C000170412

# THE ENCYCLOPEDIA OF MODERN MILITARY AIRCRAFT

THE ENCYCLOPEDIA OF

# MODERN MILITARY AIRCRAFT

**GENERAL EDITOR:** PAUL EDEN

Published in 2004 by Silverdale Books
an imprint of Bookmart Ltd
Registered Number 2372865
Trading as Bookmart Ltd
Blaby Road
Wigston
Leicester LE18 4SE



ISBN 1-84509-014-4

Produced by
Amber Books Ltd
Bradley's Close
74-77 White Lion Street
London N1 9PF
www.amberbooks.co.uk

PICTURE CREDITS
Photographs and illustrations © Aerospace Publishing Ltd, except:
Pages 5, 7 (bottom): TRH Pictures
Pages 6, 7 (top): US Department of Defense

Printed in Singapore

# Contents

***Seen from an accompanying aircraft, a Canadian Air Force F-86E Sabre fighter is put through its paces in 1950. The Sabre was the most important US fighter in the Korean War.***

AIR MOBILITY COMMAND
357

***A US Air Force B-2 Spirit stealth bomber refuels while taking part in Operation Allied Air Force over Kosovo in 1999.***



***Opposite: A US Army C-5A Galaxy heavy cargo transporter unloads a special forces MH-60 Pave Hawk helicopter. Note the refuelling probe on the starboard side and the Bendix-King 1400C colour radar in the port-side nose radome.***

***Below: A flight of three Royal Air Force Harrier II GR.Mk5s participate in operations over the British Isles in September 1988. This model included the improved Pegasus engine developed by British company Rolls-Royce.***

*Two Royal Air Force Hawk T1A fighters are put through their paces in the late 1980s. Hawk T1As were used in both training and home defence roles. These T1As are armed with Sidewinder air-to-air missiles (AAM) and 30mm (0.8in) cannon.*

# Introduction

To the majority of people, military aircraft are the fast jets that they see on television news coverage of distant combat operations. Many are likely to be familiar with various military helicopters, the Apache and Chinook perhaps being among the more readily identifiable. However, this is just the tip of the iceberg as far as modern military aviation is concerned.

Undoubtedly, attack aircraft and fighters, and assault and attack helicopters represent the spearhead of any military action, but there is a great deal more to these operations. For example, are the aircraft in use flying from land bases or aircraft carriers? Helicopters can operate from aircraft carriers with relative ease, but a fixed-wing machine must be specially designed for carrier operations, or be able to land and take-off in the shortest possible distance. Once the aircraft have left their base or carrier, their crews rely upon a whole range of technologies – many of them airborne – to carry out their mission successfully. It is virtually unthinkable that any well-equipped nation would commit its air power to combat without the support of dedicated Airborne Warning and Control System (AWACS) aircraft. Equipped with powerful radars and communications systems, these machines control the aerial battlefield, directing friendly forces and detecting hostile aircraft. In addition, should land forces committed to battle, then a select few nations are able to deploy battlefield control and surveillance aircraft, such as the US Air Force's (USAF) E-8 J-STARS (Joint-Surveillance Target Attack Radar System), to control the ground war as the AWACS controls the aerial war.

It is similarly unlikely that attack aircraft would be sent against a target without the support of dedicated SEAD (Suppression of Enemy Air Defences) platforms. these aircraft might jam enemy radar and communications systems, a mission perfected by the US Navy and Marine Corps' EA-6B Prowler, or they may take a more aggressive role, locating and attacking enemy radar emitters. In the latter case, it is common practice for F-16s flying attack missions to be supported by specially-equipped F-16CJs, carrying targeting systems and radar-homing missiles.

The key to success in any military contact, and indeed the original reason that 'flying machines' were introduced to military operations, is the gathering of reconnaissance. In recent years much of the reconnaissance mission has passed to satellite systems, but the crewed reconnaissance aircraft remains a vital asset. Tactical reconnaissance aircraft such as the Tornado GR.Mk 4A can track and obtain imagery of enemy vehicle and troop movements in real time, while strategic reconnaissance, in the forms of imagery, communications intelligence and electronic intelligence, is collected by secretive platforms, including the Nimrod R.Mk 1, RC-135 Rivet Joint and U-2.

Of course, if it all goes wrong, an effective search-and-rescue (SAR) system must be in place. Typically, the unique properties of the helicopter make it ideal for such missions and where a penetration into enemy territory is required, the heavily armed and armoured combat SAR (CSAR) helicopter is used. It is common practice for special operations teams to be dropped behind enemy lines as a means of intelligence gathering as well as providing targeting information for air strikes. The requirements of such infiltration operations have much in common with those of CSAR and a degree of cross fertilisation between the missions has produced a number of formidable helicopters, including the USAF's MH-53M Pave Low IV.

It should not be forgotten that any sustained military operation needs massive support in terms of airlift, so that none of the aircraft described so far could fly their missions without a force of transport aircraft maintaining lines of supply. While strategic aircraft – the amazing C-17A Globemaster III and the giant C-5 Galaxy above all others – move personnel and equipment across transoceanic ranges.

Almost every transport, every attack aircraft and every fighter relies totally on the provision of inflight refuelling to complete its mission and so the least glamourous machines of all, flying gas stations including the venerable KC-135 and the highly capable KC-10 Extender, fly some of the longest and most arduous missions.

*The Encyclopedia of Modern Military Aircraft* describes these disparate types in detail, so that not only will you be fully briefed on the latest front-line combat jets, but you will be able to recognize and learn about every anti-submarine aircraft, AWACS platform, helicopter, reconnaissance aircraft, tanker and transport likely to be involved in today's combat operations around the world.

***A Russian-built Indian Air Force Mi-8/1A helicopter flies above residential buildings on the outskirts of Jodhpur. First developed in the 1970s, the Mi-8 is still used in a variety of roles in many of the world's armed forces today.***

The French Aviation Légère de l'Armée de Terre (Army Light Aviation) operates around 120 SA 330 Pumas. This example belongs to det. ALAT 188 based in Djibouti, one of three permanent overseas detachments.

# Aérospatiale/Eurocopter Puma/Super Puma/Cougar

## SA 330 Puma

**In the 1970s and 1980s the SA 330 Puma became the standard medium transport helicopter for many world air forces. Only the arrival of the Sikorsky Black Hawk nudged it off its perch. Few changes were ever made to the basic design, a sure sign that it was a good one and, despite its cost and complexity, the Puma even found acceptance in the civil market.**

By the late 1960s the efficacy of the battlefield transport helicopter was not in doubt. Proven in Vietnam, no modern army could afford to be without such an aircraft. The European nations had an unsuitable collection of helicopters in service, largely based on obsolete American designs; Britain and France, in particular, had the most pressing need to replace their ageing helicopter fleets.

This led to the 1967 Anglo-French helicopter agreement, and a production/ purchase deal encompassing the Westland Lynx, Aérospatiale Gazelle and Aérospatiale Puma. While this agreement was ultimately weighted heavily in favour of the French, it did lead to three excellent helicopter designs, the largest of which was the SA 330 Puma.

The Puma story actually began several years earlier with a French army requirement to replace its S-55s and H-34s, all licence-built by Sud Aviation.

By 1962 the French were looking for a new utility transport helicopter, capable of carrying up to 20 troops and fulfilling a range of other tasks. Sud Aviation toyed with the idea of developing one of its existing (Sikorsky) designs but instead started work on a wholly indigenous design, the SA 330 – which was initially dubbed the Alouette IV. This project was launched in 1963 and the prototype first flew, rechristened as the Puma, on 14 April 1965.

Of the first three SA 330 prototypes seen here, the nearest two are carrying test instrumentation probes attached to the nose of the aircraft, away from the downwash of the rotors.

### Design profile

The Puma was built around two Turboméca Bastan VII turbines, driving a four-bladed main rotor. The high-sided main cabin, with a sliding door to port, sat on what was then a novel retractable tricycle undercarriage, with wide sponsons on either side of the rear fuselage. The helicopter could accommodate 18 passengers and two crew.

Sud Aviation went on to build a series of eight prototypes and soon re-engined the Puma with the Turboméca Turmo IIIC.4 turboshaft (as used on the Super Frelon). As the development programme progressed, UK interest in the new helicopter grew and the last prototype was transferred to Britain for evaluation. It was this that ultimately led to the selection of the Puma by the Royal Air Force as a Whirlwind and Belvedere replacement, and to the Anglo-French helicopter agreement. French Army Aviation (ALAT) adopted the SA 330B Puma as its basic aircraft. A similar version, designated Puma HC.Mk 1 (SA 330E), was acquired by the RAF. The

*For many years, a flight of RAF Pumas was based in Belize to provide the British garrison there with mobility, search and rescue and rapid response capability.*

RAF's Pumas were built under licence by Westland, at Yeovil, where all 48 HC.Mk 1s were assembled. Westland continued to have rights to the Puma design until 1988, but never sold any aircraft to any other customers. The export version of the basic aircraft, the SA 330F, was controlled by Sud Aviation and sold widely to military operators around the world.

***Both British and French Pumas have been involved in UN peacekeeping deployments into the 21st century. Often operating in potentially hostile environments, the aircraft could be fitted with infra-red decoy flares, as demonstrated by this example.***

## Company merger

In January 1970 Sud Aviation was merged with Nord Aviation and SEREB to form Aérospatiale. Aérospatiale continued to refine the Puma, developing the SA 330G powered by uprated Turmo IVC turboshafts, and aimed at the commercial market. The Puma did find favour with civil operators, mainly in the offshore oil support role. For this mission an emergency flotation system was developed, which could be fitted to the nose and undercarriage sponsons. The same equipment was fitted to SAR aircraft, such as those acquired by Portugal. The SA 330H was a military version, similar to the SA 330G, and many SA 330F operators had their aircraft upgraded to this standard.

Aérospatiale next introduced some new technology on the Puma with the addition of weight-saving composite main rotor blades. Two models were built with the new blades, the SA 330J (based on the SA 300G) and the SA 330L (based on the SA 330H). Again, several existing operators had the new dynamic system retrofitted to their aircraft. Finally, Aérospatiale used Puma airframes for test and trials duties of its own. The sole SA 330R featured a stretched fuselage and was used for development work on the SA 332 Super Puma. The SA 330Z was fitted with a fenestron tail rotor and served as a testbed for the SA 360 Dauphin project.

Aérospatiale allocated production licences for the Puma to IPTN in Indonesia and IAR Brasov in Romania. Both firms went on to build basic aircraft, chiefly for their own armed forces and government agencies – though Romania has quietly exported Pumas to several customers abroad. IPTN built approximately 20 SA 330Js from French-supplied kits and locally-built components, before moving on to build the Super Puma. IAR, on the other hand, has built close to 200 Pumas and developed its own indigenous versions. The basic Romanian Puma was designated SA 330L (IAR 330L) and, from the transport version, IAR developed a Puma gunship with 20-mm cannon in cheek-mounted pods, and side-mounted launch rails for anti-tank missiles and rockets.

***Tested during the Gulf War, where it was carried by French Army Pumas (such as this example), the HORIZON heliborne radar system is now deployed operationally on Cougars.***

## Romanian developments

Another version of the IAR 330L was developed for coastguard use and fitted with flotation gear and comprehensive navaids. IAR is producing the SOCAT Puma upgrade with Israel's Elbit. SOCAT adds a nose-mounted FLIR, a 20-mm turret-mounted cannon and advanced anti-tank missiles to the basic IAR 330L and has been ordered by the Romanian MoD.

One important customer for Romanian Pumas was South Africa, which used the SA 330s to develop its own improved, indigenous version – the Atlas Oryx. South Africa was a major Puma customer for Aérospatiale and took delivery of about 70 aircraft before arms sanctions against the apartheid regime took hold. The South African Air Force reinforced its Puma fleet with IAR 330Ls, while at the same time re-engining its aircraft with the Turboméca Makila 1A1 engine, for improved hot-and-high performance. The resultant Oryx also featured a nose-mounted radome and an improved (single-pilot) cockpit. Another Puma customer that re-engined its aircraft was Portugal, OGMA adding Makila 1 turboshafts and new composite blades to produce the SA 330S Puma.

***Over 150 Pumas have been licence-built in Romania as the IAR 330. The Romanian military aviation currently operates about 70 examples in the transport role; a current upgrade programme will provide the aircraft with a limited attack capability.***

*The Icelandic Coast Guard operates a single AS 332L2 Super Puma from Reykjavik airport for search and rescue (SAR), air ambulance and fisheries patrol work.*

# SA 332 Super Puma/AS 532 Cougar

**The Puma led, almost inevitably, to the Super Puma – a larger transport helicopter that has been built in a bewildering range of variants. Since 1990 the military aircraft have been known as the Eurocopter AS 532 Cougar family and are in front-line service around the world.**

While the original SA 330 Puma was a popular, and successful design, plans for a replacement began early. By 1974 Aérospatiale had already drawn up proposals for a 'super Puma', which would answer customer calls for more power and more lift capacity. The design that emerged was the SA 332 Super Puma, which shared the uncluttered lines of its predecessor, but was subtly different. From the beginning the Super Puma used the glass-fibre composite rotor blade technology that had been introduced on the late-model SA 330s. The most obvious change to the SA 332 was the addition of a nose radome to house a weather radar (typically either a Bendix/King RDR 1400 or a Honeywell Primus 500). Under the skin the Super Puma was completely re-engined with a pair of more powerful Turboméca Makila 1A turboshafts, replacing the original Turmo engines. Unlike the Puma, the Super Puma was aimed squarely at the civil market, though Aérospatiale did not ignore its military potential. The design incorporated several military survivability features such as a gearbox that could run without lubricants (if hit by small arms fire) and main rotors that were ballistically tolerant to up to 40 0.5-in (12.7-mm) calibre hits.

## First flight

The first Super Puma took to the air on 13 September 1978. Six prototypes were built and deliveries began in 1981. The initial production aircraft, the military AS 332B and the civil AS 332C, were no larger than the original Puma and could carry up to 21 passengers or 12-18 equipped troops. A stretched Super Puma was on the way, however, and in 1979 Aerospatiale introduced the AS 332M (military) and AS 332L (civil) models. These aircraft had a 30-in (76-cm) increase in length and could carry four extra passengers. The stretched Super Puma was certified in 1983, and cleared for operations in known icing conditions – a vital capability for offshore work and SAR missions. In 1986 the Super Puma family was up-engined with the Makila 1A1 turboshaft, and a '1' was added to all aircraft thus modified (the AS 332B becoming the AS 332B1, for example). Aérospatiale also began to introduce more specialised military variants, including the AS 332F/F1, a naval warfare variant that could be armed with two AM39 anti-ship missiles.

The maze of Super Puma designations then started to become even more complex. In the late 1980s, the basic military Super Puma was split along two lines, the AS 332M1 Super Puma Mk I and the AS 332M2 Super Puma Mk II. The Mk I was an AS 332M (stretched AS 332B) fitted with the Makila 1A1 engines. The Mk II was stretched again, this time by a further 2 ft 6 in (0.76 m), adding enough space in the cabin for an additional row of seats. It was also powered by the Makila 1A2 engine. The same process was applied to the civil AS 332L1/L2.

***The Super Puma incorporates four glassfibre rotor blades with titanium leading edges and de-icing equipment. The blades are lighter and aerodynamically more efficient than the Puma's original blades.***

***Aérospatiale 'stretched' the AS 532U2 by 2 ft 6 in (0.76 m) to provide accommodation for up to 25 passengers. The U2 variant also incorporates two extra windows and increased fuel capacity.***

***The AS 332F1 Super Puma is a navalised version which incorporates a folding tailboom for shipboard operations, and can be armed with AM39 Exocet missiles, as seen here.***

In 1990, the military line was completely reorganised once more. A new designation was adopted, the AS 532, along with a new name, the Cougar. A range of versions appeared, to which Aérospatiale (soon to become Eurocopter France) assigned designation suffixes in the form of: U, unarmed military utility; A, armed; S, anti-ship/anti-submarine; C, *court* (short) fuselage, military transport; L, long fuselage military (and civil). The basic aircraft became the AS 532UC (formerly the AS 332B1) Cougar, a short-fuselage transport version. The AS 532UL (formerly the AS 332M1) was the basic military transport model, derived from the stretched Mk I. The AS 532AC was the armed version of the AS 532UC, while the AS 532AL was the armed version of the AS 532UL. A specialised naval version of the long-fuselage AS 332F1 was developed as the AS 532SC, with the Royal Saudi Navy as its launch customer. This version could be armed with a pair of AM39 Exocet AShMs

The AS 532U2 (formerly the AS 322M2) was the stretched, up-engined military transport version, while the AS 532A2 was its armed derivative. The AS 532A2 is the basic airframe used for the French air force's new RESCO Combat Search and Rescue (C-SAR) helicopter. The RESCO Cougars are fitted with an inflight refuelling probe, FLIR, GPS-based navigation system, a personnel locator system, a sophisticated self-defence system and provision for cabin and pylon-mounted weapons. Development of the RESCO aircraft began in 1995 and the first RESCO Cougars were handed over to the French air force in 1999. Transport AS 532U2s are currently in service with the air forces of France, the Netherlands, Saudi Arabia and Thailand. The final (basic) Cougar variant was developed in 1997. This was the AS 532UB Cougar 100, a simplified 'low-cost' basic transport version without the external sponsons, with revised main undercarriage struts and a new systems fit. An armed version was designated the AS 532AB.

## Licence production

The AS 332/532 family has been built under licence by IPTN in Indonesia (as the NAS 332), CASA in Spain and F+W in Switzerland. Some air forces have given their Super Pumas/Cougars local designations, including Spain (HD.21 SAR and HT.21 VIP transport) and Sweden (Hkp 10). French Army Aviation has developed a version of the AS 532UL to carry its HORIZON battlefield surveillance radar. The earlier Orchidée system, which saw operational service during the Gulf War, has now given way to the 'full-spec' HORIZON radar and associated ground network. Four aircraft are currently in frontline service.

By late 1999 over 550 Eurocopter AS 332/532s were in service with 77 customers in 45 countries and new versions, including the EC 725, have been introduced since. Military, paramilitary or government customers include Brazil, Cameroon, Chile, China, Congo, Ecuador, Finland, France, Gabon, Germany, Indonesia, Japan, Jordan, Korea, Mexico, Nepal, Nigeria, Oman, Panama, Saudi Arabia, Singapore, Spain, Sweden, Switzerland, Togo, Turkey, Venezuela and UAE (Abu Dhabi).

***Right: The AS 532UC retains the original Puma cabin volume. However, a hatch in the floor below the centreline of the main rotor is provided for carrying loads of up to 9,920 lb (4500 kg) in an external cargo sling.***

***Below: Along with UH-1s, AB 212s and Chinooks, Spanish Army Aviation operates AS 532 Super Pumas/Cougars in the crucial battlefield mobility role.***

*First delivered in 1974, Kuwait retains a total of 16 (out of 24) Gazelles and these serve with No. 33 Squadron at Ali Salim Sabah, AB.*

# Aérospatiale SA 341 Gazelle

## Armed scout

**The Anglo-French Gazelle has proved a useful and popular light battlefield helicopter and this graceful aircraft has seen action in several conflicts, with only its fragility generating any real criticism.**

Following the success of the Alouette II, Sud Aviation began work on a new helicopter that would be faster and more manoeuvrable than its predecessor. Turboméca, the local turboshaft engine manufacturer, provided part of the formula with a more powerful engine but the Gazelle (and all subsequent French helicopters) benefited most from a 1964 agreement with Bölkow of West Germany for joint development of a glass-fibre rotor blade and an associated rigid rotor head. A new development for the time, composite-material rotors ushered in a breakthrough in blade construction through their ability to combine lightness, with strength, resistance to damage, reduced maintenance requirements and an extended fatigue life.

A fenestron was chosen as the tail rotor while the Gazelle's cockpit was of a semi-monocoque frame. Alloy honeycomb panels are used liberally through the central and rear sections of the cabin, whereas the boom and tail are produced from sheet metal. Extensive glazing is provided for the pilot and observer, and forward opening doors allow access to the cabin. The usual army skid landing gear is standard to all Gazelle versions.

What was originally known as the sud X-300 became the SA 340 by the time of its maiden flight on 7 April 1967. A proving airframe with conventional rotors, the SA 340 was followed on 12 April 1968 by a more representative prototype with rigid rotor and fenestron. Here problems began. Having tested the new rotor in a four-bladed configuration on an Alouette, Sud discovered serious control deficiencies in a three bladed layout, forcing a change to semi-articulation and the revised designation SA 341.

The aircraft became the Sud Gazelle in July 1969 but only until 1 January 1970 when Sud was absorbed into the new Aérospatiale. However, further problems meant that service entrance was delayed further.

*Soko assembled more than 250 Gazelles (local name Partizan) and has developed two distinct variants to serve in anti-tank (GAMA) and observation (HERA) duties.*

### French service

The first examples of the Gazelle entered Aviation Légère de l'Armée de Terre (ALAT) service in 1973 and these gradually began to replace the Alouette II. The original aircraft were of a basic design and were equipped with an Astazou III engine, limiting their take-of weight to 3,968 lb (1800 kg). However, later that year, Aérospatiale flew the prototype SA 342 and upon entry to service, the SA 342M (as it was designated in ALAT service) had an improved take-off weight of 4,189 lb (1900 kg) thanks to its Astazou XIVM engine. In 1985, Aérospatiale began delivering the further improved SA 342L.

The nimble and agile Gazelle exists in ALAT service today in many variants: the basic SA 341F Gazelle is used for training, VIP transport and scouting. The SA 341F2 Gazelle/Canon, with

*During the Falklands war, British Army and Marine Gazelles were extensively used and a number were lost. Those operated by No. 3 CBAS were armed with rocket pods and machine-guns, but most were unarmed and used for recce and casevac tasks.*

***An ALAT SA 342 pops above the treeline to fire a HOT missile. HOT is a Franco-German heavy anti-tank weapon, tube-launched and wire-guided.***

an M621 20-mm cannon, is used for fire-suppression and anti-helicopter missions. The SA 342ML1 Gazelle ATAM (Air-To-Air Missile) is armed with four MATRA/BAe Dynamics Mistral AATCPs (Air-Air Très Courte Portée; short-range air-to-air). The anti-tank SA 342M Gazelle HOT is armed with four Euromissile HOT missiles able to destroy any armoured vehicles at a range of up to 2½ miles (4000 m). This variant will be totally withdrawn from service in the next two years and partially replaced by the Gazelle Viviane, the latest version of the proven Gazelle. The SA 342M1 Gazelle Viviane is fitted with a night-capable laser rangefinder/thermal imaging sight for the HOT missile and with Eurocopter Ecureuil rotor blades to compensate for the increased take-off weight. The Gazelles will start to be replaced in 2003, when the first Eurocopter Tigre helicopters are delivered. Their relatively low cost, simplicity, ease of maintenance and good characteristics have made the Gazelle a popular choice for several other countries, and this helicopter is still highly regarded by its crews, who praise its remarkable agility, its low visual, radar and infra-red signatures and the unrestricted field of view offered by the canopy.

ALAT Gazelles fought successfully in the Gulf War, firing HOT missiles at Iraqi armour.

## British production

Under the terms of an 1967 agreement, Westland was granted a licence to build Gazelles. The first deliveries were handed over to the Army Air Corps in 1973 and by the time the production line finished in 1983 it had contributed 282 aircraft. All except 12 (10 for civilian use and two for the Qatari police) were for home military use, including pilot training models for the FAA and RAF.

Today, the Gazelle's presence in the UK has markedly diminished, the RAF's examples have been replaced by AS 355F1 Twin Squirrels while in FAA and Army service, the Lynx has supplemented many of the Gazelle's former roles.

Army and Royal Marine Gazelles were deployed to the Falklands Islands during the war and here they suffered mixed success. While their presence was invaluable, they proved vulnerable to small arms fire and several were lost.

## Gazelles abroad

Over 1,500 Gazelles were eventually built with some 40 countries and 29 armed forces receiving the type. Today, 21 nations including Serbia, Cameroon, Egypt, Ireland, Libya, UAE and Yugoslavia continue to operate the Gazelle.

Many have seen considerable service: Iraqi Gazelles were used against Iranian troops/armour during the first Gulf War, while Syrian Gazelles fought unsuccessfully against the Israelis during the 1982 invasion of Lebanon. Indeed, one Gazelle was captured by the Israelis and repainted in that nation's colours. Yugoslavia and Serbia had a number of Soko-built examples but after a decade of conflict, their exact number is hard to determine.

Despite its age, the Gazelle is still heavily represented in several significant air arms. It may no longer meet the standards of battleworthiness demanded from today's combat helicopters, but in all other aspects it is highly regarded as a swift, manoeuvrable and indispensable adjunct to modern army operations.

# Gazelle AH.Mk 1

**The armies of France and the UK are still the principal operators of the Gazelle, both employing the type in the scout/observation role. This example was based at the Army Aviation Centre at Middle Wallop, where it was used for training by either the Basic Rotary Squadron or No.670 Squadron, its training role denoted by the Dayglo panels for high conspicuity. Today the task is undertaken by Squirrels.**

**Stores**
In certain operational areas, stores would be carried on a boom counterbalanced across the helicopter. Equipment includes the Spectrolab SX-16 NightSun, a Canadair reconnaissance pod, 4-in (10.2-cm) flares and SNEB (2.7-in) 68-mm rocket pods.

**Fenestron tail rotor**
Thirteen light alloy blades make up the tail rotor, shrouded by the tail fin, and pitch change is obtained by movement of the blades. The disadvantage of the fenestron is that a great deal of power is used in the hover, but the flight safety advantage of the shrouded rotor was seen, at the time to outweigh this drawback.

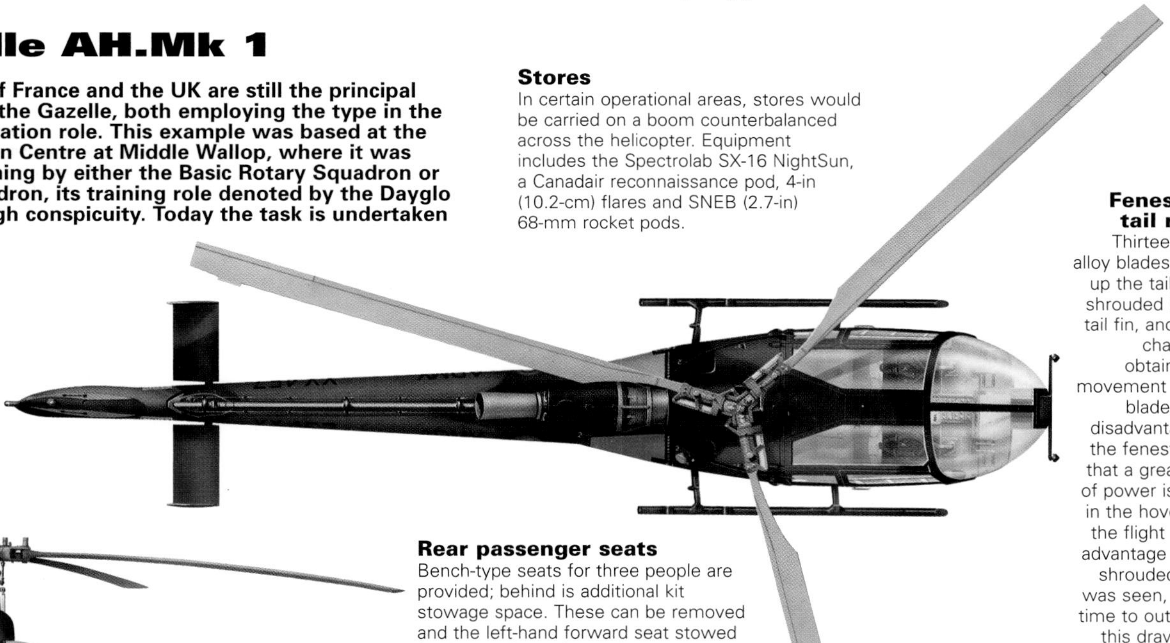

**Rear passenger seats**
Bench-type seats for three people are provided; behind is additional kit stowage space. These can be removed and the left-hand forward seat stowed for the carriage of stretchers.

**VHF/FM homer**
The ARC 340 has twin dipole aerials for radio homing; direction indication is given in the cockpit on the attitude indicator. The same radio has a communications aerial under the tailcone.

***Ching-Kuo was designed with BVR capability in an effort to counter the vast numbers of inferior fighters fielded by Taiwan's great enemy, the People's Republic of China.***

# AIDC Ching-Kuo

## Taiwan's fighter

**Beset by economic problems and the premature cessation of its production run, the Ching-Kuo has gained a reputation for being inferior to contemporary products. In fact, it represents an indigenous Taiwanese fighter with capabilities comparable to those of Sweden's JAS 39 Gripen.**

Communist China was closely aligned with the Soviet Union during the early Cold War years and, working on the principle that 'my enemy's enemy is my friend', the West, and in particular the US, saw Taiwan as an important ally. Taiwan, or the Republic of China, owes its very existence to the ousting of Nationalist forces from mainland China in 1949 and has been the last stronghold of the Chinese Nationalists ever since. Garrisoned by the US, therefore, and willingly supplied with the latest in American weaponry, Taiwan had no real defence worries.

However, even when the Cold War was at its height, any thawing in relations between Peking and Washington was felt in Taiwan in the form of delivery restrictions affecting the latest weaponry. In 1974, the US began withdrawing its forces from Taiwan and, by 1979, relations with Communist China had reached the point where US-Taiwanese relations were broken off completely. Taiwan was left with a fighter force consisting of F-5 Tiger IIs and F-104 Starfighters, with no options for their replacement and all the headaches of supporting a US fleet without access to American spares resources. Nevertheless, Northrop designed the F-20 Tigershark aimed at the Taiwanese requirement but, in the event, the US government excluded Taiwan from the list of countries eligible for Tigershark exports, as it had with the list of potential Fighting Falcon and Hornet customers.

### Indigenous solution

Luckily for Taiwan, the American restrictions on arms supply were ambiguous. Any form of technical assistance was allowed and the country took the brave decision to go it alone with a new fighter design, relying heavily on US help.

Taiwan's AIDC had already collaborated with Northrop on production of the AT-3 trainer and this experience, allied with that gained in building F-5s for the Republic of China Air Force (RoCAF), was the basis on which the Indigenous Defence Fighter (IDF) was to be built.

Initial studies began in 1980, with programme launch in 1982. The aim was to produce a lightweight fighter which was highly capable in both the air-to-air and air-to-ground roles. The codename An Hsiang (Safe Flight) was allocated to the programme as a whole, while Ying Yang (Soaring Eagle) covered the airframe, Yun Han (Cloud Man) the engine, Tien Lei (Sky Thunder) the avionics, and Tien Chien (Sky Sword) the missile armament. At an early stage, the concept of a true lightweight fighter was abandoned and US personnel were drafted in to assist the AIDC design team.

### Ying Yang

General Dynamics Fort Worth was deeply involved in the airframe development programme, supplying specifications and drawings from the F-16. It is therefore no surprise that the IDF bears some resemblance to the F-16, albeit in a twin-engined layout.

The airframe is almost entirely of aluminium alloy and offers what to most Western pilots would seem to be a cramped cockpit. The accommodation was designed with the anthropometric dimensions of Taiwanese pilots in mind, however, and provides ample space for an average crew. The cockpit features a wide-angle HUD, HOTAS controls and a Martin-Baker Mk 12 ejection seat.

### Yun Han

Allied Signal/Garrett took most of the responsibility for the IDF's twin TFE1042 turbofan powerplant. The new

***Above: In two-seat form, the Ching-Kuo loses its forward fuselage fuel tank in favour of an instructor's seat. The second seat is not raised and the instructor's view is poor.***

***Left: The wingtip rails of this aircraft mount AIM-9P AAMs, while a 275-US gal (1041-litre) drop tank hangs from the centreline. A tank in this position prevents the carriage of TC-2 AAMs.***

While, from above, it bears obvious similarities to the F-16, from below, Ching-Kuo has much in common with the F/A-18. The first three FSD aircraft, all single-seaters, wore AIDC's smart house colours.

engine was basically an afterburning development of the established TFE731, which had already found applications in the CASA C.101, AT-3 and various biz-jets. This latter fact helped to calm the minds of Americans worried about arms transfers to Taiwan, since the engines could be passed off as innocent biz-jet units. In its final form, the ITEC (AlliedSignal/AIDC) TFE1042-70 offers 6,025 lb st (26.80 kN) dry and 9,460 lb st (42.08 kN) with reheat. The engine has been given the US military designation, F125.

### Tien Lei

The heart of the IDF's avionics system was to be a multi-mode pulse-Doppler radar, offering true BVR capability. The Kam Lung (Golden Dragon) 53 GD-53, carried in the nose of the in-service Ching-Kuo (named after a former Taiwanese president), is based on the Westinghouse AN/APG-67 (V) developed for the F-20. It incorporates technology from the F-16A's AN/APG-66 and offers similar and, in some cases, superior capabilities.

### Tien Chien

In service, the Ching-Kuo has been seen with AIM-9L/P AAMs, but its primary missile armament consists of the indigenous TC-1 IR-guided AAM, which is closely related to the AIM-9, and the TC-2 BVR missile. This latter weapon has been claimed to have capabilities similar to those of AMRAAM, but this seems unlikely. It is unclear whether the TC-2 has semi-active or active radar homing. Ching-Kuo also has an internal Vulcan cannon and, for air-to-ground work, is compatible with CBUs, Mk 82 and Mk 84 bombs, and the AGM-65B EO-guided missile. GBU-12A Paveway I LGBs may also be available. For the anti-shipping role, the aircraft employs the indigenous Hsiung Feng 2 (Male Bee 2) AShM, of which up to three rounds can be accommodated.

### In service

In 1985, the IDF design was frozen and by 1989 development and production costs had risen from a predicted US$1 billion to US$5 billion. With the programme at an advanced stage, the first of four FSD aircraft (A-1) flew on 28 May 1989. These four machines were followed by 10 pre-production aircraft for a comprehensive test and evaluation programme.

Unfortunately, the first aircraft was damaged in a very public landing accident before the Taiwanese president and the world's press. A-1 was soon repaired, but the second FSD machine, A-2, was lost in a fatal accident after the port tailplane separated following severe vibration around Mach 1.

In spite of these setbacks, the first pre-production aircraft were delivered to the RoCAF around one year early, in early 1992. Production had been planned to encompass some 256 Ching-Kuos, but US promises to supply F-16s saw this requirement dramatically reduced to just 130 aircraft. This down-scaling of the programme immediately made the Ching-Kuo a very expensive product. The Block 20 F-16A/Bs being offered made greater economic sense and the Ching-Kuo was relegated to an also-ran, a position which denies this formidable aircraft the recognition it deserves.

## F-CK-1B Ching-Kuo

**The little-used alphanumeric designation for the Ching-Kuo is F-CK-1A for the single-seat aircraft and F-CK-1B for the two-seaters. This aircraft is shown in 3rd Tactical Fighter Wing colours, based at Kang Air Base. It was one of the four two-seaters in the 10-aircraft pre-production batch.**

**AGM-65B Maverick**
The AGM-65Bs carried under the wings of this Ching-Kuo are early weapons from the Maverick family. They are TV-guided and have benefited from a scene magnification optics upgrade.

**AAM carriage**
Tien Chien 1 or AIM-9L (illustrated) AAMs are carried on the wingtips, while a pair of semi-recessed TC-2 AAMs may be accommodated in a tandem arrangement of bays in the underside of the fuselage.

**Radar capability**
AIDC's Golden Dragon radar allows Ching-Kuo to detect targets at a distance of up to 93 miles (150 km). This radar, combined with Taiwanese missiles and Ching-Kuo's flight performance, makes the aircraft a formidable fighter opponent.

**Two-seat modifications**
Like the first three FSD single-seaters, the two-seat Ching-Kuo features a separate windscreen and canopy. The latter hinges to port for cockpit access. Pre-production and production single-seat aircraft feature an F-16-style single-piece windscreen and canopy which hinges aft, although a prominent frame gives the impression of a separate windscreen.

**Ching-Kuo variants**
AIDC proposed: a 'Special Missions' Ching-Kuo, intended for 'Wild Weasel' missions, with an Israeli F-16D-style bulged spine; a night-attack variant; a recce version; and an adversary trainer. The only version still being actively promoted, however, is the LIFT advanced trainer variant.

*The first prototype G222TCM, complete with a nose-mounted air data probe, is seen taxiing at Le Bourget. Large calibration markings appear on the nose, rear fuselage and rudder.*

*The major user of the G222 is the Italian air force, in whose service the aircraft has been demonstrated as reliable and extremely manoeuvrable, regularly performing barrel rolls at air shows.*

# Alenia G222 and C-27

## Mini-Hercules

**Proposed as a V/STOL transport, Fiat's G222 was, in fact, to emerge as a STOL aircraft. 'Italy's Mini-Hercules' has seen service in several different versions with 11 air arms, while the second-generation LMATTS C-27J has already gained its first order.**

Italy's G222 tactical transport was a challenging venture for its aerospace industry, and one which gave it the credentials to enter the international arena of collaborative projects. The transport has achieved moderate success on the export market as well as forming the backbone of its home air force's transport arm for over 20 years.

### V/STOL project

Today's G222 is somewhat different in operation from the aircraft first envisaged as the Fiat response to the 1961 pan-NATO NBMR-4 requirement for a V/STOL transport. Head of design was Professor Giuseppe Gabrielli (hence the 'G' in the designation), and he included the obligatory lifting jets (six Rolls-Royce RB.162s) in his submission, but deviated from the thinking of the time by a refusal to adopt jets for forward propulsion. Instead, the G222 was proposed with a pair of Rolls-Royce Dart turboprops, and the firm hedged its bets by also scheming variants with eight or two lifting engines, as well as a conventional take-off transport, a civil model and maritime patrol/anti-submarine adaptations.

Despite the abandonment of NBMR-4, the G222 continued an uncertain existence, its size and weight increasing until, in 1966, the powerplant was changed to a pair of 3,060-shp (2282-kW) General Electric CT64-820s. The AMI was, meanwhile, searching for a replacement for its Fairchild C-119, specifying the ability to carry a 5000-kg (11,023-lb) payload over a 2000-km (1,243-mile) distance. It was this prospect of a local order which kept the programme in progress, though limiting its horizons to conventional take-off. Two G222TCM unpressurised prototypes were built at Turin/Caselle for evaluation, the first making its maiden flight on 18 July 1970, by which time Fiat's aviation interests had been merged with those of others in the new company, Aeritalia.

*The liberal application of orange paint and the undernose light on this G222 reveal it to be a G222RM calibration aircraft. It is in the colours of 8° Gruppo/14° Stormo, part of 9ª Brigata Aerea, based at Pratica di Mare.*

### Performance

A commitment to purchase 44 G222s (plus the two G222TCM prototypes) was given by the AMI on 28 July 1972. The initial aircraft flew on 23 December 1975 at the start of a further trials period made necessary by several changes, not least of which were pressurisation and 14 per cent more power for hot-weather operation, available from the newly-adopted 3,400-shp (2535-kW) T64P4Ds. New engines (built under licence by a Fiat/Alfa Romeo consortium) were accompanied by an increase

***Left:** Developed to overcome restrictions on sales of US products to Libya, the G222T used Tyne turboprops in place of the T64s and European instruments. I-GAIT, the G222T prototype (converted from the 34th G222), first flew on 15 May 1980. The 20 Libyan G222s served with a transport regiment at Benghazi.*

***Below:** Typical of the export customers which ordered small numbers of the 'basic' G222 was the Argentine army, which acquired three from 1977.*

in maximum payload to 19,842 lb (9000 kg). There was a payload/range trade-off, although the G222 exceeds the original AMI specification and can carry the stipulated 5000 kg (11,023 lb) over 1,703 miles (2740 km) at cruise altitude.

In military transport roles the G222 can airdrop 32 paratroops or up to 11,023 lb (5000 kg) of freight from its 2,613-cu ft (74-m$^3$) hold. For air transport, personnel capacity is increased to 44 fully-armed troops, and 135 tie-down points are provided on the cabin floor for palletised freight, five A-22 standard-size freight containers or light vehicles.

Comfort in flight is assisted by a pressurisation system which gives the equivalent atmosphere of 3,940 ft (1200 m) at heights up to 19,685 ft (6000 m).

### Service use

The G222 has proved to be a versatile aircraft in AMI service, its duties extending far beyond mere fetching and carrying. Two squadrons of the 46ª Aerobrigata Trasporti Medi (46th Medium Transport Group), equipped at Pisa/San Guisto from April 1978 onwards, currently share a total of 33 aircraft. Six 'quick-change' kits are available so that aircraft can be converted to the aeromedical configuration, in which role they have been deployed as far afield as Kampuchea and Peru.

In August 1976 there began trials of a fire-fighting version, produced by installing a palletised Food & Machinery Corporation SAMA (Sistema Aeronautico Modulare Antincendio) kit on the opened rear ramp. SAMA includes a 1,320-Imp gal (6000-litre) tank of water or retardant and four pressurised air containers, and can be installed in under two hours to produce an 'instant' G222SAA. Six kits are in regular use for fighting forest fires.

Six of the original 46 G222s ordered for the AMI are equipped with special electronics, of which four are the G222RM model. RM indicates *radiomisure* (translated as 'calibration'), for which systems are installed so that the aircraft can calibrate a wide variety of navigational and approach aids. The computerised onboard systems require only one operator, and there is sufficient room remaining in the cabin for a light vehicle to be carried for ground tasks. Deliveries of the G222RM began in January 1983 to the 8° Gruppo Sorveglianza Elettronica (electronic surveillance squadron) of 14° Stormo at Rome/Pratica di Mare.

The other component of 14° Stormo is 71° Gruppo Guerra Elettronica (electronic warfare squadron), whose equipment includes the G222VS (Versione Speciale), alternatively known in service as the G222ECM, G222SIGIT or G222GE. Two entered service in 1983.

Further orders were placed by the AMI in 1984 for five G222PROCIVs (making 51 for the AMI in total), which it operated on behalf of the newly-established disaster relief agency, the Servizio Nazionale della Protezione Civile. Used to spray dispersants on oil slicks from a 1,320-Imp gal (6000-litre) tank in the hold and for fire-fighting, the aircraft have been replaced by Canadair CL-415s. All the G222PROCIVs were sold to Tunisia in early 2000.

### Exports

The basic transport G222 was ordered by Argentina (three for the army), Congo (three), Dubai (one, the first production G222), Libya (20 G222Ts), Nigeria (five), Somalia (six required, only two delivered), Thailand (six) and Venezuela (seven). Refusal by the US to release T64 engines for Libya forced Aeritalia to develop the G222T version, which substituted Rolls-Royce Tyne RTy 20 Mk 801 turboprops. Despite intensive efforts to secure a 50-aircraft order from Turkey, Airtech's CN-235 won the contract in February 1990. In January 1991 Aeritalia merged with the Selenia electronics concern to form Alenia.

Teamed with Chrysler Technologies, Alenia offered the G222-710A for the USAF's Rapid Response Intra-Theater Airlift (RRITA) requirement, to serve with US Southern Command in the Panama Canal Zone. Ten were ordered from 1990 as C-27A Spartans and were operated by the 310th AS/ 24th Wing from Howard AFB. The aircraft had a very short service life in the USAF, all briefly being sent to Davis-Monthan AFB for storage before the majority was issued to the US state department in 1999.

In partnership with Lockheed Martin, Alenia formed Lockheed Martin Alenia Tactical Transport Systems to produce the C-27J, a glass cockpit version with Allison AE 2100 engines. The prototype, a converted Italian air force G222, first flew on 25 September 1999. First orders for the new version are from the Italian air force which has ordered 5 with seven options (due in 2005) for partial replacement of its existing G222 fleet. Interest in the C-27J has also been reported from Australia; Greece, which has ordered 12 with three options; Malaysia; Poland and Switzerland.

***The C-27A Spartan was built by Alenia, but furnished by Chrysler Technologies for the USAF. Unfortunately, the C-27A fell victim to shrinking budgets in the late 1990s.***

# AMX International AMX

## Lightweight warrior

*Dubbed by some as a 'pocket Tornado', the joint Italian/Brazilian AMX is the only modern aircraft that has been solely designed with the attack mission in mind, a mission Italian AMXs performed with aplomb over the Balkans from 1995.*

**Although the AMX has only achieved one tentative export order, it is an effective light attack aircraft whose precision attack capabilities have led it to be compared to larger, more expensive interdictors.**

*Italian AMXs participated in the French Odax '98 exercises with the Armée de l'Air. The AMX has proved itself to be the equal of many contemporary designs and acquits itself well in comparison to supposedly 'superior' types.*

During NATO operations against Serb targets in Operation Allied Force, the Italian air force quietly flew 1,100 sorties, dropping 517 Mk 82 bombs and 79 Paveway II LGBs. Almost one quarter of the total (252 sorties) was flown (with even less fanfare) by the AMX, which also introduced the Elbit Opher imaging infra-red guided bomb, 39 of which were dropped. This was perhaps appropriate, since the Italo-Brazilian AMX has always been a profoundly unglamorous aircraft, which nevertheless performs a vital role with quiet efficiency.

The AMX was originally designed to meet an Italian requirement for an advanced multi-role attack and reconnaissance aircraft to replace various ageing F-104G Starfighters and Aeritalia G.91s. In 1978 Aermacchi and Aeritalia actually pooled their resources to design the aircraft, which represented a programme of vital importance to Italy's aircraft industry, not least as one of the few opportunities for local industry to provide an indigenous solution to an AMI requirement.

### Brazilian involvement

Brazil (with a near-identical requirement) joined the programme in 1980, and the joint procurement of 272 aircraft (six prototypes, 79 aircraft for Brazil and 187 for Italy) was agreed in 1981. This gave programme shares of 46.5 per cent for Aeritalia (later Alenia), 23.8 per cent for Aermacchi and 29.7 per cent for Brazil's EMBRAER. The resulting AMX design was a high-winged, single-engined, rather pugnacious-looking and muscular aircraft, vaguely reminiscent of the Mirage F1 in plan view.

Despite its conventional appearance, the AMX had some cutting-edge features, including virtually full-span leading-edge and trailing-edge high-lift devices which conferred superb short-field performance. The aircraft also had a state-of-the-art cockpit, with a HUD, HDD, HOTAS controls and advanced avionics.

### First flight

The first AMX prototype made its maiden flight at Turin-Caselle on 15 May 1984, with a Brazilian prototype following in October 1985. Development progressed fairly smoothly, using seven single-seat prototypes, and the first production AMX flew on 11 May 1988.

Defence cuts following the end of the Cold War brought a premature end to production for the AMI, after 136 aircraft (including 26 AMX-T two-seaters). Aermacchi built 36 of the single-seat aircraft and nine two-seaters, while Alenia built 74 and 17. These aircraft equipped six squadrons, though one of these has since disbanded, and 19 surviving Block 1 and 15 Block 2 aircraft have been placed in reserve. This left a force of 94 aircraft in service, all Batch 3 aircraft, or Batch 2 aircraft modified to the same FOC (Full Operational Capability) configuration.

The AMXs of 3° Stormo

*The two-seat AMX is used for advanced and conversion training and for operational roles in which the presence of a backseater is advantageous. This type forms the basis of the proposed **SEAD** and escort-jamming variants, and the Venezuelan air force AMX-T.*

An aerial refuelling capability was considered desirable by the Força Aérea Brasileira. AMX prototype 006 therefore conducted trials with a KC-130H (illustrated) and, later, a KC-137, at heights from 4,000-30,000 ft (1219-9144 m).

have a reconnaissance capability, using Oude Delft Orpheus reconnaissance pods, although there is an outstanding requirement for the aircraft to receive an internal sensor suite, and an external electro-optical (EO) reconnaissance pod is on order. The AMX fleet also uses recently-delivered Thomson CDLP laser designator pods, allowing the aircraft to 'self-designate' when delivering Paveway LGBs.

### Close air support

In Brazil, the AMX replaced EMBRAER EMB-326Gs (AT-26s) in the CAS/reconnaissance roles, to equip two Grupos. The Força Aérea Brasileira has 56 aircraft delivered or on order (including 11 two-seater AMX-Ts), all built by EMBRAER, with options on 23 more single-seaters. The Brazilian AMXs and AMX-Ts (known as A-1 and A-1B or TA-1 in service) differ from Italian aircraft in their avionics fit, and also feature twin DEFA 554 30-mm cannon in place of the Italian aircraft's single M61A1 20-mm weapon. The aircraft also tend to carry indigenous MAA-1 Piranha AAMs on their wingtip launch rails, while AMI aircraft generally use the US-supplied AIM-9 Sidewinder. The Brazilian aircraft also routinely carry a fixed 'bolt-on' inflight refuelling probe, following an extensive series of inflight refuelling trials using prototype 006, an FAB KC-130H and an FAB KC-137. Defence economies resulted in delivery delays in Brazil, and only one two-squadron Grupo is so far fully-equipped. Despite the slow arrival of the type, it is already proving extremely popular with its pilots, who were delighted to find that they were capable of turning with visiting USAF F-16s – not bad for an 'underpowered' fighter-bomber. The AMX avionics suite has also been the subject of much acclaim, and Brazil has asked Northrop about the possibility of upgrading its F-5Es with an AMX-based avionics suite.

The AMX will soon begin to replace the reconnaissance-configured RT-26s of 1° Esquadrão 10° Grupo. These aircraft use an underwing reconnaissance pod reportedly supplied by W. Vinten Ltd, but the exact reconnaissance fit of the Brazilian AMXs remains unknown. Theoretically, they should be equipped with any one of three pallet-mounted Aeroeletrônica photo-reconnaissance systems installed in the forward fuselage, though this cannot be confirmed. In the longer term, Brazil has a requirement for a maritime strike version of the AMX, which could be equipped with a new version of the Scipio radar, and which might feature a new Elbit Opher HUD.

The two-seat Italian AMX-T forms the basis of the proposed AMX-E escort-jammer and SEAD platform. One AMX-T has been used for AMX-E development. Venezuela has ordered a further sub-variant (the AMX-ATA, 12 of which will be delivered under the AMX-T designation from 2005) with ALX-based Elbit avionics, a digital cockpit and features of the AMI Block 3 configuration.

Development of further advanced AMX variants continues, with proposals for a version powered by a 13,500-lb (60-kN) non-afterburning derivative of the Eurofighter's EJ200 engine in place of the existing 11,000-lb st (49-kN) Spey Mk 807.

## AMX

**The 51- nosecode and cat-and-mouse fin badge identify this aircraft as one of those delivered to the first operational AMX unit, the 103° Gruppo, 51° Stormo at Istrana. The squadron was previously equipped with the Aeritalia G.91R and had been based at Treviso. The aircraft wears an overall grey colour scheme (unusual for a dedicated ground-attack aircraft), and has new-style roundels with a thin white central band for reduced conspicuity.**

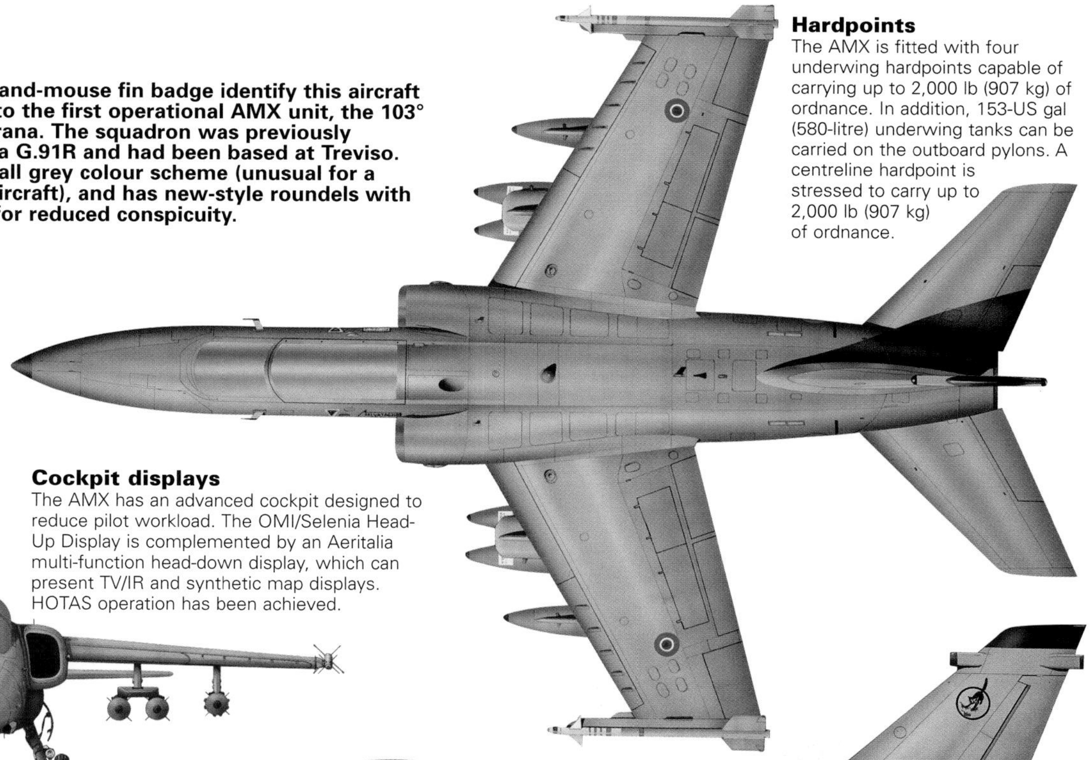

**Hardpoints**
The AMX is fitted with four underwing hardpoints capable of carrying up to 2,000 lb (907 kg) of ordnance. In addition, 153-US gal (580-litre) underwing tanks can be carried on the outboard pylons. A centreline hardpoint is stressed to carry up to 2,000 lb (907 kg) of ordnance.

**Weapons**
The AMX is cleared to use a wide variety of weapons, including free-fall and retarded Mk 82, Mk 83, Mk 84 bombs, and the Skyshark dispenser weapon. Sidewinders or Piranha AAMs can also be carried for self-defence. Further weapons have been demonstrated as potential loads, but depend on the needs of the aircraft's service users. Any export customers may demand new weapons and the aircraft has been flown by a number of foreign pilots.

**Cockpit displays**
The AMX has an advanced cockpit designed to reduce pilot workload. The OMI/Selenia Head-Up Display is complemented by an Aeritalia multi-function head-down display, which can present TV/IR and synthetic map displays. HOTAS operation has been achieved.

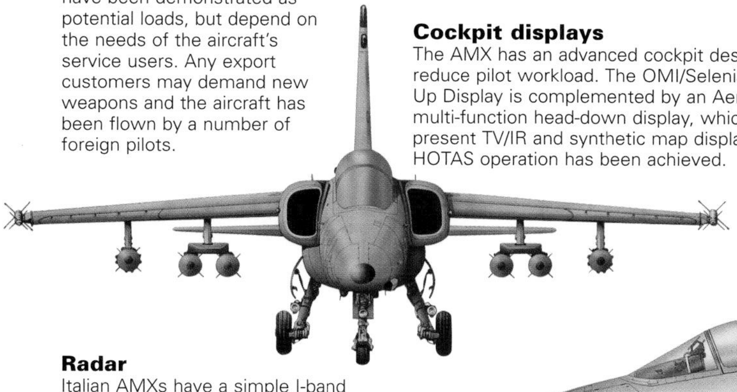

**Radar**
Italian AMXs have a simple I-band ranging radar, the FIAR-built version of the Israeli ELTA EL/M-2001B. Brazilian aircraft have a similar radar, the Technasa/SMA SCP-01.

51-14

# Antonov An-12 'Cub'

## Russia's Hercules

**For many years the An-12 formed the backbone of the Soviet transport force, playing a part in every post-war military action. Today, while largely replaced in the transport role, 'Cubs' have frequently been converted or modified for special missions.**

*Above: Where it all began...the An-8 'Camp' was the direct progenitor of the An-12, and was designed to fulfil a 1952 Aeroflot/VVS requirement for a rear-loading, twin-engined transport. About 100 were built, the An-8 design leading to the An-10.*

*Top: Considered the ultimate transport variant of the 'Cub', the An-12BK features an enlarged chin radome housing 'Short Horn' radar and has a remotely-controlled cargo-handling winch in the hold. This example serves with the Belarus air force.*

Usually regarded as the 'Soviet C-130', the An-12 is similar to the Hercules in many respects. Designed as a high-wing, four-engined, rear-loading military freighter, the Ukrainian-built aircraft has had considerable sales success in both civilian and military markets, and has been adapted to fulfil a variety of other roles. The prototype An-12 made its maiden flight on 16 December 1957. It is estimated that more than 1,200 were built at Kiev before production ceased during 1973. Furthermore, since 1972, unlicensed production in the shape of the Shaanxi Y-8 has been undertaken in China, with unconfirmed reports of up to 67 aircraft having being built.

Developed from the passenger-carrying An-10 (which was itself a stretched, four-engined derivative of the An-8, with a pressurised circular-section fuselage), the An-12 was designed from the start as a military transport and civilian freighter, with a rear-loading ramp like that of the An-8, and a partly-pressurised cabin forward of the main portion of the freight compartment. Unlike the C-130, the An-12 lacks an integral rear-loading ramp, with the upswept rear fuselage instead consisting of a pair of longitudinally-split, inward-opening doors and a third, upward-opening, door aft.

Designated 'Cub' by the ASCC (Air Standards Co-ordinating Committee), the An-12 has been produced in several versions. The An-12B is the basic military freighter, although the very earliest aircraft, which had a smaller undernose radome and other detail differences, may have had a different designation. All basic freighter variants are known to NATO simply as 'Cubs'.

Large numbers of military An-12s have been converted to perform other roles (and some production 'special duties' An-12s may also have been manufactured). Factory and air force designations for these shadowy aircraft remain unknown, and not all have separate NATO reporting names, although most remain in active front-line use with the successors to the Soviet air force. The first 'special duties' An-12 identified by NATO had blade antennas on the forward fuselage, plus other minor changes, and was a dedicated Elint platform. It is possible that this 'Cub-A' was an interim type, since most Elint 'Cubs' encountered in recent years have

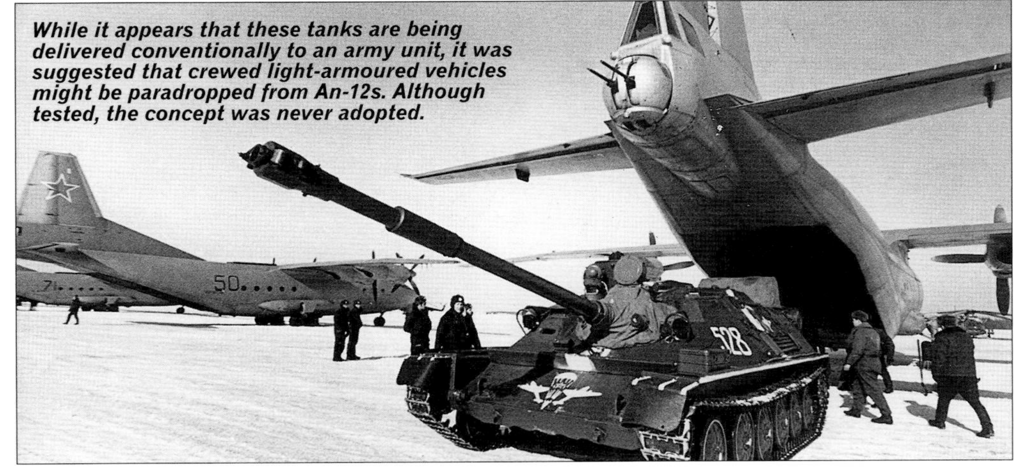

*While it appears that these tanks are being delivered conventionally to an army unit, it was suggested that crewed light-armoured vehicles might be paradropped from An-12s. Although tested, the concept was never adopted.*

***India was one of the most active 'foreign' users of the An-12, which served as a transport, bomber and even as a command post over its 40-year career. The last An-12 was withdrawn from Indian service in 1993.***

had more extensive modifications. One such aircraft had prominent 'carrot' fairings on the fin and wingtips.

The 'Cub-B' is a more obvious Elint conversion, with two prominent radomes under the belly and a host of other blade antennas. Some of these aircraft have been encountered in full Aeroflot livery and, during the 1970s, others may have worn Egyptian markings. The 'Cub-C' is understood to be a dedicated ECM platform, with palletised electrical generators and control equipment, and possibly chaff-cutters and dispensers in the cabin. Externally, the 'Cub-C' can be identified by the array of antennas on its underside, the cooling scoops and heat exchanger outlets fore and aft of the wing, and the bulged, ogival tailcone which replaces the normal gun turret. There have been suggestions that these 'stand-off' jamming platforms had a primary role of neutralising NATO air defence and surface-to-air missile radars.

The most recently identified version of the An-12, the 'Cub-D', is a second ECM platform, with a different equipment fit and characterised by huge external pods on the lower 'corners' of the forward fuselage and on each side of the base of the tailfin. Unconfirmed reports suggest the existence of an airborne command post version of the An-12, which may have seen service during the Indo-Pakistan war.

In addition to these aircraft, large numbers of An-12s have been converted as one-off test and research platforms, including a meteorological research aircraft, ejection seat test aircraft, avionics testbeds (SSSR-11417, -11700), icing rigs, and engine testbeds. In the latter category, an Egyptian 'Cub' flew with its port inner engine replaced by a Helwan E-300 turbojet, developed for a stillborn indigenous fighter. A Soviet An-12 (SSSR-11916) may have acted as the prototype for a proposed maritime reconnaissance and ASW variant.

## 'Cub' at war

The longevity of the An-12's career and the nature of its operators has meant that it has naturally gone to war in several different theatres. India was one of the earliest An-12 operators, and its aircraft were involved in resupplying troops during the 1950s border conflicts with China and the first conflict with Pakistan in which the 'Cubs' transported army units. In 1971 when India and Pakistan went to war again over the fate of Bangladesh, an An-12 was used in tactical control and co-ordination for strike packages. Other 'Cubs' were also used as makeshift bombers, attacking dumps close to the border in Kashmir. Their success prompted the OKB to develop its own 'combi-' bomber transport.
On 12 January 1972, An-12s and C-119s deployed a battalion of paratroops to cut off the city of Dacca.

## African air wars

Egyptian An-12s saw active service ferrying arms and supplies to rebel forces in the Congo during 1964. Between 1962 and 1967 the aircraft were used to support Egyptian troops fighting in Yemen and they played a limited role in the Six-Day War of 1967, where several were lost on the ground at Cairo. During the 1973 Yom Kippur war, the 'Cubs' were again used in the supply role, and a squadron of An-12PPs was deployed to Syria for jamming duties. Further south, Soviet An-12s also went to war in 1967, flying resupply missions for the Federal Nigerian forces.

Ethiopia turned to the USSR for arms following the US embargo of 1977; An-12s were among the first aircraft received and were used in the operations against rebelling Eritreans. Iraq also used its An-12s operationally and, during the war with Iran, Iraqi 'Cubs' were used for maritime reconnaissance, as targeting platforms and as inflight-refuelling tankers. The An-12s were effectively grounded during the 1991 Gulf War and at least one was destroyed on the ground by an RAF Buccaneer.

Soviet 'Cubs' were also kept busy elsewhere. They played a major part in the 1968 invasion of Czechoslovakia, flying 250 sorties delivering paratroops. In the 1979 invasion of Afghanistan, a regiment of assault troops was flown in by An-12s and An-22s on 6 and 7 December, followed by another 5,000 troops between 22 and 26 December. During the long and arduous war that followed, An-12s mounted continuous airlift resupply missions for the Limited Contingent of Soviet Forces in Afghanistan, flying from the USSR to Bagram and Kabul. By 1989, Soviet withdrawal from Afghanistan was complete, with five 'Cubs' having been lost during the conflict. A number was left for use by the local air force, though keeping them serviceable was not a priority, and they are not believed to have flown much.

More recently, Russian An-12s were used in Chechnya, when troops and equipment were shuttled to Mozdok, for onward transport into the combat zone.

There have been a number of attempts to modernise and replace the ageing An-12, but much like its Western counterpart, the C-130, its simplistic yet effective design remains unbeatable. A host of airlines currently operates the 'Cub', and the 47 year-old An-12 continues to serve with many air forces, while other nations are rumoured to have purchased or leased Chinese-built Y-8s.

***Above: Ilyushin's jet-powered Il-76 was designed as an An-12 replacement, but never managed to completely dislodge the elderly 'Cub' from Russian service. This Rostov-on-Don-based An-12 (from the 535th OSAP) is seen at Gross-Dölln in 1993 alongside a row of 'Aeroflot' Il-76MDs engaged in military transport duties.***

***Left: Originally designed to thwart enemy systems by dint of its Sirena jamming system, the An-12BK-PPS 'Cub-D' remains in service in 2004 in the EW role and is easily distinguishable by the jamming pods mounted on each side of the fuselage.***

*The An-26 became the standard WarPac tactical transport during the 1970s. Czechoslovakia received six, of which four (including the An-26Z-1 EW platform) went to the Cezch republic on partition. Slovakia (illustrated) adopted the remaining pair for service with 32/1 Letka at Piestany.*

# Antonov An-24/-26/-30/-32

## Transport family

**Built initially to swell the fleet of Aeroflot, Antonov's tough An-24 had obvious military potential. This was fully realised by the An-26 'Curl' and follow-on An-32 'Cline'.**

Antonov's An-24 had been designed to replace the Lisunov Li-2 (DC-3) in Aeroflot service. Although it was not blessed with sparkling performance, large numbers were built for the civilian market. It was not surprising that a few were bought by air forces, primarily for use as passenger/ troop transports. In 2000 the 'Coke' remains in service with Belarus, Bulgaria, Cambodia, Congo, Cuba, Czech Republic, Guinea-Bissau, Guinea Republic, Iraq, Kazakhstan, North Korea, Laos, Mali, Mongolia, Romania, Russia, Slovakia, Sri Lanka, Sudan, Syria, Turkmenistan, Ukraine, Uzbekistan and Yemen, these countries mostly flying small numbers of the type.

Two significant advances made during An-24 development led to much greater military success. Firstly, the An-24RV introduced an auxiliary turbojet in the rear of the starboard nacelle, to greatly enhance take-off performance, and secondly the An-24T (and An-24TV with turbojet) introduced a rear loading ramp in a redesigned fuselage.

Further redesign of the rear fuselage was introduced by the An-26 'Curl', the first dedicated military model. The rear fuselage was broadened and fitted with a rear loading ramp which could be slid forward underneath the fuselage in flight, so facilitating para-dropping of troops or loads. When closed, the ramp was sealed tightly: the An-26 thus became the first pressurised Soviet military transport.

All but the first An-26s were completed with a strengthened underfuselage skin to allow operations from rough fields, and all featured the auxiliary turbojet. Most were fitted with a bulged observation dome on the port side of the forward fuselage, which could be used in conjunction with a sight for accurate load-dropping.

First appearing in 1969, the An-26 was in production until 1985, by which time over 1,400 had been built. The vast majority of these went to military customers, being used for tactical transport duties. The type has proven to be rugged and reliable, and tough under fire, as was proven in Afghanistan. In that conflict the type was pressed into use as a makeshift bomber, and the aircraft of Angola and Mozambique still have bomb racks today. Some An-26s were converted for reconnaissance/ survey purposes.

In 2004 operators include Afghanistan, Azerbaijan (An-24), Belarus, Bulgaria, Cambodia (An-24RV), Cape Verde, China, Congo (An-24), Cuba, Czech Republic, Hungary, Kazkahstan, Laos (An-24), Libya, Lithuania, Madagascar, Mali, Mongolia, Mozambique, Nicaragua, Niger, Poland, Romania, Russia, Slovakia, Syria, Ukraine, Uzbekistan, Vietnam, Yemen and Zambia.

### Product improvement

During the production run notable improvements were introduced, the first of which was a change to more powerful AI-24T engines, followed by a change to AI-24VT engines in 1980. The following year the An-24B was introduced, this version featuring a roll-gang hold floor for the carriage of

*Right: The An-26 is still in widespread Russian service, in both the transport role and for a variety of specialist tasks. Bearing the flag of St Andrew, this aircraft serves with the Russian navy.*

*Below: Dubbed Firekiller, the An-32P is a fire-fighting version with fuselage-side tanks holding 17,635 lb (8000 kg) of retardant. Up to 30 smoke-jumpers can be carried internally.*

***Right:** Russian and Ukrainian An-32s have seen much service in support of United Nations operations. In the late 1980s, Indian An-32s were instrumental in keeping the Indian peacekeeping force in Sri Lanka adequately supplied.*

***Below:** This Russian An-26 has been extensively modified for military trials duties. The most important of the Soviet/ Russian special missions aircraft was the An-26RT, which performed cross-border electronic surveillance from bases in East Germany.*

pallets, and improved load-handling equipment. The cabin is reconfigurable between palletised freight, standard cargo or troop-carrying layout in about 30 minutes.

Numerous versions of the An-26 were evolved for special missions. The An-26BRL was an ice reconnaissance version with extra fuel tankage and a stub pylon on the rear fuselage, while the An-26D was another long-range version, for Siberian operations, with extra fuel tanks on the fuselage sides. There was an An-26M ambulance version and an An-26P fire-fighter. Another An-26M was an East German air force Elint version, while the An-26RT was a Soviet/Russian air force Sigint platform, distinguished by a farm of large blade antennas. There were trials versions and An-26L calibration aircraft, and several were given VIP interiors as the An-26S Salon. The An-26TS designation covered aircraft with seats and tables. Some operators performed their own conversions, including Czechoslovakia which created a single An-26Z-1 EW jamming platform.

## Uprated replacement

Replacing the An-26 in production at the Kiev plant was the An-32 'Cline'. The new aircraft was designed to offer improved take-off performance, ceiling and payload, especially under 'hot-and-high' conditions. It retains the superb cargo ramp of the An-26, and has an increased capacity (6,615-lb/ 3000-kg) internal winch. Removable roller conveyors aid air-dropping or the extraction of loads by drag-parachute. The cabin can accommodate up to 50 passengers, 42 paratroops, or 24 stretcher patients and three attendants. The normal crew consists of pilot, co-pilot and navigator, with provision for a flight engineer.

Although the An-32 was originally offered with a choice of powerplant, all production aircraft have been fitted with the 5,112-ehp (3812-ekW) Ivchenko AI-20D series 5, similar to (but more powerful than) the engine used by the An-12 and Il-18. These are mounted above the wing to give greater clearance for the increased-diameter propellers, reduce the danger of debris ingestion, and decrease noise levels in the cabin. The overwing position, however, results in very deep nacelles because the bulk of the An-26's original nacelle has been retained to accommodate the improved main undercarriage units when retracted. The overwing portion of the nacelle extended back only to about mid-chord on the An-32 prototype, but extends back almost to the trailing edge of the original underwing nacelle on production aircraft. The 'turbojet APU' of the An-26 and some An-24 versions has been replaced by a simple TG-16M APU in the tip of the starboard landing gear fairing.

The improvements to the An-32 have been extremely successful, producing an aircraft which can operate from airfields with elevations of up to 14,750 ft (4500 m) above sea level, and which has set a host of world records for payload-to-height, and sustained altitude.

In 1993 the first An-32B was seen boasting uprated powerplants with approximately 200-shp (149-kW) extra power available per engine. At the Paris air show that same year, Antonov demonstrated the An-32P water-bomber, named Firekiller. Like the similar An-26 conversion, it features side-mounted tanks, though those of the An-32 are substantially larger with a total capacity of 17,635 lb (8000 kg), and faired on. Flares are carried to induce artificial precipitation over fires. A long-range version, dubbed An-32V-200, had large tanks scabbed on to the fuselage sides.

Further development centres around the An-32B-100 with uprated AI-20D Series SM engines, or a westernised aircraft powered by the Rolls-Royce AE2100. Series production was maintained until 1992, with production to order thereafter. By the end of 1999 346 An-32s had been built. Military operators include Bangladesh, Croatia, Cuba, Ethiopia, India (locally named Sutlej), Mexico, Peru, Russia and Sri Lanka.

## Chinese copies

As well as Ukrainian production, the An-24/26 has also been built in China as an unlicensed copy. First flying in December 1970, the Xian Y-7 (An-24) serves in small numbers with the Chinese air force, as does the Y7H copy of the An-26. The latter first flew in late 1988. At least one is used for cloud-seeding, while another went to the air force of Mauritania.

***The break-up of the Soviet Union added a number of former republics to the An-26 operator list. The Lithuanian air force acquired five An-26Bs from the country's airline, although only three were put into military service.***

# Atlas Cheetah

## A South African Mirage

*Main picture: No. 2 Squadron decorated this Cheetah C to celebrate the 75th anniversary of the SAAF. The aircraft was soon nicknamed 'Spotty' by SAAF personnel.*

*Inset: All Cheetahs carry the Cheetah emblem, but this personalised form is only carried by the Cheetah C.*

**With the Cheetah, South Africa produced a capable warplane in the face of international sanctions. At the dawn of the 21st century, the aircraft has a long life ahead of it, and could be used for advanced training or be exported, after its replacement by the JAS 39 Gripen.**

The election of a socialist Labour government in Britain in 1964 led to the imposition of sanctions which cut South Africa off from what had been its main arms supplier, with Britain joining the USA and a number of other nations. France initially stepped into the breach, but South Africa was spurred into a drive for self sufficiency and 'import substitution'. Even France imposed sanctions in the late 1970s, and by the mid-1980s, the SAAF was facing severe difficulties. Ageing Canberras and Buccaneers were in urgent need of replacement, while the surviving Mirage IIIs were becoming structurally tired and were showing increasingly severe limitations, especially as the Front-Line States began to receive more modern and sophisticated fighters.

South Africa's Mirage F1s remained viable in the air-to-ground role, and it was decided that they would be augmented by upgraded Mirage IIIs. The Mirage III still offered superb outright performance characteristics, and it was felt that an ambitious upgrade and refurbishing programme would extend the type's useful service life and redress its shortcomings. The state-owned Atlas Aircraft Company had amassed considerable experience in supporting and maintaining a wide range of aircraft types, and had even licence-assembled supersonic Mirage F1AZ fighter-bombers and built MB.326s (as Atlas Impalas). South Africa had also built up close links with Israel, the two nations secretly co-operating on a number of weapons programmes.

### Mirage upgrade

The South African Mirage upgrade programme was (inevitably) based on Israel's Kfir – itself an indigenous derivative of the Mirage. The upgraded South African aircraft, known as Cheetahs, were converted from existing Mirage airframes, and retained French SNECMA Atar engines, whereas the Kfirs were newly-built, and were powered by US General Electric J79 engines. Like the Kfir, however, the Cheetah was designed as a multi-role fighter/fighter-bomber, and was equipped with much the same suite of avionics.

Atlas converted 16 Mirage IIIEZs to Cheetah E configuration (broadly equivalent to the Kfir-C7), and converted 11 Mirage IIIDZs and D2Zs to Cheetah D configuration (broadly equivalent to the Kfir-TC7). There are persistent unconfirmed reports that Atlas produced five more Cheetah Ds from Kfir or Mirage airframes supplied by IAI. The Cheetah D and Cheetah E conversions were undertaken side-by-side, and the variants respectively equipped No. 89 CFS at Pietersburg from 1 July 1986 and No. 5 Squadron at Louis Trichardt from March 1988. The Cheetah Ds may have briefly taken over the nuclear strike role prior to the retirement of the SAAF's Buccaneers in 1991, before South Africa withdrew and dismantled its six

*Common to both Cheetah and Kfir are the filled-in sawcuts in the leading edge of the basic Mirage III wing, which are replaced by a dogtooth. This Cheetah D was photographed overflying the Voortrekker Monument.*

***It is possible that the Cheetah Ds may have taken over the Buccaneer's nuclear strike role for a short time in 1990. The type also allowed the retirement of the SAAF's remaining Canberra B(I).Mk 12s and today serves in the attack and training roles.***

bombs in March 1992. They then reverted to an advanced training, long-range attack and laser designation role. The Cheetah Es were assigned a dual air defence and ground attack role, with a heavy emphasis being placed on the air-to-ground task. The Cheetah Es were officially withdrawn in October 1992, but they were replaced by a then still secret new Cheetah variant, the Cheetah C.

Under Project Bark, the SAAF was to have received six Cheetah Rs for reconnaissance duties, but in the event only one Mirage IIIR2Z was converted to Cheetah R configuration, and the reconnaissance role was assumed by Cheetah Cs carrying W. Vinten Ltd Type 18 Series 600 reconnaissance pods. The sole Cheetah R was used as the testbed for a new Advanced Combat Wing developed by Atlas, before being retired to the SAAF Apprentice Training School in 1998.

The Cheetah C was the final SAAF Cheetah, 38 of which were produced under Project Tunny, using Israeli-supplied airframe components (possibly from redundant Kfirs, possibly newly-built). These aircraft used SNECMA Atar 09 engines taken from retired Mirage F1s and acquired from abroad. The Cheetah Ds of No. 89 CFS moved to Trichardt in December 1992, forming a training flight within No. 2 Squadron, which converted to the new Cheetah C and moved from Hoedspruit. Cheetah C deliveries were completed in June 1995.

Whereas the Cheetah E had been equipped with only an ELTA EL2001 ranging radar, the Cheetah C is broadly equivalent to the Kfir 2000, and as such has a pulse-Doppler, track-while-scan EUM-2032 radar. The new variant also has a new modern glass cockpit, with a wide angle HUD and full HOTAS controls. The Cheetah C operates primarily in the air defence role, and is armed with a variety of AAMs, including the indigenous V3B Kukri, the V3C Darter, Israeli Python and Shafrir AAMs, and the new active radar-homing AAM developed by Rafael.

The surviving two-seat Cheetah Ds are currently being upgraded with Atar 09K50 engines, an uprated Cheetah C-type undercarriage and a wraparound windscreen, following the prototype conversion of one aircraft which had been damaged in a heavy landing (and subsequent fire). At one time there were suggestions that the surviving Cheetah Es would be brought up to Cheetah C standards, but the aircraft were instead simply placed in store at Pietersburg.

The Cheetahs will be replaced by the Hawks and JAS 39 Gripens ordered during 1999. In the meantime, South Africa has many more Cheetah Cs than it has pilots to fly them, and hours can be spread over all the airframes.

# Cheetah C

**Like all of the South African Air Force's active Cheetahs, this Cheetah C is flown by No. 2 Squadron, based at AFB Louis Trichardt, in the north east of the country. The Cheetah C emerged into a relative blaze of publicity in 1995 when the wraps were finally taken off what had hitherto been South Africa's most secret aviation programme. Cheetahs will give way to Gripens in the 21st century, following a $1.76 billion deal to purchase 28 of the Saab/BAe fighters.**

**Single-piece windshield**
The new single-piece windshield developed for the Cheetah C, and later available for retrofit to the Cheetah D, is a major advance over the unit inherited from the Mirage III. The stretched-acrylic transparency has better optical quality than its glass and acrylic predecessor and none of the steel struts that obscured the pilot's vision. It is also stronger, being capable of resisting a 4-lb (1.8-kg) birdstrike at >250 kt (287 mph; 461 km/h).

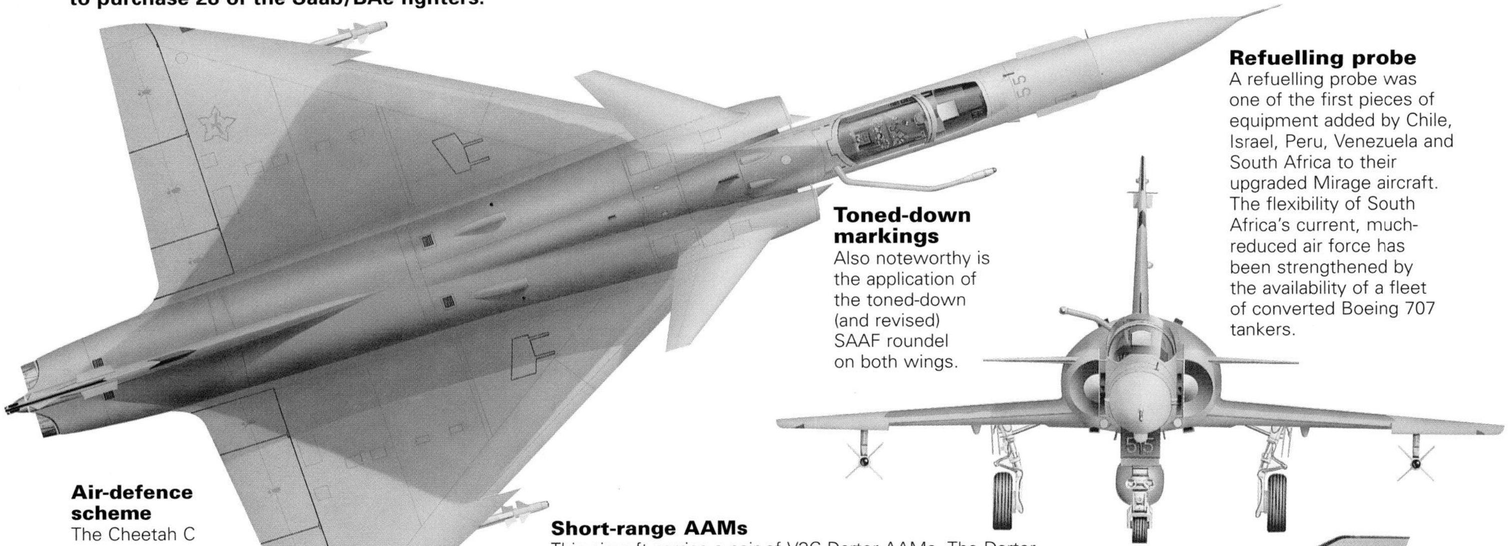

**Refuelling probe**
A refuelling probe was one of the first pieces of equipment added by Chile, Israel, Peru, Venezuela and South Africa to their upgraded Mirage aircraft. The flexibility of South Africa's current, much-reduced air force has been strengthened by the availability of a fleet of converted Boeing 707 tankers.

**Toned-down markings**
Also noteworthy is the application of the toned-down (and revised) SAAF roundel on both wings.

**Air-defence scheme**
The Cheetah C brought with it a new two-tone grey camouflage scheme that uses a large, darker diamond-shaped panel to obscure the shape of the delta wing in flight.

**Short-range AAMs**
This aircraft carries a pair of V3C Darter AAMs. The Darter entered SAAF service in 1990 and has an off-boresight capability of 20° when used with the Cheetah's helmet sight. It is believed to have been upgraded to longer-range (4.9 mile/8 km), larger warhead, U-Darter standard after delivery.

# British Aerospace Sea Harrier
## A naval 'jump-jet'

XZ451 was the second production Sea Harrier and was preceded by three trials aircraft. When the 30-mm ADEN cannon pods were not fitted, ventral strakes were added to preserve aerodynamic qualities, notably in terms of recirculating air while in the hover.

**The RAF's revolutionary Harrier had already proven the viability of VTOL operations at sea, so when the Royal Navy ditched its conventional carrier fleet in 1978, a navalised Harrier was developed to take the place of the Phantoms and Buccaneers which had previously provided the Navy's carrierborne muscle.**

When, in 1964, the Labour government cancelled the supersonic VTOL P.1154RN and bought the F-4K Phantom instead, it appeared that the Royal Navy was committed to conventional carriers. However, by the end of 1978 the Phantom and the carriers had gone, replaced by three 'Harrier-carrier' vessels ('Invincible'-class through-deck cruisers) plus an interim converted carrier (HMS *Hermes*), none able to support conventional fixed-wing aircraft. The only aircraft available was the Harrier, suitably navalised and optimised for fleet air defence.

The navalised Harrier differed from the RAF model in the vital respect that it had radar and a cockpit floor raised 10 in (25 cm) for greatly improved pilot's vision. Development problems associated with the Hawker Siddeley P.1184 Sea Harrier were few, for 24 exercises had been conducted by 'land' Harriers from 17 aircraft- or helicopter-carriers of eight navies in the 10 years since P.1127 XP831 had landed aboard HMS *Ark Royal* on 8 February 1963. As a concession to the salt air, however, magnesium components were replaced in the airframe and engine, the latter becoming the Pegasus Mk 104, still with the 21,500-lb st (96.75-kN) rating.

*Painted in chrome yellow primer and with only necessary equipment fitted, XZ450 made the Sea Harrier's first flight from Dunsfold on 20 August 1978, with little fanfare. The aircraft was actually the fourth to be built.*

### Naval roles

The military designation, Sea Harrier FRS.Mk 1, denoted fighter, reconnaissance and strike duties. As a fighter, the aircraft was intended to defend the fleet against Soviet long-range bombers approaching at medium altitude and launching first-generation cruise missiles the size of small aircraft. For this, Ferranti Blue Fox pulse-modulated I-Band radar was developed from the Sea Spray unit installed in the Lynx HAS.2 naval helicopter. This gave search and attack modes for both air and surface targets, with weapon-aiming data presented in the HUD, as well as boresight ranging for targets of opportunity. Twin 30-mm ADEN cannon pods could be fitted, the main air-to-air weapon being the Bodenseewerke-built AIM-9L Sidewinder, one of which was initially carried on each outer wing pylon. A twin-rail launcher was hastily developed during the Falklands War and entered service immediately afterwards, in August 1982.

Photographic reconnaissance was minimally catered for by a single F95 oblique camera in the nose, the principal recce role

***Seen during deck trials aboard* Hermes, *this aircraft served with No. 700A Flight, the intensive flight trials unit formed to clear the Sea Harrier for front-line service. Other trials aircraft were assigned to the manufacturer at Dunsfold and the A&AEE at Boscombe.***

***The Sea Eagle anti-ship missile was an important Sea Harrier weapon and is seen here being carried by one of the pre-production aircraft during land-based ski-jump trials.***

being considered the radar pinpointing of enemy vessels. Used only in daylight, the starboard-side F95 had two interchangeable lenses and a shutter speed of up to 1/3,000 second.

Strike implied loft-bombing with the lightweight (600-lb/272-kg) version of the British WE177 nuclear weapon, but conventional weaponry also figured prominently in the Sea Harrier's armoury. Inboard underwing pylons stressed to 2,000 lb (907 kg) could carry 1,030-lb (467-kg) free-fall and 1,120-lb (508-kg) retarded bombs, or a BAe Sea Eagle surface-skimming anti-ship missile with a weight of 1,325 lb (601 kg) and range of over 68 miles (110 km). Drop tanks were also available for this position, the original 100-Imp gal (455-litre) fitments having been augmented in August 1982 by 190-lmp gal (864-litre) tanks. For ferrying, 300-lmp gal (1364-litre) tanks could be used, but with the limitation that flaps could not be lowered with them attached. Other possibilities were Lepus flares, Royal Navy 2-in (51-mm) rocket pods of 36 rounds each and CBLS 100 carriers for small 6.6-lb (3-kg) and 31-lb (14-kg) practice bombs.

Avionics changes from the Harrier included a Ferranti attitude reference and heading system linked to Decca 72 Doppler as a replacement for the FE541 INS, which could not be aligned on a moving deck. The typical navigation error of the new system was 1.5 nm (1.7 miles; 2.8 km) after 50 minutes of flight. Smiths Industries provided a new HUD, linked to a weapon-aiming computer; there was a radar altimeter; and a new autopilot eased workload. Increased power requirements were met by two 15-kVA alternators, and the radar warning receiver was an improved version of ARI.18223. Tracor AN/ALE-40 chaff/flare dispensers were fitted internally in April 1982.

## Production programme

Hawker Siddeley received a study contract for the 'Navalised Harrier' in 1972, Ferranti receiving a go-ahead for radar development in the following year. Announcement of a contract for 24 aircraft, including three pre-series machines for development work, was made on 15 May 1975, the order complemented by a Harrier T.Mk 4A funded by the Navy, but delivered to the RAF as a payback for pilot training services rendered. Follow-on orders increased the total to 57 single-seat aircraft and four trainers, the final three being navalised T.Mk 4Ns with Sea Harrier avionics and stores management systems, Pegasus 104 engines and appropriate colour schemes, but no radar (despite a black nosecone). With its small wing, the Sea Harrier required only a port-folding nose in order to use the deck-lift aboard 'Invincible'-class vessels, but the T.Mk 4N was incapable of being struck below.

First flight of a Sea Harrier (XZ450) took place at Dunsfold on 20 August 1978, in advance of the three pre-series aircraft that had been delayed by problems not of the manufacturer's making. On 15 December 1978, the FAA's last two fixed-wing squadrons of Buccaneers and Phantoms disbanded, but it was not until 18 June 1979 that Sea Harrier XZ451 was handed over at Yeovilton as the first of a new line of fixed-wing, front-line aircraft. Apart from the short-lived trials squadron, four RN units were formed to operate Sea Harriers: 800 NAS and 801 NAS for shipboard deployment and 899 NAS as the normally shore-based headquarters and training unit. 809 NAS was established during the Falklands campaign, but disbanded soon after. The only export order was from India, which bought 23 FRS.Mk 51 single-seaters and four T.Mk 60 two-seaters. These were essentially similar to the RN machines, but used MATRA Magic missiles instead of AIM-9s and had different radios and oxygen system.

***Above: India's Sea Harriers serve with 300 INAS 'White Tigers'. After training at Yeovilton, the first aircraft left for India in December 1983 for service aboard INS* Vikrant. *In August 1987 the Sea Harriers switched to INS* Viraat, *previously the Falklands veteran* Hermes.**

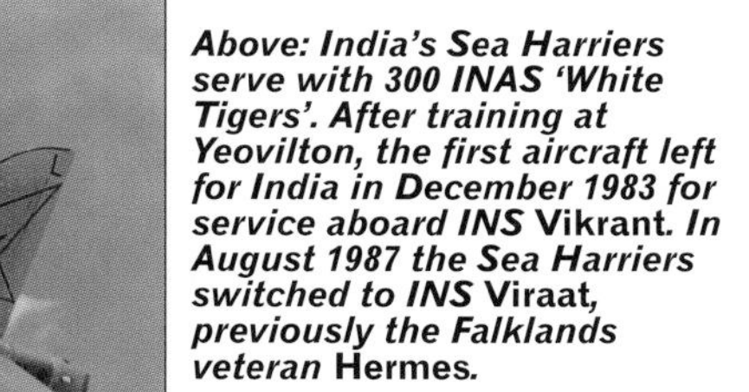


***Left: Bearing the crossed swords and trident badge of 800 Naval Air Squadron on its tail, this FRS.Mk 1 displays the all-over Extra Dark Sea Grey paint scheme adopted for the Falklands campaign.***

# Sea Harrier FA.Mk 2

*The Sea Harrier FRS.Mk 1/AIM-9L combination was a potent one in the Falklands War, and the second-generation aircraft retains Sidewinder capability. This aircraft is also fitted with two underfuselage 30-mm ADEN cannon pods, which can be replaced by AIM-120 AMRAAM launch rails or aerodynamic strakes.*

**In refining the Sea Harrier as a more capable interceptor, while retaining its reconnaissance and attack capabilities, British Aerospace made some significant changes to the airframe. The result was the FA.Mk 2, one of the most able fighters in service anywhere in the world today.**

*The Sea Harrier FA.Mk 2 was notable for being the first aircraft outside the US to be fitted with the AIM-120 AMRAAM missile. Combined with the superb Blue Vixen radar, the AMRAAM makes the second-generation 'Shar' a potent BVR fighter.*

British Aerospace received a contract in January 1985 for the project definition phase of the Sea Harrier update programme, which included two conversions of the Sea Harrier FRS.Mk 1 to FRS.Mk 2 (later FA.Mk 2) standard. Initially (in 1984) it had been reported that the MoD was planning to award a £200 million contract to BAe and Ferranti to cover a mid-life update of the entire Sea Harrier fleet, but these plans were substantially revised (in 1985) to cover an upgrade of some 30 airframes. The upgrade would include Blue Vixen radar, JTIDS, AIM-120 AMRAAM provision and an enhanced RWR fit. The original BAe proposal also covered the installation of wingtip Sidewinder rails. These additions, along with several other aerodynamic refinements, were eventually cut from the project, but a kinked wing leading edge and wing fence were retained. The first of these test aircraft (ZA195) was flown on 19 September 1988, followed by the second (XZ439) on 8 March 1989. Despite the addition of an extra equipment bay and a recontoured nose to house the Blue Vixen radar (giving the aircraft more of an elongated appearance than its predecessor), the FRS.Mk 2 is actually nearly 2 ft (0.61 m) shorter overall due to the elimination of the extended pitot head probe of the earlier variant. No increase in wingspan was found to be necessary to carry additional stores, which included a pair of 190-Imp gal (864-litre) drop tanks plus Hughes AIM-120 AMRAAMs (or BAe Alarms) on each of the outer pylons. Ferry tips are available to increase the wingspan to 29 ft 8 in (9.04 m).

The FA.Mk 2 cockpit introduced new multi-function CRT displays and HOTAS controls to reduce pilot workload. The

*Fleet Air Arm air defence: a Sea Harrier FA.Mk 2 from No. 801 Sqn shares deck space on HMS* Illustrious *with a Sea King AEW.Mk 2 from No. 849 Sqn. The Sea Harrier's Blue Vixen radar provides the pilot with an excellent air picture – in operations over Bosnia FA.Mk 2s have occasionally been used to fill in blanks in the overall AEW coverage.*

***Fitted with Sidewinder acquisition rounds, fuel tanks and gun pods, a Sea Harrier FA.Mk 2 positions itself over the carrier deck prior to landing. The bolt-on refuelling probe is regularly used for ferrying, allowing the aircraft to refuel from RAF tankers.***

FA.Mk 2 is powered by a Pegasus Mk 106 turbofan, a navalised version of the Mk 105 as fitted to the AV-8B, but with no magnesium in its construction. On 7 December 1988, a contract was awarded for the conversion of 31 FRS.Mk 1s to Mk 2 standard. On 6 March 1990, an order was placed for 10 new-build FA.Mk 2s to augment the conversions, attrition having by that time reduced the RN's Sea Harrier inventory to 39 aircraft. A further contract in January 1994 covered 18 more FA.Mk 2s and an additional five FRS.Mk 1 conversions.

Aircraft undergoing conversion are stripped down at Dunsfold, before being delivered by road to Brough for the fundamental structural work. The upgraded aircraft are then returned to Dunsfold for final assembly.

## Carrier trials

Carrier qualification trials were conducted aboard HMS *Ark Royal* during November 1990 and, among other favourable factors, these proved the FA.Mk 2 capable of operating safely from a 12° ramp. The two aircraft involved in the trials of late 1990 were configured as pre-production aircraft, although there was only one radar between the two. In order to enhance pilot conversion training, a new two-seat trainer conversion, designated T.Mk 8N, was provided with four aircraft replacing Harrier T.Mk 4Ns in 1996. Essentially a reconfigured T.Mk 4N, this variant duplicates FA.Mk 2 systems, apart from radar.

The primary air-to-air missile for the Sea Harrier FA.Mk 2 is the Hughes AIM-120 AMRAAM. The Blue Vixen radar ('A' version) was extensively flight tested in a BAC One-Eleven in a 114-hour flight programme which ended in November 1987, and again in a BAe 125 (XW930) until August 1988. Another BAe 125 (ZF130) was fitted with a complete FA.Mk 2 cockpit in the right-hand seat and later gained a B version radar in 1989. AIM-120 trials included 10 live firings against sub-scale MQM-107 drones and full-scale, supersonic QF-106 drones, commencing on 29 March 1993. A serious setback occurred with the loss of one of two radar-equipped aircraft (XZ495) in a crash in the Bristol Channel on 5 January 1994.

A trials unit was formed at Boscombe Down in June 1993, receiving the first production FA.Mk 2 (XZ497) on the 21st of that month. The Sea Harrier FA.Mk 2 OEU, currently undertaking trials at Boscombe, is an offshoot of No. 899 Sqn. Four aircraft from this OEU then undertook a limited combat cruise aboard HMS *Invincible* from August 1994, prior to full-scale deployment on HMS *Illustrious* by No. 801 Sqn in January 1995. No. 800 Sqn also formed on the type, becoming a stalwart of operations over the former Yugoslavia.

However, the Sea Harrier is now scheduled for retirement by 2006, in favour of upgraded Harrier GR.Mk 9 attack aircraft.

# Sea Harrier FA.Mk 2

**Sea Harrier FA.Mk 2 orders for the Royal Navy totalled 38 conversions from existing FRS.Mk 1s plus some 28 new-build aircraft. These serve with two front-line squadrons (No. 800 – '12x' codes and No.801 – '00x' codes) and a Yeovilton-based training unit (No. 899 Sqn). Under the 1998 UK Strategic Defence Review, the Sea Harrier force joined the RAF's Harrier GR.Mk 7 fleet in a joint-services command, allowing integrated FA.Mk 2/GR.Mk 7 air groups to be carried aboard Royal Navy carriers.**

### Blue Vixen radar

The heart of the FA.Mk 2 upgrade is the GEC-Marconi Blue Vixen, a lightweight multi-mode radar offering full lookdown/shootdown capability over sea or land. Designed from the outset to be fully compatible with AMRAAM, the radar allows the ripple-firing of all four missiles carried by the Sea Harrier. Working in I-band with variable pulse repetition frequencies, the radar offers a wide range of air-to-air and air-to-surface modes, the latter supporting sea search missions.

### Cockpit

Although it retains the original HUD (head-up display) from the FRS.Mk 1, the FA.Mk 2 cockpit has been considerably redesigned to incorporate two MFD head-down displays. All vital inputs are made via a HOTAS (hands on throttle and stick) system or via a UFC (upfront controller). JTIDS datalink integration was initially specified, then shelved, and later reinstated.

### Rear fuselage

An extra 1-ft 2-in (0.35-m) plug was inserted aft of the wing trailing edge of the FA.Mk 2 to offer greater internal capacity for avionics equipment.

### Defences

The FA.Mk 2 is adequately protected thanks to its GEC-Marconi Sky Guardian 200 radar warning receiver, which presents a threat array in the cockpit. Mechanical countermeasures are launched from ALE-40 chaff/flare dispensers.

### Air-to-ground weapons

Although tailored more closely to the air defence mission than the FRS.Mk 1, the FA.Mk 2 can carry CRV-7 rocket pods, 1,000-lb (454-kg) bombs, Lepus flares and other air-to-ground ordnance, if required.

### Missile armament

The FA.Mk 2's standard air-to-air loadout consists of four AIM-120 AMRAAMs carried under the wings and fuselage (the latter displacing the ADEN cannon). On the fuselage stations, the AIM-120 uses the LAU-106/A ejector launcher, while those carried underwing are suspended from Frazer-Nash Common Rail Launchers. The wing AMRAAMs can be replaced by up to four AIM-9 Sidewinders on LAU-7 rails. The ALARM anti-radiation missile is an option.

# BAe Hawk

## RAF jet trainer

**The British Aerospace Hawk has been in RAF service for more than 20 years. During its first 10 years, the Hawk was used as the RAF's advanced trainer, taught pilots tactics and weapons skills, became a fighter and thrilled millions as the mount of the *Red Arrows* aerobatic team.**

Today the Hawk is still in production at Warton – but as a very different aircraft to that conceived over a quarter of a century ago. The sound performance, structural integrity and handling characteristics of today's Hawk have their roots in an RAF requirement of the late 1960s.

### Genesis

The foundations for the Hawk programme resulted from a Royal Air Force need to replace the Folland Gnat and Hawker Hunter for the purposes of advanced training – a role which the two-seat Jaguar B had been due to undertake – and for the same aircraft to take over the upper end of the basic training syllabus conducted on the Jet Provost, although this requirement was later abandoned. This was encapsulated in Air Staff Requirement (ASR) 397 which was issued at the end of 1970.

However, it was recognised from the outset that the new trainer needed to be exportable, which required it to have a ground-attack potential. The contenders for ASR 397 were the Franco-German Alpha Jet, the Hawker Siddeley HS 1182 and the BAC P.59. Design contracts were issued in 1971 to the two British firms and, in October 1971, the HS 1182 was selected as the winner. A contract was place for 176 aircraft for the RAF in March 1972, the name 'Hawk' being chosen in August 1973. The design was for a tandem-seat, single-turbofan engined (Rolls-Royce/Turboméca Adour) aircraft with provision for five hardpoints.

In order to minimise the programme costs, Hawker Siddeley proposed that the Hawk should be built from the outset on production tooling, without building any prototypes. The first pre-production aircraft and the first five off the production line would be used in the flight test phase.

The maiden flight occurred on 21 August 1974, XX154 being flown by Duncan Simpson from Dunsfold airfield. Initial testing resulted in the addition of a pair of ventral stakes under the fuselage (to improve directional stability), as well as wing vortex generators and a small leading-edge fence. The first public appearance of the new aircraft was at the Society of British Aircraft Constructors (SBAC) Farnborough air show in September 1974.

### Initial deliveries

The first pair of Hawk T. Mk 1s was delivered to the RAF at RAF Valley on Anglesey, the home of No. 4 Flying Training School (FTS), on 4 November 1976. The first squadron of No. 4 FTS to re-equip was No. 1, the Central Flying School squadron responsible for standardisation and instructor training. By October 1979, the Hawk had replaced the difficult-to-maintain Gnat and

*Above: Photographed on its roll-out at Dunsfold in August 1974, the first Hawk was a pre-production aircraft, no prototypes being produced. The colour scheme was the familiar red and white.*

*Top: The major user of the Hawk in RAF service is No. 4 Flying Training School based at Valley – visible below the aircraft – where advanced pilot training is undertaken.*

*Four of the schemes worn in RAF service are those of high viz training (red and white), weapons training (camouflaged), point defence (grey) and the display team colours of the* Red Arrows.

***No. 234 Sqn of No. 1 Tactical Weapons Unit, based at RAF Brawdy, was one of four squadrons that lived on as shadow identities for the TWUs.***

Hunter (which had been used to train pilots who could not physically fit into the diminutive Gnat) in all the No. 4 FTS units. Students arrived at Valley after flying the Jet Provost, or later the Shorts Tucano, to fly just under 75 hours on the Hawk. From Valley, the newly-qualified pilots travelled to the pre-Operational Conversion Unit tactical fighter/ground-attack lead-in training courses run at the Tactical Weapons Units (TWUs).

## Weapons training

In the mid-1970s a massive fleet of Hunters was occupied in the task of training recently-qualified pilots in the art of formation flying, air combat tactics and live weapons firing. The TWU at RAF Brawdy began receiving Hawks for this role from July 1977. The weapons-carrying capability, which had been built in as part of the export potential of the aircraft, and the continuity factor for the pilot – flying the same type for advanced training and tactical weapons flying – made the Hawk ideally suited to this task. The aircraft carried the centreline 30-mm Aden gun and had two underwing pylons for rocket pods or practice bomb carriers, no provision being made for underwing fuel tanks. Instead of the training colours of red and white, the tactical Hawks wore a green/grey camouflage.

The TWU was a unit of Strike Command and its aircraft formed 'shadow squadrons'. When the TWU split into No. 1 TWU at RAF Brawdy (with shadow squadrons Nos 79 and 234) and No. 2 TWU (Nos 63 and 151 Sqn) at RAF Chivenor (after a brief stay at Lossiemouth), most of the remaining Hunters went to No. 2 TWU, which did not officially convert to the Hawk until April 1981. The TWUs had a principal war role of assisting in the low-level defence of RAF airfields.

## Point defence fighter

The successful use of the TWU Hunters as point defence fighters during exercises led to the testing of the Hawk in this role, in which it was found to be more than adequate. In early 1983, a contract was issued to convert 89 Hawks to be compatible with the AIM-9L Sidewinder air-to-air missile, to allow the aircraft to operate in the supplementary air-to-air role in times of emergency. After conversion, aircraft were designated Hawk T.Mk 1As. The idea was to illuminate enemy aircraft with the Foxhunter radar of the Panavia Tornado F.Mk 3, while the Hawk, which was to be flown by an experienced instructor, fired the missiles at the target. It was termed the 'mixed fighter force concept' and a total of 72 aircraft was declared to NATO after the last conversion was completed in May 1986.

## Red Arrows

After the training school at Valley had retired its Gnats, the only examples of this aircraft left flying, with the exception of a few on test duties with the Ministry of Defence (Procurement Executive), were those with the Central Flying School's aerobatic team, the *Red Arrows*. Deliveries of Hawks to the *'Reds'* began in August 1979 and the team began flying displays on the Hawk during the 1980 air show season. Apart from the colour scheme, their Hawks were modified with a ventral fuselage tank filled with diesel oil and red and blue dyes, ducted to three outlets above the jet-pipe for injection into the exhaust efflux. Some of the aircraft flown by the team were also part of a programme of modifications to bring them up to T.Mk 1A standard and, in an emergency, they would be used in the point defence role.

## ETPS

The Empire Test Pilot School (ETPS) received three of the late-production aircraft for the RAF, the first being received in 1981. They were fitted with recording equipment to evaluate handling parameters as part of the course run by the school. The third aircraft was later modified as the Advanced System Training Aircraft (ASTRA), a variable-stability simulator of different aircraft handling characteristics, replacing a Beagle Basset in this role.

The ASTRA Hawk was first flown after conversion by Cranfield College of Aeronautics on 21 August 1986, exactly 12 years after the Hawk's first flight.

***Above: The Empire Test Pilot School at Boscombe Down received three Hawks. Two were used for general fast-jet handling training, while the third was modified as a variable-stability aircraft, the ASTRA, to simulate the handling of a wide range of aircraft types.***

***Left: The agility of the Hawk gave rise to its secondary (wartime) role of airfield defence. Re-wired to be compatible with Sidewinder air-to-air missiles, the aircraft received an overall grey scheme and was redesignated as the Hawk T.Mk 1A.***

# Export success

**Having already established itself an enviable reputation within the RAF as a fast-jet trainer, the Hawk was actively marketed to a number of European and Middle Eastern countries. Many were to realise the potential of the aircraft, with a succession of orders being placed.**

***BAe's Hawk beat its greatest rival, the Dassault/Dornier Alpha Jet, to enter service with Abu Dhabi in 1984. Sixteen examples were delivered and were followed in 1989 by another batch of 18. These improved T.Mk 102s featured wingtip AIM-9 Sidewinder air-to-air missile rails, radar warning receivers and revised wing aerodynamics for improved handling. They were later supplemented by four Hawk T.Mk 63Cs.***

From the start of the Hawk project, the aircraft was designed for export, especially in the light attack role, albeit with the provision that such efforts would not impair its ability to meet RAF requirements. With the Alpha Jet as the main export competitor in its advanced jet trainer category, the export Hawk was initially developed privately. It was marketed at a typical 1976 fly-away cost of around $2.25 million for the standard version, with one centreline and four underwing pylons carrying up to 5,000 lb (2268 kg) of stores over a 280-nm (322-mile; 520-km) combat radius. From the beginning studies were also made of a single-seat light strike version for potential export customers, with considerably more room for additional equipment, including advanced avionics and ECM. A full-scale mock-up had been built at Kingston by early 1975. A sales point put forward by Hawker Siddeley Aviation (HSA) at an early stage in its export campaign was that, with a claimed low-level speed of around 550 kt (634 mph; 1020 km/h), the Hawk was fast enough to evade the widely-available SA-7 shoulder-launched infantry SAM. The Middle East was seen as the most likely area in which the export Hawk would find a customer. Egypt was potentially the first foreign customer for the Hawk, although it was eventually persuaded by Dassault, with the backing of the French government which offered a licence building agreement, to select Dassault's Alpha Jet.

With Egypt out of the picture, it fell to Finland to become the first Hawk export customer, placing an order for 50 T.Mk 51 versions on 30 December 1977. Only the first four Finnish Hawks were to be British-built with just the first two being assembled and flown by BAe, with Valmet in Finland responsible for some component manufacture and final assembly of the remainder. A few weeks later, on 9 February 1978, a second Hawk export order was announced, for Kenya. This involved 12 Hawk Mk 52s, which were the first to be equipped with a tail brake parachute. A third Hawk export order followed on 4 April, with an initial Indonesian air force contract for eight Mk 53s (increased to 20 on 18 May 1981), for use in the advanced flying and weapons training roles.

## Mk 50 improvements

Although generally resembling the RAF Hawks, with similar Adour engines, the Mk 50 series incorporated several improvements gained from extensive RAF experience. These included stronger wheels, tyres and brakes, a 30 per cent higher maximum take-off weight, and five stores pylons under the wings. Cockpit improvements included a Lear Siegler twin-gyro attitude and heading reference system (AHRS), a revised weapons control system incorporating a Ferranti Isis D126R lead-computing gyro sight, and more comprehensive flight instrumentation. The Finnish aircraft also

***A total of 30 Hawk Mk 65s was delivered as part of the massive Al Yamamah arms buy in 1986, followed in 1997 by a further order for 20 Mk 65As. During the Gulf War two squadrons of Saudi Hawks were stationed at Dhahran, from where they are rumoured to have flown attack missions into Kuwait.***

***Left:** To replace its elderly Vampires, the Air Force of Zimbabwe ordered eight Hawk T.Mk 61s. In doing so, the AFZ became the first customer for the uprated version. However, the first four Hawks delivered in July 1982 were badly damaged by a terrorist attack which resulted in the total destruction of one aircraft.*

***Below:** Indonesia became the third export customer for the Hawk with an initial order for eight T.Mk 53s (to be used for advanced training and weapons instruction) placed on 4 April 1978. Two follow-on orders, placed in 1981 and 1982, saw a further 12 Hawks delivered.*

***Below:** After rigorous evaluation against the Aero L-39 Albatros, Aermacchi MB-339, Dassault/Dornier Alpha Jet and Saab 105A, the Hawk gained its first export customer in the shape of the Finnish air force (Ilmavoimat). Finland operates two versions of the Hawk – the T.Mk 51, and the T.Mk 51A which incorporates structural improvements to the wings.*

## US Navy carrier trainer

On 26 January 1988, the US Navy announced the development of the T-45 Goshawk. A heavily converted carrier variant, the Goshawk features a revised wing layout and strengthened undercarriage. Entering operational service on 27 June 1992 with VT-21, the T-45 has replaced the large fleets of TA-4J Skyhawks and T-2C Buckeyes with the US Navy's training wings.

had provision for a Vinten reconnaissance pod, while the ADEN cannon was replaced by an indigenous 0.5-in (12.7-mm) machine-gun in an almost identical pod.

Engine improvements resulted in a new generation of export versions, known as the 60 series. Finland, Indonesia and Kenya remained the only customers for the 50 series Hawk.

Zimbabwe was the first customer for the Hawk 60 series, placing an order on 9 January 1981 for eight Mk 61s. The Zimbabwe order was followed on 30 June by a contract for eight Mk 61s from the Dubai Air Wing of the United Arab Emirates. Twelve Mk 64s were bought by Kuwait; 30 Mk 65s were purchased by Saudi Arabia (this total excluding 20 aircraft ordered under Al Yamamah II); 20 Mk 66s were bought by Switzerland; and 20 Mk 67s were purchased by South Korea, which has requirements for at least 20 more. The latter aircraft feature the extended nose of the Hawk 100, with a small radome for radar.

The Hawk 100 programme was launched in 1982 and incorporated a host of new avionics, including an F-16-type Singer Kerafott SKN 2415 (later BAe LINS 300 ring laser-gyro) INS. This was linked, via a dual redundant MIL STD1553B digital database, to a Smiths HUD/Weapons Aiming Computer, Smiths radar altimeter, new stores management system and air data sensor for precise low-level navigation and weapons delivery.

The Hawk's extensive range of ordnance was also further increased by the ability to carry BAe's Sea Eagle anti-ship missile and, for ground attack, the AGM-65 Maverick. These systems are designed to turn the aircraft into a truly potent light attack aircraft.

### Single-seater

Avionics developed for the Hawk 100 were later applied to the single-seat Hawk 200 derivative. Viewed as 'a more affordable fighter', it was equipped with wingtip-mounted missile rails and a Westinghouse APG-66H radar.

Oman was the launch customer for the Hawk 200 attack/interceptor, placing a contract for 12 Mk 203s on 30 July 1990, and ordering four two-seat Mk 103s at the same time.

The second customer for the Hawk 200 was Malaysia, with an order for 12 Mk 208s and 10 two-seat Mk 108 advanced systems trainers placed on 10 December 1990. Indonesia, already a Hawk customer, placed an order for 16 Mk 209s in June 1993, along with eight two-seat Mk 109s.

The US Navy made the unusual move of choosing a highly modified variant of the Hawk (the T-45 Goshawk) to fulfil its requirement for a carrier training aircraft.

The latest countries to join the ranks of Hawk operators are Australia and Canada, while South Africa's first Hawk flew in 2003. A number of nations continue to express interest in the Hawk, which is seen as the optimum solution to meet a number of firm requirements.

***In the late 1980s Oman placed a somewhat ambitious order for eight Tornado ADVs. This was cancelled in 1989 due to cost considerations. Purchased instead were 12 single-seat Mk 203 Hawks. Delivered in 1994, the aircraft serve with 6 Squadron at Al Masirah in the light attack role.***

*Resplendent in the latest BAE Systems Hawk demonstrator scheme, ZJ100 (originally the first Mk 102D production prototype) has been partially modified to LIFT standard, equipped with a 'glass' cockpit.*

# New generation Hawks

## BAE Systems Hawk 100, 200, LIF & LIFT

**Despite a relatively high 'price tag' and despite having first flown on 21 August 1974, the BAE Systems Hawk remains the 'trainer of choice' for the world's air arms. There are newer trainer aircraft in the market-place, with more advanced aerodynamics and making greater use of advanced and exotic materials, but the latest versions of the Hawk keep winning the major orders – most recently in Australia, Canada, India and South Africa.**

Although the latest Hawk variants are recognisably similar to the original 1970s vintage RAF Hawk T.Mk 1 they incorporate major improvements in many areas, and compete 'head-on' with the new generation of trainers exemplified by the Aermacchi M346, EADS Mako, Korean T-50 Golden Eagle and the MiG-AT.

Proponents of these aircraft highlight their modern fly-by-wire flight control systems (which, they claim, allow them to more faithfully simulate the handling characteristics of modern advanced fast jets), and, in the case of the T-50, stress the supposed advantages of supersonic performance capability.

*Malaysia's Hawk Mk 203s feature Lockheed Martin AN/APG-66H, wingtip Sidewinder rails, a tail-mounted RWR and a removable refuelling probe. Oman and Indonesia are the only other Hawk Mk 200 operators.*

*After receiving a batch of 29 Mk 53s beginning in 1980, Indonesia placed orders for eight Mk 109s (one of which is pictured) and 32 Mk 209s. The latter equip Nos 1 and 12 Sqns, TNI-AU.*

But there is a counter argument, and many believe that it is better for a trainer to have pleasant and viceless (but nevertheless challenging) handling characteristics. They would aver that some frontline aircraft would actually be too 'easy' to fly (from a pure handling point of view) for their handling chracteristics to be 'aped' by advanced trainers. It has also been pointed out that the Hawk is already acknowledged as excelling in the BFM (Basic Fighter Manoeuvring) role, and that the aircraft is entirely satisfactory in preparing pilots for a range of advanced modern fighters, from Abu Dhabi's Mirage 2000s, to Indonesian F-16s, Malaysian MiG-29s and Swiss F/A-18C Hornets. South Africa has acquired the type to prepare pilots for the Saab JAS 39 Gripen.

The basic RAF Hawk T.Mk 1

***Left: Mk 100 demonstrator ZJ100 is pictured here in an earlier guise, carrying a pair of dummy AGM-65 Maverick air-to-surface missiles during drop trials. Maverick was cleared for firing from the Hawk 200 in 1996.***

***Below: Australia's Hawk Mk 127s have advanced cockpit instrumentation resembling that of the F/A-18A Hornets for which they provide lead-in training. Thirty-three were ordered for the RAAF, 21 of which were assembled in Australia by BAe Australia.***

formed the basis of the original Series 50 export aircraft (which featured improved avionics, increased MTOW, four underwing hardpoints and a slightly uprated engine). The Series 60 was further improved, with an additional increase in thrust, another improvement in operating weight, and a revised wing, with four-position flaps and new 'dressing' (vortex generators and fences) on the leading edge, though it remained principally a trainer, albeit with an improved (but still secondary) ground attack capability.

## Hawk 100

The next generation Hawk 100 originated in the Hawk EGA (Enhanced Ground Attack) study, and the company demonstrator, ZA101 was incrementally modified to serve as the prototype, initially gaining an extended nose with provision for FLIR or a laser designator/marked target seeker. The aircraft flew with this new nose on 1 October 1987. The aircraft was subsequently fitted with a seven-station combat wing (with wingtip missile launch rails and combat flaps) and an uprated engine. The definitive Hawk 100, ZJ100, with an advanced digital HOTAS (Hands On Throttle And Stick) glass cockpit, first flew in February 1992. Some 40 of these aircraft were subsequently exported to Abu Dhabi, Indonesia, Malaysia and Oman between 1993 and 1996.

At the same time, BAE developed a single-seat, radar-equipped Hawk 200, which first flew in prototype form on 19 May 1987. BAE delivered 62 of these aircraft to Indonesia, Malaysia and Oman ending in 1999, but active marketing has now ceased. Recently, BAE's sales efforts have been focused on two-seaters, and especially on the latest sub-variant of the Series 100, the Hawk LIF (Lead-In Fighter) and Hawk LIFT (Lead-In Fighter Trainer).

## NATO trainers

The first of the 'new 100s' was the Mk 115, ordered by Canada in May 1998 to equip the NATO Flight Training in Canada programme. The aircraft was essentially similar to those previously delivered to Abu Dhabi, Indonesia, Malaysia and Oman – but the last of these had been ordered in June 1993.

With a five year hiatus in orders, the opportunity was taken to refine the Hawk Mk 115's cockpit. Whereas the baseline Hawk 100 had a cockpit with a single central MFD and a pure sensor display to starboard, the Hawk Mk 115 had a second MFD in place of the sensor display, albeit with limited display options.

The Mk 115 will also form the basis of the Hawks ordered by India (the order has been stalled as the result of an unrelated corruption scandal) after years of delay. The Indian Hawk (known internally as the Mk 115Y) will have a reconfigurable monochrome sensor display to starboard, and some indigenous Indian equipment including the secondary INS, the ILS and some radios. It was expected that India would receive an initial batch of BAE-assembled aircraft, followed by some assembled from kits by HAL, with the final batch being locally manufactured.

***Based at CFBs Cold Lake and Moose Jaw, alongside Raytheon T-6A Harvard IIs, the CAF's 19 Hawk Mk 115s (known locally as CT-155s) are employed for NATO Flight Training.***

***The front (below left) and rear (below right) cockpits of Hawk LIFT each feature MFDs with NVG capability, a new HUD (front cockpit only), HOTAS controls and other new systems.***

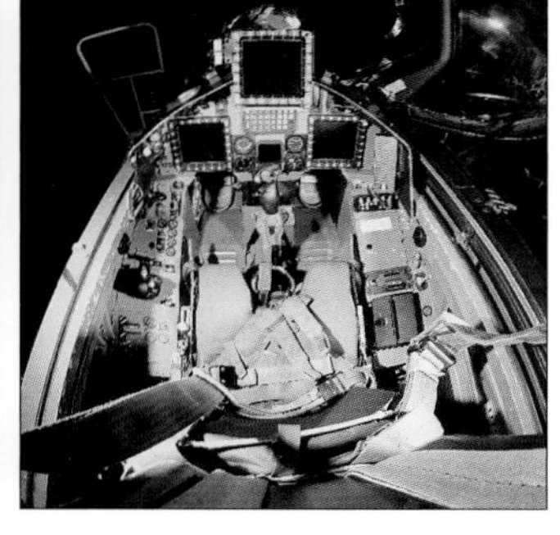

The next customer for the Hawk was Australia, whose Mk 127, ordered in June 1997, was officially designated as the Hawk LIF (Lead In Fighter). The Hawk LIF featured a new cockpit, with three colour MFDs and new avionics, including a HUD with F/A-18 symbology, an IN/GPS navigation system, and with OBOGS (On Board Oxygen Generating System), an APU and provision for a detachable, non-retractable air-to-air refuelling probe.

## Hawk LIFT

The Hawk LIF in turn formed the basis of a new variant, the Hawk LIFT (Lead In Fighter Trainer), with a further improved, fully NVG-compatible cockpit, an enhanced HUD, revised HOTAS moding and compatability with a wider range of smart weapons. The long-serving demonstrator, ZJ101, has been fitted and flown with the new cockpit, but lacks other features of the planned configuration. The new version will also gain a new powerplant, the Adour Mk 951, which incorporates FADEC (Full Authority Digital Engine Control) and technologies from the Eurofighter's EJ200 engine. A demonstrator fitted with the new engine, ZJ951, is due to fly in February 2002. Even without the new engine (which will have a thrust rating of 6,500-lb st/ 28.90 kN) the Hawk is an impressive performer, and one Australian Mk 127 has already demonstrated a speed of 568 kts (654 mph; 1053 km/h). The first LIFT-configured Hawks will be the Mk 120s ordered by South Africa in September 1999, and due for delivery from 2004.

Although by no means the cheapest trainer on the market, the Hawk does enjoy remarkably low costs of ownership, and the Canadian NFTC aircraft have already demonstrated 'tremendous' serviceability and availability rates, promising reduced through-life costs.

# British Aerospace Nimrod

## The mighty hunter

Above: Between 1971 and 1977, the RAF had a permanent Nimrod force in the Mediterranean with No. 203 Squadron based at Luqa, Malta. This example is seen in 1973, operating from RAF Gibraltar.

Top: Nimrod MR.Mk 1s were painted in a white and grey colour scheme. From late 1979, the MR.Mk 1 fleet was converted to MR.Mk 2 standard and repainted in the NATO Hemp colour.

**Derived from the world's first jet-powered airliner, the Nimrod has been constantly updated over the last 30 years to ensure that it remains one of the world's finest maritime patrol and anti-submarine aircraft.**

In 1958 the Air Ministry issued Air Staff Requirement 381 calling for a replacement for the venerable Avro Shackleton as the RAF's principal maritime patrol aircraft. At this time the NATO multinational Atlantic was under development and seemed a logical choice. However, the RAF refused to consider the Atlantic, despite it being the only post-war type to be designed specifically for this role.

By 1964, official indecision and rising costs ensured that only a derived design from a current aircraft would be affordable. The choice came down to adaptations of four British airliners – the Vickers Vanguard, Vickers VC10, de Havilland Comet and Hawker Siddeley Trident.

### Choosing the Comet

All four types underwent trials from RAF St Mawgan, evaluating low-level speed, ride comfort, fuel burn, interior accommodation and other factors. From the trials it became abundantly clear that there were excellent reasons for choosing the Comet 4C as the basic airframe. Despite being the eldest of the four designs, the Comet had an efficient wing at all speeds and altitudes in the planned mission, and crews enjoyed the handling and low-level ride. The factor which clinched the decision was that it

Above: XV148 was the first Nimrod prototype and flew initially on 23 May 1967. It lacked the equipment fit, avionics and MAD tailboom incorporated into the production version.

Right: In addition to the purely military anti-submarine role, the Nimrod MR.Mk 1 was used for long-range search-and-rescue missions and for protecting the UK's territorial waters.

**Above: During the Cold War, Nimrods often encountered Soviet navy submarines and surface vessels. Here, an MR.Mk 1 overflies a 'Kotlin'-class destroyer.**

**Right: The Nimrod MR.Mk 1's giant weapons bays held a normal load of 13,500 lb (6120 kg) of stores in six lateral rows. The fuselage aft of the bay was used for storing and ejecting sonobuoys, marine markers and other stores.**

was possible to shut down two or even three of the Comet's engines while on patrol to extend endurance. Moreover, the latter would be greatly improved by replacing the heavy and thirsty Rolls-Royce Avon 534 engines with the new Spey turbofan.

Hawker Siddeley received the go-ahead for the HS.801, later named the Nimrod, in June 1965 and started incorporating the many changes necessary to the Comet 4. The engine inlets and jetpipes were enlarged to accommodate the Spey engine. The fuselage was shortened by 6 ft (1.83 m) and an enormous unpressurised extra section was added over almost the whole length, providing room for two cavernous tandem weapons bays which accommodated almost all RAF airborne dropped stores. The engines had surface finishes to prevent saltwater corrosion and the nose contained an EMI ASV-21D surveillance radar. The landing gear was strengthened to cope with the additional weight and lateral stability was increased by the addition of a dorsal fin fillet and an enlarged fin. Two important additions at the tail were the ESM blister on top of the fin and the magnetic-anomaly detector (MAD) tailboom. A 70-million candlepower searchlight was installed in the nose of the starboard external fuel tank.

### Into service

The development was of the Nimrod proved to be painless due to the excellence of the initial design, and the first Nimrod MR.Mk 1 reached the RAF on 2 October 1969. The first unit to receive the type was the Maritime Operational Training Unit (MOTU) at St Mawgan. By August 1972, all 38 aircraft in the initial order had been delivered, equipping No. 201 Sqn at Kinloss, No. 42 Sqn and No. 236 OCU (formerly MOTU) at St Mawgan, followed by Nos 120 and 206 Sqn at Kinloss and No. 203 Sqn at RAF Luqa, Malta. From its entry into service, the Nimrod proved immensely popular, no other aircraft in its class offering anything like the same combination of performance, spaciousness, mission capability and reliability. The main tactical compartment held the mission crew, comprising a routine navigator, a tactical navigator, a radio operator, a radar operator, two sonics systems operators and an ESM/MAD operator.

To complement the Nimrod's ASW capability, provision was made to carry anti-surface vessel weaponry in the shape of underwing pylons for AS12 wire-guided missiles; however, in the event, the weapon was never carried operationally. In an additional emergency troop transport role, the Nimrod MR.Mk 1 was capable of carrying 45 fully-armed troops.

In 1974-75, a further eight Nimrod Mk 1s were built, but the British withdrawal from Malta rendered these aircraft surplus to requirements.

Seven of the eight aircraft were selected for conversion during the development of the doomed Nimrod AEW.Mk 3 airborne early warning variant.

### Nimrod R.Mk 1 – Electronic eavesdropper

In addition to 46 Nimrod MR.Mk 1s, three further aircraft (XW664-666) were ordered as replacements for No. 51 Sqn's intelligence-gathering Comets and Canberras. Security surrounding the aircraft was such that they were delivered to RAF Wyton in 1971 as little more than empty shells, with the RAF fitting virtually all the mission equipment. Shunning publicity, the R.Mk 1 entered service in 1974 as a 'calibration' aircraft, its true Elint role being disguised. The R.Mk 1 (early version pictured below) differs from maritime versions in having no MAD tailboom, instead being

fitted with dielectric radomes in the nose of each external wing tank and on the tail. Constant updating has resulted in increasing numbers of antennas above and below the fuselage as well as wingtip ESM pods. Extra internal equipment has also led to the deletion of several cabin windows and the aircraft (illustrated bottom) are currently fitted with underwing flare/chaff dispensers. The R.Mk 1s almost certainly have a computerised 'threat library', allowing a detailed 'map' of potential enemy radar stations, navaids and defence systems to be built up. With an estimated crew of about 25, No. 51 Sqn R.Mk 1s gained a Battle Honour after the Falklands War and operated from RAF Akrotiri during Operation Desert Storm. In May 1995, XW666 ditched into the Moray Firth, resulting in XV249 being converted to R.Mk 1 standard as a replacement.

**Above: RAF Kinloss hosted the Nimrod throughout its career and is now, since the withdrawal of the Nimrod from St Mawgan, home to the entire RAF fleet of MR.Mk 2s.**

# Nimrod matures

*The Nimrod fulfils three roles in RAF service: anti-submarine warfare (ASW), anti-surface unit warfare (ASUW) and search and rescue (SAR). In addition to these roles the Nimrods also assist civil agencies such as HM Customs or MAFF, when requested.*

**Constant updating has ensured that the Nimrod remains the finest maritime patrol aircraft in the world. The esteem in which the aircraft is held is re-inforced by the RAF's opinion that there is only one aircraft that can replace the Nimrod – a new Nimrod.**

Even before the first Nimrod MR.Mk 1 was built, it was recognised that in the course of a service life never approached by any previous RAF aircraft, envisaged to reach 40 years, the original avionics and mission equipment would become outdated. Accordingly, in the 1975 (two years later than planned) a largely new and immeasurably more capable equipment fit was designed. A total of 35 of the Nimrod MR.Mk 1 aircraft was completely gutted at British Aerospace Manchester Division and redelivered as virtually new aircraft, designated Nimrod MR.Mk 2 and painted in the NATO colour called Hemp, with two-colour B-type national markings.

XV236, the first Nimrod MR.Mk 2, was redelivered on 23 August 1979, and though the flight performance was unchanged, the mission effectiveness was enhanced enormously. The MR.Mk 2 had a completely new avionics and equipment suite, in which all major sensors and equipment items were changed.

## Tactical display

The aircraft received a new GEC Avionics central tactical system, used for tactical navigation and stores selection and release. The tactical display provides updated information about the Nimrod's position, showing the present and past track, passive and active sonobuoy positions, ESM bearings, MAD marks and radar contacts. A flight direction system allows course information to be displayed to the pilots and the computer can even be coupled to the autopilot, allowing the tactical navigator to steer the aircraft to the desired position. The radar installed was the EMI Searchwater which has its own data processing sub-system, allowing a clutter-free image. The radar remains one of the

*For night operations the Nimrod has an immensely powerful searchlight fitted to the starboard external fuel tank (foreground). The light is capable of illuminating an entire incident area.*

### Nimrod AEW.Mk 3

Detailed studies began in 1973 for an airborne early warning (AEW) version of the Nimrod, required to replace the RAF's Avro Shackletons in a role recognised as vital to the defence of the UK. The large-capacity fuselage and ample reserves of power in the standard MR versions of the Nimrod offered considerable potential for the carriage of alternative equipment and the performance of other roles. After deliberating whether or not to participate in NATO plans to buy the Boeing E-3A, the British government decided in March 1977 to finance instead a developed version of the Nimrod. Externally, the resulting BAe Nimrod AEW.Mk 3 version violated even further the original good looks of the Comet design. This was due mainly to the grotesquely swollen radomes mounted at each end of the fuselage, each housing a dual-frequency antenna. Because of their fore and aft location, the efficiency of these scanners was not reduced as a result of screening by other parts of the airframe, as is the case with the dorsally-mounted radar antenna of the Boeing E-3A or Grumman E-2C. The other outward sign of change in the Nimrod AEW.Mk 3 was the presence at each wingtip of a pod containing electronic support measures (ESM) equipment. An onboard digital computer controlled the flow of data from the scanners (target range, speed, height and other data) and also correlated this information with a control station on the ground. The scanners, which were interfaced with the Nimrod's IFF (identification, friend or foe) system, were also part of a pulse-Doppler radar installation capable of ship surveillance as well as aircraft detection, and highly resistant to electronic jamming. Thus, despite its AEW designation, the Nimrod's function could have been defined more accurately by the AWACS (airborne warning and control system) description applied by the Americans to the Boeing E-3A.

The first development aircraft, a converted Comet 4C (XW626), made its initial flight on 28 June 1977 carrying the nose radome only; and the first aerodynamically representative AEW.Mk 3 (XZ286) made its initial flight on 16 July 1980. An initial quantity of 11 production Nimrod AEW.Mk 3s was ordered for service with the RAF, and it was anticipated that the first of these would begin to enter service with No. 8 Squadron at Waddington, Lincs, in early 1982. However, continuing problems with the technical capabilities of the system caused the eventual cancellation of the variant. The order passed to the Boeing E-3D Sentry, the first of seven aircraft being delivered in No. 8 Squadron colours in July 1990.

*Although they have never been used in anger the Nimrod is capable of carrying two pairs of AIM-9 Sidewinder missiles. During the Falklands conflict, the type was detailed to engage any Argentinian maritime patrol aircraft it encountered.*

finest of its type in the world, with its ability to detect and classify surface vessels, periscopes, submarine snorts and other surface targets at extreme range and to track numerous targets simultaneously. The radar also has good resistance to hostile countermeasures. The AQS-901 acoustics processing and display system, with its own pair of computers, is compatible with all the important sonic sensors including the Australian Barra, the British Cambs (command active multi-beam sonobuoy), the US SSQ-41 and SSQ-53 and the Canadian TANDEM.

*During Operation Corporate the Nimrod fleet was hurriedly fitted with refuelling probes to allow long-range sorties over the South Atlantic. Refuelling from Victor tankers gave the aircraft an endurance of 19 hours or more.*

## Additional equipment

The addition of inflight-refuelling probes (initially to 16 aircraft for participation in Operation Corporate) changed the designation to MR.Mk 2P, although all aircraft have now received the modification and the designation has reverted back to MR.Mk 2. The Falklands War also resulted in the underwing hardpoints being used for the first time, giving the ability to carry AIM-9G Sidewinders for self-defence, or additional anti-ship Harpoon missiles, Stingray torpedoes, bombs or depth charges. The Nimrods operated up to 4,000 miles (6440 km) from their advanced base at Ascension Island on sorties often lasting some 19 hours which took them close to the Argentinian coastline. The Nimrods also co-ordinated air-to-air link-ups in the featureless South Atlantic and provided SAR cover in the event of ditching – a role they still fulfil on the regular fast-jet trails to the Falklands today.

New communications equipment on the MR.Mk 2 includes twin GEC Avionics AD 470 HF transceivers, a radio teletype and an encryption installation. The primary EWSM (early warning support measures) systems are the large Loral ARI-18240 wingtip pods, each with eight planar spiral high- and low-band aerials giving all-round coverage. The installation of these pods necessitated the introduction of larger rectangular finlets on each side of the tailplane. From 1981 an additional internal item is an ACT.1 airborne crew trainer which enables one of the mission crew to act the part of a hostile submarine, so allowing a complete ASW operation to be practised without using sonobuoys. The primary Nimrod MR.Mk 2 navaid is a very advanced Ferranti inertial system.

After the Iraqi invasion of Kuwait in the summer of 1990 a detachment of three Nimrod MR.Mk 2Ps was installed at Seeb, Oman to co-operate with Coalition warships in what became a naval blockade of Iraq. On 26 August – in an operation that would have been unthinkable even a year earlier – a Soviet navy warship requested and received assistance from an RAF Nimrod to intercept a suspected Iraqi blockade runner. By the time Operation Desert Storm commenced on 17 January 1991 the Nimrod MR det. at Seeb was well established, led by No. 120 Squadron with elements from Nos 42 and 206 Squadrons. The Nimrods patrolled the Persian Gulf and surrounding seas and were involved in a number of encounters including locating an Iraqi Zhuk patrol boat which was subsequently sunk by a Royal Navy Lynx from HMS *Cardiff*.

## Gulf War standard

A number of Nimrods involved in Desert Storm was modified to what was unofficially referred to as MR.Mk 2P(GM) standard through the addition of an underwing FLIR turret, BOZ pods and a towed radar decoy.

All four Nimrod squadrons are now based at RAF Kinloss, Scotland and, since the end of the Cold War and the diminishing Soviet threat, are training to cope with new threats. With more and more potentially hostile nations acquiring submarines, the Nimrods are increasingly involved in out-of-area operations, and training exercises are carried out annually around the world. The Nimrod squadrons also regularly participate in the Partnership for Peace (PfP) exercises, helping to integrate operating procedures, particularly for SAR operations, with friendly states. Most recently, the aircraft saw combat once more, with its participation in Operation Iraqi Freedom.

Despite the MR.Mk 2's capabilities, the age of the airframe and the need to integrate the newest equipment prompted the RAF to issue Staff Requirement (Air) 420 for a Nimrod replacement. After assessing the Dassault Atlantique 3 and the Lockheed P-3 Orion, the UK officially announced that an upgraded version of the Nimrod, known as Nimrod 2000, was to be procured. As well as employing the latest avionics and equipment the Nimrod MRA.Mk 4, as it will be designated in service, will be powered by BMW Rolls-Royce BR710 turbofans, boosting performance and economy.

*Although the Nimrod fleet is shared between the four operational units, No. 42 Sqn applied special markings to this Nimrod MR.Mk 2 for public displays in the UK and around Europe in the mid-1990s.*

# Nimrod R.Mk 1

## The RAF's Sigint platform

Above: This view of XV666 shows the towed decoy equipment installed under the tail radome for service during Operation Granby in the Gulf. XV666 was lost in May 1995.

**For over 25 years three unremarkable-looking aircraft have gone about their covert business, collecting Sigint data for the UK's intelligence community. Whatismore these Nimrod R.Mk 1s are likely to remain in use for the foreseeable future.**

The Nimrod R.Mk 1 (originally expected to be known as the SR.Mk 1) was developed to meet Air Staff Requirement 389, for a new Sigint (Signals Intelligence) platform for use by No. 51 Sqn. This unit then used three converted Comet C.Mk 2Rs, augmented by four Canberra B.Mk 6 (Mod)s for very high level and low altitude work, and the Nimrod was expected to replace both older airframes.

Fighting for funding for the new aircraft was fierce, and lack of support from GCHQ initially led to a focus on the tactical Elint role. In the event, though, the aircraft were equipped with both Elint (Electronic Intelligence – usually meaning radar frequency detection, location and analysis) and Comint (Communications Intelligence) receivers and equipment, and were as capable of strategic Sigint as the Comets had been, if not more so.

The new HS.801 was already on order for Coastal Command as a replacement for the Shackleton in the ASW/maritime patrol role), and the basic Nimrod airframe (as the HS.801 would become) was also selected to form the basis of the RAF's new Sigint aircraft, as the HS.801R. Three Nimrods were delivered as R.Mk 1s (serialled XW664-666), with provision for the installation of a sophisticated Sigint suite – although the aircraft were delivered as little more than empty shells, with bare equipment racks, and their secret mission equipment was fitted by the RAF at Wyton, their planned operating base.

### Larger crew

By comparison with the standard 'maritime' Nimrod, the R.Mk 1s had a much larger crew – with five flight crew and up to 23 special operators, the latter mostly sitting at sideways-facing workstations along the port forward fuselage and the starboard rear fuselage. The aircraft lost many of its cabin windows (which were blocked by equipment racks or used as mountings for flush antennas) and the distinctive MAD tailcone sting was replaced by a bulbous radome. Elint receiver antennas were mounted in the former bomb bay, and in the tailcone and the front of the fuel tank nacelles on the wing leading edges.

Pictured at its base at RAF Waddington, XV664 models the new overall grey colour scheme introduced during 2001. This scheme had already been applied to the RAF's Nimrod MR.Mk 2s.

The first of the three Nimrod R.Mk 1s was delivered to Wyton on 7 July 1971, but fitting out was a time-consuming task, and the aircraft was not rolled out until late 1973. Flt Lt Gordon Lambert captained the first training sortie on 3 May 1974, and the type was formally comissioned on 10 May. The final pair of Nimrod R.Mk 1s entered service with No. 51 Sqn in late 1974, allowing the final retirement of the Comets and Canberras.

Since then, No.51 Sqn's Nimrods have undergone a succession of modernisations, modifications and upgrades, some of which have resulted in changes to the aircraft's external configuration. The aircraft's navigation systems were upgraded in 1980, with the installation of Delco

The first R.Mk 1, XV664, is pictured early in its career. Note the lack of cabin windows compared to the MR.Mk 2; others were blanked off as internal equipment was removed/updated in later years.

***Left: XW666 climbs out of RAF Wyton, then its base, in 1982. Just visible on the dorsal extension of the tailfin is No. 51 Sqn's emblem, 'a goose volant'.***

***Below: Pictured over the Baltic during 1977/78, presumably during an intelligence-gathering flight, XV664 is shadowed by a Saab J 35D Draken of the Swedish air force.***

AN/ASN-119 Carousel INS in place of one of the two LORAN sets. One of the two navigators was dropped from the normal crew complement, and the original ASV-21 ASW radar was replaced by a C-130 type ECKO 290 weather radar.

Externally, the upgrade saw the removal of one of the LORAN 'towel rails', while revisions to the Special Operators' accommodation led to a further reduction in the number of remaining portholes. A new communications band DF system was also installed, distinguished by hook-shaped antennas mounted above the forward fuselage, above and below the wing pods, and inside the fin-top 'football'. At broadly the same time, wingtip pods (similar to the maritime Nimrods' Yellow Gate ESM pods) were also fitted.

The aircraft were also re-painted in the same 'Hemp' colour scheme as their maritime opposite numbers, as they came up for major overhaul, and some time after refueling probes were fitted, the aircraft gained a new ventral fin and new finlets above and below each tailplane.

## Operation Corporate

One No. 51 Sqn Nimrod participated in Operation Corporate (the British operation to re-take the Falklands) perhaps operating from Ascension Island, or perhaps from a base in Chile, and soon afterwards also gained an inflight refuelling probe, like those added to maritime Nimrods during the Falklands campaign. The aircraft were also fitted with underwing pylons, though these were initially used only as mounting points for a single blade antenna.

In recent years, No. 51 Sqn's Nimrods have carried modified BOZ pods on these pylons, these mounting the same 'hanging' blade antenna, and also having a forward hemisphere MAWS antenna on their nosecones. The BOZ pods themselves were probably used for carrying Marconi Aerial Towed Radar Decoys rather than their usual payload of chaff and/or flare cartridges. Rear hemisphere MAWS antennas were fitted on each side of the blunt tailcone.

No.51 Sqn's Nimrods participated in Operation Granby, and in other operations in the Middle East since then. The unit also began mounting regular deployments to Italy in June 1992, to support UN and NATO operations in the Balkans. No. 51 Sqn moved from RAF Wyton to RAF Waddington in April 1995, from where it has continued much the same pattern and tempo of operations.

## Project Starwindow

A major upgrade (Project Starwindow) saw the installation of new intercept receivers, displays and workstations, with a new digital direction finding system, and also saw the provision of new ground stations for receiving and analysing data from the Nimrods while airborne.

Flight testing of Starwindow (which is believed to have included equipment used by the USAF's RC-135V Rivet Joint aircraft) began in 1994.
No. 51 Sqn's third Nimrod was lost after a severe fire on 16 May 1995 during a post maintenance test flight. The crew ditched the aircraft safely, but the aircraft had to be replaced by converting a 'spare' MR.Mk 2, XV249. This aircraft was converted to full R.Mk 1 Starwindow standards, and entered service in April 1997.

A further upgrade (Project Extract) was launched and then cancelled on cost grounds, before a revised, more austere version of Extract was finally relaunched in early 1998.

The Nimrod R.Mk 1 is set to remain in service for the fore-seeable future, and may eventually be replaced by a converted biz-jet (such as the Global Express chosen as the RAF's ASTOR platform) or even by a UAV. Either option would entail a major change in operational philosophy, however, and a shift away from the squadron's traditional emphasis on using highly-skilled and experienced operators who manually tune and closely control their equipment.

***Above: Though overhauls are carried out at RAF Kinloss, the RAF's Nimrod fleet is painted by British Airways at London-Heathrow. In this 1993 view XW665 departs LHR for Kinloss for overhaul after being stripped of its paintwork.***

***Left: Inflight refuelling probes and associated tailplane finlets were fitted to the R.Mk 1s a short time after they were fitted to the MR.Mk 2 fleet. The mod was prompted by the need for IFR capability during the Falklands conflict of 1982.***

# Beech (Raytheon) C-12

## Military King Air

**For forces to be effective, an efficient logistic and liaison organisation is required to support the front line. For the US services, many of these unglamorous tasks are entrusted to the King Air 200. The King Air also forms the basis for a family of extraordinary electronic reconnaissance aircraft.**

***Above: Representative of the first King Air 200 utility transport variant to enter US military service, these two C-12As represent the US Air Force (foreground) and US Army.***

***Top: The flying porcupine – although rarely seen, the US Army's RC-12 family of electronic reconnaissance King Airs is the most notorious of the breed. This is the prototype RC-12N.***

Although most widely used as a corporate business aircraft, a role for which it was specifically designed, the King Air 200 has been sufficiently adaptable to fulfil a number of roles within the US armed forces and a number of overseas air arms.

Of course, earlier versions of the Queen Air/King Air had been in military service for some years (mostly under the U-21 Ute designation) before the King Air 200 appeared, smoothing the procurement path for the new variant.

Larger than its predecessors and sporting a distinctive T-tail, the King Air 200 first flew on 27 October 1972. The first three military aircraft were electronic reconnaissance aircraft known as RU-21Js, which entered service in 1973. They were followed by a much larger batch of aircraft for the utility/VIP transport role, powered by PT6A-38 engines and ushering in a new designation: C-12A. The Army, which dubbed the new type the Huron, took 60 while the USAF signed up for 30, service entry for both services being achieved in July 1975. One aircraft was also supplied to the Greek army.

In USAF service the C-12As were mainly used by Embassy Flights and overseas missions. Indeed, one C-12A assigned to the Embassy Flight at Pretoria was ordered out of South Africa for allegedly conducting spy flights with belly-mounted cameras.

In 1979 the US Navy and Marine Corps began to receive the UC-12B model, which had uprated PT6A-41 engines and a cargo door. Like those of the Army, the UC-12Bs were dispersed around airfields to act as base 'hacks' and staff transports. Sixty-six were built.

Only 14 C-12Cs were built from new, this being an Army variant similar to the C-12A but with the uprated Dash 41 engines. However, many C-12As were subsequently brought to this standard, including those of the USAF which also briefly carried a C-12E designation. The C-12D which followed had a cargo door, but around half of the 40 built for the Army were either built or converted to RC-12 standard for electronic reconnaissance duties. The USAF also took six of the C-12D variant.

*The US Navy/Marine Corps procured 66 UC-12Bs for use with base flights in the liaison role, although 12 were later adapted for training under the TC-12B designation.*

From 1984 the C-12F entered service with both the Army and Air Force. This version had Dash 42 engines and a cargo door. The Army took 20 from new, while the Air Force acquired 46. Many of these were later declared surplus and handed over to the Army. The Army's own machines were destined for the National Guard, and were given the designations C-12F-1 and C-12F-2 to denote detail differences between the batches. When ex-USAF aircraft were received, they became C-12F-3s. The Navy also took a dozen under the designation UC-12F, although two were converted to serve as radar-equipped range safety aircraft as RC-12Fs.

Chronologically, the next variant was the C-12L, a designation covering three RU-21Js stripped of their Guardrail equipment and returned to service as transports. Next came the UC-12M, of

***In January 1999 the Japanese Ground Self Defence Force received its first King Air 350 (locally designated LR-2) to replace the Mitsubishi LR-1 in the liaison/reconnaissance role.***

***Four King Air B200Ts fly on maritime patrol duties with the Malaysian air force's 16 Skuadron. Equipped with FLIR and belly radar, the King Airs can carry either drop tanks or light weapons.***

which 12 were built for the Navy. Two of these became RC-12M range safety machines, while earlier UC-12B/Fs were upgraded to the new standard, which had new cockpit instrumentation, lighting and voice comms, but was otherwise similar to the C-12F. Twenty-nine C-12Rs were bought for the Army, this being a version of the civilian B200C with EFIS cockpit. Two camera-equipped C-12R/APs are on order for the Greek army.

## C-12 in operation

With the four US services, the C-12 is employed on a range of utility transport duties. Perhaps the most important is the ferrying between bases of personnel. The Army's fleet is largely tasked by OSACOM (Operational Support Airlift Command), itself subordinate to JOSAC (Joint OSA Command). This organisation manages the OSA resources of all US services. By 2000 the once large fleets of the USAF and US Navy had been reduced considerably in size. The US Navy's UC-12s have mostly been retired to storage, while the bulk of the USAF's C-12C/D fleet has been transferred to the Army. The Embassy Flights remain, however.

The basic qualities of the King Air 200 which attracted the US services also led to significant overseas military sales, although for the most part these have been of the civilian models. A notable exception is Israel, which bought C-12Ds and RC-12D/Ks. Other overseas operators in 2004 included Algeria, Argentina, Bolivia, Cambodia, Chile, Colombia, Ecuador, Egypt, Guatemala, Ireland, Macedonia, Malaysia, Morocco, New Zealand, Peru, South Africa, Sri Lanka, Sweden, Thailand, Togo, Turkey, and Venezuela.

In several cases the aircraft are leased from civilian operators, and continue to wear civil registrations. In overseas service the King Air 200 has been put to use as a multi-engined trainer, and for special purposes such as photo-survey or maritime surveillance, as well as its more usual liaison/utility tasks.

## Maritime patrol

Of these, Malaysia's are perhaps the most interesting. Designated B200T, the aircraft have Telephonics 143 search radar and a FLIR Systems FLIR under the belly, and have wing hardpoints for the carriage of long-range tanks or weapons. They patrol the seas around Malaysia on anti-piracy, fishery and other duties, supplanting costly PC-130Hs in the role.

Having briefly dallied with the King Air 300, an improved 200, Beech/Raytheon subsequently produced the King Air 350. This has increased-span wings with winglets, a lengthened fuselage and 1,050-shp (783-kW) PT6A-60 turboprops. The US Army has bought the type as the C-12S, while a number of other air arms operate the type. The most notable of these is Japan's army, which is buying 20 (as the LR-2) to replace the Mitsubishi MU-2 (LR-1) in the liaison and reconnaissance role, the LR-2 featuring a belly sensor radome. Raytheon is marketing various special-mission variants, and also the RC-350 Guardrail battlefield Sigint platform with Elint sensors in wingtip pods and Comint antennas in a large underfuselage canoe fairing.

### Model 1900 in military service

Based on the King Air series, the Model 1900C was a new design intended for the commuterliner market. The 1900C-1 was a later 'wet-wing' version. Military interest was small, but resulted in purchases by the USAF (on behalf of the Air National Guard) under the C-12J designation. Three other air arms also bought the type. The Model 1900D was a development with stand-up headroom: only one is in military service.

***Above: Six C-12Js were bought for ANG support. Four now serve with active-duty USAF units and two with the Army.***

***Right: Two Beech 1900C-1s replaced C-47s in the transport/calibration role with Taiwan's VIP Squadron at Sungshan.***

***A single 'high-top' Model 1900D serves with the US Army's Chemical and Biological Defense Command at Aberdeen Proving Ground.***

***The Royal Thai Army Aviation Division purchased two Beech 1900C-1s to provide VIP transport from Lop Buri.***

***The Egyptian air force adopted the 1900C for electronic surveillance and maritime patrol work. The EW variant has a large canoe fairing.***

***It was the enthusiastic Canadian government which breathed life into the Twin Engined Huey programme. The first examples of the Model 212 were handed over to the Canadian Armed Forces in 1969. The Bell 412CF Griffon (above) was acquired by the Canadians to replace the CH-136 Kiowa, CH-135 Twin Huey and CH-118 Iroquois.***

# Bell 212/412

## Twin-engined reliability

**In military service, the Bell UH-1N and Model 212 built on the solid reputation of the earlier model UH-1s, while introducing all the performance improvements and advantages of a twin-engined layout. Military operators have benefited yet further from the four-bladed Model 412 which is still in production and meeting the needs of customers around the world.**

When the Bell Model 204/205 made its combat debut in Vietnam it immediately became a military superlative. Better known to all as the UH-1 'Huey', the aircraft proved it could do everything that was asked of it – but very soon, as is always the case, even more was being asked of it. Though the UH-1 outclassed any other medium transport helicopter in the theatre, it still struggled in the demanding 'hot-and-high' conditions encountered in Vietnam – most notably along the Mekong Delta. As the realisation grew in the US that the 'Huey' could do with more power, a separate initiative was being forged between Bell Helicopter, the Canadian government and Pratt & Whitney Canada. Their plan was to fit the single-engined Model 205 (UH-1H) with two PT6T-3 Turbo Twin-Pac engines. This would significantly increase all-round performance and give the aircraft much-appreciated twin-engined safety and reliability. On 1 May 1968 Bell announced that a Canadian Armed Forces order for 50 aircraft had formally launched the new project, which became the Model 212.

Once the 'Twin Huey' had received its go-ahead, the US services began to take a closer interest in the aircraft. Though the US Army did not divert any of its single-engined UH-1 orders to the new aircraft, the US Navy, US Marines and US Air Force quickly became customers. The Model 212 was allocated the new US military designation of UH-1N. Deliveries of the Canadian aircraft began in May 1971, as the CUH-1N, though these were later renamed as CH-135 Twin Hueys. In Vietnam the US aircraft were quickly used for special missions tasks, such as COIN gunships along the Mekong, and the US Marines and Navy were particularly appreciative of the UH-1N's much-improved over-water safety characteristics. The Marines and the Navy used their UH-1Ns intensively as assault transports – a role which is still paramount for the UH-1N in service with the Corps today. These veteran UH-1Ns are soon to be modernised and upgraded to UH-1Y standard (see below). After Vietnam the USAF's UH-1Ns took up base rescue flight tasks, dedicated VIP flying (VH-1N) and special support tasks – such as crew transport to strategic missile silos. In US Navy service their primary mission became SAR and base flight duties also, with aircraft designated as HH-1Ns.

The Model 212 was sold widely to forces which needed its heavier-lift capabilities, most of whom were already UH-1 operators. Military customers included Argentina, Austria, Bangladesh, Brunei, Canada, Chile, Dominican Republic, Dubai, El Salvador, Ghana, Greece, Guatemala, Guyana, Iran, Iraq, Israel, Italy, Jordan, Lebanon, Libya, Malta, Mexico, Morocco, Panama, Philippines, Saudi Arabia, Singapore, South Korea, Spain, Sri Lanka, Sudan, Thailand, Tunisia, Turkey, Uganda, Venezuela, Yemen, Zambia, United Kingdom and the United States.

### Italy's Hueys

Bell had a long-standing licence production deal with Agusta, and the Italian helicopter builder became an important supplier to markets that were sometimes not directly accessible to the US firm. Agusta-built Model 212s are known as the AB 212. In fact, so successful was Agusta at winning sales it

***Not all UH-1Ns have the NTIS forward-looking infra-red system seen here under the cockpit of a Marine aircraft, but the equipment greatly enhances the ability to operate at night.***

has often found itself in direct competition with Bell – this is particularly true of Model 412 sales (see below). Agusta also developed a range of special missions versions of the AB 212. The most widely-sold version was the shore-/ship-based anti-submarine variant, the AB 212ASW. Customers for the AB 212ASW include Italy, Greece, Iran, Iraq (not delivered), Saudi Arabia, Spain and Turkey. For its primary ASW role, the aircraft is fitted with a dipping sonar and an operator's station in the main cabin. A pair of lightweight torpedoes can be carried, and the same basic aircraft can also be equipped for anti-surface warfare missions. For this role a search radar is mounted above the forward cabin in a drum-shaped radome. Typical armament is a pair of OTO-Melara Sea Killer anti-ship missiles, though a version delivered to Turkey can be armed with the BAe Sea Skua. AB 212ASWs are routinely fitted with a SAR hoist over the starboard cabin door, and always carry emergency flotation gear above their skids. Agusta has also developed Elint and Comint versions of the AB 212, chiefly for the Italian army. The AB 212ASW also has a robust Elint capability – depending on the mission systems fitted.

## Four-bladed successor

By the late 1970s, Bell was looking to squeeze yet more performance out of the Model 212/UH-1N design, with customers increasingly looking for more speed and better range. To offer these improvements, while making the minimum change to the basic airframe, Bell introduced the Model 412. The standard Pratt & Whitney Canada PT6T-3B engines gave way to a pair of uprated PT6T-3B-1s and onboard fuel capacity was increased. The major change came through the addition of an entirely new four-bladed main rotor system which used Bell's elastometric bearings/hub technology, with all-composite blades. Two modified Model 212s acted as prototypes and the first aircraft flew in August 1979. By February 1981 full IFR certification had been achieved and the first delivery of a Model 412 was made to a commercial operator in Alaska.

Agusta undertook licence production as the AB 412 and has won several military orders, particularly to European customers. Competing against its own aircraft in several sales bids, Bell found itself being beaten out by the AB 412. A gentleman's agreement between the two companies often led to the final production being split between Bell and Agusta, but this unsettling experience has no doubt been a factor in Bell's decision not to renew Agusta's AB 412 licence. Indonesia's IPTN had a licence to build 100 aircraft as the NBell 412. Production commenced in 1984 and centred around the 412HP model. All NB 412s were built for government customers and most were delivered to the armed forces.

Developed versions of the 412 include the Model 412SP (Special Performance) with 55 per cent extra fuel capacity and increased maximum take-off weight. The Model 412HP, certified in 1991, features an uprated transmission while the Model 412EP (Enhanced Performance) is powered by a refined PT6T-3D engine and fitted with a three-axis digital flight control system. This is now the standard production model. Military and paramilitary customers for the Model 412 (AB 412) include Bahrain, Botswana, Canada, Ecuador, Finland, Honduras, Italy, Mexico, Nigeria, Norway, the Philippines, Slovenia, South Korea, Sri Lanka, Sweden, Venezuela and the UK.

Canada once again became an important customer ordering 100 aircraft, based on the Model 412EP, as the CH-148 Griffon (Model 412CF) in 1992. The Griffons were acquired to replace Canada's original CH-135s (and other types) and deliveries were completed in 1998. Italian AB 412s are known as the Grifone, while Norway has named its 19 Bell 412SPs 'Arapahos'. To the UK, which uses the Model 412EP for advanced multi-engined training at the tri-service Defence Helicopter Flying School, based at RAF Shawbury, the helicopter is known as the Griffin HT.Mk 1. A very distinct version, the Model 412EP Sentinel, has been developed for ASW and surface warfare tasks. Equipped with a dipping sonar, chin-mounted search radar and FLIR turret, the Sentinel can be armed with Penguin anti-ship missiles and Mk 46 torpedoes. Two Sentinels were converted by Heli-Dyne Systems for the Ecuadorean navy and were delivered in 1998.

As part of a major modernisation plan for its elderly helicopter fleet, the US Marine Corps is implementing a parallel upgrade for its remaining UH-1Ns and AH-1Ws. Both will be fitted with an all-new four-bladed composite rotor system and new cockpit systems, using a high-degree of common components. The upgraded Twin Hueys will be known as UH-1Ys and initial operational capabilityis scheduled for 2007 after a series of delays, with 100 examples being planned. The service life of the remanufactured UH-1Y will be reset to '0', extending the UH-1Y to beyond 2020.

Since 1986 all Bell helicopter production has been undertaken in Mirabel, Quebec, by Bell Helicopter Textron Canada. Model 212/412 production moved there in 1988/89. The 212 is still being built, largely to order, and by 2000 over 900 had been delivered. Total Model 412 production now exceeds 430, with 200 of these coming off the Canadian line.

***Sweden's Helicopterflottilj is a relatively new operator of the AB 412 Grifone, acquiring the first of its eight (now five) examples in 1993. The local designation for the aircraft is HKP 11 and the aircraft have the dual role of transport, and military and civilian medevac in the remote and unreachable parts in the north of Sweden.***

*The AH-1W SuperCobra has proved itself to be a truly effective weapons platform, able to carry a lethal mix of ordnance including TOW missiles, AIM-9 Sidewinders and Zuni rockets. Despite the AH-1W's performance, however, it is based on an elderly design, and is being upgraded for continued USMC use as the AH-1Z.*

# Bell AH-1 HueyCobra

## Attack helicopter

**Having first entered service in 1966, Bell's HueyCobra has undergone a significant number of upgrades over the years, enabling it to remain combat-capable well into the next century.**

*Right: Viewed from above, the extremely narrow and compact fuselage of the AH-1 makes it an incredibly difficult helicopter to sight. This early AH-1G is seen on a test-flight from Bell's Fort Worth production facility in Texas.*

Blooded in Vietnam and proven several times since then, the diminutive AH-1 is the father of all modern gunship helicopters. Like most great aircraft, the AH-1 has been found to be irreplaceable and is still a front line type with a host of operators around the world.

Although the idea of arming helicopters had been around since the 1950s, such machines were invariably modifications of existing types which in many cases were not ideally suited to the very different demands inherent in battle. There was clearly a need for a dedicated attack helicopter which married high performance with the ability to operate with a worthwhile payload, and was less vulnerable than interim types to ground fire, which had proven to be a constant hazard in operations over Vietnam.

*In Vietnam, Cobra crews often found themselves in the thick of the fighting, providing aerial fire-support from directly over the heads of friendly troops. During the war AH-1Gs served with more than 20 combat units and, due to the hazardous nature of their mission and their inherent vulnerability, almost 300 were lost in combat.*

Bell was only one of a number of companies engaged in research of this nature. Much of the company's pioneering work was employed to advantage on the Model 209 which was the result of a privately-funded crash project intended to meet the US Army's requirement.

In terms of physical appearance, the Model 209 was very different from the UH-1. However, in this instance, appearances were most definitely deceptive for it was, in fact, closely allied to the Iroquois in that it incorporated many of its design features, including rotor assembly, transmission system and turboshaft engine. These items were married to an entirely new fuselage of much narrower frontal section, with small stub wings to provide a measure of lift as well as somewhere to hang weapons – it was intended from the outset that the new helicopter would be heavily armed.

### Rush-job

Some idea of the urgency attached to this project can be gleaned from the fact that, although development was initiated only in March 1965, a Model 209 prototype was assembled in the summer of that year and flew for the first time on 7 September 1965. Soon transferred to Edwards AFB, California for an exhaustive series of flight trials, the Model 209 quickly convinced army personnel that the helicopter promised a new attack capability over the battlefield. By March 1965, the Army had decided to purchase Bell's gunship, placing an order for an initial batch of 112 production AH-1G helicopters, stipulating that they be ready at the earliest possible moment to permit deployment to Vietnam. This proved to be the forerunner of a series of contracts, procurement for the Army passing the 1,000 mark in 1972, while the US Marine Corps received 38 on loan pending the availability of that service's custom-built AH-1J SeaCobra derivative. Modest

***A fierce-looking yet unarmed AH-1J SeaCobra of the US Marine Corps. The Tet offensive in 1968 was the spur for the development of twin-engined versions. Typically, the SeaCobra was fitted with a M197 cannon in its universal turret.***

quantities were also supplied to Israel and Spain.

### Battle debut

The initial production version of the HueyCobra was the AH-1G, delivery of which began in June 1967. Only three months later, HueyCobras arrived in South Vietnam as part of an organisation known as Cobra-NETT, which was entrusted with introducing the type into combat. As the number of AH-1Gs increased, so operations were stepped up, to a point where the helicopters were undertaking daily missions such as escort, reconnaissance and fire-support – the AH-1's 0.3-in (7.62-mm) Gatling-type machine-gun devastated enemy bunkers and troop concentrations. The Gatling gun was soon supplemented by an M129 40-mm grenade-launcher; in this configuration and with wing-mounted rockets the AH-1s ranged far and wide over South Vietnam on attack missions.

The USMC received a modest number of HueyCobras from 1969 but sought a model of its own. Known as the AH-1J, the major difference was the installation of a Pratt & Whitney T400-CP-400 turboshaft engine (a military version of the PT6T-3 Turbo Twin Pac) and the deletion of the turret-mounted Gatling gun in favour of a single General Electric M197 20-mm rotary cannon. Some 84 AH-1Js were delivered between 1970 and 1977. A total of 202 AH-1Js was purchased by the Imperial Iranian army during the early 1970s, although it is thought that few remain airworthy despite covert assistance from the United States and Israel.

### Missile armament

TOW missile capability first emerged around the mid-1970s when about 100 AH-1Gs were modified to carry this weapon, and were redesignated AH-1Qs. Another derivative which resulted from modernisation was the AH-1R, which lacked TOW, but was equipped with a new T53-L-703 powerplant. Eventually, all AH-1Qs, AH-1Gs and AH-1Rs were brought up to improved AH-1S standard. In 1988 all survivors were redesignated AH-1F, which was the definitive US Army model.

As well as procurement of the AH-1S by means of conversion, the Army also contracted for a substantial number of new machines which were initially known as Production AH-1S before adopting the designation AH-1P, and aircraft were supplied to Pakistan, Israel and Jordan. A licence agreement with Fuji allowed production in Japan where, within the Japan Ground Self-Defence Force (JGSDF), the AH-1S was built as an equivalent of the US Army AH-1F (and is now designated as such).

The Marine Corps continued to improve its versions of the AH-1, resulting in the AH-1T, fitted with the dynamic system of the Bell 214; the 57 models entered service in 1977 and were later configured to allow the launching of TOW missiles. Further updating resulted in the AH-1T+ SuperCobra which first flew on 16 November 1983 and was later accepted by the USMC as the AH-1W. Re-engined and with distinctive widened nacelles, the 'W' can fire TOW, Hellfire and Sidewinder AAMs. New electronics in the nose allow the HueyCobra to undertake attack missions in the severest weather conditions, day or night.

### Cobra in Combat

The original AH-1Gs racked up an impressive record in Vietnam; during the closing stages of the war TOW-armed examples inflicted heavy losses on NVA armour.

Israel's small fleet of AH-1S/AH-1Fs has seen much action in support of the army in southern Lebanon. During the initial stages of Operation Peace for Galilee in 1982, the AH-1S was credited, in conjunction with Hughes Defender helicopters, with the destruction of 29 Syrian tanks and 50 armoured vehicles, for the loss of one Cobra. Iranian AH-1Js saw heavy fighting against Iraqi forces, during which Cobras are rumoured to have engaged Iraqi Mi-24 'Hinds' in combat.

The US invasion of Grenada in 1983 proved to be an inglorious debut for the USMC's AH-1T SeaCobra. Operating aboard the assault ship USS *Guam*, and flying as armed escorts two of the four SeaCobras aboard were shot down during the fighting for Fort Frederick.

### Recent action

A far more definitive mark was made by the Cobra during Operation Desert Storm in 1991. A few of the US Army's Germany-based units deployed AH-1S/AH-1Ps, though most anti-armour missions were flown by AH-64s. USMC Cobras were in the thick of the fighting, from the onset of hostilities. Four light-attack squadrons, both land- and sea-based, operated sand-camouflaged AH-1Ws. Another two squadrons of AH-1Js were also available. The AH-1Ws were used against Iraqi armour and ground positions during the battle for Khafji, and in the final battle for Kuwait city.

Despite the retirement of the AH-1 from regular US Army units, the HueyCobra will serve on into the 21st Century with a number of operators.

***Above: The prototype AH-1W SuperCobra was given a striking paint scheme to emphasise the Cobra name and its undoubted 'bite' for its debut in late 1983.***

***Left: The Spanish navy was the first export customer to receive the AH-1G variant in 1968. Of the eight delivered, four were lost in accidents, three were returned to the US and one remains in storage at Rota.***

# Single-engined variants

**The basic models of the AH-1 formed the backbone of US Army Aviation's combat units during the 1970s and the 1970s. Though the HueyCobra has now all but disappeared from US service, it continues to be a front-line type in several other countries.**

## AH-1G

The AH-1G was the first production variant of the HueyCobra. The 'G' suffix was applied by the Army which treated the AH-1 as simply a follow-on from existing UH-1 Iroquois variants. Two YAH-1G prototypes were built, an initial batch of 100 aircraft was ordered on 13 April 1966 and the type entered service in June 1967. The Army eventually acquired 1,119 AH-1Gs.

The AH-1G closely resembled the Model 209 prototype, but from the outset was built with a fixed skid landing gear. Power was supplied by a 1,400-shp (1043-kW) T53-L-13 turboshaft, derated to 1,100 shp (819.5 kW). A few early production aircraft had the tail rotor mounted to port, but the bulk of production aircraft had this position reversed. The helicopters had a distinctive rounded, conical nose which, in early versions, housed landing lights behind a transparent fairing. In later model AH-1Gs the lights were moved to retractable housings under the nose. Initially, the AH-1G was armed with an Emerson Electric TAT-102A turret, mounting a single GAU-2B 7.62-mm Minigun and 8,000 rounds of ammunition. The turret could be slewed through a 230° arc, elevated to 25° or depressed to 60°.

The single-weapon TAT-102A was later replaced by the XM28 turret which could house a GAU-2B, and an XM129 40-mm grenade launcher with 300 rounds. Experience in Vietnam led, from 1969 onwards, to an increase in firepower through the addition of a podded M35 six-barrelled 20-mm cannon under the port underwing pylon. Some AH-1Gs also employed 2.75-in (70-mm) rockets.

***Seen firing a salvo of unguided rockets during armament tests, this AH-1G is an early production example with the clear nose cone.***

The AH-1G had no sensor or target acquisition systems and was a daylight-only operations aircraft. Several trials sensor fits were flown by AH-1G testbeds, including the SMASH (Southeast Asia Multi-sensor Armament Sub-system for HueyCobra) system, which combined an early FLIR and moving target radar, and the CONFICS (COBra Night FIre Control System), which used a low-light level TV. A single JAH-1G went on to become an important testbed for new sensor and weapons systems, such as the Hellfire missile.

The AH-1G had a successful combat career in Vietnam and most surviving aircraft were later rebuilt to AH-1S, AH-1E or AH-1F standard. Between 1981 and 1986 a number of modified aircraft, stripped of all armament and armour, served with the US Customs Service. Known as 'Snakes', they were used to intercept drug-running aircraft. Despite the large numbers built, the only export customers for the AH-1G were Spain and Israel. The Spanish navy took delivery of eight M35-armed aircraft (known locally as Z.14s) in 1972 and they served until 1985. Israel took delivery of 12 aircraft, where were later replaced by AH-1Fs.

***The first prototype differed from all other HueyCobras in having a retractable landing gear. Over a six-year career, the helicopter was up-graded to virtual AH-1G standard.***

## AH-1Q

The AH-1Q was derived from the AH-1G but had a significantly improved combat capability through the addition of the BGM-71 TOW missile. In 1973 the Army took delivery of eight pre-production AH-1Qs, modified to carry the nose-mounted M65 stabilised TOW sight and four-tube TOW launchers under each pylon. The AH-1Q retained the M28 chin turret and could also carry 2.75-in (70-mm) rocket pods. Just 85 production-standard AH-1Qs were delivered, beginning in June 1975, before the introduction of the AH-1S.

## Improved AH-1S

The AH-1S became the definitive late-model Cobra variant and has itself spawned a confusing number of subvariants. The addition of new weapons and systems to the AH-1Q had left it seriously underpowered so the most important change to the AH-1S was the installation of an uprated 1,800-shp (1341-kW) T53-L-703 engine. A single YAH-1R prototype was built to test the new engine, the prototype later being redesignated YAH-1S. The AH-1Q/S was intended to bridge the gap between the cancellation of the Lockheed AH-56 Cheyenne and the introduction of the AH-64 Apache. The first service version was the AH-1S Improved (also known as the AH-1S Modified). All remaining AH-1Qs and 198 AH-1Gs were converted to this standard, and the type entered service in 1974. The AH-1S Modified/Improved airframe had several changes over the AH-1Q, including extra cooling scoops over the main engine intake and RWR antennas. Aircraft also usually carried the 'sugar-scoop' IR-suppressant shroud above the engine exhaust. As other versions of the AH-1S were introduced, these first aircraft became known simply as AH-1Ss.

## AH-1S (Production) – later AH-1P

The 100 new-build AH-1S Production-standard Cobras delivered to the US Army between 1977 and 1978 featured several small changes to the Improved/Modified aircraft. Most important of these was the addition of flat-plate cockpit canopies that reduced reflected glint off the aircraft. These aircraft retained the M28 turret, TOW missiles and associated M65 sight. They featured improved flight systems and avionics that better enabled them to undertake low-level nap-of-the-earth (NoE) flying. From the 67th aircraft onwards the AH-1S Production was fitted with tapered Kaman K-747 main rotor blades. In 1998 the AH-1S Production became the AH-1P.

Turkish Army Aviation operates approximately 30 (of 36 delivered in 1992) AH-1Ps alongside its twin-engined AH-1Ws, as part of the attack helicopter battalion based at Ankara-Güvercinlik. In 1994 Bahrain took delivery of 14 Cobras, believed to be AH-1Ps (but possibly AH-1Es), including some dual control aircraft. They form a single squadron of the Bahrain Amiri Air Force based at Shaikh Isa AB.

## AH-1S ECAS (Enhanced Cobra Armament System)/Up-Gun AH-1S – later AH-1E

The second phase of the new-build AH-1S programme added a new M197 three-barrelled 20-mm cannon in an undernose Universal turret, replacing the M28. The M197, based on the M61 Vulcan cannon, was equipped with 750 rounds of ammunition. The Up-Gun aircraft had a small but distinctive bulge housing a 10-kVA alternator in the inlet for the port engine. Most aircraft also gained wire-strike protection cutters above and below the cockpit. Ninety-eight AH-1S ECAS aircraft were delivered between 1978 and 1979. In 1988, when the whole AH-1 designation system was reorganised, the AH-1S Up-Gun became the AH-1E.

## AH-1S Modernized – later AH-1F

The final stage of the US Army's AH-1S upgrade programme resulted in 99 new-build AH-1S Modernized aircraft, plus 50 for the Army National Guard and 378 rebuilt from AH-1Gs. Deliveries took place between 1979 and 1986. The Modernized aircraft included all the improvements of previous versions, plus a new cockpit HUD, better IR suppressor, new IFF, ALQ-144 IR-jammer and a Marconi air-data sensor arm mounted on the starboard fuselage side. Many aircraft were fitted with the AN/AVR-2 laser-warning system. A bulged fairing for a laser-spot tracker, which was never actually fitted, was added to the leading-edge of the rotor mast sail.

The AH-1S Modernized/AH-1F has become the most widely exported single-engined Cobra variant. Today it is in service in Israel, Japan, Jordan, Pakistan, South Korea and Thailand. Japan is unique among export Cobra operators as its aircraft were built under licence. Fuji Heavy Industries has supplied 89 AH-1Fs to the Japan Ground Self Defence Force, and two AH-1Ss were also acquired directly from Bell. In Israeli service the Cobra is known as the *Tsefa* (viper) and 64 aircraft have been delivered to the IDF/AF since 1981. They are believed to be in service with Nos 160, 161 and 162 Sqns, based at Palmachim and Hatzerim ABs. The Royal Jordanian Air Force took delivery of 24 aircraft, from 1985, which are currently based at Amman with Nos 10 and 12 Sqns. Pakistan's Army Aviation Corps acquired 20 AH-1Fs in 1984 and they fly with Nos 31 and 32 Sqns, at Multan. The Republic of Korea Army operates a mix of approximately 60 AH-1F HueyCobras and AH-1J SeaCobras. The AH-1Fs were delivered from 1988 onwards, joining the AH-1Js that had been in service since 1978. In 1990, the Royal Thai Army Air Division began operating four AH-1Fs from its main base at Lop Buri.

## TAH-1S – TAH-1F

Dual controls were fitted to 41 AH-1Gs upgraded to AH-1S Modernized standards, for use as pilot trainers at the Army Aviation School, Fort Rucker. When the Cobra designations were changed in 1988 these aircraft became known as TAH-1Fs. They were most readily identifiable by large high-visibility red panels on the side of the fuselage (common to all US Army training helicopters) and white three-character codes. All TAH-1Fs have now been withdrawn from use.

## TH-1S 'Surrogate'

To train AH-64 Apache crews to operate the Apache sensor system, 15 early-model and unarmed AH-1Ss were fitted with the AH-64's PNVS (Pilot's Night Vision System) FLIR above the nose. These aircraft entered service at Ft Rucker in 1984/85, but have now all been retired.

**AH-1G (early)**

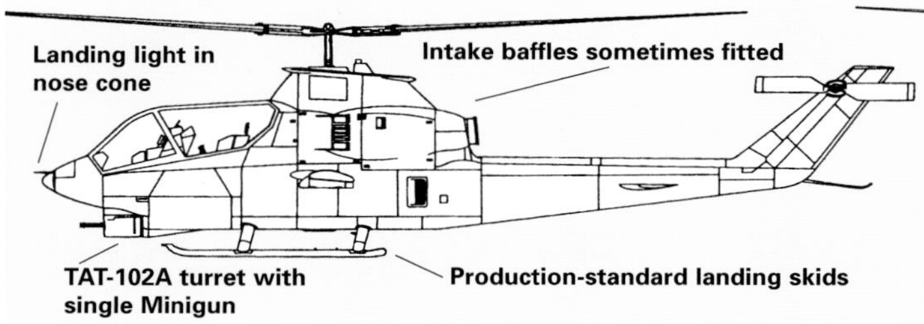

Landing light in nose cone
Intake baffles sometimes fitted
TAT-102A turret with single Minigun
Production-standard landing skids

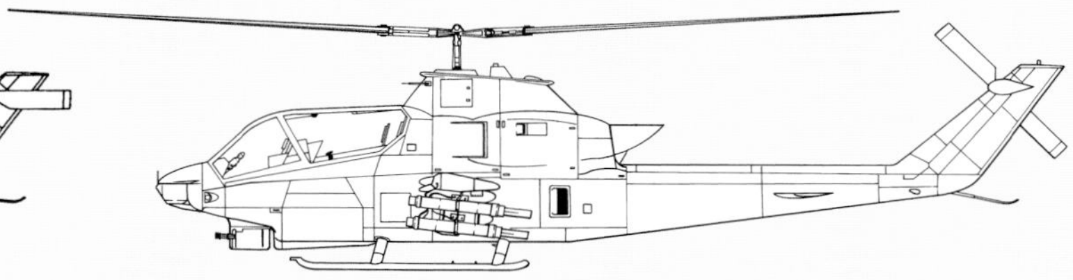

**AH-1G (late)**

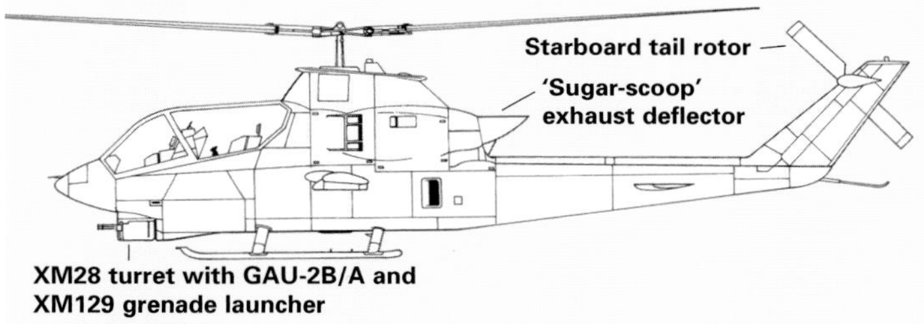

Starboard tail rotor
'Sugar-scoop' exhaust deflector
XM28 turret with GAU-2B/A and XM129 grenade launcher

**AH-1G SMASH**

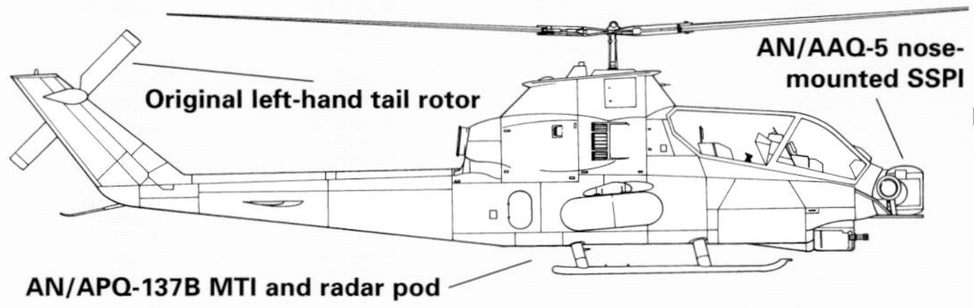

Original left-hand tail rotor
AN/AAQ-5 nose-mounted SSPI
AN/APQ-137B MTI and radar pod

**AH-1G/M35**

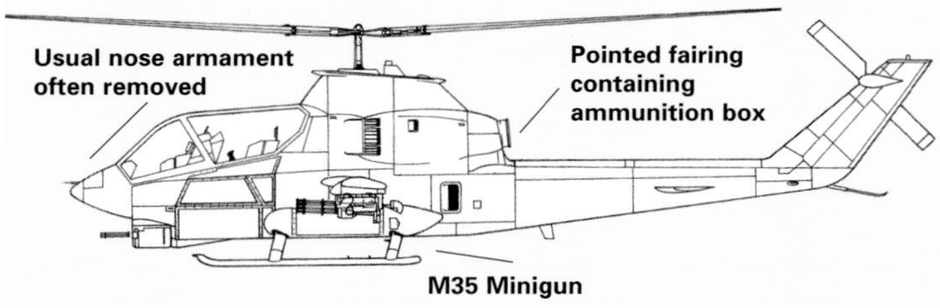

Usual nose armament often removed
Pointed fairing containing ammunition box
M35 Minigun

**Improved AH-1S**

**Up-Gun AH-1S/AH-1E**

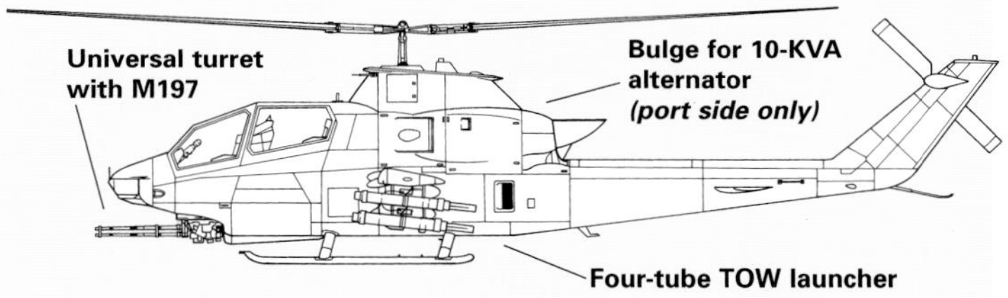

Universal turret with M197
Bulge for 10-KVA alternator *(port side only)*
Four-tube TOW launcher

**TAH-1S/TAH-IF**

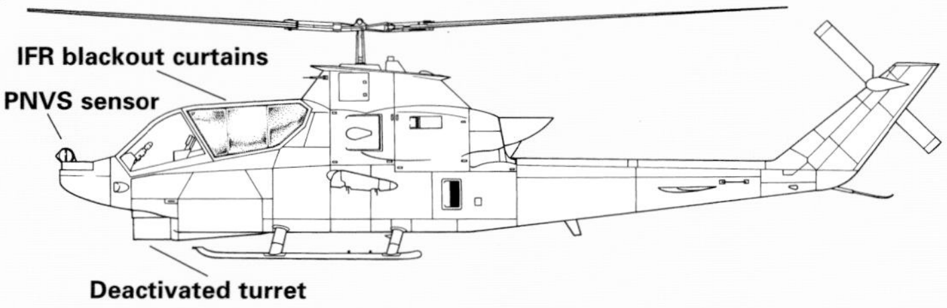

IFR blackout curtains
PNVS sensor
Deactivated turret

**Modernized AH-1S/AH-1F**

Laser spot tracker bulge (not fitted)
'Hot Brick' IR jammer
Wirecutters
Kaiser HUD
Wirecutters

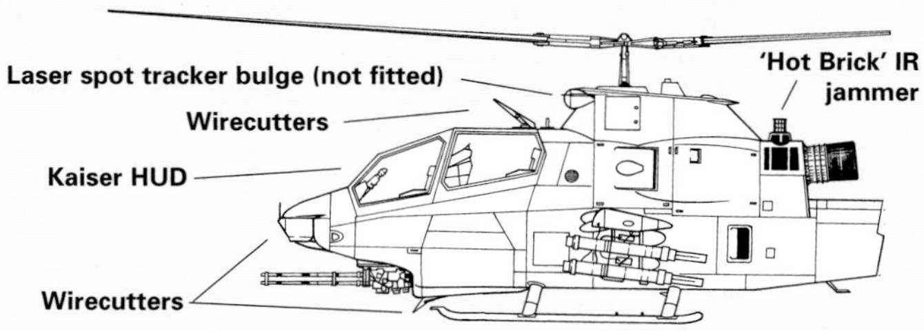

# AH-1 twin-engined variants

**Developed to meet the needs of the US Marine Corps in the late 1960s, the original twin-engined AH-1 has been constantly developed over the years, the main benefactor being the original customer.**

## AH-1J SeaCobra

As originally envisaged, the AH-1J was to have been a single-engined aircraft, similar to the AH-1G but with a rotor brake (deemed essential for shipborne operations), US Navy standard avionics and heavier armament, as well as better corrosion protection. The AH-1G was already in limited service with the USMC, and the logistic and political advantages of a common American powerplant initially overrode the Marines' traditional desire for a twin-engined machine. The 1968 Tet Offensive generated the need for massive attrition-replacement helicopter orders, and the Marines were given the go-ahead to replace their single-engined Hueys and Cobras with twin-engined machines, albeit that the engine was Canadian.

This allowed the Marines to procure a much more capable aircraft, with a Pratt & Whitney Canada T400-CP-400 (PT6T-4) turboshaft engine and a three-barrelled M197 cannon in a new undernose turret. The new weapon was basically a lightened version of the well-known six-barrelled M61, and came with an internally-mounted ammunition box containing 750 rounds. The gun had a nominal rate of fire of 750 rpm, but individual bursts were limited to 16 rounds.

The T400-CP-400, also used by the UH-1N and the Bell 212, consisted of a pair of PT6s driving a single shaft through a common gearbox. The new powerplant was appreciably more powerful than the original Lycoming T53, but its main advantage lay in the fact that it offered genuine twin-engine reliability. Since the rotor system was unchanged, the AH-1J produced more power than could be used (1,530 shp/1141 kW max continuous), but this gave a useful engine-out hover capability.

The first AH-1J was handed over in October 1969, and four were sent to Patuxent River for evaluation in July 1970. The first AH-1Js were sent to Vietnam in February 1971, where they quickly proved their worth under combat conditions. During their subsequent service, the Marines' AH-1Js were cleared to carry a wider variety of ordnance than Army Cobra variants, and all now have revised wing pylons and a new canopy-ejection system. Some surviving AH-1Js were modified to carry the AIM-9 Sidewinder, and were to have received the AGM-114A Hellfire (the latter having been abandoned). The J continued to fly with Marine Reserve units into the 1990s but have now been retired. Reserve AH-1J units were activated and sent to the Gulf.

## Model 309 KingCobra

Following the cancellation of the Lockheed AH-56 Cheyenne, Bell developed the Model 309 KingCobra. Two were built, the first a 'Marine' demonstrator powered by the same T400-CP-400 powerplant as the standard AH-1J, but with a strengthened drivetrain allowing the full 1,800 shp (1332 kW) to be used, and the second a single-engined 'Army' demonstrator powered by the Lycoming T55-L-7C, flat-rated at 2,000 shp (1492 kW).

The twin-engined aircraft made its maiden flight on 10 September 1971. The type differed from the AH-1J as its airframe was strengthened, while the tail boom was lengthened and fitted with a ventral fin to improve directional stability and to allow a larger diameter (48-ft/14.6-m) main rotor to be fitted. The single-engined 309 was similar, except for its engine pack, and indeed commonality was sufficient for the twin-engined aircraft to be rebuilt with a single engine after the original single-engined 309 was destroyed in an accident. The main rotor featured a new, very broad chord, high-lift blade with forward-swept tips and an asymmetric section. The original AH-1G-style nose was soon replaced by a longer unit housing an electro-optical or 'Visonics' sensor package, including a FLIR, a low-light TV, the TOW missile tracker and a laser rangefinder. The pilot had his own independent LLTV system mounted at the front of the rotor fairing, and this allowed him to fly in total darkness, even when the FLIR was being used by the gunner. Although not produced, KingCobra technology did find its way back into other AH-1 and UH-1 programmes.

## AH-1J International

When the Shah of Iran decided to order AH-1s for his army, he specified a TOW-compatible AH-1J derivative which incorporated many features previously tried and tested by the Model 309. The $704-million contract, the biggest single export programme ever undertaken by Bell, was signed on 21 December 1971, and covered the sale of 287 Model 214 utility helicopters and 202 AH-1Js.

The 'Iranian J', as it was sometimes dubbed, was powered by an uprated T400-WV-402, with a new transmission system derived from that of the Model 211 HueyTug flying crane. This gave the J International much improved hot-and-high performance, with a rating of 1,673 shp/1248 kW (maximum continuous). South Korea was the only other user of the AH-1J International, taking delivery of eight TOW aircraft in 1978.

## AH-1T Improved SeaCobra

The AH-1T was the first production Cobra variant with a new fuselage, necessitated by the upgraded powerplant and transmission system. Developed for the US Marine Corps, who wanted a TOW missile-capable Cobra, the AH-1T Improved SeaCobra used the 1,970-shp (1470-kW) Pratt & Whitney Canada T400-WV-402 twin-pac and a virtually unmodified Bell 214 transmission system. To absorb the extra power, the AH-1T was also given a new, 48-ft (14.6-m) diameter rotor, with blades whose chord had been increased from 27 in (69 cm) to 33 in (84 cm). The hub was strengthened, and given Lord Kinematics Lastoflex Elastomeric and Teflon-faced bearings. Swept tips were incorporated for reduced noise and to improve high-speed performance. The increased diameter of the main rotor made it necessary to lengthen the tailboom, and to provide a more powerful tail rotor with increased diameter and larger tail surfaces. To maintain the centre of gravity the forward fuselage was also stretched, making room for an additional avionics bay and 400 lb (181 kg) more fuel. Longer undercarriage skids were also used.

The adoption of the T400-WV-402 engine gave the AH-1T a dramatic increase in available power, allowing heavy payloads to be carried even with full internal fuel and giving the new variant, despite its much greater empty weight, a really impressive performance. The promise shown by the AH-1T was such that only 67 of the planned 124 AH-1Js were delivered, production switching to the AH-1T.

The last two AH-1Js built served as AH-1T prototypes, the first flying in its new guise on 20 May 1976. They were followed by 57 production aircraft. TOW compatibility was not provided from the start on the first 33 aircraft, due to budgetary constraints, but the survivors were given a retrofit programme including a nose sight, Sperry Univac helmet sights for both crew, and a recoil compensator to allow the TSU to be used with the M197 gun. This programme has given them compatibility with the TOW missile, and other modifications were to have allowed them to use the newer Hellfire. The second batch of 24 AH-1Ts was built with full TOW compatibility.

## AH-1T+

The AH-1T+ began its life as a paper proposal to Iran for a further enhanced SeaCobra incorporating the General Electric T700-GE-700 engines and transmission system of the Bell Model 214ST, which was to have been produced under licence in Iran. The new aircraft offered 75 per cent more power than the AH-1J then in Iranian service, with 25 per cent better fuel burn. It was to have had sand filters, better recoil compensation for the gun and enhanced avionics. It was also intended to demonstrate a top speed of 173 kt (199 mph; 319 km/h). The overthrow of the Shah deprived Bell of its intended customer, and the Marines made no secret of the fact that they wanted some AH-64s and did not want another 'warmed-over' Cobra. Work on the new aircraft continued, however, and an AH-1T was flown with the 1,258-shp/938-kW (max continuous) General Electric T700-GE-700 in April 1980.

## 4BW

The last production AH-1T (161022), previously the AH-1T+ and AH-1W prototype, was converted by Bell with the all-composite, bearing-free, Model 680 four-bladed rotor, first test-flown on a Bell 222. The new rotor is much simpler to make and maintain, and has a much longer life, as well as giving the SuperCobra improved manoeuvrability, increased top speed (by 20 kt/23 mph/37 km/h) and less vibration. It is much stealthier than existing rotors, and Bell hopes to demonstrate an ability to withstand direct hits by AAA of up to 23-mm calibre. Known only as the 4BW (Four-Bladed Whiskey), the former AH-1T+ demonstrator aircraft was also fitted with new tail surfaces, positioned further aft by some 60 in (152 cm), and with end-plate fins. The aircraft also incorporated a digital flight-control system and the night-targeting sights and Doppler-based navigation system under consideration for the AH-1W. With USMC evaluations complete, the 4BW prototype aircraft has reportedly been returned to stock AH-1W configuration and given back to the USMC. Many of the features tested on the 4BW will appear on the AH-1Z.

## AH-1W SuperCobra

In 1981, Congress refused to grant any funds for a Marine procurement of the AH-64; instead, Bell was given a $4.1-million contract to qualify the T700-GE-401 in the AH-1T. Bell then proceeded to add a host of new improvements and updates to the AH-1T+ prototype (161022), which was given prominent exhaust suppressors and bulged 'cheek' fairings which marked the relocation of TOW electronics previously carried in the tailboom. Sidewinders, Hellfire and TOW were all carried by the prototype, which was also given an AN/ALQ-144 IRCM set and AN/ALE-139 chaff/flare dispensers. The first production aircraft was redesignated AH-1W. An initial order was placed for 44, plus a single TAH-1W trainer, and the USMC eventually received a total of 179 newly-built helicopters. The 43 remaining AH-1Ts were modified to AH-1W configuration. Approximately 190 were in service in January 1999.

Export customers include Turkey, who received 10 of the Marines allocation. Bell is currently proposing the AH-1W KingCobra to meet a Turkish requirement for 145 locally-produced attack helicopters. Taiwan procured 42 examples between 1993 and 1997. Ambitious plans for Romania to licence-build an initial batch of 96 'Whiskey'-based AH-1RO Draculas may come to fruition.

The USMC plans to upgrade its AH-1Ws (and UH-1Ns) in a programme which will eventually see the 'Whiskey' become the AH-1Z.

## AH-1Z

After abandoning the Integrated Weapons System and the Marine Observation and Attack Aircraft programme in 1995, a two-phase improvement of the AH-1W was ordered. The first phase involved the fitting of the Night Targeting System (NTS) for dual TOW/Hellfire day, night and adverse weather targeting, while the second, more radical phase involves fitting the Bell 680 four-bladed rotor, new wing assemblies, and glass cockpits. AH-1Ws updated to Phase II standards will be re-designated AH-1Zs. The AH-1Z first flew in December 2000, with IOC scheduled for 2007. A total of 180 AH-1Zs is expected to be produced for the Marine Corps. In addition, Turkey has chosen the AH-1Z KingCobra as its new attack helicopter.

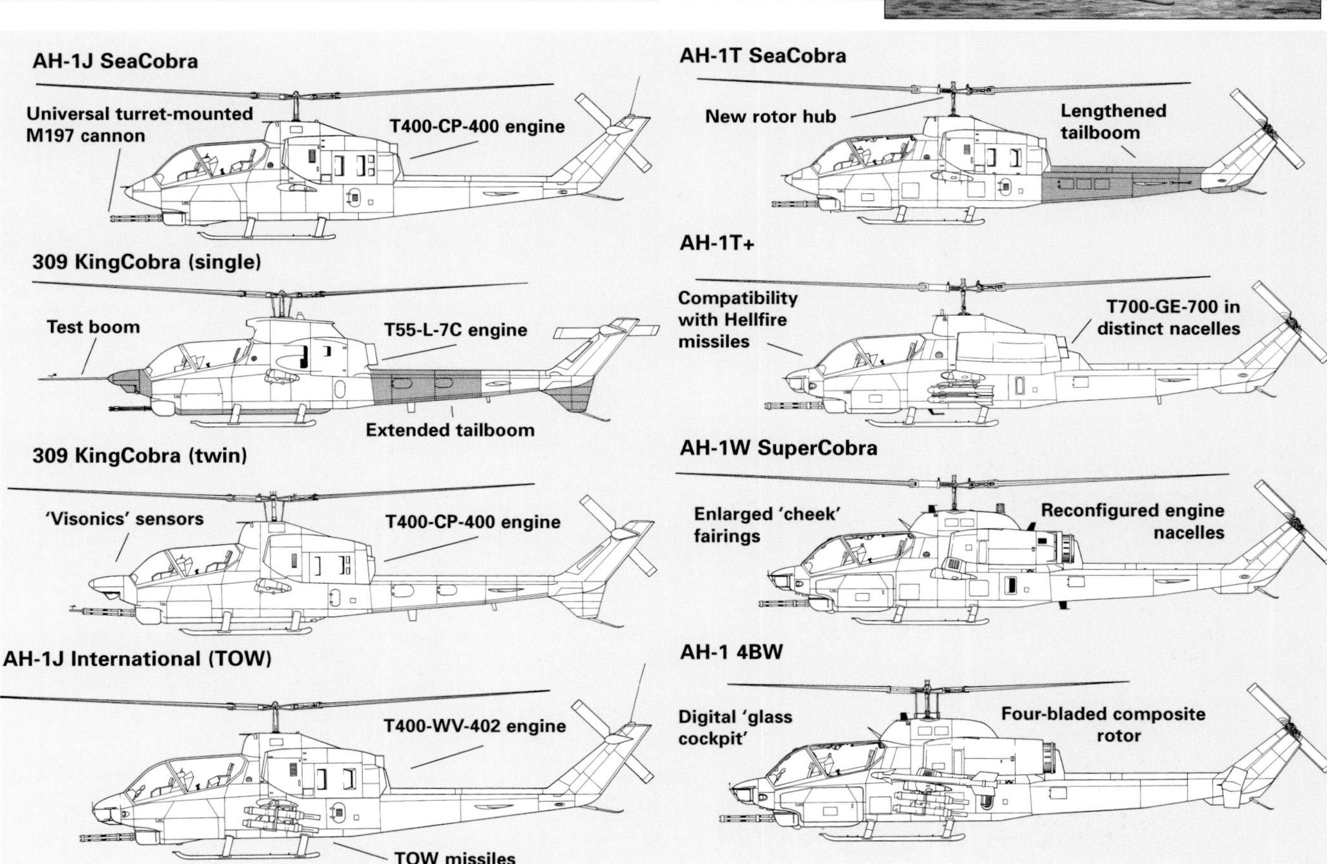

# Huey development

*The first of many: 55-4459 was the very first Bell 204 helicopter, known to the US Army as the XH-40. Years later, the type would become better known as the Vietnam-era UH-1 'Huey'.*

**In the 1950s, the US Army coined the term 'airmobility' when searching for its aircraft of the future. Bell responded with a helicopter design that looked exceedingly promising in early tests.**

Today, the Huey helicopter is one of the most familiar of all aircraft, as well known to the public as the Supermarine Spitfire, the Douglas DC-3 or the Boeing 747. However, this was not always the case.

## Korean lessons

The US Army had little to feel proud about in the early 1950s in the field of rotary-wing aviation. The army had been so late in introducing effective helicopters during the 1950-53 Korean conflict that one officer described this performance as "delinquent". This was in embarrassing contrast to the US Marine Corps, which had recognised the value of helicopters from the beginning, and now the US Army sought to correct matters.

A handful of pioneers, especially Generals James M. Gavin and Hamilton Howze, insisted that the army needed to become "airmobile". It simply made no sense, they said, to transport ground infantry troops to the battlefield by truck. In the Pentagon, officials turned to Bell Aircraft of Fort Worth, Texas, and ordered the company's Model 204 helicopter under the designation XH-40. "This will become our truck of the air," one officer told company president, Lawrence D. Bell.

*This early publicity photo of the XH-40 Iroquois shows it hovering above M60A1 (left) and M47 main battle tanks at Fort Hood, Texas. Years later, the 'Huey' would become an 'aerial tank' over Vietnam.*

## New helicopter

Powered by a 700-shp (522-kW) Lycoming XT53-L-1 turboshaft engine with a two-bladed, 44-ft (13.40-m) diameter rotor, the prototype Bell XH-40 completed its maiden flight on 22 October 1956 in the hands of Bell engineering pilot, Floyd Carlson. The tadpole-shaped XH-40 performed well, which was fortuitous – the US Army had already ordered a pre-production batch. By the end of that year, flush with enthusiasm over a number of initiatives in aviation, the army created its own system for designating military aircraft and ditched the USAF-style XH-40 nomenclature in favour of XHU-1. Soon afterwards, early production HU-1A and HU-1B models were given the popular name Iroquois, honouring an American Indian tribe indigenous to the northwest. The HU-1A designation prompted the legendary nickname 'Huey',

*Hauling an M551 Jeep during trials by the Army Aviation Board, this Olive Drab example '56-6726' was one of six YH-40 models, later to be referred to as the HU-1A in production.*

***This trials ship for the Army Aviation Board was one of half a dozen HU-1A models (later redesignated UH-1A) which validated Bell's basic utility helicopter design.***

***Although it could carry a nuclear warhead, the MGM-29A Sergeant missile was soon a footnote in history. However, like the C-130A Hercules in the background, this HU-1A Iroquois was on the brink of immortality as an aeronautical design.***

although another change in designation in 1962 made the type the UH-1.

## Early development

Nine developmental helicopters were followed by nine pre-production machines; in the mid- to late 1950s, there was plenty of funding. Soviet leader Nikita Khrushchev was brandishing his nuclear weapons, and world trouble spots were festering in Asia and Africa, especially in the Congo. By the time Bell received what the company's Bob Leder called a "no kidding, serious" production contract for 173 helicopters in May 1959, a member of the Senate, John F. Kennedy, was predicting that American troops might have to fight on real battlefields in the coming decade.

The first HU-1B made its initial flight on 27 April 1960 and demonstrated a capability to carry two pilots and seven troops at 126 mph (203 km/h) over 244 miles (393 km). In the new decade, longer and more powerful UH-1D and UH-1H models would greatly improve this performance, but the Huey was already being received warmly by troops. It was also welcome to harried US Army maintainers, who finally had a helicopter that was sensible to repair and keep flying.

The Army Aviation Board, also known to some as the Howze board after one of the army's most visionary generals, tested the new Bell helicopter in a variety of climates, conditions, and missions. The Cold War could turn hot at any time, so the army tried out the Huey as a battlefield taxi for its Honest John, Little John and Sergeant battlefield nuclear rocket projectiles. Later, when the US Air Force picked up on the potential of the Huey, it ordered the UH-1F model to supply intercontinental ballistic missile sites.

In 1961, Kennedy inspected a Huey during a visit to Fort Bragg, NC. By then, the US Army – encouraged by the new president's fascination with unconventional warfare – was establishing a unique battle formation. The 1st Cavalry Division, identified by a badge containing a silhouette of a stallion's head, would adopt a doctrine of vertical air mobility and would be redesignated as an Air Cavalry Division. Bell could now look to production orders going well above the 1,000 mark. A company memo noted that the new helicopter 'is now almost certain to be regarded everywhere as a success'. At this late juncture, no one yet knew how much of a success it would, in fact, be.

The army refined 'airmobility' tactics, showed the foresight to breed a new generation of warrant-officer pilots, and began the 1960s by supplying UH-1B Hueys to the 'First Cav' and to its training facility at Fort Rucker, Alabama.

The potential of the new helicopter in air evacuation duties was obvious and, in March 1962, soldiers of the 57th Medical Detachment (Helicopter Ambulance) at Fort Bliss, Texas, were alerted to become the first Huey operators sent overseas. At first, they thought they were going to Europe. As recounted by a UH-1B crew chief, they were finally given the word by their commanding officer.

"I know where we're going," the crew chief said to his commander. "It's in the headlines. A real hot spot. They're sending us to the Congo."

"That's wrong," the officer replied. "Our helicopters are going to a place I never heard of until last week." He paused and added, "Vietnam."

***Above: Reflecting consecutive changes in type designation, 60-3547 was an XH-40 on the drawing board, an HU-1B when it first flew, and a UH-1B, alias 'Huey', after 1962.***

***Left: Wearing high-visibility US Army colours (white fuselage, red trim), this trio of Bell HU-1Bs is pictured while on an early service acceptance flight.***

# US variants

**Bell's ubiquitous 'Huey' was in production for 28 years, between 1958 and 1986. In that time numerous improvements were introduced, the final UH-1H differing considerably from the A-model.**

## HU-1A (UH-1A from 1962)

From 1956 the H-40 was redesignated, under a new US Army Aviation system, as the HU-1 (giving rise to the 'HUey' nickname that was to be applied across the entire Iroquois range). Beginning in 1959 production UH-1As were delivered to the US Army, the first 14 of 182 being powered by a 700-hp (522-kW) T53-L-1A, the remaining examples having a 960-hp (716-kW) T53-L-5 derated to 770 hp (574 kW). The HU-1A was the first variant to see combat, equipping the Utility Tactical Transport Company in Vietnam from October 1962. A number of aircraft were field modified as armed escorts, carrying rockets and machine-guns in various combinations. Fourteen aircraft were converted as **TH-1A** instrument trainers in 1962, while a single aircraft became an **XH-1A** testbed for a gunship variant. Pictured is the first machine UH-1A, 57-6095.

## UH-1C

Essentially a late production UH-1B, the C-model had an improved main rotor system and greater fuel capacity. The Army took delivery of 767 examples between 1965 and 1967. Once again, a number were passed to Australia and Norway.

## YUH-1D and UH-1D

Based on the Model 205, the UH-1D had the same powerplant as the UH-1C, but featured an enlarged cabin able to hold 12 troops or six stretcher cases. Seven YUH-1Ds (illustrated) were built, the first flying in August 1961. Two years later, the first of 2,008 production examples for the US Army was delivered. A number were converted, in 1968, as **HH-1D** rescue aircraft, fitted with water tanks and spray booms. Many others were re-engined to UH-1H standard.

## XH-40 and YH-40

Three XH-40 prototypes (the third of which , 55-4461, is pictured) were built after Bell's Model 204 won a US Army competition to find a new utility helicopter, in 1955. Aeromedical evacuation, general utility and instrument training were among the roles envisaged for the H-40, which was powered by an 825-hp (615-kW) Lycoming XT53 turboshaft. These machines (the first of which made its maiden flight on 22 October 1956) were followed by six YH-40 service test aircraft which were tested by both the Army and USAF during 1957. These differed from the original aircraft in having a 12-in (30-cm) cabin stretch, increased ground clearance and other changes.

## YHU-1B and HU-1B (UH-1B from 1962)

Powered by 960-hp (716-kW) T53-L-5s, the four YHU-1Bs had increased chord main rotor blades, an enlarged rear cabin to accommodate eight troops (as opposed to five in the HU-1A), weapon attachment points, wiring for gunnery control systems and other detail changes. Evaluated during 1960, the four prototypes were followed by 1,014 production HU-1Bs for the US Army, later examples of which had 1,100-hp (820-kW) T53-L-11 engines. These were delivered between 1961 and 1965 (some to Australia and Norway), the first (a mixture of gunships and 'slicks') arriving in Vietnam in May 1963. A single example became an **NUH-1B** in 1963 for test purposes.

## UH-1E

Marine Corps interest in the 'Huey' resulted in a requirement being raised in 1962 for an assault combat helicopter based on the UH-1B. The 192 UH-1Es built for the Corps had T53-L-11 engines, increased fuel capacity and different avionics/instrumentation; many were later retrofitted with broad chord rotor blades. Pictured are the first two UH-1Es, BuNos 151266 and (nearest the camera) 151267, delivered in February 1964. Twenty **TH-1E** crew trainers followed.

## UH-1H and HH-1H

Equipped with a more powerful T53-L-13 engine, rated at 1,400 hp (1044 kW), the UH-1H was otherwise similar to the UH-1D and was the last production UH-1 variant. The first examples reached units in 1968; by the time the last had been delivered in 1976, production for the US Army had reached 5,435. The USAF also received 30 HH-1H base rescue aircraft, ordered in FY1970. A number of UH-1Hs have been converted for specialised roles; at least three **EH-1H**s carried jamming and monitoring gear under the codename 'Quick Fix' (a developed **EH-1U** variant was cancelled in favour of the EH-60A Blackhawk); four **JUH-1H** test aircraft were equipped with the SOTAS stand-off radar system intended for the EH-60B; **'VH-1H'** was an apparently unofficial designation for a number of aircraft converted as staff transports; as the type has been retired in large numbers during the 1990s, a number of UH-1Hs has been reworked as **QUH-1H** target drones.

## TH-1L and UH-1L

Pictured in US Navy training colours is one of the 90 TH-1L advanced training helicopters, the first of which was delivered to NAS Pensacola in late 1969. These aircraft shared their airframe and engine with the HH-1K; a small batch of eight similar UH-1Ls for utility duties with the Navy was also constructed.

## UH-1P

The USAF converted an unknown number of UH-1Fs to UH-1P standard for classified psychological warfare tasks in Vietnam. Some sources have referred to an **HH-1P** variant, possibly a conversion of UH-1Ps for a rescue role.

## UH-1V

The final UH-1 variant to enter US Army service, the UH-1V was introduced in the early 1980s, by the conversion of about 220 UH-1Hs. Advanced avionics for all-weather, low-level flight were added to these aircraft, most of which are assigned a dedicated medevac role and also carry high-speed hoists and sophisticated on-board life support systems.

## XH-48A and UH-1F

With a requirement for a missile site support helicopter, the USAF selected the Model 204 in 1963, a prototype being ordered under the designation XH-48A. First flown in February 1964 as the first UH-1F, 63-13141 (pictured) differed from earlier aircraft in being powered by a Geneal Electric T58-GE-3 turboshaft rated at 1,000 hp (746 kW). Able to carry 10 passengers, the UH-1F entered service in late 1964, 120 being delivered. A handful were deployed to Vietnam where they were converted as gunships for use by the 20th SOS, though these machines did not undergo a change of designation. Aircraft from a follow-on order for 26 **TH-1F**s were employed for instrument and rescue training.

## HH-1K

In 1970 the US Navy took delivery of 27 HH-1Ks for rescue duties. The K-model was based on the UH-1E airframe, but had a T53-L-13 engine and different avionics installed.

## UH-1M

The continuing development of the 'Huey' as a gun platform spawned the UH-1M, a conversion of the UH-1C equipped with the INFANT (Iroquois Night Fighter and Night Tracker) night vision system, produced by Hughes and comprising two nose-mounted IR seekers and IR searchlights either side of the cabin. Thirty-six UH-1Cs were fitted with T53-L-13 engines, as well as weapons slaved to the INFANT system, the first examples being deployed to Vietnam in October 1969. The aircraft remained in Southeast Asia for the duration of the war; a number were handed to the government of El Salvador in the early 1980s, though without INFANT equipment. A handful of surplus US Army aircraft finished up as **QUH-1M** target drones.

# Bell Boeing V-22 Osprey

*The second Osprey prototype takes on fuel during an evaluation exercise. When the V-22 finally makes it into service, its radical tiltrotor system will revolutionise assault transport operations.*

## Tilting troop carrier

**Development of the remarkable Osprey is continuing for operational testing with the USMC to begin during 2004. The radical programme has been beset by problems technical and political.**

During 2004, US Marine Corps squadron HMM-204, a helicopter training squadron, will be redesignated VMMT-204 and will become the first squadron to fly the Bell Boeing V-22 Osprey.

The Osprey looks in some ways like a helicopter, but the resemblance is misleading. Called a 'tiltrotor', the V-22 with its digital fly-by-wire flight controls can take off vertically like a helicopter, but, once aloft, shift into horizontal flight like a fixed-wing aircraft. This capability offers higher speed and range than the Marines' current CH-46E Sea Knight helicopter, many of which are now 40 years old, have flown up to 9,500 hours of a projected 10,000-hour life expectancy, and need to be replaced. Because it carries up to 24 troops, the V-22 can become the spearhead of an attack from offshore launched by ships that remain safely outside an enemy's coastal defenses. If technical problems can be solved, large numbers of Marines can 'hit the beach' not on a sandy, well-defended shoreline but far inland, attacking the enemy by surprise.

In its helicopter mode, the V-22 can hover, fly sideways, to the rear and forward. It can carry a variety of slung loads weighing up to 15,000 lb (6803 kg). When the rotors have tilted forward to act as turboprops, the Osprey can achieve a top speed of 315 kt (363 mph; 584 km/h). As a troop transport – even when operating from seaborne platforms in difficult conditions near an enemy's coast – the V-22 has a combat radius of 550 nm (633 miles; 1017 km) and can be refuelled in flight from a Marine KC-130F Hercules.

The pilot of the V-22 will be, in many respects, a new breed. When Bell's closely-related civil Model 609 tiltrotor reaches the civil market, the distinction between a 'fixed wing' and 'rotary wing' pilot's license will disappear inside a new category. Apart from its tiltrotor concept, the V-22 has an advanced flight deck with instruments that dispense with dials entirely. Further, the V-22 will incorporate a new helmet which will integrate both infra-red and image intensification to improve night vision; a magnetic head tracker slaved to the IR system plus any future turreted weapons systems, and display symbology like that found on a head-up display (HUD).

Boeing builds the Osprey's fuselage components at its plant in Philadelphia (Ridley Township, Pa.). This factory makes extensive use of robotics and fabricates the fuselage structure almost entirely from graphite-epoxy composite materials. The finished fuselage is then transported by air to the Bell factory in Fort Worth where it is 'mated' with wings and tail. A new Bell factory is being constructed in Amarillo, Texas and will take over the company's V-22 responsibilities in the near future.

The capabilities offered by the straight-up, fast-forward V-22 Osprey are greater than those of current helicopters. The V-22 is the USMC's biggest aviation programme. In 1997 alone, the Marines shelled out $1.18 billion for continued research, development, testing and evaluation, and for initial production. Nearly half of that money, $558.7 million, bought four low-rate initial production aircraft.

The total buy of Ospreys by all US services has been subject to much deliberation in the US Congress. The current plan is for

*The V-22 completed initial shipboard tests aboard the USS* Wasp *(LHD-1) over 4-7 December 1990. Air-to-air refuelling compatibility tests were also carried out.*

***The Osprey flies like a normal fixed-wing aircraft, with greater speed and endurance than most helicopters.***

***When nearing the landing zone, the Osprey begins the transition from wingborne flight by the translation of its radical tiltrotor system.***

***To pick up or drop its cargo, the V-22's rotors are raised like a helicopter, enabling the aircraft to descend vertically.***

the Bell Boeing team to deliver 360 MV-22Bs to the US Marine Corps, 50 CV-22Bs to US Air Force special operations forces, and 48 HV-22Bs to the US Navy. The production run is slated to stretch through 2035, and other countries may well become Osprey users.

Once an interesting experiment – presaged by earlier aircraft including the Bell XV-15 tiltrotor test ship – the V-22 Osprey is now very much a military weapon in full-scale production. This juncture was reached when the first of four MV-22B EMD (engineering and manufacturing development) aircraft (and the seventh Osprey built), BuNo. 164939, was assembled in Fort Worth and flown in January 1996. The next MV-22B (BuNo. 164940) was scheduled to fly in May 1996. The first Bell Boeing V-22 Osprey EMD aircraft, BuNo. 164939, made its first flight at Arlington, Texas on 5 February 1997. The no. 7 Osprey was ferried to Patuxent River, Maryland on 16 March. The successful ferry flight was the last milestone or exit criteria established by the Defense Acquisition Board for full funding release of Low Rate Initial Production (LRIP). The other criteria included passing 220 kt (253 mph; 407 km/h), and reaching 15,000 ft (4572 m); it now cruises at 275 kt (317 mph; 510 km/h) and dashes at 300 kt (345 mph; 555 km/h).

At least four V-22s have been lost in mishaps. The first occurred on 12 June 1991 in Wilmington, Delaware when the No. 5 Osprey went down, without loss of life. The No. 4 Osprey crashed in the Potomac River on approach to Quantico, VA, on 20 July 1992, killing seven. Two further accidents occurred in USMC service.

Personnel at Patuxent River volunteered to fly a V-22 during Operation Desert Storm but the idea was rejected by the Navy as 'premature'. US combat search and rescue efforts were not successful during that conflict – only a single coalition flier was rescued – and many believe the V-22 would have been ideally suited for rescue duties in a Middle East setting.

## V-22 Osprey

**The idea of the tiltrotor had been debated for many years, but it was not until the advent of the V-22 that the concept became operationally viable. Its advantages are numerous; it can do anything a helicopter can, but go twice as far and twice as fast. The aircraft here is the second prototype. Its initial flight tests covered flight control systems, development tests, icing and flying qualities.**

**Powerplant**
Allison won the competition to power the V-22, beating off competition from the Pratt & Whitney PW3005 and the General Electric GE27. The Allison T406-AD-400 is rated at 6,150 shp (4588 kW), and is based on the ubiquitous T56 turboprop. Each engine is fitted with a Lucas FADEC system with analog back-up. The engine is mounted in a Bell-built tilting nacelle.

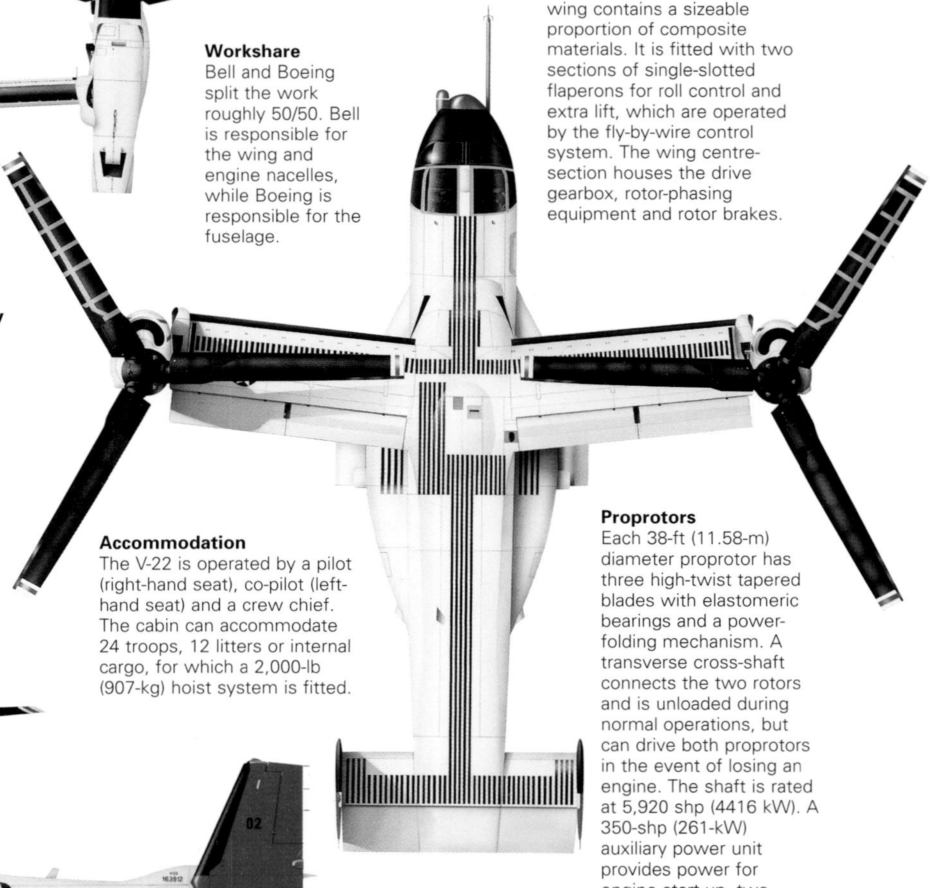

**Workshare**
Bell and Boeing split the work roughly 50/50. Bell is responsible for the wing and engine nacelles, while Boeing is responsible for the fuselage.

**Wing**
Slightly swept forward, the wing contains a sizeable proportion of composite materials. It is fitted with two sections of single-slotted flaperons for roll control and extra lift, which are operated by the fly-by-wire control system. The wing centre-section houses the drive gearbox, rotor-phasing equipment and rotor brakes.

**Accommodation**
The V-22 is operated by a pilot (right-hand seat), co-pilot (left-hand seat) and a crew chief. The cabin can accommodate 24 troops, 12 litters or internal cargo, for which a 2,000-lb (907-kg) hoist system is fitted.

**Proprotors**
Each 38-ft (11.58-m) diameter proprotor has three high-twist tapered blades with elastomeric bearings and a power-folding mechanism. A transverse cross-shaft connects the two rotors and is unloaded during normal operations, but can drive both proprotors in the event of losing an engine. The shaft is rated at 5,920 shp (4416 kW). A 350-shp (261-kW) auxiliary power unit provides power for engine start-up, two generators and an air compressor, allowing completely autonomous operations.

# Boeing AH-64 Apache

## Introduction

**Regarded as the world's premier attack helicopter, the AH-64 Apache's first real taste of combat came in Operation Desert Storm. Undertaking the first attack missions of the war, Apaches were instrumental in the destruction of Iraqi positions.**

The AH-64 Apache gives an army on the battlefield all of the advantages of a helicopter combined with the firepower of a heavily-armed combat aircraft.

Like an infantry soldier, the AH-64 uses agility to exploit its fighting prowess. It can hide, duck, rise, and fight in a fluid, fast-changing situation but, unlike the foot soldier, the AH-64 can also reach out over great distances with its weapons. When put into action as part of an integrated battle plan with assistance from E-8 J-STARS aircraft, the Apache can become the decisive weapon in a military engagement.

Anything but beautiful, with its bug-like silhouette, the AH-64 makes up for its ungainly appearance with Hellfire missiles, Hydra rockets and a M230 Chain Gun. This arsenal is directed by a high-tech array of sensors. These electronic and infra-red systems can be difficult to maintain in good running order but, when operating properly, they pinpoint the enemy by day or night.

Apache was conceived and developed in the Cold War years because the West needed an answer to that most fearsome of weapons, the main battle tank. Almost forgotten today is the challenge that faced NATO leaders when they pondered an assault on the plains of Europe by tens of thousands of Soviet and Warsaw Pact tanks. The Apache was optimised to detect tanks and to kill them, fighting in a highly mobile way using terrain and vegetation as a shield. When ready to lash out, the Apache pops up over the horizon and launches deadly missiles without ever coming within range of the tank's weapons. And if things go

*Despite recent improvements to their avionics, Apaches are able to operate in the most primitive conditions. These examples are seen in Germany where, a few years ago, they would have been tasked with halting a Russian armoured advance.*

***Above: In response to the request for a dedicated attack helicopter, Hughes Helicopters proposed the Model 77. Although completed only as a mock-up, the Model 77 displayed characteristics that would later be seen in the AH-64 Apache. Visible are the tandem-seating arrangement, under-nose cannon and pylon-mounted TOW missile launchers, which would in time appear on almost all dedicated attack helicopters around the world.***

***Right: Required to operate at low level over the battlefield to avoid hostile fire, the agility of the Apache is superb, although its ability to perform dramatic manoeuvres is reduced when carrying a large weapon load. Such is the strength of the Apache's performance that it was decided that the helicopter would have a limited air-to-air role. To perform these missions, Stinger air-to-air missiles are mounted on the stub wings. British Apaches will be equipped with the Canadian CRV-7 rocket system.***

wrong, the Apache is well armed for fighting at close quarters.

Apaches perform their task of killing targets with finesse, despite certain limitations. Most of those in service today lack global-positioning (GPS) and terrain-following systems for navigation on long missions. As a product of the 1970s, the Apache is an analog, not a digital warrior. Mission planning for any Apache mission is arduous because every eventuality must be foreseen, sketched out and planned on paper before the aircraft are in the air. Apaches fight as a team and, if the cohesion of that team is lost, so is the mission. Apache crews know the truth of Clausewitz's maxim that 'no plan survives contact with the enemy'. Communication of new ideas or intelligence is nearly impossible after launch, so Apache crews have to fly and fight in a stressful combat environment hoping that all the answers have been worked out before the shooting starts.

The long, slender Apache with its gunner and pilot in a two-seat, tandem cockpit offers excellent handling and flying characteristics and good visibility. The helicopter responds well to a skilled hand at the controls and performs as well as any battlefield helicopter in service anywhere. On the ground, its wheeled undercarriage affords easy movement for maintenance.

The Apache is a formidable weapon. But it was not the first of its kind. As a combat aircraft for army use, it was preceded by the Bell AH-1 HueyCobra from the Vietnam years.

An ambitious programme to improve the fleet of Apaches in service in half a dozen nations is at its mid-way point. The aim of the programme is to update this 1970s helicopter by means of modern-day radar and digital instruments. Once viewed purely as a helicopter to confront and halt oncoming tanks, the AH-64 Apache has evolved into a multi-role battlefield warrior. The improved AH-64 Apache variants are expected to play a vital role well into the 21st century.

***Above: An Apache attack would start with the helicopter being positioned out of the range of enemy small arms fire. Despite the vast array of high-tech weapons carried by the AH-64, unguided rockets have proved to be highly effective against so called 'soft' targets. A variety of warheads can be installed on the rockets ranging from high-explosives to white phosphorous.***

***Left: Apaches wear an overall scheme of chemically-resistant polyurethane Aircraft Type 1 Green. Squadron markings are kept to a minimum, much to the crews' annoyance, who are often left with the impression that army flying is viewed as a second-rate force. Colourful squadron markings have recently been making a return.***

# AH-64 development

**The Hughes (later McDonnell Douglas) Apache had a lengthy development history as it encountered troubles, both technical and financial. During this time, however, it matured into the most effective attack helicopter in service today.**

In August 1972, the official Request for Proposals (RFP) for the US Army's Advanced Attack Helicopter (AAH) was announced. The AAH was a replacement for the first-generation AH-1 HueyCobra, which had proven the value of a dedicated attack helicopter in the closing stages of the Vietnam War. The new AAH was intended to fight at night, in strength, on a future European battlefield.

Five competing submissions were made for the new helicopter – from Bell, Boeing-Vertol (teamed with Grumman Aerospace), Hughes, Lockheed and Sikorsky. Bell Helicopter Textron, not surprisingly, saw itself as the front-runner. It had amassed the most relevant experience of any of the competitors and its resultant YAH-63 (Bell Model 409) had the appearance of a thoroughbred. Hughes's designers developed the angular and awkward-looking Model 77 which, to the US Army, became the YAH-64.

## AAH fly-off

On 22 June 1973, the US Department of Defense announced that the Bell YAH-63 and Hughes YAH-64 had been chosen as the AAH competitors. This launched Phase 1 of the competition, whereby both firms would build and fly two prototypes, plus a Ground Test Vehicle (GTV), for a competitive fly-off. By June 1975, Hughes had begun ground tests with AV-01 (Air Vehicle-01), the prototype. This aircraft would be tasked with all the preliminary power tests, but AV-02 would be the first to fly. In fact, AV-01 never flew and served as Hughes's *de facto* GTV. In contrast, Bell had already run a dedicated YAH-63 GTV in April of that year and its apparent lead in the programme forced Hughes to hurriedly accelerate its work. The first YAH-64 succeeded in beating the YAH-63 into the air by one day, on 30 September 1975.

An intensive flight test programme was undertaken, first by the manufacturers and then by the US Army. During this period, the TOW missile armament originally planned for the AAH was replaced by the Rockwell Hellfire (HELicopter-Launched, FIRE-and-forget), a laser-guided anti-tank missile which promised effective engagement ranges in excess of 3.7 miles (6 km).

On 10 December 1976, having reviewed the evaluation results, the Secretary of the Army announced that the Hughes YAH-64 was the winner of the AAH competition. There had been some problems during the Phase 1 evaluation and the rotor system had had to be redesigned. The mast was lengthened and the blade tips were swept back. The weight of the prototype also had to be reduced and this was achieved by redesigning the tail unit and by introducing lightweight Black Hole IR-suppressors.

The Phase 2 contract called for the building of three production-standard AH-64s, conversion of the two prototypes and GTV to this standard also, and complete weapons and sensor system integration. The first flight of the modified AV-02, now in production configuration, took place on

***Above: This view of prototype AV-03 shows dummy Hellfire missiles, but also clearly illustrates the actuated trailing edge originally fitted to the AH-64's stub wings. This complicated feature was later deleted.***

***Top: AV-02, the second YAH-64 prototype, can be seen here on an early test flight – note the original shape of the nose and canopy.***

***Two competing designs were offered for the AAH's TADS/PNVS system. Developed by Martin Marietta (left) and Northrop (right), both combined FLIR and TV sensors, allowing the crew to find and designate targets – and fly and navigate – by day or night. TADS/PNVS imagery is displayed on the crew's helmet sights.***

***Hellfire testing began in 1980 and the extra stand-off range provided by the new missile made a huge contribution to the Apache's survivability on the modern battlefield. Initial testing did reveal some problems with the laser-guided Hellfire, however, particularly in fog, smoke, dust or rain – each of which could conspire to hinder the laser.***

***AV-04, the third flying prototype (AV-01 was the non-flying GTV) was the first to fly with the new 'stabilator' tail. This moving tailplane replaced a T-tailed configuration, which had been adopted to avoid problems with rotor downwash. The T-tailed solution proved unsuccessful however, as it caused the aircraft to fly nose-up. The new 'stabilator', connected to an automatic flight control system, made the YAH-64A much easier to fly.***

28 November 1977. Hellfire tests began in April 1979. Two competing TADS/PNVS (Target Acquisition and Designation Sight/Pilot's Night Vision Sensor) systems were installed on the AH-64 prototypes; AV-02 carried Martin-Marietta's system and AV-03 carried Northrop's. The last of the Phase 2 batch of three aircraft, AV-06, flew on 16 March 1980. This final aircraft was the first to fly with the definitive 'stabilator' design and extended tail rotor. In April 1980 a crucial landmark in the AAH story was reached with the selection of the Martin-Marietta TADS/PNVS for production.

Sadly, 1980 ended on a tragic note. On 20 November, AV-04 departed on a routine tail incidence/drag test, accompanied by a T-28D photo chase plane. Flying in close formation, the two collided, and only the pilot of the T-28 survived.

In May 1981, AV-02/-03/-06 were handed over to the US Army, in preparation for the AH-64's final Operational Test II (OTII) evaluation at Ft Hunter-Liggett, which was successful. One element of fall-out from OTII was the decision to move to an uprated version of the T700 engine, the T700-GE-701, rated at 1,690 shp (1259 kW). It was then, during the final stages of AAH Phase 2 testing, late in 1981, that the name 'Apache' was adopted.

## Apache go-ahead

It was not until 15 April 1982 that full-scale go-ahead for Apache production was finally given. The US Army had increased its Apache requirement to 536 aircraft, but was then forced to cut this back to 446. On this basis, Hughes estimated the total programme cost would be $5,994 million. The US Army had always accepted that the unit cost would creep up from $1.6 million (in 1972 dollars), but was now faced with a price per aircraft of over $13 million (rising to $16.2 million later that year). The AAH was faced with serious political opposition, however – the Apache had powerful friends. A letter dated 22 July 1982, from General Bernard C. Rogers NATO Commander-in-Chief Europe to the Apache's chief detractors in the Senate, spelled out the threat to Europe posed by the Warsaw Pact, and the urgent need for a counter. It ended with the words, 'we need the AH-64 in Europe now and cannot afford the luxury of another trip to the drawing board'.

## Handover

The first Apache for the US Army was rolled out in a ceremony held at Mesa, ahead of schedule, on 30 September 1983 – eight years to the day of the first flight. The stated price of the aircraft, its 'over-the-fence' cost according to the-then Project Manager Brigadier Charles Drenz, was $7.8 million in 1984 terms or $9 million in real-year terms. This equated to a unit cost of approximately $14 million when development costs were included. Hughes planned to accelerate production to a peak of 12 per month by 1986, with purchases of 144 AH-64s in FY85, followed by a projected 144 in FY86 and 56 in FY 87.

PV-01 made its 30-minute maiden flight on 9 January 1984, and, by then, the prototype fleet had logged over 4,500 hours in the air. This noteworthy event was obscured in the headlines by the announcement on 6 January 1984 that Hughes Helicopters was about to become a subsidiary of McDonnell Douglas.

## Into service

The first handover of an Apache to the US Army took place on 26 January 1984, although this was only a formality since the heavily-instrumented aircraft concerned, PV-01, would remain with Hughes/McDonnell Douglas and, in fact, it was not until the delivery of PV-13 that a US Army crew could fly an Apache away and call it their own.

Initial deliveries were made to US Army Training and Doctrine Command bases at Ft Eustis, Virginia (home of the Army logistics school), and Ft Rucker, Alabama (the US Army's centre of flying training). Apache acquisition ultimately amounted to: 138 (FY85), 116 (FY86), 101 (FY87), 77 (FY88), 54 (FY89), 154 (FY90) and a follow-on batch of 10 (FY95), for a grand total of 827 AH-64A Apaches (including six prototypes and 171 acquired in the first half of the 1980s). The first unit to convert to the Apache was the 7th Battalion, 17th Cavalry Brigade at Ft Hood, which began its 90-day battalion-level conversion in April 1986. The last of the 821 AH-64As destined for the US Army was delivered on 30 April 1996. This was the 915th production Apache.

***The official handover ceremony of the first AH-64A to the US Army, in September 1983, was held at the massive Mesa, Arizona factory, specially built to handle Apache production.***

# AH-64D Longbow Apache

## Briefing

**The AH-64D Longbow Apache represents the culmination of America's most important attack helicopter programme. US Army pilots have described the Longbow as a helicopter from the next generation.**

Since the earliest days of AH-64A operations, there have been attempts to upgrade the helicopter. In the mid-1980s, McDonnell Douglas began studies of the Advanced/Apache Plus, which was later referred to, unofficially, as the 'AH-64B'. The AH-64B would have had a revised, updated cockpit with a new fire control system, Stinger air-to-air missiles, and a redesigned Chain Gun. Aimed exclusively at the US Army, the programme was abandoned before it reached the hardware stage.

With new technologies becoming available, there was now the possibility of transforming the already formidable Apache into something of even greater capability. Operational limitations with the AH-64A became apparent during Desert Storm and provided the stimulus for developing an improved attack variant.

*Seen as a quantum leap over the AH-64A Apache, the Longbow is able to detect up to 1,024 potential targets. Of these, 128 can be classified, with attack priority being given to those 16 which have the highest threat value.*

*Above: Six AH-64D prototypes were built, the first flying on 15 April 1992, and the last on 4 March 1994. The US Army has ordered a total of 232 new-build Longbow Apaches.*

*Right: The mast-mounted Longbow radar allows the AH-64D to acquire, designate and destroy targets in all weathers, by day or night, amid hazards such as thick smoke.*

### New technology

One of the 'new' Apache's most significant developments was the mounting of a Longbow radar above the rotor head to provide millimetre-wave (MMW) guidance for specially-developed AGM-114L Hellfire missiles. When this was fully integrated into the helicopter's systems, the AH-64D was renamed the Longbow Apache.

Largely impervious to atmospheric interference, the mast-mounted Longbow radar system allows the AH–64D to fire-and-forget all 16 AGM-114L Hellfire missiles, while remaining hidden behind a tree-line. Thus, in wartime, the Longbow Apache can stay concealed while attacking targets, thereby increasing its chances of surviving retaliation from AAA or shoulder-launched SAMs.

The AH-64D is equipped with a totally new avionics system. Four dual-channel MIL-STD 1553B data buses combine with

***With its mast-mounted radar, the AH-64D can remain completely concealed while searching for potential targets, so reducing its vulnerability.***

new processors and an uprated electrical system to greatly increase and revolutionise the capabilities of the AH-64D compared to the AH-64A. The dials and 1,200 switches of the AH-64A cockpit have been replaced by a Litton Canada multi-function up-front display, two (6-in (15-cm)) square Allied Signal Aerospace colour CRT displays and just 200 switches. Improved helmet-mounted displays, an upgraded Plessey AN/ASN-157 Doppler navigation system, and Honeywell AN/APN-209 radar altimeter have also been incorporated. In service the AH-64D will have a dual embedded GPS and inertial navigation (EGI) fit plus AN/ARC-201D VHF/FM radios. The helicopter's improved navigation suite gives it near all-weather capability compared to the adverse-weather capability of the AH-64A. The larger volume of avionics in the AH–64D Longbow has forced the expansion of the Apache's cheek fairings, to become known as EFABs (Enhanced Forward Avionics Bays).

## Combat communication

The fluid nature of the battlefield has seen communication between friendly forces play an increasingly important role. Incorporating a data transfer module (DTM), the AH-64D is able to talk not only to other AH-64Ds, and OH-58Ds, but also to USAF assets such as the Rivet Joint (RC-135) and J-STARS E-8. Target information can be supplied to the Longbow Apache crew on a secure frequency, allowing them to transfer to the assigned 'killing zone'. Once the attack has begun, the Longbow radar can catalogue targets, designating those that are deemed to be the most threatening.

## Performance and power

The Apache's current General Electric GE T700-GE-701 turboshafts are to be completely replaced by uprated 1,723-shp (1,285-kW) T700-GE-701C engines. The -701C has already been fitted to existing AH-64As from the 604th production aircraft (delivered in 1990), and has proved to offer a marked increase in performance.

The US Defense Acquisition Board authorised a 51-month AH-64D developmental programme in August 1990. This was later extended to 70 months to incorporate the AGM-114L Hellfire missile. Full-scale production of 232 Longbows was authorised on 13 October 1995, with the complete US Army AH–64D contract also calling for 13,311 AGM-114L missiles. The first AH-64Ds were delivered in March 1997, with the first front-line unit expected to be operational in July 1998. Longbow Apaches will transform the composition of US Army aviation battlefield units. They will help to prove the advanced technologies that will be introduced by the RAH-66A Commanche. Should the latter enter widespread service, the two helicopters will be able to communicate with new levels of efficiency across the 21st century's 'digital battlefield'. Deliveries of the Longbow Apache are likely to continue until 2008.

## Lethal Longbow

In answer to its critics, the AH-64D Longbow received spectacular validation in a series of field tests. Between 30 January and 9 February 1995, at China Lake, a joint team of AH-64As and AH–64Ds undertook gunnery trials involving some of the most complex exercise scenarios ever devised.

The test results were staggering. The AH-64Ds achieved 300 confirmed enemy armour kills, whereas the AH-64As notched up just 75. Four AH-64Ds were shot down, as opposed to 28 AH-64As. One test official stated, "In all my years of testing, I have never seen a tested system so dominate the system it is intended to replace."

Both the Netherlands and the UK have followed the US Army's lead in ordering the AH-64D, with the Netherlands ordering 30 aircraft and the UK some 67. Sweden is also keen to evaluate the AH-64D.

***The advent of the AH-64D Longbow Apache heralds the rejuvenation of the Apache helicopter, although its high price has led some customers to opt for the AH-64A.***

# US Army operators

*All the Apache's battle honours have been won by the AH-64A model, but the replacement of this initial production variant in the US Army fleet by the latest AH-64D Longbow Apache is now gathering pace.*

**The Apache is the backbone of US Army Aviation's combat force. Since its combat debut in Panama, the Apache has been deployed to Iraq, Bosnia, Kosovo and most recently to Afghanistan.**

Beginning in 1984 the US Army took delivery of 821 AH-64A Apaches, and over 500 of these aircraft remain in the front-line inventory – with many of the 250 or so remaining AH-64As now allocated to Army National Guard and Reserve units.

In December 1995 US Army Aviation launched the transition of its Apache fleet from AH-64A to AH-64D Longbow Apache standard, when it signed an initial production deal with McDonnell Douglas (now Boeing) to rebuild and upgrade 18 aircraft as its first batch of Longbow Apaches. The following year, in September 1996, the Army completed a major five-year remanufacturing agreement for the supply of 232 AH-64Ds. During early 1997 the first two AH-64D prototype aircraft were deployed to Ft Irwin, California, to participate in the Army's Force XXI field exercise – the centrepiece of US Army efforts to rethink its tactics, techniques and procedures for combat in the 21st century.

## Army delivery

McDonnell Douglas delivered the first 'production' AH-64D for the Army on schedule, on 31 March 1997 (following its first flight on 17 March). By 4 April 1998 all 24 aircraft from the first AH-64D production lot had been delivered and, later that month, seven aircraft entered service with the Army's lead Longbow Apache unit, the 1st Battalion, 227th Aviation Regiment (1-227th), 1st Cavalry Division, based at Ft Hood, Texas. After a period of

*The AH-64 fleet consists of two models, the AH-64A, including this Bagram-based example, and the AH-64D Longbow Apache. Since production began in 1983 over 800 aircraft have been delivered.*

**Left:** *With the addition of a sophisticated fire control radar (FCR) or Longbow Fire Control Radar, the AH-64D has become arguably the most advanced production combat helicopter in the world.*

**Below:** *The emergence of the AH-64D is transforming the composition of Army aviation battlefield units, and it is ultimately expected to work alongside the RAH-66A Comanche scout.*

eight months of intensive company-level and battalion-level training, the US Army's first Longbow Apache combat battalion was certified as operationally ready on 9 November 1998. All AH-64D training, from individual to battalion level, is conducted at Fort Hood by the newly reconstituted 21st Cavalry Brigade. The Army's second Longbow Apache battalion – the 2nd Battalion, 101st Aviation Regiment, based at Fort Campbell, Kentucky – was certified as combat-ready on 2 November 1999.

## Five-year deal

Final negotiations for the remanufacture of a second batch of 298 Longbow Apaches were launched in 1999 and, on 9 December that year, Boeing (which had taken over McDonnell Douglas in August 1997) delivered the 100th AH-64D to the US Army. In September 1999, four years after work began on the AH-64A remanufacturing programme, Boeing signed a contract to provide the Army with a follow-on batch of 269 AH-64Ds, from 2002 to 2006. This second five-year deal would provide a total of 501 Longbow Apaches for Army Aviation, with around 150 already delivered at that point.

On 15 March 2001 the US Army declared its third AH-64D unit to be combat-ready – the 1st Attack Helicopter Battalion, 3rd Infantry Division (Mechanized), based at Hunter Army Airfield, Georgia. This unit was the first to send pilots through the Army Aviation training school, at Ft Rucker, Alabama, to gain initial Apache experience, before moving on to the 21st Cavalry Brigade for the fully-fledged eight-month intensive training course. By the end of April 2001 Boeing had delivered the last of 50 AH-64D Apache Longbow helicopters to be based at Ft Rucker. With the delivery of these aircraft the Army had fielded a total of 178 of its 232 'first production' AH-64Ds.

## New chapter

On 16 October 2001 the first US Army AH-64Ds to be deployed abroad arrived in Seoul, South Korea, opening a new chapter in American Longbow operations. The aircraft, all from the newly re-equipped the 1st Battalion, 2nd Aviation Regiment, were transported to Korea by sea, then reassembled and flown out. Until 1999, when it began its AH-64D conversion, the 1st Battalion had previously been an AH-64A unit in Korea.

In early January 2002 the fifth AH-64D unit was declared, in a ceremony at Ft Hood. This unit, the 1st Attack Helicopter Battalion, 101st Aviation Regiment, had won its combat-ready certification on 6 December 2001, and is based at Ft Campbell, Kentucky – the second AH-64D unit at that base. On 3 April 2002 the US Army took delivery of its 232nd and 233rd AH-64D Longbow Apache – the last example from the first five-year, multi-year production effort (Multi-Year I), and the first from Multi-Year II. Meanwhile, the Army's sixth Apache Longbow unit is now completing its training cycle at Ft Hood, while the seventh has begun its individual and unit training processes.

In recent years US Army Aviation has undergone a series of operational transformations, which have had a significant effect on the way its Apache force is organised. During the 1990s, the Aviation Restructuring Initiative (ARI) saw a reduction in the number of Apache units, but an increase in the strength of the surviving battalions from 18 to 24 aircraft. The ARI was successfully implemented, but in March 2000 the Army announced a completely new Aviation Force Modernization Plan (AFMP) – driven by the need to move away from single-purpose combat units to a more flexible, multi-purpose organisation, the prospect of the RAH-66 Comanche and the wider availability of the AH-64D.

In the future, each US Army Corps organisation will be allocated one Combat Brigade and one Combat Support Brigade. These new 'Objective Force' Combat Brigades will each comprise a Multi-Functional Battalion with 10 AH-64Ds (i.e. one company), 10 RAH-66s and 10 UH-60s.

However, until the RAH-66 becomes available the Corps will instead call on a temporary 'Transitional Force' Combat Brigade structure – each with 16 AH-64s (two companies) and one company of UH-60s.

## Transitional force

The AFMP also reorganises the Army's Divisional aviation assets. Each of the 18 currently-established Divisions (active and Reserve) will have two Multi-Functional Battalions (10 AH-64Ds, 10 RAH-66s and 10/20 UH-60s), plus a Divisional Cavalry Squadron.

Again, there will be a Transitional Force equipped with eight AH-64Ds, eight OH-58Ds and 16 UH-60s, before the final Objective Force levels become available in 2010.

# AH-64 Apache operators part 2

*Above: Greece was the first European export customer for the AH-64 Apache, initially ordering 12 examples.*

*Below: Dutch Apaches will be AH-64Ds, but will not have the mast-mounted Longbow radar. Thirty NAH-64D examples have been delivered.*

**With the role of the dedicated battlefield helicopter steadily increasing in importance, it came as no surprise to McDonnell Douglas to find that, despite its initially high purchase price, the Apache would attain a respectable list of overseas operators.**

The awesome capabilities of the AH-64 Apache were demonstrated to the world during the Gulf War. Following the conflict, McDonnell Douglas received a flood of requests from countries interested in purchasing fleets of new Apaches to reinforce their attack forces, with a view to operating them in emerging localised low-intensity conflicts.

### European operators

Constant tension between Greece and Turkey over territorial violations led Greece to upgrade its attack helicopter fleet. On 24 December 1991, Hellenic Army Aviation finalised its order for 12 AH-64As, with an option for eight more examples, which could then be increased by a further four. Delivered by sea in June 1995, a total of 24 AH-64Ds is now in service, with 12 AH-64Ds on order.

Filling a requirement for a multi-role armed helicopter to undertake escort, reconnaissance, protection and fire-support missions, the Apache proved to be the clear choice for the Netherlands. Despite objections from economic affairs advisers, the Netherlands announced its decision in favour of the AH-64D Apache on 24 May 1995, and so became the first export customer of this variant. Thirty examples are expected to be delivered during 1998, although the RNLAF AH-64Ds will not be equipped with the mast-mounted Longbow radar. The Apaches form the centre-piece of the Dutch rapid deployment Air Mobile Brigade.

### United Kingdom

The United Kingdom's search for an attack-helicopter became a priority during the mid-1980s, with approximately 127 aircraft being sought. With an invitation to tender (ITT) issued in February 1993, the AH-64D became the clear favourite over the rival RAH-66A Comanche and BAe/Eurocopter Tiger. In an announcement made on 13 July 1995, the Apache was selected as the new attack helicopter – known as the WAH-64D –for the Army Air Corps (AAC). The Westland Apache will be uniquely powered by Rolls-Royce/Turboméca RTM322 turboshafts, so maintaining a commonality with the Royal Navy's EH.101 Merlin. A reduced order of just 68 Apaches was eventually placed and British Apaches will be equipped with the Shorts Helstreak air-to-air missile. With initial crew training taking place at Ft Rucker, the first Apache unit will be No. 671 Sqn at Middle Wallop in Hampshire. The in-service date slipped from December 1998 to January 2001.

### Middle East customers

A host of Arab clients have also placed orders for the AH-64 Apache, following its performance in the Gulf War. With cost being of little concern to these oil-rich states, the United Arab Emirates Air Force received its first AH-64 Apache at a handover ceremony in Abu Dhabi on 3 October 1993, with deliveries continuing throughout the year. A total of 30 examples was received.

Saudi Arabia received 12 AH-64As in 1993 for its Army Aviation Command, based at King Khalid Military City. The Apaches operate alongside Bell 406CS Combat Scouts in hunter-killer teams, but it is not known whether Saudi Arabia received AGM-114 Hellfire missiles.

Egypt received a substantial arms package ($318 million) from the US in March 1995. This included 36 AH-64As, four spare Hellfire launchers, 34 rocket pods,

*Those countries with sufficient funds or those facing a powerful threat, have been keen to obtain Apaches. For the United Arab Emirates Air Force funding posed little problem, while instability in the Middle East was justification enough for obtaining AH-64s. As such, the UAE plans to upgrade its 30 AH-64A helicopters to AH-64D standard.*

six additional T700 engines, and one spare optical and laser turret – an additional 12 Apaches were also requested. All aircraft were to be of the latest US Army standard, with embedded GPS, but with a localised radio fit. The Egyptian Apaches are believed to have been allocated to the air force's single attack helicopter regiment. In 2000 Egypt began processing its aircraft into an AH-64D upgrade programme abd had around 34 Apaches operational in late 2003.

### Combat operations

Reformed on 12 September 1990, Israel's No. 113 Squadron became the country's first operational Apache unit. In August/September 1993, Israel received a further 24 AH-64As (plus two UH-60As) from surplus US Army Europe stocks, as a 'thank you' for support during Operation Desert Storm. All were delivered by C-5 from Ramstein AFB. The arrival of these aircraft led to the establishment of the IDF/AF's second AH-64 squadron. During November 1991, Israel became the first foreign AH-64 operator to use its aircraft in combat, when Hizbollah targets in southern Lebanon were attacked. In 2004 the country could boast 40 AH-64As, with nine AH-64Ds on order and the 'As' likey to be upgraded to 'D' standard.

### Future operators

Kuwait's requirements for a new attack helicopter led to its decision to acquire the Apachs in 1997, a deal whichcame to fruition in the form of contract signature for 16 AH-64Ds in October 2003.

Bahrain and the Republic of Korea have both expressed interest in the AH-64, with the aircraft still being considered by the latter.

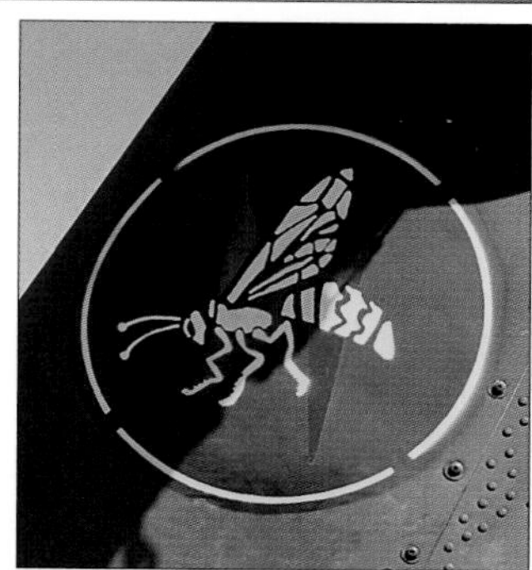

***Israel's Apache fleet has been particularly publicity-shy. Despite the substantial number of the aircraft that have been delivered over the years, only one squadron has been acknowledged to any extent by the Israelis. Although not officially identified, this is known to be No. 113 'Wasp' Squadron (badge seen opposite). The AH-64A Apache is known as the Peten (cobra) in IDF/AF service. It has been used extensively against the terrorist group, Hizbollah, operating alongside Hughes 500MDs.***

## AH-64A APACHE

**Israel became an AH-64A Apache operator in September 1990, since when its AH-64As have seen combat on the Israeli front line of southern Lebanon. On 16 February 1992, for example, a pair of AH-64As carried out an ambush on the convoy carrying Hizbollah's Secretary-General, Abbas Musawi, along the mountainous road from Jibchit to Sidon. The precision of the Apache's Hellfire system is greatly valued in attacks on small terrorist targets, which are frequently surrounded by civilian buildings and infrastructure.**

#### IDF/AF AH-64A markings

Unlike any other of its combat helicopters, the IDF/AF's Apaches are painted in an (IR-suppressive) olive drab finish. Squadron badges (in the case of No. 113 Sqn at least) are regularly seen. For operations in southern Lebanon, aircraft carry an IR-reflective 'V' identification marking on the rear of the fuselage.

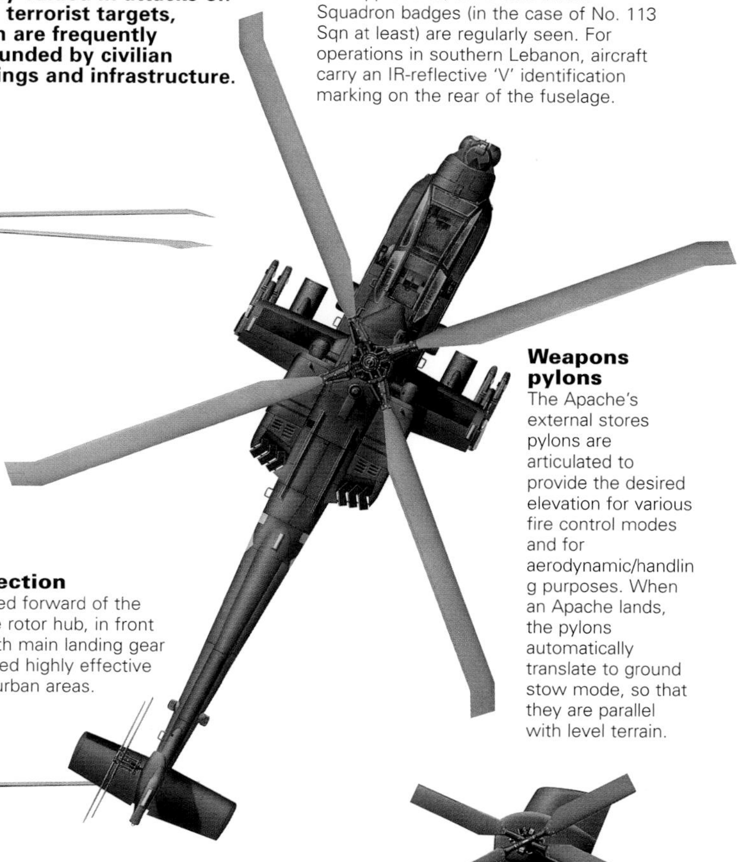

#### Weapons pylons

The Apache's external stores pylons are articulated to provide the desired elevation for various fire control modes and for aerodynamic/handling purposes. When an Apache lands, the pylons automatically translate to ground stow mode, so that they are parallel with level terrain.

#### Audio warning system

In addition to visual cues, critical threat warning and aircraft malfunctions are relayed as aural warnings through the crew's headsets. The crew members also receive a tonal signal to indicate that they are transmitting in secure radio mode.

#### Wire strike protection

Wire cutters are located forward of the nose turret, below the rotor hub, in front of the gun, and on both main landing gear legs. These have proved highly effective when operating over urban areas.

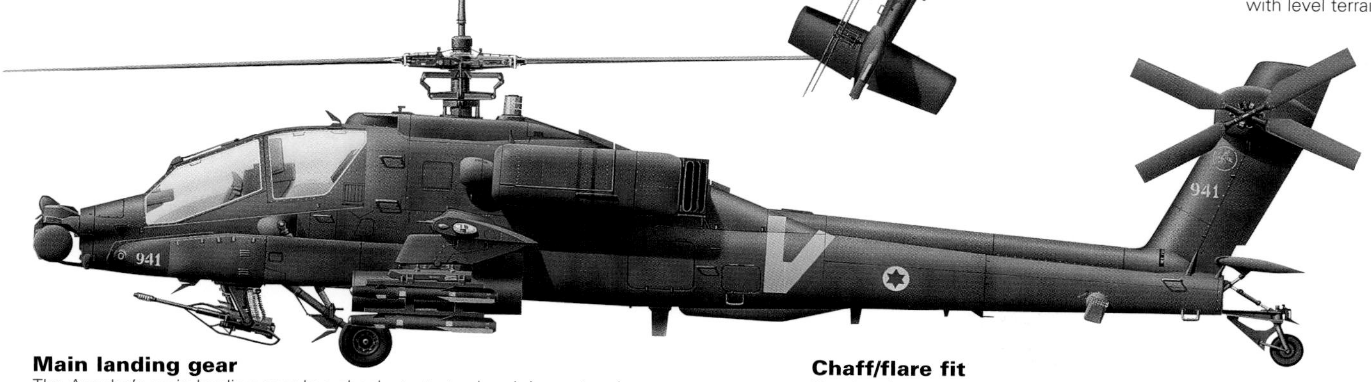

#### Main landing gear

The Apache's main landing gear has shock struts to absorb impact and a kneeling facility to allow for air transportation. Each landing strut has a one-time, high-impact absorbing capability, so reducing injury to the crew in the event of a forced landing.

#### Chaff/flare fit

The Apache can carry removable 30-round M130 chaff dispensers on a mounting to the rear of the tail boom, to starboard. The M130 can fire M1 chaff cartridges to defeat radar-guided weapons.

# Boeing B-52 Stratofortress

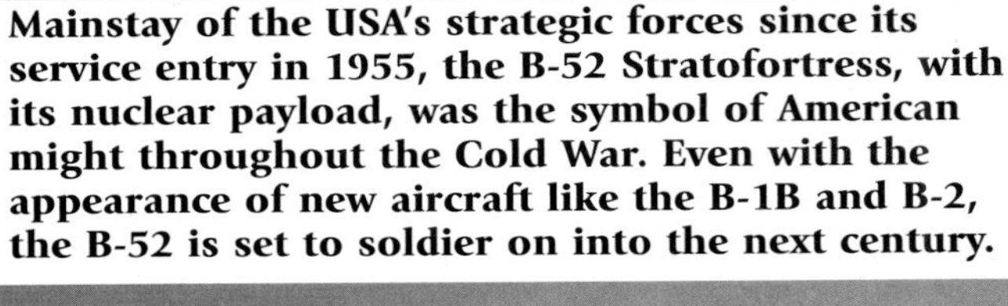

**Mainstay of the USA's strategic forces since its service entry in 1955, the B-52 Stratofortress, with its nuclear payload, was the symbol of American might throughout the Cold War. Even with the appearance of new aircraft like the B-1B and B-2, the B-52 is set to soldier on into the next century.**

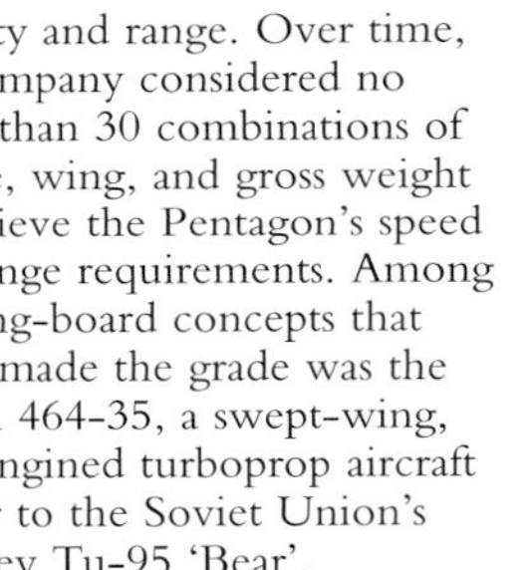

## Boeing's 'Big Stick'

As the longest-serving warplane in history, the Boeing B-52 Stratofortress is held in affection by its crews and feared by its foes. Those who fly the B-52 speak not of its age or longevity, but of its capabilities: the B-52H model in service today can carry a greater variety of weapons and perform a broader range of missions than the B-1B Lancer, B-2 Spirit, or any other bomber in service.

In 1946, Boeing was revelling in its success in building the war-winning B-29 Superfortress, but did not yet know whether or not its post-war B-47 Stratojet would succeed. Approached by the Pentagon to build a new strategic bomber, Boeing began years of design work that ultimately led to the B-52.

Boeing began with its Model 462 and 464 designs, both straight-wing, turboprop bombers of enormous size, capacity and range. Over time, the company considered no fewer than 30 combinations of engine, wing, and gross weight to achieve the Pentagon's speed and range requirements. Among drawing-board concepts that never made the grade was the Model 464-35, a swept-wing, four-engined turboprop aircraft similar to the Soviet Union's Tupolev Tu-95 'Bear'.

### 'Big Stick' shapes up

By 1950, Boeing's design efforts had yielded the Model 464-49, an eight-jet, swept-wing bomber, built for the USAF in the form of two prototypes, the XB-52 and YB-52. The prototypes had a braced tandem cockpit configuration, but otherwise were basically the same as the 744 production Stratofortresses that followed. Power was provided by the first jet engine in aviation history to generate 10,000 lb (45 kN) of thrust, the Pratt & Whitney JT-3A, known to the military as the J57-P-3.

XB-52 and YB-52 prototypes were built under conditions of great secrecy and the YB-52 became the first to fly at Seattle, Washington, on 15 April 1952 with test pilot Tex Johnston at the helm.

To win a production order, Boeing had to show that its B-52 bomber was superior to the Convair YB-60, a kind of hybrid with a B-36 fuselage, new wings and tail, and jet engines. Boeing had designed a bomber that was clearly superior in every respect, although the Convair team was held in high regard by Pentagon experts. In the end, however, it simply became obvious that the YB-60 was not a state-of-the-art aircraft.

By contrast, the B-52 had been built to the very latest design specifications. It resembled a B-47 Stratojet with its 35° swept wing, podded engines, 'bicycle' undercarriage and braced tandem canopy. From the B-52A model onward, the canopy was redesigned to provide side-by-side seating. Changes in tailfin shape and

***Above:** B-52Hs still play an important part in the USAF's Air Combat Command, which is an amalgamation of Tactical Air Command and Strategic Air Command, around 84 aircraft remaining on active front-line duty. The Air Force Reserve, Air Force Test Center and NASA also operate a number of examples.*

***Top:** Essentially a production version of the B-52A, the B-52B was outwardly indistinguishable from its predecessor, though it had uprated engines. On 18 January 1957, three B-52Bs completed a non-stop flight around the world in 45 hours, 19 minutes.*

***Although rolled out after the XB-52, the YB-52 was the first into the air by five months. During its maiden flight in 1952, it remained aloft for three hours and was well received by the test pilots (who were seated in tandem). The B-52 underwent the most rigorous testing of any aircraft of its time, and some three years elapsed before the aircraft entered regular USAF service.***

***Right:** The XB-52 was first rolled out on the night of 29 November 1951, covered in tarpaulins for security reasons. The two B-52 prototypes differed from their successors by having tandem-pilot cockpits and no tail armament.*

***Below:** The eighth production model of the B-52, the H is set to remain in service until at least 2030. The real strength of the B-52H today lies in its ability to carry a wider range of weaponry than any other US bomber.*

powerplant came later.

Fuel capacity was greater than in any previous production aircraft at 38,865 US gal (147120 litres) with external tanks, as compared with 21,000 US gal (79493 litres) for the B-36. The eight engines were podded in pairs on four underwing pylons similar to the inboard pylons of the B-47. The gigantic fin, with only its trailing edge hinged to form a rudder, brought the bomber's height to 48 ft 3⅔ in (14.72 m) and could be folded to permit the bomber to enter standard hangars. The B-52 did not rotate on take-off but, rather, popped aloft, its wing set at an incidence of 8° for a flyaway with the fuselage horizontal. On landing, the B-52 routinely employed a 44-ft (13.41-m) braking parachute, stowed in a compartment in the rear fuselage.

## B-52 variants

Remarkably, the B-52 changed little from the beginning to the end of its 10-year production run. The initial Air Force production order was for three B-52As with J57-P-9W engines, followed soon by 23 B-52Bs with J57-P-19W, -29W, and -29WA powerplants. RB-52B reconnaissance models were eventually modified to B-52C standard, in addition to 35 new B-52Cs introduced from March 1956 with larger external tanks and increased fuel capacity.

The B-52D, first flown on 14 May 1956, was built in greater numbers (170 in total). These were followed by 100 B-52Es, with minor internal changes, and the manufacture of 89 B-52Fs, beginning in February 1959.

Boeing then went on to produce 193 B-52G aircraft. The B-52G introduced a shorter vertical tail, and a new integral-tank wing with fuel capacity increased to 46,576 US gal (176309 litres) and with underwing tanks reduced in volume to 700 US gal (2650 litres) each. Weight was increased to 488,000 lb (221357 kg). The B-52G was designed for the Douglas GAM-87A Skybolt missile, a two-stage, air-launched ballistic missile which underwent extensive Anglo-American design and development work before being cancelled as a failure. The B-52G's bomb bay was also configured to carry four ADM-20A Quail decoy missiles; the aircraft also carried two North American GAM-77 (AGM-28) Hound Dog inertial-guidance cruise missiles.

On the B-52G, the gunner was relocated in the main crew compartment, operating his guns via the AN/ASG-15 fire control system. The armament of previous models, four .50-cal. (12.7-mm) machine-guns in the tail, was retained.

The USAF ordered 102 B-52H aircraft, taking delivery of the first on 9 May 1961. With the short vertical fin of the B-52G, the H model was powered by eight 17,000-lb (77-kN) thrust Pratt & Whitney TF33-P-1 or -3 turbofan engines. Tail armament of the B-52H was again remotely operated, but now comprised a single T-171 (later M61A1) 30-mm Vulcan cannon. The last B-52H was delivered to the USAF on 26 October 1962, bringing the final total of production Stratofortresses to 744.

***Right:** Range is one of the B-52's most outstanding features and it can be further increased with the aid of tankers such as this KC-135R. During the Gulf War seven B-52Gs flew from the USA to Saudi Arabia and back; the flight covered 14,000 miles (22530 km) and lasted 35 hours 20 minutes, making it the longest-ever combat mission.*

***Below:** The B-52H was never intended as a 'bomb truck' and so has less lifting capability than some earlier variants. However, it can still carry up to 51 500-lb (227-kg) Mk 82A/82SE bombs.*

# Into service

*Top: The reconnaissance/bomber RB-52B had provision for the installation of a removable two-man pressurised capsule in the bomb bays, which allowed the carriage of cameras or ECM equipment. Normal bombloads could alternatively be carried.*

*Left: Pictured after landing at March AFB, California (landing at the original destination of Castle AFB, California was not possible due to poor weather) are the three B-52s that made the successful round-the-world flight. Their historic journey was conducted at an average speed of 530 mph (853 km/h).*

**When the B-52 entered service, it represented a major leap in ability over the existing B-47s it gradually replaced. With the introduction of nuclear cruise missiles, this capability was further magnified.**

A decade of hard work by Boeing's design team reached fruition on 29 June 1955 when the first B-52B models entered service with the Strategic Air Command's 93rd Bombardment Wing (Heavy) at Castle AFB near Merced, California. The Stratofortress was crewed by two pilots, an electronic warfare officer, a navigator, a radar navigator (bombardier), and a tail gunner who was the only enlisted man on board. The B-52 was designed to carry the largest American nuclear weapons, to challenge the defences of the Soviet Union, and to get through to targets halfway around the globe via a polar route.

The USAF was only just becoming accustomed to the new bomber when it staged a demonstration of the B-52's prowess. Led by Maj. Gen. Archie Olds, five B-52s (including two spares) took off on 16 January 1957 for a round-the-world flight that followed a similar route to that taken by explorer Fernando Magellan five centuries earlier. The bombers completed the non-stop, air-refuelled 24,235-mile (39002-km) journey in 45 hours 19 minutes.

When coupled with the KC-135 Stratotanker, which first took to the air on 31 August 1956, the Buff – 'Big Ugly Fat F***er' – had global reach. Lest there be any doubt as to its purpose, during tests in the Pacific (code-named Redwing) on 16 May 1956, a B-52B dropped the first US hydrogen bomb to be released from an aircraft. This was called the Cherokee shot and was a near disaster, the Mk 15 Zombie thermonuclear bomb with its 3.75-megaton yield missing its intended target by several miles. In 1962, the year before the atmospheric test-ban treaty, B-52s dropped numerous atomic and hydrogen bombs in the Pacific.

The Redwing B-52B was slightly damaged, proving that a B-52 bomber could be five miles (8 km) from a nuclear detonation and yet still sustain harm. It was due to luck alone that the damage was not more severe (or fatal). The incident also proved that, if airmen were to fight in a nuclear war, they had to expect conditions which were different not merely in degree, but in kind from those of conventional combat. Maybe a SAC B-52 would drop one or more weapons on Moscow some day, but it was not going to be possible for a B-52 or any other aircraft to fly in a 'business-as-usual' fashion in the midst of Armageddon. As late as 1964, no-one in the USAF had any other mission in mind for the Stratofortress, revealing a complacency that would soon be overcome in the rainforests of Vietnam.

The reconnaissance mission was a temporary task in the long career of the B-52. The RB-52B

*Seen here with its predecessor, the B-47, is one of the three B-52As (foreground) received by the USAF before production switched to the B-52B. The B-52As cost the USAF the-then fantastic price of $29,000,000 each, but it is fair to say that these were essentially experimental aircraft, with much of the original R&D costs charged against them. These aircraft never reached operational status.*

**Above: Little more than a reworked production B-52A, the B-52B had the improved J57-P-19W, -29W and -29WA engines. Only 23 examples were built, and this machine (53-394) was in the last block of B models constructed. It was also the first B-52 to complete the round-the-world flight.**

**Above: The C model, an improved RB-52B, had its unrefuelled range extended by the use of 3,000-US gal (11116-litre) auxiliary fuel tanks to bring total fuel capacity to 41,700 US gal (271000 litres). The B-52C was also the first variant to use white thermal reflecting paint on its undersurfaces.**

**Above: First fired on 21 January 1961, Skybolt was America's first air-launched ballistic missile. However, this supersonic nuclear missile was later cancelled in favour of Hound Dog.**

**Above: The Hound Dog was the first cruise missile deployed on a USAF bomber. It greatly extended the aircraft's combat capabilities, allowing the B-52 to attack three targets simultaneously.**

reconnaissance model introduced a two-man pressurised capsule, equipped with camera or electronic monitoring devices, which could be carried in the bomb bay. B-52C models launched in 1956 retained the reconnaissance capability, but were not assigned an 'R' prefix. Very few details have ever been published about the Buff's reconnaissance activities and, by the early 1960s, the reconnaissance function was being ably carried out by other aircraft, whereupon the B-52 reverted to its original role as a nuclear bomber.

The B-52 had many qualities, but at the forefront was its versatility. It had been designed to attack from high altitude, but when the Soviet SA-2 'Guideline' surface-to-air missile came on the scene – rather dramatically, with the shooting-down on 1 May 1960 of an American Lockheed U-2 spyplane – the Stratofortress allowed itself to be re-tasked as a low-level bomber, eventually acquiring terrain-hugging radar and navigation gear. Designed to drop nuclear bombs that relied on gravity, the B-52 was to carry every US air-launched weapon from the Hound Dog missile of the 1960s to the Advanced Cruise Missile of the 1990s.

During its first decade as a Cold War Warrior, the B-52 flew Chrome Dome alert missions, staying aloft with nuclear weapons on board, ready to attack the Soviet Union at an instant's notice. The authorities halted the practice of flying aircraft on alert with live nuclear weapons in 1967; the practice of keeping B-52s on nuclear alert at the end of a runway was discontinued on 28 September 1991.

The grim prospect of B-52s dropping thermonuclear weapons in a nuclear holocaust was dodged in some Hollywood portrayals of the bomber and hyped in others. Film portrayals of what would go on to become one of the most famous aircraft of all time included 'Bombers B-52' (1957), 'Dr Strangelove' (1963), and 'A Gathering of Eagles' (1964). At the time, a real-life drama was about to unfold in Vietnam, in which the Stratofortress would be called upon to play a major part.

**Above: As early B-52s took off, their presence was anything but stealthy, with clouds of smoke billowing from the aircraft. This was caused by the injection of water into the engines to give greater thrust.**

**Right: The B-52D was essentially a B-52C, without the optional reconnaissance capsule.**

# 'BUFFs' over Southeast Asia

*A B-52F unloads over a South Vietnamese target during the Arc Light bombing campaign. By September 1967 the last 'Big Belly' B-52Ds had reached Guam, replacing the B-52Fs.*

**When SAC's B-52s were called upon to bolster the American campaign in Southeast Asia, it was not in a strategic bombing role, but in support of ground operations against the Viet Cong – a tactical role never envisaged for the type.**

Although use of the B-52 had been seriously considered from the beginning of the Rolling Thunder campaign (1965-68), doubts were expressed as to whether these big, lumbering aircraft could survive in the skies over North Vietnam against MiGs, SAMs and 'triple-A'.

Thus, when B-52 bombing operations began on 18 June 1965, Arc Light (as the B-52 campaign was named) was confined to targeting Viet Cong bases in South Vietnam. The aircraft employed were B-52Fs based at Andersen Air Base on Guam, these aircraft typically flying 13½-hour missions from the island, refuelling en route from KC-135A tankers over the South China Sea.

Bombs were dropped from altitudes of 30,000 ft (9144 m) and above, and were delivered with remarkable accuracy, though as the bombing intensified over the next seven years their effectiveness was often questioned, critics suggesting that they simply destroyed an awful lot of trees and little else.

*Ground crewmen at Andersen load 750-lb (340-kg) bombs on to triple ejector racks attached to the underwing pylons of the type designed for use by B-52Gs and Hs, carrying Hound Dog missiles.*

## B-52Ds replace Fs

The B-52F was limited to a conventional 'iron' bombload of 27 750-lb (340-kg) bombs and SAC was soon looking at ways of delivering more ordnance. The solution was to modify the entire B-52D fleet (170 of which were built) to so-called 'Big Belly' standard, this allowing the carriage of no fewer than 84 500-lb (227-kg) or 42 750-lb bombs internally. In addition, these aircraft were able to carry another 24 500-lb or 750-lb bombs aloft on external racks, thus bringing the type's maximum bombload up to a whopping 60,000 lb (27215 kg).

Stratofortresses made their first Arc Light foray into North Vietnam, bombing the Mu Gia Pass between North Vietnam and Laos on 11 April 1966, and later that month the first 'Big Belly' B-52Ds began to replace the B-52Fs at Andersen. The last B-52Ds were completed in September 1967 and were to bear the brunt of the heavy bombing campaign for the remainder of the war in Southeast Asia. It was during September, too, that a B-52 encountered a surface-to-air missile (SAM) for the first time. In fact, it was the first time that any high-altitude bomber had encountered a SAM, though it was to be another five years before the North Vietnamese finally downed a B-52 in this way.

*One of SAC's B-52Ds approaches the boom of a KC-135A for a top-up en route to a target in North Vietnam in 1967. Operations from U-Tapao AB, Thailand began in April, allowing shorter missions without inflight refuelling.*

## Second base

A second base for B-52 missions was opened in April 1967; the use of U-Tapao Air Base in Thailand allowed missions to be flown without the necessity of inflight refuelling. In the meantime, Arc Light continued into 1968, culminating in raids in support of the siege of Khe Sanh and, although Rolling Thunder was halted soon afterwards (having failed to stop the

**Camouflage**
For service over Southeast Asia, the B-52D fleet wore the camouflage scheme depicted here, standard TO 1-1-4 (comprising two shades of green and tan) covering their top surfaces, while undersides were finished in a gloss black.

**Powerplant**
The B-52D's eight Pratt & Whitney J57-P-29WA turbojets were required to muster all of their 12,100 lb (54.45 kN) to get the machine airborne with a 54,000-lb (24494-kg) bombload aboard. Water injection was used on take-off, increasing thrust and producing clouds of black exhaust.

**Huge span**
The B-52's 185-ft (56.4-m), 4,000-sq ft (371.6-m²) wing drooped almost low enough to touch the ground when the bomber was fully loaded; each wingtip sported an outrigger wheel to prevent this from happening.

# B-52D Stratofortress

**B-52D production totalled 170 machines, 101 from Boeing's Seattle plant and another 69 from the Wichita, Kansas factory. 56-0676 was one of the latter, allocated to the 307th Strategic Wing at U-Tapao AB, Thailand during Linebacker II. On 18 December 1972 its tail gunner, SSgt Samuel O. Turner, became the first to score an air-to-air kill, downing a MiG-21.**

**Combat crew**
B-52s went into combat with a basic crew of six – a pilot/aircraft commander, co-pilot, radar navigator (bombardier), navigator, electronic warfare officer (EWO) and tail gunner.

**Deferred retirement**
Early in the Arc Light campaign, US Secretary of Defense Robert McNamara announced that all the older-model B-52s, including the B-52Ds, would be retired by June 1971. This suggested an imminent end to hostilities in Southeast Asia, but in the event the B-52D fleet was kept on and in late 1972 over 200 aircraft (including newer B-52Gs) were bombing Hanoi.

**Tail turret**
The B-52D's only defensive armament was a quartet of 0.50-calibre (12.7-mm) machine-guns in a radar-equipped turret at the extreme rear of the aircraft. Although the North Vietnamese made claims to the contrary, no B-52 was lost to NVAF fighters, although two B-52 gunners were credited with MiG kills during Linebacker II. The second of these was claimed on 24 December 1972, A1C Albert E. Moore of the 307th SW downing a MiG-21 while aboard B-52D 55-0083.

**Massive raid**
The largest force of B-52s deployed at once during the Vietnam conflict was 117-strong, sent against Hanoi on 26 December 1972, at the height of Linebacker II.

flow of supplies from the north or force Hanoi to make concessions at the conference table), Arc Light continued.

By 1970 the number and frequency of B-52 raids over the south had been drastically reduced,with the slowdown in the pace of the war and attempts at 'Vietnamization' of the conflict, though B-52 operations over Cambodia (supposedly secret at the time) and Laos (Operation Good Luck) kept monthly sortie rates up to around 1,000 in June 1971.

## Linebackers I and II

In 1972, however, there was a massive increase in B-52 mission rates and the year also saw the loss of the first aircraft to enemy action. B-52 raids on the targets in North Vietnam resumed on 9 April in response to the invasion of South Vietnam by the North Vietnamese on 30 March – the 'Spring Offensive'. On 11 April the first strikes against the interior of the country were launched, on Vinh. Four days later, oil storage facilities near Haiphong were hit.

Operation Linebacker, aimed at crippling the entire North Vietnamese transportation system, began the following month, B-52s playing an important part in its execution. The SAC force in the Far East now comprised both B-52Ds and Gs, a proportion of which was now based at Kadena Air Base on Okinawa, as well as at Andersen and U-Tapao. These aircraft were flying over 3,000 sorties a month by June 1972.

By October the North Vietnamese appeared to have been bombed into submission and a bombing halt over the north was announced. However, the North Vietnamese took this opportunity to regroup and when they finally succeeded, on 22 November, in shooting down a B-52D from U-Tapao (operating south of the 20th Parallel) and stormed out of peace talks three weeks later, the stage was set for a last-ditch attempt by the US to force Hanoi to the peace table – by bombing Hanoi itself.

Linebacker II, otherwise known as the 'Eleven-Day War', began on 18 December, the B-52s – the largest number ever assembled and comprising one half of the SAC's worldwide force – spearheading the campaign. In all, 714 sorties were flown by over 200 B-52s, many over the treacherous Hanoi/Haiphong region. Thousands of SAMs were ranged against the waves of 'BUFFs', 15 of which were lost.

On 28 January 1973, the day on which a ceasefire was finally signed, the last Arc Light raid was flown, bringing the total number of B-52 sorties to 126,615. In all, a staggering 2,633,035 tons (2675274 tonnes) of bombs had been dropped.

# Multi-role 'Buff'

**As new as the 21st century, yet older than any other warplane, the indomitable B-52 Stratofortress survived Vietnam and the Cold War to acquire new weapons and duties. Now, the 'Buff' is ready for a new age of warfare. Incredible as it seems, this most versatile of warplanes still has decades of service ahead of it.**

*Turning among the trees became a new experience with EVS-equipped 'Buffs', which took the B-52's job down to low altitude. This daylight view hides the larger truth that crews train to fight at low level at night.*

During the quarter century since the end of the Vietnam War, the ever-familiar Boeing B-52 Stratofortress – already able to boast a remarkable record of longevity – has undergone yet another metamorphosis.

Conceived as a nuclear bomber and initially fielded with white paint on its belly to protect its crew from the heat of an atomic blast, the 'Buff' (or Big Ugly Fat F***er) emerged from Vietnam wearing camouflage and hauling conventional bombs. A common thread joined the nuclear Stratofortress of the Gen. Curtis E. LeMay era and the conventional Stratofortress which followed: both were meant to fly and fight at high altitude. With SAMs (surface-to-air missiles) becoming an increasing threat, however, American officers knew that they had no choice but to bring this eight-engined giant down to tree-top level.

As long ago as 1975, the B-52 began to sprout new appendages in the form of bumps, bulges, and the prominent jowls of the AN/ASQ-151 Electro-optical Viewing System (EVS). The latter was used to enable the bomber to fight at night, when US forces now perform at their best and a new cohort of adversaries, unlike the more sophisticated Soviets, at their worst. EVS uses FLIR (forward-looking infra-red) and LLLTV (low-light-level television), the latter usually referred to as "steerable TV" by crews.

*Seen in 1985, this B-52G wears the mid-1980s colours of two-tone green and grey over white, replaced soon afterwards with an all-over grey scheme.*

In the late 1970s and, especially, the early 1980s, Strategic Air Command began training for low-level attacks in both the nuclear and conventional roles, while also expanding the type's 'quiver of arrows'. One of the earliest additions to the B-52 arsenal was the AGM-84 Harpoon missile, enabling the bomber to support the US Navy in the anti-shipping role.

## 1990s revolution

The B-52 has acquired many other items of ordnance since then; a full list would fill an encyclopedia. Typical new weapons for the 21st century include the AGM-142 Have Nap air-to-ground missile, developed from an Israeli system (and initially named the Raptor in its American form, then

*Above: This B-52H is carrying the Israeli-sourced AGM-142 Popeye missile, also known as Have Nap. The B-52/AGM-142 combination was combat-proven over Kosovo.*

*Right: Post-Vietnam changes of mission and weapons capability saw the 'Buff' adopting a maritime role during the 1980s. This B-52G was photographed while dropping a sea mine.*

***In a real war, this would happen in darkness. The foe would have little warning that a B-52H Stratofortress, armed with a new generation of conventional weapons, was rushing in to strike. 'Buffs' served valiantly in Operations Desert Storm, Allied Force (the 1999 war over Kosovo), Enduring Freedom and Iraqi Freedom, rarely announcing their approach or arrival.***

***The AGM-86 ALCM (Air-Launched Cruise Missile) has been a primary B-52 weapon. This snow-covered B-52H hints at the all-weather capabilities of this weapons system.***

Popeye when the former name was applied to the F-22 fighter), and the nuclear AGM-86 ALCM (Air-Launched Cruise Missile). During the 1991 Persian Gulf War – often cited as an example of the new age in which the 'Buff' now finds itself – a conventionally armed version of the latter weapon was hastily developed. When B-52s from Barksdale AFB, LA launched AGM-86C CALCMs (conventional air-launched cruise missiles) against Iraqi targets, they had travelled more than 6,000 miles (9655 km) to do so and were flying the longest-ranged missions ever conducted in warfare.

A little-noticed but important change occurred in 1991, when SAC eliminated the tail-gunner position (and soon afterwards, the gun as well) from the B-52. This reduced the bomber's crew to five, namely two pilots, navigator, radar navigator (the term for the bombardier) and electronic systems officer.

Another sign of the new era came in the early 1990s when B-52Hs were assigned to an Air Force Reserve squadron. By law, Reservists cannot handle nuclear weapons. While carrying out the conventional mission, Reserve B-52 crews perform the same job as active-duty flyers.

The last B-52G was retired in the 1990s, leaving about 90 B-52H bombers as the only examples of the Stratofortress now in service. All of these are 'young' in terms of airframe hours, and are readily amenable to further modifications to keep up with the times.

In 1992, SAC itself went out of business – a dramatic sign of how times had changed, with the collapse of the Soviet Union and the shift in emphasis from nuclear to conventional war – and the B-52 force became part of the newly-formed Air Combat Command.

In the 21st century, bomber experts are forecasting the eventual retirement of the B-1B Lancer. The B-2 Spirit 'stealth' bomber is not so weary or so ready for pasture, although there has been discussion about retiring the B-2 force for other, cost-related reasons.

However, since the USAF does not plan to begin fielding a new bomber – or, more accurately, what it now terms a 'strategic power projection platform' – until 2037, the B-52 Stratofortress may well have to make up any power projection shortfall.

***Above: At the height of the Cold War, this would have been a highly unlikely sight – a B-52 in a non-nuclear role with an Air Force Reserve squadron. This B-52H and A-10 'Warthog' belong to the Reserve's 917th Wing at Barksdale Air Force Base, LA.***

***Right: The B-52H is the only 'Buff' model now in service. The aircraft have recently forsaken this two-tone scheme and are now attired in an overall Gunship Gray colour scheme.***

*The introduction of the Boeing KC-135 allowed Strategic Air Command (SAC) to deploy its fleet of B-47, B-52 and B-58 high-speed jet bombers and to adopt new tactics in a mode that was in keeping with the nuclear-oriented doctrine of the 1950s.*

# KC-135 development

**Ordered three weeks after the maiden flight of the 'Dash 80' jetliner, the KC-135 was intended to serve as an interim aircraft. Almost half a century later, SAC's Cold War workhorse remains a familiar sight in today's skies.**

In the 1950s, Boeing gambled $16 million on the likelihood that a revolution was coming. The company's decision to take risk, which it almost immediately regretted, led to the first flight of a four-jet prototype aircraft on 15 July 1954. A yellow and brown apparition in the skies over Seattle, the new craft was dubbed the Boeing 367-80, taking its model number from the Stratocruiser series of prop-driven transports. To those who worked on it and flew it, the aircraft was simply the 'Dash 80'. Until it was made public, its misleading name veiled the corporate secret that the aircraft was no relative of the Stratocruiser and had no propellers.

## SAC backing

The decision to invest in the 367-80 led to some turmoil in the corporate boardroom, where aviation pioneering was not necessarily consistent with the bottom line. In 1951, Boeing president William Allen had tried to sell a four-jet transport to the US Air Force and had been snubbed. Despite a backlog of military business, the company now faced lay-offs and stockholder discontent. The situation turned around only when Gen. Curtis E. LeMay of the Strategic Air Command threw his weight behind an innovative purpose for the new aircraft; LeMay wanted it as an air-refuelling tanker.

The US was fielding jet bombers capable of cruising speeds as high as 500 mph (805 km/h), including Boeing's B-47 Stratojet and B-52 Stratofortress, and Convair's more radical delta-wing B-58 Hustler. However, when the bombers needed to gulp down fuel from a 'gasoline station in the sky', they had to slow down to keep pace with the sluggish, prop-driven KC-97 Stratocruiser. LeMay wanted a

*Above: Douglas's C-132 (powered by four P&W T57s) is shown here in mock-up form. The C-132 design was submitted in February 1954 both for use as a logistic transport and as a tanker.*

*Representing a technological leap forward in comparison to its prop-driven KC-97 predecessor, the Stratotanker fulfilled General LeMay's wish for a truly strategic 'gasoline station in the sky'.*

***Right:* 55-3118 City of Renton *(foreground) was the first of the initial batch of 29 717-100As. It is pictured here in formation with the Model 367-80, which was itself converted to both tanker and military transport configuration for evaluation.***

***Below:* *The KC-135 A and E Stratotanker's normal wing tanks combined with the body tanks (carried in the unpressurised lower fuselage compartment) to offer a total capacity of 30,000 US gal (115562 litres) of fuel.***

tanker with the speed and altitude capabilities of the bombers. On 5 August 1954, just three weeks after the first flight of the 'Dash 80', the USAF announced that it would purchase a limited number of jet tankers.

What is often overlooked today is that the KC-135 Stratotanker was meant to have a finite airframe life and to serve as an interim aircraft, until a better design came along. Boeing was simultaneously planning an airliner (the Model 707) that would be good for hundreds of thousands of flight hours and a military tanker, (the KC-135, or Model 717) that would be a temporary solution to military air-refuelling needs. From the beginning, Boeing intended the 'Dash 80' as a proof-of-concept demonstrator for both aircraft.

## Proven IFR concept

Indeed, its military application was so essential to the 'Dash 80' that, on its seventh test flight, the 367-80 conducted rendezvous and refuelling practice with a B-52 Stratofortress. Not until later was it equipped with a 'flying boom' air refuelling rig. The refuelling boom, controlled by an operator lying prone and facing rearward, needed little testing; it was already proven on the KB-50 Superfortress and KC-97 Stratofreighter.

Today, we take the Boeing KC-135 Stratotanker for granted. It has become one of the most familiar sights in the world of military aviation. We also take for granted air refuelling as a routine tool of all military campaigns. But a 'walk-around check' of the tanker reveals features that were revolutionary at the time. A swept-back wing was still a new feature for a large aircraft. The forward crew compartment for the pilot, co-pilot, and navigator (and with a jump seat for the fourth crewman, the boom operator) was entered via an internal ladder protruding from a hatch forward of the nosewheel. The 10,500-lb thrust (46.70-kN), water-injected Pratt & Whitney J57-P-29A/43W axial-flow turbojet engine was almost identical to the powerplant as installed on other aircraft (including the B-52, which first flew shortly before the first KC-135), but was still a giant stride forward for an aircraft of this type.

It was no coincidence (Boeing had seen it all along) that most of these features were what was needed in the Boeing 707 jetliner. The USAF's LeMay was underwriting a military revolution, but the sale of the KC-135 was the touchstone that permitted Boeing to produce the first American jet airliner.

While the 'Dash 80' performed flight tests for both tanker and airliner (no one had yet decided where galleys, lavatories and a lounge should fit on a commercial transport with jet engines), Boeing persuaded the USAF that its proposed tanker was superior to anything else on the horizon. Douglas was offering a tanker version of the giant, swept-wing, turboprop C-132, but LeMay and his fellow officers never liked the proposal – and, in the end, the C-132 was never built. There was a proposal for a tanker version of the forthcoming Douglas DC-8 jetliner, powered by the J667 engine (US-built Bristol Olympus), but USAF officers found Douglas's engineering work incomplete. For a time, the USAF felt that Boeing would build an 'interim' tanker and Lockheed a longer-serving, subsequent aircraft, but it never happened. With only nominal competition, the USAF ordered an initial batch of KC-135 (Model 717) tankers – the first of a fleet that would eventually include 820 aircraft, including reconnaissance, transport, command-post, and testbed variants.

On 30 July 1954, Air Research and Development Command recommended (and LeMay concurred in) a purchase of 70 to 100 'interim' tankers, based on the 367-80, and known in Boeing jargon as the Model 367-138B, soon changed to Model 717. The initial order, announced by Air Force Secretary Harold Talbott on 5 August, was for 29 aircraft at a cost of $7.47 million each – embarrassingly, about 10 per cent above the original, projected cost. In 1954 and 1955, Boeing and USAF experts worked on cost issues while formalising the design. The prototype KC-135A (aircraft no. 55-3118) took shape on Boeing's Renton, Washington production line.

## First flight

There were technical problems with the new aircraft, some of which were not addressed as flight-testing of the 'Dash 80' continued. The KC-135 design began with a tailfin that was too short for the best stability, a handicap that was not remedied until production was well under way. The electrical and pressurisation systems of the KC-135 experienced early difficulties which, fortunately, were quickly rectified. Apart from the initial problems, the basic aircraft was sound, and there was a mood of festivity on 18 July 1956 when 55-3118 was rolled out at Renton. Test pilots 'Dix' Loesch and 'Tex' Johnston took the first KC-135A aloft for its maiden flight on 31 August 1956.

***In all, 820 C/KC-135 aircraft were assembled at Boeing's Renton plant, of which 732 were built as KC-135A Stratotankers. Boeing's own model designation for the first 29 KC-135As was 717-100A.***

***Basically a KC-135 without a refuelling boom, but with a strengthened floor and fuel dumping system, the C-135A was the answer to President Kennedy's decision to create a quick-response military airlift capability within MATS.***

# C-135 Stratolifter

**Developed from the KC-135 Stratotanker, the C-135 Stratolifter family never really achieved any great success as an airlifter. Instead, it merely served as an interim aircraft pending the delivery of the far more capable C-141 StarLifter.**

Boeing's C-135 transport made its maiden flight on 19 May 1961. Initial deliveries to the US Air Force's Military Air Transport Service (MATS) took place in January 1962, a couple of years behind civilian airlines, which were now operating Boeing 707s and Douglas DC-8s, but at last MATS was entering the jet age.

The four-engined, swept-wing C-135 seemed the symbol of a revolution. A press release from McGuire Air Force Base, New Jersey told the story: the USAF's new jet transport could carry 89,000 lb (40117 kg) of cargo, 54 ambulatory patients with medical attendants, or 126 combat troops. The C-135 transport could also carry 376 boxes of ammunition or 1,090 cases of 'C' Rations. Compared to the reciprocating engines then used on most airlifters, jet engines were more efficient and compatible with the JP-4 fuel used by in-service jet-powered fighters and bombers. Gen. Joe W. Kelly, Jr, MATS commander in 1962, said "The C-135 will give us a whole new dimension in air transport."

There were several versions of the C-135 transport. Fifteen C-135As were procured by the USAF as long-range logistics transports. The aircraft did not have a refuelling boom and could not be used as tankers. The C-135A used smoke-gushing Pratt & Whitney J57 turbojets identical to those on its air-refuelling cousin, the KC-135A tanker. The last flying C-135A, 60-0377, was operated as an NC-135A in support of the B-2 programme before its retirement in 1996.

***Only the first 15, of 45 C-135As ordered, were completed as such, the remainder being equipped with P&W TF33-P-5 turbofans. The extra installed thrust required modifications to the tail surfaces, resulting in the new designation, C-135B.***

The 30 C-135B Stratolifters purchased by the USAF and assigned to MATS employed TF33-P-5 turbofan engines with thrust reversers. This was also the engine employed by the C-135C, which was the designation for three WC-135Bs which were re-converted to the transport role. They were equipped to receive air refuelling to increase range and endurance, as the only C-135s to have this capability. Three C-135As were re-engined using Pratt & Whitney TF33-PW-102s and were given the designation C-135E. Two C-135Es are presently employed by Pacific Air Forces (PACAF) as part of the 65th Airlift Squadron, based at Hickam AFB, Hawaii; they are

***As a regular MATS airlifter, the C-135B inevitably found its way to Vietnam as part of the never-ending effort to keep the war supplied. This aircraft was photographed at Tan Son Nhut in February 1964.***

***Five aircraft from the original C-135B batch were converted as VIP transports with special comfort and communications facilities, justifying the V-prefix of their revised VC-135B designation. They were originally used by high-ranking USAF staff but, in the cutbacks of the Carter administration, the aircraft were downgraded to C-135B status.***

used as personal transports by the Commander in Chief of Pacific Forces (CINC-PAC) and the PACAF Commander. When not on VIP duties, they are used for supporting other PACAF operations.

Five C-135Bs were given VIP interiors and assigned to the 89th MAW. They were redesignated as VC-135Bs and used as staff transports for high-level officials. Four of the aircraft were later changed back to C-135Bs and the fifth to TC-135W standard.

One C-135C was modified under the Speckled Trout programme as a VIP transport for the Air Force Secretary and the chief of staff of the Air Force. Aircraft 61-2669 is operated by the Air Force Flight Test Centre and is seconded for VIP duties when the need arises.

## Brief revolution

Known in later years as Military Airlift Command (MAC) and after 1992 as Air Mobility Command (AMC), the USAF's cargo-hauling outfit was actually an unlikely customer for the C-135. It was also the least likely place for a revolution to be staged by an aircraft that lacked roll-on, roll-off capability, could not be easily loaded, and was really meant solely to carry passengers. In American service, after all, military transports do not haul people. They haul equipment. When troops are taken overseas, they travel on commercial airlines operating as contractors or, as during Desert Shield, operating as part of the Civilian Reserve Air Fleet (CRAF).

For those occasions when it did haul passengers, MAC soon had a more appropriate aircraft in the Boeing 707 (military designation C-137). For those times when it carried cargo, the C-135 was never quite right for the job. Indeed, by the mid-1960s, MAC was replacing it with a true freight hauler, the Lockheed C-141 StarLifter.

Consider, for example, the difficulty of loading the C-135. While the C-141 offered a ground-level, roll-on ramp and the Lockheed C-5 Galaxy offered roll-on, roll-off capability, the 117 x 78-in (2.97 x 1.98-m) cargo door of the C-135 was fully 10 ft (3.00 m) above the ground. This required special loading equipment which was unavailable at most locations to which the USAF might deploy. MAC tried to improve the C-135 transport and KC-135 tanker's cargo-handling capability by installing a self-contained loading device. The gadget was, in practice, of little use. It took several crew members to assemble and operate, and effectively reduced the interior height of the cargo compartment by some 14 in (35 cm).

So the C-135 was not a 'fit' for MAC's duties. But it was employed nonetheless. In October 1962, four C-135s lifted 16.60 tons of cargo and 1,232 Swedish peacekeeping troops from Stockholm to Leopoldville in the Congo. This was the USAF's first jet airlift and it seems to have gone off without a hitch, despite the lack of adequate facilities at Leopoldville. C-135s also flew humanitarian relief missions to the Congo two months later.

## Cuban missile crisis

Before the C-135 faded from the scene as a pure transport in the mid-1960s, it played a vital role in the confrontation between John F. Kennedy and Nikita Khruschev over Cuba. In October 1962, MAC C-135s provided troop and cargo support for the US military build-up in the American south – opposite Cuba – while the US and the Soviet Union came to the edge of a nuclear precipice. Ultimately, the Soviets backed down and withdrew the missiles and nuclear weapons they had installed on Cuba, but not before the first C-135 transport was lost in a crash while on approach to the US base at Guantanamo Bay, Cuba.

In the end, the primary role of the C-135 transport, now redesignated VC-135, was to carry VIPs. Jet transportation became a 'must' for world leaders and Washington dignitaries. Numerous VIPs have been assigned over the years, although the C-135 always lived in the shadow of the VC-137, which became AIR FORCE ONE when the American president was on board.

Only a handful of C-135 transports remains in service today (and even these have other tasks). The rest have been retired from service, many having been converted to other configurations as tankers, test-beds, or airborne command and control aircraft prior to this. In their earliest days, the C-135 transports were not merely revolutionary and glamorous but colourful, sporting Insignia Red trim and distinctive markings – but this era was short-lived. The C-135 Stratolifter acquired plainer garb, and was then supplanted and quickly replaced by the C-137.

***After being modified from C-135A status to EC-135N standard as part of the Apollo lunar-landing programme, three C-135s were re-engined to C-135E standard (illustrated).***

# EC-135 variants
## Command post aircraft

**During the Cold War, EC-135 command posts were the backbone of Strategic Air Command's ability to strike back at the Soviet Union in the event of a nuclear strike.**

### EC-135A

Five KC-135As (61-0262, 61-0278, 61-0287, 61-0289 and 61-0297) were converted to command posts in the early 1960s, serving initially with the 34th ARS at Offutt AFB, Nebraska. The EC-135As initiated the Looking Glass 24-hour alert on 3 February 1961. When the purpose-built EC-135Cs were delivered, the EC-135As went to the 28th Bomb Wing (4th ACCS) at Ellsworth, from where they formed part of the back-up ICBM launch command chain. The aircraft had additional communications and were equipped with the Airborne Launch Control Center equipment.

### EC-135C

The only C-135s to be purpose-built for the command post mission were 17 aircraft, powered by TF33 turbofans, serialled 62-3581 to 62-2385 and 63-8046 to 63-8057. Originally designated KC-135B, the aircraft were redesignated as EC-135C once the command post equipment had been installed. Entering service in 1964, the EC-135Cs assumed the primary Looking Glass mission from the EC-135As, and continued the 24-hour airborne alert until stood down on 24 July 1990. After that date daily missions were undertaken. As other EC-135 variants were withdrawn, EC-135Cs made occasional deployments overseas to provide theatre commanders with an airborne command post. Finally, the command post mission was handed over in its entirety to the US Navy's E-6 fleet. By the time the EC-135C was retired, four of the fleet had received the Milstars satellite communications equipment, the antenna being housed in a dorsal fairing. From the outset EC-135Cs were extensively equipped with communications, and added more as the type's career progressed. A 28,500-ft (8687-m) trailing wire and other antennas allowed the EC-135C to communicate across huge distances by very low frequency, usually with other command posts. The task of the EC-135C and its staff was simple: in the event of a nuclear attack on the US, command of Strategic Air Command's nuclear forces could be transferred to the orbiting Looking Glass, which always carried a general to provide the necessary authority to launch ICBMs. The aircraft flew on 8-hour shifts, without a break, for nearly 30 years.

### EC-135G

Four EC-135Gs (62-3570, 62-3579, 63-7994 and 63-8001) were produced by conversion from KC-135As. They were primarily intended to take over the launch of Minutemen ICBMs from their fields in the north-central US, and had Airborne Launch Control Center equipment fitted. They served with the 4th ACCS/28th BW at Ellsworth AFB, South Dakota, and with the 305th ARW at Grissom AFB, Indiana.

### EC-135J

Three EC-135Cs (62-3584, 63-8055 and 63-8057) were further modified to EC-135J standard to take the national command authority aloft in time of tension. The mission was known as Night Watch and the aircraft served with the 1st ACCS. When E-4As assumed this role in 1975, the EC-135Js were reassigned to the 9th ACCS at Hickam AFB, Hawaii to provide a command facility for C-in-C Pacific Forces.

### EC-135H

The EC-135H was produced to provide theatre commanders with their own command post, and shared many of the communications features of the EC-135C Looking Glass aircraft, including a trailing wire antenna. The first EC-135H (61-0274) was assigned to the 6th ACCS at Langley AFB, Virginia to support the C-in-C Atlantic in a mission called Scope Light. Four more EC-135Hs (61-0282, 61-0285, 61-0286 and 61-0291) were assigned to SACEUR in a programme code-named Silk Purse. They were flown by the 10th Airborne Command and Control Squadron, parented by the 513th TAW at RAF Mildenhall, UK. Having been converted from KC-135As, the aircraft initially retained J57 turbojets, as seen on the 6th ACCS aircraft (above left). However, they were subsequently fitted with TF33 turbofans and wide-span tailplanes, as illustrated by the 10th ACCS aircraft (above).

Theatre command posts were withdrawn in the aftermath of the Gulf War and the end of the Cold War. Most were dispatched to Davis-Monthan AFB for storage and eventual scrapping, although a few were modified for other special missions. EC-135Cs were deployed on an infrequent basis to practise the theatre command support mission.

### EC-135K

Not command posts in the true sense, the three EC-135Ks (55-3118 – built as the first KC-135A, 59-1518 and 62-3536) were employed by the 9th Tactical Deployment and Control Squadron to act as lead-ships for fighter formations transiting over long distances, especially across water. Two survivors were re-engined with TF33 turbofans after '536 was lost in 1977.

### EC-135L

Eight KC-135As (61-0261, 61-0263, 61-0269, 61-0279, 61-0281, 61-0283, 61-0288 and 61-0302) were converted to EC-135L standard, serving with the 70th ARS, 305th ARW, at Grissom AFB, Indiana. Three were subsequently returned to tanker standard, although they retained the inflight-refuelling receptacle added to most EC-135s. The EC-135L's main role was to act as a radio relay platform, extending the reach of SAC's Post-Attack Command and Control System (PACCS) under the mission name Cover All. One flew in Desert Storm.

### EC-135Y

This designation covered two aircraft modified as theatre airborne command posts for the Commander of US Central Command. They were converted from an NKC-135A (55-3125) and an EC-135N (61-0327). They were operated on behalf of CentCom by the 19th Air Refueling Wing at Robins AFB, Georgia.

### KC-135A Combat Lightning

During the Vietnam War, seven KC-135As (61-0268, 61-0270, 61-0271, 61-0280, 61-0288, 61-0303 and 63-8881) were modified to act as radio relays. The first two in-theatre were initially operated alongside two EC-135Ls, but further Combat Lightning conversions allowed the EC-135Ls to return to their SAC duties.

### EC-135P

Originally, five aircraft (58-0001, 58-0007,58-0018, 58-0019 and 58-0022) were modified to EC-135P configuration, although two ('001 and '018) were later returned to tanker status. The EC-135P fleet was initially assigned to the 6th ACCS at Hickam AFB in Hawaii (above), flying the Blue Eagle mission in support of CinCPAC. When the 6th ACCS acquired EC-135Js, three of the EC-135Ps were reassigned to support CinCLANT and Tactical Air Command operations, flying the Scope Light mission with the 1st ACCS at Langley AFB (above). One of the EC-135Hs, 61-0274, was also assigned to this unit, and later acquired the EC-135P designation. Following the loss of '007 in a ground fire in January 1980, an NKC-135A (55-3129) was converted to EC-135P status to maintain the 1st ACCS fleet at four aircraft. The aircraft were essentially similar to the EC-135C in terms of communications equipment although, like the other theatre-assigned aircraft, lacked the launch control equipment for ICBMs. The 1st ACCS retired its EC-135Ps to the boneyard in 1992.

# RC-135 Rivet Joint

### RC-135V/W

Despite the collapse of the Soviet threat, the disbandment of Strategic Air Command in 1992 and the introduction of modern spy satellites and J-STARS, the RC-135 remains an important type in the USAF's reconnaissance inventory. During Operation Allied Force in 1999, elements of the RC-135V/W Rivet Joint fleet operated from Mildenhall in the UK as a vital component of the electronic warfare/surveillance effort over the former Yugoslavia. Subsequently, the aircraft have been operational against Afghanistan, during Operation Enduring Freedom, and Iraq, during Operation Iraqi Freedom. It is virtually unthinkable that the US would engage in combat in any theatre without RC-135 Rivet Joint support.

*Even by -135 standards, 61-2667 has had a varied career. It was built as a C-135B and redesignated as a WC-135B in 1965. It was subsequently used by E-3 Sentry crews for inflight-refuelling receiver training. It was then used on weather reconnaissance duties, before moving to Mildenhall as a flight deck trainer in 1989. Transferring back to the US, it became a TC-135B, but was soon returned to the weather recce role again as a WC-135W. It is seen here during its time at Mildenhall as a TC-135B.*

# Special variants

**Boeing's C-135 and KC-135 series of aircraft has been employed in test and special mission roles throughout its career and has continued to fly experimental tasks into the 21st century.**

Blessed with good range and speed, excellent load-carrying performance, a capacious cabin and a tractable airframe able to absorb radical modifications, the C/KC-135 was a natural for the testing role. Furthermore, the ready availability of surplus airframes from an early stage in the aircraft's career meant that it became the backbone of the US heavy aircraft trials fleet for many years.

Aircraft chosen for test work came mostly from very early KC-135A production (and were rechristened NKC-135A, 'N' standing for 'Permanent Test') or the redundant C-135A transport fleet (becoming NC-135As). When some aircraft were later re-engined with TF33 turbofans in place of their original J57 'stovepipe' turbojets, they were redesignated as NKC-135Es. In addition, three TF33-powered C-135Es were used for testing, but without the 'N' prefix.

Most flew for much of their careers with the 4950th Test Wing at Wright-Patterson AFB, Ohio. From here, and on various detachments, the NC/ NKC-135 fleet flew on just about every imaginable research/ trials programme, from civil astronomic research to military trials missions. Most of the big US military programmes of the last four decades have involved the fleet to some degree or another: during the SDI ('Star Wars') period the fleet was extremely busy. The missions carried out have been very varied, but have included the testing of airborne telescopes, high-energy lasers, star/meteor tracking, nuclear research and airborne radar signature measurement of other aircraft, while many advanced systems which found their way in to the front line were first tested by NC/NKC-135s. One NKC-135A was given a long nose probe and winglets to test the effects of the latter aerodynamic devices. More mundane tasks, such as providing inflight refuelling for flight test programmes and the spraying of water from the boom to simulate icing conditions, are also undertaken. In the early 1990s the fleet relocated to the Air Force Flight Test Center at Edwards AFB, California, which amalgamated the work of the 4950th and 6510th Test Wings under the single banner of the 412th Test Wing. The fleet is now much reduced, the J57-engined aircraft having been retired and other aircraft converted for different missions. One NKC-135A, 55-3119, was assigned for a while to the 55th Wing at Offutt AFB to act as a Command Support

*NC-135A, 60-0371 was originally one of three such machines designed to provide a rapid-response checking facility to ensure that international bans on nuclear weapons testing were being complied with.*

*Left: NKC-135E, 55-3135, seen here in service with the 4950 TW at Edwards AFB, was built as a JKC-135A for nuclear testing. Redesignated NKC-135A, and later -135E after re-engining, it flies as a calibrated tanker for air-refuelling trials.*

*Below: Having flown as one of three 'Vomit Comet' astronaut trainers, this JKC-135A flew winglet tests from 1979 in a joint USAF/NASA programme.*

***Right:** 60-0372, seen here as a C-135E with the 4952 TS, 4950 TW, during 1993, was built as a C-135A, but soon converted as an EC-135N ARIA (Apollo Range Instrumented Aircraft). Subsequently, it was reroled and re-engined, becoming a C-135E dedicated satellite communications testbed with TF33 engines.*

***Below right:** The TC-135S is primarily assigned to training duties, but also acts as a personnel transport, as it did during the 1991 Gulf War. The aircraft has acquired the black starboard wing uppersurfaces acquired to cut down glare during photography.*

Aircraft, ferrying high-ranking military personnel. Despite the many retirements, NKC-135Es continued in use at Edwards in 2002, notably supporting F-22 Raptor flight test activities.

Two recent additions to the test fleet are a single NKC-135B (converted from an EC-135C Looking Glass command post aircraft) which serves with the 412th Test Wing's Det 2 at Kirtland AFB. It has an enlarged radome and is used on behalf of the Air Force Research Laboratory. A former WC-135B is bailed to major defence contractor Raytheon as an NC-135W, and is used for systems trials.

## Fleet support

Unconnected with the USAF's trials aircraft, two KC-135As were modified in 1977/78 with comprehensive jamming equipment to provide a realistic electronic warfare environment for US Navy fleet exercises, replacing two Boeing EB-47Es in this role. The pair, designated NKC-135A, was operated by McDonnell Douglas at Tulsa, Oklahoma, (later by Chrysler at Waco, Texas) alongside a similarly modified Douglas DC-8 (EC-24) on behalf of the Fleet Electronic Warfare Support Group. The Navy NKC-135As featured numerous antennas and fairings, including a canoe fairing and a bulged nose.

## Met recce

Ten of the fan-engined C-135B transports, which were quickly supplanted in service by the C-141 StarLifter, were released for conversion to WC-135B weather reconnaissance platforms. Operated by the 55th Weather Reconnaissance Squadron at McClellan AFB, California, the aircraft came under Military Air Command, but performed global weather recce for the Air Force as a whole. As well as internal meteorological equipment, the aircraft were fitted with particulate samplers, consisting of an open-ended cylinder with a filter. The filter collected air particles for further analysis, this work being primarily connected with nuclear fall-out from tests.

As satellites took over the weather recce role, the WC-135B fleet was released for conversion for other tasks. By 2002, only one of the aircraft remained in service, designated WC-135W. It flies with the 45th RS of the 55th Wing at Offutt AFB, and is used for nuclear particle sampling.

## Open Skies

In March 1992, 25 NATO, CIS and former Warsaw Pact nations signed the Open Skies Treaty, which allowed aircraft to overfly, by prior agreement, the territories of other signatories to monitor military activities. In October 1993 five surplus WC-135Bs were delivered to the 55th Wing at Offutt AFB, Nebraska, to support the US contingent, of which three were modified into OC-135B standard. This sports a battery of sensors consisting of one KA-91A panoramic, two KS-87B oblique and one KS-87 low-level camera. The aircraft carries 38 personnel, including foreign and host-country representatives and members of the On-Site Inspection Agency, which provides linguists and sensors for the verification missions. The OC-135Bs were originally assigned to the 24th RS, but now fly with the 45th RS 'Sylvester'.

## 'Bounce-birds'

Using fully mission-capable aircraft for the training of flight crew is a costly process, and also consumes too many hours of the airframe's life. If a 'mission-bird' should be lost thanks to an inexperienced pilot, the cost to the Air Force is huge, in terms of both money and lost operational capacity. Accordingly, the USAF introduced a few TC-135 crew trainer aircraft to serve the 'special' C-135 fleets.

For some years the 24th RS of the 6th Strategic Wing at Eielson AFB, Alaska, had used RC-135T 55-3121 as a crew trainer. When this was lost in an accident on 25 February 1985, a replacement was found in the shape of the TC-135S (62-4133), a conversion of a redundant C-135B. The aircraft was fitted with the 'Hog' nose of the operational RC-135S, but none of the sensitive recording equipment. This 'one-off' joined the 24th RS in July 1985, training aircrew for the RC-135S Cobra Ball fleet, and continues in this role today, although now assigned to the 55th Wing's 45th RS at Offutt following the disbandment of the 6th SW.

The 'Fightin' 55th' also operates examples of the TC-135W (62-4129) and TC-135B (61-2667). The former flies with the 38th RS 'Fighting Hellcats' as a trainer for the RC-135V/W Rivet Joint fleet. As well as the 'Hog' nose, the TC-135W also has the Rivet Joint's cheek Elint fairings, although they do not accommodate any mission equipment. The TC-135B is an ex-WC-135B with the 45th RS used for training OC-135B crews. After being retired from the weather recce role, it served briefly as a crew trainer with the 10th ACCS at Mildenhall (which flew the EC-135H) before reassignment and redesignation. As well as their training duties, the TC-135s are often used for crew shuttle and general transport duties.

***Above left:** Two NKC-135A aircraft fly with the US Navy. This machine was originally used on a range of tracking and monitoring duties with the USAF as a JKC-135A.*

***Below left:** In 1984, C-135E 60-0376 was assigned to support USAF Space Command. Early in its career it had been involved in tests related to nuclear weapons and space vehicle tracking, but was converted as a VIP transport for the commander of Air Force Logistics Command in 1972-73. It became the subject of congressional investigation, when Senator William Proxmire claimed that it was a 'flying playboy penthouse'.*

Charleston, SC is the backdrop for this stunning view of a 437th Airlift Wing C-17 Globemaster III in flight. The first production C-17s went to Charleston AFB.

# Boeing
# C-17 Globemaster III
## 21st century airlifter

**The C-17 Globemaster III is the great new hope for the US Air Force, this giant cargo craft being able to haul military equipment rapidly and easily to distant troublespots.**

The US Air Force's 21st century airlifter, the C-17 Globemaster III, has made one of the most remarkable turnarounds in aviation history.

### Success story

In the late 1980s, the C-17 was behind schedule and over budget, and the programme to develop the new transport was so poorly managed that several USAF officers had to be disciplined. Today, the production effort by Boeing (formerly Douglas) in Long Beach, CA, has won industry awards, the C-17 is flying with three airlift wings, and the type has appeared at every crisis spot from Korea to Kosovo. One even carried President Bill Clinton on a visit to Bosnia, thereby winning the radio call-sign, AIR FORCE ONE.

Making contrails at altitude over Edwards AFB, CA, is T-1, the first C-17 built and the only one painted in 'lizard green'.

Paratroopers of the 82nd Airborne Division float earthwards. The C-17 required minor modifications to its doors before being cleared for worldwide airdrop operations.

***To move mobile forces into place rapidly during a crisis, the C-17 must rely on air refuelling. Here, test ship T-1 carries out 'dry' refuelling mating tests with a KC-135 Stratotanker.***

***The Long Beach, CA, C-17 production line is so clean, says Boeing's George Sillia, that "you can scramble eggs on the floor".***

The C-17 is a high-wing, four-engined, T-tailed transport. It boasts an ergonomic flight deck with digital displays; the C-17's two pilots sit side-by-side and the aircraft is flown with a control stick instead of the yoke traditionally used on transports. It is the first cargo aircraft with a HUD (head-up display). The airlifter's 168-ft (51.08-m) wing is swept at 25° with a supercritical aerofoil and has winglets for fuel efficiency. Almost one third of the aircraft's structural weight lies in the wing.

The four Pratt & Whitney F117-PW-100 (company PW2040) turbofan engines are rated at a remarkable 41,847-lb (188.3-kN) thrust each, and are located ahead of, and below, the C-17's wings on cantilevered pylons.

## Airlift virtuoso

The C-17 now serves at Charleston AFB, SC, Altus AFB, OK (the training base for the type) and McChord AFB, WA. The USAF was long expected to acquire 110 Globemaster IIIs at a sticker price of around $1 million per aircraft. However, the number is now expected to rise to 134, and to include 14 C-17s intended for low-level, special operations work behind enemy lines. Progress with the C-17 has been so good that the USAF expects to retire its last C-141B StarLifter by 2001.

## C-17 history

The C-17 prototype, known as the T-1, took off from Long Beach Airport for its maiden flight to Edwards AFB, CA, on 15 September 1991. At the time, misfortunes were rife. The first flight was more than a year behind schedule. Worse, a new problem emerged on 1 October 1991: a static test C-17 had a wing structural failure in tests, but minor changes eventually resolved this structural problem.

The C-17 test programme at Edwards AFB was carried out with remarkable efficiency. Test pilots and engineers followed through with a step-by-step exploration of the C-17's flight capabilities, Unlike the development programme which preceded it, the flight test programme met cost and scheduling milestones. When aircraft P-3 made its first flight on 7 September 1992, it was a bank holiday (Labor Day) and one of the runways at Edwards was closed for repairs; Douglas obtained permission to land on the dry lake bed for the first time. Landing on the rough surface proved to be no problem at all. Soon afterwards, an M60 main battle tank became the first tracked vehicle to be loaded on to a C-17. Various loads of vehicles and armour have since been carried by the aircraft.

The first production C-17, known as P-1, made its maiden flight on 19 May 1992. Charleston's 17th Airlift Squadron, part of the 437th Airlift Wing, received its first aircraft on 14 June 1993.

The Globemaster III name, honouring the earlier C-74 and C-124 manufactured by Douglas, was applied to the C-17 on 5 February 1993 by Air Mobility Command chief General Ronald R. Fogleman, who later served as US Air Force chief of staff.

## New era

The delays and difficulties in the early C-17 programme gave way to dramatic improvements partly because Operation Desert Shield, in 1990, demonstrated the urgent nature of the strategic airlift role, and partly because Douglas management ordered thorough housekeeping and reorganisation. The manufacturer, which was then part of McDonnell Douglas, has now become part of Boeing.

## Real-world efforts

With testing, development, and production back on the right track, the C-17 began in the 1990s to demonstrate its enormous value as a key tool in the Pentagon's warfighting plans. The USAF's only other big lifter, the C-5 Galaxy, has been plagued by reliability problems and has had a 'mission-capable rate' as low as 50 per cent – this means that only one mission out of every two planned is actually launched. Mission-capable rates for the fledgling C-17 fleet have consistently been in the 80 per cent range and are rising. The C-17 is among the few airlifters that can operate easily, and reverse, on unpaved airstrips.

## Allied Force

During Operation Allied Force – the war over Kosovo – NATO forces relied heavily on the poorly-equipped airport at Tirana, Albania. The C-17 proved to be the only airlifter that could consistently haul outsized loads into Tirana, where the US Army's AH-64 Apache helicopter force was mustered. During the operation, mission-capable rates rose above 95 per cent.

To potential buyers, the C-17 is available now, while Europe's Future Large Aircraft (FLA) is still on the drawing board. Boeing has already begun construction of three 'white tail' C-17s (aircraft for which no purchaser has yet been identified). Among operators who have shown a strong interest in the C-17 is Britain's Royal Air Force, which urgently needs a big lifter and is sceptical about the FLA. Boeing has also pitched the C-17 to Japan, and has proposed USAF tanker and reconnaissance versions.

***In an early formation test in June 1992, a veritable gaggle of C-17 Globemaster IIIs wings its way over the great desert of the American southwest, near Edwards AFB.***

# Transport revolution

**It took years of tribulation to bring the C-17 Globemaster III out of the factory and into squadrons. The aircraft arrived as crisis after crisis erupted in the 1990s, all demanding the unique airlift capabilities offered by the C-17.**

The Pentagon is looking to the tremendous lifting capabilities of the Boeing C-17 Globemaster III to fill the yawning gap in American air transport needs. While the real story of the Globemaster III can be found in the quiet drone of its turbofan engines and the ease with which crews can load and unload cargoes, to members of the Airlift Action Desk in Room 4E356 in the Pentagon, the story is one of numbers – the total of 120 C-17s on order, and the way in which the USAF plans to assign them.

Due to recent changes in the rest of the airlift fleet, namely the pending retirement of the C-141B StarLifter and the reliability problems of the C-5A/B Galaxy, these figures are suddenly crucial.

C-17 delivery was scheduled to be completed by 2004, but the 'top brass' decided to acquire more Globemaster IIIs, unconcerned about the comparatively high cost of the transport which is now in the neighbourhood of $200 million per copy. Consequently, although the C-17 order had been cut back several times to the 120 aircraft level, a further order came in 2002 for 60 more aircraft. These will be built over a five year period and some will have a special forces role.

Beyond that, officials have not given up hope of raising the total 'buy' to 210 aircraft, the number that had been projected back in the late 1980s.

## 1990s challenges

While the future of the Globemaster III was still being shaped, Air Mobility Command (AMC) crews were becoming accustomed to using microchips instead of muscle to carry out the C-17's cargo-hauling responsibilities.

There was plenty of scepticism when AMC chief Gen. 'Tony' Robertson implemented the plan to fly the Globemaster III with just three crew members – pilot, co-pilot, and loadmaster. Every previous airlifter had also required a flight engineer and a navigator.

"This was a big adjustment," says Senior Airman James Baroco, a loadmaster at McChord AFB, Wash. "Those of us who were raised in the airlift culture were led to believe that we had to have a 'busy, busy' crew situation. We got that way by flying the C-141B StarLifter, which was very labour-intensive. Now, we're learning an easier way of doing things."

***Above: The loading of an M1A1 Abrams heavy tank in 1992 was a 'graduation test' which the C-17A passed.***

***Top: A C-17A joining the 437th AW at Charleston poses above the city's bridges shortly after starting work in South Carolina.***

***Night or day, this line-up of C-17s will be easier to load and unload during a crisis, thanks to the computerised system that enables a single loadmaster to handle and stow a full load of cargo.***

***Above: At Rhein-Main Air Base in Frankfurt, Germany in 1995, a light dusting of snow causes no hindrance to a pair of C-17A Globemaster IIIs of the 437th Airlift Wing carrying out a humanitarian mission to Bosnia in Operation Joint Endeavor.***

***Below: On 15 October 1999, a 7th AS, 62nd AW C-17A from McChord AFB completed the type's first landing within Antarctica, paving the way for future missions in the region.***

Although none is currently planned, Boeing is still hoping to sell new and different versions of the Globemaster III. The manufacturer has expressed the belief belief that an EC-17 airborne command post would be more economical and more flexible than the E-8B Mercury now being used in the mission, but the USAF's planned E-10 Multi-Sensor Command and Control Aircraft is almost certainly likely to offer a more likely platform for an E-8 replacement. Boeing officials also have plans for a KC-17B model which uses probe-and-drogue refuelling for the tactical mission carried out today by the MC-130 Hercules.

The C-17 has also been suggested as an alternative to the Boeing 747 (military designation YAL-1) as an airborne laser platform.

For now, the airlift role is enough of a challenge to keep the former Douglas production line at Long Beach, CA, turning out Boeing C-17 Globemaster IIIs at a prodigious rate for the next five years or more.

## C-17A Globemaster III

**Viewed from outside, the Boeing C-17A Globemaster III is deceptive. Although it resembles the earlier C-141B StarLifter, its cargo capacity is three times greater. The C-17A handles 'outsized' cargo, although its external dimensions are such that it occupies reasonable ramp space at busy airfields.**

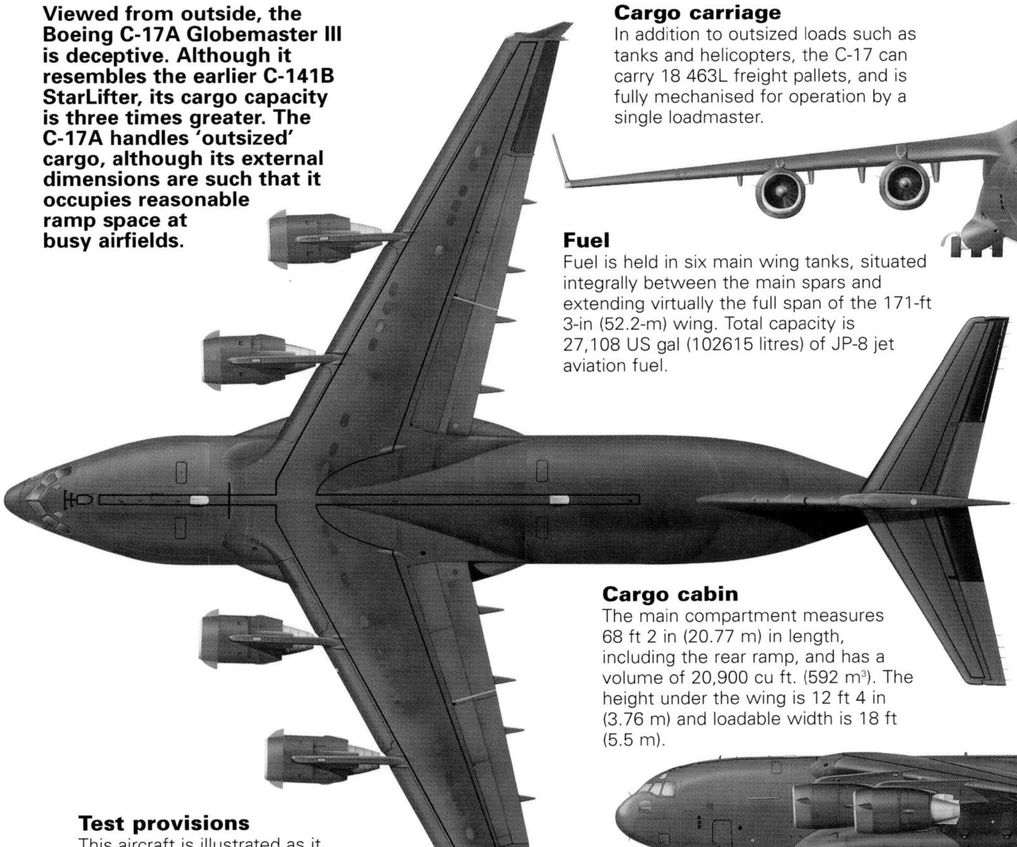

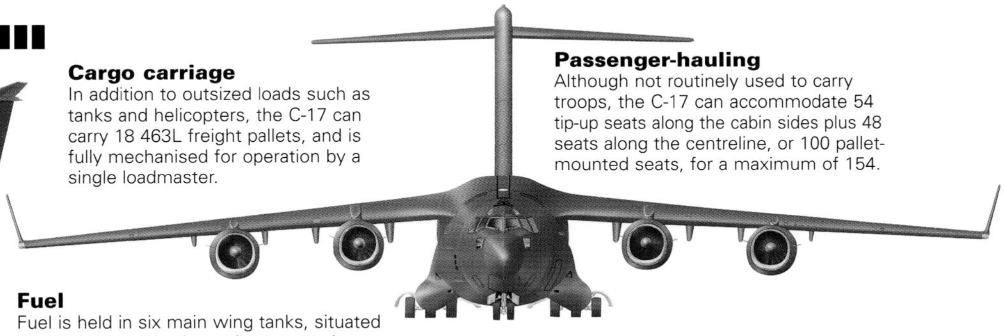

### Cargo carriage
In addition to outsized loads such as tanks and helicopters, the C-17 can carry 18 463L freight pallets, and is fully mechanised for operation by a single loadmaster.

### Passenger-hauling
Although not routinely used to carry troops, the C-17 can accommodate 54 tip-up seats along the cabin sides plus 48 seats along the centreline, or 100 pallet-mounted seats, for a maximum of 154.

### Fuel
Fuel is held in six main wing tanks, situated integrally between the main spars and extending virtually the full span of the 171-ft 3-in (52.2-m) wing. Total capacity is 27,108 US gal (102615 litres) of JP-8 jet aviation fuel.

### Airdrop
Through the open rear ramp the C-17 can drop 110,000 lb (49896 kg) on multiple platforms, 60,000 lb (27216 kg) on a single platform, 11 463L cargo pallets, or 102 paratroops. The paratroop door was slightly redesigned after tests at Fort Bragg, NC, and the C-17 is now fully certified for airborne operations.

### Dual-purpose ramp
The fully-loadable rear ramp of the C-17A was designed so that all of its surface could be used to support weight. The ramp has a 40,000-lb (18144-kg) capacity and is an integral part of the cargo compartment when closed.

### Cargo cabin
The main compartment measures 68 ft 2 in (20.77 m) in length, including the rear ramp, and has a volume of 20,900 cu ft. (592 m³). The height under the wing is 12 ft 4 in (3.76 m) and loadable width is 18 ft (5.5 m).

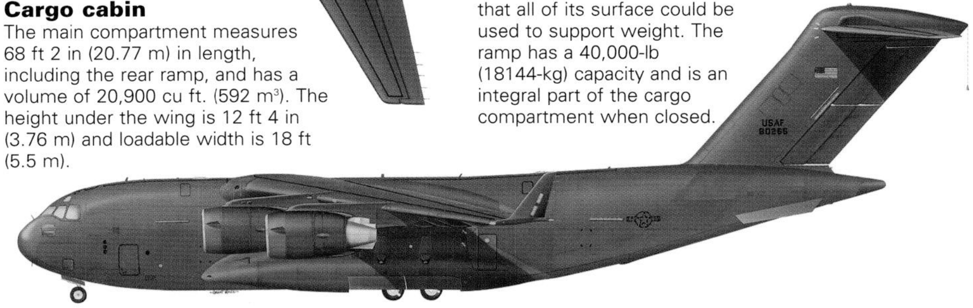

### Test provisions
This aircraft is illustrated as it appeared during flight testing, with a towed calibration cone installed in the trailing edge of its fin tip. Externally, there is little to differentiate the test and production C-17 airframes.

### Short-field lander
With landing gear designed for a high sink rate, externally blown flaps, full-span leading-edge slats, and thrust-reversing, the Globemaster III is optimised for landings on unpaved airstrips only 3,000 ft (914 m) in length, while carrying four times as much cargo as the US Air Force's only other short-field performer, the C-130 Hercules.

# Globemasters for the RAF

**The Royal Air Force has lacked a strategic airlift capability since the retirement of the hardworking Shorts Belfast in the 1970s. However, in the post-Cold War era, much of the work of the British armed forces relies on rapid deployment to trouble 'hotspots' around the globe and the RAF's veteran Hercules tactical transports were struggling to keep up with their taskings. This shortfall in outsize airlift capability was at last redressed in 2001 with the arrival of the most capable aircraft in its class – the Boeing C-17 Globemaster III.**

*A C-17A lifts off from Boeing's Long Beach assembly facility in 2001 en route to the UK. RAF crews have been impressed by the C-17's state-of-the-art cockpit, incorporating sidestick controls, MFDs and two HUDs. Sqn Ldrs Darrell Jacobs and Keith Hewitt (below) are pictured at the controls of ZZ172 in July 2001.*

The four RAF C-17s are intended as a 'stop-gap' measure until the arrival of the pan-European Airbus A400M (formerly FLA) scheduled for 2008. Their acquisition was a direct result of the UK's Strategic Defence Review in 1998. A long-term Future Transport Aircraft (FTA) Request for Proposal (RfP) was issued, along with partner European states, with Airbus' FLA favourite to win the contract. However, the aircraft was unlikely to be ready for service for a decade, and the UK's urgent need for a strategic airlifter necessitated a short-term fix, resulting in the Short Term Strategic Airlift competition. The specifications were set out in the Staff Requirement (Air) 448 specification which called for an aircraft to deploy high readiness Joint Rapid Reaction Forces (JRRF), including outsize equipment such as attack helicopters (Apache AH.Mk 1s), large military vehicles, and some Royal Engineer heavy or outsize equipment.

## Contract award

Boeing immediately tendered the C-17 to meet the requirement, having courted the UK government in previous years, recognising their growing need for just such an aircraft. By January 1999 the C-17 had been pitched against other competitors including the giant Antonov An-124 and the Ilyushin Il-76. The Globemaster emerged as by far the most suitable aircraft meeting, and in some cases, exceeding the specific payload and operating requirements outlined. The stumbling block was the price, which at a unit cost of well over $100 million, was well beyond the reach of the UK defence budget. With the other contenders deemed unsuitable the competition was terminated in August 1999 and Integrated Project Teams, involving Boeing, the UK MoD and the USAF, were established to find what could be provided within the specified budget.

Boeing returned with a unique solution. Four C-17s would be leased from the manufacturer until the entry into service of the A400M (scheduled for mid-2008). To drive down costs maintenance support and aircrew training would be handled by Boeing and the USAF respectively, and the aircraft would only be used to meet the specific requirements set out in SR(A)448. The tactical abilities

*Right: Globemaster ZZ172 is pictured at its base, RAF Brize Norton, in July 2001. The aircraft had arrived at the Oxfordshire station in June.*

*Inset: Like all US-manufactured military aircraft, including those built for foreign customers, the RAF's Globemasters are allocated US serial numbers; ZZ172 is 00-0202, indicating that it was ordered during FY2000. Part of the USAF's 'virtual fleet', the aircraft have no RAF designation and are known by their US DoD designator.*

***Left:* Carrying a temporary, but highly appropriate, civil registration (N171UK), the first of the RAF's aircraft, makes its first flight on 16 April 2001.**

***Below:* ZZ171 disgorges a load on the apron at RAF Brize Norton. Under the terms of their lease, the RAF aircraft are to be strictly employed on strategic operations.**

of the aircraft, including airborne delivery, paratroop dropping and low-level flying, would be ignored, as would the aircraft's inflight refuelling ability. This would help restrict flying hours to around 3,000 per year for the fleet and make tremendous savings in terms of training and support costs. The commercial lease contract was signed on 2 September 2000 marking the first time in over 50 years that the US government has agreed to lease a full military system package to the air aim of a foreign government.

## C-17 Block XII

The aircraft are four new-build, extended range Block XII C-17s, that incorporate an additional 10,000-US gal (37053-litre) fuel tank in the previously 'dry' bay in the wing centre-section. This adds some 600 nm (690 miles; 1110 km) to the aircraft's already extensive range with a nominal 90,000-lb (40823-kg) payload. This added range is of particular use to the RAF offsetting the decision to forsake the dormant air-to-air refuelling capability. Other improvements over the baseline C-17A included new software, allowing the aircraft to comply with future Global Air Traffic Management (GATM) requirements and redesigned cockpit multi-function displays born out of operational experience in USAF service. The aircraft itself is configured for an aircrew of just three – two pilots and loadmaster – the latter situated in a dedicated computerised station on the starboard side of the forward fuselage. The capacious cargo hold combined with a payload of 168,400 lb (76385 kg) ensure that almost any vehicle in the UK armed services can be accommodated along with RAF and Army helicopters, artillery, ammunition and troops. In order to clear specific loads, a cargo bay mock-up has been assembled at the Joint Air Transport Evaluation Unit (JATEU) at the C-17s home base of RAF Brize Norton, Oxfordshire. In the troop transport role the aircraft can accommodate 102 fully-armed soldiers, and for aeromedical evacuation nine onboard litters (along with associated medical and oxygen supplies are fitted on the starboard side of the fuselage). A total of 27 additional litters can be added if the necessity arises. The aircraft's proven short-/rough-field performance can also be utilised and with the minimum of ground support necessary (the aircraft having autonomous loading and unloading capabilities) operations into austere airfields are possible.

## Training and support

The USAF Air Education & Training Command provides training for the RAF's pilots and loadmasters at Altus AFB, Oklahoma. RAF personnel are integrated into ongoing courses run by the 58th Airlift Squadron, missing out the non-applicable 'tactical' elements of the training. Operational conversion or 'seasoning' is then completed with the RAF personnel acting as supernumerary crew members on a wide-range of missions as part of the 437th Airlift Wing. For logistical support the aircraft are integrated into the USAF's Flexible Sustainment contract with Boeing. Being part of the USAF's 'virtual fleet' offers incredible benefits including access to USAF-owned spares and support facilities around the world as well as field support and the possibility to include any modifications, upgrades or improvements for US C-17s or their systems. Boeing also has a field service team at Brize Norton providing technical support, with the RAF themselves responsible for on-aircraft maintenance including wheels, tyres and flight servicing.

## Into service

The four aircraft are operated by No. 99 Squadron. After its first flight on 16 April 2001, the first aircraft (ZZ171) was handed over to the RAF on 17 May 2001, a month ahead of schedule, and arrived at Brize Norton on the 23 May. It was followed by the second aircraft (ZZ172) on 13 June. The remaining pair (ZZ173 and ZZ174) were delivered in August and were soon on-line with the squadron. As well as JRRF taskings, the aircraft have already undertaken a variety of tasks. The first aircraft made its first 'emergency' response in July delivering an engine to a stranded RAF TriStar in the USA. Showing its versatility, it continued on to Venezuela with maritime engines for the Royal Navy, before calling in at Dover AFB to pick-up the broken TriStar engine on its return the UK. The type has also proven its worth in the Saif Sareea II exercise in Oman, during No. 99 Sqn's official work-up phase, delivering vehicles, heavy equipment and personnel. The first deployment to an operational theatre was made in August 2001 when an initial C-17 flight delivered Army Air Corps Lynx helicopters, along with its supporting equipment and crews, to Skopje, Macedonia as part of the UN peacekeeping operations. Further supply flights were made including cargoes of ambulances and Land Rovers.

It is obvious from its short time in service that the C-17 has become indispensable, and the RAF will be very reluctant to give it up if (and when) the A400M is ready for service, sometime after 2008.

### No. 99 Sqn, RAF

Reformed under the command of by Wg Cdr Malcolm Brecht to operate the RAF's four C-17s, No.99 'Madras Presidency' Sqn (motto: Quisque tenax – Each tenacious) has a history going back to World War I and, in three previous incarnations, has performed long-range bombing and transport roles. The squadron was formed at Yatesbury as a day bomber unit in the RFC in August 1917, receiving DH.9s the following April for service in France. With the end of the Great War, the squadron received DH.9As and moved to India, though it was soon renumbered No. 27 Sqn.

Reforming again in 1924, No. 99 Sqn retained its bombing role and operated Vickers Vimys, Avro Aldershots, Handley Page Hyderabads and Hinaidis, mainly from Bircham Newton, during the 1920s. Handley Page Heyfords arrived in 1933, the squadron having moved to Upper Heyford in the meantime; these were retained until more modern equipment, in the shape of Vickers Wellingtons, became available, in late 1938.

With the outbreak of war, No. 99 undertook leaflet-dropping and bombing raids from Elmdon, Newmarket and Waterbeach until early 1942, when the squadron was transferred to the Far East. Re-assembling at Ambala, initially with Wellingtons, the unit began night bombing raids on Japanese targets in Burma in November. These continued after the squadron received Liberators, for long-range operations, in September 1944. In mid-1945 No. 99 moved to the Cocos Islands in preparation for the invasion of Malaya, carrying out anti-shipping strikes in the Dutch East Indies until VJ-Day.

At the end of 1945, No. 99 Sqn reformed at Lyneham as a transport squadron. Its first aircraft were Handley Page Hastings, these aircraft being used to drop paratroops over Port Said during the 1956 Suez campaign. In 1959 re-equipment with Bristol Britannias gave the Transport (later Air Support) Command squadron a long-range transport capability that took its 'Whispering Giants' to destinations worldwide over the next 17 years, latterly from Brize Norton. No. 99 Sqn's badge comprised 'a puma salient', as seen above, on the tail of C-17A ZZ172.

# Boeing E-3 Sentry
## AWACS evolution

***Based on the Boeing 707 airliner, the E-3 Sentry represented a quantum leap over the aircraft it replaced. The large rotodome houses the radar antenna.***

**Providing airborne early warning, control and communications, the Boeing E-3 Sentry is the West's premier air warfare management asset for the modern battlefield. Defined during the 1960s, it represented a major advance over its predecessors when it entered service with the USAF.**

Large surveillance radars became airborne towards the end of World War II. Unlike previous airborne radars, they were designed to search vast volumes of sky and detect all aircraft present. The most widely used of the early generation of Airborne Early Warning (AEW) 'picket' aircraft was the EC-121 Warning Star, a series based on the Super Constellation airliner, used by the USN and USAF from the early 1950s until after the Vietnam War. The type's limitations included the fact that it was piston-engined with only modest performance, combined with a low operating altitude (the higher up the radar was taken, the greater the distance that it could cover). In the 1960s, the USAF calculated that a radar in a large jet aircraft at a height of 30,000 ft (9145 m) would 'see' up to a distance of 245 miles (395 km), increasing the time available to give warning to Air Defence Command to intercept incoming Soviet Tu-95 'Bear' bombers. The weakness of the 1950s radar system was further exposed by the move at that time towards carrying out low-level attacks. Whereas aircraft flying at high altitude – above the AEW aircraft – had no 'ground-clutter' in which to hide, by flying at low level, they were able to hide in the reflection of the radar signals from the ground. For a number of reasons, therefore, a new radar, as well as a new airframe in which to carry it, was required.

### Higher, mightier radar

In 1965, the USAF began its Overland Radar Technology (ORT) program to design a radar that could look down over the land and see small jets speeding at 'treetop height'. The answer proved to be 'pulse-Doppler' radar, a radar that uses not only successive pulses of energy, but also the Doppler phase shift of the echoes received back from the target. It works by comparing the pulse repetition frequency (PRF) of the radar signal sent out with the PRF of the echoes returned. Most signals are received back from the ground, the difference in PRF being due to the speed of the AEW aircraft. All other PRFs come from targets moving relative to the ground and are 'easy' to spot.

There are certain target angles and ranges where either the target cannot be seen, or the apparent range may be half, twice, even four times the true value. Much research was therefore needed to produce an Overland Downlook Radar (ODR) that worked. Even then, it suffered from such problems as the occurrence of false 'velocities' of leaves agitated by wind, or waves and spray blown across the sea. A very powerful, fast computer was required, which could check each one of the billions of radar pulses and echoes, and display on the operators' screens only the real targets and the true target speeds and distances. Two competing radar designs, one built by the Hughes Aircraft Company, the other by Westinghouse Electric Corporation, were produced and tested under flight conditions.

### New airframe

The AWACS (Airborne Warning and Control System) tender attracted both Boeing's Aerospace Group and McDonnell Douglas. Boeing's study included purpose-designed carrier aircraft, but these could not perform much better than the Boeing 707-320 airliner still in production. To increase endurance on station, in 1969 it was decided to fit the 707 AWACS aircraft with eight TF34 engines (as used on the A-10 ) in twin pods, but this was subsequently abandoned and the four regular TF33 engines were chosen. Boeing won the competition in July 1970, and an order for two EC-137D aircraft was placed to evaluate the competing radar designs. Of these, Westinghouse's AN/APY-1/-2 ODR emerged as the winner.

The radar is located in a saucer-like rotodome carried on two 11-ft (3.35-m) struts above the rear fuselage. On the back of this vast antenna is mounted a mass of

***Above: The combination of an airframe capable of jet speeds and altitude together with advanced search radar provides the E-3 operator with a valuable asset for offensive and defensive air operations.***

***Left: After testing the competing radars, the two EC-137Ds were refurbished and upgraded to the E-3 production standard. This is the first Sentry prototype modified as an E-3B, serving with the 552nd ACW at Tinker AFB, Oklahoma.***

***As a continuation of the military 707 line, the two E-3 prototypes were originally designated as EC-137Ds, in keeping with USAF nomenclature for its previous 707 models.***

auxiliary equipment inside a large structural beam, so preventing any distortion that might affect accuracy. Attached to this beam is a communications and digital datalink antenna which is used for IFF purposes and for secure communications with perhaps hundreds of other friendly stations. The streamlining of the radome is achieved by the saucer-shaped glassfibre sandwich, which has only a minor adverse effect on aircraft speed and handling.

## Internal systems

When the radar is in operation, the rotodome turns at speeds of up to 6 rpm, keeping the radar beam sweeping round. In the first 24 E-3s, an IBM CC-1 computer processes the incoming radar echoes at the rate of 740,000 per second and feeds the results to nine Situation Display Consoles (SDCs) and two Auxiliary Display Units (ADUs). The consoles are arranged in rows of three across the cabin, above the leading edge of the wing. Immediately behind them is the station for the duty officer. Up front are the flight crew, navigation and communications electronics, and the station for the computer operator. Further aft is the console for the radar maintenance officer while, at the rear, is a large galley and crew rest area. On a typical mission, an E-3 (with an unrefuelled endurance of 11 hours) routinely refuels and stays aloft for up to 18 hours, carrying a crew of 20, including 16 mission specialists such as weapon controllers, radar operators and communications personnel.

The radar can be operated in any of six modes. Simplest is 'Passive', which merely receives electronic signals and pinpoints their origin. In the 'Beyond The Horizon' (BTH) mode, all radar power is put into achieving range, without elevation data. 'Pulse-Doppler Elevation Scan' (PDES), in which the main beam is electronically swept up and down to cover the whole surveillance airspace, is the most widely-used mode. The received signals are analysed to determine the exact peak signal (echo) strength which, in turn, gives target elevation. At all times, target direction is determined by scanning repeatedly and comparing the scans from different positions in time and space. PDES provides the maximum amount of information and suffers from the greatest loss of range. Where the detection of distant targets is more important than knowing their height, it is possible to switch to 'Pulse-Doppler Non-Elevation Scan' (PDNES), in which vertical scanning is eliminated. The 'Maritime' mode is used to detect surface vessels in all sea surface states. The sixth operating mode – 'Interleaved' – uses various high- and low-PRF modes sent out together, optimises the crew's ability to carry out the detection of both aircraft and ship targets located beyond visual range.

***Above: This pre-delivery photograph shows three USAF E-3s on the Boeing ramp, among airliners and a 707 and 747of the Imperial Iranian Air Force. Apart from the E-3's rotodome and windowless fuselage, the external differences between it and the 707 are few.***

***Right: At the heart of the AWACS system is the AN/APY-1/-2 Overland Downlook Radar, which feeds information to the Situation Display Consoles.***

# Sentry operators

*The USAF is by far the largest user of the E-3 Sentry. Initially operated by Tactical Air Command, today Air Combat Command's 552nd ACW at Tinker AFB, Oklahoma has control over the fleet.*

**The E-3 Sentry is one of the most distinctive shapes in the sky today and is the West's principal AWACS (airborne warning and control system) platform.**

Using the airframe of a Boeing 707-320 airliner and a massive payload of radar and electronic sensors, the E-3 AWACS is a flying headquarters for C³I (command, control, communications and intelligence), employed near a combat zone to monitor aircraft and missiles and to direct friendly warplanes. Since its introduction into operational service, the distinctive E-3 Sentry has proved itself time and again to be an invaluable component in the USAF and NATO air defence systems, locating and tracking enemy intruders and directing friendly interceptors to their quarry.

## USAF procurement

Two prototype aircraft were built as EC-137Ds, the first initially taking to the air on 9 February 1972. Used to test out the new radar systems and the compatibility of the rotodome with the airframe, the aircraft were progressively improved and eventually redesignated E-3As. Two other E-3As were ordered for the FSD programme.

A total of 30 production aircraft was funded between Fiscal Years 1975 and 1983, and the first flight of an E-3 with full mission avionics was from Seattle on 25 May 1976. The first delivery to an operational unit was on 23 March 1977, to the 552nd AWAC at Tinker AFB, Oklahoma, the type reaching Initial Operational Capability in April 1978. E-3s assumed a US continental air defence role in January 1979. Since then, AWACS aircraft have been involved globally in all American combat operations, including those in Grenada (1983), Lebanon (1983), Panama (1989) and Iraq (1991).

The first 24 aircraft were delivered in 'core' standard and the final 10 to the US/NATO 'standard' with the updated AN/APY-2 radar, fitted to all export aircraft. Core E-3As were upgraded as E-3Bs with the addition of ECM-resistant voice communications, Have Quick communications gear, anti-jamming improvements, larger crew capacity, five additional consoles, and radios and numerous avionics improvements. The first E-3B was redelivered to the USAF on 18 July 1984. Under Project Snappy in 1991, seven E-3Bs were fitted with an additional (and so far unidentified) sensor for Operation Desert Storm, which eight further aircraft have also received. The 10 examples delivered to US/NATO standard were updated with Have Quick, additional computing and communications capabilities, and were redesignated as E-3Cs.

## USAF Sentry units

All operational E-3 Sentries are operated by the 552nd Airborne Control Wing, Air Combat Command, at Tinker AFB, Okla., which also allocates aircraft to two PACAF units. The 552nd ACW consists of the 963rd AACS (Airborne Air Control Squadron), 964th AACS, 965th AACS and 966th AACS; the last unit, responsible for Sentry crew training, is also equipped with a pair of TC-18Es – basically ex-airline 707s used for training. As part of its Associate Program, the Air Force Reserve Command controls the 970th ACS of the 513rd Air Control Group, providing Sentry aircrew but not 'owning' any aircraft of its own.

The Pacific Air Force (PACAF) controls two squadrons of Sentries. The 5th Air Force has the 961st AACS based at Kadena AB, Okinawa, flying E-3s with a 'ZZ' tailcode, while at Elmendorf AFB in Alaska the 962nd AACS uses the 'AK' tailcode. United States Central Command in the Middle East was responsible for aircraft to implement Operation Southern Watch. Controlled by the 4404th Wing (Provisional) with headquarters at Prince Sultan Air Base, Al Kharj, Saudi Arabia, the Sentry squadron was the 4405th Airborne Command and Control Squadron (Provisional) also at Al Kharj, operating E-3B/Cs on loan from the 552nd ACW at Tinker AFB.

## NATO aircraft

Eighteen E-3A 'standards' were delivered to NATO, which also uses three Boeing 707TCAs

**E-3 Sentry production and operators**

| | | | |
|---|---|---|---|
| EC-137D | Two prototypes (71-1407/1408) for USAF – became E-3As and finally E-3Bs. | | |
| E-3A | USAF acquired 32 (plus the two EC-137Ds). First 23 built as 'Core E-3A', rest as 'US/NATO Standard' (73-1674 updated to 'Standard'). All became E-3Bs or Cs. | | |
| | 73-1674/1675[2] | 75-0556/0560[5] | 76-1604/1607[4] |
| | 77-0351/0356[6] | 78-0576/0578[3] | 79-0001/0003[3] |
| | 80-0137/0139[3] | 81-0004/0005[2] | 82-0006/0007[2] |
| | 83-0008/0009 [2] | | |
| | NATO acquired 18 aircraft which were built to 'Standard E-3A' configuration. | | |
| | LX-N90442/N90459 [ex 79-0442/0459] | | |
| | The Royal Saudi Air Force acquired five 'Standard' E-3As as follows:- | | |
| | 1801 [ex-82-0068] | 1802 [ex-82-0067] | 1803 [ex-82-0066] |
| | 1804 [ex-82-0069] | 1805 [ex-82-0070] | |
| KE-3A | New built tankers for Saudi Arabia – eight aircraft. | | |
| | 1811/1816 [ex-82-0071/0076] | 1817/1818 [ex-83-0510/0511] | |
| E-3B | (Block 20 modifications) 22 E-3As and the two ex EC-137Ds of the USAF were upgraded to E-3B standard. | | |
| KE-3B | Proposed conversion of Boeing 707s for Saudi Arabia. | | |
| E-3C | (Block 25 modifications) 10 E-3As of USAF upgraded to E-3C standard. | | |
| JE-3C | USAF E-3C 73-1674 was bailed to Boeing to develop AN/AYR-1. | | |
| E-3D | Sentry AEW.Mk 1 for RAF, seven ordered, originally allocated serials ZH100/ZH106 but became ZH101/ZH107. Individual aircraft named after the 'Seven Dwarves' characters. | | |
| E-3F | Four aircraft for French air force, operated by CASSIC. French serials are 201/204. | | |

***Right: Not exactly what it appears to be at first glance, this E-3A – in USAF markings – is actually a Royal Saudi Air Force Sentry on a test flight, prior to delivery. The Saudi aircraft were the first to use the CFM56 engine.***

***Below: The only flying element of the Armée de l'Air's CASSIC are the four E-3Fs of the two squadrons of EDCA 36 (Escadrons 1/36 'Berry' and 2/36 'Nivernais'). The French originally required a total of six Sentries, but the options for the final two were dropped in 1988.***

for training. Dornier at Oberpfaffenhoffen integrated the systems of NATO Sentries, which were then sent to Nos 1, 2 and 3 Squadrons of the E-3A component, NATO Airborne Early Warning Force at Geilenkirchen, Germany. Ordered with US serials 79-0442 to -0459, the aircraft were registered in Luxembourg as LX-N90442 to -0459. Currently, NATO has 17 Sentries, one having been lost in a landing accident in Greece in July 1997.

## Export Sentries

In addition to USAF and NATO aircraft, the E-3 has been exported to three countries. E-3A 'standard' (as distinguished from 'core') versions were delivered to Saudi Arabia from 1986. Ordered in 1982, the aircraft were delivered in 1986, becoming 1801 to 1805 in service after being flown out in USAF colours. In service today, the aircraft fly with No. 18 Squadron at Al Kharj, having moved from Riyadh in 1997. No. 18 Squadron also uses the eight KE-3A tanker versions.

## European AWACS

Boeing gave both the UK and France a 130 per cent industrial offset. The Royal Air Force and Armée de l'Air versions differ markedly from US and NATO E-3s, primarily in the replacement of TF33 turbofans with 106.8-kN (24,000-lb st) CFM56-2A-3 turbofans (also used by the Saudis), and installation of an upper forward fuselage-mounted SOGERMA inflight-refuelling probe in addition to the refuelling receptacle. The last RAF aircraft was the final Boeing 707 airframe produced, after which the production line was closed, forcing Japan to opt for an AEW version of the much more recent twin-engined Boeing 767, using essentially E-3C equipment.

## RAF Sentries

Following the cancellation of the ill-fated Nimrod AEW aircraft for the Royal Air Force, the UK government placed a contract for six aircraft designated E-3D Sentry AEW.Mk 1 in December 1986, to replace the ancient Shackleton AEW.Mk 2s of No. 8 Sqn. An option for a seventh aircraft was converted in October 1987. The RAF's initial E-3D (ZH101) was first flown on 11 September 1989, and made its maiden flight in fully-equipped mode on 5 January 1990. RAF aircraft are distinguished by having wingtip-mounted Loral 1017 Yellow Gate ESM pods. Today, all seven aircraft (ZH101 to ZH107) are on the strength of No. 8 Sqn at Waddington. The co-located No. 23 Sqn, responsible for Sentry training, borrows aircraft as required.

## Système de Détection Aéroportée

At approximately the same time as the RAF ordered its aircraft, the Armée de l'Air placed an order – in February 1987 – for three E-3F SDAs (Système de Détection Aéroportée). An order for a fourth aircraft was added later, but options on a further two E-3s were dropped in 1988. The E-3F first flew on 27 June 1990, and they serve with EDCA36 of Commandement Air des Systèmes de Surveillance et de Communications (CASSIC - Air Signals and Ground Environment Command).

***Above: Most NATO countries were unable or unwilling to invest in national fleets of Sentries, so opted for a pooled unit of the aircraft. Based at Geilenkirchen, Germany, the fleet is dispersed to operating locations within Europe.***

***Left: The RAF could have been the first export customer for the Sentry instead of developing the Nimrod AEW.Mk 3. Eventually ordered in late 1986 and fitted with a refuelling probe, wingtip ESM pods, CFM56-2A-3 engines and finished in an overall grey scheme, the seven aircraft of the Nos 8 and 23 Squadrons are based at Waddington.***

# Boeing E-4

***The majestic beauty of the E-4B belies the aircraft's true role – in the event of a nuclear war, it would become the focus of the USA's armed response. Based on the successful 747-200, the E-4 has accumulated an excellent safety record during more than a decade of service on presidential trips overseas.***

## Briefing

**Signifying the USA's resolve to remain a cohesive force in the event of a nuclear attack, the E-4B is fitted with highly specialised communications equipment. Protected from the effects of a nuclear blast, the aircraft would be used as the Presidential command centre for America's response.**

The Boeing E-4B is the USA's National Airborne Operations Centre (NAOC), a flying command post to be used by the country's leaders in time of war. The grim purpose of the E-4B is given away by its nickname, 'the Doomsday plane'. Behind the familiar exterior of a Boeing 747-200B lies the USA's frightening potential to continue to wage war in the event that Washington is annihilated by a nuclear blast.

The E-4B, or NAOC, was developed in the 1970s to ensure the survival of the national leadership in the event of an atomic exchange with the Soviet Union. It is kept in readiness to transport the President, or others in the chain of leadership known as the NCA (National Command Authority), during the initial hours or days of a general conflict. During an attack on US soil, some leaders would be taken to an underground command post in Virginia, while others would go aboard the E-4B to direct US air and ground forces.

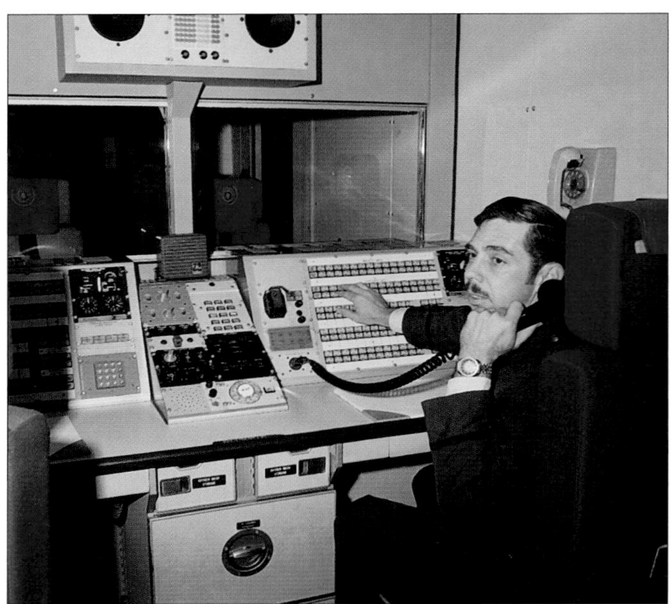

***Above: Accurate intelligence is vital following a nuclear attack and the E-4 is equipped with an extensive array of communications equipment. The systems of the E-4A (illustrated) have been greatly updated in the E-4B. The aircraft's extensive communications suite is shielded from the effects of electro-magnetic pulse.***

***Located within a dorsal blister on the E-4B is a Satellite/SHF communications antenna, allowing the aircraft to send and receive messages without risk of interception. Despite the ending of the Cold War, whenever the President is overseas, a single E-4B accompanies him. This aircraft is held on alert throughout his visit in the unlikely event of a national emergency.***

### Commercial design

When choosing the aircraft and planning its design, the USAF wanted speed, efficiency, and a degree of comfort, but the primary need was for a very large aircraft that could remain airborne for a long time. The Pentagon wanted the E-4B to remain aloft at least during the first round of a nuclear exchange, when communication would be most difficult, and airfields would not be readily available. The wide-bodied Boeing 747, with its cavernous interior, offered the size needed for redundant flight crew personnel, equipment, and 'black boxes', and also lent itself to being modified for extreme endurance. The 747 was, in addition, an ideal candidate for the extra weight caused by 'hardening' the aircraft against EMP (electromagnetic pulse), the destructive blasts of energy that accompany a nuclear blast.

***Above: By using inflight refuelling, the E-4B can stay aloft for at least 72 hours, engine oil capacity being the limiting factor. This E-4A is hooked onto a McDonnell Douglas KC-10A Extender. In times of tension, a fleet of KC-10 or KC-135 tanker aircraft would be kept at readiness, to extend the E-4B's mission duration. A relief flight crew, consisting of aircraft commander (pilot), co-pilot, navigator and flight engineer, would be carried on board the E-4B.***

Delivered in late 1974, the first three aircraft were known as E-4As, with the initial example making its maiden flight on 13 June 1973. Early equipment was that ripped from the E-4's predecessor, the EC-135J. The fourth E-4, delivered in December 1979, was modified to such an extent that a new designation, E-4B, was adopted. A subsequent modification programme saw all the E-4 fleet being upgraded to the more capable E-4B standard.

## Flying 'White House'

The E-4B uses its bulk to accommodate the President (in his role as commander-in-chief of US forces) and key members of his battle staff on its 5,500 sq ft (511 m$^2$) main deck. This is divided into five operating compartments: flight crew section, NCA area (roughly constituting a flying equivalent of the White House Situation Room), conference room, battle staff area, and a C$^3$I (command, control, communications and intelligence) planning facility. A second deck provides a rest area for mission personnel.

## Blastproof Boeing

As a 'war readiness aircraft', the E-4B is equipped with nuclear thermal shielding, LF/VLF (low frequency/very low frequency) radios, and extensive satellite communications equipment. Among this vast array is equipment allowing the aircraft to tie into commercial telephone and radio networks to broadcast emergency messages to the general population.

The E-4B is distinguished from the E-4A by the fact that, in addition to being fitted with LF/VLF communications, it also carries a SHF (super high frequency) system, with antennas housed in a distinctive dorsal blister. Every component of the aircraft, including engines, avionics, and wiring, has been optimised for maximum flight duration.

On its awesome mission, the E-4B typically cruises at 580 mph (933 km/h), is refuelled in flight, and meets a requirement of being able to remain airborne for 72 hours. In the event of a war situation, even this duration could be extended to a full week. Like the Presidential VC-25A, the other Boeing 747 derivative in the inventory, the E-4B's airborne endurance is limited only by the quantity of oil carried for the lubrication of its engines. Power is provided by four 52,500 lb (233.53 kN) thrust General Electric F103-PW-100 (CF6-50-E2) turbofan engines.

The E-4B was originally known as the AABNCP (Advanced Airborne National Command Post), and thereafter as the NEACP (National Emergency Airborne Command Post), inevitably pronounced "kneecap" by those who worked on the aircraft. Today's term, NAOC, was devised partly to reflect a changing world and additional duties.

## Future role?

With the thawing of the Cold War, the four E-4Bs are expected to remain in USAF service well into the next century, to be utilised as communications platforms during limited conflicts and natural disasters.

### Presidential transport

One of the most prestigious roles assigned to the Boeing 747 is that of Presidential transport. Operated under the designation VC-25A, two specially-equipped Boeing 747-2G4Bs are assigned to the 89th Airlift Wing at Andrews AFB, Maryland. The VC-25A can carry the President and his staff, with 70 passengers and 23 crew members, a distance of 7,410 miles (11490 km) without air refuelling. The crew includes 10 flight personnel for redundancy purposes, three communications specialists, and 10 flight attendants. The VC-25A can serve as an emergency war order aircraft to carry the President or others within the NCA during a nuclear conflict. For this role, the aircraft is equipped with 85 telephones, 19 television monitors, 11 video cassette players, and secure voice and facsimile equipment. During flight operations, the President is accommodated within the state-room equipped with twin beds, twin sinks, dressing table, shower, and lavatory. While the President is aboard the VC-25A during flight operations, the appropriate call sign 'Air Force One' is utilised. The first aircraft (82-8000) was delivered to the 89th Airlift Wing on 30 September 1990. The second VC-25A (92-9000) was delivered on 30 December 1990. The first operational mission of 82-8000 took place on 6 September 1990, taking President George Bush to Topeka, Kansas, and Tallahassee, Florida. The following day, it made its first overseas trip, taking President Bush to Helsinki, Finland.

***Thankfully, the Boeing E-4B has never had to perform its true mission. Despite the easing of tensions between the USA and Russia since the ending of the Cold War, the four E-4Bs will remain part of the USAF inventory for the foreseeable future. Recent upgrades and improvements to the fleet have seen the aircraft equipped with a tail-mounted, trailing low frequency wire antenna, and up to 46 antennas on the fuselage underside. In terms of communications, the Boeing E-4B is the best-equipped aircraft in the world.***

# E-6 Mercury/E-8 J-STARS

## Sentinels in the sky

**During the 1980s two new versions of Boeing's famous 707 appeared. The US Navy's E-6 Mercury, tasked with secure communications and command post duties, was followed into service by the USAF's E-8C J-STARS battlefield surveillance aircraft.**

*Above: The E-6A Mercury had replaced the EC-130G/Q Hercules in the TACAMO role by 1992. All E-6s have been upgraded to E-6B standard, allowing the aircraft to perform airborne command post duties in the Looking Glass role.*

*Top: Originally delivered to QANTAS of Australia as a Boeing 707-338C, N526SJ (90-0175) was purchased by the Grumman Corporation. Conversion to E-8C standard for the USAF was completed in 1995.*

*Below: A classic example of the type of intelligence provided by the J-STARS is given by this Wide-Area Surveillance/Moving Target Indicator (WAS/MTI) image, taken during the last hours of the Gulf War.*

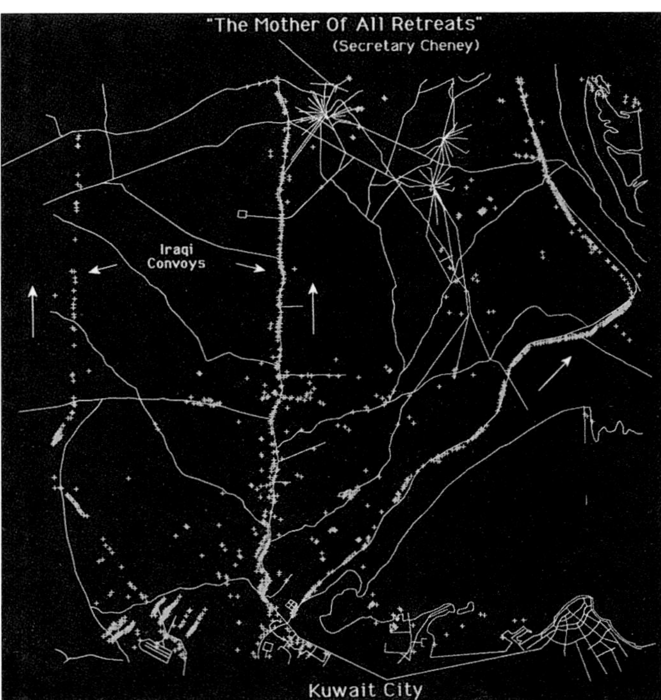


The E-6 and E-8 for the USN and USAF are two very different applications of the versatile Boeing 707-320 airframe. Not only do the two aircraft look quite dissimilar, but they are also very different in terms of age. USN E-6 Mercury TACAMO aircraft are recent, new-build examples from a second 707 production run in the late 1980s. USAF E-8 J-STARS (Joint Surveillance and Target Attack Radar System) platforms, by contrast, are rebuilt, former airline 707s from the 1960s.

### First Hermes

When the first E-6 was rolled out of the Boeing factory in Seattle on 23 June 1987, it had a name that was liked by no-one and a minor design flaw that needed to be fixed. Initially, it was called the E-6 Hermes, named after the messenger of the gods in Greek mythology. However, crews complained that the name sounded too much like the sexually-transmitted disease, herpes. USN leaders decided that the name given to the Roman version of the same God, which was also the brand name of a popular automobile, would be more acceptable, so the aircraft became the E-6 Mercury. Along the way, an early in-flight accident damaged a chunk of the E-6's fin. A minor change in fin contour solved the problem.

The US Navy acquired 16 E-6As during the free-spending 1980s to carry out a single mission – TACAMO (Take Charge And Move Out). This was the term for LF (low-frequency) radio communication between the White House and Pentagon and at-sea strategic, ballistic-missile submarines. In the TACAMO role, the E-6A Mercury replaced the EC-130G Hercules. The newer aircraft carried LF antennas that could be trailled up to 1 mile (1.6 km) behind the aircraft.

The Mercury was powered by four 24,000-lb (108-kN) thrust General Electric/SNECMA F108-CF-100 (CFM56 engines). It entered service with two USN squadrons at Tinker Air Force Base, Oklahoma in 1989. However, this was only after developmental work solved problems with the wire antenna for the E-6A's low-frequency radios, which initially had a tendency to break off and float to the ground.

Possibly by chance, possibly not, the USN ordered more E-6A TACAMOs than it needed. All have since been upgraded to E-6B standard, with improved electronics installations. The surplus aircraft have now replaced ageing EC-135 Stratotankers, employed by the USAF for the command and control of nuclear forces. Operated by US Strategic Command at Offutt AFB, Nebraska, and flown with mixed-service crews, these nuclear command posts function as an

***Unlike the USAF's E-8s, the E-6s were new-build aircraft, with production lasting from 1986-91. The aircraft operate from permanent detachments at Travis AFB, NAS Patuxent River and Offutt AFB.***

airborne alternative to ground-based command centres: they are capable of launching Minuteman intercontinental ballistic missiles from their silos.

E-6A/B Mercury TACAMO squadrons initially were VQ-3, the 'Tacamopac', at NAS Barber's Point, Hawaii, and VQ-4, 'Shadows', at NAS Patuxent River, Maryland. The TACAMO mission has now been centralised at Tinker under VQ-3 'Ironmen' and VQ-4 'Shadows'.

## J-STARS

The Noprthrop Grumman E-8 is an airborne command post outfitted for the J-STARS mission, a joint USAF/US Army programme for a battlefield management system that detects, locates, tracks and classifies enemy ground formations at long range.

Conceived for a western European scenario, J-STARS was rushed into use during Operation Desert Storm and was successful in directing fighter-bombers in attacks on Iraqi tanks and other targets detected by the E-8A's radar system.

The two prototypes, both previously-used 707s converted by Grumman, were equipped with a Norden multi-mode SLAR (side-looking airborne radar) located in a 25-ft (7.74-m) 'canoe' faired into the belly of the aircraft. This radar functions in SAR (synthetic-aperture radar) mode out to a range of 160 miles (257 km) to detect and pinpoint stationary objects such as parked tanks. The radar alternates between SAR and Doppler modes to locate and track slow-moving targets. The mission crew aboard the E-8 then directs attacks on the targets using the real-time JTIDS (Joint Tactical Information Distribution System). The flight crew of four consists of pilot (aircraft commander), co-pilot, navigator and flight engineer. The mission crew is typically 17, led by a mission crew commander, typically a lieutenant colonel or colonel.

The E-8 is powered by four 19,000-lb (85.5-kN) thrust Pratt & Whitney JT3D-7 turbofan engines, almost identical to the military TF33 turbofans employed by other 717/707 variants. The E-8C J-STARS aircraft has now replaced the E-8A, retaining the same powerplant and configuration but equipped with newer internal systems and better data-processing capability.

**Airframe**
The Boeing 707-320C was the final and definitive civil variant, having a quick-change interior for passenger or cargo operations, or a mixture of both. It was identified by the lack of ventral fin, made possible by changes to the aerodynamics.

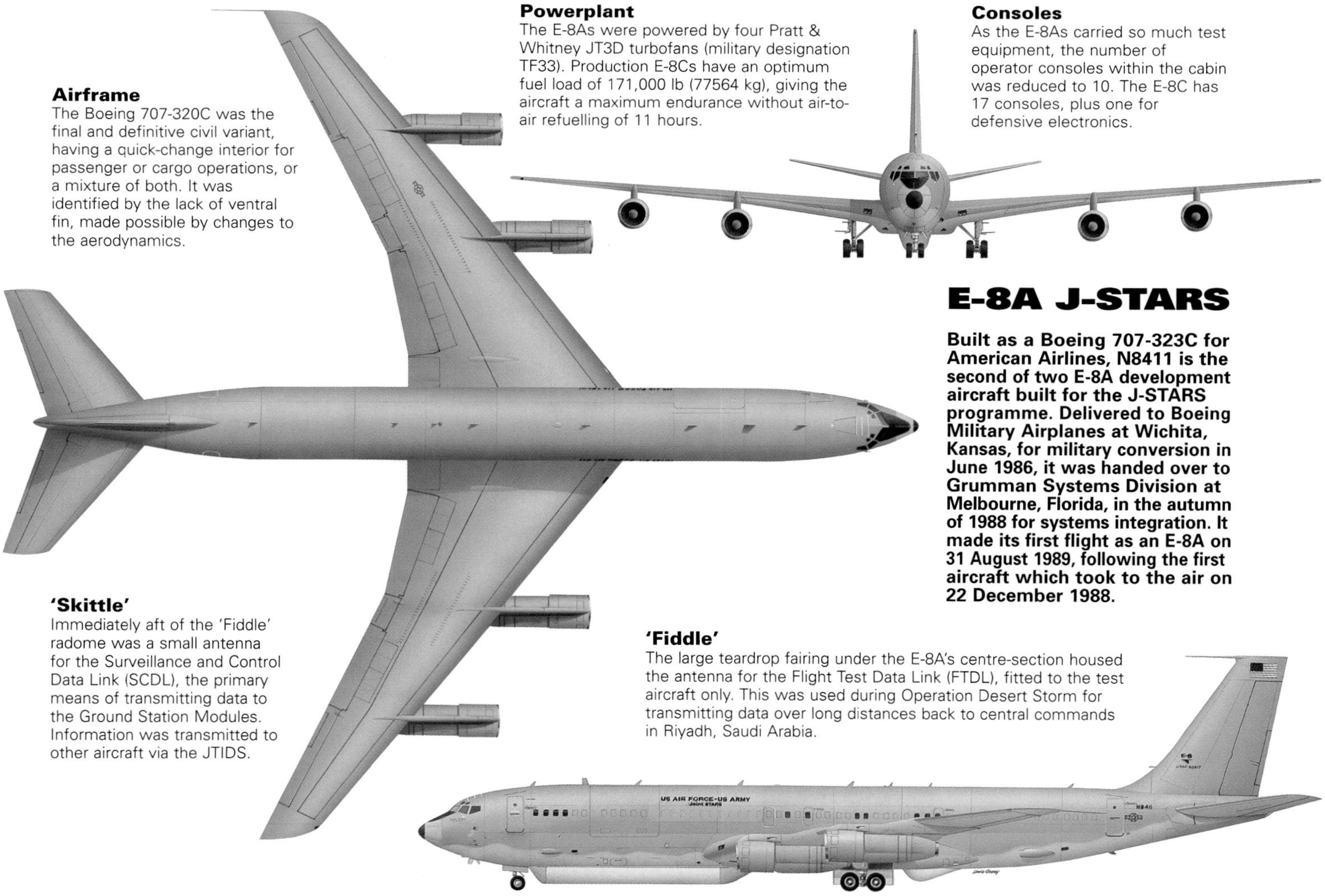

**Powerplant**
The E-8As were powered by four Pratt & Whitney JT3D turbofans (military designation TF33). Production E-8Cs have an optimum fuel load of 171,000 lb (77564 kg), giving the aircraft a maximum endurance without air-to-air refuelling of 11 hours.

**Consoles**
As the E-8As carried so much test equipment, the number of operator consoles within the cabin was reduced to 10. The E-8C has 17 consoles, plus one for defensive electronics.

## E-8A J-STARS

**Built as a Boeing 707-323C for American Airlines, N8411 is the second of two E-8A development aircraft built for the J-STARS programme. Delivered to Boeing Military Airplanes at Wichita, Kansas, for military conversion in June 1986, it was handed over to Grumman Systems Division at Melbourne, Florida, in the autumn of 1988 for systems integration. It made its first flight as an E-8A on 31 August 1989, following the first aircraft which took to the air on 22 December 1988.**

**'Skittle'**
Immediately aft of the 'Fiddle' radome was a small antenna for the Surveillance and Control Data Link (SCDL), the primary means of transmitting data to the Ground Station Modules. Information was transmitted to other aircraft via the JTIDS.

**'Fiddle'**
The large teardrop fairing under the E-8A's centre-section housed the antenna for the Flight Test Data Link (FTDL), fitted to the test aircraft only. This was used during Operation Desert Storm for transmitting data over long distances back to central commands in Riyadh, Saudi Arabia.

US AIR FORCE-US ARMY

# F-15: Eagle awakening

**Combining sophisticated technology with brute force, the F-15 is the dominant air superiority fighter in the world. Its development proceeded slowly, yet relatively smoothly, and revolutionised the face of fighter design. Today, more than 20 years after service entry, an F-15 has never been shot down by another aircraft.**

The beginning of today's F-15 Eagle occurred in February 1968 when Tactical Air Command chief General Gabriel P. Disosway signed off on an ROC (Required Operational Capability) statement. This held that any F-4 replacement to emerge from the F-X (next-generation fighter) studies must be an air superiority fighter. In May 1968, USAF Chief of Staff General John P. McConnell endorsed Disosway's package and allocated to the F-X effort his service's highest priority. In a departure from past practice, one which has since become more commonplace, the new fighter was assigned a designation (in late 1968) before an actual aircraft type had been chosen. It was to be the F-15.

A decision had been reached, it seemed. The future F-15 – whatever it looked like, whoever built it – would be optimised to engage and kill an adversary BVR, and would thus be designed explicitly for air-to-air combat. It would be able to dogfight. McConnell did not specify armament, but thought was well-advanced towards resurrecting a fighter weapon useful since World War I – the gun. The F-15 would *not* be (in the mould of the gunless F-4 Phantom) a 'multi-role' craft.

## F-15 decisions

The decision to drop the gun on the F-4 had been made at an early design stage in the 1950s by those who knew that the missile age had arrived and were preparing, next, to discard the pilot. Vietnam, at least, reversed the conventional wisdom that aerial warfare had no place for people or for shooting.

Debate persisted and, as late as 30 September 1968 (when it issued an RFP/request for proposals for a future F-15), the USAF really did not clearly know what it wanted. The RFP was, however, quite specific on some points. It stated that the new fighter should have: low wing-loading with buffet-free performance at Mach 0.9; a high thrust-to-weight ratio; long-range pulse-Doppler radar with look-down/shoot-down capability; ferry range sufficient to permit self-deployment to Europe without mid-air refuelling; and a maximum speed of Mach 2.5. The Mach 2.5 requirement was theoretically achieved, at great expense and complexity, although with missiles the F-15 is restricted to Mach 1.78.

The RFP spelled out other detailed requirements, by far the most important of which was a one-man cockpit. A maximum gross take-off weight of 40,000 lb (18144 kg) for the air superiority mission was also desired.

***Above: The use of the RPRV flying replicas to gather data in advance of the maiden flight of a major aircraft type was an unusual aspect of the Eagle's development, and was considered to be highly successful.***

***Top: In ADTAC service, the Eagle replaced the F-106. Here, TAC F-15As from the 49th TFW formate with F-106As from the 5th FIS, which itself became an Eagle operator between 1985 and 1988.***

## Three proposals

By 30 December 1968, the USAF had viable proposals from just three manufacturers – McDonnell, North American and Fairchild-Republic. All were awarded $15.4-million contracts for the Contract Definition Phase. An exhaustive evaluation by Air Force Systems Command (AFSC) led to the announcement on 23 December 1969 that the McDonnell Aircraft Company had been chosen to build the new fighter.

The initial contract called for 20 developmental aircraft, (including a preliminary batch of 10 single-seat F-15As and two two-seat TF-15As) – the two-seaters were later redesignated F-15B. In addition to the Category I aircraft, the contract specified eight Category II FSD (full-scale development) aircraft, all F-15As.

***The first F-15 to be completed was 71-0280, and is seen here on the occasion of its roll-out ceremony at St Louis on 26 June 1972. The AIM-7 Sparrow missiles were dummies.***

***The first two Category I aircraft prepare for test flying at Edwards. 71-0281 (right) was principally an engine testbed, while 71-0280 explored envelope expansion, handling and stores carriage.***

In addition to the test aircraft (the Category II machines to be upgraded to operational configuration), initial purchase plans saw 143 F-15s to be employed as attrition reserves. One hundred and eight were to be used for training (54 for command support). With 72 operational aircraft per wing, the total buy would give Tactical Air Command, USAFE (US Air Forces in Europe) and Pacific Air Forces three, two and one F-15 wings respectively.

Before the new McDonnell fighter flew, it was preceded by flight tests with three RPRVs (remotely-piloted research vehicles), which were three-eighths scale replicas of the F-15 Eagle. The National Aeronautics and Space Administration's (NASA) Dryden facility at Edwards AFB, California, dropped these remote-control mini-Eagles from its Boeing NB-52B Stratofortress mother ship.

The F-15A prototype (71-0280) – sometimes referred to as a YF-15A, with the 'Y' prefix indicating service-test duties – was rolled out at St Louis on 26 June 1972. Dismantled and transported to Edwards AFB, California, the F-15A was flown a month later on 27 July 1972. At the controls was Irving Burrows, who had many years' experience as a company test pilot. The maiden flight, in clear weather, was uneventful. Burrows has since spoken of the F-15's ease of handling.

## Test programme

An ambitious programme was embarked upon with the first 12 Eagles built; these were the USAF's Category I test aircraft, known in shorthand as F-1 through to F-10, and TF-1 and TF-2.

In 1976, an Eagle made a spectacular round-the-world sales tour covering some 34,000 miles (54716 km), attending air shows and showing itself to potential buyers. The hard-working second TF-15A (soon redesignated F-15B) wore a striking bicentennial colour scheme for 1976 during the tour.

At a late design stage, a single tail for the F-15 Eagle was rejected. The Eagle's tail unit is an all-metal structure of twin fins and rudders – remarkably thin, thanks to boron composite skin over honeycomb material – with all-moving horizontal tail surfaces outboard of the fins. Having twin fins sacrifices weight for good high-alpha performance and better survivability.

The Eagle's spine-mounted airbrake was an innovation. It could be deployed without pitch change and at any speed. Power in the early Eagle was provided by two 25,000-lb (113-kN) thrust Pratt & Whitney F100-PW-100 turbofan engines with afterburners.

## Talons of the Eagle

Given the importance of the far-reaching radar, the armament of the F-15 Eagle obviously began with BVR missiles, originally Vietnam-era AIM-7F Sparrows which have semi-active radar-homing and make it difficult for the pilot of the launch aircraft to evade. Four AIM-9J Sidewinder IR missiles (today, AIM-9M) also made up part of the fighter's arsenal, as well as a 20-mm M61A1 Vulcan ('Gatling') six-barrel cannon, which became a fallback after efforts to develop a new 25-mm cannon for the Eagle foundered.

Long range had been one goal of the F-15 programme, achieved in part with two FAST (fuel and sensor tactical) packs – flush, low-drag fuel pallets developed for the F-15 and each able to carry 5,000 lb (2268 kg) of fuel. The original FAST packs, attached to the side of either engine intake trunk and were designed to the same load factors and airspeed limits as the aircraft itself. Infact, the packs only came into use on the F-15C/D and they are now referred to as CFTs (conformal fuel tanks) because they carry fuel only, thereby extending the Eagle's range, but the original plan was for these packs to carry sensors as well as fuel.

Production of an initial batch of 30 F-15A/B fighters was announced on 1 March 1973. The first Eagle delivered to an operational USAF unit was TF-15A 73-0108 (the 21st Eagle built), christened 'TAC 1'. This aircraft was accepted by President Gerald Ford in a ceremony on 4 November 1974 at Luke AFB, Arizona, for the 555th Tactical Fighter Training Squadron, the 'Triple Nickel'.

## Front-line US service

With its RTU (replacement training unit) gearing up at Luke AFB, Arizona, the USAF assigned its first F-15s in a combat role to the 1st Tactical Fighter Wing ('FF' tailcode, for 'First Fighter') at Langley Air Force Base, Virginia. The squadron began its conversion from the F-4E Phantom to the new type on 9 January 1976.

The F-15 Eagle experienced some labour pains. At Luke, pilots were discovering that they could not mount the planned number of sorties. There were difficulties with parts and maintenance, and there persisted a more serious problem with the powerplant. Modifications to the engine provided a solution, but left the F100, even today, with a reputation for being temperamental under certain flying conditions.

Technical 'glitches' aside, the F-15 programme was a model of success in meeting projected costs, and the second unit to equip with Eagles was the 36th Tactical Fighter Wing in 1977.

***Above: Aircraft 71-0291 embarked on a major sales drive after its initial testing duties were complete. It sported French markings for just four days in April 1976, together with flags from the nations it had visited.***

***Right: Category II FSD aircraft were somewhat closer to production standard, and were engaged in further testing. 72-0118 was briefly used for operational tests, but was subsequently transferred to Israel, along with three other Category II test aircraft.***

# F-15A/B: Operations

Converting from the F-106A Delta Dart during December 1983, the 318th FIS was entrusted with the defence of the US western seaboard and maintained an air defence alert from Castle AFB in California.

**When it entered service with the USAF, the F-15 Eagle gradually began replacing the F-4 Phantom II in the interceptor role. Early model F-15s have been upgraded and remain in service.**

In March 1973 the USAF officially ordered its initial batch of 30 Eagles, with the first F-15s being delivered to an actual USAF unit on 4 November 1974. This first operational Eagle was a two-seat TF-15A trainer (73-0108) which was christened 'TAC-1'.

'TAC-1' went to the F-15 Replacement Training Unit (RTU), part of the 555th Tactical Flying Training Squadron (TFTS) at Luke AFB outside Phoenix, Arizona. As the RTU began to turn out qualified F-15 pilots, the first combat unit chosen to field the new aircraft also began to get its new mounts: the 1st Tactical Fighter (TFW) with its distinctive 'FF' ('First Fighter') tail code, based at Langley AFB, Virginia. On 9 January 1976 the 1st TFW was declared operational, having turned in its old F-4E Phantoms for new Eagles.

The following year saw the first overseas USAF unit - the 36th TFW at Bitburg, West Germany ('BT' tail code) - receive its Eagles. The same year, the 57th Fighter Weapons Wing ('FW') at Nellis AFB near Las Vegas, Nevada, activated the 433rd Fighter Weapons Squadron (FWS) to develop tactics for the Eagle, as well as conduct testing of new weapons and systems. Eventually, the 21st Composite Wing ('AK') at Elmendorf AFB, Alaska, the 32nd Tactical Fighter Squadron ('CR') at Soesterberg, Netherlands, the 33rd TFW 'Nomads' ('EG') at Eglin AFB, Florida, and the 49th TFW ('HO') at Holloman AFB, New Mexico joined the 1st as front-line combat Eagle units.

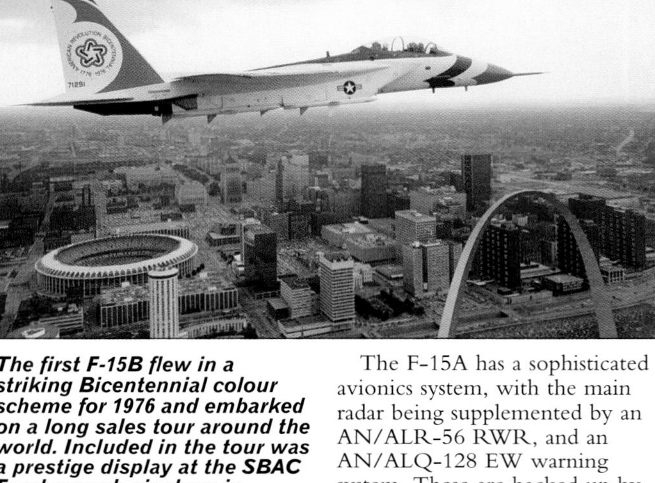

The first F-15B flew in a striking Bicentennial colour scheme for 1976 and embarked on a long sales tour around the world. Included in the tour was a prestige display at the SBAC Farnborough air show in Hampshire, England.

## Bird of prey

Problems were initially encountered with the Eagle's Pratt & Whitney F100-PW-100 engine, and the X-band Hughes APG-63 coherent pulse-Doppler radar, both of which had been designed specifically for the F-15. These have been overcome during the Eagle's service career.

The F-15A has a sophisticated avionics system, with the main radar being supplemented by an AN/ALR-56 RWR, and an AN/ALQ-128 EW warning system. These are backed up by a Northrop AN/ALQ-135 countermeasures set. Lessons learned in Vietnam proved that good pilot visibility was essential, and to this end the F-15 pilot sits high up and well forward on a McDonnell Douglas Escapac IC-7 ejection seat (later replaced

The 36th TFW at Bitburg, Germany, received the Eagle in April 1977. For many years the 36th TFW was the principal air defence unit in southern West Germany, providing an alert facility and patrolling the Air Defence Identification Zone.

The 1st FW was the first operational F-15 Eagle unit, converting to the F-15A/B in 1975. The wing's 27th FS claims to be the oldest flying squadron in the USAF, with a history dating to 15 June 1917.

***Left:** The shortest-lived Eagle operator was the 5th FIS 'Spittin' Kittens', which was tasked with CONUS air defence missions from Minot AFB, North Dakota from April 1985 to July 1988. The three CONUS-based F-15 interceptor units had previously flown Convair F-106 Delta Darts.*

***Below:** The strategic importance of Alaska was emphasised by the equipment of a single squadron (43rd TFS) of the 21st Composite Wing with F-15A/Bs.*

by an ACES II seat) under a blown canopy, with excellent all-round view. The cockpit itself is well laid out, but is equipped only with analog instruments, with no cathode ray tube multi-function displays (CRT MFDs). A head-up display (HUD) and a variety of control-column and throttle-mounted controls give hands on throttle and stick (HOTAS) operation of all important systems. The Eagle was designed to fight in the HOTAS mode, the pilot receiving all necessary information from his HUD and being able to cue the weapons system without having to look down into the cockpit.

Developed alongside the 'A' model was the TF-15A two-seat trainer. It is fully mission capable, but lacks the AN/ALQ-135 ECM and is 800 lb (364 kg) heavier than the single-seater. In 1978 the TF-15A was re-designated as the F-15B in recognition of its combat-capable status.

## Enhanced Eagles

In the 1990s, with relatively few 'new-build' aircraft being ordered apart from the F-22 Raptor, the USAF is improving its F-15A/B fighters through a Multi-Stage Improvement Program (MSIP). This programme replaces the troublesome F100-PW-100 turbofans with the slightly less powerful but more reliable -220 engines of all but the earliest production F-15Cs. It also includes new avionics and digital central computers which replace the original analog computers.

F-15A/B Eagles emerging from the MSIP differ visually from F-15C/D models by lacking the radar warning receiver antenna located next to the horizontal stabiliser. They also lack the 2,000 lb (907 kg) of extra fuel carried by the F-15C. MSIP F-15A/B aircraft replaced non-MSIP F-15C/D models with the 32nd TFS in 1992.

## Home Guard

As the Eagle entered service with front-line USAF units, seven ANG units started to receive F-15A/B models, the first being the 199th FIS, Hickam AFB, Hawaii, which replaced its F-4C Phantoms in the summer of 1987. Following the introduction of the improved F-15C into regular USAF units further ANG units have since received early Eagle variants, signifying the final withdrawal of the Phantom from the interceptor role with the USAF.

***Above:** Fifty-eight two-seat F-15Bs were procured to augment the F-15A single-seaters. Small numbers were assigned to each operational unit for continuation training, familiarisation work and check rides, the remainder being assigned to the F-15 training unit. This aircraft wears the five-star tail markings of the 555th TFTS 'Triple Nickel', the highest-scoring USAF squadron in Vietnam and the first TAC unit to get the F-15.*

***Right:** After replacement in the front line by F-15C/Ds, F-15A/Bs were 'cascaded' to Air National Guard units such as the 122nd TFS, Louisiana ANG, as illustrated here.*

The F-15Cs of the 18th Fighter Wing, USAF, at Kadena AB, Japan, periodically stand alert duty in Korea, as a result of the Okinawa-based unit's proximity to the strategically-important Korean peninsula.

# F-15C/D: Improved Eagle

**In order for the F-15 to retain its mantle of 'the world's premier fighter', McDonnell Douglas began work on a second-generation design, which would measurably improve the Eagle's performance.**

All areas of the F-15 design were looked at and improved where necessary, although the resulting F-15C/D is externally similar to the preceding F-15A/B. Internal space was found for an additional 2,000 lb (907 kg) of fuel, while the F-15C/D was the first operational model to be able to carry conformal fuel tanks (CFTs). The ability to carry a load of over 43,000 lb (19505 kg) of fuel meant that the Eagle could self-deploy to an air base in the Persian Gulf, with either two stops or inflight refuellings.

The first F-15C (78-0468) flew at St Louis on 26 February 1979, followed by the first F-15D two-seater on 19 June. Initial production C/Ds were powered by the same F100-PW-100 engines which had powered the A/B, but from November 1985 the F100-PW-220 was introduced. This new engine was slightly less powerful, but considerably more reliable.

Avionics systems were also improved, the first F-15C/Ds emerging with the improved APG-63PSP (programmable signal processor) radar and better ECM equipment. From 1989 the APG-70 radar (a much-modified APG-63) was incorporated. Using the same antenna, the APG-70 had new signal processor systems nearly five times quicker than those of the APG-63, while able to handle much larger volumes. C- and D-model Eagles were rapidly delivered to front-line fighter units around the world, and by the time the last of the second-generation F-15s had been delivered to the USAF, some 408 F-15Cs and 62 F-15Ds had been produced.

## Middle East Eagles

When the American C/D-model Eagles came on the scene, the IAF was already interested in a further F-15 procurement. Project Peace Fox III delivered 18 F-15Cs and eight F-15Ds from the FY1980 and 1983 Eagle production runs. In IDF/AF service, the F-15C/D acquired the name Akef (buzzard). Later, five additional F-15Ds were delivered from FY90 production under Peace Fox IV, these probably being based on the F-15E airframe rather than the F-15D, as the latter was no longer in production. The aircraft serve with the IDF/AF's 106 Squadron, which flies alongside the A/B-equipped 133 Squadron at Tel Nof. Like the earlier A/B models, they are equipped with locally-produced EW equipment. Weapons include the Python 3 and the latest Python 4 AAMs, which have largely replaced the AIM-9 Sidewinder.

In the 1970s, the Royal Saudi Air Force (RSAF) began to consider procuring an interceptor to replace its BAC Lightnings. An Eagle purchase, which was tied to a force of Boeing E-3 AWACS aircraft, was opposed by Israel and its lobby in the American Congress. The details of the sale became part of the contents of the Camp David Peace Accords between Israel, Egypt and the US, stating that only 60 of the Eagle airframes would be allowed on

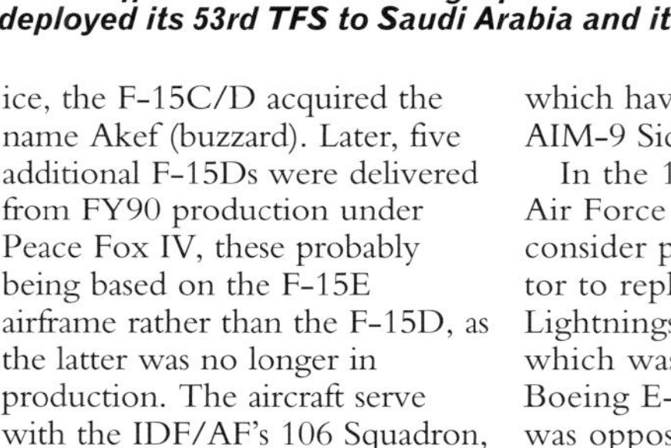

A Bitburg-based F-15C of the 36th TFW suffers a 'flame out' during a take-off in June 1989. During Operation Desert Storm, the wing deployed its 53rd TFS to Saudi Arabia and its 525th TFS to Turkey.

Front-line Japanese Eagles wear a standard air superiority camouflage, consisting of two shades of grey. The first half of the six-digit serial system corresponds to the procurement year (5: 1985), aircraft class (2: twin-engined), and basic role (8: all-weather fighter); the last three digits refer to the individual aircraft number in sequence.

*Right: The F-15 is a big fighter by any standards, but this size is emphasised when compared to the RAF's diminutive Hawk. The 'tennis court' wing is lightly loaded, combining with a high thrust-to-weight ratio to provide good manoeuvrability.*

*Below: Israel's F-15C/D Akefs are operated by 106 Squadron at Tel Nof. This aircraft combines a Python 3 on the outer launch rail with an AIM-9 on the inner. Locally-built EW technology replaces some equipment, including the ALQ-128 RWR.*

Saudi territory at any time. Since the RSAF order was for 62 C/D-model F-15s, two were to be held back as attrition aircraft.

Procured under Project Peace Sun, the initial RSAF F-15s were ordered from the FY80 and 81 production runs. In 1991, a further order of 12 attrition aircraft was contracted under Peace Sun VI, and these were delivered from February 1992. They quickly showed their teeth when, on 5 June 1984, two RSAF F-15s shot down a pair of Iranian F-4s over the Persian Gulf. By 1990 three RSAF Eagle squadrons were in service: No. 5 at Taif, No. 6 at Khamis Mushait and No. 13 at Dhahran. By this time, the restriction of only allowing 60 RSAF F-15s had been dropped, and two dozen additional F-15Cs and F-15Ds were rushed to the RSAF during the 1990-91 Persian Gulf crisis, forming No. 42 Squadron at Dhahran.

During the Gulf War, the RSAF's finest moment came when a pair of Eagles, led by Captain Ayehid Salah al-Shamrani of No. 13 Squadron, shot down a pair of Exocet-carrying Iraqi Mirage F1s.

## F-15J/DJ

The second overseas customer for the Eagle was the Japanese Air Self-Defence Force (JASDF), which evaluated the F-15 in 1975. The JASDF versions of the Eagle (the F-15J is the single-seat version, and the F-15DJ a two-seat fighter trainer) were co-produced by Mitsubishi Heavy Industries (MHI), but were functionally almost identical to early-production C/Ds in USAF service. Initially, the procurement, run under Project Peace Eagle, was for 123 aircraft, but by early 1998 totalled 213 (169 F-15Js and 44 F-15DJs), with further low-rate production likely to be added to the currently planned total of 224.

Initial F-15J production was undertaken at St Louis, where two aircraft were built, the first undertaking its maiden flight in June 1980. The next eight F-15Js were supplied to Mitsubishi as kits for final assembly at MHI in Japan, the first of these flying at Komaki on 26 August 1981. Subsequent F-15J production was at MHI. All F-15DJ production from FY1988 onwards was by MHI (this coincides with MDC production conversion to the F-15E). F-15Js began entering service (with 202 Hikotai) in 1981 after initial service testing had been performed by the Koku Jikkendan at Gifu.

Currently, the JASDF is conducting a major mid-life upgrade of the F-15J/DJ fleet, which will result in the aircraft being given a 'Plus' designation. This includes installation of F100-IHI-220E engines (licence-produced versions of the F100-PW-220) and an upgraded radar designated APG-63U, probably equivalent to the upgraded APG-70. Eventually, the indigenously-designed AAM-4 air-to-air missile will be fitted.

*Above: The 57th Wing, ACC's fighter tactics and weapons test and evaluation establishment, is based at Nellis AFB, Nevada. The 422nd TEWS 'Vampires' operated the F-15C, and provided aircraft for the Fighter Weapons School F-15 syllabus.*

*Right: The F-15's cockpit was designed to minimise the amount of time the pilot had to spend with his 'head down' during combat. Consequently, the cockpit is dominated by a large head-up display, presenting the pilot with vital combat information.*

# F-15E: The 'Mud Hen'

**Turning the West's best air-to-air fighter into a nocturnal mud-mover was an idea opposed by many. However, today's F-15E is without doubt the most capable strike/attack platform in the world, while having lost little of its air combat prowess.**

***Above: For many years an F-4E user, the 4th Wing at Seymour Johnson, North Carolina is now the premier F-15E operator, with four squadrons assigned. These examples are from the 335th FS 'Chiefs'. The squadron undertook strike missions over Iraq during Operation Desert Storm in 1991.***

***Right: The F-15 is potentially the most capable warrior over the battlefield. However, to use the F-15E and its systems to the full requires not only thorough instruction and practice, but also close co-ordination between the two cockpits.***

All F-15s were built with air-to-ground capability, and wired for the carriage of air-to-ground ordnance. They were originally intended as dual-role aircraft, but the ground attack role was abandoned in 1975, when it was decided not to incorporate the relevant software.

Trials of an air-to-ground F-15 began during 1982, when McDonnell Douglas modified the second TF-15A as the 'Strike Eagle', funding the project itself. The aircraft was conceived as an ETF (Enhanced Tactical Fighter) replacement for the General Dynamics F-111 and was chosen in preference to the 'cranked-wing' F-16XL Fighting Falcon. The 'Strike Eagle' demonstrator was joined by an F-15C and F-15D, which conducted trials with a variety of fuel and ordnance loads, usually with Conformal Fuel Tanks (CFTs) fitted. The resulting F-15E was given the go-ahead on 24 February 1984 and the first production aircraft made its maiden flight on 11 December 1986. McDonnell's 'Strike Eagle' name was not adopted, although some unofficial epithets such as 'Beagle' (Bomber Eagle) and 'Mud Hen' have been used on occasion.

In introducing new avionics and equipment for a 'mud-moving' role not assigned to earlier variants, the F-15E is very much a second-generation Eagle. The aircraft introduced redesigned controls, a wide field of vision HUD, and three CRTs providing multi-purpose displays of navigation, weapons delivery and systems operation. The rear-cockpit WSO employs four multi-purpose CRT terminals for radar, weapons selection and the monitoring of enemy tracking systems. The WSO also operates an AN/APG-70 synthetic aperture radar and Martin-Marietta LANTIRN navigation (AN/AAQ-13) and targeting (AN/AAQ-14) pods. The navigation pod incorporates its own terrain-following radar, which can be linked to the aircraft's flight control system to allow automatic coupled terrain-following flight. The targeting pod allows the aircraft to self-designate GBU-10 and GBU-24 laser-guided bombs. Basic flight controls are provided for the WSO and the crew sit on ACES II zero-zero ejection seats.

Power for the new variant was initially provided by F100-PW-220 turbofans, as used by the F-15C, with a digital engine control system. However, the powerplant was soon replaced under the Improved Performance Engine programme, whereby GE F110-GE-129 and P&W F100-PW-229 engines were both flown in F-15Es under competitive evaluation;

***In Strike Eagle guise, McDonnell Douglas's two-seat F-15B demonstrator, 71-0291, was an awesome aircraft. It is illustrated with a full load of Mk 7 Rockeye CBUs on its wing and fuselage pylons. The aircraft wore both overall grey and two-tone schemes.***

***This Lakenheath-based F-15E from the 494th 'Panthers' was suitably decorated in tiger-stripe markings. This enabled it to participate in NATO's annual squadron meet of those units carrying a tiger as their emblem.***

the Pratt & Whitney engine was eventually selected. Since August 1991 the new engine (from aircraft 90-0233) has been fitted on the production line, and other aircraft will be retrofitted. To adapt the F-15E to the rigours of the low-level role, the aircraft was structurally redesigned for a 16,000-hour life and loads of up to 9*g*. More use was made of superplastic forming and diffusion bonding in the rear fuselage, engine bay and on some panels. The fuel tanks were filled with reticulated foam, reducing capacity to 2,019 US gal (7643 litres).

In 1988, the 405th Tactical Training Wing at Luke AFB, AZ, became Tactical Air Command's replacement training unit for the F-15E Eagle, a role since taken over by the 58th Fighter Wing in Air Education and Training Command. The first operational F-15Es were delivered to the 4th TFW, Seymour Johnson AFB, NC, replacing the F-4E Phantom.

On 12 August 1990, as the US began Operation Desert Shield, F-15E Eagles from the 336th TFS, 4th TFW, deployed to Al Kharj air base, Saudi Arabia. F-15Es of that wing's 335th TFS followed. During Desert Storm, F-15Es were assigned strike missions against a variety of targets, including five/six-hour sorties in search of 'Scud' missile launch sites. Out of 2,200 sorties totalling 7,700 hours, just two F-15E Eagles were lost in combat.

In 1991, the Secretary of Defense overruled USAF leaders who wanted to keep the F-15E Eagle in production. Although the F-15E is an exceedingly potent warplane for the strike mission, critics point out that its low wing-loading produces a rough ride, especially for the backseater, and that the aircraft's payload is less than that of the 30-year old F-111. However, this short-sighted decision was later reversed and another small batch of F-15Es was ordered.

In addition, long-standing F-15 operator Saudi Arabia, ordered 72 aircraft, designated F-15S, similar to the American aircraft but lacking certain ECM equipment. Responding to this potential threat from its near neighbour, Israel followed suit with a total order for 25 F-15Is. Known as the Ra'am (Thunder) within IDF/AF service, the aircraft were built almost to the full specification of USAF examples. A further customer emerged in 2002 in the form of South Korea, whose 40 General Electric F110-229 powered F-15K aircraft are due for delivery in 2005-08.

### English Eagles

Since the 1960s, RAF Lakenheath has been a cornerstone of Western European defence. Equipped with F-84s, F-86s, F-100s and F-4s, the 48th TFW adopted the F-111F in 1977. It took the 'Earth Pig' into action against Libya and in a starring role in Desert Storm. Following the Gulf War, the wing began winding down F-111F operations in preparation for the F-15E, the first example, (illustrated) arriving on 21 February 1992. The two F-15E squadrons, 492nd and 494th, have made regular deployments to Aviano to provide night attack cover for the UN ground forces in Bosnia. Another ongoing commitment has been to Operation Provide Comfort – policing the UN safe haven in Northern Iraq.

## F-15E Eagle

**This aircraft represents that of the 48th FS wing commander, based at RAF Lakenheath, Suffolk, UK. The wing retired its four squadrons of F-111Fs in favour of two F-15E squadrons in 1992. Today, the aircraft fly alongside one squadron of F-15C/D 'fighter' Eagles.**

**CFTs**
The conformal fuel tanks each hold 723 US gal (2737 litres) of fuel, and have a continuous pylon (with three attachment points) and three stub pylons for the carriage of weapons.

**Cockpit**
The F-15E has a state-of-the-art cockpit, the pilot having a wide-angle HUD and three MFDs. The WSO has four MFDs. All vital flight and attack inputs are made via an upfront control and stick/throttle controls.

**Powerplant**
Late production F-15Es, like this one, are fitted with the F100-PW-229 IPE, each offering 29,100 lb (130.9 kN) of thrust with full afterburning.

**Radar**
At the heart of the F-15E's capability is the APG-70 radar, a vastly-improved version of the F-15C's APG-63. As well as having improved air-to-air modes, the APG-70 offers a high-resolution synthetic aperture mapping mode. This allows highly accurate 'patch maps' to be taken of the target area which, in turn, allow the precise designation of the desired aimpoint.

**LANTIRN pods**
The LANTIRN system consists of the AAQ-13 navigation pod under the starboard intake and the AAQ-14 targeting pod under the port. The AAQ-13 consists of a wide-angle FLIR, which projects an image on the pilot's HUD, and a Texas Instruments terrain-following radar, which interfaces with the aircraft's autopilot system to provide safe low-level flight in all conditions.

**Armament**
This F-15E is loaded for a close air support/battlefield air interdiction mission with 14 SUU-30H cluster bombs. AIM-9s are carried for self-defence. Lakenheath F-15Es also carry AIM-120 AMRAAMs on the outer launch rail, with Sidewinders on the inner rail.

# USAF/ANG operators

***An F-15C of the 390th Fighter Squadron, 336th Wing takes off from its base at Mountain Home. The 366th was one of Air Combat Command's first composite wings – in effect air forces in miniature, with several different aircraft types.***

**Although the McDonnell Douglas F-15 Eagle has been operational for more than a quarter of a century, it is still one of the world's best fighters, and remains the mainstay of America's air defences.**

The Eagle entered service with the 1st Tactical Fighter Wing at Langley AFB in Virginia in January 1976. Over the next decade it replaced F-4 Phantom and F-106 Delta Dart interceptors with Tactical Air Command, and was also deployed to the UK, Germany, Alaska and the Far East with USAFE (US Air Forces Europe) and PACAF (Pacific Air Forces).

In Europe, the F-15 was on the Cold War front line with fighters on alert with the 32nd FS at Soesterburg in the Netherlands and with the 36th Fighter Wing at Bitburg. With the easing of tensions after the collapse of Communism, most F-15s were withdrawn from the continent, and now the only Eagle fighters serve alongside F-15E Strike Eagles at RAF Lakenheath in England.

Pacific Eagles are based in Alaska, where during the Cold War they regularly intercepted Soviet reconnaissance bombers, and at Kadena in Okinawa. With the reduction in the US fighter presence in Korea, the Kadena Eagles became an increasingly important element in the US commitment to defend Korea, though the rapprochement between North and South, to gether with Japanese unease at the presence of US Forces on Okinawa make their future a matter for debate.

As the original single-seat F-15As and F-15Bs were replaced with front line operators by the improved F-15C and F-15D, their old mounts were handed on to Air National Guard Units. The first ANG F-15 unit was the 122nd FS of the Louisiana ANG, which began to trade in its F-4C Phantoms for F-15As in June 1985. The 173rd FW, Oregon ANG is the first unit to operate F-15Cs and -Ds.

Apart from combat and reserve units, Eagles are also flown by the Air Education and Training Command at Tyndall

**WINTER 2003/04 US-BASED COMBAT UNITS**

| Base | Wing | Sqn | Variant |
|---|---|---|---|
| Eglin AFB, Florida | 33rd FW (ACC) | 58th FS | F-15C/D |
| | | 60th FS | F-15C/D |
| | 53rd Wing (ACC) | 85th TES | F-15C, F-15E |
| Elmendorf AFB, Alaska | 3rd Wing (PACAF) | 12th FS | F-15C/D |
| | | 19th FS | F-15C/D |
| | | 90th FS | F-15E |
| Seymour Johnson AFB, North Carolina | 4th FW (ACC) | 333rd FS | F-15E |
| | | 334th FS | F-15E |
| | | 335th FS | F-15E |
| | | 336th FS | F-15E |
| Langley AFB, Virginia | 1st FW (ACC) | 27th FS | F-15C/D |
| | | 71st FS | F-15C/D |
| | | 94th FS | F-15C/D |
| Mountain Home AFB, Idaho | 336th FW (ACC) | 390th FS | F-15C/D |
| | | 391st FS | F-15E |

***The 159th Fighter Wing, Louisiana Air National Guard was the first ANG unit to re-equip with the Eagle. Known as the 'Coonass Militia', the unit flies ex-49th FW F-15As and -Bs.***

**TEST/TRAINING/EVALUATION UNITS**

| Base | Wing | Sqn | Variant |
|---|---|---|---|
| Tyndall AFB, Florida | 325th FW (AETC) | 1st FS | F-15C/D |
| | | 2nd FS | F-15C/D |
| | | 95th FS | F-15C/D |
| Nellis AFB, Nevada | 53rd Wing (ACC) | 422nd TES | F-15C/D |
| | 57th Wing (ACC) | Weapons School | F-15C Division, F-15E Division |
| Edwards AFB, California | 412th TW (AFMC) | 445th FLTS | All variants |
| Warner Robins AFB, Georgia | Air Logistics Center (AFMC) | Maintenance | All variants |

AFB in Florida, by Air Combat Command's Weapons School at Nellis AFB in Nevada, and by the Air Force Material Command's test and evaluation unit at Edwards AFB in California. Maintenance is carried out at AFMC's logistics centre at Warner-Robins AFB in Georgia.

***Above: The 57th Fighter Interceptor Squadron flew missions from Iceland for much of the Cold War, exchanging its Phantoms for F-15C Eagles in 1985. The squadron was disbanded in 1995, its mission being taken by detachments from other F-15 units.***

***Above: The 'WA' tailcodes identify these aircraft as Eagles from the F-15 Division of the USAF Weapons School. The school, part of Air Combat Command, is located at Nellis AFB in Nevada.***

## AIR NATIONAL GUARD F-15 UNITS

| Base | Wing | Sqn | Variant |
|---|---|---|---|
| **Florida** | | | |
| Jacksonville, IAP | 125th FW (FL ANG) | 159th FS | F-15C/D |
| Homestead, ARB | | 159th FS (det) | F-15C/D |
| **Missouri** | | | |
| St Louis IAP | 131st FW (MO ANG) | 110th FS | F-15A/B |
| **Louisiana** | | | |
| NAS New Orleans | 159th FW (LA ANG) | 122nd FS | F-15A/B |
| **Massachussetts** | | | |
| Otis ANGB | 102nd FW (MA ANG) | 101st FS | F-15A/B |
| **Oregon** | | | |
| Portland IAP | 142nd FW (OR ANG) | 123rd FS | F-15A/B |
| Klamath Falls IAP | 173rd FW (OR ANG) | 114th FS | F-15A/B/C/D |
| **Hawaii** | | | |
| Hickam AFB | 154th Wing (HI ANG) | 199th FS | F-15A/B |

## OVERSEAS-BASED F-15 UNITS

| Base | Wing | Sqn | Variant |
|---|---|---|---|
| **Japan** | | | |
| Kadena AB, Okinawa | 18th Wing (PACAF) | 44th FS | F-15C/D |
| | | 67th FS | F-15C/D |
| **United Kingdom** | | | |
| RAF Lakenheath | 48th FW (USAFE) | 492nd FS | F-15E |
| | | 493rd FS | F-15C/D |
| | | 494th FS | F-15/E |

## ICELAND-BASED F-15 UNITS

| Base | |
|---|---|
| Keflavik AB | ACC, AFRC, ANG F-15 sqns on TDY |

**33rd Fighter Wing**
Seen in the markings it carried in the early 1990s, this aircraft accounted for four out of the 58th TFS's 16 kills during the Gulf War. Among its victorious pilots were Colonel Rick Parsons, Captain David G. Rose and Captain Anthony R. Murphy.

**Nomenclature**
When it first flew Eagles, the unit this aircraft belongs to was part of Tactical Air Command, and was known as the 58th Tactical Fighter Squadron, 33rd Tactical Fighter Wing. With the USAF re-organisation of the 1990s it is now the 58th Fighter Squadron, 33rd Fighter Wing of Air Combat Command.

# McDonnell Douglas F-15C Eagle

**The F-15 has been the USAF's premier fighter since the 1970s, and during that time it has seen continuous development. The latest improvements go to front-line squadrons first, but eventually they find their way to the whole Eagle community.**

**MSIP**
The Multi-Stage Improvement Program has seen the F-15C/Ds of Air Combat Command, PACAF and USAFE fitted with improved radar, weapons control, avionics and countermeasures.

# Israeli operators

Israel's F-15A/Bs, including this F-15A single 'MiG-killer' are operated by No 133 'The Twin-Tailed' Sqn at Tel Nof. This aircraft carries Python 3 AAMs on the outer underwing launch rails. It also carries AIM-7 Sparrows.

**The F-15 forms the nucleus of Israel's current fighter and ground-attack force. Israel continues to update its inventory and is now acquiring the F-15I.**

Israeli air crews evaluated the manufacturer's TF-15A 'dog ship' in 1974. Despite an effort during the Carter years (1977-81) to limit US transfers of advanced warplanes to foreign users, the Jewish state has received Eagle deliveries taking place in instalments.

Four F-15A FSD (full-scale development) aircraft arrived in Israel beginning 10 December 1976, apparently for developmental work, in the Peace Fox I programme. It has been reported by an Israeli source that the government later fell because their arrival violated the Sabbath. These were followed by 19 F-15As and two F-15Bs under Peace Fox II, offered at preferential financing to help offset sale of the same aircraft type to Saudi Arabia. Thereafter came 18 F-15Cs and eight F-15Ds in Peace Fox III. No. 106 Sqn was formed specifically to operate the F-15C/D.

The F-15C/D was given a different name in IDF/AF service – Akef (buzzard), wheras the F-15A/B is known as Baz (eagle). The F-15Cs for Israel were given additional air-to-ground capability through installation of MER-10N bomb racks and a datalink pod for guiding GBU-15 glide bombs. IDF/AF F-15C/Ds do not have the Electronic Warfare Warning Set (EWWS) or the Tactical Electronic Warfare System (TEWS) that had been provided on the USAF version, since these items were considered too sensitive for export. Israeli Eagles use AN/ARC-109 radios instead of AN/ARC-164s. All Israeli F-15s can carry FAST pack conformal fuel tanks and these can carry tangential bomb pylons. Israeli Eagles are equipped with the IG-7 ejection seat rather than the ACES II seats of the USAF version. They can carry the indigenous AL/L-8202 electronics countermeasures pod in addition to the US-supplied AN/ALQ-119(V) and AN/ALQ-132 pods.

The units which operate the F-15 fighter variant are Nos. 106, 133 and 148 Squadrons (F-15A/B/D) at Tel Nof.

## Eagle action

The first IDF/AF action with Eagles took place on 27 June 1977, during a mission in which a mixed force of F-15s and Kfirs provided top cover for other IDF/AF aircraft carrying out an attack on terrorist bases near Sidon in southern Lebanon. A number of Syrian MiG-21s attempted to intercept the attacking force, but Israeli Hawkeye AWACS detected this flight and directed the top cover against them. In the ensuing battle, five MiGs were shot down (one by a Kfir), without loss.

An IDF/AF KC-707 tanker carries out in-flight refuelling on three F-15I Ra'ams during Israeli Independence Day celebrations in April 1998.

On 24 September 1979, Eagles shot down five Syrian fighters and on 27 June 1980 at least one more. In may 1982, two Syrian MiG-23s were claimed. On 7 June 1981, Eagles equipped with FAST packs flew a 1,000-mile (1610-km) mission to rpovide top cover for F-16 attacks on Iraq's Osirak nuclear reactor. To date, the most successful deployment of F-15s occurred during Operation Peace for Galilee, the Israeli invasion of Lebanon in June 1982. Israeli aircraft succeeded in destroying no less than 92 Syrian fighters during operations between 5-12 June over the Beka'a Valley, and F-15s were responsible for a large proportion of these victories, including three high-flying MiG-25s destroyed with 'snap-up' AIM-7 intercepts. Unconfirmed reports suggest that Israeli F-15Ds participated in a raid against PLO headquarters in Tunis on 1 October 1985.

Following Desert Storm, Israel received a batch of early production block F-15As from the USAF that were not scheduled for the MSIP (Multi-Stage Improvement Program). These deliveries supposedly took place as a reciprocal exchange for Israel's decision not to retaliate against Iraqi 'Scud' launches during the Gulf War. No Israeli F-15s have been lost in combat, but at least three have been lost in training accidents.

On 27 January 1994, the Israeli government announced

***Bearing the markings of the 601 Flight Test Centre unit, this F-15I was delivered to Israel on 14 September 1999 after a time with AFFTC at Edwards AFB. It carries the standard three-tone IDF/AF attack scheme.***

***Above:** The F-15I serves with No. 69 'Hammer' Sqn at Hatzerim. Outwardly similar to the late production F-15E, the F-15I features certain Israeli-built components, including the EW suite.*

***Below:** This Tel Nof-based No. 106 Sqn F-15C Akef wears six Syrian 'MiG kills'. The IDF/AF's F-15 fighter force maintains a high-alert status in order to ensure the nation's air defence.*

that they intended to purchase the F-15I. A contract was signed on 12 May 1994 and deliveries began under the Peace Sun V/VI programme in January 1998. In order to ensure a night-fighting capability, the F-15Is were fitted with some of the 30 Sharpshooter targeting pods intended for Israel's F-16 fleet, prior to Israel buying new LANTIRN pods, completing the F-15I night vision suite.

Known as Ra'am (thunder) in Israel, the F-15I incorporates new and unique weapons, avionics, electronic warfare, and communications capabilities that make it one of the most advanced Eagle variants. The F-15I, like the US Air Force's F-15E, is a dual-role fighter that combines long-range interdiction with the Eagle's air superiority capabilities. All the aircraft are configured with F100-PW-229 engines by direct commercial sale; NVG compatible cockpits; an Elbit display and sight helmet (DASH) system; conformal fuel tanks; and the capability to employ a variety of air-to-surface munitions. Israeli ordnance can also carried by the Ra'am, including the Python 4 AAM.

F-15 production, which began in 1972, was extended into 1999 by the F-15I orders. On 22 September 1998 the US Department of Defense announced the sale to the Government of Israel of 30 F-15I aircraft, although only 25 have been received; 30 AN/APG-70 or AN/APG-63(V)1 radars; and 30 each LANTIRN navigation and targeting pods. Associated support equipment, software development/integration, spares, flight test instrumentation, training and other requirements to ensure full programme supportability will also be provided at an estimated cost of $2.5 billion.

## F-15C Akef

**This F-15C Akef (buzzard) wears the markings of Israel's No. 106 Squadron, based at Tel Nof, and carries four victory markings claimed during Operation Peace for Galilee. The nicknamer *Skyblazer* is carried on the nose in Hebrew. Like the F-15A/B, the F-15C/D models carry locally-produced EW equipment. IDF/AF F-15s are claimed to have achieved a kill tally of at least 57 without loss.**

### Internal armament

The F-15 is fitted with a single 20-mm M61A1 Vulcan six-barrelled cannon in the starboard wingroot, and carries 940 rounds of ammunition in a drum in the centre of the fuselage.

### Missile armament

Israeli F-15s can carry the same mix of AIM-9L/M Sidewinder and AIM-7M Sparrow AAMs as their USAF counterparts, but can also carry the highly-agile indigenous Python 3 IR-homing missiles, shown here, or the latest Python 4.

### Powerplant

The F-15C is powered by a pair of Pratt & Whitney F100-PW-100 turbofans, each rated at 25,000 lb st (111.2 kN) with afterburning.

### Radar

Although the Eagle is extremely fast and remarkably agile, at the heart of its success is a superb weapon system, built around the Hughes AN/APG-63 I/J-band pulse-Doppler radar.

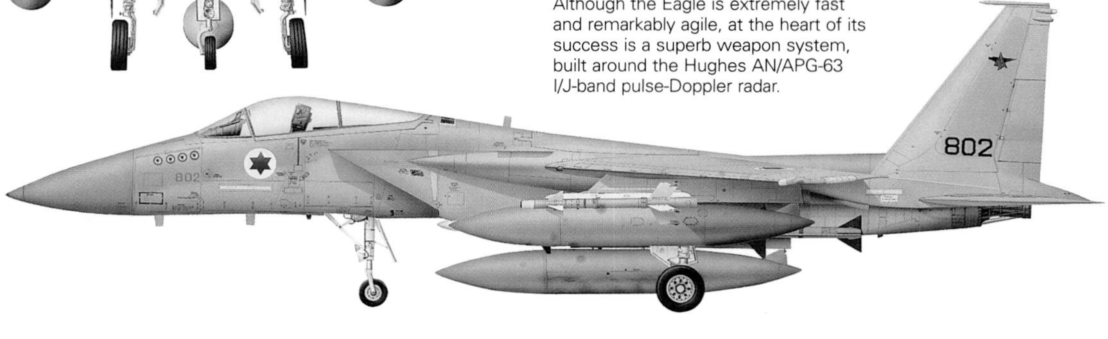

Carrying a set of three 610-US gal (2309-litre) drop tanks, F-15J 72-8882 gives a spirited display at Hamamatsu AB.

# JASDF Eagles

**Eight of the JASDF's interceptor squadrons continue to operate the Mitsubishi-built F-15J/DJ and most are likely to do so for the foreseeable future. One hundred surviving aircraft are about to undergo a major mid-life upgrade which will bring the aircraft close to F-15C MSIP-II standard from 2004. New engines, an upgraded radar and central computer and a new, indigenously-developed AAM (AAM-4) are key elements.**

*Above: Like most Eagles worldwide, the **JASDF**'s F-15s are armed primarily with AIM-9 and AIM-7 AAMs. This late-production F-15J carries a single **S**idewinder on its port inner shoulder pylon.*

*Based at Hyakuri AB and Chitose AB, respectively, Dai Hiko-tai 204 (above) and Dai Hiko-tai 201 (below) are two of the eight F-15 units split between three air defence force regions.*

*Its air brake deployed in typical fashion, an F-15J of Dai 203 Hiko-tai touches down. This unit was the first operational squadron to convert to the F-15; the first four units to convert to the Eagle had all previously flown the F-104 Starfighter.*

***Left:** The F-15 partially equips the Hiko Kyodo-tai – Japan's 'aggressor' training squadron – stationed at Nyutabaru AB. The unit is allocated seven F-15DJs and two T-4s, and provides air combat training for JASDF fighter squadrons. The F-15DJs of this unit wear a distinctive camouflage finish.*

***Below:** The first F-15DJ was delivered in 1981 and the last in the mid-1990s. 82-8065 is one of four built in 1988 and is seen in 'aggressor' camouflage.*

***Below:** A handful of two-seat F-15DJs serve alongside the F-15Js with each squadron. This aircraft wears the dragon's head badge of Dai 303 Hiko-tai, based at Komatsu AB. The aircraft is carrying a prototype of Japan's new ASM-2 (Type 93) air-to-surface missile.*

### Dai 203 Hiko-tai

Dai 203 Hiko-tai was formed at Chitose AB as the third F-104 squadron on 25 June 1964. Conversion to the F-15J/DJ was finished on 13 April 1983 and the unit became the JASDF's second F-15 squadron. In 2000, Dai 203 Hiko-tai was the only squadron to operate its aircraft entirely from hardened aircraft shelters.

### Powerplant

As built the JASDF's Eagles are powered by a pair of Pratt & Whitney F100-PW-100 turbofans. These will be replaced by a pair of F100-IHI-220Es (licence-built F100-PW-220s) as part of the F-15J MLU.

### ECM

Among the indigenous equipment fitted to the Japanese Eagles is the J/ALQ-8 ECM suite and the XJ/APQ-1 radar warning system.

## F-15J Eagle

**F-15J 72-8898 carries the tail markings of Dai 203 Hiko-tai, the first front-line Japan Air Self Defense Force unit to achieve operational status, in 1983. It was preceded by Dai 202 Hiko-tai, the Eagle OCU.**

### Unit markings

The unit's bear (panda) badge has two red stars (for 2 Koku-dan) and stylised lightning bolts on either side of the aircraft that echo the '2' and '3' of the squadron designation.

### Camouflage

Japanese F-15s wear this standard camouflage consisting of two tones of grey. National insignia and squadron badges are carried in full colour and are often elaborate.

# Desert Eagles

*The arrival of the F-15 and the replacement of the Lightning in the interceptor role dramatically improved the Saudi ability to defend its own airspace, a fact illustrated in 1984 when two Iranian Phantoms were shot down.*

**In an effort to maintain Middle East peace, the US elected to supply F-15s to Saudi Arabia following sales to Israel. Considerable restrictions were placed on the force, which were only lifted when the invasion of Kuwait revealed the vulnerability of the world's largest oil-producing nation.**

During the 1970s and 1980s, US arms sales to Saudi Arabia were controversial - because of the tense situation between the Arab nation and Israel - and the equipping of the RSAF (Royal Saudi Air Force) with F-15 Eagles became an especially contentious domestic American issue.

Riyadh initially ordered 62 airframes, consisting of 47 F-15Cs and 15 F-15Ds, under Project Peace Sun as a replacement for the Lightning fighter. Delivery consisted of 46 F-15Cs (80-0062/0106 and 81-0002) and 16 F-15Ds (80-0107/0121 and 81-0003). The total of 62 includes two attrition replacements, since the US imposed a limit (in 1980) of 60 Eagles which could be 'on board' in Saudi Arabia at any given time.

## F-15 build-up

The RSAF began receiving its first F-15C/D aircraft in January 1981 and apparently reached IOC (initial operating capability) in August 1981. Early aircraft were temporarily dispatched to the 555th TFTS at Luke AFB for training purposes. Original Saudi units were: No. 5 Squadron at Taif, No. 6 Squadron at Khamis Mushait and No. 13 Squadron at Dhahran.

The controversial sale of this modern fighter aircraft was eased by Saudi assurance that the Eagles would be used solely in the air defence role. Still restrictions were imposed which at first prevented delivery of CFT (conformal fuel tanks) to the RSAF, and because of political sensibilities a 1989 request for 12 more attrition replacement F-15C/D Eagles was not accommodated.

During a period of border tensions, two Saudi F-15Cs shot down two Iranian F-4E Phantom IIs over the Persian Gulf on 5 June 1984. It was possibly the first time one McDonnell Douglas product had scored an aerial victory over another.

When Saddam Hussein's forces invaded Kuwait on 2 August 1990 and immediately threatened the rich oilfields of Saudi Arabia, the F-15 Eagles and Tornado ADVs of the RSAF were on full alert as the primary counter to any further Iraqi ambitions. Soon joined by USAF F-15s and RAF Tornado F.Mk 3s, the three forces pooled their resources at the base at Dhahran to provide continuous combat air patrols to protect Saudi airspace, a task which continued throughout the entire Desert Shield/Storm period.

The Iraqi invasion of Kuwait had altered the Middle East equation and dramatised Saudi Arabia's status as a nation comparatively weak in military terms, with fewer than 60,000 personnel under arms. The constraint limit of 60 aircraft 'in country' was therefore dropped. Twenty four F-15C/D Eagles were rushed to the Saudis from US Air Force stocks in Europe in September-October 1990. During Desert Shield and Desert Storm, Saudi F-15C Eagles shared combat air patrol duties with British Tornado F.Mk 3s and American F-15Cs. The aircraft supplied from USAFE units were easily identified during Desert Storm by the fact that their nose titles were hastily applied, using stencilling in place of the smarter lettering of the original Saudi machines.

*These 13 Sqn F-15s carry AIM-9P Sidewinders. During Desert Shield the unit shared its facilities with USAF F-15s of the 1st TFW.*

These multi-national CAPs made few engagements. On one occasion however, Captain Ayehid Salah al-Shamrani of RSAF's No. 13 Squadron was vectored onto two Mirage F1EQs by a Saudi E-3 AWACS. The intruders were believed to have been attempting an Exocet launch against coalition shipping in the Persian Gulf. Captain Al-Shamrani shot down both aircraft. For Saudi fighter pilots however, this proved to be the war's shining moment.

In mid-1991, McDonnell began filling an order for 12 more F-15s which had been ordered by Saudi Arabia before the Gulf War under a $333.5-million FMS (Foreign Military Sales) contract by delivering the first two machines in this dozen (nine F-15C, three F-15D). On 12-August 1991, McDonnell formally received the FMS for this purchase under the Peace Sun VI programme. The aircraft were to

***Left: Saudi Arabia received the F-15S, an export version of the F-15E lacking some air-to-air and air-to-ground capabilities. The request for 72 aircraft was approved in late 1992.***

***Below: Saudi Eagle pilot Capt Al-Shamrani employed two AIM-9s to claim a brace of Iraqi Mirage F1s on 24 January 1991. Many Saudi Eagle missions during Desert Storm were supported by USAF KC-135s and KC-10s as well as RSAF KE-3A tankers.***

be delivered at the rate of two per month by February 1992. The first two were delivered by mid-August.

With the USAF Strike Eagle programme coming to an end, the McDonnell Douglas marketing team was looking everywhere for ways to keep the F-15 production line 'warm' into the 21st century. Fortunately, the Strike Eagle's performance in Desert Storm made it an automatic choice for several nations that had been most involved in that conflict. In late 1991, the RSAF began to consider a buy of 24 modified F-15Es, which would have been equipped with only one seat. The F-15F would have had many of the F-15E features, including the common engine bay, F100-PW-229 engines, and the ability to carry LANTIRN pods if desired. However, the US Congress rejected any attempt to sell the aircraft. In its place came the F-15H, a downgraded two-seat F-15E. This, too, was vetoed, being replaced by a third proposal known initially as F-15XP (export). This variant was finally given the Congressional go-ahead on 10 May 1993, and emerged as hardware in the form of the F-15S Eagle.

### Saudi 'Strike Eagles'

Following the F-15F sales effort, an industry rumour surfaced that the RSAF wanted 72 additional Eagles, although the type and purpose was unspecified. Eventually, the order crystallised for the F-15S. Originally, it was intended that the 72 aircraft of the RSAF buy would not have all the capabilities of the domestic F-15E. Once again, the power of the Israeli lobby in Congress came to bear, and the low-level TFR capabilities of the LANTIRN navigation pod were to be deleted so that the low-level penetration capabilities of the aircraft would be lessened. However, when word got out that the Israelis themselves were planning to procure a batch of Strike Eagles, the Departments of Defense and State decided to sell RSAF the new aircraft, designated F-15S, with only slightly downgraded equipment. Some modes of the AN/APG-70 are down-tuned while, as with all export Eagles, nuclear weapon wiring is deleted and certain sensitive ECM systems are replaced with older equipment, or deleted altogether. Other systems which had originally been the subject of debate, such as CFTs and tangential stores carriage, were supplied. The aircraft are powered by the latest F100-PW-229 IPE engines.

The Saudi Eagles are essentially stock F-15E airframes, the first of which flew on 19 June 1995. The first was officially handed over at a ceremony at St Louis on 12 September. A first pair were delivered to Saudi Arabia in November 1995, and the final two aircraft were received in July 2000. Twenty-four are optimised for the air-to-air role, with the remainder assigned a dual-role F-15E-style tasking. Combined with the purchase of the AGM-65D/G Maverick, AIM-9M/S Sidewinder, CBU-87 submunitions dispenser and GBU-10/12 laser-guided bomb, the Saudi F-15S fleet is expected to hold a set of targets at risk that includes everything from traditional targets in Iraq to possible nuclear threats and terrorist installations in Iran and Yemen.

## F-15D Eagle

**Two-seat capability**
The dual control F-15C retains full combat capability, although the rear seat replaces the Internal Countermeasures Set (ICS) and necessitates the carriage of an external AN/ALQ-131 ECM pod.

**Weapons**
Saudi F-15C/Ds were originally supplied with AIM-9P Sidewinders, as shown here, but the all-aspect AIM-9L/M series became available later in the aircraft's career. Four AIM-7Ms are also carried for longer-range work.

**Early Saudi service**
The Royal Saudi Air Force initially formed four F-15C/D squadrons, No. 5 at King Fahd AB, Taif and No. 6 at Khamis Mushait/King Khalid AB, both in the south west, close to the Red Sea; No. 13 at Dhahran/King Abdullah Aziz AB (illustrated) on the Persian Gulf coast, close to Iran and Iraq, and No. 42. This latter squadron was hastily formed at Dhahran in 1990 to operate the Eagles supplied directly from the 32nd TFS and 36th TFW in Europe.

***Always a great fighter, the YF-17 lost in the USAF's ACF competition. Its potential was realised by McDonnell Douglas, however, which transformed the machine into the F/A-18.***

# Birth of the Hornet

**Having lost to the YF-16 in the USAF's Air Combat Fighter fly-off, the YF-17 was developed into the potent F/A-18 Hornet following a controversial period of gestation. Today, the F/A-18 competes for export orders against its old rival.**

***Left: The F-18's maiden flight was on 18 November 1978. Nine single-seat and two two-seat aircraft were involved in the flight test programme.***

Today's F/A-18 Hornet owes its origin to Northrop, which in the 1950s and 1960s excelled in the lightweight fighter (LWF) business. The P-530 Cobra of 1966 was the best-known of these LWFs. A few USAF veterans of combat against the light and simple MiG-17 believed in a Cobra-like machine, but the USAF had no requirement for it and decided in 1969 to buy the costly F-15 Eagle.

In the late 1960s Northrop designers revised and redesigned the Cobra. They kept it simple but introduced new features such as a HOTAS (hands on throttle and stick) cockpit, which enabled the fighter pilot to keep his eyes up, out of the cockpit.

By 1971, the future of the F-15 was secure and supporters of the LWF finally managed to persuade Congress to fund an LWF technology demonstration programme with flying prototypes from two manufacturers. On 13 April 1972 Northrop and General Dynamics were awarded contracts to build two prototypes. Fourteen days later, the US Secretary of Defense dropped a bombshell, announcing that he felt it "appropriate to consider full-scale development and eventual production of an Air Combat Fighter" which would provide an alternative to "high-cost tactical aircraft while maintaining a credible tactical air force". This effectively turned the Northrop and General Dynamics aircraft into competing prototypes of a new USAF Air Combat Fighter (ACF) and caused a storm of controversy. While the LWF was an experimental machine it was welcomed by the USAF, but as a production aircraft it could only threaten the future production of the all-important F-15 Eagle. Objections were overruled and the LWF evaluation became the ACF competition.

## Fighter prototypes

Flown for the first time on 9 June 1974 Northrop's fighter was the YF-17, the end result of the Cobra studies. It had the competitive disadvantage of being powered by unproven engines, two new General Electric J101 'leaky turbojet', or shallow bypass, engines. The stakes were huge. The winning aircraft in the General Dynamics YF-16/Northrop YF-17 contest could remain in production beyond the end of the century, serving the USAF and replacing the F-104 Starfighter in NATO air forces.

On 13 January 1975, after months of head-to-head competition, the YF-16 was declared the winner. The decision stunned Northrop. Although a superb fighter, the YF-17 seemed to be dead. One last, outside chance was to sell the aircraft to the US Navy, which had been directed to make the maximum use of USAF-LWF/ACF technology for its own lightweight fighter. Recognising that it would have to buy a low-cost complement to the F-14, the US Navy looked to the ACF competition and the YF-17. Although the aircraft was not

***Below: With its hook deployed, the third pre-production Hornet is about to 'trap a wire' during carrier qualification aboard USS** America **in early 1982.***

***Left:* Climatic tests were undertaken at the McKinley Climatic Laboratory, Eglin AFB. Such laboratory simulations reduced the need for expensive and time consuming overseas climatic tests.**

***Below:* The Hornet was developed from Northrop's YF-17. Compared to the YF-17 the Hornet has a larger wing, a redesigned radar-carrying nose, an improved powerplant and carrier compatibility.**

designed for carrier operations, the result was a foregone conclusion. Navy pilots who flew the YF-17 (or against it) during the ACF evaluation preferred the Northrop aircraft, which seemed to have greater potential for development into a radar-equipped multi-role aircraft which could replace the A-7 Corsair II and the F-4 Phantom II. Perhaps, above all it was twin-engined, with all the flight safety advantages which that entailed. Northrop had the right aircraft, but not the experience or the expertise, and accepted an offer from McDonnell Douglas to collaborate on a naval YF-17. Teamed together, Northrop and McDonnell Douglas outbid General Dynamics and LTV, who wanted the Navy to acquire a carrier-based version of the F-16. Overnight, a new designation came into use. The new aircraft was the McDonnell Douglas F/A-18 Hornet.

### Hornet takes shape

Northrop and McDonnell Douglas agreed that the latter would market the F-18 Hornet to the Navy (with Northrop as prime subcontractor, with major responsibility for building sub-assemblies). At the same time, Northrop would sell a land-based version of the Hornet, known as the F-18L.

Although it retained the aerodynamic shape of the YF-17 including its twin tails, the F-18 was in most respects an entirely new aircraft. Changes included the addition of 50 sq ft (4.65 $m^2$) of wing area (from 350 to 400 sq ft/32.5 to 37.2 $m^2$), with increases in both span and chord to improve performance in the low-speed regime of an aircraft-carrier pattern.

The aft fuselage width was increased by 4 inches (10 cm) and the engines were canted outward at the front in order to create more internal space for fuel - addressing the need for greater range, which had been a problem in the YF-16/YF-17 contest and was to remain a problem for the new aircraft. In addition, the Hornet required an enlarged nose shape for the 28-inch (71-cm) radar dish needed to meet the Navy's weapons system search range requirement of more than 30 nm (34½ miles, 55.6 km). The change in nose shape brought the biggest change in appearance of the F-18 from the YF-17.

Power for the F-18 Hornet was to be provided by an improved version of the General Electric J101/F101, designated F404-GE-400. Although the powerplant was unproven, it produced 16,000 lb (71.2 kN) of thrust. As development continued, the USN soon revealed plans to acquire some 780 Hornets in A-18 attack and F-18 fighter configurations.

***Above:* Inflight refuelling allows the Navy to extend the reach of strike packages using carrier-based tankers. This facility was particularly important for the short-ranged F/A-18. The number one Hornet was used for inflight-refuelling trials with a KA-3B Skywarrior during the early 1980s while both aircraft were assigned to the Naval Air Test Centre.**

***Right:* VFA-113 'Stingers' was the first US Navy squadron to re-equip with the F/A-18. This 1984 picture shows the toned down markings and overall grey camouflage of the service aircraft. This aircraft is seen dropping a pair of 500-lb (227-kg) Mk 82 general-purpose bombs on a training mission, having launched from the deck of USS Constellation.**

# Hornet matures

*Although the compatibility of the Hornet with carrier operations was by no means certain, the F/A-18 quickly proved itself to be an ideal naval aircraft.*

**With the US Navy and Marine Corps committed to the Hornet programme, development continued in the face of increasing acrimony between the principal contractors, McDonnell Douglas and Northrop.**

On 18 November 1978, McDonnell Douglas test pilot Jack Krings completed the first flight of the F-18 Hornet. Krings put the new fighter through exhaustive manoeuvres and found the F-18 to be remarkably stable and easy to handle. Full flight tests began in January 1979 at the Naval Air Test Center (NATC), Patuxent River, Maryland.

Some nine F-18A single-seat and two TF-18A two-seat Hornet prototypes (the latter in due course redesignated F-18B) entered an intense flight test programme. Rather than scatter the flying prototypes at locations near manufacturers of major systems (engines, avionics, airframe) where tests on separate tracks might be conducted, the Hornet was put through its trials under a new Principal Site Concept which stationed all the aircraft in one place, with the US Navy in charge of flying.

*Hornet No. 5 performed many of the early missile-firing trials. Here, the aircraft is seen having just launched an AIM-7 Sparrow. Such was No. 5's capability that it had soon acquired 12 target drone 'kill' markings below its cockpit.*

*Above: Offering exceptional visibility and supreme agility, the F/A-18 has matured into an excellent fighter and attack aircraft. It was the first fast jet to introduce a glass cockpit into regular service.*

Despite experience acquired on the YF-17, the F-18 Hornet encountered difficulties in flight testing which needed to be remedied. A too-high nosewheel lift-off speed was corrected by filling in the dogtooth in the horizontal stabiliser which gave the stabiliser greater authority at a lower speed, and by toeing in the rudder on take-off. Problems with the flight control software that controlled the leading-edge flaps also had to be solved through internal changes, although problems with the flaps were to recur and later cause a NASA aircraft to be lost. It was also observed that cockpit and avionics bay cooling was using too much fuel, diminishing the F-18's already marginal range.

## Hornet carquals

Carrier qualification (carqual) trials were carried out from 30 October-3 November 1979, with the third prototype operating from USS *America* (CV-66) in the Atlantic.

Having evolved from a purely land-based design, there was always the chance that the F-18 might not prove suitable for

***Left: Representing a new and unusual shape on the US Navy's carrier decks, the F/A-18 revolutionised operations with its complex avionics and dual-role capability.***

***Below: In the face of competition from the F-16 and with Northrop's F-18L a dead project, McDonnell Douglas won an order from Spain for 72 Hornets on 31 May 1983.***

carrier operations. In fact, two US Navy test pilots made 17 touch-and-go landings and 32 catapult-take-offs and arrested landings, and flew the aircraft in a carrier environment on eight flights over 14 flying hours. There was not a single hitch.

## The VFA is born

With tests showing that the F-18 was sturdy and versatile enough to carry out both fighter and attack roles, the US Navy abandoned its plans for separate F-18s and A-18s. In order to accommodate this change within its squadrons, the USN introduced a new type of unit, the strike squadron (VFA), sometimes loosely called a fighter attack squadron, which would be equipped with dual-role F/A-18s. To illustrate the F/A-18'sverstility, the aircraft replaced both F-4 fighters and A-7 attackers on 'Midway'-class carriers, which were too small to take Tomcats.

Its range aside, the F-18 seemed to be the hottest thing in the air. It was therefore a cause for concern that costs were rising during the period 1979-81, and Congress was looking at the programme with concern. The Navy/Marine 'buy' was now up to 1,366 aircraft and the F-18, spawned by a supposedly inexpensive, lightweight fighter, was now reaching the point where it cost almost as much as the sophisticated and expensive Grumman F-14 Tomcat.

With accusations of cost overruns flying about, this was a poor time for relations between Northrop and McDonnell Douglas to deteriorate. Under the terms of the agreement, Northrop was to receive 30 per cent of the development work and 40 per cent of any production work for the carrier-based F-18. When foreign purchasers seemed interested in the F-18, McDonnell Douglas mounted a sales effort, putting the carrier-based aircraft in direct competition with Northrop's land-based F-18L.

In a series of lawsuits launched during October 1979, Northrop argued that McDonnell Douglas was unfairly using the Northrop technology of the F-18L to sell its own F-18 abroad. Northrop also charged that McDonnell Douglas was endeavouring to sell Israel a version of the F-18 which competed directly with its own F-18L. Finally, Northrop requested – among other things, in a complex legal case – that McDonnell Douglas be constrained from offering to sell to or produce for any foreign government any version of the F-18 which took advantage of Northrop technology to the detriment of the latter company.

Nevertheless, in May 1980, a production F-18 Hornet was delivered to the Pacific Fleet's Fleet Replacement Squadron (FRS), the 'Rough Riders' of VFA-125 at NAS Lemoore, California. An FRS is the replacement training unit that prepares pilots to operate a particular aircraft type in the fleet. Reflecting the purchase of the Hornet by both the Navy and Marine Corps, the first machine had 'NAVY' painted on one side and 'MARINES' on the other. VFA-125 had a Navy commander and Marine Corps executive officer.

The hottest jet in the sky was now going operational – everybody was celebrating, but the critics were circling like vultures, ready to point out any failing. And the two companies that had brought the McDonnell Douglas F/A-18 Hornet into being were at each other's throats.

***Above: Destined to replace both the F-4 and A-7 in US Navy and Marine Corps squadrons, the F/A-18A soon began to enter regular service. VFA-125 (aircraft 1from this unit illustrated) was the first unit to be declared operational with the type on 13 November 1980.***

***Left: Originally designated TF-18A, then F-18B, the original two-seat Hornet model eventually became known by the designation F/A-18B. This example shows the robust undercarriage necessary for high-sink carrier landings.***

***The 'Black Knights' of VMFA-314 was the first front-line Hornet unit, and took the aircraft into action against Libyan targets in 1986, flying from USS* Coral Sea. *An F/A-18A from VMFA-314 displays the type's responsiveness, despite a load of eight 500-lb (226-kg) bombs.***

# F/A-18A/B

**Early F/A-18s were eagerly received into service and soon managed to chalk up several export orders, although they were besieged by a number of problems. A and B models still serve with Australia, Spain and the USMC, among others, despite the fact that the more potent C variant is now in service.**

McDonnell Douglas and Northrop were announced as winners of the US Navy's NACF (Navy Air Combat Fighter) programme in May 1975, and the first F/A-18 flew in November 1978. It was a new aircraft, sharing only its general layout with the YF-17. Compared with its predecessor, it was larger and more powerful, incorporating the stronger structure and landing gear that were necessary for carrier operations.

In many respects, the F/A-18 was technologically more advanced than its great rival, the F-16A. Its 'fly-by-wire' flight control system used digital rather than analog processors, and it used more composite materials (in the wing skins, for example). It had a multi-mode radar and a cockpit which used cathode-ray tube (CRT) displays in place of conventional dial-and-pointer instruments. It was designed from the ground up to accept pods for electro-optical navigation and targeting aids, and the AIM-7 medium-range air-to-air missile – none of these could be carried on the F-16. McDonnell Douglas touted the new fighter as a true multi-role type, as opposed to the simpler F-16A.

Canada and Australia, both with large fleets of older supersonic fighters, were persuaded by these arguments and selected the F/A-18A over the F-16 before the new fighter had finished its flight tests. One of the F/A-18's rivals was Northrop's land-based F-18L, similar in size to the F/A-18, but with an almost completely redesigned structure. Unfortunately for Northrop, the export customers found that the lower risks of the F/A-18A, already in full-scale development for the US Navy, outweighed the higher performance promised by the Northrop design.

## Advantages

Canada, with its large expanses of Arctic terrain, and Australia, with its overwater interception mission and the need to overfly the Australian interior (known to pilots as the GAFA, or the Great Australian ****-All), assigned some value to the F-18's twin engines. In fact, the new fighter's General Electric F404 was proving to be trouble-free, in sharp contrast to the F-16's F100 engine.

The F/A-18's new-technology cockpit was also widely acclaimed, and its radar and weapons integration drew no criticism. This was just as well, because other important attributes of the new aircraft were attracting sharp criticism.

During development, the F/A-18 underwent some major changes. Dog-teeth disappeared from the wing and stabiliser leading edges. The wing itself was reinforced and the lateral controls were revised, because the long, thin wing proved insufficiently stiff – leading to a severe shortfall in roll rate. Long slots in the LERXes were sealed along most of their length, to reduce drag.

Even these measures, however, barely touched the basic problem. The F/A-18 was failing, by a large measure, to meet its warload and radius specifications. Both of the aircraft which it was supposed to replace (the F-4 and A-7) could carry larger loads over a greater distance. Weight and drag increases also meant that the F/A-18 was limited in its 'bring-back' capability. With normal fuel reserves, the new fighter could not land aboard a carrier at an acceptable approach speed with more than a minimal ordnance load.

In 1982, US Navy test squadron VX-5 recommended that the F/A-18 programme be suspended until some way of alleviating the range shortfall could be found. Among other measures, McDonnell Douglas proposed a thicker wing and an enlarged dorsal spine, which would have improved the aircraft's range at the expense of transonic acceleration and speed.

The US Navy, however, rejected these suggestions and overrode VX-5's recommendations. By that time, the service had other priorities, including the development of modernised

***Spain initially acquired 72 F/A-18A/Bs from the St Louis production line and then augmented its force with 24 ex-US Navy Hornets. They have since been upgraded to near F/A-18C status.***

***The US Navy's* Blue Angels *display team operates eight F/A-18As, from which the six-ship team is drawn. A two-seater F/A-18B is also kept on strength for training and 'media orientation' flights.***

*Left: F/A-18As and Bs still have a part to play in US Navy aggressor units. Examples serving with VFC-12 'Omars' are used to represent aircraft such as the MiG-29 or Su-27.*

*Above: Canada was the first and largest customer for the Hornet. In Canadian service, the CF-188 is a true multi-role fighter, employed on a 50/50 basis for air defence and ground attack. The Canadians also pioneered the use of 'fake' cockpits on the underside of their Hornets, with the intention of disorientating an opponent in ACM.*

versions of the A-6 and F-14, and the definition of a long-range, 'stealthy' bomber to carry the war to the Soviet navy's land bases. All these aircraft were expensive, however, and would not be built soon, or in large quantities. Meanwhile, the USN's carrier fleet was expanding, and ageing F-4s and A-7s, dating back to the Vietnam War, had to be replaced. Cancelling or delaying the F/A-18 would leave the US Navy short of modern aircraft, so the USN decided to put the aircraft into production without attempting to solve the range problem.

### Two-seat Hornet

Basically identical to the F/A-18A, the two-seat F/A-18B was developed alongside the single-seater. In consequence, two examples of the TF-18A (initial designation, later replaced by F/A-18B) featured in the original contract which covered the procurement of a batch of 11 prototype aircraft for RDT&E tasks. The provision of a second seat in tandem was accomplished at a modest six per cent penalty in fuel capacity. Otherwise, the F/A-18B was unaltered, possessing identical equipment and near-identical combat capability.

Subsequent procurement of the F/A-18B for service with US Navy and Marine Corps units ended with the 40th production example, and this version has never been employed by front-line forces. Apart from a few examples assigned to test agencies, the F/A-18B serves only with VFA-106.

### The end of the F/A-18A

The F/A-18A garnered a total of three export customers – Canada, Australia and Spain. They were in a rather better situation than the US Navy, because the limitations on the Hornet's range and bring-back capability could be alleviated when it was operated from land bases. Canada, for instance, developed a 480-US gal (1800-litre) external tank to supplement the 330-US gal (1250-litre) tanks used by the US Navy. The US Navy did not adopt this external tank because it would not fit on the centreline. In spite of moves to solve the F/A-18's problems, such as that stated above, the aircraft's deficiencies, combined with the arrival of the F-16C/D, ushered in a long sales drought.

Pilots were – as always – enthusiastic about the F/A-18A/B when it entered service in 1983. However, historical fact tells a different story. Some 410 of this initial version were built until production switched to the F/A-18C/D in 1987. By 1995, the US Navy had retired most of the A/B models from carrier-based service, the shortest first-line career of any modern fighter. Apart from a small 'top-up' batch of aircraft delivered to Spain from USN stocks in 1995, there are no plans at present to offer these aircraft for export, or to upgrade them – unlike the older and more austere F-16A/B.

The fact was that VX-5 had been right. The F/A-18A/B was a somewhat inadequate aircraft, which validated the adage 'jack of all trades, master of none' in its full and not altogether complimentary sense. It took a series of upgrades to produce a Hornet variant which could be called the master of most of its many missions. This process started with the first F/A-18C/D, delivered from September 1987. Basically designed to accommodate new technologies and weapons, the first F/A-18C/Ds have formed the basis for a series of Hornets whose exterior resemblance to the original A/B is entirely deceptive.

*Above: All of Australia's Hornet squadrons were former Mirage III operators. No. 77 Squadron re-formed on 1 July 1987, receiving its first aircraft shortly afterwards. The unit is primarily responsible for the development of air-to-ground tactics and techniques.*

*Right: USMC Hornets have been subject to worldwide defence cuts, and F/A-18A-equipped VMFA-451 'Warlords' was deactivated in 1998.*

***The F/A-18C represented a major addition to the US Navy's strike force. The Hornet was considered so important by the Navy that its tactics were changed to accommodate the aircraft's somewhat limited range.***

# F/A-18C/D

**Despite early teething troubles, the F/A-18 has evolved into the C/D models which, with their new avionics and weapons, far surpass their predecessor.**

When the F/A-18A/B entered service in 1983, it proved popular with pilots and its appearance was generally greeted enthusiastically. However, when one looks at the historical facts, a different perspective emerges. Some 410 of the original version of the Hornet were built until production switched to the F/A-18C/D in 1987. By 1995, the US Navy had retired most of its A/B models from carrier-based service, the shortest first-line career of any modern fighter. The fact had been that the Hornet was a somewhat inadequate aircraft which validated the old adage "Jack of all trades, master of none". It took a number of steps to produce a Hornet variant that could be called the master of most of its missions. This process started when the first of the F/A-18C/Ds were delivered from September 1987. Designed to accommodate new technologies and weapons, the first F/A-18C/Ds formed the basis of a series of Hornets whose exterior resemblance to the original A/B was entirely deceptive.

## Airframe development

The F/A-18C/D airframe is not very different to that of the A/B, and has not changed significantly since it entered production. The reason was not so much that the original design was perfect, as that it had run into a hard limit on its growth.

The F/A-18 had been designed for an approach speed of 125 kt (143 mph; 231 km/h), but development problems raised this to 134 kt (155 mph; 250 km/h), a respectable speed for a land-based fighter but a little high for a carrier-based aircraft. This in turn set a cap on the Hornet's maximum landing weight which, coupled with the fact that the navy requires its carrier-borne aircraft to retain large fuel reserves for landings, meant that the Hornet could not undergo major airframe modifications without sacrificing the number of weapons carried or reducing the already limited range of its operations. In fact, the only visible outboard changes to the Hornet have been the addition of antennas and a pair of strakes or 'billboards' above the LERX. These help to break up vortices at angles of attack above 45°. These strakes have been retrofitted to most Hornets.

## 'Stealthy' Hornet

One significant change, though far from visible, is the addition of 'stealthy' materials to the Hornet. During the 1970s and 1980s, new types of RAM (radar-absorbent material) were developed which were lighter and more durable than their predecessors. As a result, both the navy and air force initiated programmes to reduce the RCS (radar cross-section) of their aircraft. Under the 'Glass Hornet' programme, F/A-18s were given a gold-tinted canopy, coated with a thin layer of indium-tin oxide (ITO) in order to reflect radar signals away from the transmitter. RAM paint on the engines and engine inlets also helped to absorb radar signals. However, the price of this 'stealthiness' was a weight gain of 250 lb (113 kg) which further reduced the Hornet's bring-back load.

## Engine development

Although the Hornet has changed little externally, one significant development has been the changes to the F/A-18's engines. General Electric's F404 had been free from handling limits and, by 1988, the basic F404-GE-400 engine had accu-

***Above: The C/D-model Hornets stole back orders from the F-16 on account of their proven ability and sophistication. Meanwhile, the F-14 has been steadily edged off the carrier decks by US Navy Hornets.***

***Left: One of the first of 64 Finnish F-18s lands at Pirkkala Airport in Tampere, Finland after its non-stop journey from the McDonnell Douglas St Louis facility. Valmet was granted a licence to manufacture the Hornet and built all but the first eight F-18Ds. They will have a range of Finnish equipment, including instruments with metric calibration.***

***The F/A-18 has four fuselage fuel tanks and two wing tanks, and runs on JP-8 aviation fuel. F/A-18C/Ds are fitted with an enhanced electronic fuel system that monitors usage and automatically adjusts the aircraft's centre of gravity as fuel is consumed. In the case of damage being sustained, all fuel tanks are self-sealing, with a foam infill system.***

***One of several non-US operators of the F/A-18C/D, Switzerland decided to purchase the Hornet over competing aircraft such as the Mirage 2000. This caused a great deal of consternation, and a national referendum was held on whether Switzerland had a need for a new fighter at all.***

mulated 700,000 flight hours, and reliability and maintainability statistics were good. However, some problems did surface at the million-hour mark. A number of fires broke out in these high-time engines, causing the loss of several aircraft; these fires were attributed to FOD (foreign object damage) eroding the coating on the compressor casing which resulted in the titanium blades and any debris rubbing together and therefore causing a fire. A number of new safety coatings was developed to cover these blades and to prevent any burning through friction, but the installation of a new engine was inevitable.

To meet Swiss requirements for its Hornets, the F404-GE-402 Enhanced Performance Engine (EPE) was developed and this became the standard powerplant on all Hornets from 1992. Delivering 10 per cent more static sea-level thrust than its predecessor, the EPE also offers 18 per cent more excess power at Mach 0.9 and 10,000 ft (3048 m), and increased transonic acceleration. A typical runway-launched interception profile, from brake release to Mach 1.4 at 50,000 ft (15240 m), takes 31 per cent less time than before.

## Avionics

The F/A-18 was the first true 'digital aircraft'. Many aspects of what the Hornet pilot sees on the cockpit displays are determined by a core mission computer, or by processors built into the other avionics sub-systems. Because of this, the introduction of new software packages every couple of years has steadily improved the Hornet's capability. The centre of the avionics suite is the mission computer. On the F/A-18C/D, this is the XN-8 system, which is expected to last until 2002/3; the XN-8 will also be the computer system fitted to the first F/A-18E/Fs.

The presence of the multi-sensor integration (MSI) system is another important aspect of the C/D-model Hornets. With the MSI, the computer receives inputs from different sensors, correlates them and displays them so that each target appears clearly on the pilot's display. This can be used in an air-to-air or air-to-ground role and is particularly useful in improving the suppression of enemy air defences (SEAD) mission, where the HARM seeker, radar and RWR can be integrated to locate threats and display them to the crew.

***Kuwait's first Hornets arrived in February 1992 and the KAF now operates two squadrons: the 9th (tasked with air defence) and the 25th (ground-attack).***

## Radar

By 1994, all later-model F/A-18s were fitted with the new APG-73 radar, as opposed to the APG-65 of earlier variants. The -73 uses the same antenna and travelling-wave tube (TWT) transmitter as its predecessor, but the rest of the hardware is new. The receiver/exciter unit is more sophisticated and provides much faster analogue-to-digital conversion, allowing the radar to cut the incoming signal into smaller fragments and therefore achieve better range resolution. What is more, air-to-air detection and tracking ranges are up by 7 to 20 per cent. For air-to-ground mapping and bombing modes, the APG-73 also offers higher resolution than before.

Other systems fitted to the later Hornets include NITE Hawk (Navigation IR Targeting Equipment) FLIR, which can track moving targets on the ground and designate them for laser-guided bombs. A new, more reliable Identification Friend or Foe (IFF) system was also incorporated after Kuwait decided upon it for its Hornets and, soon after, it was fitted to US Navy and Marine Corps Hornets.

The Advanced Tactical Air Reconnaissance System (ATARS) fits into the Hornet's nose and incorporates a low- and medium-altitude EO sensor and an infra-red linescan imager, all produced by Loral. The first of the ATARS systems was fielded by USMC F/A-18Ds over Yugoslavia in 1999.

## Weaponry

Representing a massive leap forward in air-to-air capability over the AIM-7 Sparrow is the AIM-120 AMRAAM. The AMRAAM has its own radar, datalink and inertial navigation system. It is also lighter and faster (at Mach 4) than the Sparrow, and has been operational on the F/A-18C/D since September 1993. A wide range of stand-off weaponry is also available for the Hornet. This includes the land-attack derivative of the Harpoon missile, the SLAM, and its extended-range variant, the SLAM-ER. For shorter-range stand-off attacks, the AGM-154 Joint Stand-Off Weapon (JSOW) will be used by C/D-model aircraft. The Hornet is also taking over as the main exponent of SEAD missions and of the AGM-88C High-speed Anti-Radiation Missile (HARM).

## Operators

As mentioned, both the US Navy and Marines operate the F/A-18C/D. For the navy, the Hornet is fast becoming its most important aircraft, with most carrier wings operating three F/A-18C/D squadrons. It has taken the place of the Intruder and supplemented the F-14 Tomcat in many areas. Marine Corps D-model Hornets are used for night-attack missions, while single-seat aircraft are used for SEAD and other ground-attack missions.

While the original Hornet sold comparatively well outside the US, it was not until the night-attack version of the F/A-18C/D became available that sales of the later Hornet took off. It was the aircraft's night-attack capability that swayed Kuwait into purchasing 40 C- and D-models. Switzerland, Finland and Malaysia have also purchased varying numbers of the later-model Hornet.

*Super Hornet sea trials were undertaken aboard USS Harry S. Truman (CVN-75) during March 1999. With 'everything down' this F/A-18F makes one of many test approaches to the carrier during the 12-day trial.*

# F/A-18E/F Super Hornet

**Although superficially an enlarged F/A-18C/D, the Super Hornet is very much a new aircraft of considerably more tactical capability. Born out of the cancellation of the Grumman A-12 and rejection of upgraded Intruders and Tomcats, the Super Hornet has invoked both criticism and praise.**

When the original F/A-18A (the 'Heritage Hornet') made its debut, it was regarded by many as being the world's leading multi-role fighter, and became the benchmark against which all rival fighters were judged. Possessing a formidable BVR capability (endowed by what many described as the world's foremost fighter radar) the F/A-18 was also as agile as the leading lightweight air superiority fighters (and in some respects was more agile), and had a genuine multi-role flexibility, able to 'swing' from air-to-air to air-to-ground operations 'at the flick of a switch'. But the passage of more than 20 years has seen the emergence of new fighter prototypes, and while the baseline F/A-18 remains a class leader, new fighters are waiting to supplant it and to steal its crown.

Remarkably, one of these successors is the Super Hornet, known as the F/A-18E in single-seat form, and as the F/A-18F in two-seat guise. The Super Hornet is still very much an F/A-18, an evolutionary development of the earlier aircraft, and which looks superficially the same as its progenitor. But initial appearances are deceptive, and airframe commonality between the F/A-18A and the F/A-18E is put at only 10 per cent, while the new F/A-18E/F is 25 per cent larger, with massive rectangular-section, stealthy raked intakes, bigger LERXes and with larger control surfaces, tailfins and tailplanes. The new variants have a sawtooth wing leading edge and a lengthened fuselage, giving a one third boost in internal fuel capacity. But the imaginative use of advanced materials and modern manufacturing techniques has allowed this growth to occur without major weight penalty, and with a 42 per cent reduction in parts count.

The Super Hornet originated from a 1987 requirement for an F/A-18C/D replacement for the US Navy and US Marine Corps for service in the early years of the 21st century. At that time, it was envisaged that the new Hornet derivative would be augmented on US Navy carrier decks by the Naval ATF (replacing the F-14) and the General Dynamics A-12 (replacing the A-6E Intruder). These latter new types were subsequently cancelled, and the Super Hornet will now fulfill the carrier strike/attack and fighter/intercept

*In the combat tanker role a Super Hornet, equipped with four underwing tanks and a centreline HDU, can carry 30,000 lb (13608 kg) of fuel. A jamming/SEAD EA-18G variant will replace the EA-6B.*

roles, effectively replacing the F-14 and A-6, while the smaller, lighter JSF will replace the first generation Hornets. This has been made possible by a post-Cold War shift in emphasis from 'blue water' to littoral operations, for which the Super Hornet is ideally suited.

Using some key technologies from the earlier 'Hornet 2000' and YF-23 programmes, the F/A-18E retained a high degree of avionics commonality with the original Hornet, resulting in a low unit cost (within 15 per cent of the cost of the F/A-18C) and a smooth and swift transition of production and aircrew from one version to the other. The high commonality figure tends to mask the fact that the F/A-18E/F has a refined FBW flight control system, now without mechanical back-up, as well as a much-improved cockpit.

The aircraft attracted some early controversy (much of it stirred up by those who favoured the development of a longer-range strike aircraft based on the F-14) and there were some early technical difficulties with the aircraft's new F414 engines, even though these were derived from the original Hornet's F404, with the core of the A-12's F412. Wind tunnel tests prompted a minor redesign of the LERXes, while further minor modifications cured handling issues raised in early flight testing of the aircraft.

While retaining the agility of the original Hornet, the F/A-18E/F is less 'draggy' and enjoys a lower approach speed, despite its higher maximum landing weight. This all helps the F/A-18E/F enjoy a much-improved 'bringback' capability - allowing the aircraft to land with unused ordnance which the original Hornet would have to jettison before landing.

***Until new pulse-rocket or ramjet-powered missiles are available, AIM-120 AMRAAM (one of which is seen being test fired from the second F/A-18F prototype) will be the Super Hornet's primary air-to-air weapon.***

***Cancellation of the planned replacements for the A-6 Intruder and F-14 Tomcat have left the F/A-18E/F as 'the only game in town' as far as equipping the USN's 12 carriers in the 21st century is concerned.***

## First frontline unit

Following a successful Opeval by VX-9, VF-122 received its first Super Hornets in late 1999, for instructor training. The first frontline unit, VFA-115 at NAS Lemoore, transitioned to the F/A-18E in late 2000. Under current plans, the US Navy is to buy 548 Super Hornets and 222 of these have been contracted for. The Super Hornet adds real long range heavy attack capabilities to the F/A-18's capability portfolio, and will even be able to serve as an inflight refuelling tanker aircraft. The F/A-18E/F may also be adapted for the recce role using the SHARP pod, and a further development, tentatively known as the 'F/A-18G', or 'Growler' could replace the EA-6B in the SEAD/ECM role. With Boeing making aggressive efforts to reduce the aircraft's unit price from $48 milllion to the 'low $40 milllion range', the Super Hornet seems set to enjoy export success, too.

# F/A-18E Super Hornet

**Stationed at NAS Lemoore, California, VFA-122 was established in late 1998 and welcomed the Super Hornet to the fleet in January 1999. As the first F/A-18E/F training unit, VFA-122 will produce its first graduates on the type in early 2001. As plans stood in 2000, the first operational unit was expected to be VFA-115, this unit being slated to take the Super Hornet on its first cruise, in USS *Abraham Lincoln*, in 2002.**

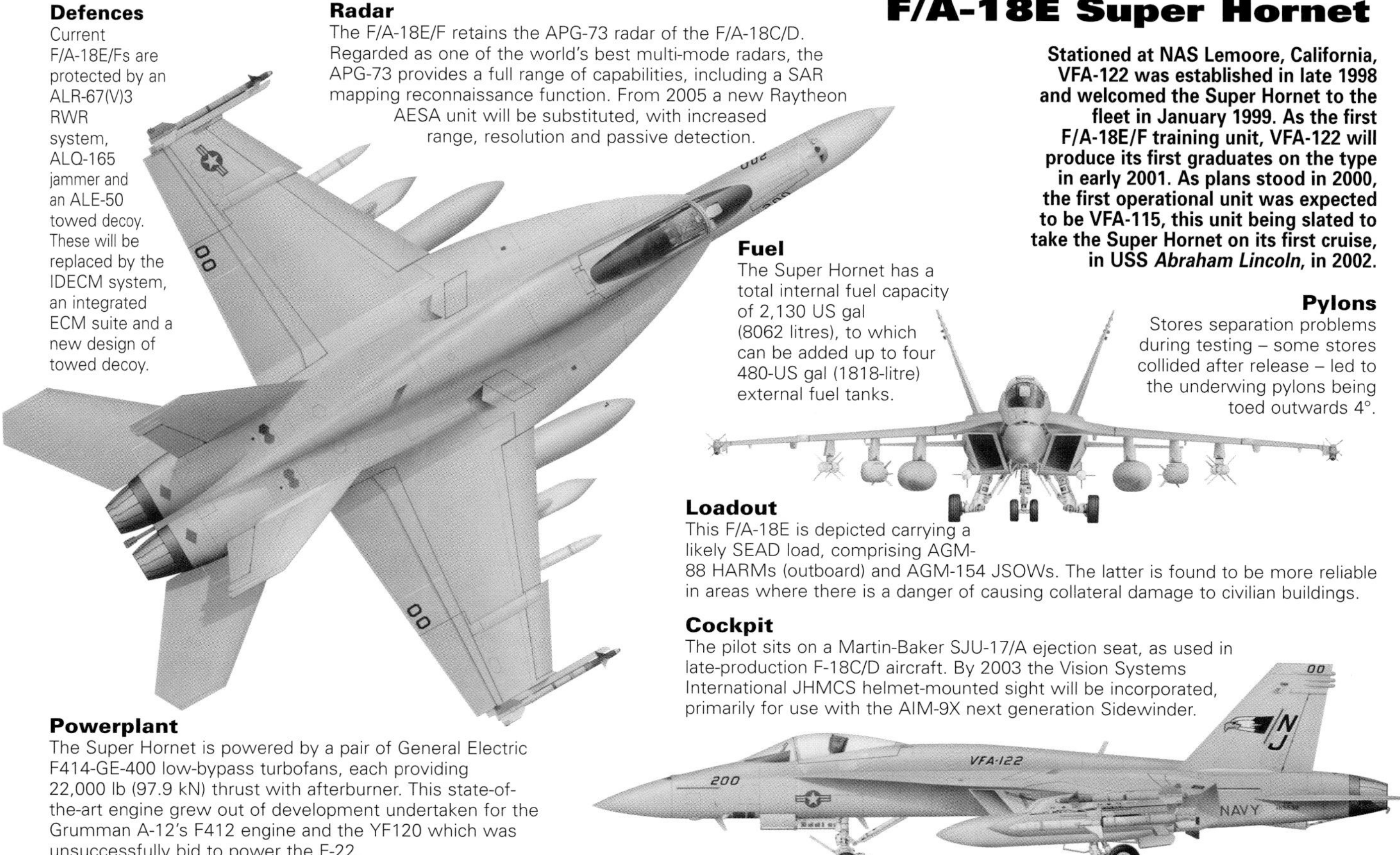



**Defences**
Current F/A-18E/Fs are protected by an ALR-67(V)3 RWR system, ALQ-165 jammer and an ALE-50 towed decoy. These will be replaced by the IDECM system, an integrated ECM suite and a new design of towed decoy.

**Radar**
The F/A-18E/F retains the APG-73 radar of the F/A-18C/D. Regarded as one of the world's best multi-mode radars, the APG-73 provides a full range of capabilities, including a SAR mapping reconnaissance function. From 2005 a new Raytheon AESA unit will be substituted, with increased range, resolution and passive detection.

**Fuel**
The Super Hornet has a total internal fuel capacity of 2,130 US gal (8062 litres), to which can be added up to four 480-US gal (1818-litre) external fuel tanks.

**Pylons**
Stores separation problems during testing – some stores collided after release – led to the underwing pylons being toed outwards 4°.

**Loadout**
This F/A-18E is depicted carrying a likely SEAD load, comprising AGM-88 HARMs (outboard) and AGM-154 JSOWs. The latter is found to be more reliable in areas where there is a danger of causing collateral damage to civilian buildings.

**Cockpit**
The pilot sits on a Martin-Baker SJU-17/A ejection seat, as used in late-production F-18C/D aircraft. By 2003 the Vision Systems International JHMCS helmet-mounted sight will be incorporated, primarily for use with the AIM-9X next generation Sidewinder.

**Powerplant**
The Super Hornet is powered by a pair of General Electric F414-GE-400 low-bypass turbofans, each providing 22,000 lb (97.9 kN) thrust with afterburner. This state-of-the-art engine grew out of development undertaken for the Grumman A-12's F412 engine and the YF120 which was unsuccessfully bid to power the F-22.

*An F/A-18C Hornet of US Navy squadron VFA-147 'Argonauts' flies over a Kuwaiti oil production platform during Operation Southern Watch. The Hornet and its developments will remain the US Navy's most important carrier-borne combat aircraft well into the 21st Century.*

# US operators

**Designed for the US Navy and US Marine Corps, the versatile Hornet is the most important tactical aircraft currently in service with each air arm.**

### US Navy Hornets afloat, Summer 2001

| Squadron | Type | Number | Shore base |
|---|---|---|---|
| **CVW 1** (USS *John F. Kennedy* CV-67): Tailcode 'AB' | | | |
| VFA-82 'Marauders' | F/A-18C | (12) | MCAS Beaufort, SC |
| VFA-86 'Sidewinders' | F/A-18C | (12) | MCAS Beaufort, SC |
| *VMFA-251 'Thunderbolts'* | *F/A-18C* | *(12)* | *MCAS Beaufort, SC* |
| **CVW 2** (USS *Constellation* CV-64): Tailcode 'NE' | | | |
| VFA-137 'Kestrels' | F/A-18C | (12) | NAS Lemoore, CA |
| VFA-151 'Vigilantes' | F/A-18C | (12) | NAS Lemoore, CA |
| *VMFA-323 'Death Rattlers'* | *F/A-18C* | *(12)* | *MCAS Miramar* |
| **CVW 3** (USS *Enterprise* CVN-65): Tailcode 'AC' | | | |
| VFA-37 'Bulls' | F/A-18C | (12) | NAS Oceana, VA |
| VFA-105 'Gunslingers' | F/A-18C | (12) | NAS Oceana, VA |
| *VMFA-312 'Checkerboards'* | *F/A-18C* | *(12)* | *MCAS Beaufort, SC* |
| **CVW 5** (USS *Kitty Hawk* CV-63): Tailcode 'NF' | | | |
| VFA-27 'Royal Maces' | F/A-18C | (12) | Atsugi, Japan |
| VFA-192 'Golden Dragons' | F/A-18C | (12) | Atsugi, Japan |
| VFA-195 'Dambusters' | F/A-18C | (12) | Atsugi, Japan |
| **CVW 7** (USS *George Washington* CVN-73): Tail code 'AG' | | | |
| VFA-131 'Wildcats' | F/A-18C | (12) | NAS Oceana, VA |
| VFA-136 'Knighthawks' | F/A-18C | (12) | NAS Oceana, VA |
| **CVW 8** (USS *Theodore Roosevelt* CVN-71): Tailcode 'AJ' | | | |
| VFA-15 'Valions' | F/A-18C | (12) | NAS Oceana, VA |
| VFA-87 'Golden Warriors' | F/A-18C | (12) | NAS Oceana, VA |
| **CVW 9** (USS *John C. Stennis* CVN-74): Tail code 'NG' | | | |
| VFA-146 'Blue Diamonds' | F/A-18C | (12) | NAS Lemoore, CA |
| VFA-147 'Argonauts' | F/A-18C | (12) | NAS Lemoore, CA |
| *VMFA-314 'Black Knights'* | *F/A-18C* | *(12)* | *MCAS Miramar* |
| **CVW 11** (USS *Carl Vinson* CVN-70): Tail code 'NH' | | | |
| VFA-22 'Fighting Redcocks' | F/A-18C | (12) | NAS Lemoore, CA |
| VFA-94 'Mighty Shrikers' | F/A-18C | (12) | NAS Lemoore, CA |
| VFA-97 'Warhawks' | F/A-18C | (12) | NAS Lemoore, CA |
| **CVW 14** (USS *Abraham Lincoln* CVN-72): Tail code 'NK' | | | |
| VFA-25 'Fist of the Fleet' | F/A-18C | (12) | NAS Lemoore, CA |
| VFA-113 'Stingers' | F/A-18C | (12) | NAS Lemoore, CA |
| VFA-115 'Eagles' | F/A-18C | (12) | NAS Lemoore, CA |
| **CVW 17** (USS *Dwight D. Eisenhower* CVN-69): Tail code 'AA' | | | |
| VFA-34 'Blue Blasters' | F/A-18C | (12) | NAS Oceana, VA |
| VFA-81 'Sunliners' | F/A-18C | (12) | NAS Oceana, VA |
| VFA-83 'Rampagers' | F/A-18C | (12) | NAS Oceana, VA |

## US Navy

The major strike power of the US Navy at sea lies in more than 20 squadrons of McDonnell Douglas F/A-18 Hornets. Ordered in late 1970s, the first of more than a thousand aircraft destined for USN/USMC units were delivered to the Navy in May 1980. VFA-113 was the first operational Navy unit, forming in October 1983, and along with with VFA-25 embarked aboard the USS *Constellation* in February 1985.

The original 'A' and 'B' models were followed in production by the improved single-seat F/A-18C and two-seat F/A-18D in 1986. As the newer aircraft entered frontline service, the older machines were transferred to reserve units and to test and evaluation squadrons. Proposed in 1991 as a replacement for a variety of tactical aircraft, the stretched F/A-18-E/F Super Hornet first flew in 1995, and has entered squadron service with VFA-122, the Pacific Fleet's Replenishment unit.

### Shore-based Navy Hornets, Summer 2001

| Squadron | Type | Number | Base |
|---|---|---|---|
| **Strike Fighter Wing Atlantic, NAS Oceana** | | | |
| Fleet Replenishment Squadron: Tail code 'AD' | | | |
| VFA-106 'Gladiators' | F/A-18A, C/D | (12/13) | NAS Oceana, VA |
| **Strike Fighter Wing Pacific, NAS Lemoore** | | | |
| Fleet Replenishment Squadrons: Tail code 'NJ' | | | |
| VFA-122 'Flying Eagles' | F/A-18E/F | (5/2) | NAS Lemoore, CA |
| VFA-125 'Rough Riders' | F/A-18A/B | (16/24), | NAS Lemoore, CA |
| **Naval Strike Warfare School** | | | |
| NSWAS | F/A-18A/B | (24/4) | NAS Fallon, NV |
| Strike Wing Detachment | F/A-18A/B | (10/8), | NAS Fallon, NV |
| **Navy Fighter Display Squadron**, Tailcode 'BA' | | | |
| "Blue Angels" | F/A-18A | (10) | NAS Pensacola, FL |
| **Test Wing Atlantic**, Tail code 'SD' | | | |
| Strike Squadron | F/A-18A | (12) | NAWC Patuxent River, MD |
| USN Test Pilot School | F/A-18A/B | | NAWC Patuxent River, MD |
| **Weapons Test Wing Pacific**, Tail code 'AI' | | | |
| NWTS 'Dust Devils' | F/A-18A/C/D | (16) | NAWC China Lake, CA |
| **Test and Evaluation Squadron** | | | |
| VX-9 'Vampires' | F/A-18A<br>F/A-18E/F | (11) | NAWC China Lake, CA |

### NAVAL AIR RESERVE FORCE, Summer 2001

| Squadron | Type | Number | Base |
|---|---|---|---|
| **CVW(R)-20** Atlanta: Tail code AF | | | |
| VFA-201 'Hunters' | F/A-18A | (12) | NAS Dallas/Fort Worth, TX |
| VFA-203 'Blue Dolphins' | F/A-18A | (12) | NAS Atlanta, GA |
| VFA-204 'River Rattlers' | F/A-18A | (12) | NAS New Orleans, LA |
| VFC-12 'Fighting Omars' | F/A-18A | (12) | NAS Oceana, VA |

## US Marine Corps

The primary function of US Marine Corps aviation assets is to provide close air support. The two main aircraft used in this mission are the McDonnell Douglas (now part of Boeing) AV-8B Harrier and the F/A-18 Hornet. Marine Corps Hornets are fully carrier capable, and four squadrons are assigned to carrier air wings, serving alongside Navy VFA squadrons. The Marines began using the Hornet even before the Navy, and the first operational F/A-18 unit was VMFA-314 'Black Knights' which converted to the type in 1982. The first Marine Corps carrier deployment came in 1985, when VMFA-314 and VMFA-323 embarked alongside VFA-131 and VFA-132 aboard the USS Coral Sea. Marines use the two-seat F/A-18D as an all-weather fighter-bomber and as a 'Fast FAC' forward air control/tactical reconnaissance platform. Marine Corps VMFA(AW) squadrons began to convert to F/A-18Ds in 1990, just in time to take part in the Gulf War.

### Marine Corps Hornet units, Summer 2001

| *Squadron* | *Type* | *Base* | *Tailcode* |
|---|---|---|---|
| **MAW-1**, MAG-12, Iwakuni,Japan | | | |
| VMFA-122 'Crusaders' | F/A-18C (TDY) | | DC |
| VMFA(AW)-242 'Batman' | F/A-18D (TDY) | | DT |
| **MAW-2**, MAG-31, Beaufort 'SC' | | | |
| VMFA-115 'Silver Eagles' | F/A-18A | | VE |
| VMFA-122 'Crusaders' | F/A-18A | | DC |
| VMFA-251 'Thunderbolts' | F/A-18C | | DW |
| VMFA-312 'Checkerboards' | F/A-18C | | DR |
| VMFA(AW)-224 'Bengals' | F/A-18D | | WK |
| VMFA(AW)-332 'Moonlighters' | F/A-18D | | EA |
| VMFA(AW)-533 'Hawks' | F/A-18D | | ED |
| **MAW-3**, MAG-11, MCAS Miramar | | | |
| VMFA-232 'Red Devils' | F/A-18C | | WT |
| VMFA-314 'Black Knights' | F/A-18C | | VW |
| VMFA-323 'Death Rattlers' | F/A-18C | | WS |
| VMFA(AW)-121 'Green Knights' | F/A-18D | | VK |
| VMFA(AW)-225 'Vikings' | F/A-18D(R) | | CE |
| VMFA(AW)-242 'Bat' | F/A-18D | | DT |
| VMFAT-101 'Shooters' | F/A-18C/D,T-34C | | SH |
| **MAW-4 (Reserve)**, | | | |
| VMFA-112 'Cowboys' | F/A-18A | Fort Worth | MA |
| VMFA-142 'Flying Gators' | F/A-18A | Atlanta | MB |
| VMFA-134 'Smokes' | F/A-18A | Miramar | MF |
| VMFA-321 'Hell`s Angels' | F/A-18A | Andrews | MG |

### Marine Corps Reserve Hornet units, Summer 2001

| | | | |
|---|---|---|---|
| **MAW-4 (Reserve)**, | | | |
| VMFA-112 'Cowboys' | F/A-18A | Fort Worth | MA |
| VMFA-142 'Flying Gators' | F/A-18A | Atlanta | MB |
| VMFA-134 'Smokes' | F/A-18A | Miramar | MF |
| VMFA-321 'Hell`s Angels' | F/A-18A | Andrews | MG |

## National Aeronautics and Space Administration

NASA uses at least seven F/A-18 Hornets. The Hornet has become the standard NASA chase plane in place of ageing Lockheed F-104 Starfighters, six aircraft being acquired between 1984 and 1991. It is fast enough to keep up with most experimental aircraft, and the two two-seaters can transmit live video imagery back to the engineers at the Dryden research centre. However, Hornets are also experimental platforms in their own right: for ten years from 1987, the F/A-18 HARV (High-Alpha Research Vehicle) was used to investigate flight at high angles of attack, demonstrating the ability to fly in a controlled fashion at low speeds and with a nose-up angle in excess of 65° Currently a former Navy F/A-18B has been modified as a systems research aircraft to investigate new technologies in the areas of flight controls, air data sensing and advanced computerised avionics.

Above: The earliest and latest generations of jet aircraft in Canadian armed forces service are pictured. The CT-133 Silver Star (background) was the primary jet trainer until 1974; today, it provides instrumentation, communications and electronic warfare training.

Left: Canada is the largest export customer for the F/A-18, acquiring 138 single-seat CF-188As and two-seat CF-188Bs from 1982. However, cuts in the Canadian defence budget have reduced the Fighter Group's fleet of CF-188s to around 60 operational aircraft.

# Canadian service

**The Canadian armed forces will be reliant on the CF-188 well into the future. The type is the focus of a planned life-extension programme, probably funded by the sale of some of the fleet.**

Even with a substantial fuel load (internal and external), the CF-188 is hard-pressed to cover the vast expanse of Canadian territory on its own, and uses CC-130 tankers to extend its range.

***Left: From a peak of eight squadrons, the CAF is now down to four CF-188 units. The force has been ruthlessly cut back but its taskings have not, and national defence policy decrees that two squadrons must be prepared for deployment anywhere in the world.***

***Below: This 410 'Cougar' Squadron aircraft was specially marked to celebrate the defence of Canada. Its port fin carried an image of a World War II fighter pilot.***

By the late 1970s, Canada decided that a single fighter type would be needed to replace its F-101 Voodoos and F-104 Starfighters. Consequently, the F/A-18 was chosen and was given the designation CF-188 for Canadian service; the name 'Hornet' was not adopted as the French word for 'Hornet' is 'Frelon', leading to likely confusion with the Frelon helicopter.

The first export customer for the F/A-18, Canada ordered 138 aircraft, including 24 two-seaters. Canadian Hornets began their service life with 410 OTS in 1982. The CF-188s operate over the great expanses of the Canadian wilderness and were used to defend the nation's airspace, often in conjunction with fighters from the USA. Canadian CF-188s were also part of the NATO framework and, as such, were based in Germany. However, in line with the end of the Cold War and Canada's ever-shrinking defence budget, the CF-188s returned from Germany to Canada.

During the Gulf War, Canada sent a total of 40 CF-188s to the Persian Gulf, although there were never more than 26 there at any one time. The 'Desert Cats', as they were known, performed in the air-to-air, ground-attack and Coalition fleet defence roles.

As soon as the CF-188s returned from the Gulf, defence cuts ensured that a decision was made to reduce severely the number of CF-188s in service. Of the original 138 aircraft, only 60 remain in front-line squadrons today. The OTU has a further 23 aircraft, mostly two-seaters. Each of the four operational squadrons has a unit establishment of 15 aircraft, although they often have a few more on hand. The remainder are stored for varying lengths of time by Canadair, which cycles them back into the active fleet to keep the number of flying hours per aircraft relatively even. However, some of the oldest CF-188s are very close to the end of their airframe hours and are unlikely to fly again.

In theory, each of the four front-line squadrons (416 and 441 at Cold Lake, 425 and 433 at Bagotville) is dual-role but, in practice, each specialises in either air-to-air (and is NORAD-dedicated) or air-to-ground (NATO-dedicated). For a while, each squadron switched roles twice a year, but the cost in terms of time and loss of capability during the transition was too great and the change is now made on an approximately annual basis. In addition to NORAD, NATO and potential overseas missions, CF-188s are also employed in other national tasks such as counter-drug operations.

## Improving the fleets

Air-to-ground capabilities received a significant boost with the introduction of precision-guided munitions, this leading directly to the deployment of six aircraft to Aviano AB between August and November 1997. For the first time, Canadians on the ground were supported by their countrymen overhead, during peacekeeping operations in Bosnia. During the Gulf War, Canadian CF-188s – flying in Operation Friction – had been limited to dropping 'dumb' bombs when they were authorised to conduct ground-attack missions partway through the war. Canada flew a total of 77 training sorties and 261 operational sorties in support of the Stabilisation Force (SFOR). A typical warload consisted of one 500-lb (227-kg) laser-guided bomb, two AIM-9 Sidewinders, one AIM-7 Sparrow and one Maverick missile. The Canadians' most recent conflict, Operation Deliberate Force over Kosovo, saw 14 CF-188s engage in air-to-ground operations, armed with GBU-10s.

There is no current plan to upgrade from what are essentially F/A-18As and Bs to the new Es and Fs. The former Chief of the Air Staff has been quoted as saying that Canada could conceivably 'cash in' the 126 surviving CF-188As and 188Bs and, with the money available for the CF-188 life-extension programme, buy 20-30 Es and Fs.

Although reliant on the CF-188, Canada has recently made a CN$10 million 'buy-in' to the Joint Strike Fighter programme, so as to be kept fully advised of its progress.

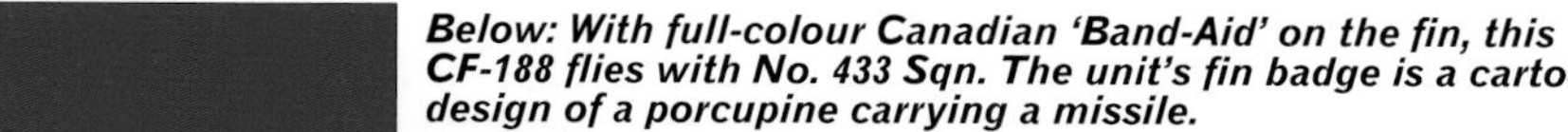

***Below: With full-colour Canadian 'Band-Aid' on the fin, this CF-188 flies with No. 433 Sqn. The unit's fin badge is a cartoon design of a porcupine carrying a missile.***

***Left: A flight of four No. 433 Squadron CF-188s, based at CFB Bagotville, releases infra-red decoy flares. The 'Porcupines' are a French-language unit and have been equipped with CF-188s since December 1987.***

# Foreign operators

**While not matching its great rival, the F-16, the Boeing (McDD) Hornet has notched up several high-profile export sales.**

## Australia

Australia selected the Hornet in October 1981 as its next-generation tactical fighter and Mirage III replacement. The US$2,788 million deal included 57 F/A-18As (AF-18As) and 18 F/A-18Bs (AF-18Bs), all but two of which were assembled at Australia's own Government Aircraft Factory. Hornets were delivered to four units between 1985 and 1990 – No. 2 OCU (re-equipped May 1985), No. 3 Sqn (August 1986), No. 77 Sqn (July 1987) and No. 75 Sqn (May 1988). Three of these are based at Williamtown, NSW, which was refurbished to become the main base of RAAF Hornet operations between 1983 and 1985. No. 75 Sqn is based at Tindal, NT. The Aircraft Research and Development Unit (ARDU), based at Edinburgh, SA, routinely has an AF-18A and an AF-18B on strength for weapons and systems trials. Hornet squadrons regularly make mass deployments to other bases and FOLs, such as Curtin and Schergar. Australian Hornets are being upgraded with APG-73 radar in place of the APG-65, and AIM-132 ASRAAM short-range missiles.

## Finland

After a long and exhaustive evaluation of various fighter types, Finland chose the Hornet to replace its elderly Drakens and MiG-21s in April 1992. An order, placed on 5 June 1992, covered 57 F/A-18Cs and seven F/A-18Ds. The two-seaters were all built at St Louis, the first flying there on 21 April 1995. The single-seaters were assembled by Valmet in Finland, the first taking to the air in 1996. All had been delivered by 2000. The Finnish Hornets are fitted with APG-73 radar, ALQ-165 ECM and F404-GE-402 EPE engines, and are armed with AIM-9M Sidewinders and AIM-120B AMRAAMs. They undertake a purely air defence role, and are consequently known as F-18s. Three squadrons fly the type: HävLLv 11 at Rovaniemi, HävLLv 21 at Pirkkala and HävLLv 31 at Rissala, covering the northern, central and southern sectors of the country, respectively.

## Kuwait

The Kuwait air force selected the Hornet to replace its A-4KUs and Mirage F1CKs in 1988, placing a September order for 32 F/A-18Cs and eight F/A-18Ds, plus associated AIM-9L, AIM-7F, AGM-65 Maverick and AGM-84 Harpoon missiles. The 1990 invasion of Kuwait affected Hornet deliveries, but the first three arrived in-country on 25 January 1992, with deliveries completed on 21 August 1993. The aircraft are designated KAF-18C/D in service. Initially operating from Kuwait International, the Hornets moved to Ahmed al Jaber AB once it had been rebuilt. The aircraft serve with No. 9 Squadron on air defence tasks and with No. 25 Squadron on attack duties. An option for 38 was cancelled in 1992, and Kuwait is seen as a potential Super Hornet customer.

## Malaysia

Faced with replacing a large force of F-5s, Malaysia adopted an unusual two-tier approach, whereby MiG-29s were bought for the air defence role, and two-seat F/A-18s were acquired for the attack role. The 28 October 1993 Hornet order covered eight 'missionised' F/A-18Ds, with APG-73 radar, F404-GE-402 EPE engines, Nite Hawk FLIR, AIM-9S, AIM-7M, CRV-7 rockets, AGM-65 Mavericks and AGM-84 Harpoons. The aircraft are operated in the attack role with an accent on night/precision work, in the same fashion as the US Marine Corps' 'missionised' two-seaters. Four F/A-18Ds arrived at their new base at Butterworth on 27 May 1997, for operation by 18 Skuadron. The initial eight-aircraft order was viewed in Malaysia as a precursor to larger follow-on orders, but the Asian economic crisis intervened. An expected 12-aircraft purchase failed to materialise, although the procurement of Super Hornets remains high on Malaysia's 'shopping list'.

## Switzerland

After one of the most drawn-out and controversial procurement programmes of recent years, Switzerland eventually ordered the Hornet as a Mirage III and (partial) F-5 replacement on 22 June 1993, following a national referendum. The order covered 26 F-18Cs and eight F-18Bs, equipped to a very high standard with APG-73 radar, EPE engines and ALQ-165 jamming system. Initially supplied with AIM-7Ms, the Hornets now also carry AMRAAMs. On 31 October 1996 the first of two St Louis-built aircraft made its first flight: subsequent Swiss aircraft were assembled by SF at Emmen, and all had been delivered by 1999. The Hornets serve with Fliegerstaffel 16 and 17, both based (in peacetime) at Payerne. The aircraft are to undergo a Hornet 2000 upgrade programme.

## Spain

Following a five-year evaluation, the Hornet was chosen by Spain to fulfil its FACA (Futuro Avión de Combate y Ataque) requirement in 1983. An initial requirement for 144 aircraft was halved to 72, split between 60 EF-18As and 12 EF-18Bs, known under the Ejército del Aire (EdA) designation system as C.15 and CE.15, respectively. The first was delivered on 10 July 1986.

Between 1992 and 1994 the fleet underwent an upgrade programme, after which the aircraft were known as EF-18A+/B+. The modification improved the central computer, added wiring for carriage of the AIM-120 AMRAAM (ordered in 1990) and AAS-38 Nite Hawk FLIR, and integrated the EW jamming system into the overall defence suite via a new Mil Std 1553 databus. Additional weapons available to the upgraded Hornets included the AGM-84 Harpoon, AGM-88 HARM, Paveway II LGBs and AGM-65 Mavericks.

In December 1995 the EdA began receiving 30 more ex-US Navy Hornets, which were given similar modifications to the existing EF-18A+/B+.

On 25 May 1995 EdA Hornets dropped bombs in anger for the first time, two EF-18A+s dropping self-designated GBU-16 LGBs on Serb positions at Pale. Subsequent actions were undertaken, leading to full participation in Allied Force over Kosovo.

The current fleet is allocated to Grupo 12 at Torrejón, Grupo 15 at Zaragoza, Grupo 21 at Morón and Ala 46 at Gando. Additional aircraft are assigned to CLAEX, the EdA's trials unit at Torrejón.

## Thailand

On 30 May 1996 Thailand signed for the supply of four F/A-18Cs and four F/A-18Ds. However, the Asian economic crisis forced the cancellation of this sale in April 1998.

# Boeing Helicopters CH-47 Chinook

## Heavylift twin-rotor

**In service for nearly 40 years, the Chinook has become the West's primary medium-lift helicopter. Its capacious cabin and and weight-lifting capability have made it a highly versatile battlefield helicopter.**

*Above: The first **CH-47C** lifts off on its maiden voyage. The aircraft was actually a converted **CH-47B (66-19103)**, re-engined with the uprated **T55-L-11s** that constituted the main change from the earlier model.*

*Top: The **YCH-1B** development programme was to have involved five flying prototypes, but the first was badly damaged in a ground-running accident. The nearest of this pair is extensively tufted on the undersides, around the nose and on the front rotor pylon to allow the accurate monitoring of airflow patterns.*

The origins of the CH-47 Chinook lie in the Vertol Model 114 of 1958 (the Vertol company was originally named after Frank Piasecki, pioneer of the tandem-rotor configuration, and has been part of Boeing since 1960). The straightforward idea behind the Chinook was to devise a more capable development of the maker's earlier Model 107 twin-engined assault transport helicopter, better known today as the US Marine Corps' CH-46E Sea Knight, or 'Bullfrog'. The US Army did consider the Model 107 in 1959 under the military designation YCH-1, but found it too small. Curiously, when the Chinook came along, it was given a follow-up designation of YHC-1B, subsequently changed to CH-47A.

From 1965, the US Army relied heavily on the CH-47A, CH-47B and CH-47C for lifting duties. It is claimed that no fewer than 10,000 downed aircraft were retrieved from Vietnamese rice paddies and mountain sides, and brought home for salvage or repair slung beneath the belly of a Chinook. Considering that A, B and C models were all hampered by having only one sling point to which to attach a load – replaced by three sling points in the post-Vietnam CH-47D – this was quite an achievement. The Chinooks became a familiar sight throughout the country, virtually all painted flat olive drab and devoid of any colour or noteworthy markings. By 1971, the Vietnamese air force was also equipped with the CH-47.

The Chinook has the most available and usable cargo space of any US Army helicopter. Its fuel supply is carried externally in pods running the length of the fuselage, which results in a constant cross-section cabin, similar to that of many fixed-wing transports. The cabin measures 30 ft x 8 ft 3 in x 6 ft 6 in (9.14 m x 2.51 m x 1.98 m), provides an area of 1,440 cu ft (40.78 m$^3$), and is long enough to accept two M551 Jeeps – the standard tactical vehicle in use at the time of the helicopter's design. Only a single example will fit – just – of today's standard US Army tactical vehicle, the M998 'Humvee'.

For most routine cargoes, the Chinook's cargo space is more than ample and the type is usually called the US Army's heavylift helicopter, although it technically falls into the medium-lift category. Around the Chinook's cargo space, the helicopter's surrounding fuselage is remarkably compact.

### Twin-rotor design

The Chinook's tandem rotor design allows the entire length of the fuselage to be put to good use, since none of it is required as a boom for a tail rotor. Loading and unloading can be accomplished through a full-length rear ramp, which can be lowered to the ground or raised to match the level of truck beds. One soldier using a built-in winch can pull cargo in or out of the aircraft. Extremely long cargo can extend beyond the opened rear ramp, if necessary.

The Chinook's high rotor blades allow soldiers to enter or exit the helicopter quickly and safely, even with the rotors turning. The standard troop load is 44 fully-equipped troops on

*The third production **CH-47A** demonstrates the ability of the Chinook to deliver paratroops. A standard load was 33 fully-armed troops, although this figure later rose to 44. During the Falklands War, the sole in-theatre **RAF** Chinook once carried 81 troops.*

### Chinook gunships

The ACH-47A, initially known simply as the 'Armed CH-47A', was the battlefield gunship version of the Chinook. Boeing modified four helicopters in 1965 for operational evaluation in Vietnam. In the ACH-47A, engineers deleted all cargo-handling equipment, soundproofing, and all but five troop seats, then added 2,000 lb (907 kg) of armour plating and weapons pylons on each side of the aircraft outboard of the front wheels, plus a nose gun installation. Nicknamed 'Guns A Go-Go', the ACH-47A carried two 20-mm fixed forward-firing, pylon-mounted cannon, up to five 0.50-in (12.7-mm) machine-guns (two on each side of the aircraft plus one firing down from the ramp), and two pylon-mounted XM128 19-round pods of 2.75-in (70-mm) rockets, plus a single chin-mounted M5 40-mm automatic grenade-launcher. In February 1964, the US Army established a requirement for the use of a heavily-armed helicopter in combat operations, and ordered four modified CH-47As in June 1965.The prototype ACH-47A made its initial flight on 6 November 1965 and an official roll-out ceremony was held four days later. The First Air Cavalry Division took three of the four ACH-47A gunships to Vietnam in June 1966.The Vietnam detachment of 'Guns A Go-Go' was the 228th Aviation Battalion of the First Cavalry Division, which flew numerous sorties, providing direct support to American and Australian ground combat troops. Eventually, the development of the smaller, more nimble AH-1 Cobra made a Chinook gunship unnecessary, and the concept was not developed further.

standard sidewall seating, but the Chinook can carry up to 59 infantrymen by placing additional seats in the centre aisle. For medical evacuation missions, the cabin can take 24 litters and two medical attendants.

Although its four-point undercarriage is nothing more than a logical solution for an aircraft of this size and shape, it has proven aptly suited to harsh environments. The quadricycle landing gear provides good stability during loading and unloading operations, preventing roll-overs when landing at unprepared sites.

Every Chinook's hull is sealed at the factory so that the helicopter can land and take off from water in conditions up to Sea State 3; this amphibious capability enables it to operate from a larger number of locations, but is rarely used in everyday operations.

### Chinook at war

The 1st Air Cavalry Division brought a new form of warfare to the world in 1965, creating the largest helicopter base ever hacked out of the jungle (at Anh-Khe) and launching infantry attacks in which air cavalrymen leapfrogged the enemy. The UH-1 Huey was the principal player in this new kind of fighting, but the supporting role played by the Chinook was invaluable.

The Pentagon stepped up CH-47 production and the Army experimented with methods, tactics and crew composition. In Vietnam, a Chinook's crew complement consisted of pilot, co-pilot, flight engineer/crew chief (who also doubled as a gunner) and gunner. In the combat zone, soldiers removed the rear cabin windows, and sometimes other windows, to create rifle ports for onboard infantrymen. Chinooks in Vietnam carried a pintle-mounted 0.30-in (7.62-mm) M60D machine-gun in the port escape hatch opening and a second M60D on a mounting in the forward starboard crew door.

The widespread use of the CH-47C in Vietnam and elsewhere ended complaints that the type was underpowered. The CH-47C was both more powerful and more capable. It was able to carry four bladder-type internal fuel tanks in the cargo compartment, making possible a ferry range of over 1,000 miles (1610 km) when flying at 10,000 ft (3048 m).

In a real-world environment, it is rarely possible to self-deploy a Chinook force, and US Army personnel were frustrated during 1990's Operation Desert Shield when it took nearly 30 days to deliver Chinooks to the war zone, taking into account 'cocooning', sea lift, unloading and rebuilding needs. Still, the CH-47D proved invaluable. In Operation Desert Storm in 1991 – in company with British Chinook HC.Mk 1s, among many other types – CH-47Ds participated in the famous 'left hook' ground manoeuvre that isolated much of the Iraqi army.

Inflight refuelling to extend the range of the Chinook has always been a possibility but has been pursued only with a few specialised aircraft. The MH-47D and MH-47E special operations variants later appeared with refuelling booms and include air-refuelling as part of their routine tactics.

### Foreign Chinooks

Despite competition from other, possibly superior, types, the Chinook has enjoyed notable sales success, with 14 international users operating the type. The first overseas customer was Australia, which took delivery of 12 CH-47C models. The Italian firm Agusta acquired rights to manufacture the CH-47C in 1968 and sold its first batch of 20 to Iran. Agusta-built CH-47Cs also equip the Italian army. Further examples went to Egypt, Greece, Libya and Morocco.

Kawasaki became a builder of Chinooks for the Japanese ground and air arms, and still manufactures a few today, the only overseas builder to produce an aircraft comparable to the US Army's CH-47D.

Taking advantage of the substantial upgrade of the military Chinook when it was being modified into the CH-47D, Boeing announced in the summer of 1978 that it had completed the market evaluation of a commercial version. The target was the growing North Sea oil business, in which drilling operations were being pushed further from the mainland. The availability of the Commercial Chinook was instrumental in British Airways Helicopters (BAH) obtaining a seven-year contract from Shell to service its large Brent/Cormorant oil field off the Shetland Islands. In November 1978, BAH ordered an eventual six Model 234s and the type entered service on 1 July 1981. However, a catastrophic crash in the mid-1980s led BAH to retire the type, and it is now used for other duties, including construction operations and logging.

***Below: The interim MH-47D was the first Chinook to carry a refuelling probe as standard. The type equips the 3/160th SOAR at Fort Campbell, Georgia, although this machine is a Boeing demonstration aircraft.***

***Below: The MH-47E is optimised for covert low-level penetration, usually undertaken at night. As well as Special Forces insertion, it has an important 'fat cow' forward refuelling point role.***

# CH-47 Chinook Operators

**The Boeing CH-47 Chinook is the standard Western medium/heavy-lift helicopter. It has served with the armed forces of 18 nations and remains in service with all but two of these.**

## South Korea, Taiwan and Thailand

The South Korean air force and the army both use the Chinook. Six air force Chinooks (equipped with winches), designated HH-47Ds, are operated by the 235th Squadron for SAR work. The army uses 17 CH-47Ds in a transport squadron based at Taegu. The Taiwanese army uses three Boeing-Vertol BV 234MLRs and nine Boeing Helicopters CH-47SDs. Thailand (below) received four CH-47As in 1972, which were replaced by five new CH-47Ds in 1989 and augmented in 1991 by three upgraded CH-47Cs.

## Previous operators – Vietnam and Canada

In late 1972, under the Enhance Plus programme, South Vietnam (above right) received 20 CH-47As. They served with the 237th Helicopter Squadron, until the fall of Saigon, when they were operated by the Communists for a while. In the early 1990s they were offered on the world market. Canada (above) operated nine CH-47Cs as CH-147s between late 1974 and mid-1991, serving with Nos 447 and 450 Squadrons. Seven were later acquired by the Dutch air force.

## United States of America

The US Army is the largest operator of the Chinook today. It initially received 349 CH-47As, followed by 108 improved CH-47Bs from May 1967. From early 1968 270 Boeing-built CH-47Cs were acquired and 11 Agusta-built CH-47Cs in 1985. This version served as a medium-lift helicopter, while four were converted to ACH-47As for the gunship role in Vietnam. From 1982 the US Army received the first of 472 upgraded CH-47Ds, remanufactured from earlier As, Bs and Cs. After successfully operating a number of MH-47D special operations aircraft, 26 improved MH-47Es were produced. Both types were remanufactured from older variants. The current plan for US Army Chinooks again includes remanufacture – to the improved CH-47F standard.

## Australia

Australia became the first overseas operator of the Chinook, when 12 CH-47Cs (above) arrived aboard HMAS *Melbourne* on 9 April 1974 to fulfil a medium-lift helicopter requirement. Delivered to No. 12 Squadron RAAF, they served until July 1989 when they were retired, the army taking responsibility for battlefield helicopters. A lack of US army airlift capability resulted in a deal in which seven of the CH-47Cs were transferred to the US Army, thus paying for the remaining four (one having crashed in 1985) to be returned to Boeing for upgrade as CH-47Ds. They re-entered service in mid-1995 with the army's C Sqn, 5 Aviation Regiment, based at Townsville. Two new CH-47Ds were added to the fleet in early 2000.

## Japan

Japan is one of two countries to licence-produce the Chinook. Kawasaki Heavy Industries builds CH-47Js (equivalent to the CH-47D) and CH-47JAs (equivalent to the CH-47SD/Model 414-100) for both the Japanese Air Self-Defence Force (JASDF), for logistical support of radar sites, SAR and other transport duties, and the Japanese Ground Self-Defence Force (JGSDF), which uses them in the heavy-lift transport role. The JASDF fleet is divided among SAR flights based at Misawa, Iruma, Kasunga and Naha. The first two Japanese-built Chinooks were delivered on 26 December 1986, one going to each service, but they were preceded by two Boeing-built examples (above, wearing the standard JGSDF scheme). Procurement of the type continues, and by 2004 the JGSDF had a requirement for 50 and the JASDF 31, two more CH-47JAs for the JGSDF and two Js for the JASDF being added in 2000.

## European CH-47s – UK, Holland, Greece, Spain and Italy

Five European nations use the Chinook. The first to order the type was the UK's RAF (top right), which ordered 15 CH-47Bs in 1967. This order was cancelled, reinstated in 1971 and again cancelled, before 33 Chinook HC.Mk 1s were ordered in 1978. The first arrived in October 1981, with No. 18 (based at RAF Odiham) being the first squadron to gain them after No. 240 OCU. They were followed by No. 7 Sqn and No. 1310 Flt in the Falklands (which later became No. 78 Squadron). Another eight were ordered in 1983. Upgraded to Chinook HC.Mk 1B status with glass-fibre rotor blades, 32 of the fleet were further modernised to HC.Mk 2 standard (similar to the CH-47D). No. 27 Squadron (ex-No. 240 OCU) was the first unit to operate the Mk 2. In September 1995 a

further three HC.Mk 2s were ordered, with six HC.Mk 2As and eight special operations HC.Mk 3s. The latter were subsequently cancelled.

The latest European operator of the Chinook is the Netherlands (right), which uses seven ex-Canadian CH-147s upgraded to CH-47D standard and six new-build Ds. All are operated by No. 298 Squadron based at Soesterberg, as part of the Tactical Helicopter Group.

The Greek army's 3 Loko/2 TEAS (3rd company/2nd Hellenic army aviation battalion), based at Megara, operates 16 CH-47D/DGs. Initially, five Meridionali-built CH-47Cs were delivered in the early 1980s, five more coming from the air force in 1988. All were upgraded to CH-47DG standard, and seven more CH-47Ds were acquired.

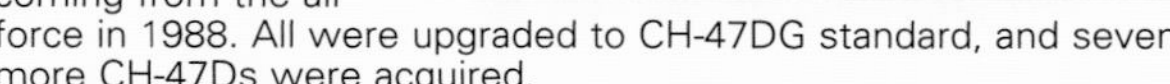

Spanish army unit BHELTRA (transport helicopter battalion) V's fleet of 17 Chinooks (above left) consists of BV 414s, CH-47Cs and CH-47Ds. The BV 414s (five) and CH-47Cs (two) have been upgraded to D standard. They are based at Colmenar Viejo.

A total of 35 Agusta-built and two Boeing-built CH-47Cs have served with the Italian army (left) in the heavy-lift role since 1972. Currently based at Viterbo, the helicopter is known as the ETM-1 in the Italian army designation system.

## Argentina

Argentina acquired two CH-47Cs for the Comando de Aviación del Ejército Argentino, one of which was lost in the Falklands War, and three for the Fuerza Aérea Argentina. One now serves with the FAA, having been upgraded with nose radar – it flies with Grupo 7 on Antarctic duties.

## Egypt, Libya and Iran

Ten of 15 Agusta-built CH-47Cs delivered are still in use with the Egyptian air force (below left), these aircraft being reinforced by an order for four CH-47Ds placed in 1997. The Chinooks are based at Kom Awshim. Libya received 20 from the Italian production line, commencing in 1976. Six were used by the air force and the remainder by the army. Serviceability of the type in Libyan use is thought to be low, because of the arms embargo. Iran (above left) was the largest operator of the type after the US Army, taking 95 from Italy (38 built from kits supplied by Boeing). Despite years of isolation and conflict, around 25 Chinooks still remain operational with the air force and army.

## Morocco

Morocco bought a fleet of nine Agusta-built CH-47Cs, the first being delivered in 1979. Nine are apparently in use with a heavy helicopter squadron based at 1 Air Base, Rabat-Sale. The fleet was heavily used in the fighting against the Polisario guerrillas in the south of the country.

*The US Navy has employed the UH-46A utility transport, of which 14 were delivered, the HH-46D dedicated search and rescue variant and the improved UH-46D utility model. USN Sea Knights have been principally employed on vertrep tasks.*

# Boeing-Vertol H-46 Sea Knight

## Naval twin-rotor

**Destined to remain the backbone of the US Marine Corps' assault helicopter fleet until the introduction of the MV-22 Osprey, the H-46 Sea Knight dates back to the civil Model 107 of 1958.**

The Boeing-Vertol Model 107, or US military H-46 Sea Knight series, is a familiar sight in the helicopter world, widely recognised as the vehicle that has carried US Marines into combat from the Vietnam era to the present day. Four decades after a prototype took to the air in April 1958, the Sea Knight is still the mainstay of the Marines' mobility. Due to be replaced eventually by the tilt-rotor Bell Boeing MV-22B Osprey, the Marine Corps' Sea Knight is likely to be further modernised and kept in service for at least another decade before it is finally retired. R. A. (Art) Sifuentes, Programme Manager for the H-46 series at Boeing in Philadelphia, PA, insists that the H-46 is "very much alive" and "very much an ongoing concern for all of us".

The role of this twin-tandem helicopter in other countries receives less attention, but Sweden operates one version for anti-submarine work and Canada flies another for SAR (search and rescue). Canada designates this helicopter the CH-113 Labrador and employs it in often unfriendly, northern climes where any rescue mission is inevitably made more difficult by that nation's harsh climate and terrain.

The H-46, or Model 107, owes its origins to the pioneering work of Frank Piasecki, the engineer who developed the tandem-rotor or 'flying banana' configuration, with a series of earlier rotorcraft including the USN HRP and HUP (designated H-21 and H-25 by the US Army).

The first CH-46 Sea Knights (known prior to delivery by their HRB-1 designation, for Helicopter, Transport, Boeing) joined US Marine Corps squadron HMM-265 in June 1964. It had not been an easy decision, the FMF (Fleet Marine Force) traditionally being equipped with Sikorsky designs (plus a few Bell HTL-4s in Korea and the Kaman HOKs stateside in the late 1950s). There was shock and disbelief when it was

***The first military Model 107s received the designation HC-1A (denoting Helicopter, Cargo). This YHC-1A prototype, procured for US Army evaluation, became known as the YCH-46C after 1962.***

***Delivered from 1964-5, the CH-113A Voyageur assault transport was operated by the Canadian army. The RCAF, meanwhile, procured the CH-113 Labrador for SAR duties.***

***Above: The CH-46F, typified by this HMM-261 example, was the final production model for the USMC. Most have now been updated to the definitive CH-46E standard.***

***Left: A UH-46D operated by Gulf veterans HC-8 'Dragon Whales', Det 6, is seen aboard the USS*** **San Diego*****. The UH-46D utility transport variant was acquired for the USN both in the form of new-build airframes, and by conversion of at least five earlier CH/UH-46A helicopters.***

announced that the replacement for Sikorsky's much-loved UH-34D would be the CH-46 and not a Sikorsky design.

As the new primary assault helicopter, it brought a greatly increased payload, cruising air speed, and ease of loading/ unloading people and cargo while retaining all of the UH-34's virtues. Powered by two General Electric T58-GE-8B turboshaft engines rated at 1,250 shp (933 kW), the 'Frog', as it became known, hauled up to 17 combat troops on missions in Vietnam. Retrofitted with armour around the pilots' positions – and, on occasion, locally-devised floor armour – the CH-46 was described by Marine Gen. Victor 'Brute' Krulak as "one tough bird" that "can get hit by a whole confetti of flying steel and bring Marines home safely".

All went smoothly in Vietnam until a series of catastrophic accidents in 1967 resulted in the CH-46s being grounded. For a time, they flew only on emergency operations that could not be flown by other aircraft. Many of these accidents involved the machine coming apart in flight, and it is easy to imagine how aircrews felt when dispatched on flights before a simple, structural change was found to be the necessary corrective action.

## Khe Sanh resupply

While the 'Frog' distinguished itself throughout its service in RVN, surely the battles around Khe Sanh and its outposts were high points. In generally bad weather and from bases near the coastline, CH-46s shuttled supplies throughout the mountainous Khe Sanh area. They constantly moved medevacs, people, and supplies as the tactical situation required, often under IFR (instrument flight rules) conditions, all the while being strenuously opposed by crack North Vietnamese army regulars. Operations around Khe Sanh took place over a prolonged period, severely taxing the endurance of aircrews and maintenance personnel. That the NVA finally packed up and withdrew was due in no small part to the CH-46 and its steadfast aircrews.

Boeing built 160 CH-46A and 265 CH-46D troop-carriers, plus 14 UH-46As and 10 UH-46Ds for USN vertical replenishment (vertrep) duty. The final new-build Sea Knights were 174 improved CH-46Fs. Today, the current Marine version is the CH-46E, an upgrade of previous airframes. In all, Boeing built 669 of these helicopters, not counting production in Japan by Kawasaki.

Sweden and Japan operate Kawasaki-built versions of the Sea Knight. Canada acquired 18 Labradors from Boeing and operates these with great success, although they are due to be replaced by the AW320. Bigger, longer-legged and more robust than most rescue helicopters, the CH-113 is every bit as highly regarded as the Vietnam War's Marines version.

### H-46 transport operations in Vietnam

From early 1966 the USMC began replacing its three squadrons of UH-34Ds with CH-46Ds, starting with HMM-164 at Marble Field Mountain, Da Nang in March. Just after midnight on 10 May 1967, three CH-46s were sent to rescue seven Marines, part of a reconnaissance team which had come under Viet Cong attack near Quang Tri, South Vietnam. All three helicopters were hit during the mission, with one co-pilot killed, six crewmen wounded and four Marines on the ground dead. The CH-46 began to be criticised after a series of eight different accidents in mid-1967, and a vulnerability to the sandy conditions encountered in the Vietnamese lowlands. As a result, the CH-46's tail assembly was strengthened, along with other modifications. From 1 September 1967, HC-7, equipped with a variety of helicopters, including UH-46Ds, took over SAR responsibilities from the earlier HS units, until September 1973, by which time they had effected 140 rescues. HC-7 aircraft were based on carriers and a range of escort vessels close to the North Vietnamese coast. The last American casualties of the war were the crew of an HMM-365 CH-46D, which crashed in the sea off USS *Hancock* during Frequent Wind, the final evacuation from Saigon in April 1975. Pictured right is one of the crewmen of a Cubi Point, Philippines-based Sea Knight passing over the Mekong Delta during a 10-hour 'Whitehat' airline mission, while temporarily stationed at Tan Son Nhut, while HMM-262 aircraft, based at Ky Ha, are pictured above and below at an LZ.

# RAH-66 Comanche

## Introduction

**The Comanche was conceived as the most advanced and sophisticated helicopter ever built. It was designed to be a 'stealthy' scout, operating on a high-threat European battlefield, using the very latest technology to find targets and kill them if necessary, defend itself from any threat and remain undetected throughout. However, it has fallen foul of budget cutbacks and technological hitches that have significantly delayed its introduction.**

The RAH-66 sprang from the US Army's LHX (Light Helicopter Experimental) requirement of 1982, which sought to replace 5,000 UH-1, AH-1, OH-6 and OH-58 scout/attack/assault aircraft. These numbers were later cut back to 2,096 in 1987 and to 1,292 in 1990 – the latter is still the US Army's desired total. Several years were spent redefining requirements (and cutting back on numbers) before an RFP (request for proposals) was issued in 1988. The 'First Team' of Boeing and Sikorsky won the competition in April 1991 and was awarded a contract to build four demonstration/validation prototypes.

The RAH-66 is the world's first 'stealthy' helicopter. Its surface area is faceted (like the F-117) to cut down its radar reflectivity, and is covered in radar-absorbent material and IR-suppressant paint. To further reduce its radar signature, all weapons are carried internally on foldaway pylons. Its airframe and five-bladed rotor system is all-composite and highly ballistically tolerant. The shrouded rear 'fantail' fenestron tail rotor reduces the overall noise signature of the helicopter, a huge challenge to helicopter designers and operators.

In addition to generating noise, the blades of any helicopter give a substantial radar return and the technology used to reduce this on the Comanche remains one of the project's most closely guarded secrets.

The Comanche is powered by two LHTEC T800-LHT-801 turboshafts, rated at 1,432 shp (1068 kW).

### Cockpit technology

The avionics systems, and much of the airframe technology, are derived from the Lockheed Martin F-22 fighter programme. Each RAH-66 crewmember has two large LCD MFDs (Multi-Function Displays) in a fully-NVG compatible cockpit – they will also each have HIDSS (Helmet-Integrated Display and Sight System) to provide 'heads-up' flight information and sensor imagery. Each RAH-66 will have a second-generation FLIR, laser designator/rangefinder, TV and other optical sensors, while one

*Only a third of the Comanche fleet will be fitted with Longbow radar, but the passive electro-optical system in the aircraft is probably the finest anywhere in the world (the RAH-66 is pictured here on its first flight on 4 January 1996).*

*Right: The crew sees the battlefield through a revolutionary binocular helmet-mounted sight, as the optimum method of taking in a mass of information while flying and fighting at tree-top level.*

*Despite the difficulties in catering for conflicting requirements like ballistic protection, stealth and noise reduction, the RAH-66 uses some of the most advanced rotor technology ever used.*

**The Comanche is built like no other helicopter. Notable features include the engine behind the main gearbox, the flush side-mounted intakes, the faceted fuselage and fenestron tail. The result is the world's first stealth helicopter.**

third of the fleet will be fitted with a version of the AH-64D's Longbow MMW radar. A 'stealthy' LPI (low probability of intercept) radar altimeter system will also be fitted.

The Comanche is armed with a three-barrelled 20-mm cannon in a nose turret. Each folding weapons pylon can carry up to three AGM-114 Hellfire missiles and four air-to-air Stingers. Extra stub pylons can be fitted to boost the RAH-66's weapon-carrying capability (adding eight Hellfires or 16 Stingers), but at the expense of increasing its radar signature.

The flight control system is a dual redundant triplex digital fly-by-wire system and each crewmember has a novel sidestick cyclic with standard collective controls. In 1994 all FY96-2001 production funding ($2.1 billion) for the RAH-66 was again cut completely from the defence budget by the Pentagon. Scaled-down production of just two prototypes was allowed, to be followed by six EOC (early operational capability) aircraft which would form the first army trials unit in 2001.

The following year, funds for the development phase were restored. A full-scale production decision was postponed until 2003, though the army still hopes to have its first operational RAH-66 unit fielded by 2007 (using all eight initial aircraft with no offensive systems). More recent budget cuts have pushed the programme back by some months, but it remains essentially on track.

**Above: Attack team of the future – while the Comanche can kill tanks by itself, its more usual role will be to find targets for the AH-64D Apache and its lethal AGM-114K Hellfire laser-guided missiles.**

**When operating in the armed scout role, the Comanche will carry its weapons internally. Although it can accommodate far fewer weapons this way, it will have the advantage of getting in the first shot while undetected by the enemy.**

## First flight

Assembly of the first prototype began at Sikorsky's Stratford plant and Boeing's Philadelphia plant in November 1993. These sub-assemblies were brought together for final assembly at Stratford in 1994. The first RAH-66 (94-0327) was rolled out on 25 May 1995. It was transferred to Sikorsky's Flight Test Center at West Palm Beach, Florida, in June 1995. However, it was not until 4 January 1996 that the first Comanche made its (39-minute) maiden flight, flown by Rus Stiles and Bob Gradle.

This flight had originally been postponed from August to November 1995, and further delays were caused by structural problems and software defects.

Ground tests of the Comanche's dynamic system revealed resonance problems in the gearbox which delayed the second flight of the prototype. With a power limit imposed on its engines, the first RAH-66 flew again on 24 August 1996, this time for 54 minutes.

The single Comanche prototype continues to conduct flight tests and envelope expansion. It is now scheduled to be joined in the air by the second prototype in 1999 (delayed from September 1998). In the meantime, the flying prototype has demonstrated a cruise speed of 162 kt (186 mph; 298 km/h), a 'dash speed' of 172 kt (197 mph; 317 km/h), backwards and sideways flight at up to 70 kt (80 mph; 129 km/h) and 180° snap turns in 4.5 seconds. The FY99 request for $367.8 million in aircraft development funding, plus $62 million for accelerated MEP (mission equipment package) development, was approved in early 1998.

A further $24 million was added to the overall Comanche budget by the Senate Armed Services Committee – a sign of renewed Congressional support for the project, which was once conspicuously absent.

## Mission package

In FY02 Boeing/Sikorsky planned to add the full armed reconnaissance MEP to the first Comanche. At this point, a fully-functional gun was slated for fitting, along with missile-firing capability. In FY03 attack MEP integration was planned, allowing full external stores carriage.

The Comanche's first combat 'warfighter' evaluation, dubbed Corps 04, should be held in 2004. If this is successful, initial operational test and evaluation (IOT&E) is scheduled for FY05, with IOC in FY06.

The RAH-66 is a crucial element in the US Army's Force XXI future battlefield concept, which calls for fully-integrated 'digital' forces to work together seamlessly on the ground and in the air. The RAH-66 will work closely with the AH-64D Longbow Apache, scouting targets and performing its own security and attack missions. The Comanche will also be able to 'talk' easily to armoured and artillery units elsewhere on the battlefield. The RAH-66 is also being eyed keenly by US Army Special Operations Command which sees its 'stealthy' capabilities, long range and punch as ideal for its special needs.

***The only operator of the Atlantic outside Europe, Pakistan purchased three refurbished ex-Aéronavale Atlantics in 1975 and a fourth ex-MLD airframe in the 1980s. Another batch of three former French aircraft followed in the mid-1990s, principally as a source of spare parts. One of Pakistan's aircraft was shot down by an Indian Air Force MiG-21 during a confrontation between the two countries in 1999.***

# Breguet/Dassault Atlantic/Atlantique 2

## The first generation

**NATO's collective resolve to counter the potential menace of Warsaw Pact submarines and surface vessels led to the development of the multinational maritime patroller, the Dassault-Breguet Atlantic.**

Commissioned in 1956 to meet NATO Basic Military Requirement No. 2, the Atlantic was intended as the primary NATO maritime reconnaissance aircraft, but this position was weakened by US preference for the Lockheed P-3 Orion and the British decision to develop the BAe Nimrod. Nevertheless, 87 Atlantics were built for four NATO countries.

### Br.1150 wins NBMR-2

Unusually, the name Atlantic had been chosen for the NBMR-2 even before the Breguet Br.1150 submission was chosen in October 1958 as the winner of a design competition. Breguet later joined Dassault in an amalgamation of French industries, although the true builder of the Atlantic was SECBAT (*Société d'Etude et de Construction du Breguet Atlantic*). Led by Breguet, which built the centre fuselage and cockpit and was responsible for final assembly at Toulouse, SECBAT also involved Seeflug (Dornier and Siebel of West Germany) for the rear fuselage and tail; Fokker (Netherlands) for the wing centre section; Sud Aviation (later part of Aérospatiale) for the outer wing panels; and ABPAP (SABCA, Fairey and Belgium's FN ) for the engine nacelles. Italy, a latecomer to the programme, received work associated with the engines, airframe and equipment. The UK's bond with the Atlantic was forged through its two Rolls-Royce Tyne RTy.20 Mk 21 turboprop engines, each of 6,097 shp (4548 kW), although

***Above: The primary detection systems aboard the Atlantic include the search radar (below the forward fuselage), MAD (in the tailboom) and ESM gear (in the fintop fairing).***

***Below: Aéronavale's 40 Atlantics equipped 21 and 22 Flottilles at Nîmes-Garons from 1965/66 and 23 and 24 Flottilles at Lann-Bihoué from 1967/68. Detachments also served in Dakar, Senegal.***

***Left:* The Atlantic has been France's primary maritime reconnaissance platform since 1975 and, in its updated Atlantique 2 guise, will remain in service for years to come.**

***Below:* This view gives an indication of the Atlantic's weapons-carrying capacity. Assorted types of ordnance, including mines and depth charges can be carried by the ventral weapons bay. The four underwing pylons and the weapons bay have a total capacity of 7,716 lb (3500 kg).**

these came from licensed production by Hispano-Suiza of France.

Traditional lines were retained for building the Atlantic, notably the 'double-bubble' fuselage cross-section that provides a pressurised crew compartment above and a spacious weapons bay below. Of all-metal construction, with bonded honeycomb sandwich skin covering the crew area, the fuselage is joined to a wing of high aspect ratio (10.94) for economical cruising during the long-range patrol task. An internal fuel capacity of 4,619 Imp gal (21000 litres) delivers a maximum endurance of 18 hours at the normal patrol speed of 170 kts (313 km/h; 195 mph). Missions of up to 10 hours are usually considered the maximum for the aircraft's 12-man complement, although a complete exchange crew can be accommodated.

Long-range surface detection was by a CSF radar mounted in a retractable 'dustbin' in the lower fuselage, a MAD (magnetic anomaly detector) installation is fitted in the tailboom and an ARAR ESM (electronic support measures) equipment is installed on top of the fin. An Autolycus 'sniffer' identifies fumes from diesel-powered submarines.

## NATO weaponry

The Atlantic has been designed to accept a broad spectrum of NATO maritime weaponry, including the full range of standard bombs; depth charges; homing torpedoes and, on the four wing pylons, anti-ship missiles and HVARs (High Velocity Aircraft Rockets).

The prime movers of the Atlantic programme were France and West Germany, whose navies acquired 40 and 20 respectively, taking simultaneous delivery of their first in December 1965.

Five of West Germany's aircraft were fitted with a comprehensive monitoring suite for gathering Elint, installed by the US firm E-Systems Corp under a programme codenamed 'Peace Peek'. Identifiable by a radome below the weapons bay and small wingtip pods, the aircraft patrolled the East German, Polish and Soviet coastlines.

In 2004, Germany and Italy continued to operate first generation Atlantics, albeit with upgraded systems. Pakistan also had at least two Atlantics, while France replaced its aircraft with new-build Atlantique 2s.

### European customers

Germany's *Bundesmarine* equipped two squadrons (14 aircraft) within *Marinefliegergeschwader 3* with the Atlantic from late 1965 (bottom right); the remaining six of 20 ordered were 'Peace Peek' Elint aircraft. The Netherlands' Marine *Luchtvaartdienst* became the third Atlantic operator in June 1969, when the first of nine aircraft was delivered to No. 321 Squadron at Valkenburg, receiving the local designation SP-13A (right). The type was grounded for 11 months in 1981, then phased out as Lockheed P-3C Orions began arriving. Italy (below) bought 18 Atlantics, which it received between mid-1972 and mid-1974, when the production line closed. Assigned to the navy, the aircraft were operated by the air force and flown by joint crews.

***A key sensor of the 'Nouvelle Génération' Atlantique 2 is the Thomson-CSF Iguane radar, housed in a retractable 'dustbin' radome. Here it is seen deployed on the first production aircraft.***

# Atlantique 2

**Faced with replacing the original Atlantic, Dassault looked no further than the existing durable airframe. However, new systems made the resulting Atlantique 2 a far more capable maritime patroller.**

Though designed as a replacement for all first-generation Atlantics, the Atlantique 2 (originally Atlantic Nouvelle Génération or ANG) was adopted only by France, and the original requirement for 42 aircraft was subsequently slimmed-down to only 30, and the programme has since been trimmed further. These, it was said, would replace France's original 41 Atlantics (and five attrition replacements purchased from the Netherlands).

Design definition began in July 1977, and development began in September 1978. After prolonged studies, the Atlantique emerged as a minimum-change but new-build derivative of the basic aircraft, with the same airframe and engines, albeit with much-improved anti-corrosion protection, a detailed structural redesign giving a 30,000-hour fatigue life, better sealing between panels and improved bonding. Generally, airframe improvements were made only on a 'spend-to-save' basis, to increase service life and reduce operating costs and the cost of ownership.

Externally, the new version featured flattened rectangular wingtip pods (housing D/F antennas for the Thomson-CSF ARAR-13 ESM system) and with a strangely-contoured fin-top, scooped away from the leading edge with its ARAR-13 frequency analysis radome, and lacking the Atlantic's 'football'. A prototype was converted from a production Atlantic 1, and this made its maiden flight on 8 May 1981, and a second (again converted from an Atlantic) followed on 26 March 1982.

Production aircraft (authorised on 24 May 1984) featured an Astadyne gas turbine APU and larger Ratier-BAe propellers. The first of these made its maiden flight on 19 October 1988.

Internally, the Atlantique was 'all-new' however, with a redesigned digital mission avionics fit. This was based on digital databus architecture, and linked a new Thomson-CSF Iguane frequency-agile radar, Thomson-CSF Sadang sonics processing, an SAT/TRT chin-mounted Tango FLIR, a NATOL Link 11 datalink, and a Sextant Avionique (Crouzet) MAD. The Atlantique carries up to 100 sonbuoys, and these are launched from four automatic Alkan pneumatic launchers, or a freefall chute. It also carries up to 160 smoke markers or flares.

***The two prototypes of the Atlantique (this being the first) were produced from Atlantic 1 airframes. Key external differences are the large wingtip antennas for ESM equipment, and the replacement of the fin-top 'football' with a pointed fairing.***

***The second prototype Atl.2 is seen wearing the badges of all four Aéronavale Atlantic units. In the event, only three converted to the new variant, and one (Flottille 24F) was subsequently disbanded.***

**_Above: By 2000 there were just two Atlantique 2 units: Flottille 21F at Nîmes covering the Mediterranean, and Flottille 23F covering the Atlantic from Lann-Bihoué._**

**_Left: The forward observer position of the Atlantique provides an extraordinary view. Beneath the window is the Tango FLIR turret._**

The main weapons bay has three side-by-side pairs of hardpoints, allowing the carriage of eight Mk 46 or seven Murène torpedoes, six 551-lb (250-kg) mines, or eight depth charges, or of two AM39 Exocet missiles, or of a single Exocet and three torpedoes, mines, or depth charges. Exocet was a new weapon option for the Atlantique, freeing the type from reliance on the obsolete Martel used by the original version. Internal weapons carriage can be augmented by stores (weighing up to 7,716-lb/3500-kg) on four underwing hardpoints.

### Atlantic 1 upgrade programmes

In Pakistan Thomson-CSF has upgraded four Atlantic 1s with the AMASCOS mission system, with an Ocean Master radar, DR3000A ESM, and Sadang C1 sonics processing, as well as a GPS-based navigation system. A similar upgrade has been applied to Pakistani Fokker F27s and to Indonesian CASA 212s. German Atlantics have also received a mid-life upgrade at the hands of Dornier. The aircraft received a Texas Instruments radar with a new digital cockpit display, improved Litton LN-33 Decca-updated inertial navigation systems, a new sonobuoy launcher, an Emerson Electric sonar system with increased frequency range and improved processing, and new Loral ESM equipment in wingtip pods. A further upgrade, launched in 1996, will add 12,000 hours to the lives of the country's 18 Atlantics, extending their Out-of-Service Date to 2010. The 1996 programme also adds FLIR, further navigation system improvements and further improved ESM equipment. In Italy, Aeronavali (a subsidiary of Alenia) incorporated a new ESM system on 18 Atlantics (below), and also incorporated the ALCO improvement programme, adding Iguane radar and GEC-Marconi Avionics ASQ-902 acoustic processing.

The new Atlantique finally entered service with the Aéronavale's west coast squadrons first. Flottille 23F at Lann-Bihoué converted in 1989, with conversion completed by 1991, with Flottille 24F following suit in 1992. The Mediterranean squadrons at Nîmes-Garons were to follow, but in the event only Flottille 21F converted, becoming operational in February 1994. Flottille 22F disbanded on 1 October 1996, before it could convert, ending the Aéronavale career of the original Atlantic.

With only three squadrons, the total of Atlantiques was reduced to 28 from 30, and in 1996 it was announced that six of these would be placed in storage pending possible re-sale.

## Advanced developments

Dassault has continued to market derivatives of the Atlantic/Atlantique, including the 1990 Europatrol (intended as a replacement for European P-3 Orions in the wake of the cancellation of Lockheed's own P-7), the 1991 Jet Atlantique (offered to Britain as a Nimrod replacement) and the more extensively upgraded Atlantique 3, first proposed in 1988 but re-promoted in 1995.

The Jet Atlantique featured a choice of Allison T406 or General Electric T407 engines in place of the original Tynes, and with additional podded turbojets (probably Garrett TFE731s) underwing.

The Atlantique 3 was offered as a potential Nimrod replacement in 1995, and then featured Allison AE2100H turboprop engines with six-bladed Dowty 945 propellers, an inflight refuelling probe, a two-crew EFIS cockpit (with six large LCD display screens), a high proportion of UK-supplied avionics and systems and provision for four defensive AAMs.

Although withdrawn from the Nimrod replacement contest in 1997, the Allison-engined Atlantique 3 has continued to be promoted to meet a German requirement for an Atlantic replacement (12 aircraft), for a similar Italian requirement (16 aircraft) and also as a potential MLU configuration for the Aéronavale's own Atlantique 2s. The new version promises a 15 per cent reduction in fuel consumption, allowing improvements in range and endurance. A version of the Atlantique 3 has also been marketed which retains the original Tyne engines, though this would not offer the same benefits.

These various 'Super Atlantiques' represent a long-term (and high-cost) solution to the requirement to replace first generation maritime patrol aircraft, and in the interim, all Atlantic operators are upgrading their aircraft.

Although built in small numbers, the Atlantic and Atlantique seem set to enjoy many more years in productive service, and the family could yet spawn a 'third-generation' version. It is certainly too early to write an obituary for the aircraft which began life as the Breguet Br.1150.

**_This impression shows what an Atlantique 3 might look like, with modern turboprops driving six-bladed propellers. Atlantique 3 is currently on offer to Germany and Italy._**

*In 2004, Pakistan's air force is the last major operator of the Mirage III/5 family, having acquired second-hand examples from various sources including Australia, France and Lebanon.*

# Dassault Mirage III

## Dassault's deltas

**Dassault's concept of a lightweight, ultra high-performance fighter resulted in a simpler and cheaper aircraft than its more sophisticated contemporaries. Many advances were incorporated and the aircraft spawned a myriad of variants that achieved considerable export success.**

Unquestionably, the aircraft that restored the global reputation of France as a leader in aeronautical design was the Dassault Mirage III. Devastated by World War II, the local aircraft industry strove valiantly in the following decade to catch up with Britain and the United States and was gradually able to satisfy national pride with an increasing proportion of home-designed combat aircraft in the inventory of the Armée de l'Air. Some export successes were gained, but it was with the advent of the Mirage family that the world began to take serious notice of the French arms industry in general, and Générale Aéronautique Marcel Dassault in particular.

'Mirage' has become a generic name for almost all subsequent Dassault fighters and strategic bombers, the initial series being the III, 5 and 50. Adopted by a score of air forces, the remarkably tractable, combat-proven Mirage has enjoyed a production history in excess of three decades, and even now is being refurbished and modified for further service, guaranteeing that it will mark its 50th anniversary while still in harness. Few other aircraft can match the Mirage's diverse history of production, licensed production and pirate production, during which the aircraft has been de-sophisticated and re-sophisticated to meet diverse customer requirements.

Genesis of the Mirage may be traced back to early 1952 when Dassault received a study contract for a variant of its Mystère fighter series, designated M.D.550 Mystère Delta. Some preparatory work had therefore been done when, on 28 January 1953, the Air Staff promulgated a requirement for a light fighter, incorporating what it thought were the lessons being learned in the Korean War. Parameters included a 4-tonne maximum weight, top speed of Mach 1.3, carriage of a single 441-lb (200-kg) air-to-air missile and a landing speed less than 112 mph (180 km/h). Power choice was to be made from – if necessary in combination – the new SNECMA Atar afterburning turbojet, light turbojets, liquid-fuel rocket motors and even solid rockets. Unmanned aircraft were permitted.

Responses included the Breguet 1002, Nord Harpon and Morane-Saulnier 1000, but it was the Sud-Est Durandal, Sud-Ouest Trident and Dassault Mystère Delta that received orders for two prototypes each. First flown on 25 June 1955, the rocket-boosted Mystère Delta – soon to be re-named Mirage I – was too small to carry radar plus effective armament. Also on the drawing boards were the twin-engined Mirage II; the Mirage III with a single Turboméca Atar turbojet and 'area ruled' fuselage later incorporating simple, but effective variable-geometry air intakes; and the Mirage IV.

### Futuristic project

The last-mentioned and most futuristic project impressed upon the Air Staff that the light fighter concept was a *cul de sac* in combat aircraft design and strategic defence. Accordingly, in 1956, the original specification was upgraded to 'Stage II', which called for a multi-role, radar-equipped fighter, which only Dassault was in a position to supply before the end of the decade.

Skipping the Mirage II stage, the firm developed the III to the required standard, while the IV was scaled up into a strategic bomber. With incredible speed, Dassault produced a Mirage III fuselage within the year, permitting the aircraft to take to the air on 17 November 1956.

Turning a research machine

*Above: The first production Mirage IIIC was developed from the considerably smaller Mystère Delta research aircraft, via the Mirage III (seen here) and Mirage IIIA. The III was the first of the development airframes to use a SNECMA Atar powerplant.*

*Below: Powered by an Atar 9 turbojet, Mirage IIIA '05' was the first Mirage completed with a production-standard airframe. Although it had a nose radome, the Cyrano Ibis radar was not fitted.*

Initially, the RAAF considered having its locally-built Mirage IIIOs powered by Rolls-Royce Avon turbojets and, although a prototype was flown, the Atar was finally chosen in the interests of simplicity. Of 100 examples, all but two were built by the Commonwealth Aircraft Corporation, the type serving with the RAAF until 1988.

into a service fighter was the task of 10 pre-production Mirage IIIAs, which gradually incorporated CSF Cyrano Ibis intercept radar and combat avionics during 1958-59. Considerable time was spent perfecting the SEPR 841 rocket installation in the lower rear fuselage, although it was little used in squadron service and aroused no interest in foreign customers. The rocket was to improve high-altitude performance, and was certainly not necessary lower down where, on 24 October 1958, IIIA No. 01 achieved twice the speed of sound with only the Atar operating. This was the first unassisted turbojet flight at that speed by a European aircraft, for the Mirage III beat the English Electric Lightning to Mach 2 by one month.

Deliveries of the definitive Mirage IIIC interceptor to the first operational squadron began in July 1961. Despite being an advanced aircraft, the Mirage required little in the way of specialised handling and was flown by pilots straight out of training with not much more than 300 hours in their logbooks. Only on the landing approach is special care required because of the narrow delta configuration and correspondingly nose-high attitude. From the outset, training included 'dead-stick' landings – something not attempted in contemporary deltas.

Equipped with Cyrano II air intercept radar, the Armée de l'Air's Mirage IIICs were armed with a large MATRA R.511 (later R.530) radar-homing AAM under the fuselage as a complement to twin internal 30-mm cannon. Ground attack ordnance could also be fitted, and during the 1980s a pair of underwing MATRA Magics was added to replace the optional AIM-9 Sidewinders.

The Mirage became truly multi-role on 5 April 1961 with the maiden flight of the first 'stretched' IIIE. The IIIEs were assigned a battlefield air superiority role as well as surface attack with conventional ordnance or the AN52 tactical nuclear weapon. A related variant, the IIIR, provided all the tactical reconnaissance for the French air force until phased out in 1988.

### Export success

Australia adopted the Mirage III as its only single-seat fighter, and Israel made it the top combat machine in the IDF/AF. It was in the Six-Day War that the Mirage III conclusively demonstrated its versatility. On 5 June 1967, wave after wave of Mirages and other IDF aircraft decimated the Egyptian, Jordanian and Syrian air forces on the ground.

Israel was well pleased with the Mirage and ordered a follow-on batch of a simplified variant, lacking radar. A fighter-bomber with fair-weather visual intercept capability, the resultant Mirage 5 opened new markets for Dassault by offering a low purchase price and reduced maintenance requirements.

Abu Dhabi, Egypt, Libya and Pakistan all received aircraft with 'Mirage 5' painted on the side, but which were IIIEs in all essential respects, including Cyrano radar. Perhaps this ploy was to obviate political and press criticism of high-technology exports, although it certainly has confused aviation historians since.

### Other derivatives

Meanwhile, the Mirage 5 launch customer had been denied its aircraft when France correctly divined that there was more money to be made by selling arms to the neighbouring Arab nations. After its Mirage 5s were embargoed, Israel built its own copy, the IAI Nesher, from 1971. A redesigned derivative with an American engine and Israeli avionics, the IAI Kfir, followed and was first delivered to squadrons from April 1975 onwards.

Chile and Venezuela purchased the Mirage 50, a Mirage 5 variant with an uprated Atar 9K50 engine of the type fitted to the Mirage F1.

Several Mirages underwent mid-life improvement programmes featuring upgraded avionics and other changes. Chile and South Africa utilised Israeli technology to produce their own upgraded aircraft, namely the Pantera and Cheetah, respectively. In all (including licensed production), 1,422 Mirage IIIs, 5s and 50s were built.

The key to the Mirage's ubiquity and longevity was found in the careful blending of simplicity with adapted technology. It was a 'minimum risk' programme, relying on constructional materials and manufacturing techniques readily available in Europe during the mid-1950s. Likewise, the Atar turbojet lagged behind equivalent British and US engines in efficiency even when installed in the prototype Mirage III, yet has stood the test of time. One must be clever to make things look simple, and the genius of Dassault was to make an aircraft that was more than the sum of its component parts.

**Above: As with most new single-seat fighters of the period, there was a two-seat trainer variant – the Mirage IIIB. Examples were purchased by the Armée de l'Air and the air forces of Israel (IIIBJ), Switzerland (IIIBS) and South Africa (IIIBZ).**

**Left: Spain's Mirage IIIEEs were known locally as C.11s. Like many Mirage operators, the Ejército del Aire planned to upgrade its Mirages, but budget cuts saw their premature retirement in 1992.**

# Mirage III in service

Above: The South African Air Force operated a plethora of Mirage III variants, though only the advanced Cheetah C remains in service today. This IIIEZ of No. 2 Squadron is seen firing a salvo of rockets at a ground target.

**The Mirage III family is typical of Dassault products in that it has been sold to a wide range of customers, many of whom could not afford, or were forbidden, to own the latest American aircraft and so turned to France to meet their needs.**

The Armée de l'Air took delivery of 59 Mirage IIIB trainers, 95 Mirage IIICs and 183 Mirage IIIEs, together with 70 Mirage IIIRs and IIIRDs. The trainers and combat aircraft equipped the 2e Escadre de Chasse at Dijon/Longvic from 1961 (consisting of EC 1/2 'Cigognes', ECT 2/2 'Côte d'Or' and EC 3/2 'Alsace'), the 3e Escadre de Chasse at Nancy/Ochey from 1965 (consisting of EC 1/3 'Navarre', EC 2/3 'Champagne' and EC 3/3 'Ardennes'), the 4e Escadre de Chasse at Luxeuil from 1966 (consisting of EC 1/4 'Dauphine', and EC 2/4 'La Fayette'), the 5e Escadre de Chasse at Orange from 1966 (consisting of EC 1/5 'Vendée' and EC 2/5 'Ile de France'), the 10e Escadre de Chasse at Creil (with one squadron in Djibouti) from 1974 (consisting of EC 1/10 'Valois', EC 2/10 'Seine' and the Africa-based EC 3/10 'Vexin'), and the 13e Escadre de Chasse at Colmar from 1966 (consisting of EC 1/ 13 'Artois', and EC 2/13 'Alpes').

The Mirage IIIRs served with the 33e Escadre de Reconnaissance at Strasbourg from 1963 (consisting of ER 1/33 'Belfort', ER 2/33 'Savoie' and ER 3/33 'Moselle'). EC 5 converted to the Mirage F1C in 1975, while EC 10 followed between 1981 and 1988. EC 2 converted to the Mirage 2000C in 1983, EC 4 stood down prior to re-equipping with the Mirage 2000N in 1987, while EC 3 converted to the Mirage 2000N in 1994. EC 1/13 converted to the Mirage F1CT in June 1992, while EC 2/13 had converted to the Mirage 5F in 1977. The reconnaissance unit, ER 33, re-equipped with Mirage F1CRs between 1983 and 1988.

## Export aircraft

The Spanish air force received the first of 30 Mirage IIIs (six IIIDE trainers and 24 IIIEE fighters) in June 1970, equipping Ala de Caza 11 at Manises/Valencia. Initially used in the interceptor role, with AIM-9B Sidewinder and Matra R530FE AAMs, the aircraft were later relegated to the fighter bomber role, due mainly to the type's lack of EW equipment.

Switzerland procured a fleet of 61 Mirage IIIs, mostly IIIS interceptors, but also including a single Mirage IIIC, four IIIBS and two IIIDS trainers and 18 IIIRS reconnaissance aircraft. Some 34 of the IIISs, three BS trainers and the reconnaissance aircraft were locally built. The aircraft entered service during the mid-1960s, replacing Hawker Hunter fighters, which were relegated to the ground attack role, while the reconnaissance aircraft replaced de Havilland Venoms. The Mirage IIIS fighters flew with Fliegerstaffeln 16 and 17. All of the surviving aircraft were upgraded with canards, RWRs and improved equipment during the 1980s, and the IIISs received a new air superiority grey colour scheme. The IIIS interceptors were eventually replaced by F/A-18 Hornets, and were finally retired on 31 December 1999, leaving only the IIIRS recce aircraft and the trainers in service.

Israel received 72 Mirage IIICJs between July 1961 and July 1964, and five Mirage IIIBJ trainers. These equipped Israel's front-line air defence fighter squadrons until they were themselves replaced by F-4E Phantoms and the indigenous Nesher and Kfir Mirage derivatives from the late 1960s, following relatively heavy attrition during Israel's various wars. Known Mirage III operators were Nos 101, 113, 117, 119, and 190 Squadrons. The final 19 Mirage IIICJs and three Mirage IIIBJs were sold to Argentina in 1982.

## South America

Argentina ordered 10 Mirage IIIEAs and two IIIDAs in

Spain's Mirages received a modest upgrade (with new RWRs) in 1978, but plans for more ambitious upgrades were cancelled in 1991, and the aircraft were withdrawn from service in 1992.

Switzerland's reconnaissance Mirage IIIRSs served with detachments of Fliegerstaffel 10 until 1992, when these were redesignated as Fliegerstaffel 3 and Fliegerstaffel 4.

*This Mirage IIIB is seen wearing the markings of SPA94 of ECT 2/2 'Côte d'Or', the old Mirage conversion and training unit for the Armée de l'Air's Mirage IIIs. This unit now operates Mirage 2000-5Fs as EC 2/2.*

October 1970, and these finally entered service in July 1973. Seven more IIIEAs (compatible with the R530 AAM) were delivered in 1979. These equipped Grupo 8 de Caza's I Escuadrón de Caza at Buenos Aires, operating detachments at Comodoro Rivadavia and Rio Gallegos during the Falklands War. The unit gained two more trainers post-war, but the parent Grupo 8 disbanded in February 1988, and I Escuadrón transferred to Grupo 6 at Tandil. Here it joined the Daggers of Escuadrónes II and III de Caza. A total of 19 ex-IDF/AF Mirage IIICJs and three Mirage IIIBJs was delivered as attrition replacements and equipped Escuadrón 55 (numbered in remembrance of the 55 aircrew killed in the Falklands War) which formed within Grupo 4 at El Plumerillo, Mendoza, in 1983. The Mirage IIICJs were grounded in 1996, apart from a handful used for test/trials duties, and Escuadrón 55 was disbanded.

Brazil received the first of 20 Mirage IIIEBRs and eight IIIDBR trainers in 1972. These equipped 1° Grupo de Defesa Aerea at Anápolis. The last six aircraft (four single-seaters) were ex-Armée de l'Air machines delivered from 1988, after refurbishing and modernising with new avionics, canard foreplanes and other improvements. Brazil's 10 surviving original EBRs and two DBRs were subsequently upgraded to the same standard.

Venezuela's fleet of Mirages consisted mainly of Mirage 5s and 50s, but included seven IIIEV interceptors (equivalent to Armée de l'Air Mirage IIIEs) and three IIIDV trainers. All were upgraded to Mirage 50 standard, with refuelling probes, canard foreplanes and advanced systems, from 1990. The aircraft serve with Grupo Aéreo de Caza 11 at El Libertador.

The Royal Australian Air Force took delivery of 49 fighter-configured Mirage IIIO(F)s and 51 IIIO(A) fighter-bombers, together with 16 Mirage IIID two-seat trainers. Deliveries began in 1963, equipping No. 81 Wing at Williamtown and No. 78 Wing at Butterworth, Malaysia. The Williamtown wing initially consisted of No. 2 OCU, No. 75 Squadron, No. 76 Squadron and No. 77 Squadron, with No. 75 deploying to Butterworth in May 1967 where it was later joined by No. 3 Squadron. Between 1968 and 1971, all surviving single-seaters were brought to a common IIIO(F/A) standard.

No. 76 Squadron was disbanded in 1973, while No. 2 OCU passed its training role to No. 77 Squadron in January 1985, thereafter becoming the F/A-18 conversion training unit. Conversion to the F/A-18 began in July 1987, and the last nine Mirages retired in 1987.

No. 75 returned from Malaysia to Darwin in 1983, finally converting to the Hornet in late 1988. No. 3 Squadron stood down in 1986, pending conversion to the F/A-18, but its aircraft were taken over by the newly-formed No. 79 Squadron which remained active until April 1988, when the RAAF presence in Malaysia came to an end. The last RAAF Mirages were retired by the Aircraft Research & Development Unit (ARDU) in early 1989, and 50 aircraft were then sold to Pakistan.

## SAAF Mirages

South Africa evaluated the Mirage III in 1961, and ordered 16 Mirage IIICZ interceptors and three IIIBZ trainers in 1962. These equipped No. 2 Squadron at Waterkloof, moving to Hoedspruit in 1975. They were followed by 17 multi-role Mirage IIIEZs and by three Mirage IIIDZ and 11 Mirage IIID2Z trainers, and four IIIRZ and four IIIR2Z reconnaissance aircraft. Most of the Mirage IIICs were withdrawn from use in 1990, though No. 2 Squadron did not officially disband, and two Mirage IIIs were retained for display use even after the unit re-equipped with the Cheetah C between 1993 and 1995. No. 3 Squadron at Waterkloof passed its IIIEZs and D2Zs to No. 85 AFS (later ACS) in April 1975, which used the type until the aircraft were withdrawn for conversion to Cheetah standards, from 1983 to 1988.

The two-seat Cheetah Ds initially served with the new 89 CFS at Pietersburg from July 1986, passing to No. 2 Squadron's training flight at Louis Trichardt in 1992. The single-seat Cheetah Es served with No. 5 Squadron at Trichardt from March 1988 until October 1992, when the squadron disbanded, and the Cheetah Es were placed in storage. No. 2 Squadron has operated the advanced Cheetah C since 1993.

Pakistan ordered 18 Mirage IIIEP interceptors in 1967, augmenting these with three Mirage IIIRPs and three Mirage IIIDP trainers. These equipped No. 5 Squadron at Sargodha from late 1967, later moving to Rafiqi in 1984-85. Two IIIDPs and 10 IIIRPs arrived in 1970 and 1975, accompanying a number of Mirage 5s. The IIIDPs were used by the newly-forming Mirage 5 units, while the reconnaissance aircraft went initially to No. 20 Squadron, before being gathered together with the IIIEPs in No. 5 Squadron. Pakistan subsequently purchased 50 ex-RAAF Mirage IIIOs and IIIDO trainers, and after these arrived in 1990, refurbished enough of them to equip two air defence units.

*Above: No. 77 Squadron, RAAF swelled in size with the absorption of the training role from No. 2 OCU and the gaining of a fleet support commitment, and by 1985 the unit had 40 Mirages on charge.*

*Right: Today, the Brazilian F-103E (Mirage IIIEBR) fleet operates as a single squadron, 1°/1°GDA at Anápolis.*

*Belgium's Mirage 5BA fleet began to undergo the Mirage Safety Improvement Programme (MirSIP) (foreground) in 1989. This incorporated the addition of canards, zero-zero ejection seats and advanced avionics. Nevertheless, the type was retired as the programme was being completed.*

# Mirage 5/50

**While the original Mirage III is disappearing from active service, the later Mirage 5 and 50, along with a host of derivatives, serve with several air forces whose resources do not stretch to fourth-generation fighters.**

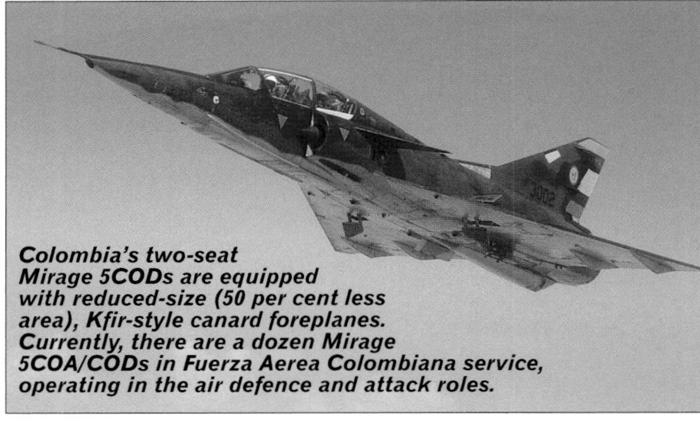

*Colombia's two-seat Mirage 5CODs are equipped with reduced-size (50 per cent less area), Kfir-style canard foreplanes. Currently, there are a dozen Mirage 5COA/CODs in Fuerza Aerea Colombiana service, operating in the air defence and attack roles.*

In its second incarnation, the 'fifth' Mirage was briefly known by the Roman numeral 'V' before adopting the Arabic '5'. It stemmed from an Israeli requirement for an attack aircraft having as much as possible in common with the Mirage III already in service, but with radar and some other equipment removed for reduced cost and faster turnaround. Based on the Mirage III airframe, the 'new-old' aircraft retained Mach 2+ performance and semi-prepared airfield operating capability, but dispensed with the SEPR rocket and added sixth and seventh hardpoints at the rear junction between wing and fuselage. Armament capability remained at 8,818 lb (4000 kg), however.

The most noticeable alteration was the removal of the nose radome, the sharper 'solid' cone increasing fuselage length by 20¾ in (0.53 m). The pitot tube was now attached slightly below the tip of the nose so that an EMD (Electronique Marcel Dassault) Aïda ranging radar (not to be confused with the Super Aïda originally intended for the Mirage IIIC) could be fitted if required. Repositioning some electrical equipment in the nose produced extra space in the equipment bay to the rear of the cockpit, this being used for a further 103 Imp gal (470 litres) of fuel, boosting capacity to 750 Imp gal (3410 litres) and combat radius from 745 to 800 miles (1200 to 1288 km).

First flown on 19 May 1967, the Mirage 5 suffered a setback when the 50 ordered Israeli 5J aircraft were embargoed by the French government. They went instead to the Armée de l'Air (AA) as Mirage 5Fs in the attack role with almost the full range of 'extras' including radar warning receivers, VOR aerials, ESD Aïda ranging radar in a small nose radome, and a finroot fillet. Eight more were delivered from 1983-85, No. 58 becoming the 465th and last Mirage III/5 supplied to the AA. External stores include RPK100 110-Imp gal (500-litre) fuel tanks with attachments for bombs, Belouga cluster bombs, rockets and air-to-air missiles.

The elements that constitute a Mirage 5 have never been accurately defined by the manufacturer, although in the late 1980s Dassault did reassess its sales totals to classify as Mirage IIIs those radar-equipped aircraft previously described as Mirage 5s. Two-seat trainers and reconnaissance versions are similarly indistinguishable from their progenitor. Optional items included Aïda ranging radar (Abu Dhabi, Egypt, Gabon, Libya, Pakistan, Venezuela), VOR aerials (Abu Dhabi, Colombia, Peru, Venezuela, Zaïre), radar-warning receiver (Abu Dhabi, Egypt, Gabon, Libya, Pakistan) and finroot fillet (Colombia, Egypt, Gabon, Libya, Peru, Venezuela, Zaïre).

Export variants of the attack-optimised Mirage 5 lacking search radar were the 5AD for Abu Dhabi (12), the 5BA for Belgium (63, of which 62 were built by SABCA/Avions Fairey), the 5COA for Colombia (14), the 5E2 for Egypt (16), the 5G/5G2 for Gabon (three and two), the 5D for Libya (53), the 5PA for Pakistan (28), the 5P/5P3/5P4 for Peru (22, 10 and two), the 5V for Venezuela (six) and the 5M for Zaïre (eight).

## Mirage 50

This out-of-sequence designation derives from the fitment of an Atar 09K-50 powerplant in place of an 09C to both the basic Mirage III and non-radar 5. Similar in dimensions to its predecessor, the -50 develops 11,055 lb st (49.20 kN) 'dry' and 15,870 lb st (70.60 kN) with afterburning, its air mass flow being increased to 158 lb (72 kg) per

***Most of the Mirage 5s that Chile purchased from Belgium had undergone the MirSIP programme, and in Chilean service were known as Elkan-status Mirages. However, the type still proved inferior to the indigenous Chilean ENAER Pantera C (illustrated).***

***Although high Alpha capability is increased, approach angle of attack (and thus speed and landing speed) is limited by the danger of tailscrape . No extra braking systems were incorporated in the MirSIP aircraft, so landing distances remain high at 1830 m (6,004 ft).***

second. All compressor stages are steel, but detail changes (such as provision for interior inspection by boroscope) are such that there is only 45 per cent parts commonality with the 09C. External signs of -50 installation are air intake splitter plates which, instead of being straight, curve forwards towards the point at which they meet the half-cone centrebody and a pair of cooling air intakes on the upper part of the rear fuselage. The Mirage 50 uses 90 per cent of the structural parts of the III or 5 and 95 per cent of the systems, while its additional thrust gives advantages such as a 15-20 per cent reduction in take-off run; 1,896 lb (860 kg) extra gross weight; 87 miles (140 km) of additional range – or a combat radius of 807 miles (1300 km); sea-level climb rate increased by 30 per cent to 607 ft (185 m) per second; 35 per cent reduction in time-to-height at Mach 2 and typical patrol time increased by 40 per cent.

At first the Mirage 50 was seen as an uprated Mirage 5, with Aïda 2 ranging radar, TRT radio-altimeter, Crouzet air data computer and gyro weapons sight. Options were the 50A with Agave radar and 50C with Cyrano IV, and all could have EMD RND 72 Doppler coupled with a Crouzet 93 computer or a conventional INS.

The Thomson-CSF Cyrano IV-M3 represents a considerable advance on the original Cyrano II. The -M3 combines the basic Series IV (as fitted to Mirage F1s) with technology developed for the RDM and RDI radars (Mirage 2000), but is still compatible with the avionics of older-generation aircraft. Modular in design, it has air-to-air, -ground and -sea modes, presenting information to the pilot in head-up and -down displays as well as providing navigation functions such as ground-mapping, IFR letdown and iso-altitude splitting. INS and nav/attack computer are standard for this and the Mirage 5/50 – which can either be non-radar or can mount the maritime-optimised Agave for use with Exocet anti-ship missiles. Some Mirage 5/50 versions have the seven-hard-point option, but the norm is five, with individual load maxima of 2,601 lb (1180 kg) on the centreline, 3,704 lb (1680 kg) on the inboard wing position and 370 lb (168 kg) outboard, although the total must not exceed 8,818 lb (4000 kg).

Claimants to the title of Mirage 50 prototype are legion. The first Atar 09K testbed was the Mirage IIIC-2, while the 09K-50 became airborne in the Milan S-01 (IIIE No. 589) on 29 May 1970. Next, four IIIR2Zs were exported to South Africa without fanfare, despite being the first 'production' aircraft. Then, on 15 April 1975, having relinquished its 'moustaches', the former Milan flew as the official Mirage 50 'preliminary' prototype with an Aïda nose. It was supplanted on 15 May 1979 by the IIIR No. 301, now complete with search-radar nose and also purporting to be No. 01.

First Mirage 50s to be exported under that designation were eight Mirage 50FCs delivered to Chile during 1980 in the form of re-engined AA Mirage 5Fs, the initial new production concerning a further six for the same customer, designated Mirage 50C and fitted with search radar in the nose, radar warning receivers and fin-base fillet. Also delivered were three Mirage 50DC two-seat trainers, the first two apparently having Atar 09C-3 powerplants. Venezuela is standardising its fleet on the 50EV and 50DV trainer, acquiring six and one respectively from new production, plus nine and two by conversion.

## Mirage 5BR

**This Mirage 5BR wears the striking colours applied in celebration of No. 42 Smaldeel/Escadrille's 70th anniversary. Red and gold flames were applied to the leading edges of this reconnaissance Mirage 5, and the squadron's traditional 'Mephisto' was painted below the centre-section. The squadron was part of No. 3 Wing, based at Bierset (at first alongside No. 8 Smaldeel/Escadrille), moving when No. 2 Smaldeel, and the previously Bierset-based No. 1 Smaldeel, converted to the F-16 at Florennes.**

**Fuel tanks**
The Mirage 5 has two integral tanks in each wing, with a combined capacity of 150 Imp gal (685 litres) per side. Total internal fuel capacity is 733 Imp gal (3330 litres), which can be augmented by underwing fuel tanks totalling up to 220 Imp gal (1000 litres).

**Guns**
The Mirage 5BR, like the Mirage IIIR and IIIRD, retains twin DEFA 552 30-mm cannon, each with up to 125 rounds.

**Operational equipment**
For the reconnaissance role, the Mirage 5BR was equipped with five British-made Vinten-type 360 cameras, although one of these could be replaced by a panoramic Vinten in station 2. Loral Rapport II ECM pods were fitted from mid-1978.

**Powerplant**
The Mirage 5BR is based on the airframe and engine combination of the Mirage IIIE, and thus has the same stretched forward fuselage (with intake lip behind the rear edge of the canopy) and the same variable-area petal-type afterburner nozzle associated with the 13,228-lb st (58.80-kN) Atar 09C-3 turbojet. Engines for Belgian Mirages were locally assembled and tested.

*Pakistan is the last major operator of the Mirage III family, with these Mirage 5PA3s equipping No. 8 Squadron at Masroor. However, the airframes are aging and, due to Pakistan's military imbalance with India, the Pakistani Fiza'ya is looking to replace its Mirages – a variant of the Mirage 2000 or Su-27 'Flanker' are the favoured options.*

# Mirage 5/50s in service

**Like their predecessor, the Mirage III, the Mirage 5 and 50 have achieved sales success around the world. Despite their age, they still equip the air forces of several nations and are occasionally involved in combat missions, especially over the Kashmir border and in South America.**

Belgium acquired 106 Mirage 5s, consisting of 63 Mirage 5BA tactical fighters, 27 Mirage 5BR reconnaissance aircraft and 16 Mirage 5BD trainers. The first of each variant was built by Dassault, but the remainder were built under licence by SABCA at Gosselies. The aircraft equipped 1 Escadrille of No. 3 Wing at Bierset, and Nos 2, 8 and 42 Escadrilles of No. 2 Wing at Florennes, with No. 42 Escadrille operating the reconnaissance aircraft.

Some 20 of the Belgian aircraft began to undergo an upgrade to allow them to serve until 2005, but all were then withdrawn from use as part of post-Cold War defence cuts. The MirSIP upgrade was completed on 10 aircraft (to cancel it entirely would have attracted a hefty cancellation fee), but the aircraft did not re-enter service and were stored before being sold to Chile.

Following the embargo on Israel of the delivery of 50 Mirage 5Js, the aircraft were delivered to the Armée de l'Air as Mirage 5Fs. Eight were subsequently transferred to Chile as Mirage 50FCs, and were replaced by eight new-build Mirage 5Fs. In Armée de l'Air service, the Mirage 5F equipped Escadrons de Chasse 3/13 (from March 1972 until 1993) and 2/13 (from February 1977 until 1994).

In addition to its Mirage IIIs, Pakistan took delivery of 70 Mirage 5s. These comprised two Mirage 5DPA2 trainers, 28 basic radar-less Mirage 5PAs, 28 Mirage 5PA2s with Cyrano WM radar, and 12 Mirage 5PA3s with Agave radar and Exocet ASMs. These were delivered from 1982, and equipped Nos 8, 9, 18, 20 and 33 Squadrons and No. 22 OCU. The type remains in use with No. 22 OCU and with No. 8 Squadron.

*The first Mirage 5BA flew from Bordeaux on 6 March 1970 and the subsequent 62 examples replaced the F-84F that was in service with the Belgian air force at that time. Despite the beginning of the MirSIP update programme, the last Mirages were retired in 1993.*

Although designated as Mirage IIIR2Zs, South Africa's last four reconnaissance Mirages were powered by the SNECMA Atar 09K-50 engine and, as such, were effectively Mirage 50s. These machines served with No. 2 Squadron at Hoedspruit.

## Africa/Middle East

Libya took delivery of 110 Mirage 5s, comprising 53 basic 5Ds, 15 two-seat 5DDs, 32 radar-equipped 5DEs and 10 5DR reconnaissance aircraft. Deliveries began in 1971, and small numbers still remain in use today.

Saudi funds paid for 32 Mirage 5SDEs and six Mirage 5SDE trainers for Egypt (the single-seaters being broadly equivalent to the Mirage IIIE with Cyrano

*In the wake of the Arab-Israeli war, Saudi Arabia financed the purchase of 38 Mirage 5s for the Egyptian air force. However, political sensibilities meant that the aircraft had to wear the distinctive green and white markings of the Saudi air force until their delivery in October 1974.*

***Left:** A pair of Mirage 5s from EC 3/13 'Auvergne' and EC 2/12 'Alpes' formates with a Mirage III from EC 1/13 'Artois'. In all, France received 58 Mirage 5Fs – 50 retained from an embargoed Israeli order and eight new-build machines. The last examples were replaced in 1994 by the Mirage F1CT.*

***Below:** Chile acquired 25 of the upgraded ex-Belgian air force Mirage 5s between March 1995 and April 1996. In Chilean service the aircraft have been further upgraded and are known as Elkans.*

radar and Doppler), delivered from 1973. Early aircraft were painted up in RSAF markings for delivery and pilot training, though they were delivered straight to Egypt. Egypt subsequently bought 22 more SDEs, six reconnaissance-configured SDRs and 15 Mirage 5E2s which lacked radar, but which had an avionics package equivalent to that of the Alpha Jet MS2.

Gabon ordered four two-seat Mirage 5DGs, five single-seat Mirage 5Gs and two Mirage 5RGs in two batches in 1975 and 1982, though the reconnaissance aircraft were never delivered.

The former French colony of Zaïre received eight single-seat Mirage 5Ms and three two-seat 5DM trainers from 1975, six further single-seaters remaining undelivered due to funding problems. The 11 aircraft delivered equipped the 211[e] Escadrille at Kamina, but are now grounded.

Abu Dhabi received 12 Mirage 5AD fighter bombers, 14 radar/Doppler-equipped Mirage 5EADs (Mirage IIIEs in all but name), three Mirage IIIDAD trainers and three Mirage IIIRAD reconnaissance aircraft. Delivered from 1974, the aircraft equipped two squadrons, and were initially flown by seconded Pakistani pilots. A total of 26 surviving aircraft was rotated through overhaul in Pakistan from 1990, and are almost certainly now in storage.

Following the embargo on the delivery of the 50 Mirage 5Js to Israel, indigenously built IAI Neshers were supplied instead, these being broadly equivalent.

## South America

Argentina's Mirage IIIEAs and Daggers were augmented by 10 ex-Peruvian Mirage 5Ps delivered as attrition replacements following the Falklands War. These had originally been supplied 'on loan' and had equipped a Grupo 6 detachment at Rio Gallegos, subsequently being donated to Argentina and coming under the control of Grupo 10. The aircraft (which took over serials of shot-down Daggers) were upgraded to Mara standard (broadly equivalent to Dagger/Finger standard) and remain in service.

Eight ex-Armée de l'Air Mirage 5Fs were refurbished and modified to Mirage 50FC standard (with Atar 09K-50 engines) and were delivered to Chile in 1980. These were augmented by six new-build, radar-equipped Mirage 50CHs and two Mirage 50DCH trainers in 1982-83, with an attrition replacement trainer being delivered in 1987. These aircraft served with Grupo 4 at Santiago until 1986, when they moved to Punta Arenas.

All were upgraded locally by ENAER (with IAI assistance) to Pantera configuration, with Kfir-type noses and canards, and with a fixed refuelling probe, a new INS, HUD, RWR and chaff/flare dispensers. The Pantera programme commenced in 1986 with flight-testing of a canard-equipped Mirage 50, with the full modernised version flying two years later; deliveries began in 1992.

Chile's Panteras were augmented from 1995 by the 15 Belgian Mirage 5BAs and 5BDs which had been converted to MirSIP standard, together with five additional aircraft, all of which were further modified with Chilean-specified avionics and defensive systems as Mirage 5MA and 5MD Elkans. Chile also received four unmodified Mirage 5BRs for reconnaissance duties, and one unmodified trainer. The new aircraft re-equipped Grupo 8, replacing ageing Hawker Hunters.

Peru received 40 Mirage 5s under 10 contracts, comprising 22 Mirage 5Ps, 10 Mirage 5P3s, two Mirage SP4s and six Mirage 5DP and 5DP3 trainers. Ten Mirage 5Ps were supplied to Argentina in 1982, and the remaining survivors were converted to Mirage 5P4 and 5DP4 standards. About eight single-seaters and three two-seaters remain in service with Escuadrón de Caza 611.

Venezuela received six Mirage 5Vs alongside its original Mirage IIIs in 1972-73, and subsequently received nine upgraded, canard-equipped Mirage 50EVs and a Mirage 50DV two-seater in 1990-1991, when the surviving Mirage IIIs and Mirage 5s were modified to the same standard. The aircraft equipped Grupo Aéreo de Caza 11 at El Libertador, where two squadrons remain operational.

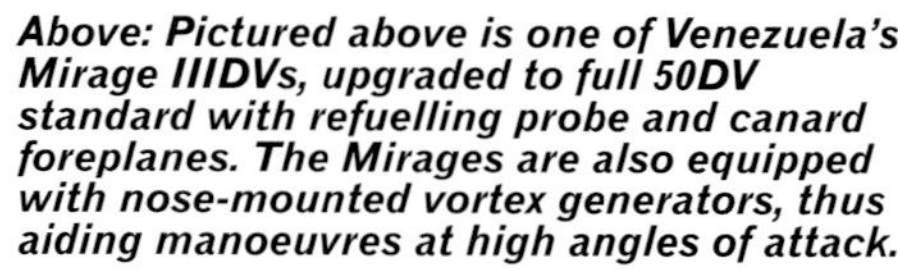

***Above:** Pictured above is one of Venezuela's Mirage IIIDVs, upgraded to full 50DV standard with refuelling probe and canard foreplanes. The Mirages are also equipped with nose-mounted vortex generators, thus aiding manoeuvres at high angles of attack.*

***Left:** Colombia took delivery of 14 Mirage 5COAs, two Mirage 5COD trainers and two reconnaissance-configured Mirage 5CORs from 1972 – these equipped Escuadrón 212 at Palanquero. The survivors were upgraded to Kfir-C7 avionics standard from 1988, with a Kfir-style nose, inflight refuelling probe and half-size canards.*

***Powered by a SNECMA M53 turbofan, the F1E was developed as a private-venture export fighter for entry into the 'Sale of the Century'. The latter, to supply a common NATO fighter, was won by the F-16. Nevertheless, when the Armée de l'Air placed an order for the F1C, the second-generation Mirage gained the added credibility of a home customer.***

# Mirage F1 Development

**An attack aircraft somewhat foisted upon an interceptor-demanding Armée de l'Air, the F1 was developed from a series of designs that explored the benefits of VTOL and variable geometry.**

The thrust of Armée de l'Air (AA) thinking in the early 1960s was towards a dual-role aircraft which, as an interceptor, could perform a Mach 2.5 dash, sustain Mach 2.2 at 50,000 ft (15240 m), manoeuvre at 3 *g* at Mach 2, and carry an armament of two internal 30-mm cannon and one or two collision-course AAMs. In tactical fighter guise, requirements included the carriage of a tactical nuclear bomb or conventional ordnance over a lo-lo radius of 300 nm (345 miles/556 km) – the last 80 nm/93 miles/150 km at Mach 0.9 dash speed – a Mach 0.7 cruising speed, operability from a 2,625-ft (800-m) runway, and 3 *g* manoeuvrability at 300 kt (343 mph; 553 km/h).

Four potential answers were built and flown in a short period of time, some more as proof-of-concept designs than actual production-ready examples. Designations in the Mirage III series were used, though they had only a tenuous link with the IIIE fighter-bomber in production. The Mirage IIIT was a single-seat tailless delta, the IIIF had a conventional high-mounted wing plus horizontal tail surfaces, the IIIG and IIIG8 were variable-geometry Mirage III derivatives, and the IIIV was a VTOL example.

However, the tailless IIIT had poor handling and the VTOL IIIV was impractical with its dead-weight lifting engines. The Mirage G8 showed more promise and became the basis for the G8A, or Avion de Combat Futur (ACF), until high costs killed the programme in 1975.

The VG Mirage programme had deviated on 17 May 1965 when the UK and French governments agreed to the joint development of an AFVG (Anglo-French VG) aircraft, from which France unilaterally withdrew on 5 July 1967. While development of the Mirage G proceeded, the Mirage IIIF was left to meet near-term requirements. Of the two officially sponsored aircraft, the IIIF2 had a fuselage and tail surfaces nearly identical to those of the IIIG. As its intended TF306 engine was not ready because of protracted development difficulties, prototype No. 01 was first flown on JTF10 power by Jean Coureau at Istres on 12 June 1966. To meet AA requirements, the IIIF2 had to have an approach speed of less than 140 kt (160 mph; 260 km/h), eliminating the tailless delta configuration. Two days after its maiden sortie, IIIF2-01 exceeded Mach 1.2. On 29 December 1966 a flight at Mach 2.0 was followed by a landing run of only 1,575 ft (480 m), convincingly demonstrating the short-field performance of what was then known as the Mirage F2. That was to no avail, for six days previously another version of the same aircraft, destined for greater success, had first taken to the air. This was a smaller, private-venture machine which Dassault called the Super Mirage F1.

***An early F1 formates on one of the variable-geometry Mirage IIIGs. The Mirage G family, like the F, was an enlarged design derived from the original Mirage III to meet an Armée de l'Air requirement for a new tactical fighter/interceptor. The swing-wing Mirage IIIG was felt to show huge promise, and several sub-types were planned, including single- and twin-engined designs and even a carrierborne fighter for the Aéronavale.***

## All sizes

The Mirage F2 was shrunk to Mirage III size, leading – in two stages – to the F1 and F3. To create the F1, the cut-down F2 was fitted with Mirage IIIE avionics and a tried-and-tested Atar 09K afterburning turbojet from the Mirage IVA bomber. The resultant F1 was launched late in 1965 under the temporary designation IIIE2 and proceeded through the design stage at remarkable speed. The F1 was seen as a multi-role aircraft,

***The first Mirage F1 prototype retained a short, blunt, Mirage IIIE-style radome, and bore the legend 'Mirage F1C' on the nose. Designed with exports in mind, the Mirage F1 was intended to be a cheap multi-role warplane.***

***The second prototype Mirage F1 was originally labelled 'Super Mirage F1' on the nose. It had a longer Cyrano IV/Mirage 50-style nose radome, but was otherwise externally identical to the ill-fated first prototype.***

having a higher maximum weight than the F3 in spite of a less powerful engine and a thrust to weight ratio of 1:2.1.

The F3 was constructed as the second officially-funded IIIF. Placed between the F2 and F1 in terms of size, the F3 was optimised for interception and, accordingly, had a high thrust:weight ratio of 1:1.3. All three Mirage Fs had two internal cannon and provision for bombs, rockets and guided missiles.

## F1 lift-off

Marked 'Mirage F1C' on the nose, and powered by an Atar 9K, prototype No. 01 lifted off at Melun/Villaroche on 23 December 1966 with chief test pilot René Bigand at the controls. On only the fourth sortie, on 7 January, Bigand and No. 01 achieved Mach 2.0 and then landed at 120 kt (138 mph; 221 km/h).

A few days later, the French Armed Forces Minister announced that the AA had sufficient attack aircraft and needed more interceptors. Consideration was being given to ordering 100 Mirage F1s, the decision to be made in February. The programme was formally launched in March, but an announcement was delayed until 26 May 1967, the official contract for three prototypes following in September.

Sadly, Bigand and the first F1 crashed during practice for a display routine near Fos, Marseilles, on 18 May. No. 01 had broken up in the air due to airframe flutter, the aircraft being completely destroyed and Bigand fatally injured.

However, the loss had no effect on the programme to place the Mirage F1 in military service. Lightning conversion of the AA to the Mirage F1's merits has never been satisfactorily explained, but may have more than a little to do with Dassault's belief that it was a better export prospect than the larger and more expensive Mirage F2 or the specialised F3. However, the Armée de l'Air now received an attack aircraft when it really needed an interceptor with no extraneous capabilities, and would have been better off with the Mirage F3. The partially-completed F3 prototype was scrapped in 1967, denying the AA an opportunity of comparing it with the F1 in flight test.

No official requirement had existed for the Mirage F1 until March 1967, when a specification was written round a production version of the aircraft. Jean-Jacques Samin was transferred from the now-defunct Mirage F2 to lead the F1 design team, although most of No. 02's changes were internal in nature. Marked 'Super Mirage F1', the aircraft was completed in December 1966. It was dismantled for road transport to Istres, where assembly was completed by 20 January, ready for vibration trials. Pending availability of the definitive Atar 9K-50 powerplant, No. 02 had a 9K-31B(3), rated at 14,770 lb st (65.7 kN) with reheat.

## Test programme

The test programme began in confident style, but a couple of weeks behind schedule. Taking off from Istres on 20 March 1967, No. 02 was airborne within 1,475 ft (450 m) and conducted trials of the undercarriage, flaps and airbrakes before 'cleaning up' for a high-level run to Mach 1.15. Landing at the end of a 50 minute-sortie, Saget brought No. 02 to a halt in 1,310 ft (400 m). The following day, Saget was again airborne to demonstrate the aircraft's speed range by flying at Mach 1.5 and then slowing to 115 kt (132 mph; 213 km/h). For landing, the approach speed was 135 kt (155 mph; 250 km/h), followed by touch-down at 125 kt (144 mph; 232 km/h).

No. 02 was stood down on 27 June after 62 flights, having completed Phase 1 testing. This had included a flight above 50,000 ft (15240 m), low-altitude operation at 808 mph (1300 km/h), carriage of military loads including wingtip Sidewinder missiles and under-wing drop-tanks, and exploration of the full flight envelope. No. 02 was then re-engined with a 15,873-lb st (70.6-kN) pre-series Atar 9K-50 and returned to flying in August.

No. 02 had reached 77 sorties and 80 hours when Saget flew No. 03 at Istres for the first time on 18 September 1969. The pair completed Phase 2 testing in December after 120 sorties/ 135 hours, after which No. 02 went to the Centre d'Essais en Vol (CEV) on 22 December for armament testing. The 137th flight by No. 02, on 21 February 1970, was the first with a production Atar 9K-50 installed, and was marked by the achievement of Mach 2.15 at 53,000 ft (16155 m) that day. The joint 200th sortie, and the 50th by No. 03 alone, was celebrated on 11 March 1970, by which time carriage trials had begun with a MATRA R530 AAM on the centreline pylon. No. 4 flew on 17 June 1970, undertaking interception and air-to-ground firing trials at the CEAM test establishment just over a year later.

The prototypes demonstrated beyond doubt that the addition of a conventional wing and tailplane to the basic Mirage III fuselage had produced an aircraft of greatly increased capabilities, despite only a modest increase in installed thrust. The delta had been chosen for the first-generation Mirage partly because it could achieve the low thickness:chord ratio needed for supersonic flight, without resorting to very thin wings, which were then difficult to construct.

Compared with the Mirage IIIE, an F1 requires a 23 per cent shorter take-off run and has a 20 per cent slower approach speed, yet is 80 per cent more manoeuvrable and carries 43 per cent more fuel. This is despite having a 29 per cent smaller wing area and 2.5 tonnes added to the take-off weight.

***Above: Launch customer of the prototype two-seater Mirage F1B – a conversion and continuation trainer – was Kuwait, rather than France. Previously content with Mirage IIIBs and IIIDs, the Armée de l'Air changed its mind once the F1B became available.***

***Left: Production avionics were the principal feature of No. 04 when it flew on 17 June 1970. This aircraft conducted interception and air-to-ground firing trials at the CEAM test establishment in August 1971, performing well despite poor operating conditions.***

# Mirage F1 operators

**Dassault was assured of a ready-made home market for the Mirage F1, but also wished to continue the export success achieved by the Mirage III/5 series. The F1 did not match its predecessor, but did notch up sales to 10 export customers.**

## France (Armée de l'Air)

F1 deliveries to France consisted of 20 F1B two-seaters, 162 F1C single-seat fighters and 64 F1CR tactical reconnaissance aircraft. Major fighter units were 5e Escadre de Chasse (EC 5), EC 10, EC 12 and EC 30, of which EC 30 at Reims-Champagne was the first to become operational, receiving its initial aircraft on 20 December 1973. In addition to France-based units, the F1C also equipped a detachment in Djibouti (EC 4/30, now EC 4/33). All of the F1CRs (an example in desert camouflage is shown top right) were delivered to the 33e Escadre de Reconnaissance (ER 33) at Strasbourg. When the Mirage 2000 replaced the F1C in the air defence role, 55 survivors were modified as F1CTs for a multi-role attack tasking, being delivered to EC 13 (right) at Colmar. This unit has subsequently renumbered as EC 30, and together with EC/ER 33 is the last French F1 operator. A handful of trials units have also operated the type.

## Ecuador (Fuerza Aérea Ecuatoriana)

Unable to buy Kfirs, Ecuador turned to France in the late 1970s, resulting in 16 Mirage F1JAs (similar to the F1E) and two F1JE trainers being delivered in 1978-80. The aircraft serve with Escuadrón de Caza 2112, part of Grupo 211 at Base Aérea Taura, Guayaquil. Ecuador's Mirages have a multi-role tasking, and have been updated by Israel. Israeli-made bombs are among the available weaponry.

## Greece (Elliniki Polemiki Aeroporia)

Greece's inability to procure F-4 Phantoms in the early 1970s led to an order for 40 Mirage F1CG single-seaters to equip 334 and 342 Mire of 114 Ptérix at Tanagra for the defence of Athens. Such was the urgency of the order that 16 F1Cs were diverted from an Armée de l'Air batch. Virtually identical to French F1Cs, the Greek aircraft initially did not have BF radar warning receivers, although these were subsequently added. The arrival of Mirage 2000s for the defence of Athens saw 334 Mira move to Iraklion as part of the 126a Smirna Makis, while 342 Mira remained at Tanagra until the type was retired.

## Iraq (al Quwwat al Jawwiya al Iraqiya)

Iraq ordered a total of 110 Mirage F1EQ single-seat multi-role aircraft and 18 F1BQ two-seaters, although not all were delivered because of arms embargoes. Following 16 F1EQ and 16 F1EQ-2 air defence aircraft were 28 F1EQ-4s with attack and reconnaissance capability. More important were the 20 F1EQ-5s with Agave radar, in place of Cyrano IV equipment, and Exocet missiles. These were used during the Iran-Iraq war in the mid-1980s, during the course of which F1EQs accounted for about 35 kills, including an F-14 Tomcat. A few F1EQ-6s were delivered. Several Mirage F1s were shot down during Desert Storm and others were destroyed on the ground. Twenty-four F1EQs were among the aircraft which escaped to Iran, where they were subsequently impounded.

### Jordan (al Quwwat al Jawwiya al Malakiya al Urduniya)

Having been denied F-16s, Jordan acquired 17 Mirage F1CJs and three F1BJs with Saudi funding. Intended for air defence, this first batch was delivered in light grey to No. 25 Squadron at Azraq. A subsequent batch comprised 17 F1EJs for multi-role duties, these camouflaged aircraft (below) going to No. 1 Squadron.

### Libya (al Quwwat al Jawwiya al Jamahiriya al Arabiya al Libyya)

Libya acquired 38 Mirage F1s, comprising 16 F1AD radarless attack aircraft, six F1BD trainers and 16 F1ED multi-role fighter-bombers (below). They saw some action in the 1980s during operations in Chad. The survivors are believed to serve at Okba bin Nafi, near Tripoli, with an interceptor and a ground-attack squadron.

### Kuwait (al Quwwat al Jawwiya al Kuwaitiya)

Kuwait acquired 18 Mirage F1CK interceptors with two F1BK trainers to replace its elderly Lightnings in the air defence role. These were followed by nine F1CK-2s and four F1BK-2s. The aircraft served with Nos 18 and 61 Squadrons at Ali al Salem. Fifteen escaped to Saudi Arabia when Iraq invaded, one Iraqi helicopter being shot down in the process. The aircraft were subsequently stored, pending sale.

### Morocco (al Quwwat al Jawwiya al Malakiya Marakishiya)

Morocco's 50 Mirage F1s break down as 30 F1CHs and 20 F1EHs, six of the latter being equipped with refuelling probes. First deliveries were made in 1978. The aircraft saw action in the 1977-88 war with Polisario guerrillas, during the course of which at least three were lost to SAMs. The survivors continue to serve with an interceptor and a ground-attack squadron at Sidi Slimane.

### Qatar (al Quwwat al Jawwiya al Emiri al Qatar)

Having first equipped a training squadron in France, Qatar's Mirage F1s did not arrive in-country until July 1984, where they were assigned to No. 7 Squadron at Doha. The order comprised 12 Mirage F1EDAs and two F1DDA two-seaters. The aircraft had a multi-role tasking, and could carry reconnaissance pods. Having undertaken local air defence missions during Desert Storm, they were sold to Spain.

### South Africa (Suid-Afrikanse Lugmag)

South Africa became the first customer for the radarless Mirage F1AZ attack variant, receiving its first of 32 aircraft in November 1975. Sixteen F1CZs were also acquired. The F1AZs served with No. 1 Squadron while the CZs were operated by No. 3 Squadron, both at Waterkloof. Mirage F1s were active in the skirmishes in Angola, including two confirmed kills over MiG-21s. No. 3 Squadron was disbanded in 1992 and its F1CZs retired.

### Spain (Ejército del Aire)

Between 1975 and 1983 Spain received 45 Mirage F1CEs (local designation C.14A), six F1BE trainers (CE.14A) and 22 F1EE multi-role aircraft (C.14B). The CEs were used to equip two squadrons of Ala 14 at Albacete/Los Llanos, while the F1EEs (illustrated below) went to Escuadrón 462 of Ala 46 at Gando, in the Canaries, and are easily identified by their slate-grey camouflage. Subsequently, Ala 11's Escuadrón 111 also transitioned to the type, flying from Manises. Attrition has been made good by the acquisition of surplus F1Cs from France, and by the purchase of the Qatari F1EDAs and F1DDAs, the latter equipping Esc 111. The remaining variants had been due to retire in late 1998, but around 65 aircraft remained in service into 2004.

# Mirage F1 Variants

**Though intended for the air interception role, the Mirage F1 proved itself able to perform attack and 'recce' missions, leading to a host of variants.**

*Above: The Armée de l'Air ordered only a limited number of F1B two-seat conversion trainers, and these were not delivered to squadrons until some way into the single-seat operational service. The F1B retains full combat capability.*

*Top: Performing both air interception and ground attack missions, Ecuador's F1JAs are similar to the F1E. The aircraft have recently undergone a major upgrade programme which allows them to carry eight Israeli P-1 bombs.*

Despite its suffix, the Mirage F1C was the initial production version. The private venture prototype flew on 23 December 1966 and was officially adopted in May 1967, when three service prototypes were ordered. Power was provided by a 15,873-lb st (70.61-kN) SNECMA Atar 09K50 reheated turbojet which offered good manoeuvrability at all speeds.

To meet the prime requirement for an all-weather interceptor, the F1C is equipped with a Thomson-CSF Cyrano IV monopulse radar operating in the I/J band. A later modification to IV-1 standards added limited look-down capability, but as ground attack is only a secondary role for the F1C there are no ground mapping or continuous target ranging options. Only single targets can be tracked, and radar performance is noticeably degraded by poor weather.

## French service

The Armée de l'Air acquired 83 basic F1Cs beginning in 1973, of which the final 13 were fitted with Thomson-CSF BF radar warning receiver 'bullet' antennas on the fin. Later models were delivered with fixed refuelling probes and are designated F1C-200. Probe installation requires a small plug in the forward fuselage, increasing the aircraft's length by 3 in (7 cm).

The Armée de l'Air ordered 20 F1B tandem-seat trainers for pilot conversion. Incorporation of a second cockpit adds only 12 in (30 cm) to the standard F1C's length, as remaining space is made by deleting the fuselage fuel tank and both internal cannon. Empty weight increases by 441 lb (200 kg), due partly to the installation of two French-built Martin-Baker Mk 10 zero-zero ejection seats (the F1C having Mk 4 seats with a forward speed limitation). Otherwise, the F1B is combat capable. Refuelling probes occasionally fitted to F1B aircraft are, in fact, dummies for training with C-135FR tankers.

Exports of the F1C have been made to six countries, four of which went on to adopt the multi-role F1E. South Africa received the first of 16 F1CZs in 1975 for No. 3 Squadron at Waterkloof. They saw action in the confrontation with Angola.

## Reconnaissance variant

As soon as it was clear that the Mirage F1 would support a major production run, Dassault studied a dedicated reconnaissance version, the customer being the Armée de l'Air. Designated Mirage F1CR-200, the first example flew on 20 November 1981. For its mission the Mirage F1CR carries a wealth of reconnaissance equipment both internally and externally. An SAT SCM2400 Super Cyclope infra-red linescan unit is installed in place of the cannon, and an undernose fairing houses either a 75-mm Thomson-TRT 40 panoramic camera or 150-mm Thomson-TRT 33 vertical camera. Other internal equipment includes a Cyrano IVMR radar with extra ground-mapping, blind let-down, ranging and contour-mapping modes, when compared to the fighter's radar, and provision of a navigation computer and ULISS 47 INS.

Additional sensors are carried in various centre-line pods, these including Thomson-CSF Raphaël TH side-looking airborne radar, HAROLD long-range oblique camera or Thomson-CSF ASTAC electronic intelligence pods. Various combinations of cameras can also be mounted in a pod. An inflight refuelling probe is fitted on the starboard side of the nose.

Sixty-four F1CRs were ordered, of which 52 remain in service. The first production aircraft flew on 10 November 1982, and the first squadron, Escadron de Reconnaissance 2/33 'Savoie', became operational at BA124 Strasbourg/Entzheim in July 1983. ER 1/33 'Belfort' and ER 3/33 'Moselle' followed, conversion from Mirage IIIRs being completed in 1988. F1CRs were dispatched to Saudi Arabia for participation in Desert Shield/Desert Storm, where they were used for reconnaissance missions before being grounded to prevent confusion with Iraqi Mirage F1EQs. When allowed to resume flying, they displayed their little-known secondary ground attack role by bombing Iraqi positions, their radar making them more effec-

*Pictured participating in a USAF Red Flag exercise at Nellis AFB in Nevada, this French F1CR displays the bulged under-nose fairing housing the aircraft's panoramic camera. The F1CR is also able to carry the Raphaël SLAR 2000 pod on its central fuselage pylon.*

tive than the alternative Jaguars.

While most export customers for the Mirage F1 interceptor series were content to specify aircraft based on the original Armée de l'Air F1C, Dassault recognised the advantages of a simplified version for day attack missions. The Mirage F1A is visually distinguished by having a slender conical nose, resulting from the removal of the large Cyrano IVM radar. In its place is the ESD Aïda II ranging radar. The large instrument boom housing the pitot/static heads is attached on the underside of the nose, out of the way of the Aïda set. The main advantages of the Mirage F1A are its relatively low cost and extra range. The main avionics racking is moved from behind the cockpit to the nose, making room for an extra fuselage tank. Other additions are a Doppler radar, and an IFR probe. In addition to Aïda radar, South African F1AZs are fitted with a laser-ranger.

On 22 December 1974 Dassault flew a prototype Mirage F1E, powered by the then-new M53 engine. This aircraft failed to win large orders, and the M53-powered version was abandoned. Instead, the designation was then applied to an upgraded multi-role version for export customers. Outwardly resembling the F1C, the F1E has a SAGEM inertial system, EMD.182 central digital computer, and VE.120C head-up display. Like all F1 versions, the F1E can be fitted with radar-warning receivers, chaff/flare dispensers and ECM jammer pods. The Mirage F1D is essentially similar to the F1B trainer procured by the Armée de l'Air, differing only in being based on the F1E export variant, although it is also fitted with SEMMB Mk 10 zero-zero ejection seats.

Most export F1D/Es have been fitted with bullet antennas for the Thomson-CSF BF radar warning receiver and VOR aerials located in the fin. In addition, some aircraft received an HF fillet aerial at the forward joint of the fin. Basic multi-role aircraft (F1EQ, F1EQ-2) were followed by the F1EQ-4 with refuelling probe and reconnaissance pod capability, and F1EQ-5 and F1EQ-6 with Thomson-CSF Agave radar and Exocet capability. The F1EQ-6 had RWRs from the outset, and these were also retrofitted to F1EQ-5s.

A logical product of the shortfall in French ground attack capability and a surplus of air defence fighters following Mirage 2000C deliveries, the Mirage F1CT derives its designation from being a tactical air-to-ground version of the F1C interceptor – specifically, the probe-equipped F1C-200. Two prototypes were converted by Dassault at Biarritz (the first flying on 3 May 1991) and 55 more followed from the air force workshops at Clermont-Ferrand/Aulnat by 1995. Deliveries began on 13 February 1992, allowing one squadron of 13 Wing at Colmar to achieve IOC in November of that year.

***Five variants of the F1 serve with the Spanish air force: F1CEs (illustrated), -BEs, -DDAs and -EDAs and -EEs. This example wears the newly adopted light grey air defence colour scheme.***

### Latest upgrades

The F1CT programme upgrades interceptors to a similar standard to the tactical recce F1CR. Radar changes from Cyrano IV to IVMR, with additional air-to-ground modes, and is backed by a SAGEM ULISS 47 inertial platform, Dassault Electronique M182XR central computer, Thomson VE120 HUD, Thomson-TRT TMV630A laser rangefinder beneath the nose, Martin-Baker Mk 10 zero-zero ejection seat and improved radar warning receiver.

Structurally, the cockpit is rebuilt and the wing strengthened and modified for activation of the outboard hardpoints, while the port cannon is removed to make space for the additional equipment. Strengthening of the centre-line pylon permits carriage of the large, 484-Imp gal (2200-litre) tank. Externally, the blue-grey air defence camouflage is exchanged for wrap-around green and grey. The F1CT carries bombs and rocket pods for its new mission, but retains the ability to launch Super 530 and Magic 2 AAMs as a pure interceptor.

## Mirage F1AZ

**The last South African Mirages wore this distinctive camouflage scheme. National and squadron insignia were often over-sprayed. This aircraft served with No. 1 Sqn, at Hoedspruit, the last SAAF Mirage F1 user before the type's retirement in late 1997.**

**Fuel**
Total internal capacity is 1,136 US gal (4300 litres) in 14 bag tanks located in the fuselage and inner wing. This is augmented by 317 US gal (1200 litres) in each of two underwing drop tanks.

**Radar warning**
The fin mounts forward- and rearward-facing antennas for the Thomson-CSF BF radar warning receiver. Sideways cover is provided by disc antennas flush with the fin sides.

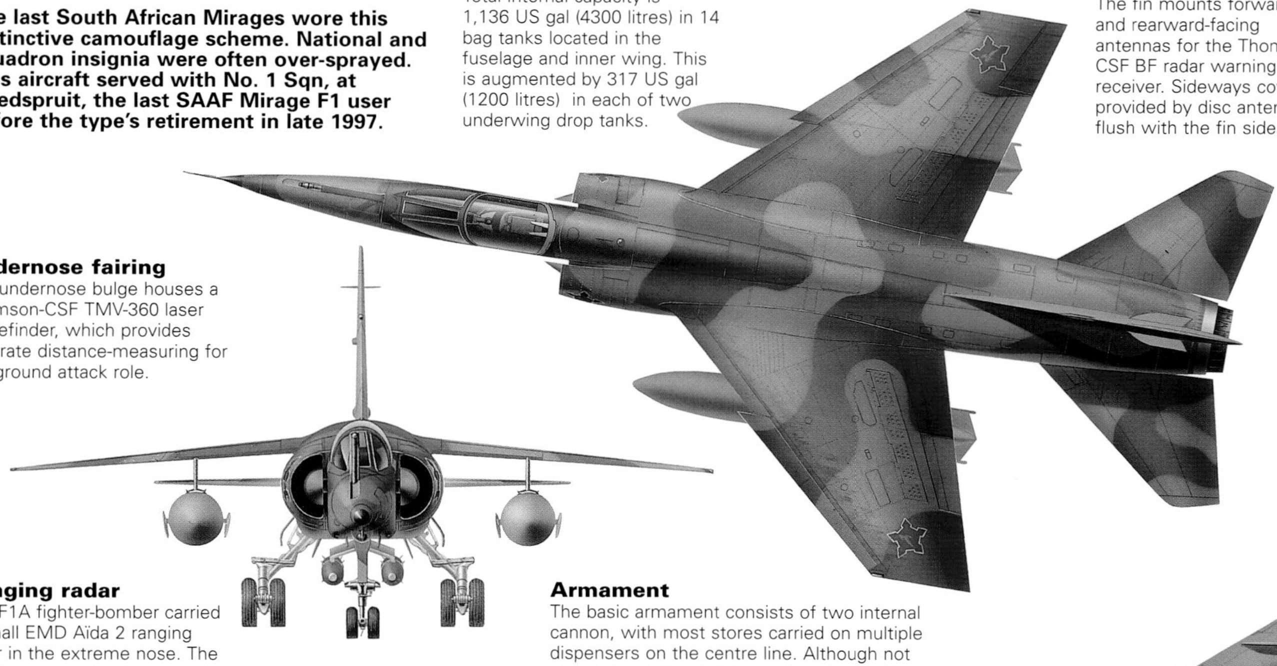

**Undernose fairing**
The undernose bulge houses a Thomson-CSF TMV-360 laser rangefinder, which provides accurate distance-measuring for the ground attack role.

**Ranging radar**
The F1A fighter-bomber carried a small EMD Aïda 2 ranging radar in the extreme nose. The radar has a fixed antenna and provided automatic search, acquisition, ranging and tracking for targets within its 16° field of view. Data was presented to the pilot in his gyro gunsight.

**Armament**
The basic armament consists of two internal cannon, with most stores carried on multiple dispensers on the centre line. Although not shown here, the F1AZ could be fitted with wingtip launch rails for the V3B Kukri or V3C Darter indigenous air-to-air missile.

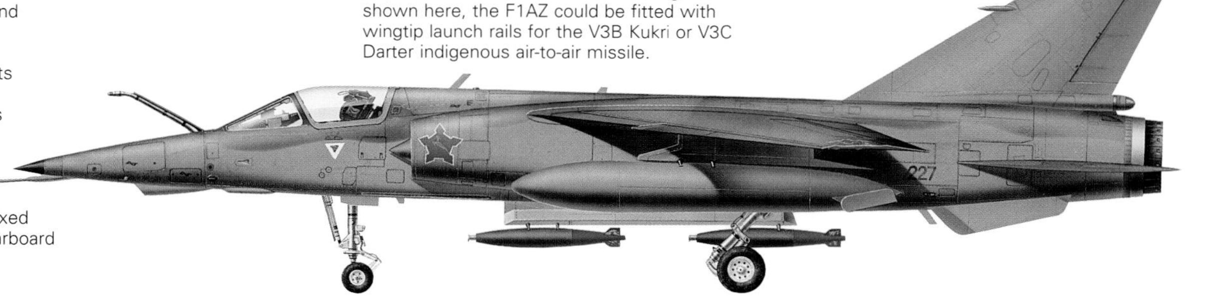

**Probe**
South Africa's F1AZs had fixed refuelling probes on the starboard side for inflight refuelling.

# Mirage 2000
## Development

Befitting its multi-role capability, Mirage 2000B-01 is seen carrying dummy bombs, dummy air-to-air missiles and two fuel tanks.

**Developed using elements of the cancelled ACF, the Mirage 2000 contained many typical Dassault features, yet possessed vastly superior capabilities to earlier Mirage fighters.**

During the 1970s, France began to study plans for an Avion de Combat Futur (ACF) with Mach 3 ability and Dassault came up with the G8A. This 14-tonne monster was soon shelved, though, as problems with its size and cost made it an unfeasible project.

The real news story centred on an unknown aircraft which had been metaphorically rolled out at the same council meeting and authorised on the spot to replace the ill-starred Mirage F.8 fighter development of the G8. By this time, the design was known as Delta 2000, quickly to become Mirage 2000. In March 1976 – and not for the first time – the AA wrote an official requirement around a set of Dassault performance estimates and put its weight behind getting the aircraft into service as soon as possible, with the first 10 to be delivered before the end of 1982.

The second-generation Mirage was to be a more agile and tractable performer than the Mirage F1 at all but high level, where acceleration and supersonic ceiling were reduced in comparison to the Mirage III. Greater thrust, compact avionics and better use of internal space gave the F1 improvements in range and combat load, but there was a practical limit to exploitation of these areas. With considerable experience of both pure delta and conventional swept-wing fighter design, Dassault elected to combine the best of both while eliminating many of their negative aspects. The Mirage 2000 adopted negative longitudinal stability in conjunction with an automatic flight control system (AFCS) and 'fly-by-wire' control surface movement.

In this, the Control-Configured Vehicle (CCV) approach, the aircraft is made longitudinally unstable by having the centre of gravity behind the aerodynamic centre, instead of in front of it. The AFCS computer maintains stability and translates the pilot's commands into manoeuvres. Compared with the case of a Mirage III forcing itself back onto the runway when raising the elevons to lift the nose, the Mirage 2000 slightly lowers its elevons to pivot the aircraft – and increases lift in the process. Similarly, landing is simpler, with the Mirage 2000 approaching at 162 mph (260 km/h), compared to the Mirage III's 211 mph (340 km/h).

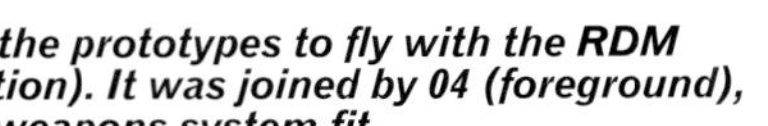

Aircraft 03 was the first of the prototypes to fly with the RDM (Radar Doppler Multifunction). It was joined by 04 (foreground), which also featured a full weapons system fit.

A mock-up of the Aérospatiale ASMP nuclear stand-off missile was fitted to the centreline of aircraft B-01 for aerodynamic work associated with the 2000N programme.

By recourse to computer-aided design, Dassault was able to maximise the size of the wing-root fairings with minimal drag penalty. The extra space in these 'Karman fairings' accommodated fuel and equipment which would otherwise have had to go further outboard, demanding stronger and heavier wing construction. The Mirage 2000 'added more lightness' by using new constructional materials, benefiting from such projects as trials of a boron-fibre rudder tested on a Mirage III and a complete stabilator fitted to a Mirage F1 soon afterwards. Titanium and carbon-fibre similarly combine strength and lightness, bringing the aircraft close to its goal of a thrust:weight ratio of unity.

The basics of design thus satisfied, the Mirage 2000 had a long way to go before entering service. Some items from the ACF were salvaged, one of the most vital being the M53 engine. A single-shaft reheated turbofan, the M53 was first bench-tested in February 1970 and taken aloft in a pod on a Caravelle testbed on 18 July 1973. French jet engines tend to be less sophisticated than those built in the UK and USA, but that is not to deny that the M53 is a comparatively light and simple powerplant.

Of modular construction, it has a straightforward design featuring only three low-pressure turbine stages, five high-pressure stages and two turbine stages, all on a single spool. Its afterburner can be used without restriction throughout the flight envelope, which extends to Mach 2.5 at high altitude. Development orders totalled 20, comprising three for bench trials, 10 for air- and ground-testing, three for supersonic trials and four for the ATF programme. M53 met Dassault for the first time at Istres on 22 December 1974 when one of the three supersonic engines was flown in the prototype Mirage F1E.

The F1E's career ended as a testbed for the Mirage 2000 programme, initially with the M53-2, following completion of its 150-hour bench test at Saclay in April 1976. In this form, the M53 was rated at 18,739 lb (83.34 kN) with reheat, improved to 19,842 lb (88.25 kN) in the M53-5 version with which series manufacture was launched. For this variant, the successful 150-hour trial was accomplished in May 1979.

***Dassault's plant at Argenteuil was made responsible for fuselage production, and it was from here on 7 June 1982 that the first recognisable element of Mirage 2000C-01 (left) was taken by road to Bordeaux-Mérignac. There, it was joined with wings from nearby Martignas and a fin built by Aérospatiale at Nantes. Thomson-CSF provided the RDM radar and SNECMA the M53-5 turbofan. The aircraft conducted its maiden flight on 20 November 1982, with Guy Mitaux-Maurouard in command.***

### First Mirage 2000

Three prototype Mirage 2000s ordered in December 1975 had increased to four and to a Dassault-funded two-seat aircraft within a year. A commendable 27 months after the ACF had been cancelled, Mirage 2000 No. 01 was airborne. Hand-built at Dassault's St Cloud facility, the prototype was taken by road to Istres for assembly, flying from there on 10 March 1978 in the hands of Jean Coureau. During the 65-minute sortie, No. 01 accelerated to Mach 1.02 on the 12,125 lb (53.92 kN) of thrust of its M53-2, then climbed to 40,000 ft (12192 m) for an afterburner run at Mach 1.3. By the end of May, No. 01 had demonstrated Mach 2 and an indicated airspeed of 749 mph (1205 km/h) during a total of 13 sorties. The slow-speed characteristics were convincingly demonstrated in public at Farnborough during September 1978, despite the machine having accumulated only some 60 hours.

In a similar but more closely monitored vein, Maurouard and Jean-Marie Saget flew 22 sorties from Istres between November 1980 and March 1981, following which the Mirage 2000 was cleared for all manoeuvres between zero airspeed and 920 mph (1480 km/h). For these trials, various combinations of external fuel tanks and weapons were fitted to No. 01, which was flown at angles of attack exceeding 30°. Fitted with four air-to-air missiles (AAM), the aircraft demonstrated a roll rate of 270° per second throughout the flight envelope. At the same time, the first of two static airframes (No. 06) in the Toulouse fatigue rig was used to clear the Mirage 2000 for high load factors.

It was with an M53-5 installed that 2000-02 first flew at Istres on 18 September 1978, Maurouard being in command for the 50-minute mission. Early trials work concerned the SFENA digital autopilot and weapons carriage and separation. A dummy MATRA R.550 Magic was dropped on 9 March 1981, followed by a MATRA Super 530F on 27 July, while several missions were flown with 374-Imp gal (1700-litre) underwing tanks. After contributing over 500 sorties to the trials programme, No. 02 met an untimely end – and Saget very nearly so – when contaminated fuel caused it to flame out at 250 ft (76 m) while on approach to Istres on 9 May 1984.

Earmarked for weapons trials, No. 03 first flew at Istres on 16 April 1979, fitted with nine hardpoints – although not until 13 November 1980 did it become the first Mirage 2000 to fly with radar. In the course of official trials by all three aircraft at the Centre d'Essais en Vol section at Istres during May 1980,

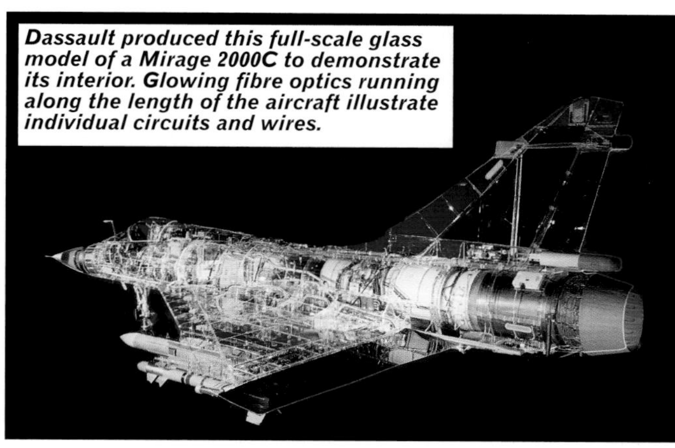

***Dassault produced this full-scale glass model of a Mirage 2000C to demonstrate its interior. Glowing fibre optics running along the length of the aircraft illustrate individual circuits and wires.***

Mirage 2000 hours topped 500, including six sorties flown by pilots of the military trials unit, CEAM. The brief programme enabled the AA to see in detail what was happening to 43 per cent of its equipment budget. Afterwards, No. 01 was fitted with an M53-5 powerplant and then progressed to the definitive M53-P2. The prototype ended its career with retirement to the Museé de l'Air at Le Bourget in 1988. No. 03 flew firing trials of the Super 530F and Magic missiles in 1982, then received an RDI radar for the first launch of a Super 530D from a Mirage 2000 on 26 October 1984.

No. 04 joined its companions in the air on 12 May 1980, fitted from the outset with the full weapons system and being to proposed production standards in other respects. Few changes had to be made to the Mirage 2000 as a result of early flight-testing, but of those which were the most noticeable was a reduction in fin height, in conjunction with an increase in fin sweep. This was brought in with No. 04 and retrospectively applied to earlier aircraft (starting with No. 01 early in 1979), as were extensions to the Karman wingroot fairings to well beyond the trailing edge line. More searching examination would reveal redesigned air intake boundary layer diverters, while an internal modification concerned the FBW system. Mechanical back-up had been available to the triplicated system first installed, but the Mirage 2000 progressed subsequently to quadruplex FBW on roll and pitch axes and triplex FBW for rudder deflection. Nos 03 and 04 flew proving trials with an AA Boeing C-135F tanker in the autumn of 1980 and remained at Istres for more weapons and ECM development work. Like the two before them, the third and fourth aircraft initially flew unpainted. No. 02 received a smart colour scheme of white overall, with French patriotic red and blue trim, for the 1979 Paris air show, and was later joined in this guise by No. 01. No. 03 adopted a purposeful light grey and blue disruptive camouflage scheme.

Last of the five prototypes to fly, the Mirage 2000B-01, was airborne at Istres on 11 October 1980 with Michel Porta as pilot. The sortie increased Mirage 2000 flying hours to 660 and was followed by a further 19 flights and 17 hours by B-01 during the next four weeks. An RDM radar was also installed early in 1981.

A useful demonstration vehicle for an increasing number of interested foreign pilots, B-01 also participated in refuelling trials, and was painted white overall. Further reflecting the Mirage III and F1 programmes, the first production version of the new fighter was the Mirage 2000C, there having been no 2000As.

*The Mirage 2000B is a fully combat-capable training version of the fighter 2000C. Mirage 2000B/Cs serve with six Armée de l'Air squadrons in a primary air defence role. Around 25 per cent of the training, however, is in the ground attack role, for which the aircraft can carry Mk 82 or SAMP general-purpose bombs, ARMAT anti-radiation missiles and MATRA F4 pods for 68-mm rockets.*

# Mirage 2000

## First-generation fighters

**As initially developed, the Mirage 2000 was optimised for air defence, although it also has a secondary attack and reconnaissance capability.**

Mirage 2000 deliveries to 2 Escadre de Chasse (EC 2) commenced in 1984. The first 2000C single-seaters were of the S1 production variant, which featured RDM radar. This did not have a continuous-wave (CW) illuminator, and so the aircraft could not fire the intended MATRA Super 530F missiles. Effectively, armament was restricted to Magic 1 infra-red homing missiles and the internal DEFA 554 30-mm cannon.

The next batch of 2000C-S2s had improved radar, but it was not until the 2000C-S3 that the aircraft gained the CW illuminator needed for Super 530F launch. All S1s and S2s were subsequently brought up to this standard. Delivered alongside the S3s were a number of 2000B two-seaters, which were initially of S3 configuration. Production of single-seat aircraft with RDM radars totalled 37, most serving with EC 2 or with trials units. Power came from the interim M53-5 engine.

A change to the definitive M53-P2 engine and RDI radar heralded the 2000C-S4 and S5. The RDI radar is a pulse-Doppler unit which allows the use of the improved Super 530D missile which has a much-expanded envelope. From very early in the Mirage's operational career the improved Magic 2 IR missile has also been available.

The S4/S5 became the definitive first-generation fighter version, and equips EC 5 and EC 12 in addition to some with EC 2. The S5 has further improved radar compared to the S4, but many of the latter have been upgraded. The electronic warfare suite has also been significantly upgraded, late-production S5s having the automatic Spirale chaff/flare system in place of the earlier Eclair.

Production of S4/S5s reached 87, bringing 2000C deliveries to the Armée de l'Air to 124. The service also received 30 2000B two-seaters, which were completed in S3, S4 and S5 configuration. The trainers are spread throughout the three wings, with the majority being

*The Mirage 2000 did not repeat the extraordinary export success of its delta predecessor, the Mirage III/5, but has notched up useful sales. These Greek 2000EGs display this variant's upgraded EW system, which includes Spirale chaff/flare dispensers just below the fuselage roundel.*

*Seen over Iraq during a Southern Watch sortie, this 2000C-S3 displays the typical air-to-air missile load and the bolt-on refuelling probe.*

***This is one of Abu Dhabi's camera-shy 2000RADs. The tiny Gulf nation's commitment to the type resulted in a 1998 order for the second-generation 2000-9. Older aircraft are to be upgraded.***

concentrated in EC 2/5, the type OCU. The 2000B retains full combat capability, sacrificing some internal fuel to make room for the second seat.

Some of the French single-seaters are being brought up to 2000-5F standard with RDY radar, while the RDI radars released by this programme are being fitted to the survivors of the S3s. More improvements have come about largely as a result of operations over Bosnia, with the addition of SAMIR missile launch warning systems to some aircraft.

## Exports

The 2000C/B, collectively known as the 2000DA (Défense Aérienne), formed the basis for the 2000E (single-seat) and 2000BD (two-seat) export versions. There were five customers for the first generation of Mirage 2000, built in two main series. The first series (2000EM/BM for Egypt, 2000H/TH for India and 2000 P/DP for Peru) was based closely on the standard 2000C/B with RDM radar (with CW illuminator) and standard French-specification EW suite.

However, there were some small but significant differences. India's first few aircraft had the M53-5 engine and were known as 2000H5s and 2000TH5s. They were subsequently re-engined with M53-P2s. The Egyptian aircraft featured an additional radar warning antenna on the fin.

In terms of armament the first export batch had similar weapons to the French Cs, including Super 530F and Magic 2 missiles. Attack options include a variety of free-fall bombs and laser-guided weapons, designated by the ATLIS II pod.

India also procured the ARMAT anti-radiation missile, while Peru uses the Intertechnique 231-300 buddy refuelling pod also employed by the French.

Confusion surrounds India's 2000Hs, as it has often been suggested that they had the Antilope 5 radar from the 2000N/D, and are thus optimised for a strike/attack role.

The second export series comprised 2000EG/BGs for Greece and 2000EAD/DADs for Abu Dhabi. This batch has the improved ICMS Mk 1 EW suite, characterised by additional antennas on the fin. Radar in the Greek aircraft is designated RDM3, with unspecified improvements over the original unit.

Armament options are also expanded, Greek aircraft being able to launch Exocet anti-ship missiles, while Abu Dhabi's Mirages have been integrated to take the GEC-Marconi PGM series of guided missiles.

## Reconnaissance

Included in Abu Dhabi's batch were eight aircraft designated 2000RAD. These are for reconnaissance, Abu Dhabi being the only customer for this variant. Externally, the 2000RAD differs little from the standard single-seater, but has the ability to carry one of three reconnaissance systems on the centreline.

These comprise the Raphäel side-looking imaging radar, HAROLD long-range oblique photography camera and the COR2 multi-sensor general-purpose reconnaissance pod, which contains cameras and an infra-red linescan.

# Mirage 2000C-S4-2

**This aircraft was the last of the S4 variants to be built, fitted with the RDI J2-4 radar. It is seen as it appeared during Operation Daguet (France's contribution to Desert Storm) while based at Al Ahsa AB in Saudi Arabia.**

**5 Escadre de Chasse**
Based at Orange, EC 5 was the first unit to be supplied with the RDI radar-equipped S4 Mirage, and was naturally the first choice to deploy aircraft to the Gulf. In 1998 the wing took over the Mirage 2000 training tasking from EC 2.

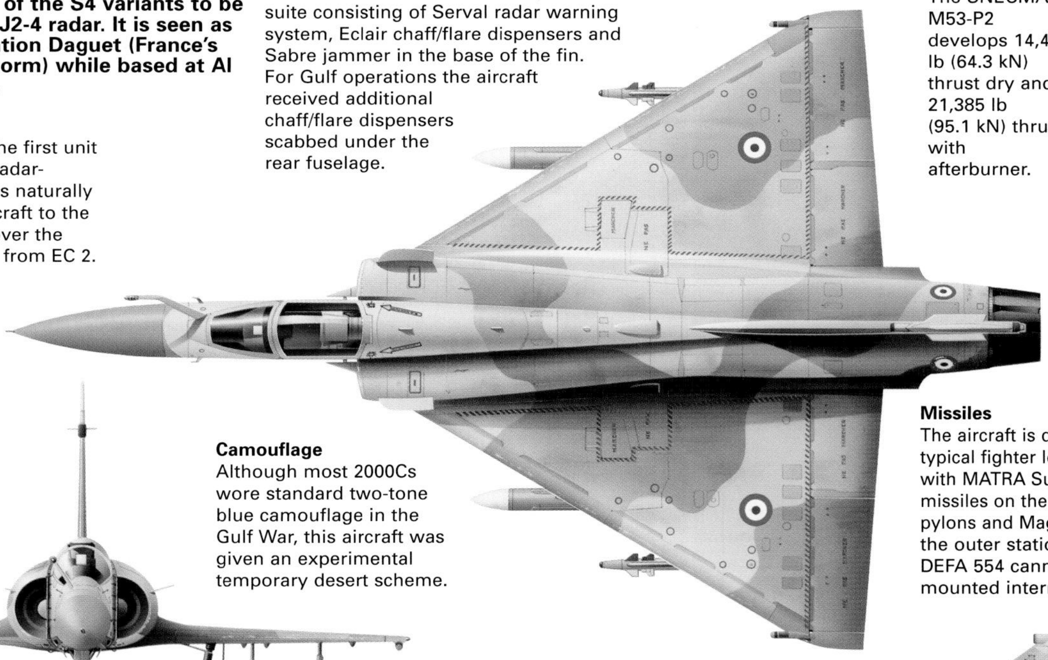

**Desert 2000s**
EC 5 dispatched 14 2000Cs to Al Ahsa for Operation Daguet, beginning CAP operations over Saudi Arabia on 12 December 1990. These continued until later in the war, when the 2000Cs escorted Jaguar and Mirage F1CR attacks. The Mirages did not encounter any Iraqi aircraft.

**Fuel**
Internal fuel capacity is 875 Imp gal (3978 litres), to which is normally added a 286-Imp gal (1300-litre) RPL 522 centreline drop tank. 374-Imp gal (1700-litre) and 440-Imp gal (2000-litre) wing tanks are available.

**Defences**
The 2000C has a standard self-protection suite consisting of Serval radar warning system, Eclair chaff/flare dispensers and Sabre jammer in the base of the fin. For Gulf operations the aircraft received additional chaff/flare dispensers scabbed under the rear fuselage.

**Camouflage**
Although most 2000Cs wore standard two-tone blue camouflage in the Gulf War, this aircraft was given an experimental temporary desert scheme.

**Powerplant**
The SNECMA M53-P2 develops 14,460 lb (64.3 kN) thrust dry and 21,385 lb (95.1 kN) thrust with afterburner.

**Missiles**
The aircraft is depicted in typical fighter loadout, with MATRA Super 530D missiles on the inboard pylons and Magic 2s on the outer stations. Two DEFA 554 cannon are mounted internally.

5-OP

74

# Mirage 2000N
## France's nuclear deterrent

*The primary role of the Mirage 2000N is to be a launch platform for the ASMP nuclear missile. This aircraft, 301, the first production 2000N, carries the standard configuration of an ASMP, with self-defence Magic 2s and large wing tanks.*

**Designed to replace the ageing Mirage IVP, the Mirage 2000N – with the ASMP missile – provides France's sole aerial nuclear attack capability. Later models are also used in a conventional strike role.**

When the Mirage 2000 was being designed, one of its envisaged roles was that of a nuclear penetrator. The aircraft would be used to deliver the new tactical stand-off weapon designed by Aérospatiale and known as the ASMP (Air-Sol Moyenne Portée – Air-to-Ground Medium-Range) missile. Originally, this weapon was carried by the Mirage IVPs of the Strategic Air Forces and the navy's carrier-based Super Etendards. The cancelled ACF (Avion de Combat Futur) had been another candidate for the ASMP. However, due to the age of the Mirage IVP, Dassault received a contract for two prototypes of an interdictor version of the new Mirage 2000, to be designated 2000P ('P' for 'Pénétration'). However, the designation was soon changed to 2000N ('N' for 'Nucléaire') to avoid confusion with the ageing Mirage IVP.

### Designing the 2000N

Due to the high pilot workload that would be encountered during an interdiction mission at low-level, it was decided that a WSO would be needed to undertake radar navigation, control the ECM equipment and manage the armament. The 2000N was based upon the 2000B trainer, but the airframe was strengthened to withstand the stresses of high-subsonic, low-level flight. Some internal equipment was also modified from the original Mirage 2000C interceptor and this reflected the need for greater positional accuracy. In the nose, a Dassault Electronique/Thomson-CSF Antilope V radar replaced the RDM/RDI and this set featured terrain-following, air-to-air, air-to-sea, air-to-ground, ground-mapping and navigation-updating modes.

For self-defence, the 2000N was fitted with Magic 2 AAMs on the outboard wing pylons and

*Above: It was soon realised that a single pilot could not handle the intense workload involved in nuclear interdiction missions, so the two-seat Mirage 2000B trainer was strengthened and modified to withstand the rigours of low-level attack flying.*

*Left: The Mirage 2000N-01 first prototype flew initially on 3 February 1983 at Istres, and is seen here carrying an ASMP missile and the original smaller wing tanks.*

**_4 Escadre de Chasse (EC 4) was formed as the first Mirage 2000N wing and was assigned to nuclear duties with the ASMP missile. Aircraft 306 was an early K1 variant, lacking any conventional ordnance ability, and originally delivered without the Spirale mechanical countermeasures system._**

Dassault Electronique Sabre jammers plus a Serval radar warning receiver. The aircraft could also be fitted with the MATRA Spirale integrated decoy system. Although early 2000Ns lacked Spirale as standard, since 1989 it has been fitted to all aircraft.

The initial requirement was for 100 Mirage 2000Ns, which would be allocated 75 ASMP missiles, some of which would have come from ex-Mirage IVP stocks. However, delays with the Dassault Rafale programme and the need for an interim replacement for the Mirage IIIE meant that a further 70 Mirages were added to the conventional attack role, with the ASMP interface deleted. Generally regarded as 'non-nuclear' aircraft, they were given the designation Mirage 2000N' (N Prime). A reassessment of nuclear requirements resulted in later changes to the number of Ns and N's and, to simplify the distinction between the two, the latter was designated Mirage 2000D in 1990.

## Weaponry

The first 2000Ns, with ASMP capability, were designated K1 sub-types. The ASMP, which is carried on the centreline pylon, delivers a 150- or 300-kT warhead over a maximum range of 50 miles (80 km) from a low-altitude launch point. Provision is made for a pair of large, 528-US gal (2000-litre) drop tanks underwing. From the 32nd 2000N onwards, the designation K2 was used and these aircraft were capable of carrying conventional ordnance or a nuclear payload. The same weaponload is available for the 2000D, 'D' standing for 'Diversifié' (Diversified), the prototype of which (D01, ex-N-01) first flew on 1 January 1990. Weapons that can be carried include the Aérospatiale AS30L and MATRA BGL (Bombe Guidée Laser – laser-guided bomb), both of which are guided by the ATLIS 2 laser designator pod. The MATRA APACHE stand-off dispenser, ARMAT anti-radar missile and AM39 anti-ship missiles are also available to the 2000D.

## Operators

At present, six Escadres de Chasse fly the Mirage 2000 in its 'D' or 'N' form. Mirage 2000Ds are part of the Commandement de la Force Aérienne de Combat (CFAC), France's largest command, which performs air defence, conventional ground-attack and tactical reconnaissance missions. Three squadrons fly from Nancy: EC 1/3 'Navarre', EC 2/3 'Champagne', and EC 3/3 'Ardennes'. Mirage 2000Ds are expected to serve well into the next century and they will be the last of France's current warplane fleet to be replaced by Rafale. It is estimated that, by 2015, the French air force will have a fleet of 300 Rafales and Mirage 2000Ds.

Mirage 2000Ns operate as part of the Commandement des Forces Aériennes Stratégiques (CFAS). The main mission of the strategic air forces is to provide a nuclear deterrent. Since the withdrawal of the Mirage IVP and the phase-out of the ballistic missiles at the Plateau d'Albion, the CFAS nuclear deterrent rests solely with the three Mirage 2000N units. Equipped with the ASMP missile they, together with the French navy's ballistic missile submarines, provide France with its nuclear strike capability. EC 1/4 'Dauphiné' and EC 2/4 'Lafayette' from Luxeuil, while EC 3/4 'Limousin' operates from Istres. Tanker support for the 2000Ns is provided by Istres-based C-135FRs.

## France's airborne nuclear deterrent

**Augmenting and eventually replacing the Mirage IVP in the nuclear strike role, the Mirage 2000N (Nucléaire), with its ASMP missile, is France's primary nuclear strike aircraft. The prototype N-01 first flew in February 1983. Later that year, it flew at the Paris air show, wearing a grey and green upper-surface camouflage to indicate its low-level role. Aircraft N-01 later went on to become the 2000D prototype.**

### ASMP

Designed to provide a more credible penetration capability than Mirage IVs armed with free-fall weapons, the ASMP missile has a reported range of 50 miles (80 km) from low-altitude launch and 155 miles (255 km) from high altitude. A solid propellant booster accelerates the missile to Mach 2, when a ramjet takes over. Intakes for this motor are mounted on the sides, and guidance is inertial with terrain-mapping.

### Spirale

The 2000N-K1s were not originally fitted with Spirale countermeasures, but these have been retrofitted. The system consists of integral infra-red warning receivers, and an interface with the radar warning receivers. These trigger the launch of chaff (starboard) or flare (port) cartridges from boxes in the wing and fuselage fairings. A missile plume detector is located in each Magic launcher.



### Radar

The Dassault Electronique/Thomson-CSF Antilope V is a J-band attack radar, providing ground-mapping and terrain-following functions with additional air-to-air capability. The data are presented on a HUD and on a colour head-down multi-function display.

### Powerplant

The 2000N is powered by the M53-P2, rated at 14,462 lb (64.3 kN) thrust dry and 21,385 lb (95.1 kN) with afterburning. The engine is 16 ft 7½ in (5.07 m) long and has a diameter of 3 ft 5½ in (1.06 m).

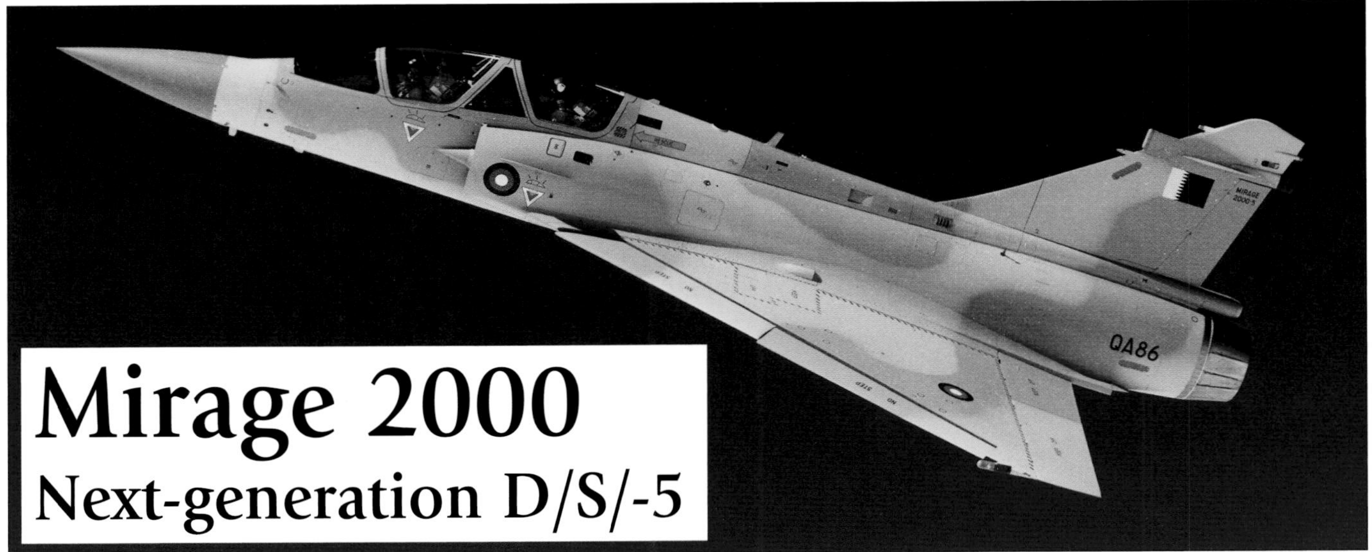


# Mirage 2000
## Next-generation D/S/-5

*Both Dash 5 export customers have acquired two-seaters, in full operational fit. The Qatari aircraft QA86 was the first Qatari Mirage 2000 to fly, late in 1995, and was handed over in France in a ceremony on 8 September 1997.*

**With the D, S and -5 variants of the Mirage 2000, Dassault has dramatically improved the type. The capacity to carry laser-guided bombs and an increased air-to-air capability have ensured that these modern Mirages are selling well, not only in France, but on the export market as well.**

In producing a conventional attack version of the Mirage 2000N – the 2000D – Dassault took the opportunity to install later versions of some equipment to upgrade the aircraft's capabilities. External differences between the two include the deletion of the nose pitot, the addition of ICMS Mk 2 countermeasures, a spine antenna for GPS, and cockpit transparencies covered in gold film to reduce radar reflectivity. Technological advances mean that the crew of the 2000D have more integrated HOTAS controls and are accommodated in what is well on the way to being a 'glass' cockpit.

Dassault proudly proclaims that the 2000D designation stands for the aircraft's Diversifié (diversified) potential; French Air Force squadrons operating other, less heavily-laden fighters call it the '2000 Diesel'.

The key to much of the Mirage 2000D's extra potential in terms of precision weapons is the 750-lb (340-kg) Thomson-CSF PDLCT TV/thermal imaging pod carried on a pylon beneath the starboard air intake. This Pod de Désignation Laser à Caméra Thermique (Laser Designation Pod with Infra-Red Camera) is effective by day or night and is used to direct either an Aérospatiale AS30L missile or MATRA/BAe BGL 1000 bomb. One missile or LGB is carried on the starboard inner wing pylon while two laser weapons and an RPL 522 can be carried on shorter missions, or when aerial refuelling is available.

From 2000, the MATRA/BAe APACHE will be available. This stand-off weapon has a small turbojet, wings, INS and a radar to enable it attack airfields up to 87 miles (140 km) from the release point.

Variants of the D include the Mirage 2000D-R1N1L (this designation was given to the first six Mirage 2000Ds). This variant initially had the ability only to launch the AS30L and BGL 1000, plus Magic AAMs. It gained IOC on 29 July 1993, giving the French air force an urgently needed LGB capability. By June 1995, all had been upgraded to full R1 standard.

The 2000D-R1N1 could carry an increased range of weapons, with possibly as few as four aircraft being supplied in this configuration. Another variant, the Mirage 2000D-R1, is able to operate with all the conventional weapons detailed above, apart from the APACHE (armée propulsée a charges éjectables) and SCALP (a development of APACHE).

In late 1999, production will switch to the Mirage 2000D-R2, which will have the added ability to launch APACHE, as well as full automation of the self-defence suite by integration of the SAMIR missile plume detector with chaff/flare dispensers and jammers, and provision for ATLIS II laser guidance pods. A third production standard,

*The two-seat strike/attack variants outnumber the single-seat fighters in French service. Based on the 2000N, which in turn came from the 2000B trainer but with airframe strengthening to cope with the rigours of low-level buffet, the 2000D has a new weapon system, with Antilope 5 or 53 radar providing various ground-mapping functions and terrain avoidance.*

*This 2000D is in typical precision attack fit for a longer-range mission, carrying two Aérospatiale AS30L laser-guided missiles. The latter is the primary weapon of the 2000D, with designation provided by the PDLCT FLIR/laser pod or ATLIS II TV/laser pod. Like the Super 530D air-to-air missile, AS30Ls are flight-time limited and are carried sparingly for training.*

***Left: Taiwan's 48 Mirage 2000-5EIs serve with the 2nd TFW at Hsinchu. Optimised for air defence duties, they were supplied with MATRA/BAe Magic 2 and Mica missiles.***

***Below: Marked simply 'S' on the fin and carrying the legend 'Mirage 2000S', this aircraft is, in fact, a standard 2000N masquerading as the export version.***

designated Mirage 2000D-R3, was originally proposed with provision for SCALP and a reconnaissance pod. Cancellation of the -R3 was announced in June 1996 as part of defence economies.

### Mirage 2000S

Dassault used the 2000S designation for a non-nuclear interdictor to be offered for export. Essentially a parallel to the 2000D, it was quietly dropped from promotional literature in the mid-1990s before any could be sold. However, two Mirage 2000Ns had been marked with the '2000S' logo for air show exhibition in 1989 and 1990.

### Mirage 2000-5

The Mirage 2000-5 brings together the Thomson-CSF RDY radar, the APSI cockpit, MATRA/BAe Mica missiles and the ICMS Mk 2 self-defence system in a major update of the original interceptor weapons system. This was first achieved in a two-seat aircraft, 'CY1', which flew initially on 27 April 1991 wearing '01' on the fin (it was subsequently converted to the single-place prototype).

Internal aspects of the 2000-5 include the uprating of the engine-driven generators and the installation of an advanced HUD for the pilot. For export, the fully-automated ICMS Mk 2 significantly improves upon the self-defence suite of the Mirage 2000D by adding a receiver/processor in the nose and secondary DF antennas on the wingtip pods.

### 2000-5 variants

Originally indifferent to the private-venture 2000-5, the French air force was eventually prevailed upon to allocate funding to the conversion of 37 existing airframes to 2000-5F standard. The initial 'production' conversion, No. 38, was handed over at Istres on 30 December 1997 to meet contractual obligations, but did not transfer to CEAM to begin pilot conversions until April 1998. The initial standard of conversions for the French air force differs slightly from the 2000-5 baseline as promoted for export, most notably in the omission of the two superhet antennas from the fin. The Mirage 2000-5F-SF1 retains the French standard self-protection equipment (Serval, Sabre and Spirale), but with slight modifications. Armament is optimised for the air defence role, the normal configuration being four Micas on pylons beneath the wingroots and a pair of Magic 2s outboard. When available, the IR version of Mica will replace Magic. The Mirage 2000-5F-SF2 is a projected French air force upgrade.

Exports of the Mirage 2000-5 were launched in November 1992 and designated 2000-5E, on receipt of a major order from Taiwan for 60. Qatar later announced a contract for 12 and Abu Dhabi (for the UAE) added 30 more to the order book, as well as funding an upgrade for 33 older aircraft (the UAE batch is described under the 2000-5 Mk II heading). Qatar's order (contract Falcon) of July 1994 included nine single-seat aircraft, designated Mirage 2000-5EDA. The air-to-air missiles are Mica and Magic 2, but the aircraft also have an air-to-ground role with the MATRA/BAe Black Pearl stand-off missile; AS30L and BGL 1000, with appropriate designator; and BAP 100, Durandal and Belouga air-to-ground weapons.

Mica and Magic are also the prime armament of Taiwan's 48 single-seat Mirage 2000-5EIs, the first squadron of which gained IOC in November 1997. Their configuration is similar to the air defence-optimised -5F, apart from having all five fin antennas. Deliveries to Taiwan began with the arrival of the first five by sea on 5 May 1997.

### Mirage 2000-5 Mk II

After a protracted competition, Abu Dhabi ordered 30 new Mirage 2000s in December 1997, requiring delivery to take place between late 1998 and late 2001. All 33 remaining Mirage 2000EADs, RADs and two-seat DADs will also be modified to this standard, originally named 2000-9, but rechristened Mirage 2000-5 Mk II in 1999. The $3.4 billion deal was not finalised until November 1998, with an attendant slippage in delivery dates.

The -9 was specifically developed to satisfy Abu Dhabi's requirement for a long-range attack aircraft, which could also carry six Mica missiles. In November 1998 it was announced that the -9 would be armed with the MATRA/BAe Dynamics Black Shaheen, a development of the SCALP EG/Storm Shadow being produced for the RAF and Armée de l'Air.

The original Mirage 2000B prototype served as a radar test-bed before being fully upgraded to become the first 2000-5. It carried the identity 'B01' and was broadly representative of the export configuration, apart from lacking the third forward-facing fin antenna.

Export trainers with RDY radar have been supplied to two overseas operators of the Dash 5E. Qatar's three Mirage 2000-5DDAs are partners to nine 5EDAs. Taiwan has 12 Mirage 2000-5DIs, of which aircraft No. 2051 was the first export Mirage 2000-5 to fly, in October 1995. The initial aircraft was handed over in France on 9 May 1996.

***Above: In maximum-range configuration, the 2000-5F carries a centreline RPL 522 tank and wing-mounted RPL 541/542 tanks which can increase endurance from one and a half to three hours. Endurance can be further improved with the addition of a a bolt-on refuelling probe.***

***Right: Originally 'CY1', the first Mirage 2000-5, this aircraft went on to become the 2000-5 demonstrator and is seen here completed in export configuration with the ICMS Mk 2 EW suite.***

# Mirage 2000 operators

**Mirage 2000s, despite their cost and complexity, achieved notable sales success in the early 1980s. A slump in the late 1980s and early 1990s resulted in the Dash 5, which is beginning to win back orders.**

## India

India placed an order for 40 Mirage 2000s, including 36 single-seaters, in October 1982. To expedite deliveries, the first 26 were produced with M53-5 engines, and carried a '5' in their designation. KF101 flew on 21 September 1984 and, after pilot training in France, the first batch of seven was delivered by air from 20-29 June 1985. The local name of 'Vajra' loosely translates as 'Thunderbolt'. Ten final aircraft from the first Indian contract and a follow-up batch of six, ordered in March 1996 and delivered by October 1988, were supplied with M53-P2 engines. The earlier 26 were upgraded to this standard in India. Configuration and colour scheme (black radome) was as for the French 2000C but, by 1993, at least two had received mid-brown and dark-green upper surface camouflage, suggestive of low-level tasking. IAF Vajras have always had a dual role, being able to carry MATRA ARMAT anti-radar missiles, Durandal anti-runway bombs and Belouga cluster bombs as alternatives to Magic and Super 530 missiles. However, at the arrival ceremony for the first seven aircraft, it was stated that the 2000H has an Antilope 5 radar and a second ULISS 52 INS, implying it to be a single-seat version of the 2000D interdictor. This apparent contradiction has never been fully resolved. Operating squadrons are Nos 1 and 7 at Gwalior.

## Peru

The Peruvian air force's intention to order 14 2000Ps was announced in December 1982 and renegotiated in July 1984 due to financial problems. In all, 10 were delivered to Escuadrón 412 at La Joya from December 1986 onwards, together with Thomson-CSF ATLIS laser designators, 2,205-lb (1000-kg) MATRA guided bombs, MATRA AS30L missiles and a selection of free-fall bombs. Peru's Mirage 2000Ps, along with Venezuelan F-16s, are arguably 'top dog' in South America. Along with the nation's MiG-29s, they represent the most modern fighter design in the region.

Peru was initially to have acquired three two-seaters, but this was reduced to two 2000DPs. They serve with Escuadrón de Caza-Bombardeo 412 at La Joya. Peru's Mirage 2000Ps have a dual-role tasking, and are often seen armed with bombs. They also have the ability to fit ATLIS for the designation of AS30L missiles and MATRA BGL bombs.

## Qatar

Qatar's order of July 1994 included nine single-seat 2000-5EDAs. They have the full ICMS Mk 2 defensive aids suite, including five fin antennas, secondary wingtip sensors and provision for Spirale, plus a GPS aerial in the spine. Air-to-air missiles are MICA and Magic 2, but the aircraft also have an air-to-ground role with the MATRA/BAe Black Pearl stand-off missile (which is an export adaptation of APACHE); AS30L and BGL 1000, with appropriate designator; and BAP 100, Durandal and Belouga. An 882-lb (400-kg) Thomson-CSF ASTAC ground radar locator pod can also be carried. The first four Qatari aircraft (including three -5DDAs) arrived on 18 December 1997, after training in France.

## Egypt

Egypt was the first export customer for the Mirage 2000, but the second recipient. The contract placed in December 1981 included 16 single-seat 2000EMs, the first of which flew in December 1985. A unique feature of the 2000EM is a single, rear-facing antenna above the Serval DF unit, high on the fin trailing edge. Based at Berigat, the aircraft are in a colour scheme of medium-grey upper surfaces (with a black radome, however) and light-grey undersides. Armament includes Magic, Super 530, ARMAT ASMs and AS30L ASMs, with an ATLIS laser designator.

## France

The Armée de l'Air marked its 50th anniversary in 1984 by receiving its first squadron of Mirage 2000Cs. Escadron de Chasse 1/2 'Cigognes', the famous 'Storks' squadron, was based at Dijon where, by early 1985, it had achieved full squadron strength, including trainers. Two further wings were soon equipped with the 2000C, replacing Mirage IIIEs and Mirage F1Cs. Incorporated into the Force Aérienne Tactique, Mirage 2000Cs are assigned to home defence and overseas intervention, where they have been involved in conflicts such as Desert Storm and Deny Flight over Bosnia. Once the interceptor and air defence roles had been established, thoughts turned to that of nuclear attack. Equipped with the ASMP nuclear stand-off missile, the two-seat 2000N, which was based on the trainer 2000B, was delivered to two squadrons, replacing Mirage IIIEs and Jaguars. EC 1/4 'Dauphine' was the first unit to receive the 2000N on 12 July 1989. Due to delays in the Rafale programme, further 2000Ns were ordered, including a version without the ASMP interface, and this was eventually designated 2000D. The Ds are used for precision attack, with laser-guided weapons such as the AS30L, and equip three squadrons, all based at Nancy. The advanced 2000-5 is slowly entering service with the Armée de l'Air, with the first squadron (EC 2/2) receiving its examples in July 1999. These aircraft are refitted Cs and incorporate new avionics and weapon capabilities.

## Taiwan

Orders for the Dash 5 Mirage 2000 were led by Taiwan, which has acquired 60 as part of the major revamping of the RoCAF fighter forces. These comprise 48 2000-5EIs and 12 -5DI two-seat trainers. Magic 2 and MICA air-to-air missiles were included in the deal, and the 2000-5EIs are tasked with air defence missions. Taiwan's Dash 5s serve with the 2nd TFW at Hsinchu and, like the aircraft for Qatar, the Taiwanese Mirages have the full ICMS Mk 2 electronic countermeasures suite. Deliveries to Taiwan began with the arrival by sea on 5 May 1997 of the first five aircraft. There is a requirement for a second batch of 60.

## Greece

Greece's 36 Mirage 2000EGs were ordered in March 1985 and were delivered from March 1988 onwards to 331 and 332 Squadrons at Tanagra for air defence duties with Super 530D and Magic 2 AAMs. The exact version of radar is reported to be RDM3, which was initially covered by a black radome, later changed to grey. Greece operates four two-seaters, fitted with full mission equipment, including ICMS Mk 1. Greece's 40 aircraft were bought primarily for the defence of Athens. They have been considerably upgraded, and some now have a secondary Exocet anti-ship capability. In addition, Greece placed an order for 18 Dash 5 Mk II aircraft in 2000 and announced its intention to upgrade ten earlier aircraft to a similar standard.

## Abu Dhabi

Between May 1983 and 1985, Abu Dhabi ordered 22 Mirage 2000EADs. Acceptance was delayed by the customer's dissatisfaction with the standard of equipment installed, and not until November 1989 were the first flown to the Middle East. Self-defence aids include Spirale chaff/flare dispensers in the Karman fairings and Elettronica ELT/158 radar warning receivers and ELT/558 jammers in place of the standard French equipment, the new fit being known as SAMET. A further unusual feature is the adaptation to carry AIM-9 Sidewinder AAMs as alternatives to Magic (which is also used). Nos I and II Squadrons fly Mirage 2000s at Maqatra. Abu Dhabi was also the only purchaser of the 2000RAD reconnaissance sub-variant, of which eight were acquired. Six 2000DAD two-seaters were also included in Abu Dhabi's first batch, finished in a grey scheme. After a protracted competition, Abu Dhabi ordered 30 new Mirage 2000s in December 1997, requiring delivery to take place between late 1998 and late 2001. All 33 remaining Mirage 2000EADs, RADs and two-seat DADs will also be modified to this standard, originally named 2000-9, but rechristened Mirage 2000-5 Mk II in 1999. This includes the ability to launch Black Shaheen, an export version of Storm Shadow/SCALP.

*On its very last flight on 24 January 1994 the Rafale A technology demonstrator led all five aircraft for this fine family portrait. Rafale A was slightly bigger than the four operational prototypes which followed, which comprised a single-seat Armée de l'Air aircraft (C 01), two-seater (B 01) and two single-seaters for the Aéronavale (M 01 and M 02).*

# Dassault Rafale

## French superfighter

**Rafale is a French combat aircraft with French engines and French avionics – a flagship for its home country's military industries and an affirmation of French determination to be second to none in the Europe of the 21st century.**

Public knowledge of what was to become Rafale dates back to June 1982, when Dassault announced that studies were under way to develop a successor to the Mirage 2000, under the acronym ACX (Avion de Combat Experimental). France was then holding discussions with Britain and West Germany with regard to a new multinational fighter, although all three nations continued with their own developments. ACX proceeded with a contract for two (later reduced to one) technology demonstrator aircraft on 13 April 1983.

Development of ACX continued apace, even as the international collaborative effort foundered, mainly on the insistence by the French that Dassault should have design leadership, and irreconcilable requirements (France was determined on an 8-tonne fighter, whereas the other partners wanted a 9.5-tonne aircraft). In April 1985 ACX was christened Rafale (squall), shortly before Britain, West Germany, Italy and Spain announced that they would proceed without France on what would become the Eurofighter, based on BAe's EAP project.

*To start its test programme as early as possible, the Rafale A demonstrator initially flew with General Electric F404 engines (as used by the F/A-18). From February 1990 it began flying with the intended M88 engine, initially fitted in the port bay only. Rafale A eventually contributed 865 flights to the flight test programme.*

*Still struggling along with ancient F-8P Crusaders in the fighter role, the Aéronavale had the most pressing need for re-equipment with Rafale. Consequently, two of the four prototypes were of the carrier-capable Rafale M variant, which became the first variant in service. The second of these was the main testbed for the operational avionics suite. Here, M 02 launches from FNS Foch with a typical air-to-air load of MICA and Magic 2 missiles.*

There was never any doubt that Rafale would not proceed at full pace and, on 14 December 1985, the Rafale A technology demonstrator was taken by truck from Dassault's St Cloud plant to Istres, from where it made its first flight on 4 July 1986, piloted by Guy Mitaux-Maurouard. During the first flight it achieved Mach 1.3, 36,000 ft (10973 m) and pulled 5 *g*. The aircraft showed its Mirage origins by having a near-delta wing, but featured the fourth-generation fighter trademarks of underslung intakes and canard foreplanes. Power initially came from a pair of General Electric F404 turbofans, as SNECMA's new M88 powerplant was far from ready. During early tests Rafale A easily achieved Mach 2, vindicating the intake/forward fuselage design. On 14 February 1987 the French government formally announced

***Following Gulf War experience, Armée de l'Air planners altered the requirement to tailor the Rafale B two-seater (previously regarded as a combat-capable trainer) to operational attack missions, the workload in combat being perceived to be too high in single-seat attack types for one pilot alone.***

nosewheel then extends as the aircraft launches, forcing the nose upwards. A series of dummy deck trials in the United States allowed Rafale M 01 to undertake the type's first carrier landing, on *Foch*, on 19 April 1993.

Next of the prototypes to fly was the two-seater Rafale B 01, which took to the air on 30 April 1993, followed by the second Rafale M on 8 November 1993. The two naval aircraft were extensively involved in a series of deck trials to clear the aircraft for carrier operations with a variety of loads. This signified the urgency placed on replacement of the Crusader on French carrier decks, notably to equip the new nuclear-powered carrier *Charles de Gaulle*.

that Rafale would be developed for combat.

During 1987 the aircraft made an important series of approaches to French navy carriers to validate the type's suitability for naval operations. After a lay-up, Rafale A flew again on 27 February 1990, fitted with an M88 engine in the port bay. The other F404 was later replaced by the intended engine.

Rafale A ended its flight test programme in January 1994, by which time it had been joined by four pre-production combat aircraft. The first of these to fly was C 01, the single-seat prototype for the Armée de l'Air. As well as being smaller than the A, the Rafale C introduced a host of new features, including reshaped wingroot fairings and gold-coated canopy which were part of the 'stealth' features. The airframe was liberally sprinkled with antennas (or, at first, their mountings) for the SPECTRA self-defence suite, reputedly one of the most advanced in the world and capable of directional jamming. The recontoured nose was yet to house the multi-mode RBE2 radar, which was first flown in B 01. Rafale C 01 took to the air on 19 May 1991, demonstrating 'supercruise' (flying supersonically in dry thrust) on this maiden flight.

On 12 December 1991 Rafale M 01 joined the test fleet. The M is the carrier version for the Aéronavale, and features a vastly strengthened undercarriage, arrester hook and unique 'jump strut' nosewheel. Held compressed during the initial phase of the catapult stroke, the

In a change of requirement, the Armée de l'Air announced in May 1992 that the majority of its aircraft would be two-seaters, intended to replace attack-roled Jaguars. Rafale Cs are required to replace Mirage F1 interceptors and F1CR reconnaissance aircraft. Initial deliveries will be to a lower equipment standard than fully specified in order to get Rafale into service as quickly possible. However, budgetary stretch-outs have slowed down the production programme considerably – the first production example, a Rafale B, took to the air in December 1998. On 4 December 2000, the first of 60 Aéronavale Rafale Ms was accepted, while the Armée de l'Air will debut the B/C aircraft in service from 2005. France and Dassault have intimated that they would also grant priority to any export customer.

***Above: The Rafale's cockpit (this is M 01) is one of the most advanced in the world, fully utilising touch-sensitive screen and HOTAS technology. The primary displays are three large multi-function displays and a wide-angle single-glass HUD. The latter can have FLIR imagery overlaid to provide the pilot with a 'window in the night'.***

***The Armée de l'Air will procure both single- and two-seaters, with a preponderance of the latter. Both air force variants are known collectively as the Rafale D (Discret = discreet), alluding to the type's 'stealthy' properties.***

# Rafale nears service

*Rafale M1, the first navalised production aircraft, maintains 80 per cent structural and systems commonality with the single-seat Rafale C. The initial software standard permits air defence missions against multiple targets. Later, F1.1-standard software will add IR-guided MICA AAMs, and a datalink for communication with the E-2C.*

**The Rafale prototype flew before the rival Eurofighter, and for some years the French programme seemed to stay 'ahead' of the multi-national Eurofighter effort. This is perhaps unsurprising, since Rafale is a simpler, less capable aircraft, while most of Eurofighter's delays were a function of domestic German political difficulties.**

In recent years, however, funding problems have delayed the Rafale programme, and the aircraft is only now on the verge of entering service, five years after it was originally planned.

The original Rafale A demonstrator flew between 4 July 1986 and 24 January 1994, and was followed into the air by four further prototypes, though these were officially defined as pre-production aircraft. They consisted of a single Rafale C prototype, which flew on 19 May 1991, two carrier-capable Rafale Ms (these flying on 12 December 1991 and 8 November 1993) and a single Rafale B two-seater, which flew on 30 April 1993.

The French Armée de l'Air was originally expected to receive predominantly single-seat Rafale Cs, but in 1991 switched its preference to an operationally-equipped two-seat Rafale B, announcing that 60 per cent of its aircraft would be two-seaters. It had once been intended that the aircraft would enter service in three successively more developed standards (*Standard Utilisateur* 0, 1 and 2), though these were replaced by a single Armée de l'Air standard, with an export equivalent, with three successive software standards (F1, F2 and F3).

*The first production Rafale B (301) first flew on 24 November 1998. The first two aircraft have been assigned to the CEV. Once in service, the B will be capable of one- or two-crew operations.*

## Production begins

Production of the Rafale was formally launched in December 1992, but was then suspended in November 1995, with work on the first production aircraft halting in April 1996. The programme was effectively relaunched in January 1997, with Dassault and the French MoD agreeing a 48 aircraft production programme (28 firm orders and 20 options) for delivery between 2002 and 2007. The French requirement for Rafales is much greater, of course, with the Armée de l'Air expected to take about 212 aircraft (reduced slightly from the 139 Rafale Bs and 95 Rafale Cs outlined in 1992), and the Aéronavale taking 60 Rafale Ms.

The first production Rafale (a two-seat Rafale B, 301) made its maiden flight on 24 November 1998, and then flew to the CEV (Centre d'Essais en Vol) at Istres for development work. The first production Rafale M (No.1) followed on 7 July 1999, and a second Rafale B production aircraft (302) flew later in 1999.

It was once planned that the first ten Armée de l'Air Rafales would be rushed into service to equip a trials and export promotion half squadron, but these plans were quickly abandoned and deliveries are now expected

*B01, the first Rafale B prototype, and M01, the first naval prototype, demonstrate different weapon loads. The wingtip pylons accept either MICA (B01) or Magic (M01) AAMs. A maximum of three external tanks can be carried.*

***Rafale M01 fires a MICA AAM development round during trials. Both IR- and active radar-guided variants of this new weapon are available; Rafale can carry as many as eight in the air defence role.***

from 2002, with IOC being achieved in 2005.

## First ALA squadron

The first operational Armée de l'Air Rafales will enter service at St Dizier Robinson with Escadre de Chasse 7. The unit is presently equipped with the SEPECAT Jaguar, and reduced from three Escadrons to a single enlarged Escadron in mid-2001. Its first Rafale will be the third production Rafale B, No.303, which will also be the only Armée de l'Air Rafale with the original baseline F1 software standard. The rest of EC 7's 34 early Rafales will have the multi-role F2 software, which will give the RBE2 radar a number of air-to-ground modes, and which will allow the aircraft to use the new Apache/Scalp stand-off missile. F2 Rafales will also have Link 16 MIDS and the OSF IRST system, and will use IR-guided Mica in place of the ageing R550 Magic AAM. The Rafale is expected to be declared operational in 2005, allowing the last Jaguars to be withdrawn from use.

Subsequent Armée de l'Air Rafales will have F3 software, giving compatability with the ASMP cruise missile, the new ANF anti-ship missile (being developed to replace Exocet), a range of recce pods, a buddy-buddy inflight refuelling store and a Topsight E helmet-mounted sight (HMS) system for the pilot. All Armée de l'Air Rafales will be brought up to this software standard during routine depot-level maintenance. Details have not yet been released, but it is expected that the first F3 standard Rafales will be used to supplant the Armée de l'Air's remaining Mirage F1s, which are expected to disappear from service entirely by 2015, when 140 Rafales will have been delivered.

Development work on the Rafale continues, and the first service aircraft may incorporate additional features. At the 2001 Paris Air salon at Le Bourget, for example, a Rafale appeared with massive conformal tanks on each side of the fuselage spine, and there have been frequent reports that various 'stealth' features are still being developed for the aircraft.

Dassault and the Aéronavale began catapult and arrested landing trials of the Rafale M at NAS Patuxent River and NAS Lakehurst in July-August 1992, with a second series of trials following in January-February 1993. Deck trials were then carried out on the carrier *Foch*, before two further US trials in November-December 1993 and October-December 1995. The first prototype was joined by the second for trials on Foch in January-February 1994 and the second aircraft then undertook a third series of deck trials aboard *Foch* in October-November 1994.

## Aéronavale deliveries

The Aéronavale is expected to take delivery of ten aircraft with the original F1 (air defence only) software standard, and eight of these equipped 12 Flotille aboard the *Charles de Gaulle* from mid 2001, gaining IOC during 2002. The basic F1 software standard will quickly be replaced on these aircraft with an F1.1 release, adding compatability with the IR-homing version of the Mica AAM, and a MIDS datalink to allow secure communication and data transfer with the Aéronavale's new Grumman E-2C Hawkeyes. The next 15 will have F2 software, and will allow the formation of the second unit, 11 Flotille, from 2005. The final 35 aircraft will have F3 software (which will be retrofitted to all earlier Rafale Ms by 2008) and the force will be brought up to three squadrons, all shore-based at Landivisiau, and using a core fleet of 40 aircraft, with 20 more kept in reserve. With the French Navy having reduced from a two-carrier force (with *Clemenceau* and *Foch*) to a single carrier fleet (with the new carrier *Charles de Gaulle*) significant further Rafale M orders seem unlikely.

***Different air-to-surface and air-to-air weapon load-outs are demonstrated in these two views of Armée de l'Air development airframe B01. In the photograph above, the aircraft is armed with Matra BAe APACHE stand-off weapons dispensers, three external fuel tanks and wingtip IR-guided MICA self-defence AAMs. At left, the aircraft carries a similar load of fuel, in conjuction with four inert GBU-12 laser-guided bombs and wingtip Magic AAMs. Note also the detachable (fixed) in-flight refuelling probe. On a low-level penetration mission with 12 551-lb (250-kg) bombs, four MICA AAMs and 880 Imp gal (4000 litres) of fuel in three external tanks, the Rafale has a combat radius of 655 miles (1055 km).***

# Super Etendard

Selected largely for political reasons, in preference to a maritime variant of the Anglo-French Jaguar, the Super Etendard, although quite fast, has a very poor radius of action when carrying weapons.

**The combination of Super Etendard aircraft and Exocet missile was used with devastating effect during the Falklands conflict and in the Persian Gulf. However, the combat successes of the Super Etendard cannot hide some serious deficiencies in performance, range and payload capability.**

Once the Super Etendard had achieved all of its development criteria, 71 production aircraft began replacing Etendard IVs and F-8E(FN) Crusader interceptors in the Aéronavale's Flottilles 11, 14 and 17 from June 1978.

By the time the Falklands War started, in April 1982, the Argentine navy (sole Super Etendard export customer) had received the first five of 14 aircraft on order to equip CANA's 2º Escuadrilla at BAN Cdte Espora when not carrier-based, together with five AM39 Exocets. Operating from Rio Gallegos, these made their operational debut sinking HMS *Sheffield* off the Falklands on 4 May 1982, followed by the destruction of the supply ship *Atlantic Conveyor* on 25 May, for no Super Etendard losses. At least three have since been lost by 2º Escuadrilla of 3º Escuadra, which still operates the rest from Cdte Espora.

In October 1983 five Aéronavale Super Etendards were leased to the Iraqi air force and a substantial number of AM39s were sold for use against Iranian tankers in the Iran/Iraq war, scoring many successes. The four surviving aircraft were returned to France in early 1985, following replacement by Agave-equipped Mirage F1EQs.

A mid-1980s upgrade programme costing some FFr 2 billion ($400 million) was planned to extend the long-range attack and anti-ship strike capabilities of the Aéronavale's nearly 60 surviving Super Etendards. Some 53 had already been modified at Cuers to launch the 300-kT Aérospatiale ASMP stand-off nuclear weapon. Main changes were avionics modernisation, including new cockpit instrumentation, HOTAS, and a new Electronique Dassault Anémone radar which incorporated track-while-scan, air-to-surface ranging, ground-mapping and search functions. Provision has also been made for night-vision goggles, while airframe changes to ensure a 6,500-hour fatigue life will help to extend Super Etendard service until about 2008.

The prototype upgraded Super Etendard first flew from Istres on 5 October 1990, Dassault modifying two more for operational development. Following disbandment of Flottille 14 in July 1991, prior to its eventual re-equipment as Aéronavale's first Rafale M fighter unit, its Super Etendards replaced the last 11 Etendard IVPs of Escadrille de Servitude 59S at Hyères. They were used for the operational conversion of French naval pilots after deck-landing training in Fouga Zéphyrs at the same base.

## 'SuE' today

Operation Tridente, the overall French contribution to Operation Allied Force, marked the first time that Aéronavale Super Etendards had taken laser-guided weapons and designators to war. The ongoing Super Etendard Modernisée (SEM) five-stage modernisation programme has enabled the 'SuE' to use such weapons. By the time of Allied Force, 16 of the so-called Standard 3 SEMs had been delivered, this version being able to drop the 500-lb

*With one of its Etendard ancestors looking on, an early production Super Etendard taxis into position for take off. This aircraft (No. 10) belonged to the first operating squadron, Flottille 11.*

***Right:** The first of 14 Super Etendards for the Argentine naval air arm is seen in France during 1981, prior to delivery. Five aircraft had been handed over by the time the Falklands War started, of which one was used as a spares source. The others destroyed two British ships.*

***Below:** The Super Etendard's most recent, and almost certainly its last, combat appearance was over Kosovo, where aircraft operating off* Foch *were utilised in the attack and reconnaissance roles.*

(227-kg) GBU-12 Paveway II LGB and fire the AS30L laser-guided missile, both employing the ATLIS laser designator. All were embarked with Flottille 11 on the aircraft-carrier *Foch*, which sailed into the Adriatic in January 1999 as part of Task Force 470.

Six of the 16 were equipped with ATLIS and designated targets for the other SEMs, which carried either a single AS30L or up to two LGBs. The Standard 3 SEMs are not capable of carrying the ATLIS as well as the LGBs. This forced 11F to conduct LGB operations using the buddy-lasing concept.

During Allied Force the SEMs flew 412 offensive combat missions, dropping 266 bombs and firing two AS30L missiles. Eighty-eight missions were cancelled, largely due to bad weather and the high probability of collateral damage.

The next phase of the Super's modernisation programme will incorporate modifications to allow the LGB/ATLIS combination to be carried simultaneously by one aircraft. This Standard 4 will also include the option of carrying a new reconnaissance pod that would be carried semi-recessed under the belly. The internal cannon would have to be removed. When the four Standard 4s became operational, the Aéronavale retired the last Etendard IVPs. The Aéronavale tested the prototype of this combination in January 1999 aboard *Foch*.

Standard 4 also incorporates a new self-defence package, consisting of the Sherloc radar warning receiver, programmable chaff/flare dispensers to be attached to two new underwing pylons, and a new secure frequency-hopping radio. The development of the final standard (Standard 5) started in early 2000, and incorporates a night precision attack capability for operations from 2003. FLIR and night-vision goggles are the main characteristics of this standard. The Aéronavale is currently looking for a laser designator pod for night operations, since the electro-optical ATLIS is daylight-only.

## Super Etendard

**In service for over 20 years, the Super Etendard, despite suffering many failings, is only now preparing itself for retirement, with the Rafale being its designated successor. This example belonged to the now defunct 14 Flottille, which was based at Landivisiau.**

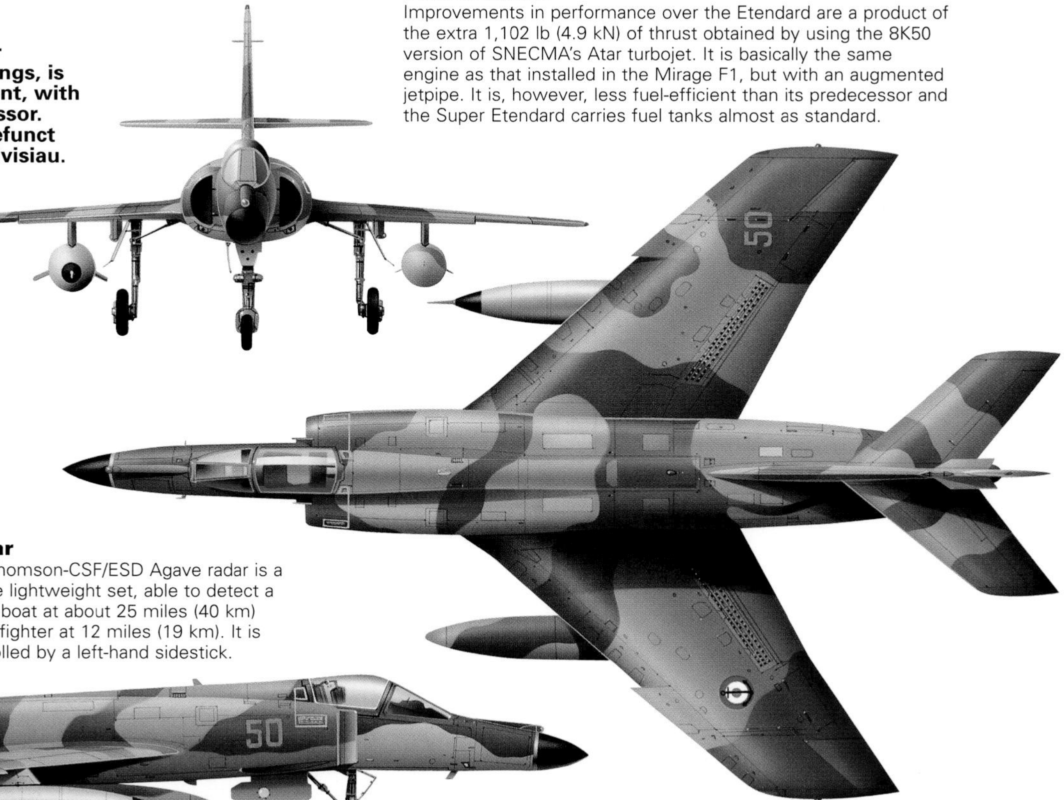

**Performance**
Improvements in performance over the Etendard are a product of the extra 1,102 lb (4.9 kN) of thrust obtained by using the 8K50 version of SNECMA's Atar turbojet. It is basically the same engine as that installed in the Mirage F1, but with an augmented jetpipe. It is, however, less fuel-efficient than its predecessor and the Super Etendard carries fuel tanks almost as standard.

**Armament**
Until recent developments, the Super Etendard's (at least in French service) weapon options began with the AN 52 tactical nuclear weapon of 15-kT yield. Conventional armament included two DEFA 552 cannon, four LR 150 rocket launchers and six 551-lb (250-kg) or four 882-lb (400-kg) bombs. For air defence, a MATRA R550 Magic AAM is fitted to each outer wing pylon in conjunction with a 132-Imp gal (600-litre) centreline fuel tank.

**Radar**
The Thomson-CSF/ESD Agave radar is a simple lightweight set, able to detect a patrol boat at about 25 miles (40 km) and a fighter at 12 miles (19 km). It is controlled by a left-hand sidestick.

# Dassault/Dornier Alpha Jet

## More than just a trainer

*In celebration of NATO's Tiger Meet held at Beja, Portugal in May 1996, this Alpha Jet from Escuadra 301 'Jaguares', PAF was appropriately decorated in 'tiger stripe' markings.*

**Developed by France as a jet trainer and Germany as a light-attack aircraft, the Alpha Jet has served its home nations well. The aircraft remains active in France and, for a number of export customers, has proved to be an ideal training and attack platform.**

One of the first of a new category of light multi-role military aircraft, the Alpha Jet can perform advanced flying training, weapons instruction and ground-attack missions. Developed jointly by France's Dassault and Germany's Dornier, over 500 Alpha Jets have been delivered to 10 air forces, making this one of Europe's most successful post-war aircraft.

The story of the Alpha Jet goes back to the 1960s, when the air staffs of France and Germany first discussed their future requirements for a jet trainer aircraft. The French planned to replace their Fouga Magister basic trainer, the Lockheed T-33 advanced trainer, and the Dassault Mystère IVA weapons trainer during the course of the 1970s. The Germans apparently considered the development of a training aircraft, but then decided to continue to use American facilities (training on the Cessna T-37 and Northrop T-38) in order to have the advantage of year-round good weather. However, Germany would clearly have to replace the Aeritalia/Fiat G91R, of which the Luftwaffe had over 300 in the light ground-attack role. On 22 July 1969 the two governments therefore announced a joint requirement for a new aircraft that could perform either in the training or close support roles, with the intention that each country would buy 200 of the type.

The Alpha Jet is a twin-turbofan aircraft with a high-set swept wing, with the engines mounted in what might be termed conformal pods on the fuselage sides. The two crew members sit in tandem, with the rear cockpit raised considerably so that, in the flying training role, the instructor can see straight ahead over the student pilot's head. The pilots are provided with Martin-Baker ejection seats in the case of French-built Alpha Jet Es, and Stencel seats in German-built A models, both types being produced locally under licence. Other external differences, between the two include the fitting of a rounded nose with strakes to the French Alpha Jet for improved spin handling, whereas the German close-support aircraft has a finely pointed nose. Other characteristics of the German aircraft are the installation of a Litton Doppler navigation radar, Kaiser/VDO HUD, and a belly-mounted 27-mm Mauser Mk 27 cannon pod. French Alphas carry a ventral 30-mm DEFA cannon pod with 150 rounds. Both variants have four underwing pylons for up to 5,511 lb (2500 kg) of stores, including bombs, rockets, missiles or drop tanks. Towards the end of the Alpha Jet production run, the ability to carry the AM.39 Exocet anti-ship missile was provided. Along with the Exocet, the Alpha would be able to carry two Matra Magic 2 AAMs and a 138-Imp gal (625-litre) drop tank, thus

*Above: The French air force aerobatic team, the* Patrouille de France*, traded in its ageing Fouga Magisters for Alpha Jets in 1980. The team's highly polished displays have undeniably helped sales of the aircraft around the world.*

*Left: With the establishment of two assembly lines, at Toulouse (France) and* Oberpfaffenhofen (Germany)*, four prototypes were constructed, two for each partner. The first to fly, prototype 01, is illustrated lifting off from Istres, France on 26 October 1973.*

***The French air force uses the Alpha Jet E for advanced pilot training, weapons instruction and as the mount of its national aerobatic team. Its current fleet comprises 55 aircraft, which are based at Tours, western France.***

demonstrating a capability far exceeding that of its original trainer role.

### Training the world

Alpha Jets entered service with the Armée de l'Air training units in May 1979, in the process replacing all of the Lockheed/ Canadair T-33s which, by this time, had been in service for over 20 years. The Luftwaffe received its first aircraft a few years later, and immediately the Alpha Jets were assigned a more potent role than their French cousins– that of providing close support to NATO's front-line troops. German Alphas were also seen as the ideal aircraft to attack the large fleets of Russian 'Hinds' which were anticipated at that time. Alphas remained as potential helicopter-killers until more suitable attack helicopters entered service with NATO allies.

### Export success

The success was not restricted to Europe. A number of countries purchased the design, in order to fulfil their training and attack requirements.

The first customer for the aircraft was Belgium, placing an order for 33 aircraft to replace both its T-33s and Fouga Magisters in the basic and advanced training roles. Further afield, Alpha Jets were ordered by Togo, the Ivory Coast, Qatar, Nigeria and Morocco, whose aircraft have seen combat. Moroccan Alpha Jets also serve in the aggressor training role, for which they carry large red and yellow numbers and stars on their noses. These sales have often been hard won, as the Alpha Jet's main rival is viewed as BAe's Hawk, and it was this aircraft, albeit in a modified form, that was to beat the Alpha Jet in its bid for the US Navy's carrier training aircraft. Despite this lack of success and the eventual withdrawal of the type from front-line Luftwaffe squadrons, Dassault/Dornier continues to offer upgrades to the basic design, such as the fitting of FLIR and CRT displays. As modern fighters become more complex, the need for highly efficient pilot training assumes an ever more important role, one that the Alpha Jet continues to fulfil for several operators.

***The Alpha Jet NGEA is an improved attack version, incorporating the nav/attack system developed for the Egyptian MS2. This example is armed with a pair of Matra Magic AAMs and a single Exocet anti-ship missile inboard.***

## Alpha Jet E

**Belgium received 33 Alpha Jets for the training role, delivered between December 1978 and July 1980. Located at Beauvechain, the aircraft are split between 7 Smaldeel and 11 Smaldeel, which provide advanced and initial flying training, respectively.**

**Powerplant**
The SNECMA/Turboméca Larzac 04-C6 (of which two are installed in nacelles on the fuselage sides) generates 3,175 lb st (13.24 kN). This is a turbofan of 1.13 bypass ratio with a two-stage fan, four-stage HP compressor, single-stage HP turbine (having cooled blades) and single-stage LP turbine.

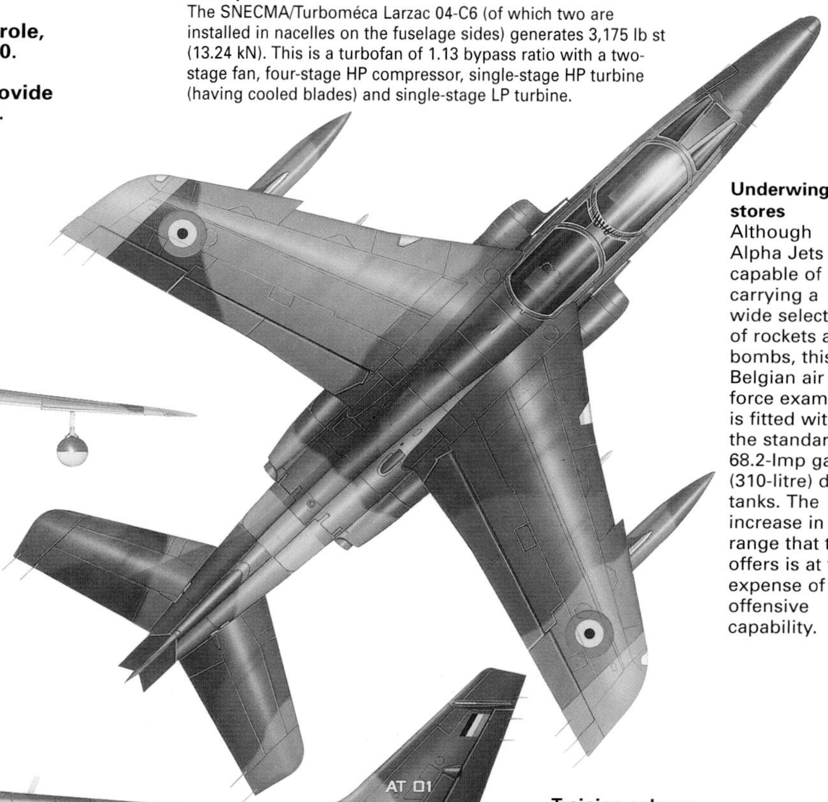

**Cockpit layout**
The two crewmembers are accommodated under individual transparencies on tandem-positioned Martin-Baker Mk 10 ejection seats; the forward pilot is provided with a simplified HUD. Instruments for front and rear cockpits are duplicated.

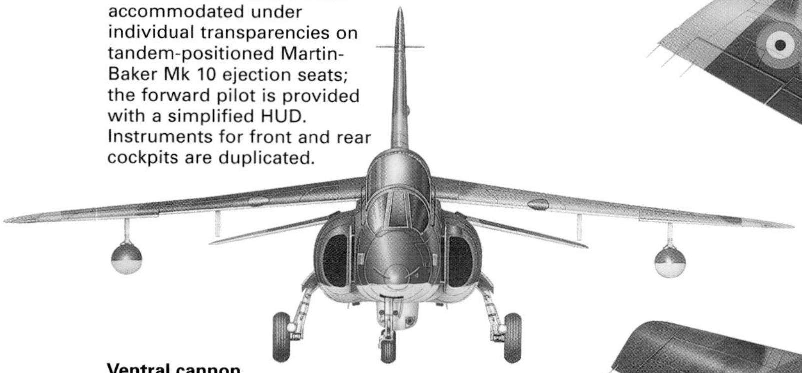

**Underwing stores**
Although Alpha Jets are capable of carrying a wide selection of rockets and bombs, this Belgian air force example is fitted with the standard 68.2-Imp gal (310-litre) drop tanks. The increase in range that this offers is at the expense of offensive capability.

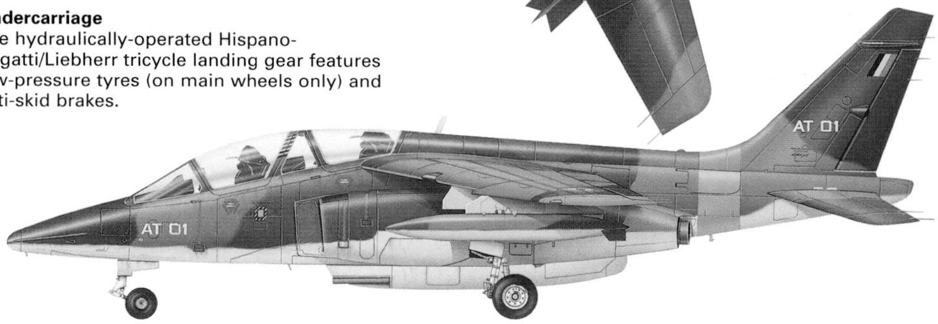

**Ventral cannon**
This Belgian aircraft is depicted carrying the ventral cannon pod which contains a DEFA 30-mm cannon and 150 rounds. German examples were fitted with a 27-mm Mauser cannon.

**Undercarriage**
The hydraulically-operated Hispano-Bugatti/Liebherr tricycle landing gear features low-pressure tyres (on main wheels only) and anti-skid brakes.

AT 01

**Training colours**
This Alpha Jet E displays the original training colours worn by the aircraft upon their entry into service. Recently, aircraft returning from overhauls have been repainted in a two-tone grey camouflage, although the orange training bands have been retained.

# Operational history

**In the face of extreme competition, especially from BAe's Hawk, Dassault/Dornier achieved considerable export and home sales success with its eminently practical Alpha Jet.**

With its excellent twin Larzac engines and light-attack capabilities, the Alpha Jet is an eminently sensible advanced/weapons trainer and light attack aircraft. Produced to meet a Franco-German requirement, the Alpha Jet programme was launched with the huge advantage of a large guaranteed production run, and the two 'launch customers' took an eventual total of 351 aircraft, although this was lower than had originally been required. The aircraft was effectively a combination of features from the Breguet 126 and Dornier P.375, and was selected after a 'paper' competition with the SNIAS/MBB E.650 Eurotrainer and the VFW-Fokker VFT-291.

Launched in 1970, the Alpha Jet replaced the Lockheed T-33 in the advanced trainer role, the Mystère IVA in the weapons training role, and light-attack Luftwaffe G.91s. This spread of capabilities forced the design team to produce a versatile basic aircraft (though Germany and France received specialised sub-variants to meet their specific requirements) and this enhanced the aircraft's export sales potential. The twin-engined configuration was dictated by German concerns (which had been raised by heavy attrition of the F-104). With Dassault acting as *de facto* 'senior partner', many expected the aircraft to be the most successful trainer of its generation, though these hopes were not realised. In fact, production of the Alpha Jet reached only 504 aircraft, and terminated in 1991. Most of the export customers for the aircraft were French-speaking nations (Belgium, and some former French colonies such as Cameroon, Côte d'Ivoire, Morocco and Togo) which traditionally turned to France for their military aircraft requirements and, with the exception of Nigeria, the others (Egypt and Qatar) were all existing operators of the Dassault Mirage. Even Nigeria was hardly a new market for the Franco-German partners, having received large numbers of ex-Luftwaffe Dornier Do 27s, Do 28s, Do 128s and Piaggio P.149s, as well as new MBB Bo 105s.

Unfortunately, the Alpha Jet faced fierce competition in the jet trainer market. For customers who were prepared to pay for the best, the BAe Hawk was recognised as the 'Rolls-Royce' among jet trainers, while aircraft like the Czech L-39 Albatros and Italian

***Above: The Fighter Pilots' School at Meknes operates the Royal Moroccan Air Force's Alpha Jet Hs, delivered from 1979. This pair flanks Alpha Jet Es from GE.314, an Armée de l'Air unit that can trace its origins back to service in Morocco in 1943.***

***Right: Most French Alpha Jet Es have worn this two-tone upper and grey lower scheme in service. However, in 1999 an all-over grey scheme was adopted.***

***Above: The first Belgian air force Alpha Jet is seen prior to gaining its green and brown camouflage. The order gained SABCA the production contract to build the aircraft's nose and flaps.***

***Left: Alpha Jet 'AJ58' is seen with four pylons instead of the more widely used two, carrying a pair of rocket pods and four dumb bombs, and the tail-mounted VOR 'winglets', not adopted by all users.***

*Left: The Luftwaffe was one of the original customers for the type, ordering 175 Alpha Jet A close support versions to replace the Fiat G.91R, but was also the first service to retire the aircraft.*

*Above: With its bulged dorsal spine, NAF 451 is the second of the Nigerian air force's 24 Alpha Jet Ns, seen prior to delivery. About 18 of the aircraft survive, but serviceability is low.*

Aermacchi MB.339 offered superb performance at relatively low cost. There was also a plethora of nations producing their own indigenous trainers and light attack aircraft, or licence-building competing designs.

Later entrants to the market included Argentina's IA 63 Pampa, Chile's Halcon, the Sino-Pakistani K-8, India's Kiran II, Poland's I-22 Iryda, Romania's IAR 99 Soim, South Africa's Impala, Spain's C.101, Taiwan's AT-3 and Yugoslavia's G-4 Super Galeb. High-performance turbo-props were typified by the PC-9 and EMB-312 Tucano.

The Alpha Jet proved unable to achieve a major 'breakthrough' sale, losing out to the BAe Hawk in the US Navy VTX-TS competition, and failing to deflect the Indian air force from its choice of the Hawk, though a firm order has yet to be placed. More embarrassingly, when the requirement for a French navy carrier-capable trainer emerged, it soon became clear that the Alpha Jet was the 'second-choice' behind its old rival, the Hawk, in its 'beefy' T-45 Goshawk guise. In the end, it was decided that Aéronavale aviators would train with the US Navy (on the T-45) which saved France the embarrassment of 'buying British'.

The first of four prototypes made its maiden flight on 26 October 1973, just over two years after the rival Hawk. The basic production versions of the aircraft featured increased-thrust Larzac 04 engines, extended outboard leading edges, single-slotted Fowler flaps and servo-controls, and were the Alpha Jet E (for Ecole, or School) for the Armée de l'Air and the Alpha Jet A (for Appui Tactique, or Attack) for the Luftwaffe. The Alpha Jet A featured Martin-Baker ejection seats and had a rounded, 'blunt' nose which gave the improved high AoA and spin recovery handling characteristics necessary in a trainer. In its weapons training role, the Alpha Jet E can carry a ventral gun pod containing a single DEFA 553 30-mm cannon with 150 rounds of ammunition.

All first-hand export customers use aircraft based on the French Alpha Jet A, although Egypt's first batch of trainers was designated Alpha Jet MS (or MS1) and featured an enhanced avionics fit. The Alpha Jet MS2 was a dedicated light attack aircraft with a new, more pointed nose, accommodating a Thomson-CSF TMV 630 laser rangefinder. The digital databus-equipped MS2 also featured a Sagem Uliss 81 INS, a Thomson-CSF VE110 CRT HUD and a TRT-9 radio altimeter.

The Alpha Jet E, as an operational aircraft, had Stencel ejection seats and a generously appointed nav-attack suite, with a Litton Doppler, Lear-Siegler twin-gyro INS, and a Kaiser HUD. The aircraft carried a Mauser MK 27 cannon in a ventral pod.

Dassault-Dornier has produced a number of advanced Alpha Jet studies, but none has been purchased by customers. The Alpha Jet 2, or Alpha Jet NGEA (Nouvelle Génération Ecole/Appui) was based on the MS2, but added provision for Magic AAMs and uprated Larzac 04-C20 engines (which were retrofitted to Luftwaffe Alpha Jets). Even more advanced was the Alpha Jet 3 or Alpha Jet ATS (Advanced Training System) – also known as the Lancier. This featured two new colour MFD displays in each cockpit, for use with Agave or Anenome radar, FLIR-, TV-, or laser-based sensors. The Alpha Jet ATS remains a possible upgrade configuration for Armée de l'Air Alpha Jets, with an upgrade gradually gaining favour over the option of procuring a new successor aircraft type.

The Alpha Jet later enjoyed something of a mini-renaissance, however, thanks mainly to Germany's desire to sell off its considerable fleet of stored aircraft. The country retired the type from front-line use in 1993, and the last few surviving trainers in June 1997. Germany had already cascaded 50 Alpha Jets to Portugal in 1993, and although there were reports that 30 might go to France to replace higher-houred Alpha Jet Es, and that Greece wanted 60 aircraft, nothing happened.

The German aircraft are now available at 'rock-bottom' prices, and can be fully refurbished (and upgraded) before delivery. The low price and immediate availability of the type has resulted in at least one very surprising new Alpha Jet customer, the UK's DERA ordering 12 (of which seven will be 'fliers'); these will replace ageing Hunters in the drone-chase, test pilot training and trials support roles. The British Alpha Jets will later also replace a Meteor drone trainer and may eventually supplant two Canberra target launchers.

A further 20 (plus five 'spares ships') have been ordered by the Kingdom of Thailand, and the UAE requested 30 machines, plus two non-airworthy airframes to be used for spares recovery, although none seems to have entered service.

*Five Alpha Jet Cs remain intact with the Côte d'Ivoire's Escadrille de Chasse (Fighter Flight). Only two of the aircraft are airworthy at any point in time. Orders for six more were cancelled.*

*Aggressive marketing will surely see the civil EH 101 Heliliner achieve a large number of sales. The aircraft is eminently suitable as an S-61N or Super Puma replacement.*

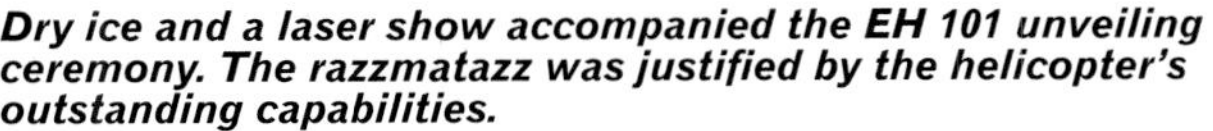

*Dry ice and a laser show accompanied the EH 101 unveiling ceremony. The razzmatazz was justified by the helicopter's outstanding capabilities.*

# EH Industries EH 101

## Anglo-Italian Sea King replacement

**The EH 101 is a European helicopter design that soon promises to be one of the most advanced heavyweight military helicopters in service. Designed to be a dual-role anti-submarine/troop transport aircraft, the EH 101 has now evolved to handle, additionally, a range of civil missions.**

The EH 101 was born out of a late-1970s European NATO naval requirement to replace the H-3 Sea King in the shipborne ASW role. This requirement was driven by the Royal Navy which decided to combine with the Italian navy, and award the new project to a specially-established joint venture between Westland and Agusta, EH Industries. The aircraft that emerged was a large but sleek, three-engined design with a five-bladed swept-tip main rotor system (featuring Westland's BERP technology), the EH 101. British aircraft would be powered by the Rolls Royce/Turboméca RTM332 turboshaft, while Italy chose the General Electric CT7-6 engine, built under licence by Alfa Romeo Avio and Fiat.

The naval version would be fitted with a 360° maritime search radar, dipping sonar, sonobuoys and external weapons (including torpedoes and anti-ship missiles). The EH 101 weighed in at 15,700 lb (7121 kg) and its substantial size allowed it to incorporate a rear ramp that would be all-important for the military transport mission. This was originally only an Italian requirement but, in 1995, a second version was selected for the RAF as a Wessex replacement. The same basic transport aircraft was also well-suited to civil applications, such as offshore support. The EH 101 programme was officially launched in 1981, for formal go-ahead in 1984.

### First flight

The first prototype (PP1) made its maiden flight on 9 October 1987. A series of nine prototypes (PP1 to PP9) was built, each dedicated to a specific development role. The Westland-built PP1 (ZF641) served as an engine test-bed and as a trials aircraft for the Royal Navy's Merlin HM.Mk 1 version. Agusta's PP2, which flew on 26 November 1987, was built to a similar standard as an Italian navy ASW aircraft. The Westland-built PP3 (G-EHIL), which flew on 30 September 1988, was the first civilian-standard EH 101 and undertook the certification programme for the Heliliner commercial transport variant. On 15 June 1989 Westland's PP4 (ZF644) took to the air and served as a general trials aircraft for the naval version. It was followed into the air, on 24 October 1989, by PP5 (ZF649), again built by Westland. This was the dedicated Merlin development aircraft for the RN and undertook the first shipboard landings in 1991. It was also the first aircraft to receive the full mission avionics fit, in 1996. The sixth prototype, PP6 (I-RAIA, MM-X-605), made its maiden flight on 26 April 1989. Built by Agusta, this aircraft became the Italian navy's dedicated naval trials EH 101, and made the first Italian shipboard landings in 1991. PP7 (I-HIOI) first flew on 18 December 1989, and served as Agusta's testbed for the military utility version, fitted with the rear ramp. The penultimate EH 101 development aircraft, Westland's PP8 (G-OIOI), flew on 24 April 1990 and joined PP3 on civil flight trials work. Lastly, Agusta's PP9 (I-LIOI), which flew on 16 January 1991, was the second aircraft to be built with a rear ramp, and it too was tasked with civil test duties.

### Multiple versions

Current plans call for a range of versions to serve with the EH 101's prime customers. Italy will adopt an ASW/ASVW (Anti-Submarine Warfare/Anti-Surface Vessel Warfare) version, and an AEW variant revealed in 1994. The ramp-equipped utility version will also serve with the Italian

*PP9 was the first Agusta-built civil EH 101. The aircraft has been used in a variety of trials, including hot-and-high tests at Mesa, Arizona. It was the second EH 101 with a rear ramp.*

# EH 101 PP5 (Merlin HM.Mk 1)

**PP5 was initially used for trials with the Type 23 frigate HMS *Norfolk*. It then moved onto trials with HMS *Iron Duke*, the latter including sonobuoy drop trials. Subsequently, it became the second RTM 322 test airframe and was fitted with full Merlin avionics. Latterly, it has been involved in drop tests with the Stingray torpedo.**

### Undercarriage
The hydraulically-retractable tricycle undercarriage with steerable nosewheel was developed by AP Precision Hydraulics in association with Officine Meccaniche Aeronautiche. Westland has drop-tested the EH 101 to a survivable velocity of 35 ft (10.6 m) per second.

### Orange Reaper
Racal's Kestrel airborne ESM system bears the Royal Navy name, Orange Reaper. It employs six antennas, located above the nose, above the sponsons and on the upper rear fuselage.

### Rotor head
The EH 101 rotor uses both fibre-reinforced and metal components. The system is resistant to hits from 23-mm shells and will continue running for 45 minutes with no oil in the gearbox.

### Emergency flotation gear
The Merlin relies on four Kevlar-reinforced polythene floats, inflated by bottled helium. The system, developed by BAJ Ltd, features four floats, one on either side of the nose, and two in the undercarriage sponsons.

### Structure
The fuselage has been designed in four sections, with the front, centre-sections and tailcone common to all versions. The tailboom in the ramp-loading versions is slimmer and dispenses with the tail-folding option. The fuselage structure is mainly of honeycomb aluminium-lithium alloy with bonded composite panels.

navy, and total Italian EH 101 orders currently stand at 16 (down from an original requirement for 42). The Royal Navy will acquire 44 Merlin HM.Mk 1 aircraft, with a primary ASW tasking. There are plans to introduce a Merlin HM.Mk 2 upgrade to expand the aircraft's ASVW capabilities. The RAF will acquire 22 Merlin HC.Mk 3 aircraft, equipped with a FLIR, IFR boom, integrated defensive aids system (with laser-warning, radar-warning and IR decoy systems) and a rescue winch. The Merlin HC.Mk 3 will be optimised for battlefield transport missions and CSAR (combat search and rescue). The first production standard Merlin for the RN flew on 20 January 1997 and was handed over to the Merlin programme prime integrator, Lockheed Martin, in May. Lockheed Martin is managing the Merlin programme for the UK MoD, overseeing the critical integration of all missions systems in the airframe. On 1 December 1998 the RN's Merlin Intensive Flying Trials Unit (IFTU), No. 700(M) Squadron, was commissioned at RNAS Yeovilton. In March 1999 three EH 101s travelled to the USN's Atlantic Undersea Test and Evaluation Center (AUTEC), in the Bahamas, for two months of weapons and ASW sensor trials. The three aircraft will return to AUTEC in early 2000. The first Merlin HC.Mk 3 flew on 24 December 1998, followed by the second aircraft on 14 June 1999. The HC.Mk 3 entered service with the re-formed No. 28 Sqn at RAF Benson, in 2000.

On the export market the EH 101 was involved in a bitterly contested competition to provide the Canadian forces with a new ASW and SAR helicopter, for which it was selected in 1987. Canada ordered 15 CH-149 Chimo SAR aircraft (replacing its CH-113 Labradors) and 35 CH-148 Petrel ASW aircraft (replacing its CH-124 Sea Kings). This substantial, and costly, order became an election issue in 1992/93 and was abruptly cancelled after a change of government in 1993. As a result, Canada was forced to pay substantial cancellation penalties and re-opened both competitions. The arguments in favour of EH 101 remained unchanged, however and, in 1997, Canada re-ordered the EH 101 once again, as its new long-range SAR helicopter. The 15 aircraft concerned are dubbed AW320 Cormorant by EH Industries, concealing the fact that they are almost identical to the version that Canada ordered 10 years earlier and should now already have in service. The first Cormorant will finally enter service in February 2001. When a decision is made on a Sea King replacement for Canada, the EH 101 must again be the obvious choice. EH Industries also became involved in the Nordic Standard Helicopter requirement. For this, Denmark, Finland, Norway and Sweden joined forces to evaluate and adopt a single helicopter type, to serve in the shipboard and military transport roles. However, only Denmark chose the EH 101, for service from 2004. In November 2003, Portugal signed a contract for 12 EH 101s for use in the long-range SAR and fisheries proection roles, while a VIP version of the helicopter is being offered to the US.

*PP2 undertook deck-landing trials aboard the Italian navy frigates* **N Grecale** *and* **Maestrale** *(illustrated). The aircraft was lost in an unrelated crash on 21 January 1993.*

*The only export order, apart from the Canadian deal, to December 1999, came from Japan, where the Tokyo Metropolitan Police took delivery of one utility transport aircraft in March 1999.*

# EMBRAER EMB-312 Tucano

## Fighting trainer

**In the Tucano, Brazil's enterprising aircraft industry produced a world-class turboprop trainer which secured export success and notable orders from the UK and France. Now the type has been developed into a potent fighter to tackle drug traffickers.**

Development of the turboprop, high-performance EMBRAER EMB-312 Tucano (Toucan) trainer started in 1978, in response to a Brazilian air force specification for a Cessna T-37 replacement. Designed from the outset to provide a 'jet-like' flying experience, the Tucano has a single power lever governing both propeller pitch and engine rpm, ejection seats, and a staggered tandem-place cockpit. Four underwing hardpoints can carry up to 2,205 lb (1000 kg) of ordnance for weapons training. Economically a better proposition than a jet type, the Tucano is less demanding from the viewpoint of student pilots in the earliest stages of flight training.

A total of 133 was ordered for the Força Aérea Brasileira, the initial batch of 118 being bolstered by 'top-up' batches of 10 in 1990 and five in 1992.

First flown on 16 August 1980, the initial T-27 Tucano was delivered to the Academia da Força Aérea (air force academy) near São Paulo in September 1983, for service in the advanced training role with 1° Esquadrão de Instrucão Aérea. The majority of Brazilian Tucanos fly with this unit. The Brazilian air force formation aerobatic team, the *Escuadron de Fumaca* (*Smoke Squadron*), received T-27 Tucanos to replace its ageing North American Harvards.

### Armed trainers

Some Brazilian Tucanos are known as AT-27s, these aircraft being armed, with underwing hardpoints carrying 0.3-in (7.62-mm) C2 gun pods, seven-round rocket pods or light bombs. AT-27s serve with four-aircraft flights in the more remote areas of Brazil, detached from 1°/7° and 2°/7° ETA (Esquadrão de Transporte Aéreo). Although the unit designator might suggest otherwise, these Tucanos are used for armed patrols against drug-smugglers, including the interception of aircraft. Peru's Tucanos also operate in this role, and a number of air-to-air kills have been recorded.

In FAB service these Tucanos have been augmented by A/TA-29 ALXs. Further AT-27s serve with the FAB's jet fighter squadrons as weapons continuation trainers and 'hacks', and with the advanced weapon training unit 1°/5° GAv.

An export order for 134 Tucanos was concluded with Egypt in September 1983. All except the first 10 of these were licence-assembled at Helwan. The Egyptian air force operates only 54 locally-assembled Tucanos, about 80 aircraft having been supplied to the Iraqi air force. Further deliveries from Brazil were made to the air forces of Argentina (30), Colombia (14), Honduras (12), Iran (25), Paraguay (six), Peru (30) and Venezuela (31).

Another major order came into effect in October 1991 (though it was placed in July 1990) when France announced its intention to purchase 80 EMBRAER-built EMB-312F aircraft. This French version boasts an increased fatigue life, ventral

***Above:** The first (inverted) and second YT-27 Tucano prototypes cavort during an early test flight. As well as the two fliers, two static test aircraft were included in the prototype contract.*

***Top:** Brazil operates armed AT-27 Tucanos (note seven-round rocket pod and machine-gun pod) against drug-smugglers. This aircraft is from the Boa Vista-based 1°/7° ETA.*

*The best known Tucanos in the Americas are those of the Esquadrão de Demonstração Aérea – or 'Esquadrão da Fumaca' – Brazil's national display team based at Pirassununga.*

*As well as the large batch of TPE331-engined Tucano Mk 1s for the RAF, Shorts also built the T.Mk 51 for Kenya, and the T.Mk 52 (illustrated) for Kuwait.*

*Left: The Tucano sold well in South America: this group comprises aircraft from (front to back) Venezuela, Peru, Brazil and Argentina. Colombia and Paraguay later joined the club.*

airbrake and French avionics. The first aircraft had been delivered to the CEV test establishment at Mont-de-Marsan by July 1993, another going to CEAM. Service with Groupement d'Instruction 312 at Salon-de-Provence began in July 1994, the Tucano replacing the Fouga Magister in the advanced training role.

In 1985 the RAF selected the Tucano – to be built in the UK by Shorts under the model number S312 – following an international competition that also involved the Pilatus PC-9, the Hunting Turbo-Firecracker and the AAC/Westland A 20. The Tucano was selected as a replacement for the Jet Provost in the basic training role. Considerable modification was undertaken to tailor the basic airframe to British requirements, including reshaped wingtip fairings, substituting a 1,100-shp (820-kW) Garrett (now Honeywell) TPE331 turboprop in place of the original Pratt & Whitney PT6A – which significantly improved the rate of climb – and reprofiling the cockpit to provide commonality with the BAE Systems Hawk. EMBRAER flew a Garrett-engined prototype in Brazil in February 1986 and delivered this to Shorts in Belfast as a pattern aircraft, the first Tucano T.Mk 1 making its maiden flight on 30 December that year. The total RAF production order covered 130 aircraft, first delivery to the Central Flying School at Scampton taking place in June 1988. The balance of the RAF order was completed in 1993. Tucanos went on to equip No. 1 FTS at Linton-on-Ouse, No. 3 FTS at Cranwell, and No. 6 FTS at Finningley, with others at Scampton with the CFS. In 2000 the Tucano fleet was restricted to 1 FTS and the CFS (at Topcliffe).

To extend the Tucano's capability in both military training and counter-insurgency roles, Shorts conducted a series of Tucano weapon trials in the spring of 1991 using twin FNNH machine-gun pods, the FNNH heavy MG and rocket launcher and the LAIJ32 seven-round rocket launcher, plus bombs up to 551 lb (250 kg). Overseas customers for the armed S312 were Kenya (T.Mk 51), which received the last of 12 in June 1991 and Kuwait (T.Mk 52), which took delivery of 16 aircraft from 1995 for service with No. 19 Squadron.

*The first (foreground) and second EMB-312H/314 prototypes demonstrate some of the weaponry available to the type. Notable is the MAA-1 Piranha missile carried by PP-ZTV.*

### EMB-314 Super Tucano and ALX

Spurred by the USAF/USN JPATS competition for a basic trainer to replace the T-34C and T-37, EMBRAER announced in June 1991 the EMB-312H Tucano H, featuring an uprated P&WC PT6A-68A engine. Fuselage plugs fore and aft totalling 4 ft 6 in (1.37 m) were inserted to accommodate the 1,300-shp (970-kW) turboprop, and to maintain stability and centre of gravity. The EMB-312H was offered for the JPATS competition in association with Northrop. A converted Tucano (PP-ZTW) toured bases in the US during August 1992, before the first of two new-build prototypes (PP-ZTV) flew on 15 May 1993. These were subsequently redesignated EMB-314 and renamed Super Tucano to reflect the considerable improvements made to the type.

Under the name ALX, a version of the Super Tucano – the EMB-314M – was chosen for the Brazilian air force's SIVAM project, which provides for a border and remote region patrol force of light attackers/fighters to counter a variety of illegal activities, including logging, pollution and drug smuggling. SIVAM also includes a force of EMB-145SA/RS (R-99A/B) surveillance platforms.

Designated A-29 (single-seat) and TA-29 (two-seat) in FAB service, the EMB-314M has a more powerful 1,600-shp (1193-kW) PT6A-68-1 turboprop and comprehensive equipment fit (including SAFIRE FLIR and GPS). Armament consists of one 0.472-in (12-mm) machine-gun in each wing with 200 rounds, and four underwing and one centreline hardpoints for a variety of bombs, gun pods and rockets. Weapon options include laser-guided and cluster bombs, and the indigenous MAA-1 Piranha air-to-air missile.

An initial FAB order for 99 ALXs (49 A-29s and 50 TA-29s) has been placed, the first of which (YA-29 5700) made its first flight in 1999. In service 60-plus A/TA-29s are expected to operate in the SIVAM role with a newly-established 3° Grupo, while 30 TA-29s are due to replace EMB-326 Xavante jets in the weapons/tactical training role with 2°/5° Grupo at Natal. The EMB-314 is being actively marketed around the world by EMBRAER.

*5700 is the first EMB-314M, completed as a single-seat YA-29 (the 'Y' prefix denoting test status) and finished in the camouflage expected to adorn the fleet. This variant introduces fixed armament for the first time, with a machine-gun in each wing.*

# Eurocopter Tiger

## European wildcat

**'The most advanced combat helicopter in the world today' is the description given to the Tiger by its manufacturer, Eurocopter, although this joint French/German aircraft has yet to secure any export orders.**

***Above:** Eurocopter emphasises that the Tiger offers the latest technology, with 80 per cent of the airframe being of composite materials and with the aircraft having low-radar, infra-red and visual signatures.*

***Right:** French aircraft PT1, in HAP/Gerfaut configuration, displays its 30-mm GIAT AM-30781 cannon, 22-round SNEB pods, Mistral AAMs and roof-mounted STRIX sight.*

The Eurocopter Tiger has its origins in Germany's early 1980s requirement for a second-generation anti-tank helicopter (Panzerabwehr-Hubschrauber, or PAH-2). With the French army seeking an anti-tank helicopter (Hélicoptère Anti-Char, or HAC) in a similar category, a Memorandum of Undertaking was signed in 1984 for the joint development of a new aircraft. To handle the programme, Aérospatiale in France and MBB in Germany set up the jointly-owned Eurocopter Tiger GmbH in September 1985; subsequently, all helicopter activities of the two companies have been merged under the Eurocopter name, but the Tiger project remains outside this formal structure as it is a unique single government contract. On 30 November 1989, after several revisions, the main development contract was awarded and the Tiger name was formally adopted.

The Tiger (the generic name for the helicopter) has a slender low-drag fuselage with two seats in tandem, stepped and offset to each side of the centreline. Each cockpit is built around two colour LCD MFDs and the crew will have helmet-mounted sights. The structure makes extensive use of composites, and uses an advanced four-bladed composite semi-rigid main rotor. The three-bladed tail rotor is an Aérospatiale Spheriflex design and a fixed tricycle undercarriage is fitted, with single wheels. Weapons carriage is on anhedral stub wings with provision for a cannon turret undernose. Power is supplied by two MTU/Turboméca/Rolls-Royce MTR 390 turboshafts, each rated at 1,285 shp (958 kW) for take-off and 1,171 shp (873 kW) for continuous running.

The Tiger is to be built in three different versions for its two primary customers. These designs have been subject to several revisions – due mostly to the disappearance of the Soviet armoured threat in Europe. Two basic types exist, the dedicated anti-armour U-Tiger and the scout/escort HCP (Hélicoptère de Combat Polyvalent, multi-role combat helicopter). Germany is acquiring just one Tiger variant, the UHT (Unterstützungshubschrauber), which is a multi-role combat helicopter with a primary anti-tank role. The UHT replaces the previous PAH-2 concept and adds a new air-to-air capability not previously required. The UHT can carry HOT 3 or Trigat anti-tank missiles, Stinger AAMs, rocket and gun pods. It will have a mast-mounted electro-optic/FLIR sight, with laser rangefinder, and a pilot's FLIR in the nose. A nose-mounted 30-mm cannon may be added later. The French anti-tank version is known as the Tigre HAC and will be of a similar

*Initially, F-ZWWW was fitted with a mast-mounted sight, but was reconfigured a year later with the Gerfaut/HAP's roof-mounted sight and nose-gun. PT1 was withdrawn from flight tests for ground fatigue testing in early 1996.*

***Left:** The prototype French Gerfaut escort/scout (foreground) formates on the first Tigre anti-tank helicopter. Both were involved in the flight test programme.*

***Below:** The Tiger was brought to public attention when it was used in the James Bond film 'Goldeneye', in which its technology supposedly made it invulnerable to the effects of an EMP (Electro-Magnetic Pulse).*

configuration to the German UHT. France will also acquire a second variant derived from the HCP design, the Tigre HAP (Hélicoptère d'Appui et de Protection), for escort and fire-support missions. Until 1993 this version was known as the Gerfaut, and the main difference between it and other Tigers is its nose-mounted 30-mm GIAT AM-30781 cannon. The HAP will not operate with an anti-tank missile armament, but instead will carry a heavy load of 68-mm SNEB rockets and MATRA/BAe Mistral AAMs. The HAP also replaces the mast-mounted sight with a roof-mounted system.

## Development

The 1989 contract provided for five prototypes: three unarmed aerodynamic aircraft, one escort Gerfaut/HAP and one full anti-tank configuration. An Aérospatiale Panther was used as a testbed for the MTR 390 engines, flying for the first time on 14 February 1991. Three other testbeds – two Pumas and a Dauphin – were used to test the mast-mounted sight, the night-vision sight and the fire control system. The first prototype (PT1, F-ZWWW) flew at Marignane on 27 April 1991 while PT2 (F-ZWWY), the second aircraft, a Gerfaut/HAP airframe with all essential basic avionics, was rolled out at Ottobrunn on 9 November 1992 and first flew on 22 April 1993. After completing its test programme, including radar cross-section trials, PT2 was reconfigured as a HAP, and redesignated PT2R.

PT3 (F-ZWWT, later 98+23) followed it into the air on 19 November 1993. This aircraft flew initially with the full core avionics suite and was later brought up to full UHT standard in 1997, becoming the PT3R.

***Left:** Australia evaluated the 'Aussie Tiger' before placing an order for 22 of the type. This is based on the French HAP, with roof-mounted sighting system and a number of modifications to suit domestic needs.*

PT4 (F-ZWWU) was built as the dedicated HAP/Gerfaut prototype, with a functioning roof-mounted sight, and became the first Tiger to fire live weapons. It flew on 15 December 1994 and undertook cannon and Mistral firings between 1995 and 1997. This aircraft was heavily involved in efforts to attract export sales for the Tiger and underwent evaluation in Sweden and Australia. Unfortunately, it crashed in Australia during a night evaluation flight on 17 February 1998, and was written off.

PT5 (98+25) was the dedicated UHT testbed and first flew on 21 February 1996. It undertook the German weapons trials, including HOT, Stinger and 12.7-mm gun pod firings, during 1997.

## Defence cuts

The Tiger programme has been badly hit by major defence budget cuts in both France and Germany, driven by the end of the Cold War. Production and delivery schedules have also slipped considerably. The original Tiger requirement was for 427 aircraft (75 HAPs and 140 HACs for France and 212 PAH-2/UHUs for Germany. Germany's 1995 budget submission included funds for only 75 aircraft, and this drove the development of the lower-cost UHT variant. The German order has now been restored to 212, with the intention of funding 112 aircraft between 2001 and 2009. In 1994, the French order was amended to 115 HAPs and 100 HACs, though this may yet be revised downwards to an overall total of 140.

The Tiger's fortunes were not helped by the UK's decision to acquire the Boeing/McDonnell Douglas AH-64D in July 1995. British Aerospace had teamed up with Eurocopter to bid for the 90-helicopter order, and the UK had been offered full membership of the Tiger project, should the aircraft be selected for the British army. Eurocopter is believed to have offered a 'risk-free' deal to the UK MoD as the Tiger's development costs were already underwritten by the French and German governments.

It was not until May 1998, after much doubt regarding its future, that the Tiger received renewed official approval, guaranteeing production – despite ongoing defence reviews in Germany and a much-restricted French budget. However, in January 1999 France and Germany again delayed (by six months) signing the first firm order for 160 aircraft, despite earlier promises that the $3.8 billion contract would be finalised by the end of 1998. This delay will mean that the first deliveries to the German army, scheduled for late 2001/early 2002, were put back. French HAP deliveries remianed on track for first delivery in 2003.

***A Tiger buy by the UK was encouraged to promote pan-European defence and industrial ties. The failure to win the UK order came as a major blow to Eurocopter, and was followed by prevarication by its two partner governments, who delayed signing firm orders for their own aircraft.***

# Service status

**Eurocopter's Tiger has made slow, but steady progress. Though it is one of many European defence projects that have been hamstrung by a lack of finance – and changing priorities in a post-Cold War world – the Tiger is at last preparing to enter service.**

Throughout the late 1990s, the Tiger programme struggled to make meaningful progress in the face of shrinking defence budgets from its two primary customers – France and Germany. While Eurocopter continued to wait for the elusive production contract to be signed, the Tiger failed to make headway in any of the international competitions in which it was a contender. The continuing lack of support from the home governments left the Tiger sales team on shaky ground when it came to convincing other customers to invest in the aircraft. In May 1998, the first small step forward was made when the German and French authorities signed a Memorandum of Understanding (MoU) committing to serial production. But this was not the firm order that had been hoped for. The MoU covered an initial batch of 160 helicopters – 80 for Germany and 80 for France. The German army's total requirement for the Tiger remained at 212, with 215 for the French Army. At the time it was hoped that deliveries would commence in 2001, but soon after the MoU announcement this date was delayed yet again.

It was not until a year later, on 18 June 2000 during the Paris air show, that the final production contract for the Tiger was at last signed. This covered a first batch of 160 helicopters (as set out in the 1998 MoU). Production and final assembly of the aircraft would be undertaken at the Eurocopter plants in Donauwörth (Germany) and Marignane (France). The latter will produce the HAP (*Hélicoptère d'Appui et de Protection*) combat support version, ordered by the French army, while Donauwörth will manufacture the HAC (*Hélicoptère Anti-Char*) and UHT (*Unterstützunghubschrauber Tiger*) anti-tank versions for the French and German armies, respectively. Cost and workshare has been divided equally between the two partner countries. The first Tiger deliveries began in 2003.

***Above: The third Tiger prototype was the German Army's UHT 'utility' or multirole anti-tank and fire-support helicopter testbed, seen here with with Trigat missiles on the port inner hardpoint.***

***Top: The Tiger programme won its first all-important export order – to Australia – leaving it in a fine position to secure a sale to Spain. Pictured is the victorious HCP 'Aussie Tiger'.***

## Export offers

On the back of this firm go-ahead for the project, Eurocopter was able to turn to the international market with renewed confidence. In September 1999 Eurocopter made an offer to Poland, which had just been granted NATO membership and was planning a major modernisation of its front line forces. Initially Poland had hoped to

***Formerly known as the Gerfaut, the Tiger HAP, seen with a Leclerc MBT, is the French army's escort/fire-support version. GIAT produce the HAP's 30-mm (1.18-in) cannon as well as the Leclerc.***

***The weapons options for the HAP and HCP export version include Mistral AAMs, 12-round or 22-round 68-mm (2.68-in) TDA rocket pods and HOT 3 or Trigat AC3G air-to-ground missiles. The 30-mm automatic cannon is provided with 150-450 rounds of ammunition.***

acquire 96 locally-designed and built P.Z.L. W-3H Huzar armed helicopters, fitted with either the HOT-3 or NT-D Spike anti-tank missiles – but these plans were abandoned. To meet Poland's revised anti-tank and armed reconnaissance helicopter requirement, Eurocopter then offered the Tiger in its German army UHT configuration – featuring HOT-3 missiles, Stinger air-to-air missiles and 20-mm gunpods. If selected, Eurocopter promised a substantial industrial participation deal to helicopter manufacturer P.Z.L.-Swidnik. Though Poland has since opted to pursue an interim upgrade of its Mi-24 force, and postponed any wider decisions on a new type, a future combat helicopter acquisition is still being planned for and the Eurocopter Tiger remains a strong contender.

## Export potential

Another important customer has turned out to be Spain, which is replacing its fleet of missile-armed BO 105s with a special Tiger variant. With an eye on the Spanish army's requirement for about 30 new aircraft, Eurocopter signed an agreement with EADS-CASA to establish Eurocopter Espana, in September 2000. Operational in 2001, Eurocopter Espana is now the third company in the Eurocopter Group and its formation brings Spain much closer to the Tiger programme – and other Eurocopter projects in general.

On 21 December 2000 a major milestone in the Tiger story was reached when the first pre-production standard aircraft made its maiden flight at Marignane. This HAP-standard aircraft (PS1) was manufactured and assembled using the full-standard production assembly process (unlike the earlier prototypes that were all assembled with development tooling).

At the same time as PS1 took to the air, Eurocopter announced two other noteworthy achievements. The first was the completion of qualification tests for the HAP weapon systems, including the Mistral AAMs, 68-mm (2.7-in) rockets and the GIAT 30-mm gun turret. Mainly conducted with the PT2R2 prototype, these trials involved crews from Eurocopter, the DGA flight test centre and the French Army Air Corps firing at 53.8-sq ft (5-m$^2$) diameter targets from a range of to 3,280-4,921 ft (1000-1500 m). Trials involved stationary and moving targets in the air-to-ground mode, and then in the air-to-air mode. At 1000 m, nine of the 10 rounds hit the target and at 1500 m, six out of 10 were on target.

Eurocopter also announced that together with partners Thales Detexis, Dornier and MS & I, it had been awarded a contract by SPAé (French aeronautical programmes) to develop an airborne tactical datalink for the Tiger.

With the Tiger now progressing smoothly towards its service debut, the programme received a massive boost at the end of 2001 when the winner of the hard-fought Australian Armed Reconnaissance Helicopter (ARH) competition was finally announced. Otherwise known as Project AIR 87, the ARH competition developed into a roller-coaster ride in procurement as the final decision dragged on well past the original deadline and then, in 2000, the whole thing was cancelled and restarted. The 'Aussie Tiger' proposal faced stiff competition from the Boeing AH-64D Apache, Bell ARH-1Z and the Agusta A 129 Scorpion, but on 21 December 2001 the Australian Minster of Defence announced that a contract had been signed with Eurocopter International Pacific for 22 Tigers, worth $1.3 billion. Deliveries to the Australian Army Air Corps will begin in December 2004, and the Tiger ARHs will be assembled in Queensland by Australian Aerospace Pty Limited (recently acquired as a subsidiary of EADS in Australia). As part of the deal Eurocopter will also establish a production line to build the EC 120 light helicopter in Australia. A new facility will produce from 30-50 helicopters per year for the Australian, New Zealand and Asian markets.

***Right: Type qualification of the UHT is scheduled for December 2002. Mid-life upgrades may add a 30-mm Mauser chin gun to the UHT and a mast-mounted pulse Doppler radar to the HAC.***

***Below: The U-Tiger serves as the basis for both UHT and HAC versions, carrying the mast-mounted sight common to both aircraft. All three configurations share 80 per cent commonality.***

# EF2000/ Typhoon

**Stretching back over 15 years, the Eurofighter programme has become a byword for political disagreement and delay. However, the aircraft has been making steady gains recently and is now on the eve of service.**

As a follow-on to the tri-national Tornado programme, the Eurofighter consortium was formed in June 1986 by the same three countries – Britain, Germany and Italy (soon joined by Spain) – to produce an air superiority fighter by the late 1990s. Other European countries, notably France, had been involved in earlier European Fighter Aircraft (EFA) discussions, but shunned the final consortium to pursue their own independent programmes.

Much experience of the main EFA concepts had been gained from BAe's Experimental Aircraft Programme (EAP). These concepts included an unstable aerodynamic configuration with canard foreplanes, active digital fly-by-wire control system, complex avionics, multi-function cockpit displays, carbon-fibre composites and extensive use of aluminium-lithium alloys, titanium and even direct voice input (DVI). The EAP had been funded (after German withdrawal) by the UK MoD and industry with some Italian participation. First flying on 8 August 1986, the twin-engined RB.199-powered EAP amassed invaluable data in 259 test sorties totalling over 195 hours before retirement in 1991.

Finalised in September 1987, the EFA European Staff Requirement for Development specified a relatively light and sophisticated twin-turbofan single-seat fighter. Optimised for BVR and close air combat, it was also to be capable of secondary air-to-surface roles and operation from short, austere air strips, with a low radar cross-section and high supersonic performance, agility and carefree handling. Germany and Italy sought only air-to-air roles, but accepted the common specification of a 21,495-lb (9750-kg) basic empty weight, 538.2-sq ft (500-m²) gross wing area, and 20,233-lb (90-kN) reheat thrust per engine. These were new EJ200 twin-spool turbofans from the Eurojet consortium, with some 30 per cent fewer parts than the Tornado's RB.199, and with a 13,488-lb (60-kN) maximum dry thrust.

***Above: The third phase of Eurofighter FCS clearance involved air-to-air refuelling. DA.2 flew the first air-to-air refuelling trials, making dry 'prods' into a drogue from a No. 101 Squadron VC10.***

***Top: Current military experience has demonstrated the need for aircraft that are capable of undertaking offensive counter-air and attack missions on the same sortie. RAF Eurofighters were designed around this specification from the planning stage.***

A £5.5 billion contract signed on 23 November 1988 covered the building and testing, until 1999, of eight prototypes (including two two-seat versions): three in Britain, two in Germany, two in Italy and one in Spain. The aircraft were funded in proportion to national industrial participation: 33 per cent each by BAe and MBB (now EADS Deutschland), 21 per cent by Alenia (as it was by now), and 13 per cent by CASA (now EADS CASA).

## Eurofighter systems

Eurofighter will rely primarily on the AIM-120 AMRAAM as its primary air-to-air weapon. However, in the future, this could be supplemented or replaced by the Meteor, a combination of BAe's S225X and DASA's A3M. For shorter-range engagements, RAF Eurofighters will use the ASRAAM, while German aircraft will have the MBDA IRIS-T. An air-to-air configuration could include up to six AMRAAMs and four ASRAAMs. In the air-to-surface role, the Eurofighter's 14,300-lb (6486-kg) payload allows it to carry up to three Paveway III LGBs plus a TIALD designator. Other weapons carried could include the BAe/MATRA Storm Shadow or the Hellfire-derived Brimstone missile.

The Eurofighter is equipped with the ECR.90 radar which is

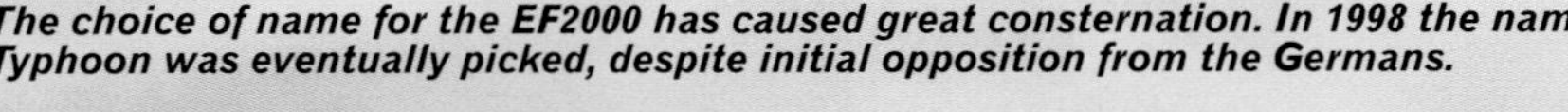

***The choice of name for the EF2000 has caused great consternation. In 1998 the name Typhoon was eventually picked, despite initial opposition from the Germans.***

regarded as being a highly capable and flexible part of the overall attack and identification system. It offers air-to-air and air-to-surface modes, with all-aspect look-up and look-down capability, as well as automatic threat prioritisation and identification. The radar can perform real beam ground-mapping, moving ground target indication and tracking, high-resolution (Doppler-beam sharpening) mapping, sea clutter optimised mapping, terrain avoidance and ranging functions. The system also provides automatic weapon release computation. The radar has a very long range and is highly resistant to ECM.

The ECR.90 is supplemented by an infra-red search and tracking system (IRST), with passive multi-target tracking and imaging, for which the Eurofirst group of FIAR (Italy), Thorn-EMI Electronics (UK) and Eurotronica (Spain) received a development contract in mid-1992. This followed orders for integrated defensive aids sub-systems placed with a Marconi Defence Systems/Elettronica consortium to cover missile approach, laser and radar warning systems, wingtip ESM/ECM pods, chaff/flare dispensers and towed decoys, although Germany and Spain may seek cheaper off-the-shelf equipment.

### First flight

The first two EFA prototypes, DA.1 (98+29) and DA.2 (ZH588) flew on 27 March and 6 April 1994 from Manching and Warton, for 45 and 50 minutes, respectively. BAe's DA.4 was the first two-seat EFA and also the ECR.90 development prototype, while DASA uses the DA.5 for avionics and weapons integration. CASA assembled and flew the second two-seat prototype (DA.6), with Alenia building the DA.7, now the last development aircraft following the cutbacks which deleted two prototypes from the programme.

It is far too premature at present to predict final production numbers for Eurofighter, even for the four original customers. The UK remains committed to 232 Eurofighters which will provide a front-line establishment of 140 aircraft. In Germany the present tally is 180, including a second batch of 40 as Tornado replacements. To this total, there may be an additional 15-20 aircraft for training in the USA and a further batch for the reconnaissance role. The Italian requirement currently stands at 121 aircraft and Spain is committed to 87 Eurofighters. The Eurofighter was projected to be in service by 2002, but in fact this date slipped to 2003, albeit with service test detachments. This date can be compared to a service entry date of 2006 for the French air force Rafale, and 2008 or later for the F-22. The latest estimates seem to indicate that the first Eurofighter squadrons will attain combat ready status during 2005 and the first ground attack squadrons in 2008.

***Germany's DA.1 is seen over the golden sands of Blackpool, during a series of trials in the UK in July/August 1997. Based at Warton, DA.1 flew a number of sorties over the Irish Sea, testing structural stresses at high dynamic pressure.***

## Eurofighter DA.6

**The first two-seat Eurofighter to fly was the second aircraft to be built – the CASA-constructed DA.6 (XCE.16-01). DA.6 took to the air on 31 August 1996. In fact, DA.6 beat both DA.4 and DA.5 (DASA's second single-seat aircraft) into the air.**

**Fuel system**
Eurofighter can carry fuel tanks on three of its hardpoints. A 330-Imp gal (1500-litre) tank may be carried on the centreline and on the underwing hardpoints (restricting the aircraft to subsonic speeds) or 220-Imp gal (1000-litre) supersonic tanks may be carried under the wings.

**Aircraft structure**
Advanced materials (carbon-fibre composites) make up 70 per cent of Eurofighter's surface area. The percentages by weight are 40 per cent CFC, 12 per cent titanium and 20 per cent aluminium-lithium.

**Intakes**
The need to ensure a good performance at all speeds and at all angles of attack necessitated the design of an extremely versatile and flexible intake. The configuration chosen was an underfuselage ('chin') intake with a hinged lower lip or 'varicowl'. An ogival splitter plate helps to ensure that clean air is supplied to the compressor throughout the flight envelope by removing sluggish boundary layer airflow.

**Avionics**
The basic avionics system is entirely digital and each part was supplied by one of the four companies. DASA took responsibility for the attack and identification systems, while BAe built defensive aids, displays and controls, and monitoring, test and recording equipment. Alenia provided navigation and armament control systems and CASA took responsibility for communications.

**Canard foreplanes**
The use of canard foreplanes has contributed to Eurofighter's unstable aerodynamic configuration, with an aft centre of gravity. The foreplanes have also added to total lift on take-off or in a turn (rather than generating downforce, as does a tailplane), and reduced drag. Strakes on the fuselage sides smooth out vortices from the canard foreplanes, and have reportedly been used as footsteps by pilots – indicating their strength.

**Undercarriage**
The undercarriage is extremely robust, and is stressed to allow a constant angle of attack during approach and landing, giving the shortest possible landing distance. Eurofighter is fitted with advanced carbon-carbon brakes, which are computer-controlled and fan-cooled.

# Eurofighter nearing service

**By 2001, all seven Eurofighter prototypes had flown, and although production has been delayed by political difficulties in Germany, the partner nations began receiving their first production-standard Eurofighters in 2003 and more similar machines are already taking shape on their high-tech assembly lines.**

Eurofighter's factories and assembly facilities are the most modern aircraft facilities in Europe, with highly advanced computer-controlled machine tools and assembly jigs and an atmosphere of scrupulous tidiness and clean efficiency.

Modern production techniques and concepts will allow Eurofighter to be built more quickly than its predecessors, allowing deliveries to be so rapid that early diversions for future export customers will have little impact on the plans of the four original customers.

By the time the 20th aircraft is in production, for example, BAE aim to have streamlined the assembly process so that it will take only 16 weeks, this comparing with 30 weeks for the 'fastest' Tornado.

The Eurofighter will enter service virtually simultaneously in Germany, Italy, Spain and Britain. Despite the similarity of the aircraft being delivered to the four partner nations and despite the similar timescale, all four operators will have separate training units, and their will be no Eurofighter equivalent to the combined Trinational Tornado Training Establishment run by Germany, Italy and the UK.

## First German deliveries

The first operational German Eurofighters will be delivered to JG 73 at Laage in 2002, followed by JG 74 at Neuberg, JG 71 at Wittmund, and JG 72 at Hopsten. Germany's 180 aircraft will include 33 two-seaters and 40 multi-role aircraft equipped with the full DASS (defensive aids subsystem) suite and available for multi-national operations. The remainder will be dedicated to the air defence role, and are presently planned to have a more austere defensive aids suite.

In Italy 121 Eurofighters (including 15 two-seaters) will equip 4° Stormo at Grosseto, 37° Stormo at Trapani and 53° Stormo at Cameri. Spain will take 87 aircraft (15 or 16 of them two-seaters) and these will equip an OCU, 113 Escuadron, from January 2004 and the first frontline unit, 111 Escuadron will follow in 2007. 112, 141 and 142 Escuadrons will form between 2010 and 2015.

***Built in Italy by Alenia, DA.7 (above and right) was the last of the EF2000 prototypes, making its first flight in early 1997. Employed for navigation and communications, performance and weapons integration trials, DA.7 was followed by five instrumented production aircraft. The first of these (IPA.1, built by BAE Systems) was a two-seater and flew for the first time on 15 April 2002.***

Great Britain will be the largest Eurofighter operator, having ordered 232 Eurofighter Typhoons (including 37 two-seaters), and these will equip an OEU (No.17 Squadron), an OCU (No.29 Squadron) and seven frontline squadrons. The OEU and OCU formed at Warton during 2003, and the first 16 RAF pilots and 248 groundcrew will be trained there under 'Case White'. This unusual and pioneering arrangement is intended to reduce risk and ensure a particularly smooth transition to service. The co-location of the first RAF aircraft alongside BAE's Warton-based Eurofighter development team will allow the service to benefit from on-site support by the manufacturer, and should facilitate useful exchange of experience and ideas. The OEU and OCU should move to Coningsby in 2004, where they will be joined by the first frontline air defence squadrons in 2005 and 2006. Two more front-

***During 2000, ZH558 (DA.2), the first British-built prototype, was painted black to improve its conspicuity during envelope expansion and handling trails. Here the aircraft is seen over Blackpool, near its Warton, Lancashire base.***

line air defence squadrons will form at RAF Leeming in 2006 and 2007, and one dedicated Offensive Support squadron and two multi-role units will finally form at Leuchars during 2008-2010.

The 13 or so 'Case White' Batch One Eurofighter Typhoons (ten of them two-seaters) will be 'relatively immature, interim' aircraft. They will be fitted with radar and a partial DASS, but will lack IRST, helmet-mounted displays, and the planned data link. Despite this, the aircraft will be fully compliant with OCU training requirements and will mark a quantum leap over the latest Tornado F.Mk 3 standard. By the time the first front-line Squadron is declared to NATO in January 2006, it will be operating a full-specification Air Defence aircraft which will have IRST, a helmet mounted display, the full-spec DASS, a full digital ASRAAM capability, and a datalink.

The Eurofighter declared to NATO in 2006 will be fully capable in the air defence role, and will be cleared to use the internal gun in the air-to-ground strafe role, and to drop Paveway II Laser Guided Bombs and fire ALARM anti-radar missiles. It will, however, still be some way short of the full-spec Swing Role Fighter described in some marketing material. The aircraft's planned air-to-ground capabilities will be introduced in stages, starting with the introduction of the DSD (Development Standard D) Captor Radar, a laser targeting pod, Paveway III LGBs and Brimstone ATGMs.

## 'Swing role'

As soon as it is cleared to operate in the air-to-ground role, the Eurofighter Typhoon will be capable of operating in the 'swing Role' mode and Typhoon pilots will be able to 'swing' from the air-to-surface role to the air-to-air role 'at the push of a button'.

Although Eurofighter Typhoon has won only one confirmed export order, for 18 aircraft from Austria, marketing campaigns have reached an advanced stage in a number of potential customer countries. The best prospects are believed to be Brazil, Greece (which has promised to purchase 60 aircraft after the 2004 Olympic Games), the Netherlands, Norway, Saudi Arabia and Singapore.

The Eurofighter Typhoon is believed to be cheaper but more capable than the rival Dassault Rafale and is bettered only in some respects (and then by only a narrow margin) by the prohibitively expensive F/A-22. The USA's JSF programme is less mature than the Eurofighter programme, and a production JSF will not be available for some years. Even when it is available for export the JSF is unlikely to be significantly cheaper than the Typhoon, nor will it have the Eurofighter's advanced BVR air-to-air capabilities. For the smaller air arm, requiring a genuine multi-role swing fighter at an affordable price, Eurofighter seems likely to be the best and most sensible option.

# Eurofighter DA.2

**DA.2 (ZH588) was the first British-built Eurofighter prototype, the first aircraft to be completed but the second to fly. When it made its maiden flight on 6 April 1994, DA.2 was powered by a pair of RB.199 engines; these were later replaced with EJ.200s at Warton, the aircraft being reflown in late August 1998.**

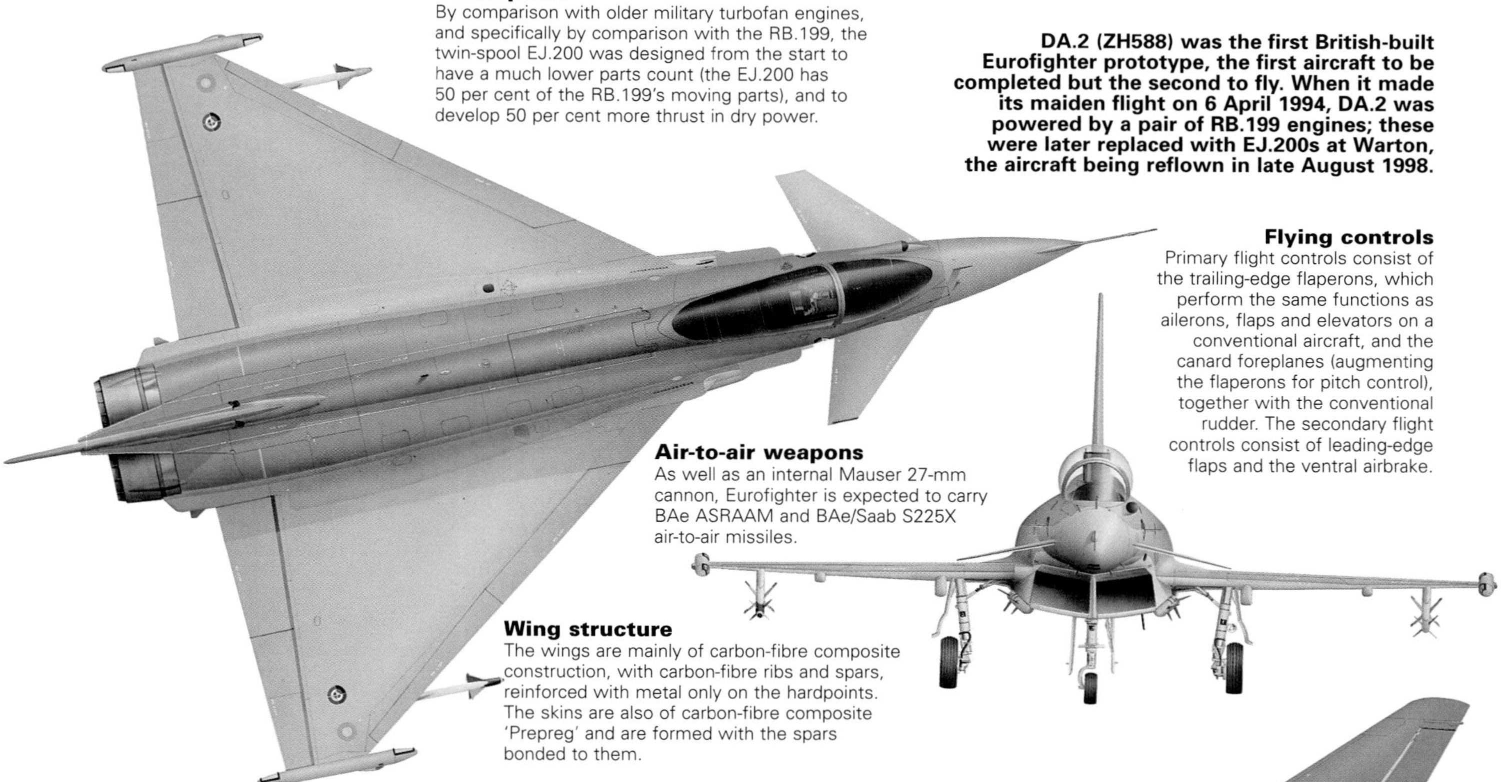

**Powerplant**
By comparison with older military turbofan engines, and specifically by comparison with the RB.199, the twin-spool EJ.200 was designed from the start to have a much lower parts count (the EJ.200 has 50 per cent of the RB.199's moving parts), and to develop 50 per cent more thrust in dry power.

**Flying controls**
Primary flight controls consist of the trailing-edge flaperons, which perform the same functions as ailerons, flaps and elevators on a conventional aircraft, and the canard foreplanes (augmenting the flaperons for pitch control), together with the conventional rudder. The secondary flight controls consist of leading-edge flaps and the ventral airbrake.

**Air-to-air weapons**
As well as an internal Mauser 27-mm cannon, Eurofighter is expected to carry BAe ASRAAM and BAe/Saab S225X air-to-air missiles.

**Wing structure**
The wings are mainly of carbon-fibre composite construction, with carbon-fibre ribs and spars, reinforced with metal only on the hardpoints. The skins are also of carbon-fibre composite 'Prepreg' and are formed with the spars bonded to them.

**Ejection seat**
Eurofighter's Martin-Baker Mk 16A ejection seat was developed from the same company's lightweight Mk 15. With a moderately raked back (18° rather than the F-16's 30°), the seat weighs less than 140 lb (63.5 kg), and uses the twin propulsion tubes as load-carrying structures.

ZH588

# A-10 Thunderbolt – Development

**Following bitter experience in Vietnam, the USAF sought to develop an attack aircraft that would be able to survive above a modern battlefield.**

The Attack Experimental (AX) programme was launched in June 1966 with a view to replacing the successful but outmoded Skyraider, and a requirement for a suitable attack aircraft was issued in that September. The Air Force issued the Request For Proposal (RFP) for AX design studies to 21 companies on 6 March 1967. Before these could be submitted, follow-on study contracts were awarded to General Dynamics, Grumman, Northrop and McDonnell on 2 May 1967. These called for detailed research on exactly how armour should be configured and located, and how fuel, hydraulics and other systems should be best protected and routed and, where necessary, duplicated. The use of turbofan engines was suggested as these had proved to be more economical than turboprops. By removing the propellers, the engines could be located closer to the aircraft's centreline in an effort to provide protection from ground fire and, in the event of losing an engine, to reduce asymmetric handling problems. The final choice of engines was left, however, to each respective manufacturer.

Responses were received from Boeing, Cessna, Fairchild, General Dynamics, Lockheed and Northrop on 10 August 1970. Northrop and Fairchild-Republic were declared the winners on 18 December 1970, each winning the right to build two prototypes.

The first YA-10 flew from Edwards AFB on 10 May 1972, in the hands of Republic division chief test pilot Howard 'Sam' Nelson. This was shortly followed by the Northrop YA-9 flying on 30 May 1972, also from Edwards, in the hands of the unrelated Lew Nelson. The second YA-10 made its first flight on 21 July 1972.

The US Air Force's formal evaluation of the two prototypes lasted from 10 October until 9 December 1972, with the YA-9s logging 307.6 hours, and the YA-10s 328.1 hours. Pilots preferred the handling qualities of the YA-10, but the real advantage was the ease of access to its underwing hardpoints. Other

*Above: A head-on view of the A-10 reveals some important design features. The ability to survive hostile ground fire required the engines to be positioned far apart and to be shielded to some extent by the tailplanes.*

*Top: The prototype YA-10 lugs a heavy load of six AGM-65 Mavericks during an early trial flight. The prototype was originally flown with an M61A1 20-mm Vulcan cannon in place of the intended GAU-8/A Avenger.*

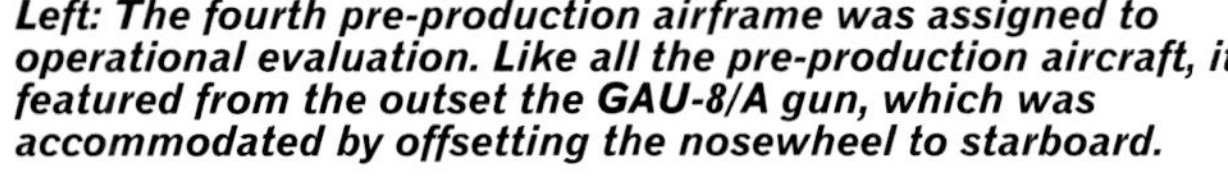

*Left: The fourth pre-production airframe was assigned to operational evaluation. Like all the pre-production aircraft, it featured from the outset the GAU-8/A gun, which was accommodated by offsetting the nosewheel to starboard.*

*Below: A contender for the AX competition was the Northrop YA-9. Although a highly capable aircraft, problems were encountered with the YA-9's high-set wing during re-arming exercises. The two examples built were subsequently retired and placed in museums.*

***Above: The first service unit to receive the A-10 was the 355th Tactical Fighter Wing, which was established as the training unit. The unit quickly took its aircraft on a tour of Europe. However, during a display at the Paris Air Salon on 3 June 1977, Fairchild test pilot Sam Nelson was killed when his aircraft (illustrated) hit the ground after performing a series of low-level loops.***

***Right: The A-10 went through a succession of paint schemes before the USAF replaced the early pale grey colour with a series of greens and grey. Known as the Charcoal Lizard scheme, this became the standard camouflage for many years although the aircraft have recently been painted in an overall grey.***

factors included the shorter, easier transition from prototype to production aircraft, the Fairchild aircraft having been built to what amounted to a production standard, at least structurally. The use of an existing engine (the TF34 was also used on the US Navy's S-3 Viking) was also a deciding factor. However, the defeated YA-9 was not without advantages, the most notable being its unique side-force control system that linked the split airbrakes and rudder, and allowed the pilot to track a ground target without worrying about bank angle or fuselage direction. Both aircraft exceeded the specification and, while the Northrop aircraft was judged to have superior handling characteristics, with less roll inertia, this was felt to be counterbalanced by the maintainability and survivability of the A-10.

### Winning design

Fairchild-Republic was announced the winner on 18 January 1973, and set about building 10 (later reduced to six) pre-production YA-10s after signing the production contract on 1 March 1973; simultaneously, General Electric received a contract for TF34 engines for these aircraft. Modifications to the engine were very minor, being largely confined to those necessary to meet the USAF's left/right interchangeability requirements.

From 16 April until 10 May 1974, a fly-off was held at McConnell AFB, Kansas against an A-7D Corsair II. Despite the initial doubts about the YA-10, the aircraft proved to be far more capable than the Corsair II, being able to spend two hours over the target area, compared to the A-7's 11 minutes.

Following this fly-off, the first prototype YA-10 was placed in flyable storage on 15 April 1975, after completing 467 sorties and 590.9 hours of flight time. The second YA-10, 71-1370, finished the 37-month prototype programme when it was placed in flyable storage on 13 June 1975, after completing 354 flights and 548.5 flight hours.

Pre-production YA-10s joined the test programme from February 1975. The six aircraft were each tasked with specific parts of the test programme. The sixth aircraft was later lost on 8 June 1978 when both engines flamed out while a new gun propellant was being tested. Its pilot was forced to use his Douglas ESCAPAC ejection seat; production aircraft were later fitted with McDonnell ACES II seats.

Since there were only a total of six YA-10As, testing – although successful – soon fell behind. Apart from this, the only factor to mar the early development work was the tragic loss of one example at the Paris Air Salon.

The first production aircraft, 75-0258, flew on 10 October 1975 and was delivered to the USAF on 5 November 1975. The first operational A-10As were delivered to the 355th TFW in March 1976, five months behind the original schedule.

### Final rounds

Final operational test and evaluation work was carried out by the 355th which, in late 1977, took part in a series of trials known as JAWS (Joint Air Weapons System). These were critical in defining the role and tactics to be followed by the new aircraft, in particular the ways in which it would operate in conjunction with army attack helicopters.

The A-10 was christened the 'Thunderbolt II' by the Pentagon during the ceremony to mark the delivery of the hundredth aircraft on 3 April 1978. By then the A-10 was already developing into a deadly battlefield warrior within the USAF.

## YA-10B: Night/Adverse Weather variant

**Fairchild bailed back the first pre-production YA-10A to produce the Night/Adverse Weather (N/AW) A-10 variant. The major change to this aircraft, apart from the addition of the second seat, was the enlarging of the vertical tails. The aircraft was equipped with an LN-39 INS and AN/APN-194 radar altimeter but, extraordinarily, armour was not extended to the rear seat.**

**Sensor pods**
The YA-10B carried its FLIR and radar sensors in pods but, had there been a production order for the night version, the sensors would have been relocated into the 'kneecaps' of the main undercarriage fairings.

**Combat roles**
Fairchild promoted the YA-10B as a combat-ready trainer and, later, as a defence suppression aircraft, but both these failed to interest the USAF. In one final attempt, the YA-10B was marketed overseas as a maritime strike aircraft. However, once again, the project met with no success.

# A-10A/OA-10A Service history

**The 'Warthog' is best known for its service in Europe, where it equipped the USAF's largest wing. However, it also served as far afield as Alaska, Korea and locations in the United States.**

Naturally, the first USAF unit to get its hands on the A-10 was the 6510th Test Wing at the Air Force Flight Test Center, Edwards AFB. This unit was responsible for the pre-service tests and trials, using prototype and pre-production aircraft. Another early recipient was the 3246th Test Wing at Eglin AFB, which performed armament trials.

The next step in the introduction to service was the establishment of a training unit, the 355th Tactical Fighter Wing at Davis-Monthan AFB, Arizona, which began trading in Vought A-7s for A-10s in March 1976. The initial squadron was the 333rd Tactical Fighter Training Squadron ('Lancers'), joined soon after by the 358th TFTS 'Lobos'.

It was the 354th Tactical Fighter Wing at Myrtle Beach, South Carolina, that was the first operational unit to trade in A-7s for A-10s, a process which began in late 1976. The wing stood up three squadrons (353rd, 355th and 356th TFS) and these were instrumental in pioneering operations with the new aircraft. This task was taken over by the 57th Tactical Training Wing, at Nellis AFB, Nevada, which began its operational evaluation work with the 'Warthog' in October 1977. At about that time the critical JAWS (Joint Attack Weapons System) trials took place, which set down the way A-10s would work with artillery and battlefield helicopters.

### Central Europe

With training, trials and a US-based organisation in place, it was time to begin equipment of what was arguably the most important wing to receive A-10s: the 81st Tactical Fighter Wing in England. Central Europe was where the A-10 was expected to fight and a large proportion of the front-line force was earmarked for the 81st TFW. From the first aircraft arriving on 26 January 1979, the 81st built up to a six-squadron wing (78th, 91st, 92nd, 509th, 510th and 511th TFS) accommodated at the twin bases of RAF Bentwaters and Woodbridge. From here, the A-10s could deploy to six Forward Operating Locations (FOLs) in West Germany, each squadron being assigned a specific FOL. The FOLs were spread across both 2 ATAF and 4 ATAF areas, and regular deployments allowed squadron pilots to familiarise themselves with the terrain in the areas they would be expected to defend in time of war. A-10 operations were naturally aimed primarily at the anti-armour role, and the pilots used their peacetime detachments to identify natural tank-killing grounds and potential vehicle choke points.

*Top: Slow when compared to other battlefield types, the A-10 relies on its excellent low-level agility to survive. The traditional anti-armour role has been expanded to include FAC missions.*

*Above: The 354th TFW was the first operational A-10 unit, this pair demonstrating the initial paint scheme to be adopted: MASK-10A. The Wing's aircraft were soon busy on overseas deployments.*

### In the reserves

Following the establishment of the European unit, attentions turned to swelling the ranks of US-based operators who could be called upon to reinforce the 81st in a European war. Five Air National Guard squadrons (103rd TFS/CT, 104th TFS/MA, 128th TFS/WI, 174th

*The 355th TFW was the nominated A-10 training unit, although it later added an operational role. The clear skies and extensive ranges of Arizona offered excellent training conditions.*

***Right:** Initially envisaged for the war in Southeast Asia, the A-10 was eventually tailored to the Central European theatre. Six squadrons were based in England throughout the 1980s, poised to rush into pre-prepared forward bases in Germany to blunt a WarPac armoured thrust.*

***Below:** For operations in snow, the A-10 has been painted with temporary white camouflage. This example is seen during a 1982 exercise in Alaska.*

TFS/NY and 175th TFS/MD) were equipped with the type, beginning with the 103rd in May 1979. This was significant as it represented the first time that an ANG unit had received new aircraft directly from the manufacturer, as opposed to having used equipment 'cascaded' from active-duty units. In 1990-91 two more ANG units began flying the OA/A-10 (110th TFS/MI and 111th TFS/PA).

Air Force Reserve units also began to receive A-10s in the same time-frame, beginning with the 917th TFW in October 1980. Others were the 442nd TFW, 926th TFW and 930th TFW.

More active-duty units were also formed in the early 1980s, consisting of the 23rd TFW at England AFB, Louisiana as a second Stateside unit, plus the 51st and 343rd Composite Wings. Both of the latter were based in the Pacific region, the 51st in Korea and the 343rd in Alaska. Both received A-10s in the winter of 1981/82 to complete the initial deployment of the A-10 force.

## 1980s changes

The A-10 force disposition remained little changed for a decade, although two squadrons of the 81st split off to form the 10th TFW in RAF Alconbury in 1988 – their operational task remained unchanged, however. In October 1987 the 602nd Air Control Wing at Davis-Monthan AFB began its adoption of the 'Warthog' in the Forward Air Control (FAC) role as the OA-10A, introducing a new arrow to the A-10's quiver.

A-10s went to war in a variety of roles during Desert Storm, aircraft coming from a number of units in the US and Europe to fly with the 23rd and 354th TFW (Provisional), but returned home to face uncertainty. Once slated for complete retirement, the A-10 convinced planners in the Gulf War that it still had much to offer, especially in the FAC role and for combat search and rescue support. In areas of low-density defences, the A-10 could still operate in its traditional close support roles.

Nevertheless, the end of the Cold War caused dramatic changes in the A-10 community, not least of which was the dismantling of the vast USAFE force, leaving just one squadron based with the 52nd FW at Spangdahlem AB in Germany. This unit has since seen considerable action. Elsewhere, the CONUS force was reduced to just one active-duty unit (355th Wing) and several ANG/AFRes units, while a squadron remains in Korea. Today, each 'Warthog' squadron operates a mix of A-10As and OA-10As, illustrating a mixed attack/FAC tasking. In reality, there is no difference between the two variants and both have seen extensive combat in recent operations over the Balkans, Afghanistan and Iraq.

***Above:** CONUS-based A-10As were a key part of the rapid-reaction forces, being able to fly at very short notice to troublespots. Here, an A-10 taxis in past EAF F-4 Phantoms at an Egyptian base during Exercise Bright Star 1982.*

***Left:** Alaska has been an important base for the A-10 since the first example arrived with the 18th TFS in late 1981. As well as deterring any land aggression from across the Bering Strait, the A-10s were also on alert for rapid deployment to the Korean peninsula to bolster US forces there.*

# FMA IA-58 Pucará

*Four early production Pucarás formate for the camera, displaying the initial silver colour scheme worn by Argentine examples. A variety of camouflage schemes have subsequently been applied.*

## Pampas warrior

**With a history of ambitious aircraft projects behind it, the Argentine state aircraft factory designed and produced an aircraft specifically for the role of counter-insurgency: the Pucará.**

The design team at Fabrica Militar de Aviones (FMA) began development work on what was then known as the Delfin (Dolphin) in August 1966. An unpowered aerodynamic prototype first flew on 26 December 1967 before the first powered version, with imported Garrett TPE331 turboprop engines, made its initial flight on 20 August 1969. A second prototype (AX-02), with Turboméca Astazou turboprops, made its maiden flight the following summer and it was this version that attracted an initial order for 30 by the Argentinian air force. A shortage of facilities and money delayed production and it was not until 1976 that the FAA began to receive the first production aircraft.

As the first locally-designed combat aircraft to enter service with the FAA for some 30 years, the Pucará (a type of stone fortress built by the early South American Indians) featured the Astazou XVIG engine and Martin-Baker Mk AP06A zero-zero ejection seats. Brakes and tyres were provided by Dunlop, avionics were mainly American and weapons French or Belgian, the rest of the aircraft being locally produced.

Designed from the ouset as a COIN machine, the Pucará's initial purpose was to destroy the lightly-armed rebel forces and insurgent bands in the Argentinian hinterland. The Pucarà was therefore made capable, as far as possible, of surviving bullet strikes. Capable of single-engined operation, and of surviving heavy battle damage, the cockpit floor was covered beneath by a sheet of armour resistant to rifle-calibre fire, the windscreen was bullet-proof and both cockpits had flight controls. To facilitate operations from small unpaved airstrips the Pucará has slotted high-lift flaps fitted to the long-span wing, plus long undercarriage legs giving exceptional ground clearance and low-pressure tyres capable of operating from almost any surface except the softest sand or snow.

From the outset the aircraft incorporated impressive firepower. Fixed forward-firing guns consisted of two Hispano HS804 20-mm cannon (later replaced by DEFA 30-mm cannon on the IA-58B) mounted inside the belly of the fuselage, supplemented by four FN-Browning 0.3-in (7.62-mm) machine-guns mounted in pairs on each side of the forward fuselage. A wide range of stores of up to 3,307-lb (1500 kg) can be carried on three hardpoints (one beneath each wing and one below the fuselage) including rockets, bombs and napalm tanks. The only aiming device is a conventional SFOM Type 83A3 reflector sight. This can be set up for any desired dive angle, the pilot manually operating a 'pickle' switch at the top of the control column at the appropriate moment. Alternatively, the crew may elect to activate the Bendix AWE-1 programmer on the instrument panel, with which stores may be released in any desired sequence or 'ripple' mode.

IA-58As have full blind-flying instruments and night lighting. Avionics, however, as might be expected for a COIN aircraft, are confined to HF and VHF communications, ADF, VOR and ILS.

Deliveries began in spring 1976 to 2° Escuadrón de Exploración y Ataque, and some of the first production examples were detached to the military aviation school at Córdoba. Offensive

*Wearing a non-standard camouflage scheme, this IA-58A Pucará was one of five built for, but never delivered to, Mauritania.*

### Pucará in the Falklands

At the beginning of April 1982 the 3° Grupo of the Fuerza Aérea Argentina, equipped with the Pucará, departed from Reconquista AB for deployment to the newly occupied Islas Malvinas. The 25 aircraft were deployed to the airfields at Puerto Argentino (Port Stanley), Calderon naval air base (Pebble Island) and Condor AB (Goose Green). Used for harassing British troops, the 25 Pucarás had little effect and, as the war continued, losses mounted. On 1 May a 3° Grupo Pucará was destroyed by a cluster bomb dropped by a Sea Harrier. On 15 May six further aircraft were destroyed at Pebble Island by an SAS raid . Several more were downed by small arms fire and missiles, and a Sea Harrier downed a further example by cannon. One Pucará did, however, down an Army Air Corps Scout AH.Mk 1 using cannon fire. None of the 25 aircraft survived to return to Argentina after the war. Five survivors are now resident at various museums in the UK, one of which was flown by the A&AEE in 1983 where it impressed during combat assessment before being grounded at the end of the year: it now resides at the Cosford Aerospace Museum.

*A 3° Grupo Pucará flies low over a pier in Puerto Argentino (Port Stanley) on its way to attack British troop positions.*

*Within days of the ceasefire the surviving Pucarás at Stanley were made safe and grouped together beside the runway.*

***Above: Pucará A-515 was captured at Stanley and transported by ship to the UK for evaluation by the A&AEE with the serial ZD485.***

***Left: For the first time since the prototype, the Pucará returned to Garrett power with the IA-66 variant, of which a single example (AX-06) was produced form a production IA-58A.***

missions commenced against insurgent bands said to be members of the communist ERP party some 310 miles (500 km) away near Tucumán. In these early engagements the aircraft acquitted itself well, despite the long radius of action. The simplicity of maintenance was a contributing factor to successful remote base operations. The self-sealing fuel tanks can be filled using an ordinary hose and filler cap on top of the mid-fuselage, external stores were found to be simple to attach, and the gun magazines could be replenished in 20 minutes. In addition, the view from the cockpit was found to be outstanding, both occupants having a rear-view mirror and the upward hinged Plexiglas canopy offering unobstructed and almost undistorted vision.

The fact that the Pucará suffered badly in the Falklands conflict in no way invalidates the worth of the aircraft in the role for which it was intended. The aircraft's exceptional COIN warfare abilities, combined with a low unit cost, led to a number of reported contracts, including 50 IA-58As for Egypt, 12 for the Central African Republic and 20 for Iraq. However, these failed to materialise, being either cancelled or vetoed by the Argentine government. This has left Uruguay (six), Colombia (three) and Sri Lanka (four) as the sole export customers for the IA-58A.

Several developments of the Pucará emerged in the late-1970s and 1980s. The IA-58B incorporated uprated cannon in the form of two 30-mm DEFA 553s, a deeper forward fuselage and improved avionics. The prototype made its maiden flight on 15 May 1979 and flew extensive trials before the decision was taken to further modify the design as the IA-58C 'Pucará Charlie'. Proposed as a rebuild option for the IA-58A in light of experiences gained in the Falklands Conflict, the IA-58C had the front cockpit faired over and an enlarged rear cockpit protected by further armour. Weapons options included two 30-mm DEFA cannon, Martin Pescador ASMs and MATRA Magic AAMs and additional avionics were to include a radar altimeter and a radar warning receiver. First flying in December 1985 the IA-58C showed considerable promise but the prevailing financial situation in Argentina forced the suspension of the project in the late 1980s.

From the sixth production airframe FMA developed the IA-66 which appeared in 1980 powered by Garrett TPE-331 turboprops, however, like other developments, no production orders materialised.

## IA-58A Pucará

**This aircraft is one of six supplied to the Fuerza Aérea Uruguaya (Uruguayan air force) for counter-insurgency (COIN) work. It carries Argentine-supplied 242.5-lb (110-kg) bombs in triplets under the fuselage (six) and wing pylons (three each).**

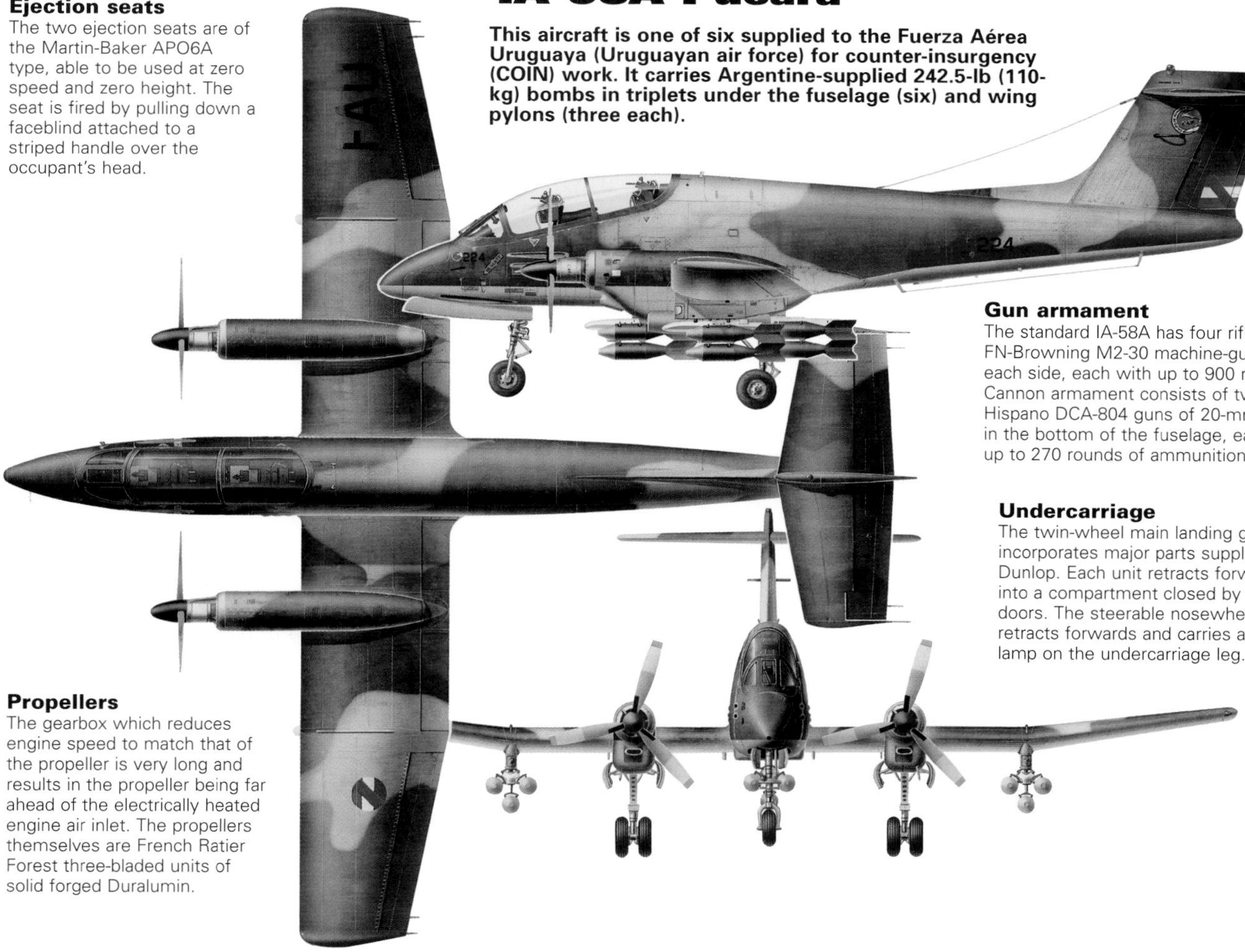

**Ejection seats**
The two ejection seats are of the Martin-Baker APO6A type, able to be used at zero speed and zero height. The seat is fired by pulling down a faceblind attached to a striped handle over the occupant's head.

**Gun armament**
The standard IA-58A has four rifle-calibre FN-Browning M2-30 machine-guns, two on each side, each with up to 900 rounds. Cannon armament consists of two Hispano DCA-804 guns of 20-mm calibre in the bottom of the fuselage, each with up to 270 rounds of ammunition.

**Undercarriage**
The twin-wheel main landing gear incorporates major parts supplied by Dunlop. Each unit retracts forwards into a compartment closed by twin doors. The steerable nosewheel also retracts forwards and carries a taxi lamp on the undercarriage leg.

**Propellers**
The gearbox which reduces engine speed to match that of the propeller is very long and results in the propeller being far ahead of the electrically heated engine air inlet. The propellers themselves are French Ratier Forest three-bladed units of solid forged Duralumin.

Proudly wearing its SAC 'Milky Way' sash, 67-0159 was the first production FB-111A. The F-111's variable-geometry wing was the key to the design's ability to combine a Mach 2+ top speed with the acceptable low-speed handling necessary for operations from aircraft-carriers.

# 'McNamara's Folly'

*Inset above: Just prior to touchdown, the first production F-111A displays its double-slotted Fowler flaps, wingroot rotating glove vane and robust landing gear, the latter designed for 'rough field' use.*

## F-111 development

**One of the more readily visible results of Defense Secretary McNamara's involvement in the TFX programme was the fact that the resulting F-111 only received an official name on the eve of its retirement from USAF service. For a while it was derisively known as 'McNamara's Folly', such were the problems inherent in trying to produce two aircraft from one design for entirely different roles.**

*Above: This F-111A was modified as the sole RF-111A, with a camera pack in the weapons bay. Development of this variant and an RF-111D (based on the F-111D) were cancelled, though the RAAF later modified four aircraft to RF-111C standard.*

In the late 1950s it was discovered that most aerodynamic problems encountered by experimental variable geometry aircraft, such as the Bell X-5 (based on the German P.1101 design) and Grumman XF10F-1, could be alleviated by using dual pivot points placed outboard of the fuselage. Rather than build another experimental aircraft to explore the practical aspects of this theoretical breakthrough, the Air Force used it as the basis for Specific Operational Requirement (SOR) 183 (issued on 14 June 1960), calling for a tactical fighter specialising in nuclear strike missions. This new design was to have an unrefuelled range of 3,300 nm (3,795 miles; 6107 km), the ability to dash for 400 nm (460 miles; 740 km) at Mach 1.2, and be capable of using 'unprepared' airfields.

At the same time, the US Navy was developing a new fleet air defence fighter. The fixed-wing Douglas F6D Missileer was to be a subsonic aircraft with good loiter capability which would rely on its Eagle missiles to engage the enemy. Partly because its large radar dictated a wide fuselage, it was to feature side-by-side seating similar to the Douglas F3D Skyknight. As the Eisenhower administration ended in December 1960, the F6D was cancelled because the design was seen as a step backward from the F-4 it was intended to replace.

The new Kennedy administration's Secretary of Defense, Robert Strange McNamara, saw an opportunity to save money by using the same aircraft to fulfil both the US Navy and US Air Force missions. Three weeks after taking office, on 14 February 1961, he ordered a study to determine the feasibility of using a design based on SOR 183 to perform close air support (CAS), air superiority and long-range interdiction missions. By May 1961 the CAS mission was split off into a separate programme which resulted in the LTV A-7 Corsair II, while the remaining requirements were to be satisfied by a single bi-service

*This view of the flight line at GD's Fort Worth plant in 1965 shows three of the eight pre-production F-111As. In all, 17 aircraft were employed in the RDT&E effort required before the type entered service with the USAF in 1967.*

### F-111 intake designs

The effort to remedy the engine stall problems encountered early in the TFX programme led to three different engine intake designs being employed during the F-111's production life. Triple Plow I intakes (right, as fitted to all production F-111As and Cs) allowed the highest top speed; Super Plow (middle right, a single F-111B and FB-111A) introduced a pair of blow-in doors behind the intake lip; Triple Plow II (far right, all F-111D/E/F and most FB-111As) had three blow-in doors.

design (led by the US Air Force) which was called the tactical fighter, experimental (TFX).

McNamara ordered development of the TFX on 7 June 1961, USAF and US Navy attempts to dissuade him proving unsuccessful. The two services could not agree on compatible requirements, which resulted in McNamara himself setting the design's basic characteristics in September 1961, with a request for proposals (RFP) being issued in October 1961, calling for initial operational capability (IOC) to be reached by October 1965.

There followed four design competitions, all of which were won by Boeing. Howls of protest were heard in the Pentagon on 24 November 1962 when McNamara overruled everyone and decreed that the team of General Dynamics (GD) and Grumman would build the TFX. The main stated reason was the greater commonality of GD's design, although the political benefits of having it built in then-Vice-President Johnson's home state probably did no harm.

After its award, the TFX became known as the F-111. On 21 December 1964 the USAF's F-111A flew for the first time from GD's Fort Worth, Texas, plant. The USN's F-111B followed on 18 May 1965 from Grumman's Bethpage, New York, facility. What followed was one of the most painful and controversial development programmes ever endured by the US military: not only were the aircraft overweight and over budget, but they did not work.

## Radical innovations

The F-111 introduced a number of radical innovations to combat aircraft, including variable-geometry wings, terrain-following radar and afterburning turbofan engines. Three features were insisted upon by the USN: the crew escape capsule, side-by-side seating and the weapons bay. Including these made the F-111B so big that the USN was able to extricate itself from the programme after spending $238 million on seven airframes. In the process, the design went through four weight reduction programmes which reduced its vaunted commonality with the USAF version from 80 per cent to less than 30 per cent.

Like the Douglas F6D Missileer it replaced, the F-111B was not designed for classical air-to-air combat, but rather to engage the enemy from a distance of up to 100 nm (115 miles; 185 km) with AIM-54 Phoenix missiles. Its targets would be tracked by the AWG-9 radar system (which could track up to 24 at a time), with missiles being launched against as many as six. After the demise of the F-111B programme on 10 July 1968, several of the seven completed aircraft served as testbeds for the AWG-9/AIM-54 weapon system. Three of the seven F-111Bs crashed, with the loss of four lives. The last aircraft were grounded in May 1971.

Congress gave the go-ahead for the USN fighter, experimental (VFX) programme, which became the Grumman F-14 Tomcat, simultaneously with cancelling the F-111B. It used the F-111B's AWG-9/AIM-54 armament and TF30 engines in an airframe which was smaller and lighter by virtue of its use of ejection seats and tandem seating, as well as the deletion of the weapons bay.

The F-111 was the first operational aircraft to employ variable-geometry, or 'swing', wings. With 20/20 hindsight, it has been convincingly argued that the aerodynamic location of the wings was incorrect. Certainly, the interaction between the wings, fuselage and air inlets caused serious developmental problems.

## 'Wings that fell off'

Despite the aerodynamic benefits of swing wings, there were natural suspicions about this radical innovation. These increased dramatically in late December 1969, when a wing separated from an F-111A during recovery from a dive-bomb attack. The entire F-111 fleet was grounded for seven months while the problem (eventually determined to be due to poor quality subcontracting) was located and fixed. Although wings have been known to depart unintentionally from fixed-wing aircraft, it was because the F-111's wings were designed to move that it gained an undeserved reputation of having 'wings that fell off'.

The F-111's Pratt & Whitney TF30 engines gave it superior fuel efficiency in the low-altitude, high-speed regime. When flown with stable power settings the engines seldom stalled, although early in the programme stalls caused by the interface between the wing, fuselage and inlets caused one of the biggest design challenges of the F-111 programme.

***After the cancellation of the ambitious FB-111H (based on an FB-111A rebuilt for a strategic role, powered by F101 engines and armed with up to 10 SRAMs), GD proposed the FB-111B/C (illustrated) – similar to the FB-111H, but based on a reworked F-111A/D.***

### NASA's TACT F-111

Based at Edwards AFB, NASA's Dryden Flight Research Facility operated the 13th F-111A RDT&E aircraft (63-9778) during a joint USAF/NASA advanced wing design research programme known as TACT (Transonic Aircraft Technology). Boeing fitted a supercritical Mission Adaptive Wing (MAW) with an unbroken surface made of flexible fibreglass. The benefits of this feature at variable camber and wing sweep angles were investigated.

# Variants

*Wearing the final camouflage scheme adopted by the Aardvark, this **F-111G** from the 428th **TFS** (operating from **Cannon AFB**) wears the light blue fin band of the 'Buccaneers'. A distinguishing feature of the **G** model was the bulge forward of the cockpit, which had previously housed the astrotracker navigation system (**ANS**).*

**Although plagued throughout its career by maintenance problems the F-111 emerged as a highly capable deep-penetration bomber, giving rise to a succession of sophisticated variants.**

## F-111A

The F-111A made its first flight on 21 December 1964, 16 days ahead of schedule, with its wings locked at 26° (maximum sweep angle at which flaps and slats can be used). The second flight occurred on 6 January 1965, and saw the wings swept fully aft. The twin TF30-P-1s, the first afterburning turbofan engines to be developed, enabled the F-111 to fly long distances at high speed, with low fuel consumption (later F-111As were powered by P-3s). Later in the programme, the A-model suffered a succession of compressor stalls due to problems with the engine inlets and, despite modification to the inlets and engine blades, the problems persisted. Illustrated is the fifth test aircraft, 63-9770, which had a different tail design to that used on later production F-111s. F-111As were deployed to Vietnam under Operation Combat Lancer in 1968, during which three aircraft were lost. The aircraft were quickly withdrawn, but returned at the end of 1972 to much greater success.

## F-111B

Intended as a US Navy replacement for the F-4 Phantom II, the F-111B was built by Grumman, and was planned as a cost-saving measure whereby one common aircraft was developed for both the USAF and US Navy. It was not designed for classic air-to-air combat, but to engage the enemy from up to 115 miles (185 km) away, with its combination of AWG-9 radar in a shortened radome, and AIM-54 Phoenix missiles. The B model was equipped with long-span wings, (illustrated below) and an arrester hook mounted between the engines on the underside of the fuselage. Seven aircraft were completed, with carrier trials taking place aboard USS *Coral Sea* in July 1968 (right). The F-111B was well-suited to carrier operations, posing no problems during launch, approach or deck/hangar handling. Of the seven aircraft completed, three crashed, with the loss of four lives. Despite the success of the trials, the F-111B was eventually cancelled due to the aircraft's spiralling increase in weight. Despite frantic weight reduction efforts by Grumman, the programme was cancelled in favour of Grumman's own proposal, the F-14 Tomcat, which was to utilise the engines and weapons system of the F-111B. The remaining airframes were finally retired in May 1971. The US Navy would have received 231 F-111Bs, which theoretically would have been delivered between 1968 and 1975.

## F-111C

The F-111C is an F-111A built for the RAAF. It differs from the US F-111A in its longer wings (as used on the FB-111A) and a removable right control stick. The F-111C also has the larger and stronger landing gear, brakes, and tyres of the FB-111A. The first F-111C made its first flight in July 1968, and was quickly followed by 23 further examples. In September the Australian government accepted its first F-111C. After this, all 24 aircraft were put into storage where they were left until problems with the USAF F-111s were corrected. During this period, F-4E Phantoms were leased until the F-111Cs finally arrived on 1 June 1973. Four examples were modified for the reconnaissance role, while upgrades to the fleet included the addition of AVQ-26 Pave Tack pods to enhance laser-guided bombing. The retirement of the F-111 from USAF service saw numbers within the RAAF increase. Two main variants are currently in service – the F-111C (illustrated) and F-111G.

## F-111D

The F-111D followed the F-111E into operational service. It featured an advanced Mk II avionics system, improved environmental control systems, and uprated TF30-P-9 engines. Other changes in the F-111D included the use of larger tyres and parts of the FB-111A's stronger landing gear. This permitted the F-111D to operate at heavier gross weights. The airframe was essentially the same as that of the F-111E, including the Triple Plow II intakes, which featured triple 'blow-in' doors to increase the inlet area. Problems encountered with the Mk II avionics system caused a reduction in the number of D models delivered, the first of which arrived in service on 1 November 1971. The F-111D's unique equipment and its low number of airframe hours made the variant superior to other models. The F-111D, including this 27th Fighter Wing aircraft, ruled the roost at Cannon AFB for 21 years. The wing later transitioned to the F-111F, sending its D models to AMARC at Davis-Monthan.

## F-111E/F

The second tactical version of the F-111, the E model became operational in October 1969. It was essentially similar to the F-111A apart from modified air inlets and some minor improvements to the nav/attack system, along with the addition of terrain-following radar (TFR) and a strike camera. All E models were equipped with TF30-P3 engines. Further improvements to the F-111 resulted in the F-111F, which was equipped with the powerful TF30-P-100 engine, but had inferior avionics compared to the D model. It was fitted with Triple Plow II inlets which gave the aircraft a slightly higher speed than earlier models, With the addition of the Pave Tack pod, F-111Fs were able to undertake fully autonomous laser-bombing. During the Gulf War, the majority of LGBs dropped by the USAF was via the Pave Tack system – illustrated is an F-111F in classic 'laser-bomber' configuration, with its Pave Tack pod fully deployed, an ALQ-131 ECM pod under the rear fuselage and GBU-10 Paveway IIs under each wing.

## EF-111A Raven

Following the Vietnam War, the US Navy possessed the best electronic jamming aircraft in the world, namely the EA-6B Prowler. An equivalent aircraft was required by the USAF, which would use the ALQ-99 jamming system, and the result was that the ALQ-99 was mated with an aircraft which possessed the required speed and range. The aircraft chosen was the F-111A, those aircraft selected for modification having an average airframe life of 2,000 hours. The first production EF-111A Raven was rolled out on 19 June 1981. The aircraft dispensed with the traditional three-tone Southeast Asian camouflage, instead adopting a two-tone grey scheme. The jamming system is an improved version of that used in the EA-6B, and is designated ALQ-99E, the jammers being housed in a canoe fairing in the former weapons bay. UK-based EF-111As, of the 42nd Electronic Combat Squadron at Upper Heyford, served during Desert Storm. The Ravens jammed Iraqi radars, and during one mission, a crew outmanoeuvred an Iraqi Mirage F1 fighter, forcing it to crash into the ground.

## FB-111A

The FB-111A was based on the F-111A, but incorporated the longer wings of the F-111B, stronger landing gear, extra fuel, and TF30-P-7 powerplants. An improved and expanded avionics suite was also fitted. In addition to carrying nuclear bombs, the FB-111A was unique among Aardvarks in that it was the only variant to be equipped with the astrotracker navigation system (ANS), which was located in front of the canopy, and to have provision for the SRAM (Short-Range Attack Missile) in addition to the incorporation of an Air Force satellite communication capability and an SMS optimised for its mission as a nuclear bomber. It was also unique in that it had no provision for manually releasing weapons – all releases were via computer. Following the re-structuring of the USAF in 1992, which saw the break-up of SAC, FB-111s had their nuclear capability removed, and served instead in the training role. Redesignated F-111G, the aircraft were soon withdrawn from US service, and a number was later sold to the RAAF.

*A8-274 of No. 6 Sqn carries 60th anniversary markings. The unit began flying the Anson in 1939, followed by the Hudson and Beaufort and, post-war, the Lincoln, Canberra and Phantom II.*

*In a practice that was supposedly outlawed by USAF F-111 operators, this RAAF F-111C dumps surplus fuel from the tailcone fuel vent into the afterburner plume, with spectacular results. RAAF F-111s have now lost their USAF-style, three-tone Southeast Asia camouflage and black undersides in favour of a grey scheme, more effective both over water and in the hazy tropical skies of northern Australia.*

# Amberley's Aardvarks

**The Royal Australian Air Force remains the final military F-111 operator, with two Amberley, Queensland-based squadrons in service with No. 82 Wing, providing the most potent airborne strike force in the Pacific and Southeast Asia zone.**

Having celebrated over 25 years of service, and been bolstered by the purchase of ex-USAF F-111Gs, the F-111 looks set to remain a familiar sight in Australian skies until 2020. Beating the Mirage IV, TSR.2, F-4 Phantom II and A-5 Vigilante, the F-111 was chosen by the Australian government to replace the ageing RAAF Canberra fleet. An order for 24 aircraft was placed in October 1963, initially for the F-111A, but was later changed to the unique F-111C.

Australia's F-111Cs are a hybrid version, combining the fuselage, avionics and engines of the F-111A with the longer-span wings, heavier landing gear and wing carry-through box of the strategic-configured FB-111A.

Due to problems with the wing carry-through structure of USAF F-111As, the aircraft were placed into storage at Fort Worth in 1968, amid much controversy in Australia, and it was not until July 1973 that the first four touched down at Amberley, near Brisbane. Twenty-four F-4E Phantoms had been leased from the USAF to cover the shortfall.

The aircraft entered service with Nos 1 and 6 Squadrons, as part of No. 82 Wing, and were joined by four ex-USAF F-111As in 1982 as attrition replacements. These latter aircraft were brought up to F-111C standard at Amberley, the only noteworthy difference now being the retention of the lower-strength wing carry-through box.

The original order included six RF-111As, but this version was not produced and the RAAF had to wait until 1979 before gaining a reconnaissance capability; this was provided by the conversion of four F-111C airframes to RF-111C.

Fifteen ex-TAC F-111Gs were offered to Australia in 1992, in the post-Cold War contraction of US forces, and were duly transferred to RAAF ownership. A number of these are operated by the F-111G Flight of No. 6 Squadron, with the balance being held in rotational storage.

No. 82 Wing has long been the supreme strike force in the Southeast Asia/Pacific region,

*Ex-USAF F-111Gs are flown by No. 6 Sqn, which serves as the F-111 OCU. F-111G ordnance options differ from those of the baseline F-111C, and include Mk 82 iron bombs in various guises, Mk 36 Destructor bombs, GBU-10 LGBs and the AN/ALE-40 CMDS (countermeasures dispenser system).*

*A Pave Tack-equipped AUP F-111C shelters from the sun in its purpose-built 'carport' hangar at Amberley. The underfuselage AN/AVQ-26 Pave Tack provides target tracking and designation.*

*Carrying a pair of practice bomb dispensers, this No. 6 Sqn Aardvark displays toned-down markings and overall Gunship Gray colour scheme.*

*Displaying old-style No. 1 Sqn markings, this Harpoon-armed Aardvark flies low over South Queensland during the early 1990s. The AGM-84D provides a potent anti-ship capability.*

and remains so to this day. It is perhaps not widely appreciated that the Strike and Reconnaissance Group (parent unit of No. 82 Wing) fields the only night-capable strike force south of the USAF bases in Japan and Korea.

In order to allow operation up to the planned retirement date, several shortcomings have had to be addressed, particularly with the 1960s vintage avionics suite. Accordingly, an F-111C/RF-111C Avionics Upgrade Programme (AUP) was designed, and has recently been completed.

The digital AUP upgrade confers much greater capability, and allows closer interoperability between the two models. The F-111Gs had been given a broadly similar, but less extensive upgrade by the USAF, and a further upgrade is planned, though not yet funded.

Coincident with the AUP has been the installation of the more powerful TF30-P-109 to the F-111C and a hybrid TF30-P-107/109 (dubbed P-108) to the F-111G. The latter engine, developed by RAAF technicians in conjunction with Pratt & Whitney, is planned to overcome installation difficulties associated with the different airframe.

## Maritime missions

The primary wartime role of the fleet is to fly interdiction sorties within Australia's maritime approaches and provide a precision strike capability. No. 1 Sqn is the (peacetime) operational unit (Strike and Reconnaissance), with No. 6 Squadron fulfilling the role of Operational Conversion Unit.

Accordingly, the aircraft are equipped with a range of Mk 82 and 84 bombs, Paveway LGBs, the AGM-84D Harpoon, and will shortly introduce the AGM-142 Raptor, providing a much-needed stand-off capability. The major shortcomings of the aircraft are the current lack of anti-radiation and area-denial weapons. The ubiquitous AIM-9M is used for self-defence, but is expected to be replaced by the AIM-132 ASRAAM (the missile selected as the next close-in missile for the Hornet force) in due course. All F-111Cs are fitted with the AN/AVQ-26 Pave Tack pod (the F-111G has no self-designating capability at the present time), the RAAF now being the sole operator of the system.

Amberley remains home to the F-111, though wartime would find it operating from one or more of the bases around the northern coastline of Australia. These bases are manned by a skeleton staff in peacetime, but would play host to several diverse units as tensions increase. The two squadrons would then transfer from No. 82 Wing/Strike & Reconnaissance Group, to the (hostilities-only) No. 95 Contingency Strike Wing. The latter would possibly be a composite unit comprised of other RAAF assets (e.g. Orions and Hornets) and units from Australia's allies.

With 25 years of dependable service behind it, and thanks to the recent upgrades, the F-111s of the RAAF Strike and Reconnaissance Group at Amberley are likely to remain in service into 2010.

*This No. 6 Sqn RF-111C is one of the unit's four reconnaissance-configured aircraft. Many prizes were taken during No. 6 Sqn's participation in the USAF's 1988 Reconnaissance Air Meet.*

## F-111C Aardvark

**Today, the RAAF's Nos 1 and 6 Squadrons fly a total of 13 F-111Cs, from the total of 24 originally ordered, and delivered in 1973. Of the other aircraft from the initial F-111C batch, seven have been lost in accidents, and another four converted to RF-111C standard. In order to replace attrition losses, four ex-USAF F-111As were delivered in May 1982 and brought up to near-F-111C standard. They are often referred to as F-111A(C). This aircraft wears the blue flash and boomerang markings of No. 6 Sqn.**

**Pave Tack**
The AN/AVQ-26 Pave Tack underfuselage-mounted guidance/delivery pod was introduced to the F-111 fleet in the mid-1980s. Only 10 pods were delivered, requiring them to be shared among the F-111C fleet. Pave Tack provides precision delivery capability for 500-lb (227-kg) GBU-12 and 2,000-lb (907-kg) GBU-10 LGBs. The winged 2,000-lb (907-kg) GBU-15 has been acquired, but can only be used within visual range.

**'Strategic' wing**
The F-111C inherited the strengthened undercarriage, higher operating weight and the increased-span wing of SAC's FB-111 medium-range strategic bomber. In common with the F-111A, however, this F-111C retains the lower-powered P&W TF30-P-3 turbofans (it has not yet received the complete AUP upgrade), each providing some 18,500 lb (82.32 kN) thrust with augmentation.

**Sidewinder**
The AIM-9L/M (or in this case AIM-9P) Sidewinder can be carried for self-defence upon twin outboard shoulder pylons. The locally-designed Karinga cluster bomb is another option, principally for CAS missions.

**No. 82 Wing**
Located at RAAF Amberley, near Brisbane, Queensland, No. 82 Wing comprises two squadrons, No. 1 Sqn (yellow lightning flash, number '1', or kookaburra) and No. 6 Sqn (blue lightning flash and boomerang). No. 1 Sqn is the main operational unit, undertaking overland and maritime strike missions, as is No. 6 Sqn (pictured) which, additionally, is tasked with conversion and recce duties.

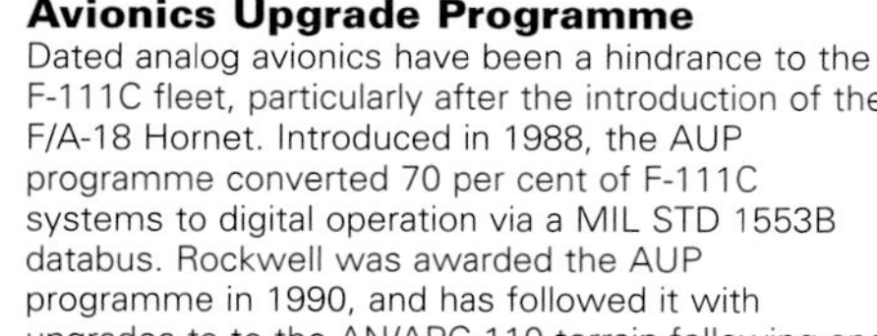

**Avionics Upgrade Programme**
Dated analog avionics have been a hindrance to the F-111C fleet, particularly after the introduction of the F/A-18 Hornet. Introduced in 1988, the AUP programme converted 70 per cent of F-111C systems to digital operation via a MIL STD 1553B databus. Rockwell was awarded the AUP programme in 1990, and has followed it with upgrades to to the AN/APG-110 terrain-following and AN/APQ-113 attack radars and flight control system.

**Ordnance options**
This F-111C carries a typical precision attack load of four 2,000-lb (907-kg) GBU-10 Paveway II LGBs. Other F-111C stores include the AGM-84D Harpoon anti-ship missile, 500-lb (227-kg) Mk 82 bombs (LDGP, AIR or SEHD (Snakeye high-drag)), Mk 36 Destructor mines, ACMI pod, 500-lb (227-kg) GBU-12 Paveway II LGB, AN/ALE-28 CMDS, and AGM-84E SLAM. The AGM-142 Raptor is due to be introduced in 1999.

# Electronic Prowler

*EA-6Bs equip US Navy and USMC squadrons. Of these, part of the USN force provides electronic support to USAF expeditionary squadrons.*

**In service since 1972, the EA-6B Prowler is the prime electronic warfare aircraft of the US military services, and is constantly in demand to support carrier deployments and USAF operations.**

Based on the original A-6A variant of the Intruder, the Grumman EA-6A was conceived in response to a Marine Corps requirement for an EF-10B Skyknight replacement and entered service with three composite reconnaissance/ electronic warfare squadrons in the mid-1960s. Production totalled just 27 airframes, of which a dozen were essentially conversions of existing A-6As, and most were retired from front-line service in the late 1970s.

Externally, the most visible difference between the EA-6A and its attack-dedicated A-6A counterpart was the bulbous fin-top fairing, which housed antennas associated with the electronic warfare equipment. Although mainly employed for electronic warfare, the EA-6A evidently retained a limited attack capability, although it appears that this was seldom used, especially in Vietnam, where it saw extensive service in support of strike aircraft and as a gatherer of intelligence for the North's electronic order of battle.

A handful of EA-6As remained in service into the 1990s, operating with VAQ-33 from Key West, Florida, under the overall direction of the Fleet Electronic Warfare Support Group. Their principal task was to act as electronic aggressors in the training of US Navy air- and seaborne forces, but they have now been withdrawn.

## EA-6B Prowler

Fundamentally a four-seater variation of the well-proven Intruder, the EA-6B entered service during 1971 as a replacement for the EKA-3B Skywarrior. Key equipment includes the TJS (Tactical Jamming System), which is capable of operating in fully-automatic, semi-automatic and manual modes and employs 'noise' jamming originating from a maximum of five external transmitter pods.

*The first EA-6A refuels from a pod-equipped A-6A on its maiden flight. The aircraft was completed without the wingtip airbrakes, but the main distinguishing feature was the fintip fairing, housing receivers for the ALQ-86 system.*

Progressive update initiatives have resulted in the appearance of ever more capable versions. Excluding three prototype conversions of A-6As and five development airframes, the first 23 production aircraft were to 'Basic' standard, using ALQ-99 TJS and ALQ-92 with an EW potential that was limited to four specific frequency bands. They were followed in 1973 by the first of 25 Expanded Capability (EXCAP) airframes with improved equipment and the ability to cover threats across eight bands using ALQ-99A TJS.

The next version to appear was Improved Capability (ICAP), which made its debut in 1976 and incorporated new display and reduced reaction times, along with AN/ALQ-126 multiple-band defensive breakers, updated radar deception gear and the automatic carrier landing system. In addition to 45 new-build machines, 17 surviving Basic and EXCAP airframes were brought to the full ICAP standard.

Software and display improvements were among the changes made on the ICAP-II version, which flew for the first time in June 1980, with all 55 surviving ICAPs being upgraded. ICAP-II is the current service model and is able to handle groups of weapons systems, embodying such refinements as power management and improved identification of hostile emitters, while being more reliable and more easily maintained than its predecessors. As with the original ICAP, it has a crew of four and it has also recently acquired the ability to use more direct methods in countering the threat posed by enemy surface-to-air missile (SAM) sites, for it is now able to function as a 'shooter' with the AGM-88A High Speed Anti-Radiation Missile (HARM) defence suppression missile. The

*It was the Marine Corps which was the prime mover behind the EA-6A. The Corps took the EA-6A into battle, with aircraft serving with VMCJ-1 and VMCJ-2 in Vietnam. This aircraft displays the markings of VMAQ-2 which was created in 1975 with the merger of the EA-6A units.*

***Right:* In 1967, Grumman converted an EA-6B flying demonstrator created from the A-6A Intruder (BuNo. 149481) and this aircraft made its first flight on 28 May 1968.**

***Below:* Aircraft 156482 was part of a batch of five new-build pre-production aircraft and has been regularly used as a testbed. It can be seen here serving as the test-ship for the ADVCAP variant. The most notable new feature of this upgrade is the bulge at the bottom of the fintop 'football' fairing and additional antennas.**

ICAP-II/Block 86 can be distinguished by three new swept-back antennas on the spine and under the nose, associated with HARM capability.

### New-build and conversions

Procurement of ICAP-II also followed a twin-track approach, with the US Navy and Marine Corps receiving a mixture of remanufactured and new-build aircraft to this standard. These presently equip about a dozen deployable Navy squadrons, which are mostly concentrated at Naval Air Station (NAS) Whidbey Island, WA, from where they routinely embark aboard aircraft-carriers of both major fleet organisations.

Marine Corps usage of the Prowler is more limited, comprising four front-line squadrons at Marine Corps Air Station (MCAS) Cherry Point, NC.

Production of the US Navy's standard carrierborne electronic warfare aircraft terminated in July 1991 with 170 aircraft built. However, since the Prowler's inception, it has undergone a series of upgrades to ensure that it is capable of beating the latest threats. After the early ICAP-II variants came the ADVCAP (Advanced Capability) or Block 91. EA-6Bs have been upgraded to two ADVCAP configurations. The basic ADVCAP has new jammer transmission and passive detection capabilities and an expanded AN/ALE-39 chaff dispenser fit.

An Avionics Improvement Program led to a remanufactured ADVCAP/Block 91 EA-6B with new displays, radar improvements, an improved tactical support jamming suite, AN/ALQ-149 communications jamming system and a digital autopilot. Aerodynamic improvements were developed under the Vehicle Enhancement Program (VEP) project and comprise the addition of fuselage strakes, slats, speed brakes and a fin extension. The VEP prototype first flew on 15 June 1992 and featured uprated powerplants and two additional dedicated HARM pylons. A more advanced ADVCAP model never made it into service due to spiralling costs. ICAP-II Block 86, 89 and 89A EA-6Bs have progressively added new radios, cockpit instrumentation improvements and additional antenna and safety features.

To keep the Prowler serving into the next century, the remaining airframes are beginning to undergo ICAP-III development, which is replacing the ALQ-99 with improved TJS receivers, introducing a fully integrated communications jamming system and giving the Prowler the ability to react to the latest SAMs such as the SA-10, -11, -12 and -17.

With the often-criticised decision to retire the F-4G in 1994 and the EF-111 in 1998, the EA-6B has now assumed full responsibility for the electronic warfare mission in US service, with joint USAF/USN squadrons operating the type. Though the Prowler has less range and a lower speed than the EF-111, its ability to operate from carriers, employ HARM missiles and degrade enemy communications, as well as having a greater number of crewmen among whom to share the work, ensured its survival.

The Prowler has had a long and successful history and is expected to remain in service, infurther upgraded forms, to at least 2015. It will be replaced by the EA-18G Growler EW variant of the F/A-18E/F Super Hornet, which is being jointly developed by Northrop Grumman and Boeing.

## EA-6B ICAP-II (Block 89) Prowler

**This aircraft was one of those attached to VAQ-134 'Garudas' when that unit sailed aboard the USS *Ranger* before the ship was decommissioned on 10 July 1993. VAQ-134 is now a joint expeditionary Prowler unit.**

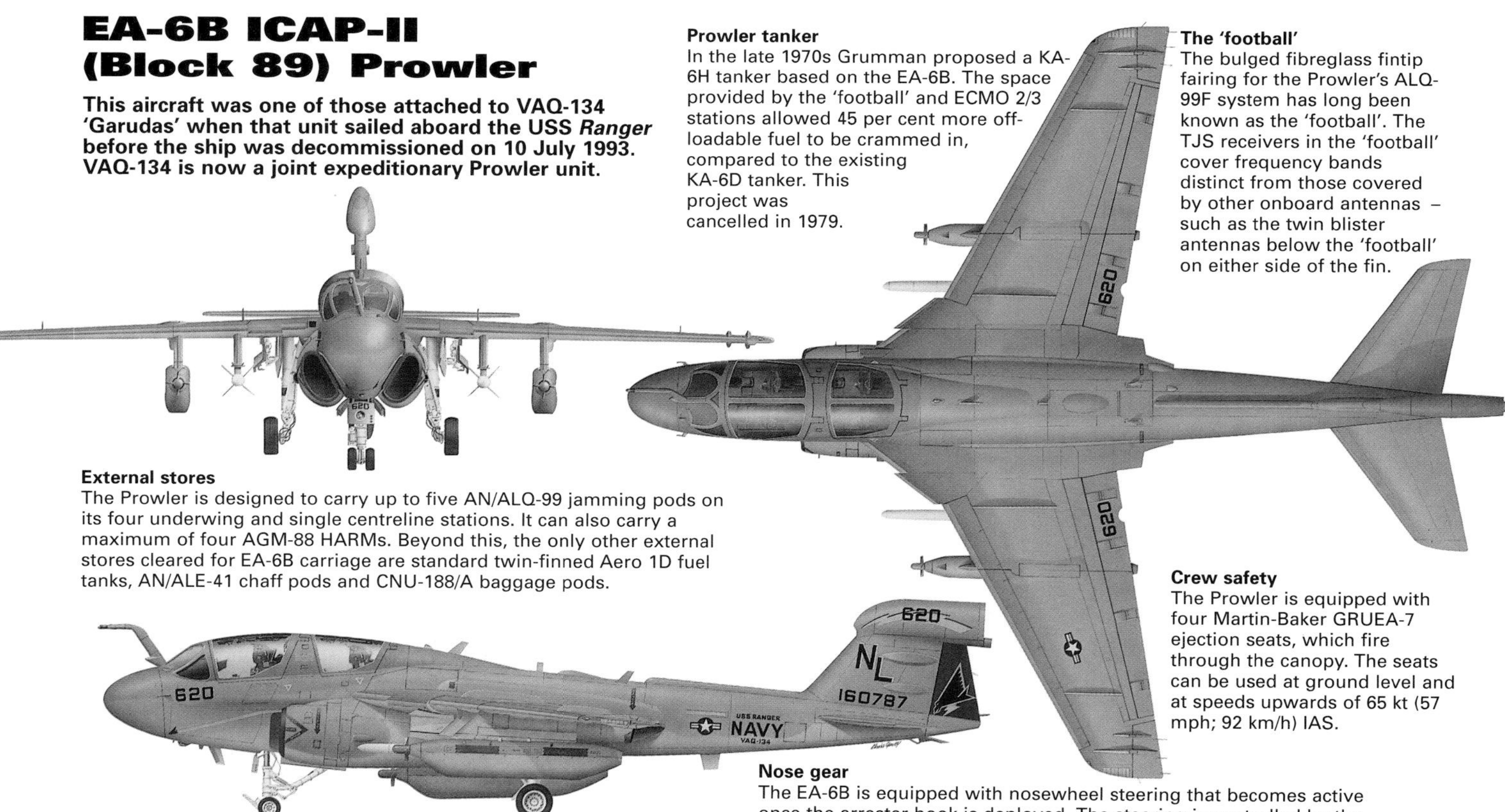


**Prowler tanker**
In the late 1970s Grumman proposed a KA-6H tanker based on the EA-6B. The space provided by the 'football' and ECMO 2/3 stations allowed 45 per cent more off-loadable fuel to be crammed in, compared to the existing KA-6D tanker. This project was cancelled in 1979.

**The 'football'**
The bulged fibreglass fintip fairing for the Prowler's ALQ-99F system has long been known as the 'football'. The TJS receivers in the 'football' cover frequency bands distinct from those covered by other onboard antennas – such as the twin blister antennas below the 'football' on either side of the fin.

**External stores**
The Prowler is designed to carry up to five AN/ALQ-99 jamming pods on its four underwing and single centreline stations. It can also carry a maximum of four AGM-88 HARMs. Beyond this, the only other external stores cleared for EA-6B carriage are standard twin-finned Aero 1D fuel tanks, AN/ALE-41 chaff pods and CNU-188/A baggage pods.

**Crew safety**
The Prowler is equipped with four Martin-Baker GRUEA-7 ejection seats, which fire through the canopy. The seats can be used at ground level and at speeds upwards of 65 kt (57 mph; 92 km/h) IAS.

**Nose gear**
The EA-6B is equipped with nosewheel steering that becomes active once the arrester hook is deployed. The steering is controlled by the rudder pedals and will allow turns of up to 60°.

# Birth of the Tomcat

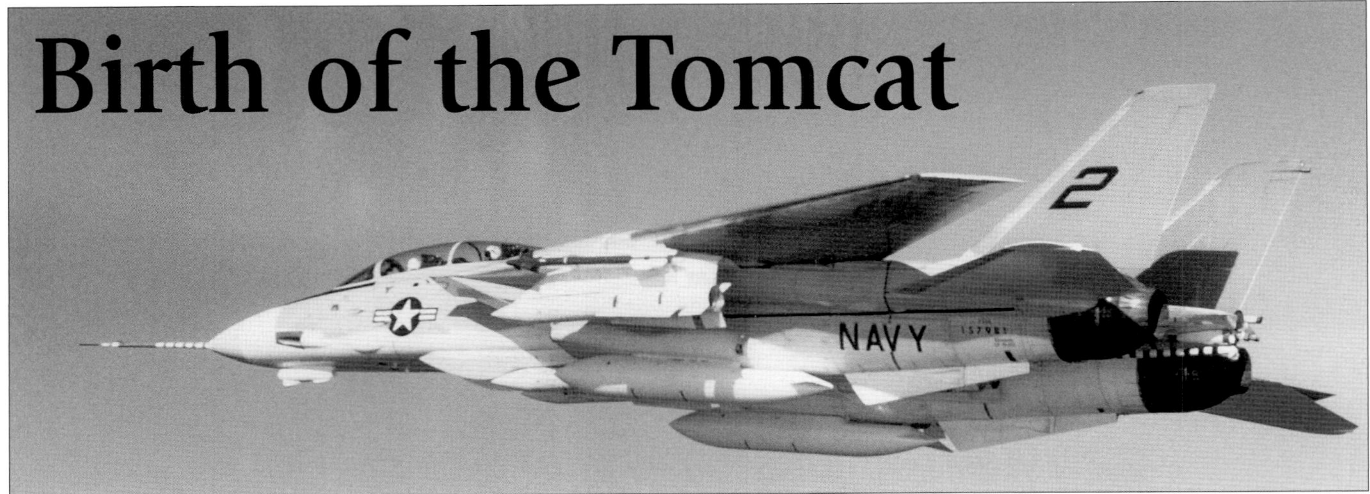


**Emerging from an earlier failure by Grumman to produce a shipborne fighter, the F-14 Tomcat's development suffered some early setbacks, yet it soon emerged into an exceptional interceptor.**

***Above: The first F-14 made its maiden flight one month ahead of schedule, on 21 December 1970. Nine days later, during the aircraft's second flight, disaster struck when a primary hydraulic system failed. The aircraft can be seen speeding back to Grumman's Calverton facility, trailing a plume of hydraulic fluid.***

***Top: The second F-14 prototype explored the low-speed flight envelope, including spinning and stalling. For spinning trials, the aircraft was fitted with retractable canard strakes on the nose, running forward from the canopy arch to the radome.***

During the 1950s, the US Navy began to seek an aircraft that could defend carrier battle groups against long-range bombers carrying stand-off anti-ship missiles. An aircraft able to fulfil these tasks would have to be able to remain aloft for long periods of time and would need to carry missiles with long-range target detection abilities. The only critical parameter was that the aircraft would have to be small enough to be able to operate from an aircraft-carrier; the missile would do the rest of the work.

In 1957 Bendix produced the AAM-N-10 Eagle missile, which had a Mach 4 capability and a 110-nm (126-mile; 203-km) range. In addition, Douglas won a competition between rival aircraft manufacturers to build its XF6D-1 Missileer. This aircraft would be able to loiter for up to 10 hours and carry six Eagle missiles. However, the Missileer was eventually scrapped as it lacked agility and was unarmed apart from the long-range Eagle missiles. Ultimately, one aspect of the Missileer programme did survive and that was the Hughes AN/AWG-9 fire-control system. More than just a radar, the AN/AWG-9 was an integrated target detection and weapon control system with a long-range IR detection system, lightweight computers, advanced cockpit displays and a two-way datalink to allow aircraft and ship or ground station or even other aircraft to be linked together. The Eagle missile was also reborn as the AAM-N-11 Phoenix (later AIM-54) after the technology was transferred from Bendix to Hughes.

## McNamara's plan

With President Kennedy's inauguration in 1961, Robert S. McNamara was made Secretary of Defense and with him came a host of new ideas on how to run the military. One of his major ideas on how to save money was a decree that the US Air Force and Navy should adopt a common fighter called the TFX (Tactical Fighter Experimental). However, the Air Force had been looking for a long-range fighter-bomber while the Navy was searching for a fighter capable of long-range and close-in combat. McNamara was ignorant of the specialist requirements of each service and pressed ahead with the single aircraft idea, despite a campaign by the respective Secretaries of the Navy and Air Force.

A request for proposals was issued on 1 October 1961 and a number of aerospace manufacturers submitted designs; it was ultimately General Dynamics that was successful and it set about producing an F-111 to fulfil the roles of both services. General Dynamics' bid had been made in association with Grumman and it was the latter, with its extensive naval aviation knowledge, which was charged with designing the rear fuselage and landing gear of all F-111s and of the F-111B, the TFX-N naval version. Grumman had also done much work on the variable-sweep wing with its XF10F-1 Jaguar, which had never achieved service. While the Jaguar was discarded, its 'swing' wing and Phoenix missile were incorporated into the F-111B.

The nautical F-111 prototype was first flown in May 1965. However, as tests progressed, it soon became apparent the F-111B was too heavy, had an unreliable and old engine, was too complex and too slow, and so was not suited to carrier missions. What is more, the inadequate view from the cockpit and the fact that the landing gear was judged to be too far forward meant that landing was tricky and therefore dangerous. The Navy was vehemently opposed to the F-111B and made every attempt to highlight any problems with the aircraft, which were further magnified by the loss of a prototype. Perhaps the most significant problem with the F-111B was that it seemed to offer no benefit over the F-4 Phantom it was replacing. In a Senate Armed Services Committee, the chiefs of the Navy and the Naval Secretary expressed their severe misgivings about the naval variant and work on it was halted. The TFX programme, the notion of commonality and the F-111B programme were all

***This mock-up of the Tomcat was created from the original Design 303E model which only had one dorsal fin and outward-folding ventral fins. Sparrow missiles are also present below the belly, despite the fact the aircraft was designed around the AIM-54 Phoenix.***

***Above: Engineers sift through the wreckage of the Tomcat prototype which crashed on approach to Grumman's Calverton base. The pilot and back-seater had ejected safely beforehand.***

killed off, though the USAF's F-111 did mature into a potent low-level, long-range bomber.

## F-14 genesis

Although the F-111B was totally discredited, the Navy still pushed ahead with its requirement for a new fighter. F-8 Crusaders and F-4 Phantoms were considered to be reaching obsolescence and the rapid advancement of Soviet aircraft, especially later-model MiG-21 'Fishbeds', offered a major threat. 'Badger' and 'Blinder' bombers, which attacked naval targets, also had to be stopped, as did the missiles that they fired.

The VFX (Carrier-based Fighter Experimental) programme was initialised and a number of companies submitted designs. In October 1967, Grumman proposed the idea of developing a new aircraft which would, however, retain the avionics, missiles, engines and weapon systems of the discredited F-111B. The Navy had no objections to this and Grumman came up with a design that promised to be superior to the F-111B in all aspects. Though some suggested that the F-4 could do a similar job, the Navy pointed out that to redesign the Phantom would be both costly and impractical. The following year, McDonnell Douglas's Model 225 and Grumman's Design 303 were selected for further testing. Ultimately, it was Grumman's design that was chosen and, in January 1969, it was awarded a contract for the building of six prototypes, and a provision for the subsequent production of 463 aircraft.

The aircraft was now known as the F-14 Tomcat; it would utilise the AWG-9 weapon control system and would be fully compatible with the Phoenix missile. The first 67 aircraft, including the prototypes, would be powered by the TF30-P412 turbofan engine, while subsequent aircraft would be built to VFX-2 standard which would have a new, more powerful advanced engine, and would be designated F-14B. This new engine was cancelled and then later reinstated: VFX-2 eventually resulted in the F402-engined F-14B. The F-14B was meant to enter service in December 1973, but was ultimately cancelled. An F-14C with all-weather and ground-attack capabilities was also proposed, but a request for more funds to fuel development was refused, killing off the project.

Eventually, two full-scale mock-ups of the F-14A were produced, with the original version only having a single fin – the second model introduced the now familiar twin fins. The design was then frozen in March 1969 and the first prototype rolled out of the Grumman plant later that year. A first flight for the new fighter was earmarked for January 1971, but the aircraft had actually made it into the air in the preceding December. On 21 December 1970, company chief test pilot Robert Smythe and project test pilot William Miller had flown two wide circuits of the airfield, laden with dummy Sparrow missiles. The flight was cut short because of darkness and a threatening weather front, but it revealed the fighter's great potential. Nine days later, another flight ended in disaster when a hydraulic system failed. Miller was manoeuvring cautiously back towards a landing, using the nitrogen bottle to blow down the landing gear, when the secondary system failed as well. This had supplied power to the rudders and tailplane and, without these, the pilot had no control over the aircraft. The two men ejected only 25 ft (7.6 m) above the trees, suffering minor injuries. The Tomcat itself was destroyed.

A correction to the Tomcat's hydraulic system was relatively easy to fix and, on 24 May 1971, the next fighter flew. This aircraft was assigned to low-speed and critical stall/spin trials. It also went on receive wing sweep and it eventually tested the F-14's gun. No. 3 aircraft flew envelope-expanding trials with steadily increasing loads and speeds. Nos 4, 5 and 6 went to NAS Point Mugu, the fourth for integration of the AWG-9/AIM-54 system, the fifth for systems, instrumentation and compatibility tests, and the sixth for weapon system and missile separation tests. Of these, No. 5 was lost during a Sparrow separation on 20 June 1973.

***Below: Three Tomcat prototypes in flight show different wing sweep angles and some of the varied colour schemes applied to the pre-production aircraft.***

***Expecting the large F-111B to be an effective carrierborne fighter was an example of extreme optimism. The aircraft was too heavy and its long nose made it easy to lose sight of a carrier beneath it.***

***Most of the F-14 Tomcat prototypes carried large areas of Dayglo to increase conspicuity and enhance optical tracking by ground-based observers.***

No.3 flight test YF-14A prototype (BuNo. 157982) carries four AIM-54 Phoenix AAMs and a pair of drop tanks during one of its numerous test flights.

*Inset: Initial carrier suitability trials were carried out aboard USS* Forrestal *(CVA-59) in mid-1972, using the 10th YF-14A airframe.*

# Development

## Trials and tribulations

**The 12 YF-14As were joined by additional airframes to speed development and testing and ensure that the type entered service on time. However, problems remained and political knives were being sharpened.**

The first Navy Preliminary Evaluation (NPE1) was performed between 2 and 16 December 1971. This examined flying qualities, carrier compatibility, maintainability and 'human' considerations, at different speeds and altitudes. The aircraft involved flew 73.9 hours in 39 flights. The NPE pilots were enthusiastic about the aircraft, exhilarated by the aircraft's pure performance. Emory Brown, the F-14 OPEVAL Manager, later recalled, "The sheer excitement of strapping on the most advanced tactical fighter aircraft in the world, going from brake release to lift-off in 1,200 ft (365 m), rotating immediately to 70° nose up, then looking back over your shoulder as you pass through 15,000 ft (4570 m) and seeing that you are still within the airport boundaries....well, that's exhilarating. I had to stifle the urge to leave her in zone five afterburner and to recite 'High Flight' over and over and over again. At that moment there was no man in the world with whom I would have traded jobs."

Tomcat No. 7 became the test ship for the F-14B with F401 engines, its first flight being delayed, and No. 8 was used to test the production configuration and to provide contractual guarantee data. Nos 9 and 11 went to Point Mugu for radar evaluation and auxiliary system trials, respectively. No. 11 also flew air-to-ground gunnery trials.

No. 10 was delivered to the Naval Air Test Center at Patuxent River, and from there it was flown on structural trials and then carrier-compatibility work. On 15 June 1972 this aircraft made the F-14's first shipborne catapult launch, from the USS *Forrestal*, and made the first 'live' arrested landing aboard the same ship on 28 June 1972. Emory Brown, the fourth Navy pilot to fly the F-14, was the first pilot to land the type aboard a carrier.

### Another crash

During preparation for an air display, the no. 10 aircraft crashed into the sea, killing the pilot, Bob Miller, who was flying the aircraft solo. No. 17 replaced this aircraft on carrier-compatibility tests just as No. 12 (redesignated No. 1X) had replaced the first prototype on high-speed flight trials. This aircraft was the most comprehensively instrumented of the test Tomcats, able to transmit up to 647 measurements back to the ground, and fitted with hydraulic 'shakers' for flutter testing. 1X – actually the third F-14 to fly – had exceeded Mach 2.25 by December 1972.

Completing the trials fleet were various aircraft from the initial F-14A production batch: No. 13 (anechoic chamber work for compatibility of the electromagnetic systems), No. 20 (climatic trials at Point Mugu) and Nos 15, 16, 18 and 19 (pilot conversion). These extra airframes were allocated to the trials programme to shorten development time, and to bring forward the service entry date. Although only the first 12 Tomcats were officially funded as prototypes, the first 16 were built in prototype jigs at Grumman's Bethpage facility. Subsequent aircraft, starting with No. 17, were built on a modular basis and consisted of separate forward, mid and aft fuselage section modules, intake ducts, tail section and a glove module. Adoption of the new method of construction allowed the production rate to rise from two

*Above: As the first Tomcat fitted with an AWG-9 FCS, the fourth aircraft became heavily engaged in the Phoenix test programme. Here the aircraft is seen with a test round.*

*During 1973 a Tomcat was flown against a slatted F-4J in a series of pre-briefed engagements and dogfight manoeuvres. The F-14 displayed superior turn performance and was always able to outrun the Phantom.*

***Left:* Its wings in the fully forward position, the second Tomcat prototype leads a formation comprising the first and fourth aircraft.**

***Below:* After the loss of the first prototype, the 12th aircraft was redesignated No. 1X and took over the high-speed flight test phase of the test programme.**

to three aircraft per month, and paved the way for the transfer of production from Bethpage to Calverton by February 1973, with the 36th aircraft.

## Fire-control system

The AN/AWG-9 fire-control system had already reached a high degree of maturity through trials in the F-111B and a trials TA-3B. Such trials had included live missile firings, most of which had been judged successful. Once the No. 4 Tomcat had flown with AN/AWG-9 fitted (from early 1972), it was only a matter of time before missiles were fired from the F-14 itself.

The fourth prototype F-14A was joined by the ninth, and the two aircraft together flew 357 hours (in 184 sorties) during 1972, firing 11 Phoenix, four AIM-7E Sparrow and two AIM-9G Sidewinder missiles. In early December 1972, a Tomcat made the first multiple Phoenix launch, firing two missiles at targets representing an enemy bomber and the ASM it had just fired. The missile target was successfully destroyed, but the second missile developed a fault and missed its target. An even more ambitious demonstration was mounted. On 20 December 1972, a Tomcat flying at Mach 0.7 and 31,500 ft (9600 m) successfully engaged a formation of five target drones flying at Mach 0.6 and between 20,000 and 25,000 ft (6095 and 7620m), shooting down four of them with its four Phoenix missiles. The three QT-33s and two BQM-34s were destroyed at relatively short range (the missiles were fired at ranges of between 25 and 30 miles (40 and 48 km) and in quick succession, not simultaneously. This was nevertheless a very convincing demonstration of the Tomcat's capability.

There were technical problems, of course, though snags encountered with the AN/AWG-9 fire-control system were minor, although the system's very high cost was a serious deficiency in the hostile political and economic climate. By March 1973 it was being reported that Grumman was considering the use of a simpler, cheaper weapons system based on that of the USAF's F-15. It was estimated that this would have saved $1 million per aircraft, although it would have removed AIM-54 compatibility and would have reduced radar range quite dramatically.

It was the cost overruns and technical problems with the F-14A that prompted a sharp reminder to Grumman from the DoD on 7 April 1971. A hostile report by Democratic Senators Hartke and Bingham was motivated primarily by the high cost of the Phoenix, and by the perceived low level of capability of the F-14 without the AIM-54. The F-14's cost overruns and technical difficulties made the aircraft an obvious and easy target, and even a popular one. They foresaw an eventual $13.5 billion saving by axing both projects, or even as much as $25 billion taking into account whole programme costs, with immediate FY72 savings of $538 million to $776 million.

## Naval hostility

The F-14 earned the opprobrium of more than just left-wing and pacifist anti-war politicians. Some naval officers and aircrew were alarmed that the aircraft was over-specified, overweight and far too costly, and that this threatened the maintenance of a sufficiently large force of fleet fighters. Such people wanted a lighter, cheaper fighter, with a lighter, cheaper radar, and, if necessary, a shorter range.

In the end the project was dramatically pruned, with procurement being slashed from the planned total of 722 F-14s to only 313. Fortunately, the AIM-54 Phoenix missile survived the axe, although some observers expected it to be cancelled. Subsequently, politicians frequently attempted to further downscale the F-14 programme, although it was never again in danger of outright termination. However, cost-cutting measures were demanded. Fortunately the F-14 had a powerful ally in the person of the Chief of Naval Operations, Admiral Elmo R. Zumwalt, Jr, who was determined to keep Phoenix capability in all fleet Tomcats, and who strove to ensure that any stripped version of the aircraft would be as close as possible to the service F-14A. Under his direction, Grumman and the Navy came up with a series of minor modifications to the basic F-14A which would have saved money. The goal of the entire package of modifications was to save $2 million per aircraft.

### Engine problems and the F-14B

The original engine for the F-14A was the 12,350-lb (54.94-kN) thrust Pratt & Whitney TF30-P-412 which introduced minor improvements over the TF30-P-12 tested exhaustively in the F-111B, and adopted for the F-111D. This engine had caused severe problems in the F-111, and was destined to prove equally troublesome in the F-14. The TF30-powered F-14A was underpowered, and the engine was notably intolerant of disturbed airflow in the intake and embarrassingly prone to compressor stalls. Engine problems directly led to the loss of 40 aircraft, worth over $1 billion ($1.5 billion, if an average price of $36 million per aircraft is assumed). The TF30 remains the powerplant for the Navy's remaining F-14As in 2001, and remains the Tomcat's only real Achilles heel. Had early plans been followed, the TF30 problem would have been a minor inconvenience, since only the first 67 Tomcats had been scheduled to be powered by this engine, and even these aircraft were then to have been re-engined as F-14Bs. The original F-14B was to have been powered by the General Electric F401-PW-400. This engine was a derivative of the JTF-22, which also spawned the USAF's advanced-technology fighter engine, the F100. It offered much higher thrust and maintainability than the TF30, with lower fuel consumption, but development proved trouble-prone and costly at a time when the F-14 programme was itself under threat. To test the original F-14B, Grumman had intended to modify two aircraft to F-14B standard to fly the Pratt & Whitney F401 turbofan engine. A test ship bailed to Grumman – hard-working BuNo. 157986 – was actually modified and flown with the F401, beginning 12 September 1973. Problems with the highly advanced new engine led to the cancellation of plans to build 400 F-14Bs and to the termination of work on the F401 itself in April 1974. The second test aircraft, 158260, was nearly completed to F-14B standard when the programme was cancelled, and this aircraft reverted to F-14A configuration without ever even flying as a B model.

# Tomcat today

*A VF-102 F-14B takes the wire during exercises. The F110 engine employed by the F-14B and F-14D, allows the aircraft to be launched in military power, increases combat radius by 62 per cent and gives the pilot the benefit of carefree engine- handling during ACM.*

**By 2008, when the last Tomcats are due to retire, the F-14 will be almost four decades old. Its replacement, in a process that has already begun, is the multi-role F/A-18, especially in its E/F forms.**

During the late 1970s the Grumman F-14 Tomcat was widely regarded as the most important aircraft in the US Navy, and was the dream billet for any ambitious trainee naval aviator. Every US Navy aircraft-carrier (apart from the tiny *Coral Sea* and *Midway*) embarked a pair of F-14 Tomcat squadrons, and these units were the oldest, most historic and proudest fighter squadrons in the Fleet. Only the Tomcat was felt to be capable of defending the Carrier Battle Group from long-range cruise missile carriers, with its unmatched potential to fire off a salvo of up to six ultra long-range Phoenix AAMs against high- or low-flying targets, and then to deal with any 'leakers' with AIM-9 Sidewinders or the internal 20-mm cannon. And nor was the Tomcat a lumbering bomber-destroyer. Agile and with phenomenal acceleration, the F-14 was a better dogfighter than the F-4 it replaced and was even superior in a close-in fight to the much-loved F-8 Crusader.

## The 'Top Gun' legacy

Remarkably, even 25 years after it entered service, the now-ageing F-14 retains a ragged glamour, and many still regard it as being the pivotal element within any carrier air wing. However, the credibility of the AIM-54 Phoenix has been dented by a poor showing in combat and trials, while the F-14 still cannot carry today's leading AAM, the AIM-120 AMRAAM. Plans to integrate the AIM-120 have, at the time of writing in late October 1999, been cancelled again, leaving the aircraft reliant on the ageing AIM-7 Sparrow and the AIM-54, whose reputation may be more impressive than its actual capability.

The only time six AIM-54s were ever fired together (against a helpfully close-packed formation of radar-signature augmented drones), just three missiles actually hit their targets. Impressive as an air-to-air dogfighter when it entered service, the F-14's agility has never been on a par with that of the slightly newer teen-series fighters (F-15, F-16, and F/A-18), nor of aircraft like the MiG-29 and Su-27. Against such aircraft, the Tomcat relies

*Above: Iran possesses a strong F-14 force, maintained mostly from local spares sources. The Hawk SAM has been integrated onto at least two aircraft, possibly in an attempt to produce a Phoenix replacement.*

*Right: Pictured here is a USN F-14A painted for aggressor training. As well as serving in the adversary role with the Naval Strike Air Warfare Center, F-14s perform various test duties.*

***The Tomcat could be gone from US (above) service by 2007, where it is being ousted by Boeing's Super Hornet, especially the two-seat version. Iran (right) will likely retain its aircraft somewhat longer.***

on its BVR capability, on superior tactics, and on the greater situational awareness that a good, well co-ordinated two-person crew can enjoy.

The original F-14A model (which still outnumbers the re-engined F-14B and F-14D) remains severely constrained by the unreliability and limitations of its TF30 engines, which have accounted for heavy losses of aircraft and aircrew in the past. For many years, the Tomcat had little multi-role versatility, although it has proved a remarkably useful tactical reconnaissance platform when equipped with the TARPS pod, and every Carrier Air Wing has always included two or three TARPS-capable F-14s. This reconnaissance capability has been enhanced in recent years by the addition of a digital TARPS reconnaissance pod and by the ongoing development of real-time data-links.

## Reduced fleet

A shortage of F-14 airframes, coupled with the realisation that the F/A-18 Hornet was a better, more versatile aircraft, especially in the post-Cold War world, led to a dramatic reduction in the F-14 fleet. The composition of the Carrier Air Wing was revised, with only a single F-14 unit and three squadrons of F/A-18s (which could include a USMC Hornet unit) deployed aboard most carriers. Only two Air Wings (CVW-7 aboard the USS *Dwight D. Eisenhower* and CVW-8 aboard the USS *Theodore Roosevelt*) retain paired Tomcat squadrons – this is a result of a shortfall in F/A-18 numbers rather than a deliberate 'pro-Tomcat' choice. The Tomcat force has thus reduced from 28 squadrons (with separate training units for the Atlantic and Pacific Fleets) to just 12, with a single training unit. All of these (except VF-154) are based at NAS Oceana, Va. The exception is based at NAS Atsugi in Japan, where it supports CVW-5 aboard the USS *Kitty Hawk*.

This drawdown left three squadrons with the F-14D (VF-2, VF-11, and VF-31), four with the F-14B (VF-102, VF-103, VF-143, and VF-211) and five with the F-14A (VF-14, VF-32, VF-41, VF-154 and VF-213). A shortage of F-14Ds led to the conversion of VF-11 to the F-14B in 1997, though since then VF-213 has re-equipped with the F-14D, VF-211 has transitioned back to the F-14A, while VF-32 has gained F-14Bs. Plans to deploy a mix of Tomcat variants in all Fleet squadrons have now been cancelled.

The Tomcat also found a single export customer, and speculation abounds concerning the status of these Iranian F-14As. A peek beneath the veil of security surrounding the aircraft reveals that as many as six squadrons may be operating the type late in 1999.

The US F-14 force began assuming a limited clear-weather attack capability in 1992, and some began referring to the aircraft as the 'Bombcat'. Limited all-weather air-to-ground PGM capability has since been provided through the integration of the LANTIRN (Low-Altitude Navigation and Targeting Infra-Red for Night) laser designator, and the aircraft can now deliver a range of LGBs (Laser-Guided Bombs), dumb 'iron' bombs, CBUs (Cluster Bomb Units) and unguided rockets. Work is progressing on integrating GPS-guided munitions, including JDAM (Joint Direct Attack Munition) though, even with all these capabilities, the only real advantage of the 'Bombcat' over the F/A-18C/D (let alone the new, far more capable F/A-18E/F now entering service) lies in its superior range and radius of action. Its disadvantages include very poor serviceability and huge operating costs.

The F-14A-equipped squadrons have been among the first to re-equip with the single-seat F/A-18E Super Hornet and the two-seat F/A-18F. The F-14B/D will remain in service until about 2007-09.

***Open air maintenance is standard practice at NAS Oceana. The base previously housed A-6s alongside its F-14s, but the A-6 apron has been turned over to the F/A-18. It is only a matter of time before the 30-year old Tomcat follows suit.***

# Hughes OH-6 Cayuse/ Model 500 Defender

***Hughes had hoped to build around 4,000 OH-6As for the US Army, but the combined effects of manufacturing snags, cost escalation and politics conspired to limit production to just over 1,400 examples.***

## 'Loach' & 'Little Bird' – the OH-6 family

**Though it started with technical brilliance leading to outstanding success, the OH-6 suffered reverses leading to the indigenous market going to a rival. Undeterred, the designers just improved their product and the universally-named 'Loach' swept up a world market.**

Design of what evolved as the Hughes Model 500 started in 1960, when the US Army issued a stiff requirement for a new light observation helicopter. The OH-6A differed from its Bell and Hiller rivals in several respects. The design was aimed clearly at manoeuvrability and low drag (leading to high speed and low fuel consumption) and featured a then-unusual, part-hingeless four-bladed rotor. instead of being anchored to the hub by conventional flapping and feathering hinges, each rotor blade was linked to the opposite blade by 15 flexible stainless steel straps. Because of these design features, there were no penalties in complexity and maintenance cost to offset the advantages of a four-bladed rotor: better control response, smaller diameter and lower vibration at high speeds. Better controllability stemmed from the more optimised blade design that was possible with a four-bladed rotor, and meant that unlike its rivals, the Hughes helicopter could be designed with a simple manual control system, with no hydraulic boost and no need for a stability-augmentation system. Because the rotor was smaller, the tail boom could be shorter and lighter, and the helicopter could fly through smaller spaces in 'nap-of-the-earth' combat flying.

### Low drag airframe

Concern for low drag was evident in the fuselage design. The cross-section was tailored to the two front-seat occupants, and the powerplant and transmission were designed to fit entirely within it. The engine was installed in the rear fuselage, its driveshaft pointing upwards at 45° and ending in a bevel gear on a common shaft driving the main and tail rotors; the entire main transmission had only two gear meshes. Because the rotor was relatively stiff, it could be mounted close to the fuselage without striking it during manoeuvres, reducing weight and drag. Even so, the short rotor pylon was neatly faired.

Structurally, the core of the OH-6A was the cargo compartment, a crash-resistant alloy cage located directly beneath the rotor and accommodating folding seats for two passengers. The rotor spun around a fixed mast attached to the top of the cargo compartment; the front bulkhead carried the pilots' seats and the engine was installed to the rear, while the lower corners served as attachment points for the skids. Fuel and batteries were installed under the floor, and a pylon for a 0.3-in (7.62-mm) six-barrelled Minigun or XM75 grenade-launcher was installed on the port side of the fuselage.

The OH-6A proved to be several hundred pounds lighter than the empty-weight target which the US Army had set for the LOH, and smaller and lighter than either of its rivals. It was also faster, and, having a similar maximum weight, it could carry more payload or fuel and had a

***Two of the YOH-6A prototypes are seen during early flight testing. The shape of the tail unit changed later in the development process.***

***In 1972, Hughes used one of the original YOH-6As in a test programme aimed at reducing helicopter noise. Named 'The Quiet One', the helicopter was fitted with an acoustically-treated engine exhaust and inlet system, as well as a new rotor hub carrying five blades. These tests provided the basis for the considerably improved Model 500D, flown in August 1974.***

***The NOTAR (NO TAil Rotor) concept was tested on OH-6A 65-12917 in 1982. In place of the tail rotor, NOTAR aircraft have a special tail boom, pressurised by an engine-driven fan. Air escapes through a 0.33-in (8.5-mm) wide slot running the entire length of the boom, causing air to circulate around the boom and so develop thrust to counter rotor torque. Advantages include low noise, improved safety and low maintenance costs.***

greater range. Finally, it was more manoeuvrable and nicer to fly. After a seven-month evaluation in which more than 5,000 hours were flown at Fort Rucker, Alabama, the OH-6A was declared the winner in May 1965, and the US Army placed an initial order for 714 aircraft. Total orders for more than 4,000 of the type were expected.

## Manufacturing problems

Named Cayuse, in the US Army's Indian tradition for aircraft, the OH-6A entered service in 1966. Production accelerated rapidly to meet the needs of the Vietnam War, and by 1968 Hughes was building 70 Cayuses every month. But there were problems: military and civil aircraft production, particularly in southern California, was expanding so fast that several manufacturers, including Hughes, began to fall behind production targets. Materials and components were sometimes hard to obtain, and prices rose. Meanwhile, Bell had redesigned its unsuccessful LOH contender, the Model 206/OH-4A, into the vastly improved Model 206A JetRanger civil helicopter. Unhappy with the price and delivery problems affecting the Cayuse programme, the US Army re-opened the LOH competition in late 1967. This time, the Texans had their revenge, and a modified JetRanger, the OH-58A Kiowa, was selected as the winner. Existing orders covering just 1,434 Cayuses were filled, in three batches, before production ended in August 1970.

The OH-6A established a high reputation in combat in Vietnam, being the US Army's main scout helicopter through the years of most intense fighting. OH-6As flew more than two million hours in Vietnam, winning a name for reliability and high resistance to battle damage. Thanks to the type's compact and rugged construction, pilots considered the Cayuse to be the best of all helicopters in a crash.

Another remarkable achievement came in 1966, when OH-6As were used to set 22 helicopter records, including the absolute world records for range, speed in a closed circuit and sustained altitude, and a string of records in the light- and medium-weight classes.

After Vietnam (where over 950 'Loaches' were lost in combat and accidents), the surviving Cayuses were replaced by Kiowas in US Army regular units. By 1984, there were 350 still serving with the Army National Guard; around 250 of these were brought up to a so-called 'Series IV' (or, unofficially 'OH-6B') standard from 1988, with a 420-shp (313-kW) Allison T63-A-720 engine (250-C20B) and 'Black Hole' exhaust suppression (both features of the Model 500MD Defender), provision for an undernose FLIR, wirestrike protection and an adjustable landing light. An OH-6D variant was also proposed for the Army's Advanced Scout Helicopter (ASH) competition, but the programme failed to secure funding and it was decided to upgrade Bell OH-58As to OH-58D AHIP (Army Helicopter Improvement Program) standard instead.

The OH-6A was finally retired by the Army National Guard in 1995, leaving the 160th Special Operations Aviation Regiment (Airborne) as the only major Army command still using the type.

## Special forces aircraft

The use of the Hughes 500/Cayuse derivatives by US special forces became apparent in 1983 when, during the American invasion of Grenada, variants of the Hughes Model 500MD Defender were noted being flown in support of Army and Navy special operations forces. Known in their multi-mission and light attack guises as 'Little Birds' and 'Little Bird Guns', respectively, these aircraft are also known to have participated in American attacks on Iranian gunboats in the Persian Gulf in 1987 and in the invasion of Panama in 1989. A number of variants have been identified, including two employing NOTAR technology. Trialled as a means of improving stealth characteristics, NOTAR was eventually abandoned as it was shown to reduce speed and range performance.

### Special Operations H-6s

The full story of the use of the Cayuse by US Army special forces has yet to emerge; the aircraft are rarely seen and even more rarely photographed. Aircraft first noted in 1983 were known to various trade journals as 'OH-8s', while the DoD is known to have since referred to AH-6A light attack and MH-6A transport/reconnaissance versions of the OH-6A. More recently a number of variants have been identified, as follows:

**EH-6B:** Four OH-6As modified in 1982 for SIGINT duties; fitted with 400-shp (298-kW) 250-C20 engine and 'Black Hole' exhausts
**MH-6B:** 23 OH-6As modified as scout/light attack aircraft, with same engine/exhaust as EH-6B, NVG compatibility, a FLIR turret and external mounts for two 0.3-in (7.62-mm) Miniguns or troop seats
**AH-6C:** 15 aircraft (11 OH-6As, one EH-6B and three MH-6Bs) brought up to a common standard close to that of the MH-6B, but with ability to carry Hydra-70 2.75-in (70-mm) rockets and BGM-71 TOW anti-tank missiles
**EH-6E:** Three Model 500Ds procured under a covert budget for electronic surveillance operations; a quiet four-bladed tail rotor, 'Black Hole' exhausts and advanced avionics were among features
**MH-6E:** 15 new multi-mission aircraft, plus one conversion from an EH-6E, based on the Model 500MD Quiet Advanced Scout Defender, with 425-shp (317-ekW) 250-C30 engine
**AH-6F:** 10 new-build light attack aircraft (ordered in 1984) combining the airframe, engine and rotors of the MH-6E with the armament of the AH-6C and a mast-mounted sight; a 30-mm M230 Chain gun and a pair of Stinger AAMs could also be carried
**AH-6G:** Five new-build aircraft (ordered in 1984) derived from the Model 500E or MD530F, plus seven obtained by re-engining AH-6Fs
**MH-6H:** 12 MH-6Es and two EH-6Es re-engined to same standard as AH-6G, but for multi-mission role
**AH-6J/MH-6J:** MD530N NOTAR derivatives for light attack and multi-mission roles, respectively; development believed abandoned

### The LOH contenders

Design of what evolved as the Hughes Model 500 started in 1960, when the US Army issued a requirement for a new light observation helicopter (LOH), to replace not only its existing Bell and Hiller helicopters but also its fixed-wing Cessna L-19 liaison aircraft. It was to be powered by a small turboshaft engine, have a cruising speed of 125 mph (201 km/h), be capable of hovering outside ground effect at 6,000 ft (1830 m) and have an endurance of 3 hours in the observation role. Ease of maintenance and low cost were high priorities. All the major US helicopter companies competed for the LOH requirement, and in 1961 three of them were awarded contracts to build five prototypes each for evaluation. From the US Army's existing light-helicopter suppliers came the Bell OH-4A (upper left) and Hiller OH-5A (left), both owing a great deal to their piston-engined predecessors. The Hughes OH-6A, or Model 369, was completely new; the company's only previous helicopter, apart from the vast and freakish XH-17, had been the much lighter Model 269, which had only just entered production. All three contenders made their first flights during the winter of 1962-3.

# Defender series

**By developing its already successful OH-6 helicopter, Hughes produced a family of light, inexpensive, but highly capable combat and combat-support helicopters. The latest in the series remains in production by MD Helicopters in 2002.**

While Hughes was working on OH-6 production for the US Army, it was also developing a civil version of this military helicopter as the Model 500. This machine spawned the military Model 500M Defender, a helicopter which was first sold to Colombia. Such was its popularity that the 500M became the subject of licence manufacture in Japan, by Kawasaki as the OH-6J, for the Japan Ground Self Defence Force and in Italy, by BredaNardi, as the NH-500M for the Guardia di Finanza and later as the 'hot-and-high' NH-500MC. An ASW version of the 500M was sold to Spain, complete with MAD bird and torpedo capability, as the Model 500M/ASW.

## Model 500MD

Early in the 1970s, Hughes tested an OH-6A with a number of new features including a five-bladed main rotor. It also modified a second OH-6A to OH-6C standard, with a more powerful 400-shp (298-kW) Allison 250-C20 engine and a T-tail. Elements from both these experimental aircraft then found their way into a new civilian Model 500D. Clearly, this improved machine had great military potential and the Model 500MD Defender was soon notching up sales. In fact, the first military version of the 500D was built by Kawasaki in Japan as the OH-6D, while production by Hughes began in earnest in the latter part of the 1970s.

Powered by a 420-shp (313-kW) Allison 250-C20B turboshaft, the 500MD featured armour protection, IR exhaust suppressors and a wide range of weapon fits.

The first aircraft were delivered to Colombia and Mauritania, and the type was soon under licenced production in South Korea and Italy. In the latter country Agusta's Monteprandone Works, which had formerly been BredaNardi, supplied the NH-500MD to the Guardia di Finanza and to Malta.

*The MD 530MG Defender can be fitted with the rounded nose of the 500MD, as illustrated by this example. The 530MG's integrated crew station allows HOLAS (hands on lever and stick) operation, communications, flight and weapons controls being located on the collective and cyclic controls.*

*Right: Israel's 500MD TOW Defenders were the country's primary airborne anti-armour weapon before the AH-1 and AH-64 entered service. They have since been relegated to a training role.*

*Below: Italy's Guardia di Finanza retains a large fleet of NH-500M, NH-500MC and NH-500MD (illustrated) helicopters for border and maritime control and law enforcement.*

***Various equipment options can be specified for the Defender series. This MD 530MG has a mast-mounted sight for its TOW missiles, as well as an undernose FLIR turret for low-light operations. It also has the rounded nose profile.***

Hughes again offered an ASW version, the Model 500MD/ASW adding a nose-mounted search radar to the equipment of the 500M/ASW, while a more austere combat version, armed only with rocket or gun pods, was designated Model 500D Scout Defender. Perhaps the most important of the 500MD models however, is the Model 500MD/TOW Defender. This formidable helicopter packs a powerful punch into a very small and affordable airframe. It is armed with four TOW missiles, mounted on fuselage outriggers and aimed by means of a nose-mounted sight. Gun and rocket pods are alternatives to the TOW launchers. The 500MD/TOW Defender allowed poorer countries, including Kenya, to achieve an advanced attack capability. The type was also available with a mast-mounted sight as the Model 500MD/MMS-TOW Defender and as the Model 500MD Quiet Advanced Scout Defender when fitted with a low-noise four-bladed tail rotor and other specially-developed noise-reduction features.

## McDonnell Douglas

In 1985 McDonnell Douglas purchased Hughes, the Model 500MD continuing in production as the MD 500MD. A number of MD 500D and 500MD helicopters found their way into US Army special forces use around this time. Known as 'Little Birds', the aircraft are likely to have had the Allison 250-C30 engine of the more advanced MD 530F and were equipped for a number of roles as EH-6E, MH-6E and AH-6F helicopters. Eight MD 500E machines may also have been involved, these featuring the pointed nose profile introduced by Hughes on its civil Model 500E design.

McDonnell Douglas Helicopter's quiet MD 500MD Defender II seems to have come to nothing, while subsequent developments were based on the more advanced MD 500E as the MD 530MG Defender. Powered by a 650-shp (485-ekW) 250-C30 turboshaft derated to 425 shp (317 ekW) and with a fully-articulated main rotor, the new helicopter clearly offered greater capability, especially in 'hot-and-high' conditions. First flown under Hughes ownership in 1984 as the Model 500MG, the MD 530MG quickly gained orders and was appreciated for its high-tech control and weapons systems. The Nightfox version added NVG and FLIR technology to these systems, while in recognition of the lesser capabilities required by police and other paramilitary operators, a more basic MD 530MD Paramilitary Defender was also offered.

The US Army upgraded some of its existing 'Little Birds' to this new standard retaining the original rounded nose profile. These, along with a number of new-build helicopters, resulted in the Army obtaining a fleet of MH-6H, AH-6G, AH-6J and MH-6J helicopters.

***The MD 530MG is comprehensively equipped for anti-armour and general attack operations in all weathers and at night. Nap-of-the-earth flying operations are easily accomplished.***

## NOTAR

Interestingly, while the US Army tested two NOTAR MD 530s, it found them unsuitable to Special Ops due to their high fuel consumption and reduced speeds. Few other NOTAR helicopters have been sold to other military operators.

Having purchased McDonnell Douglas in 1997, Boeing sought to sell off the MD 500 range. It was bought by MD Helicopters in 1999 and in early 2002, this company had the MD 500MG Defender (based on the 530MG, but with Rolls-Royce (formerly Allison) 250-C20B engines and an MD 500E rotor system), TOW Defender (with the original round nose and a choice of -C20B, -C20R or -C30 engine), Paramilitary Defender (with -C20B, -C20R or -C30 engine), MD 530MG Defender and Nightfox in production. In addition, it was working on the MD 520N Defender version of the NOTAR MD 520N.

***Chile's MD 530Fs are its primary combat helicopters. The 530F is particularly suited to Chile's requirements, being optimised for 'hot-and-high' operations with the 650-shp (485-ekW) 250-C30 turboshaft.***

# IAI Kfir

*By adding canards and a US engine to the Mirage III, IAI improved the airfield performance and manoeuvrability of the French aircraft while also overcoming an embargo on its engine.*

## Desert Lion

**Forged in the face of embargoes and hostile conditions, IAI's Kfir has fought successfully in the wars of the Middle East and has also been exported to several air arms around the world.**

Israel was the first export customer for the Dassault Mirage III, and used the type to great effect during the 1967 and 1973 wars with its Arab neighbours and during the lower-intensity hostilities. Despite its success, Israel was aware of the shortcomings of the Mirage, which included very fast take-off and landing speeds and consequently a long take-off and landing run, lack of thrust, and primitive avionics. The obvious need for improvement, coupled with arms embargoes, forced Israel first to upgrade its Mirages and then to build its own improved Mirage derivatives.

This process resulted first in Project Salvo, under which Israel's Mirage IIICJs were rebuilt and upgraded, and then in the IAI Nesher, an unlicensed Mirage 5 copy, and eventually in the IAI Kfir (Lion Cub). The development of the Kfir was made possible by Israel's purchase of the F-4 Phantom and its General Electric J79 engine. The first J79-engined Mirage was a French-built two-seater, and this made its maiden flight on 19 October 1970, joined by a re-engined Nesher in September 1971.

The J79's 11 per cent greater mass flow and higher operating temperature necessitated the provision of enlarged air intakes and extensive heat shielding of the rear fuselage. A large air scoop was added to the leading edge of the tailfin for afterburner cooling. Other airframe changes included a strengthened undercarriage with longer stroke oleos.

There have been persistent reports that some Mirage IIICJs were re-engined with the J79, receiving the local name Barak (Lightning), but such conversions seem unlikely and have never been photographed. A similar rumour concerned the production of a radar-nosed Kfir, this being caused by photographs of an early aircraft which had its forward fuselage painted black as though it were a radome. The more observant immediately noticed that the nose contours were unchanged, and the pitot position remained the same. The basic Kfir was produced in small numbers (27) and most were later upgraded to Kfir C1 configuration, with small narrow-span fixed canards on the intakes and rectangular strakes behind the ranging radar, on the sides of the nose. Twenty-five survivors were later lent to the US Navy and US Marines for adversary training (between 1985 and 1989) as F-21As.

### Avionics upgrades

The Kfir C2 was the first full-standard variant, equipped with nose strakes and large fixed canard foreplanes from the outset. The new variant also had a dogtooth wing leading edge. Canards and strakes were first flown on the J79-powered Mirage IIIB which had served as the Kfir prototype, during July 1974. These aerodynamic alterations improved turn and take-off performance along with controllability.

The Kfir C2 also introduced new avionics, including an ELTA M-2001B ranging radar. Other equipment included an MBT twin-computer flight control system, angle of attack sensor vane on the port side of the forward fuselage (retrofitted to early aircraft), Elbit S-8600 multi-mode navigation and weapons delivery system (alternatively Elbit/IAI WDNS-141), Taman central air data computer and Israel Electro-Optics HUD. One hundred and eighty-five C2s and TC2 trainers were built, and about 120 of these remained in service until recently.

After long delays in gaining US approval to re-export the J79 powerplant, 12 Kfir C2s were sold to Ecuador in 1982, and

*The US Navy and Marine Corps used the Kfir for dissimilar air combat training in the late 1980s and the latter has recently again started using Kfirs, flown by a civilian contractor.*

***Three late-series Kfirs of the Israeli air force carry underwing Rafael Python 3 advanced IR-homing air-to-air missiles. This air superiority grey colour scheme was gradually adopted during the late 1980s.***

another 11 went to Colombia in 1988-89. Both export customers also took delivery of a pair of Kfir TC2s. The latest customer for the Kfir was Sri Lanka which purchased eight of the aircraft and has used them in offensive actions against the Tamil Tiger rebel group. Virtually all surviving Israeli Kfir C2s and TC2s were upgraded to Kfir C7 and TC7 standards, but it is uncertain as to whether any were built as new aircraft.

The C7 designation is applied to upgraded aircraft delivered from 1983 onwards. These incorporate a number of avionics improvements, and have what is effectively a HOTAS cockpit. Equipment improvements involve a WDNS-391 weapons delivery and navigation system, an Elbit 82 stores management system, armament control display panel, video subsystems and the ability to release 'smart' weapons. Aerial refuelling provision with either probe or receptacle is optional. Most C2s in IDF/AF service have been upgraded to C7 standard, and the potential is present to replace ranging radar by an Elta EL/M-2021 I/J-band multi-mode radar as installed in Israel's F-16s. Not all C2s had RWRs – at least initially – but late-production machines have an Elisra SPS-200 comprising two hemispherical sensors under the lower forward fuselage and two on the fin, immediately above the rudder. Jamming pods such as the Elta E/L-8202 can be fitted on the port inboard wing pylon.

The only external difference is the provision of an extra pair of hardpoints under the engine intakes, bringing the total to nine and increasing warload to a maximum of 13,415 lb (6085 kg). An engine overspeed provision, referred to as 'combat plus', can be used to boost thrust to 18,750 lb st (83.41 kN) for brief periods.

During 1993, Israel began seeking export customers for its surplus Kfir C2/C7s and, to this end, IAI proposed a further upgrade as the Kfir C10. Features of this version, benefiting from Lavi technology, include a new cockpit fit, new radar in an enlarged radome, more external fuel and provision for an IFR probe. Recently, Israel has retired its remaining Kfirs as they are inferior to the more modern F-15s and F-16s.

South Africa, which also operated the Mirage III, has also upgraded its aircraft to Kfir standard with new avionics and foreplanes. The Cheetah C is a South African-developed aircraft that owes much to Israeli engineering and innovation. In fact, the bulk of the airframes for the new Cheetahs came from ex-IDF/AF stocks. The Cheetah C is now the South African Air Force's main fighter.

A further, more advanced Kfir variant, the Kfir 2000, had a substantial airframe upgrade and new avionics including a BVR ability and a new Elbat radar in the radome, and was developed by IAI to be offered to foreign customers.

## Kfir C2

**Ecuador operates one squadron of Kfirs. Escuadrón de Caza 2113 has both C2s and TC2 two-seat trainers. The Kfirs were involved in Ecuador's 1995 conflict with Peru over disputed territory and, along with their Mirage F1 counterparts, they have made three confirmed aerial kills.**

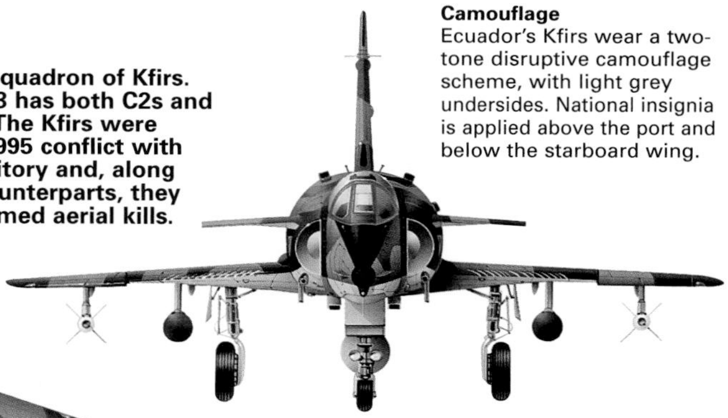

**Camouflage**
Ecuador's Kfirs wear a two-tone disruptive camouflage scheme, with light grey undersides. National insignia is applied above the port and below the starboard wing.

**Canards**
Ecuadorian Kfirs are fitted with the full-size fixed foreplanes associated with the Kfir C2 and C7. These reduce the take-off run by some 1,500 ft (457 m) and have a similarly dramatic effect on turn performances, reducing longitudinal stability by generating lift ahead of the centre of gravity.

**Armament**
Ecuador's Kfirs are primarily used in the air-defence and interception role, though as part of a multi-role wing, they also undergo training in fighter-bomber operations. The aircraft are normally armed with a pair of Rafael Shafrir IR-homing air-to-air missiles. Like all Kfirs, they have a pair of Rafael Defa 553 30-mm cannon ahead of the wingroots, each with 125 rounds of ammunition. In the ground attack role, the aircraft can carry a variety of US, Israeli or French free-fall bombs, but do not have the extra under-intake hardpoints associated with the Kfir C7.

**Wing**
The Kfir's wings lack the sawcut leading-edge of the Mirage III and instead have extended outboard leading-edges, giving a pronounced saw-tooth leading edge discontinuity.

**Powerplant**
The most powerful production variant of the General Electric J79 engine; the J79-J1E powers the Kfir. Because it has greater mass flow than the original Mirage Atar engine, installation of the J79 necessitated larger intakes, and its increased operating temperatures required provision of a dorsal airscoop.

The unarmed Il-76T 'civilian' version was, together with other Aeroflot assets, operated on behalf of Military Transport Aviation (Voyenno Transportnaya Aviatsiya, VTA) during the Soviet period. This example was used to transport freight to Soviet airbases within East Germany.

# Ilyushin Il-76/Il-78 & A-50

## 'Candid', 'Midas' & 'Mainstay'

**Developed as a successor to the An-12, with short-field and adverse weather capability, the Ilyushin Il-76 was intended for service with both transport elements of the Soviet air force and Aeroflot.**

In the same way that the USAF had purchased the jet-driven C-141 to augment propellor-driven C-130s, so the Soviet air force turned to a jet aircraft to augment (and eventually supersede) its An-12s. However, in certain roles, the Soviets found the turboprop An-12 superior, and the Il-76 never entirely replaced the Antonov design in Soviet service. Larger, heavier and more powerful than the C-141, the Il-76 uses extensive high-lift devices, thrust reversers and a high-flotation undercarriage to achieve superior short- and rough-field performance, at the expense of only slightly inferior payload and range.

### Design philosophy

The Il-76 displays many of the traits of a typical post-war Soviet transport. Most military variants carry a gun turret (with a twin-barrelled GSh-23L 23-mm cannon) in the tail, and all transport versions have an extensively glazed navigator/drop master position in the lower part of the nose. The cargo hold is fully pressurised and has a titanium floor, with fold-down roller conveyors, and can be rapidly reconfigured by using interchangeable passenger, freight or air ambulance modules. Three such modules can be fitted (each 20 ft/6.10 m long and 8 ft/2.44 m wide), the passenger modules containing 30 passengers in four abreast seating.

Loading is accomplished with the aid of a pair of internal overhead winches, each of which can mount two 6,614-lb (3000-kg) or four 5,511-lb (2500-kg) hoists. The ramp itself can be used as a lift, with a capacity of up to 66,150 lb (30000 kg).

The first prototype Il-76 made its maiden flight in March 1971, and by 1974, a development squadron was in VTA service, flying tail gun-equipped Il-76s. Series production of the Il-76 began at Tashkent, Uzbekistan,

The first prototype Il-76, seen here, was first flown by Eduard Kuznetsov at Khodinka on 25 March 1971. Five pre-production examples followed, including a single civilian-configured example.

Above: In Indian Air Force service, the Il-76MD is known as the Gajaraj (king elephant), and replaced the An-12BK. The IAF received 24 examples, which are shared by Nos 25 and 44 Sqns.

Below: The definitive military 'Candid' variant is the Il-76MD, as exemplified by this Russian air force machine in Aeroflot colours. Note the rear turret and clamshell thrust reversers.

## Il-78 'Midas' – Russia's tanker

The 'Candid' tanker was first trialled using a converted Il-76MD (no. 78782) in 1977, and the design was refined over a period of 10 years, prior to service entry of the Il-78 'Midas-A' at Uzin in 1987, replacing the 3MS2 and 3MN2 'Bison'. The Il-78 carries 90 tonnes of fuel in the wing, and 28 tonnes in the fuselage, including cylindrical tanks in the hold totalling 64000 litres (14,080 Imp gal). The initial Il-78 service aircraft carries a single UPAZ-1A hose-drum unit (HDU) scabbed on the port side of the rear fuselage (below right). A crew of seven is carried. The nose navigator station and radars are similar to those of the Il-76MD, but an observer station replaces the standard military tail turret. Formation lights and ranging radar are carried in the underside of the ramp door. From 1989, UPAZ-1A pods were added under each wing, creating the definitive, non-convertible, Il-78M 'Midas-B' (below left). Limits for contact are 6,560-29,530 ft (2000-9000 m) at speeds of 249-373 mph (400-600 km/h). The 'Midas' is operated by Russia (200 Guards Aircraft Refuelling Aviation Regiment, Engels) and Ukraine (409 Aircraft Refuelling Aviation Regiment, Uzin Chepelevka), whilst India ordered two examples in 1997.

in 1975. The initial production version of the Il-76 received the NATO reporting name 'Candid-A'. The unarmed Il-76T retained the 'Candid-A' codename, but was essentially a civil conversion, featuring additional fuel tankage in the wing centre section. The final 'Candid-A' variant is the unarmed Il-76TD, with upgraded avionics, strengthened wings and centre fuselage, and uprated Aviadvigatel D-30KP-2 engines, which maintain full power at higher outside air temperatures, and offer improved 'hot-and-high' take-off performance.

Maximum take-off weight and payload are increased compared to earlier models, and range is increased by 745 miles (1200 km) with the carriage of an additional 22,046 lb (10000 kg) of fuel. A single sound-proofed and specially-equipped Il-76TD was operated in support of Soviet Antarctic expeditions from Molodozhnaya Station, flying via Maputo, Mozambique from 1986.

In 1975 examples of the Il-76 set 25 records, including payload-to-height records, circuit records and group paratroop jump records.

Similar to the Il-76T is the dedicated military Il-76M 'Candid-B', with provision for the carriage of up to 140 troops or 125 paratroops as an alternative to freight. This version carries a rear gun turret as standard, although this is not always fitted to exported 'paramilitary' examples. for self defence, the Il-76M carries small ECM fairings (optional for export) between the centre windows at the front of the navigator's compartment, on each side of the front fuselage, and each side of the rear fuselage. Packs of 96 IRCM flares are fitted to the landing gear fairings, and further packs can be scabbed onto the rear fuselage sides. Generally similar is the Il-76MD 'Candid-B', which introduced the improvements of the Il-76TD to the dedicated military Il-76M.

Based on the Il-76MD are the Il-76LL testbeds of the Gromov Flight Research Institute, which have carried a number of engines, including the NK-86, PS-90A and D-18T turbofans, and the D-236 propfan. The Il-76MDP is a fire-bomber conversion carrying up to 44 tonnes of retardant in two cylindrical tanks in the hold, with aiming devices for accurate delivery. The equipment can be installed or removed in four hours, and the tanks take 12 minutes to fill. The tanks can be discharged simultaneously or in series in just over six seconds. The aircraft can carry up to 384 meteorological cartridges for weather modification, or 40 fire-fighting parachutists.

The Il-76PP is a version of the Il-76MD equipped for ECM, with a Landysh avionics suite in lengthened undercarriage panniers. The type was not adopted for front-line service.

The Il-76VPK (Il-82) airborne command post, is based on the Il-76MD, with a prominent 'doghouse' fairing over its satellite communications/IR antenna, a ventral canoe radome and strakes, 14 blade antennas, VLF trailing wire, new APU, and HF probes under the outer wings. Examples are operated by the 8th Special purpose Aviation Division, Chkalovsky.

### 'Candids' overseas

In addition to around 500 Il-76s built for the Soviet military (including the AV-MF naval arm), and around 120 for Aeroflot service, 'Candids' were exported to the military air arms of Algeria, Cuba, India, Iran, Iraq, Libya, North Korea, Syria and Yemen. Former Soviet states with 'Candids' in their military inventory include Azerbaijan, Belarus and Ukraine. Iraq's fleet includes drogue-equipped tanker conversions, the abortive Baghdad-1 with Thomson-CSF radar inverted under the tail, and Adnan-1 with AEW&C rotodome and large strakes.

By 1997, series production of the Il-76 series had exceeded 900 airframes, although production by the end of the 1990s numbered nearer 10 per year, compared to 10 per month at its peak in the 1980s. Minor 'Candid' versions in service include the Il-76MDK initial cosmonaut training conversion, enabling occupants to experience brief periods of weightlessness in a dive.

The commander of Russian Military Transport Aviation stated in 1996 that the stretched and re-engined Il-76MF was to be one of three major transport types to be operated in the 21st century, although its future must now be regarded as uncertain.

### AEW conversions

Developed from the Il-76MD from the 1970s as a replacement for the Tu-126 'Moss', A-50 'Mainstay' conversions were begun by Beriev at Taganrog from the early 1980s. After service entry in 1984, the A-50 was active over the Black Sea during the 1991 Gulf War. The baseline A-50 carries a conventionally located 'saucer' radome and a Liana AEW&C radar, derived from that carried by the Tu-126. The more capable A-50U is equipped with improved Vega Shmel-M radar system in place of the Liana. The 'Mainstay' is equipped for inflight refuelling and has accommodation for 10 mission operators with colour CRT displays. Around 25 'Mainstays' are operational with the Russian air force at Pechora, principally tasked with the control of counter-air fighters for home defence.

Related aircraft include the A-60 airborne laser testbed and the Be-976 (or Il-76SKIP) surveillance platform and range control aircraft for the observation of missile and aircraft flight tests, the latter aircraft being externally similar to the A-50, except for the retention of the navigator's station in the nose.

***The Beriev A-50 'Mainstay', in its latest guise with three-dimensional pulse Doppler radar and digital MTI subsystem, is capable of the passive detection of hostile ECM sources, and the detection of a MiG-21-size target within a search radius of 143 miles (230 km). The A-50U can track 50 targets, and guide the interception of up to 10 of them simultaneously. Endurance on internal fuel, at maximum take-off weight, is 4 hours at 621 miles (1000 km) from base.***

The last Seasprites in service with the US Navy belonged to HSL-84 and HSL-94, reporting to the Commander, Helicopter Wing Reserve, Naval Air Reserve. This example is seen unwinding its ASQ-81(V)2 Magnetic Anomaly Detector.

# US service

## SAR and ASW

**The Kaman SH-2 Seasprite is enjoying an unexpected revival in the export markets, but its days in the US Navy are numbered, with only two reserve squadrons operating the type.**

The president of Kaman Aerospace International Corporation (KAIC), Admiral Huntington Hardisty, calls the Super Seasprite the "most advanced and robust small ship maritime helicopter designed". The United States Navy has cut back its once-substantial Seasprite fleet to just two Reserve squadrons of modernised SH-2Gs, which are scheduled to remain in the US Navy until at least 2000. Since the sea service is retiring its few remaining 'smaller' warships from which the SH-2G routinely operates, the more distant future is uncertain for the squadrons HSL-84 'Titans' and HSL-94 'Thunderbolts'.

### Utility background

The Seasprite has a long history of naval service in single- and twin-engined versions, in a variety of duties, dating to before the US involvement in Vietnam. Built in response to a 1958 US Navy requirement for a ship-based light utility helicopter, the prototype HU2K-1 (company K-20) made its first flight at Bloomfield on 2 July 1959. It became the only Kaman helicopter to go into production with a conventional main and tail rotor configuration, rather than the intermeshing twin rotors found on other Kaman products. The HU2K series was redesignated H-2 on 1 October 1962. Kaman manufactured 190 UH-2A and UH-2B single-engined Seasprites for liaison, utility, SAR (search and rescue) and combat rescue (four YUH-2A, 84 UH-2A, 102 UH-2B).

The Kaman UH-2A was seen by Kaman as the ideal airframe for a US Army requirement for an interim gunship and

*Built as the second of four prototype YUH2K-1s (later YUH-2As), BuNo. 147203 shows the lines of the type before the adoption of the rescue and ASW roles added varied lumps and bumps.*

*From mid-1964 a single UH-2A was used for a joint US Army/ Navy evaluation as the Compound Seasprite. Fitted with a General Electric YJ85 turbojet on the starboard side and wings from a Beech Queen Air, it reached speeds of 225 mph (362 km/h).*

BuNo. 149785 was modified as the Tomahawk for evaluation from October 1963. Fitted with two nose-mounted gun turrets and stub-wings the army was sufficiently impressed to order 220 examples. Political pressure forced the army to acquire more UH-1s instead – the only other Seasprite to acquire US Army titles being used in compound helicopter research.

### Medal of Honor

On 19 June 1968, UH-2A Seasprite pilot Lieutenant Clyde E. Lassen of squadron HC-7 launched from USS *Preble* (DLG-25) on a night mission to attempt the rescue of two downed F-4 Phantom crewmen. Lassen and his crew shot it out with North Vietnamese troops close by, collided with trees, and rescued both crewmen. Together with an A-4 Skyhawk pilot, Lassen became one of only two naval aviators to be awarded the Medal of Honor in Vietnam. It was a swansong of sorts – by the 1970s, single-engined Seasprites were beginning to vanish from Navy decks and were being replaced by twin-engined HH-2C and HH-2D rescue helicopters.

### LAMPS

The twin-engined Seasprite helicopter was introduced in the ASW role in October 1970 when the Navy selected the SH-2D as an interim Light Airborne Multi-Purpose System

***Six UH-2As were converted to gunships as HH-2Cs with a chin-mounted turret housing a 0.3-in (7.62-mm) TAT 102 Minigun, a pair of waist-mounted 0.3-in (7.62-mm) guns, armour, self-sealing fuel tanks and a hoist cable. They were used by HC-7 in Vietnam.***

(LAMPS) platform. This version introduced an undernose radome housing a Litton LN 66 search radar and an ASQ-81 MAD on the starboard fuselage pylon, and a removable sonobuoy rack in the fuselage port side for 15 SSQ-47 active or SSQ-41 passive sonobuoys. Twenty were converted from HH-2D rescue craft and entered service in 1972.

Kaman began delivering the definitive SH-2F LAMPS I aircraft in May 1973. Its primary role was to extend the outer defensive screen of a carrier battle group. The SH-2F had upgraded General Electric T58-GE-8F engines offering 1,350 shp (1007 kW); Kaman's advanced '101' rotor that gave longer life (3,000 hours), improved performance, reliability and maintainability; and a strengthened landing gear. An identifying feature was the tail wheel, which was relocated forward by 6 ft (1.83 m) for greater deck-edge clearance when operating from smaller warships. These modifications enabled the SH-2F to operate at higher all-up weights than the SH-2D.

## Improved radar

The SH-2F featured an improved Canadian Marconi LN 66HP surface search radar, which is also on the subsequent SH-2G, where it adds to the helicopter's versatility with its ability to spot small surface targets, including submarine periscopes and the helmets of airmen downed at sea. The SH-2F also had an AN/ASQ-81(V)2 towed MAD (Magnetic Anomaly Detector) 'bird' on a starboard pylon, and a tactical nav/comms system, necessitating a sensor operator in addition to the two pilots. Offensive capability comprised two Mk 46 torpedoes to engage sub-surface threats. Eighty-eight aircraft were converted from earlier variants (using virtually every surviving airframe). Sixteen surviving SH-2Ds were also brought up to SH-2F standard in a programme completed in 1982.

In March 1972, Kaman completed two YSH-2Es as test-beds for the Navy's LAMPS II programme with a new Texas Instruments APS-115 radar in a reconfigured nose. The Navy cancelled the programme later the same year. Kaman proposed a derivative of the SH-2 known as the Sealamp as a contender for the LAMPS III requirement that was eventually fulfiled by the SH-60B. This aircraft remained unbuilt, although several SH-2s were used to test LAMPS III systems and equipment.

SH-2F LAMPS I aircraft remained on duty aboard US Navy 'Knox'- and 'Kidd'-class frigates, 'Truxton'-class cruisers, and the first two 'Ticonderoga'-class cruisers. All but the first 'Belknap'-class cruisers carried SH-2Fs, as did the first and third through the 25th 'Oliver Hazard Perry'-class ASW frigates.

In 1981, the Navy ordered production of 60 new-build SH-2Fs in addition to those already converted from earlier airframes. The last six were delivered as SH-2Gs. In 1994, the SH-2F – once operated by 11 squadrons: Norfolk, Virginia-based HSLs 30, 32 and 34; North Island, California-based HSLs-31, 33, 35 and 84; Mayport, Florida-based HSL-36; Barbers Point, Hawaii-based HSL-37; South Weymouth, MA-based HSL-74; and Willow Grove, PA-based HSL-94 – was phased out, leaving the Navy with today's two SH-2G Reserve squadrons.

From 1987, 16 SH-2Fs received a package of modifications to allow them to operate in the Persian Gulf. The package included the provision of AN/AAQ-16 FLIR under the nose, AN/ALQ-144 IR jammer, AN/AAR-47 and AN/DLQ-3 missile warning and jamming equipment, and new radios. During the Gulf War of 1991, SH-2Fs tested the ML-30 Magic Lantern laser sub-surface mine detector, a predecessor of the Magic Lantern system placed into service aboard SH-2Gs in 1997.

## SH-2G Super Seasprite

The SH-2G programme began in 1985 when Secretary of the Navy John Lehman told a Senate panel that it would be more cost-effective to upgrade an operational helicopter than to develop a new one to increase anti-submarine capabilities. The prototype YSH-2G, which flew on 2 April 1985, was simply a conversion of an SH-2F to serve as a testbed for the powerplant for the new model, two General Electric T700-GE-401/401C turboshaft engines each rated at 1,723 shp (1285 kW). The new engines, offering 10 per cent greater power and 20 per cent lower fuel burn, were the principal change from the SH-2F to the SH-2G. The G model is essentially rebuilt above the roof, with the engines being heavier and more powerful.

The Kaman SH-2G Seasprite is a conventional helicopter light enough (design gross weight of 13,500 lb/6124 kg) to operate from small warships. It still combines compact external dimensions, a rugged dependable airframe, and the good handling characteristics of earlier Seasprites, but has far more installed power and a capable new mission equipment suite. The crew is composed of a pilot, co-pilot/tactics, and an enlisted crewman operating the ASW (anti-submarine warfare) or Magic Lantern equipment.

The key ASW system in the SH-2G was the AN/UYS-503 onboard acoustic processor, which gave this version of the Seasprite the ability to autonomously hunt submarines – the LAMPS I helicopter datalinking sonobuoy returns to the ship.

***Above: The SH-2D was the first LAMPS version of the Seasprite. NHH-2Ds pioneered the concept before 20 H-2s were converted to SH-2D standard as an interim type before the SH-2F.***

***Below: Now in the twilight of its career with the US Navy, the SH-2G Super Seasprite served the 'Oliver Hazard Perry'-class guided missile frigates until their helicopter decks were lengthened. 'NW-01' is BuNo. 163545 of HSL-84, based at NAS North Island, California.***

# Export operators

*New Zealand's first new-build SH-2G(NZ) completed a maiden flight at Kaman's Bloomfield, Connecticut, headquarters on 2 August 2000. The SH-2G(NZ) was ordered as a Westland Wasp replacement in 1997.*

**The SH-2G Super Seasprite is available as either a remanufactured SH-2F airframe or as a new-build aircraft and has found success among operators seeking an intermediate naval combat helicopter.**

The basic Seasprite was in service for more than ten years before the emergence of the definitive SH-2F LAMPS I helicopter in 1973. In the interim, a single-engined utility helicopter had matured into a twin-engined ASW platform, with undernose Litton radar and a fuselage mounted towed MAD 'bird'. The latter proved so useful that in addition to new production, virtually every available utility and SAR Seasprite was converted to ASW duties. In the SAR and utility roles, the UH-2 enjoyed a distinguished career in Vietnam, and one Seasprite pilot became one of only two naval aviators to be decorated with the Congressional Medal of Honor.

Ten years later, in 1985, Kaman finally flew the prototype of the improved SH-2G, with a new titanium roof structure supporting new T700-GE-701 engines, and with composite rotor blades and a digital avionics suite. The new engines offered a useful 10 per cent boost in power, but reduced fuel burn even more dramatically, and reduced maintenance requirements. Kaman upgraded most surviving USN SH-2Fs to the new standard, though large numbers of F-models remained in storage in the Boneyard. From then until the type's withdrawal from frontline US Navy service in mid-1994, Kaman found no overseas customers for this versatile shipborne anti-submarine helicopter, though it performed with distinction on board those US Navy warships which could not accommodate the larger SH-60B LAMPS III helicopter, and the type saw combat service during Desert Storm, most notably in the mine-hunting role.

Desert Storm modifications included an undernose FLIR, door-mounted machine guns, IR jammers and chaff/flare dispensers, all features which would subsequently be refined for export variants. The type continued in limited service with a pair of US Navy Reserve squadrons until the retirement of the last 'Oliver Hazard Perry'-class frigates in 2000, bringing the type's US Navy career (which was to have lasted until 2006) to a premature close. However, with the end of the Cold War, small frigates were rapidly retired from the US Navy Reserve.

The withdrawal of the type from USN and USNR service provided a pool of airframes for refurbishing, upgrade and export, and Kaman has enjoyed a belated 'Indian Summer' of export

*Above: The RAN's SH-2G(A) aircraft are remanufactured SH-2Fs. The first three machines were completed to an interim standard, with fully operational versions becoming available in 2003.*

*Left: Egypt was the first SH-2 export customer, and received its first remanufactured SH-2G(E) in October 1997.*

***Left:* An early task for the RNZN's Seasprites was taking part in the UN-conducted Multi-national Interception Force in the North Arabian Gulf, where the aircraft monitored shipping activity.**

***Below:* The SH-2G(A) can launch the AGM-119 anti-ship missile and provide over the horizon targeting for frigates. Although able to carry Mk 46 torpedoes, ASW is not a priority for the SH-2G(A).**

success, with what it refers to as the Super Seasprite.

The first export customer for the Seasprite was Egypt, which received ten SH-2Fs remanufactured to SH-2G(E) standards between October 1997 and November 1998, to operate from a pair of second-hand 'Knox'-class frigates, and three 'Oliver Hazard Perry'-class ships. The Egyptian aircraft uniquely received dipping sonar equipment.

The SH-2's relatively compact dimensions belied its relatively 'heavyweight' payload and performance, while the G model enjoyed very high specific excess power and an impressive fatigue life, though some believe that deck handling characteristics are significantly poorer than those of the Anglo-French Lynx. The SH-2 was naturally well-suited to operation from the ships which had carried it in US Navy service, and many expected Greece, Turkey and Thailand to be among the first export customers. In the event though, the next export contract would be for aircraft to serve aboard indigenously built 'ANZAC' frigates and British-built 'Leander'-class ships.

## New Zealand order

The next customer for the Super Seasprite was New Zealand, which ordered four (later five) SH-2G(NZ)s in 1997, with a temporary batch of four SH-2Fs being delivered from 1998 for training, and as provisional replacements for the Navy's ageing Wasps. These have now given way to full-standard SH-2Gs, uniquely equipped with IR-imaging (and TV-guided) AGM-65 Maverick ASMs for the surface attack role. The New Zealand SH-2G(NZ)s have proved popular in service.

The most advanced Seasprites so far are the eleven SH-2G(A)s ordered by Australia in 1996 and delivered from 2001. With their T700 engines and UYS-503 acoustics processors, the SH-2Gs enjoyed considerable compatability with the RAN's S-70B-2s. These aircraft were based on the US Navy's SH-2G (although they were remanufactured from SH-2F airframes) but featured a new Integrated Tactical Avionics System, with a new glass cockpit, Telephonics APS-143 ISAR radar, an Elisra integrated EW suite and Kongsberg Penguin Mk 2 Mod 7 ASMs. Systems development problems delayed delivery of the first three aircraft, which were completed to an interim standard.

The Australian aircraft are now reported likely to be a minimum of three years overdue when they finally enter service and will not have a full combat capability when delivered. There are concerns that the programme has also major cost-overruns. At one time, some expected an SH-2 variant to be selected to meet the Australian Army's Project Air 87 requirement for an armed battlefield helicopter, or for additional SH-2s (perhaps bringing the total to 29) to be procured to allow two SH-2Gs to be embarked on vessels which usually carried a single S-70B.

Today, the SH-2G Super Seasprite competes head-on against the Westland Super Lynx, versions of the SA 365 Dauphin and AS 565 Panther, and against larger naval helicopters like the S-70B. A number of nations had also been mentioned as potential operators of the Super Seasprite, including Malaysia and Singapore. Perhaps surprisingly, no export customers have bought SH-2Gs equipped with Kaman's innovative 'Magic Lantern' laser-based mine detection system, a forerunner of which proved devastatingly effective during Desert Storm.

***Right:* The Royal New Zealand Navy's first two SH-2G(NZ)s are pictured during assembly at Kaman Aerospace's facility. The SH-2G(NZ) has APS-143 radar and a FLIR Systems thermal imager.**

***Below:* The SH-2G(E) is equipped with the AN/AQS-18A active dipping sonar and digital hover coupler. Aircraft Stabilisation Equipment (ASE) allows an automatic approach and departure.**

# Kamov Ka-50/52 'Hokum'

Cavorting at the 1993 Dubai air show, one of the Ka-50 pre-production aircraft demonstrates the agility conferred by Kamov's unique co-axial main rotor configuration.

## Werewolf/Alligator

**Conceived at the height of the Cold War, the Ka-50 flew in prototype form and was comprehensively evaluated as the Soviet Union split apart. The Ka-50 programme was then starved of funding, leaving several prototypes and demonstrators flying, but with no firm orders.**

The original Ka-50 'Hokum' is unique in being a single-seat attack helicopter, and critics of the aircraft maintain that single-crew operation in this role is impossible, even if the pilot enjoys the latest avionics systems to reduce his workload and allow him to act simply as a systems manager. It is widely agreed that Kamov is capable of producing a superb helicopter airframe/engine/dynamics system package. But it is also generally believed that it is still beyond the capability of the Russian aviation industry to produce the kind of avionics systems that would be required to make a single seat attack helicopter viable, even with the easy, low-workload handling characteristics conferred by Kamov's co-axial main rotor configuration.

### Co-axial main rotor

What became the Ka-50 was designed from the start to take advantage of Kamov's innovative co-axial main rotor configuration, whose contra-rotating main rotors obviate the need for a conventional anti-torque tail rotor. Kamov initially concentrated on meeting Navy and civilian requirements, producing the Ka-25 'Hormone' and the larger Ka-27/-28/-29/-31/-32 'Helix' family. The Design Bureau first began producing designs to meet Army requirements during the late 1960s, with the unbuilt Ka-25F, which competed against the Mil Mi-24. During the final stages of that competition, Kamov offered the tandem-rotor V-50, but this was too revolutionary, and was rejected. During the mid 1970s, work began again resulting in the V-80, later Ka-50. This was designed to meet a Soviet Army requirement for a close-support helicopter that would augment and eventually even replace the Mi-24 'Hind'. Heavily influenced by dedicated Western attack helicopters like the McDonnell Douglas AH-64

***Above:** The silver-painted third V-80 prototype took over the flight test responsibilities of the ill-fated first prototype. The first two V-80s had dummy 'second cockpit' windows painted on the fuselage, behind the cockpit.*

***Left:** Seen here is the Ka-52 prototype, with a LLTV/FLIR system in the nose, an Arbalet mast-mounted radar, and a roof-mounted gyro-stabilised sighting system.*

***Above: The Ka-50 is fast, extremely agile, and packs a heavy punch, though doubts about its single-seat cockpit remain the biggest obstacle to customer acceptance, resulting in the recent concentration on two-seat derivatives.***

***Above: The Kamov Ka-52 prototype initially flew with a smooth-contoured, streamlined nose, lacking the undernose sensor package. It is believed to have been converted from the last pre-production Ka-50 airframe.***

***Below: A Ka-50 takes shape in the Kamov OKB's own workshops. Production will be undertaken at the Arseneyev Progress plant.***

Apache and Bell AH-1 Cobra, the Soviet requirement outlined a small, compact, high performance helicopter with sufficient agility for Nap of Earth operation, and a heavy anti-tank weapon load. Kamov and Mil were given contracts to produce initial prototypes for competitive evaluation. The first of three Kamov prototypes made its maiden flight on 17 June 1982, five months before the first of two rival Mi-28 'Havoc' prototypes. A second Kamov (with some operational equipment and a cannon) joined the test programme on 16 August 1983. Both of the first two Ka-50s (then known simply by the Kamov internal designation of V-80) had dummy windows painted on to give the appearance of being tandem-seat two-crew helicopters.

The first V-80 prototype was lost in an accident on 3 April 1985, and its place was taken by the third prototype. Kamov claimed victory over the rival Mi-28 in the original state comparative programme, which ended in August 1986, and built five more pre-production aircraft for further testing and evaluation. Mil, meanwhile, built two improved Mi-28A prototypes, and the competition continued.

## Ka-50 the winner

Following a major evaluation at Torzhok in 1993, the Ka-50 was judged winner of the competitive evaluation (by Presidential decree), and in August 1994 was ordered into production. Four production aircraft were funded initially. These were built and delivered, but before a further batch of 15 could be completed, funding was terminated and a revised requirement (which placed greater emphasis on the night attack role) was issued in 1998. This favoured the two-seat Mi-28, development of which had continued even after its official termination in October 1994. Indeed, development of a dedicated Mi-28N, with enhanced night vision equipment and a mast-mounted sight had been funded by the Russian army from January 1994. In response, Kamov developed its own Ka-50N, with new night systems including FLIR and LLTV, converting one of the pre-production Ka-50s to serve as the prototype. This made its maiden flight in its new guise on 4 March 1997. Flight testing and evaluation of the single-seat Ka-50N (also known as the Ka-50Sh) underlined the limitations of the single-seat configuration.

Attention switched to the two-seat (side-by-side) Ka-52 Alligator, development of which had been announced in 1995. The first prototype (converted from the last pre-production Ka-50) made its maiden flight on 25 June 1997. Kamov maintained that the two-seat Ka-52 would augment and not replace the Ka-50, and that the two types would operate in mixed formations, although by 2004 only the single-seater had entered limited service with the Russian army, while the Ka-52K remained in the running for a South Korean requirement.

## Export derivatives

Kamov has drawn up a number of derivatives for the export market including a side-by-side two-seat Ka-50-2, a tandem two-seat Ka-50-2 and the similar Ka-50-2 Erdogan (the latter to meet a Turkish requirement). These have been offered with various avionics fits, including systems designed and integrated by IAI Lahav. But full scale production of this innovative design remains just out of reach for Kamov.

***This production Ka-50 was used in the making of a Russian feature film, resulting in this gaudy colour scheme. The 'Black Shark' name has been used for marketing, replacing the 'Werewolf' and 'Helicopter Soldier' names used previously.***

# C-130 Hercules Development

Above: As the first YC-130 took to the air, few could have possibly imagined the future success of the portly transport. Even Lockheed was uncertain that the aircraft had a promising future, choosing to build the type away from its headquarters plant.

**Lockheed first flew its YC-130 in 1954, three years after its specification had been issued by the USAF. Since then, its avionics and systems have been upgraded, but the basic design has remained faithful to that first prototype.**

The C-130 is rare in engineering terms, in that its basic design was right from the very beginning and, in fact, remains relatively unchanged in almost 50 years.

The C-130 owes its configuration to the humble Laister-Kauffman CG-10 Trojan Horse assault glider which was able to land on rough tactical airstrips. This glider was ultimately cancelled for political reasons, however, in favour of the Chase CG-14, which resulted in the C-123 Provider.

During World War II, a number of transport types were used, although most had shortcomings. The C-46 and C-47 did not have a level floor, an obvious problem when loading cargo, while the floor of the C-54 was level, but was 11 ft (3.40 m) off the ground. In this era, aircraft designers were more interested in an aircraft's aerodynamic properties than in its ease of cargo handling.

Specialised cargo-haulers like the Curtiss C-76 Caravan and Budd RB-1 Conestoga were never built in sufficient numbers, while the more successful C-82 did not have sufficient range and was limited by what it could carry. However, these aircraft set a trend for level, low-floored, easily accessible and rough field-capable aircraft. Despite this, the USAF persevered with other designs like the low-wing, front-loading C-124 Globemaster. Eventually, the decision was made, by both the USAF and commercial operators, to develop a 'flying truck', designed as such from the beginning.

On 21 April 1951, a harried and otherwise busy colonel on the Air Staff issued a specification for a new transport aircraft which he believed was unattainable, therefore enabling him to get on with other work. The requirement called for 'a medium transport, that can land on unimproved ground, be extremely rugged, be primarily for freight transport, have a troop-carrying capability, and carry about 30,000 lb (13608 kg) over a range of 1,500 miles (2414 km)'. Boeing, Douglas, Fairchild and Lockheed all brought forward designs and Lockheed's designs was chosen only three months later, on 11 July 1951.

Out on its first flight, YC-130 '33397' crosses the Sierra Nevada mountain range on its way from the company airfield at Burbank to Edwards AFB.

Since its entry into service, the C-130 has proved indispensable to American forces, wherever they have been deployed. No other airlifter has been able to compete with the Hercules' full range of capabilities and, as a result, air forces the world over are still keen to invest in the aircraft.

The Lockheed design team had quickly settled upon turboprop engines and selected four Allison T56-A-1As, each capable of 3,750 shp (2800 kW). These powerplants, linked to variable-pitch constant-speed Curtiss Turboelectric propellers, gave the new transporter a cruising speed of 360 mph (579 km/h). This was only slightly slower than that of the sleek passenger aircraft of the day such as the L-1649 Starliner or Viscount.

For cargo-loading purposes, the aft cargo door opens directly upwards and the ramp comes straight down. The height restriction of 76 in (1.93 m) is generous and allows easy cargo-loading. When the ramp is closed, the C-130 can be fully pressurised at around 28,000 ft (8668 m) and the ramp itself can store 5,000 lb (2276 kg) of cargo. When loading and unloading in a confined area, the 'Herk' can turn itself in 170 ft (52 m) with the nose gear canted to its maximum of 60°.

Lockheed's design exceeded the goals specified by the Air Staff and, in fact, remains little altered today. However, in spite of its many positive features, Lockheed was not supremely

***The C-130A soldiered on with the USAF Reserve until the early 1980s – ex-USAF aircraft are still operated today by a number of nations, including Honduras, Mexico and Peru.***

confident about its new aircraft and decided to shift production from Burbank (where the prototypes had been built) to the lesser known (and government-owned) plant in Marietta, Georgia. If the transport failed, the company could shut down its Marietta operation without endangering its reputation at its better-known corporate headquarters.

When Lockheed rolled out the first two Burbank-built YC-130s in August 1954, the still unnamed transport was clearly aimed at meeting the USAF's needs, but was also seen as the answer to the needs of all the United States' civil freight carriers. It was noted at the time that Lockheed's new 'air truck' could carry a maximum payload of about 40,000 lb (18143 kg), whereas the DC-6A cargo carriers being used by Flying Tiger Lines and Slick Airways were carrying a maximum permissible payload of 32,000 lb (15515 kg). Lockheed's sales team believed that US domestic air freight business would quadruple by 1960 and that a vast civilian 'air trucking' business lay just around the corner. It seemed certain that if the YC-130 succeeded, it would become an important part of the civil scene.

### Into service

The first YC-130 to fly was actually the second aircraft built and it took to the air from Burbank on 23 August 1954; first flight of a production C-130A was made at Marietta on 7 April 1955.

The USAF received its first C-130A on 9 December 1956 and it joined the Tactical Air Command's 463rd Troop Carrier Wing at Ardmor AFB, Oklahoma. The 'Roman' nose on early models, which fell straight down following the profile of the windscreen, was soon replaced by a 'Pinocchio' nose housing an AN/APN-59 radar. The vertical tail outline, once rounded at the top, was squared off to mount a rotating red anti-collision light. With early production models, a shift was made to an Aeroproducts propeller, still an interim model with three blades. The first flight made using this propeller was by the sixth C-130A on 26 November 1955. In August 1957, Lockheed and the USAF jointly announced the development of the C-130B which incorporated more powerful Allison T56-A-7A engines rated at 4,050 shp (3020 kW), and increased tankage in the wings inboard of the engines. Its strengthened structure and undercarriage permitted operation at a take-off weight of 135,000 lb (61235 kg), compared with the 124,000 lb (56245 kg) of the C-130A.

The second change of propellers saw the C-130B flying with four-bladed 13.5-ft (4.17-m) Hamilton Standard hydromatic 54H60-39 propellers to replace the three-bladed unit, thus reducing tip speed. The Hamilton Standard propeller was much later retrofitted to the surviving early 'Herks'.

The first C-130B was rolled out in September 1958 and made its first flight two months later. This model remained in service until the 1990s and was the only version of the aircraft not to be equipped with external fuel tanks.

The Hercules soon found itself in service around the world, the first overseas customer being Australia which purchased a total of 11 C-130As and has gone on to acquire others since. Britain and more than 50 other nations have received later versions of the C-130. The civilian variant of the Hercules, the L-100 and its subsequent derivatives, has also seen service with worldwide freight haulers and organisations which have included the CIA's shadowy airline Air America.

***Above: Troop transportation was the secondary role of the Hercules. The troops departing this early C-130A are from Fort Bragg and are demonstrating how easily their on-board complement of 92 can be disembarked. Early aircraft were also tested in the medevac role.***

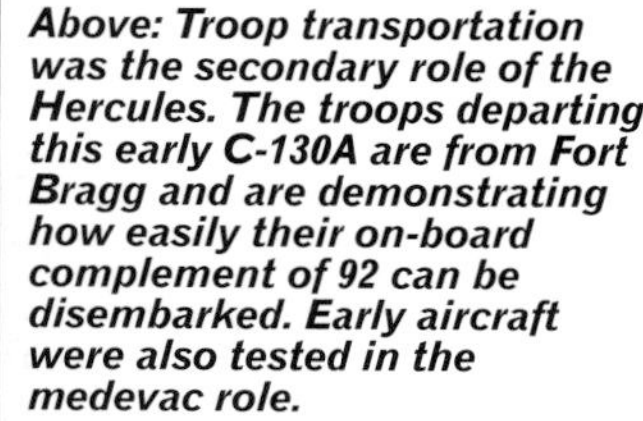

***Left: YC-130 '33397', was the second aircraft built, but the first to fly. It, along with its predecessor, are unique in being the only C-130s built at Lockheed's Burbank plant rather than at Marietta.***

# C-130J Hercules

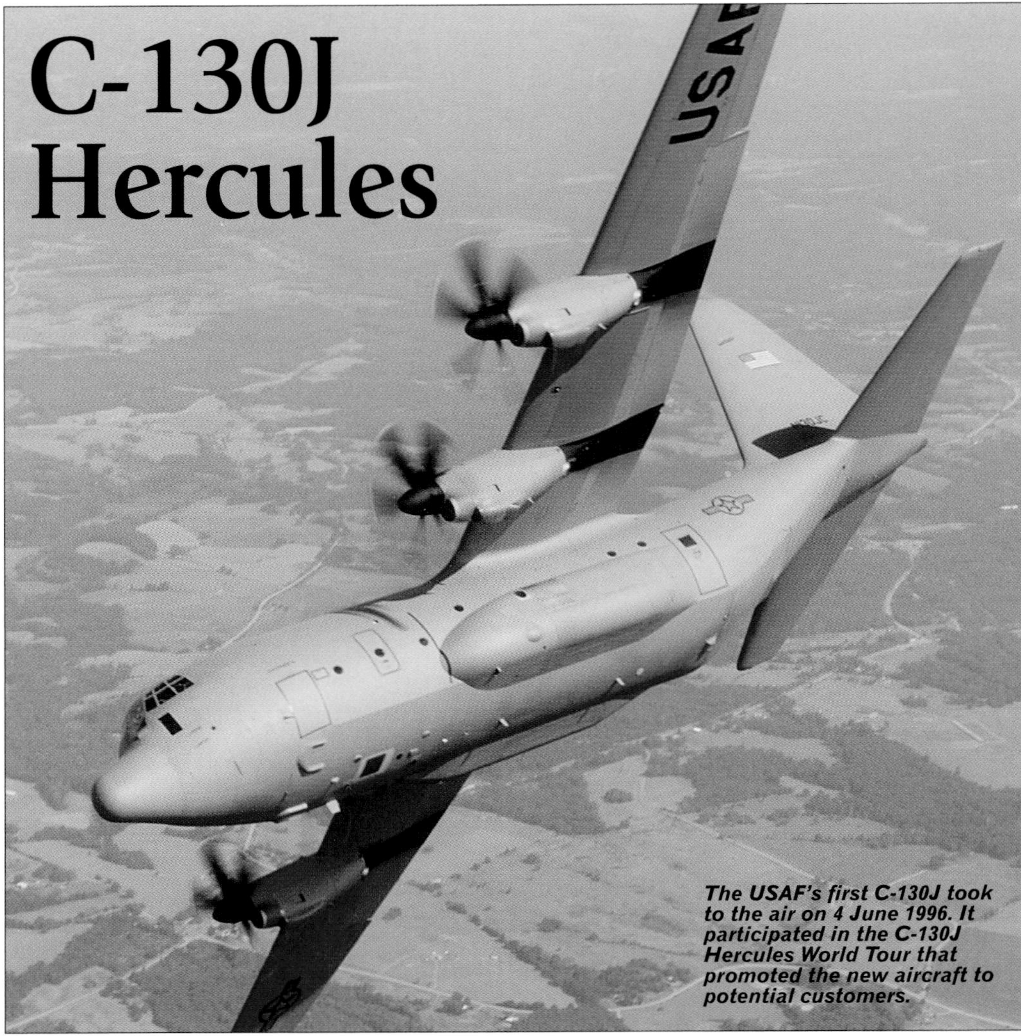


The USAF's first C-130J took to the air on 4 June 1996. It participated in the C-130J Hercules World Tour that promoted the new aircraft to potential customers.

**Although at first glance it looks like a slightly improved version of the classic C-130, the C-130J is, in fact, a revolutionary new aircraft conceived for the air forces of the 21st century.**

Representing the latest in the line of the incredibly successful Lockheed C-130 Hercules is the C-130J, nicknamed by some the 'Hercules II'. The most advanced turboprop airlifter ever built, the C-130J combines the latest in aerospace technology with the sturdy, proven frame of the Hercules, giving it an increased capability and greater operational efficiency.

The C-130 Hercules has been in service since the 1950s and the original design was so good that, physically, it has changed little in all that time. There has been a wide range of variants to suit various customer requirements and the Hercules has seen service all over the world. However, modern scenarios require a level of performance that the traditional C-130 has been unable to meet, and the demand has grown for a successor to this versatile tactical airlifter.

## Design

Starting from the premise that the design of the airframe remains adequate, the Lockheed designers instead decided to improve the C-130's mission effectiveness. The heart of these improvements is the new mission computer, which is connected to electronically operated propellers and engine, 1553B databus architecture and digital avionics. The result of this is a transformed two-seater cockpit that is without the traditional air engineer and navigator, though the flight deck does provide a third seat for an additional crewmember if needed. The mission computer provides increased navigational capability and better situational awareness, and enhances short-field performance. The situational awareness and mission capability are improved still further by the presence of a holographic head-up-display (HUD) – revolutionary in military transports – multi-function liquid crystal displays, station-keeping radar and a topographical map display. The instrument panel, centre console and overhead panels are very different from earlier versions, with only the two central columns, captain's nosewheel steering wheel, parking brake and the two crew seats looking familiar. Moreover, Lockheed Martin has decided that, to meet 'anthropometric requirements', a smaller yoke is to be fitted, replacing the original control columns.

***Above: With Lockheed Martin's chief test pilot at the controls, the prototype C-130J prepares for landing. All the basic flight, navigation and systems information is displayed on four LCD units on the instrument panel.***

## Performance

The performance of the new aircraft is also suitably increased; the C-130J can climb to 29,000 ft (8839 m) in just under 20 minutes and can go on to reach 35,000 ft (10668 m). In doing so, the C-130J uses less fuel than the old C-130E/H and, overall, the C-130J can boast a 40 per cent greater range, 40 per cent higher cruising ability, 50 per cent decrease in time-to-climb, 21 per cent increase in maximum speed and a 41 per cent shorter maximum effort take-off run than its predecessors. This improved performance results directly from the C-130J's new propulsion system. Four Rolls-Royce Allison AE2100D3 turboprops, each rated at 4,591 shp (3425 kW), are allied to new, more efficient Dowty R391 six-bladed, composite propellers, which generate up to 30 per cent more thrust while using some 15 per cent less fuel. It is these propellers that are one

***The first C-130J to enter service in the US was the weather reconnaissance WC-130J which operates with the Air Force Reserve. Other nations may order non-transport variants such as the KC-130J, EC-130J and C-130J-30AEW. Italy includes tanker/transport C-130Js in its fleet and may equip a further two for Elint duties.***

***Above:* N130JA/ZH865 was the first of 10 RAF C-130J-30s (Hercules C.Mk 4) aircraft, the sevice also taking 15 short-fuselage Hercules C.Mk 5s. Nos 24 and 30 squadrons operate the new aircraft.**

***Left:* A Royal Australian Air Force C-130J displays the Dowty six-bladed, composite propellers, one of the features that distinguishes the C-130J from its predecessors.**

of the most notable new features on the C-130J, six-bladed rather than the conventional four, and with a distinct curved shape that improves efficiency due to a reduction in drag; this new design has only recently become possible with new manufacturing methods and modern technologies.

Development work on the C-130J first began in 1991, with two variants being planned: the basic version which is similar to the C-130H but with new equipment, and the C-130J-30 which has a fuselage increased in length by some 15 ft (4.57 m). The building of the initial production variant commenced in autumn 1994 with the first aircraft, a C-130J-30, rolling out on 18 October 1995, and the initial C-130J appearing two days later. The following spring saw both variants fly for the first time.

In 1996, Lockheed Martin began a worldwide tour with the C-130J to promote the new aircraft's abilities to the dozens of countries which already operated variants of the C-130, and to attract new customers. In mid-1998, the aircraft began testing with the FAA to ensure that the stringent safety certificates needed to operate a new airframe were being met. Deliveries commenced in summer 1998.

## Customers

As of May 1998, there had been a number of firm orders, with the RAF destined to be the biggest recipient of the first batch of aircraft, a combination of 10 C-130Js and 15 stretched C-130J-30s. The USAF will receive four C-130Js, the US Air Force Reserve nine weather-monitoring WC-130Js, the US Air National Guard eight C-130Js and two EC-130Js for electronic warfare purposes. The US Marine Corps has ordered five KC-130Js for aerial refuelling. Elsewhere, Australia will receive 12 of the stretched variants while the Italian Air Force has ordered 18 C-130Js.

At present, there are also a number of prospective purchases, the most significant being around 168 aircraft earmarked for the USAF and a possible further purchase for the RAAF. Denmark has three C-130Js with a fourth on option and the Greek and Norwegian, air forces have also shown great interest.

# C-130J improvements

**Compared to the C-130E and C-130H, the C-130J is a far more capable aircraft in terms of flight performance, thanks to its new Allison AE2100 powerplants.**

**Cost savings**
The C-130J's range, climb rate and cruise altitude are the areas of greatest improvement. This permits better fleet utilisation, allowing a smaller number of aircraft to do the work of a more numerous fleet of older C-130s. This is one of a number of cost savings that Lockheed Martin is keen to emphasise as it markets the new aircraft.

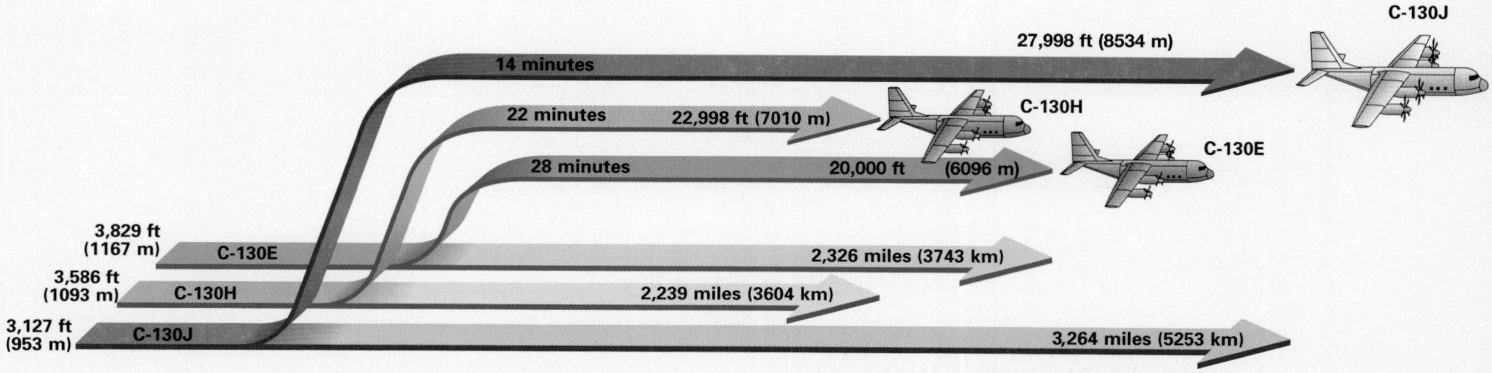

# Electronic variants

**The tremendous versatility of the C-130 has given rise to a host of specialised variants. These electronic scouts and communications centres were first used in the Vietnam War and are regularly used to provide electronic intelligence and support.**

At various times during the development of the C-130, Lockheed proposed electronic versions of the Hercules. Based on what at the time was the definitive transport variant – the C-130E – these electronic spooks initially received the designation EC-130E. However, this has been the source of much confusion, resulting in completely unrelated variants receiving this designation as well.

These highly specialised electronic scouts entered service with the USAF in the late 1950s and operated covertly within regular C-130 transport squadrons. Often wearing similar style markings to the transport aircraft, the EC-130s probed the borders of the Warsaw Pact nations. As tensions around the world increased, ever more sophisticated electronic variants were developed, but it was in Vietnam that the full potential of the EC-130 was realised. Serving in the Airborne Battlefield Command and Control Centre (ABCCC) role, EC-130Es of the 314th TCW operated from Da Nang Air Base, South Vietnam. Equipped with a module in the cargo bay that housed a comprehensive communications fit (UHF, VHF, FM and UHF transceivers, voice/data recorders and secure teletypewriters), the EC-130s also provided accommodation for up to 16 operators and command staff. These aircraft were instrumental in co-ordinating search and rescue (SAR) missions over North Vietnam. The same aircraft, but with updated avionics and now designated ABCCC III, controlled nearly half of all air attack missions flown during operation Desert Storm.

## Rivet Rider

By far the most visually distinctive electronic series of C-130s are those converted under the Rivet Rider programme, which are equipped with large blade antennas under the wings and forward of the tail fin, and wire aerials beneath the tail cone and outer wing panels. These EC-130E(RR)s are operated by the 193rd Special Operations Squadron (SOS) Air National Guard, based at Harrisburg International Airport, Pennsylvania. The aircraft are regularly deployed to Europe and the Far and Middle East. Further variants of the basic Rivet Rider configuration have resulted in the Volant Solo and Comfy Levi. Each of these models has received progressively updated electronic equipment to undertake psychological warfare (Psywar) missions, broadcasting colour-TV propaganda. Although the true nature of their work remains highly classified, both variants have travelled extensively throughout the world, with Rivet Riders being heavily committed to Psywar and psycological operations (Psyops) during Desert Storm.

## Naval operations

The US Navy acquired four C-130s through the USAF, which it modified to EC-130G TACAMO (TAke Charge And Move Out) configuration to provide a link between the National Command Authority and submerged fleet ballistic missile submarines. Messages were received over the VLF to UHF range and transmitted via two trailing antennas on the tail and in the cargo door. EC-130Gs were later supplemented and eventually replaced by EC-130Qs, which utilised the C-130H airframe and could be distinguished by their wingtip ESM pods.

Although the US Navy operated only two electronic variants, the USAF continued to develop more sophisticated models. With blister fairings mounted on either side of its rear fuselage and support struts for wire antenna arrays, the EC-130H Compass Call variant serves as a Command, Control and Communication

***Above:** Ten aircraft were converted for use in Vietnam as airborne command posts. Known as EC-130E (ABCCC)s, the aircraft were used to co-ordinate air strikes using information supplied by forward air controllers (FACs) and ground observers.*

***Top:** The tail-mounted antenna of the EC-130H consists of a huge number of suspended wires, forming a network around the aircraft's tail surfaces. During the Cold War the 43rd Electronic Combat Squadron (ECS) was based at Sembach, Germany, from where it prepared to fly communications jamming missions in the event of a Central Front war. The squadron has since disbanded and the aircraft are now assigned to the 41st ECS at Davis Monthan Air Force Base (AFB), Arizona.*

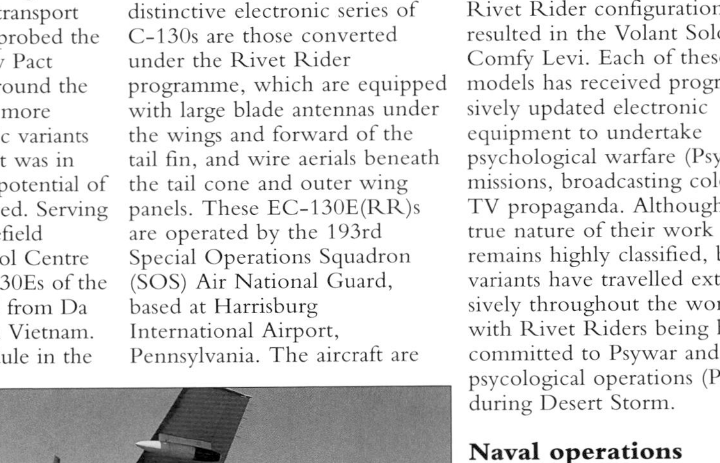


*Four C-130s were converted to Rivet Rider/Volant Solo configuration. The aircraft, fitted with blade antennas under the wing and forward of the tail, serve as airborne radio/television relay and transmission stations to provide emergency broadcast in the event of a national disaster or emergency, and during special operations.*

## Electronic variants

**While most of the electronic C-130 variants are radically modified, some are intended to appear outwardly little different to their unsophisticated transport cousins. On closer inspection, they exhibit a wealth of aerials and antennas on the fuselage and flying surfaces. Typifying this practice is one of the latest variants – the Senior Scout. Following the completion of a mission, the airframe can be stripped of its specialised equipment and so revert to the transport role.**

### EC-130E (ABCCC)

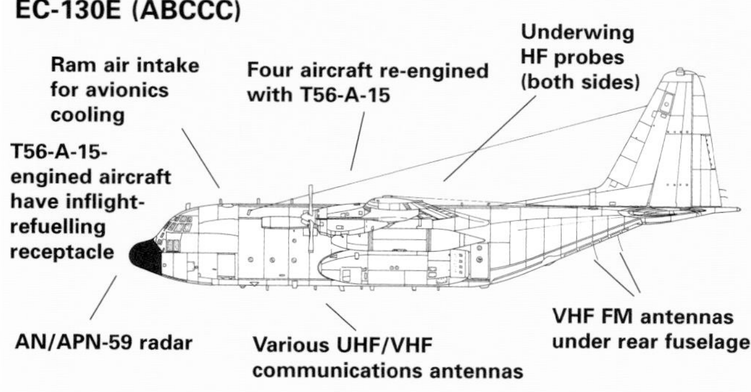


### EC-130E(RR) Volant Solo upgrade

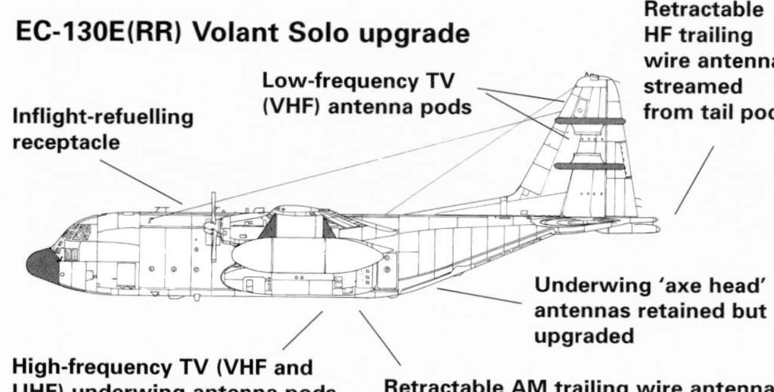


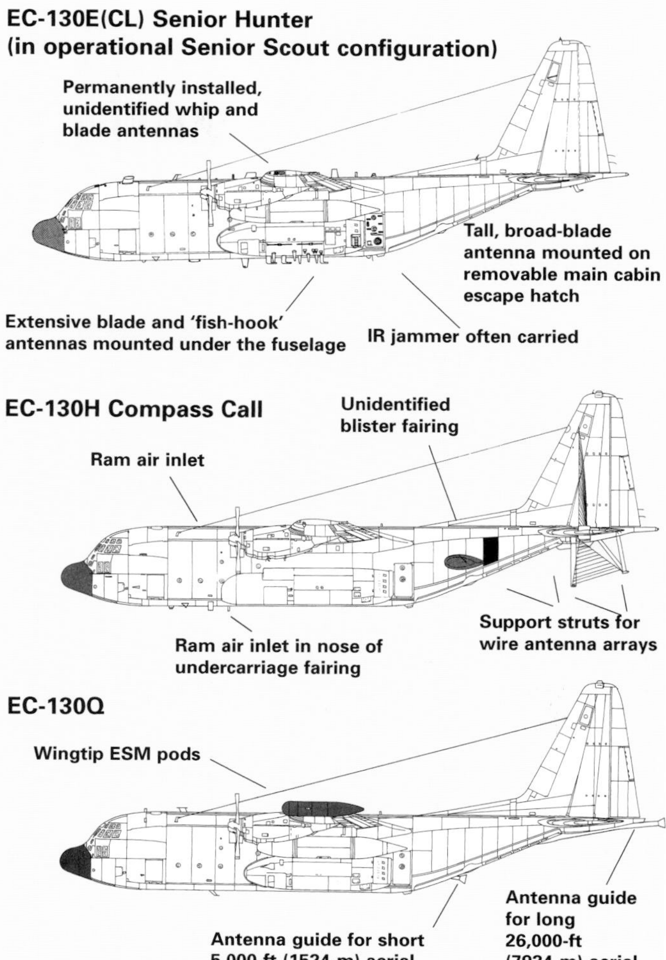


Countermeasures ($C^3CM$) platform. The role of Compass Call is to jam hostile communications. EC-130Hs from the 41st and 43rd Electronic Combat Squadrons, operating from Riyadh King Khalid International Airport, conducted numerous support missions during Desert Storm, jamming Iraqi radars during combat missions by strike packages. Compass Call aircraft remained in the theatre after the war to provide assistance during Operation Proven Force and served again during Operation Iraqi Freedom.

### Drug interdiction

The growing drugs problems in the US led to an intensification in the interdiction campaign against drug runners in the late 1980s. Following its use of borrowed E-2 Hawkeyes, the US Coast Guard (USCG) decided to procure its own AEW platform by converting an HC-130H to EC-130V configuration. General Dynamics undertook conversion work to install the E-2's AN/APS-145 radar above the C-130's fuselage and three palletised operators' consoles inside the cabin. The aircraft went into service with the USCG at Clearwater, Florida in 1991. However, following extensive evaluations in interdiction patrols lasting up to 10 hours, the programme was considered to be too costly and so was subsequently cancelled.

The basic C-130 transport Hercules airframe has been dramatically improved through the C-130J by the incorporation of advanced avionics and the adoption of Rolls-Royce Allison AE2100D3 turboprops. With this new variant, the trend of utilising the C-130 for electronic intelligence-gathering is set to continue, with funding provided for two EC-130J Coronet Solo aircraft for the 193rd SOS, Pennsylvania Air National Guard (ANG).

Though much of the work of these sophisticated electronic spies is classified, their long operational career combined with the plethora of variants and the reluctance of the US to export the type indicate that, whatever missions the EC-130s fly, they are performing them successfully.

***The EC-130Q has been replaced by the Boeing E-6 Mercury in its task of communicating with US Navy ballistic missile submarines in time of war. Following removal of TACAMO equipment, the aircraft were operated as TC-130Q trainers and utility transports.***

***The EC-130V combines the capability of the E-2C Hawkeye with the endurance of the C-130. After the cancellation of USCG operations, the single EC-130V was handed over to the USAF on 1 October 1993, for use in an undisclosed 'black programme', rumoured to be the monitoring of cruise missiles, in the hands of the 6545th Test Squadron at Hill AFB, Utah. The aircraft has since been retired to the Aircraft Maintenance and Regeneration Center (AMARC).***

# Special variants

**The versatility of Lockheed's C-130 has meant that a number of variants has been built for limited service or for use in experimental, special forces or clandestine duties.**

## HC-130H-7

The Coast Guard operates 22 HC-130H Hercules aircraft. While other air arms use the 'Herk' as a transport, to drop paratroops, or for utility missions, the Coast Guard also operates its HC-130H-7s in the search and rescue, ice patrol and maritime surveillance roles. The potential replacement for the HC-130H-7 (of which the oldest was delivered in 1973) is the second-generation HC-130J Hercules.

## KC-130

The US Marine Corps required a tactical transport which could double as an inflight-refuelling tanker using the probe and drogue system. In August 1957 two US Air Force C-130As were borrowed and each fitted with two 506-US gal (1915-litre) tanks in the fuselage and two underwing pods containing the hose equipment. So successful were the trials that 46 Lockheed KC-130F Hercules were ordered for delivery from 1960. The KC-130F is based on the C-130B airframe, initially fitted with Allison T56-A-7 engines, but later re-engined with the T56-A-16. To cope with attrition, the USMC ordered 14 KC-130R tankers based on the C-130H and later purchased 22 KC-130Ts. In addition, 11 KC-130Js are on order. Although not in service with US forces, the KC-130H (similar in most respects to the KC-130R) has been successfully exported to several countries such as Argentina, Brazil, Israel and Spain (illustrated). In the UK, the Falklands War resulted in an urgent RAF demand for increased tanker support. At least four Hercules C.Mk 1s were modified to tanker configuration, incorporating four 900-Imp gal (4091-litre) tanks and a single FR.Mk 17B HDU (hose drum unit) attached to the rear cargo ramp door – the aircraft was designated Hercules C.Mk 1K. In addition, the C-130J is being produced for the USMC as the KC-130J, while Italy has tanker-capable C-130Js.

## DC-130

The Lockheed DC-130 Hercules is a drone controller aircraft, used for a variety of missions as a mother ship and launcher for RPVs (remotely-piloted vehicles). These are carried on four underwing pylons. Eight DC-130A (illustrated) aircraft were supplied to the US Air Force. DC-130As launched Combat Dawn reconnaissance RPVs in the Vietnam conflict and in a short-lived effort in Korea. Five of the USAF aircraft were subsequently transferred to the US Navy for drone target work. Three ex-US Navy DC-130As are operated by Tracor Flight Systems on behalf of the Naval Air Warfare Center at Point Mugu, CA. Seven similar DC-130Es were used for carrying reconnaissance drones during the Vietnam War, but all were converted back to transport configuration. A single DC-130H, capable of launching and controlling four drones was completed in 1976. It was later redesignated NC-130H for classified work.

## LC-130

The Lockheed LC-130F/H/R Hercules transports are winterised aircraft designed for support operations (as denoted by the 'L' prefix) on the Antarctic ice shield and DEW (distant early warning) line, and are equipped with skis. With slightly redesigned fuselage and intended for very long-range operations, LC-130F/H/Rs can be equipped with RATO (rocket-assisted take-off) gear for short-distance take-off from ice fields. The C-130D was the first ski-equipped Hercules; this variant has been replaced by four LC-130H (pictured) aircraft with the 139th Airlift Squadron, 109th Airlift Wing, NY ANG – the only unit to operate LC-130s in the USAF. The LC-130F was the first US Navy variant for Antarctic operations; four joined VXE-6 'Puckered Penguins' in 1969. The LC-130R (six built) is the final ski-equipped Hercules, initially joining VXE-6, but later transferring to the USAF. LC-130Hs made the headlines in October 1999 due to their rescue of Dr Jerri Nielsen, an American scientist suffering from breast cancer who was working at the Amundsen-Scott research station at the South Pole.

## HC-130H

Intended as a long-range search and rescue aircraft, the Lockheed HC-130 Hercules has served with the USAF and USCG. The most numerous examples are the 43 HC-130Hs (above) delivered to the USAF from 1965-1966. These snub-nosed Hercules are fitted with a large distinctive radome for the AN/ARD-17 Cook Aerial Tracker above the forward fuselage and a large observation window in the port fuselage to locate satellite capsules during re-entry from orbit. Intended as a combat-capable rescue aircraft, the HC-130N differed from the HC-130H in being equipped with inflight-refuelling HDUs underwing. Soon after came the HC-130P (later redesignated MC-130P), which combines the appearance and ability of the HC-130H with the air-to-air refuelling role of the HC-130N; these aircraft are used to refuel rescue and special operations helicopters. In 1991 the first of a new-build version, the HC-130H(N), was delivered to the 210th RQS, Alaska ANG, differing from earlier aircraft mainly in having extensively modernised avionics.

## MC-130E

US Air Force interest in variants of the Hercules tailored to the support of Special Forces began in the Vietnam War, when 17 C-130Es were converted to C-130E-I standard, with Fulton STAR recovery gear on the nose for the mid-air retrieval of agents from the ground. Fulton was not used in combat, but the aircraft themselves undertook special missions in night and poor weather conditions. In the late 1970s, the designation MC-130E Combat Talon was adopted as standard for the Special Forces Hercules. The basic MC-130E featured inflight-refuelling capability, uprated T56-A-15 engines and Omega and inertial navigation systems. There are three current sub-variants: the MC-130E-C (Clamp) which has Fulton STAR equipment and a nose radome extended downwards to house the radar in a lower position; the MC-130E-Y (Yank) which has a standard 'Pinocchio' nose; and the MC-130E-S (Swap) which is reportedly used for Sigint work. MC-130Es feature the APQ-122(V)8 weather avoidance and long-range navigation radar, to which a terrain-following function has been retrofitted. Combined with a FLIR sensor in a retractable turret, this allows the crew to penetrate hostile airspace at night or in adverse weather at very low level and to navigate accurately to a set position where Special Forces can be inserted by parachute, or supplied from the air.

## MC-130H

One of the latest variants to enter service with the USAF is the MC-130H Combat Talon II, 25 of which were delivered with a view to the eventual replacement of the MC-130E fleet. These have new radar (APQ-170) in a revised radome, with a FLIR turret underneath. Specialist equipment includes a low-level aerial delivery and container release system, and comprehensive defensive countermeasures. The aircraft were manufactured by Lockheed with minimal equipment, and delivered to IBM Federal Systems Division for the installation of mission equipment. The first aircraft flew in December 1987, and began equipment flight trials at Edwards AFB in spring 1988. The 8th Special Operations Squadron of the 1st SOW received its first MC-130H in June 1990. The 15th SOS was later formed to operate all operational US-based MC-130Hs, while the 7th SOS/352nd SOG at RAF Mildenhall flies four MC-130Hs. The 58th SOW at Kirtland AFB was said to have operated four MC-130Hs for training.

## NC-130A

Even though the 'N' prefix is supposed to identify aircraft on permanent special test status, three of the six C-130As known to have carried the NC-130A designation were at some point brought back to the C-130A configuration, and one became a DC-130A. NC-130As were notably operated by the Air Force Special Weapons Center at Kirkland, New Mexico. In 1986, 55-0022 (illustrated) of the 4950th Test Wing, Aeronautical Systems Division (ASD), at Wright-Patterson AFB, was modified as a sensor and seeker testbed for terminally-guided air-to-ground weapons.

## WC-130

Fifteen HC-130Hs were modified to supplement the WC-130Bs and WC-130Es of the Air Weather Service in the weather reconnaissance/hurricane- and typhoon-hunting role. They were distinguished externally from the WC-130Es by their enlarged radome. The first of at least nine WC-130Js entered service late in 1999.

## NC-130B

One C-130B was converted as a prototype for a STOL version in which the US Army was interested, and was fitted with a rudder of increased chord, single-hinged flaps instead of Fowler flaps and a boundary-layer control system. Bleed air from two Allison YT56-A-6s, the latter operating as gas producers and slung beneath the outer wings, was blown over the flaps and rudder to enhance lift and controllability. The modified machine was flown for 23 hours, but the army cancelled its requirement. Placed in temporary storage, the NC-130B was eventually fitted with standard wings and rudder and delivered to NASA as N929NA (later N707NA – illustrated) for use in the Earth Survey programme. This involves gathering information on forestry, agriculture, land use and land cover, hydrology and geology. The aircraft is fitted with an enlarged nose radome, zenith and nadir viewpoints and external antennas. Sensors and support equipment include cameras, multispectral scanners and microwave scatterometers. The aircraft has also been involved in testing satellite sensors before they are sent into space.

# Lockheed C-141 StarLifter

*The StarLifter can carry a variety of palletised loads and most vehicle types, with the exception of main battle tanks. The C-141's load-carrying ability has been called upon many times by the USAF, actions including the Vietnam War, the 1973 'October War' in the Middle East, Operation Urgent Fury in Grenada in 1983, Operation Just Cause in Panama in 1989, Desert Storm in 1991, and the ongoing Enduring Freedom and Irqqi Freedom operations.*

## Introduction

**Constant, effective support is essential for any military force, particularly when that force is spread around the world, with a vast range of operational needs. For over 35 years, the C-141 has answered the call for quick and effective logistic support.**

At the beginning of the 1960s most of the USAF's Military Air Transport Service (MATS) strategic transport aircraft were prop-driven types. With increasing demand for rapid deployment capability, it was clear that modern jet-powered equipment was urgently needed.

As a result, MATS obtained four dozen examples of the C-135 as a short-term palliative. These, the first true jets to join the MATS airlift inventory, were in many ways inadequate, unable to accommodate much in the way of the heavy or bulky equipment that MATS was regularly instructed to transport around the world, and the C-135 was primarily employed to airlift troops.

Meanwhile, the veteran C-124 continued to serve in considerable numbers as the backbone of MATS' heavy-lift capability, supported by a modest number of C-133s. It was mainly to replace the C-124 that the USAF issued SOR-182, inviting designs for a new turbofan-powered cargo/troop-carrier aircraft as part of a new integrated logistics support system.

The USAF judged Lockheed's candidate as best suited to fulfilling the requirement, ordering an initial batch of five RDT&E aircraft in August 1961.

*For much of the 1980s, the USAF's C-141 fleet wore the familiar 'Lizard' camouflage scheme, adopted for European operations.*

*The C-141A emerged as a four-engined, high-wing aircraft incorporating rear-loading doors facilitating the carriage of extremely lengthy and heavy items, including ICBMs.*

Flown for the first time on 17 December 1963, the C-141A began to enter operational service with the 1501st Air Transport Wing (subsequently the 60th Military Airlift Wing) at Travis AFB, California, on 23 April 1965. This occurred eight months before MATS underwent a considerable upheaval, being retitled as Military Airlift Command on 1 January 1966. In 1966-77 the StarLifter went on to enter service with five more front-line transport units, these being the 62nd MAW at McChord AFB, Washington; the 63rd MAW at Norton AFB, California; the 436th MAW at Dover AFB, Delaware; the 437th MAW at Charleston AFB, South Carolina; and the 438th MAW at McGuire AFB, New Jersey. A modest number was also allocated to MAC's principal training unit, the 443rd MAW(T) at Tinker AFB, Oklahoma. In 1973, a realignment of 21st Air Force airlift assets resulted in the 436th MAW becoming a C-5A unit, the C-141s previously operated being reassigned to the 437th MAW, which henceforth was equipped only with the StarLifter. Thus, five front-line units and a training element continued to operate the C-141 from 1973 onwards, a line-up which remained essentially unchanged until the 1990s, although the 443rd MAW moved to Altus AFB, Oklahoma, in May 1969.

***With events in Southeast Asia occupying centre stage during the mid-1960s as the C-141A began to join MATS/MAC in considerable numbers, the aircraft was soon committed to supporting the war effort.***

***Below: Modification from C-141A to C-141B (foreground) standard entailed adding a 13-ft 4-in (4.06-m) long plug directly ahead of the wing and a 10-ft (3.05-m) long plug immediately aft.***

The first operational airlift base to receive the StarLifter, Travis served as a key link in the supply chain to Vietnam and, as a consequence, at the height of the war witnessed a near-constant stream of airlift aircraft departing for Southeast Asia. The C-141A was employed to ferry troops and urgently-needed 'red ball' supplies across the Pacific to forward bases such as Tan Son Nhut in South Vietnam.

In addition to being employed in support of forces engaged in combat in Vietnam, the StarLifter also began to undertake its fair share of 'special airlift missions'. This involved a diverse range of activities including mobility training exercises, ICBM and outsize cargo shipment, humanitarian tasks and specialised support operations.

## Global transport

As the number of C-141s in MAC's inventory rose, the type took over responsibility for many 'routine' scheduled airlift tasks, becoming an increasingly familiar sight at US bases overseas. By 1967, when a substantial proportion of the 284 examples that were eventually procured had been delivered to MAC, the StarLifter was likely to appear at any point where American influence was strong or where the US had a vested interest.

Operational experience acquired during the late 1960s and early 1970s revealed that, although in many ways suited to MAC airlift tasks, in its initial form the C-141A suffered from some shortcomings. At the time the C-141A entered service, the US maintained a large number of overseas bases and its aircraft could usually pass without let or hindrance in most parts of the world. By the mid-1970s, however, the situation had changed somewhat in that many of the overseas stations had closed and the lack of suitable staging bases made life very difficult when MAC was required to undertake Operation Nickelgrass – an airlift in support of Israel during the course of the 1973 'October War'. Since the C-141 could not be refuelled in flight, much of the resupply task fell to the C-5A which, by virtue of its inflight-refuelling capability, could reach Israel without the need for an en route landing.

If it were to possess true global range, the C-141 would require modification in order that it too might be refuelled in flight. At the same time, consideration was given to the C-141's payload capability, the type usually being volumetrically-limited, or tending to 'bulk-out', meaning that the aircraft was physically full before reaching its maximum permissible weight. Between them, these two shortcomings eventually resulted in the appearance of a new variant, the C-141B.

Although nothing could be done to increase the cross-section of the StarLifter's hold, it was feasible to 'stretch' the aircraft so that it could operate at weights rather closer to the permissible maximum. In 1976, Lockheed received a $24.30 million contract covering the conversion of a single C-141A into the YC-141B prototype.

***Left: Operationally, the advent of the C-141B made a considerable difference to Military Airlift Command's airlift potential, with the ability to refuel in flight meaning that the C-141's range became limited only by crew fatigue considerations.***

Modification allowed an increase in the number of standard Type 463L pallets which can be accommodated from 10 to 13. Improved wingroot fairings were fitted, reducing drag and resulting in a slightly higher maximum speed and lower fuel consumption.

## Stretching the StarLifter

IFR capability was installed on the YC-141B, which first flew on 24 March 1977. Prototype-testing in mid-1977 led to a decision to modify all of MAC's 270 or so remaining C-141As, this project getting under way at Lockheed's Marietta, Georgia, facility in 1978. Acceptance of the first 'production' C-141B took place in December 1979 and the modification programme terminated in June 1982 when the last example was re-delivered to MAC, slightly ahead of schedule and at less than the originally anticipated cost. The fleet-wide modification initiative provided MAC with the equivalent of an additional 90 C-141As at modest cost and without the need to find additional aircrews.

The 'new' StarLifter has emphatically demonstrated its value on numerous occasions since entering the MAC inventory, having 'grown' in both the literal and metaphorical senses since entering service. The process of attaining maturity has resulted in an aircraft which continues to provide MAC with the ability to move cargo and/or personnel virtually anywhere in the world at short notice. Beautiful the StarLifter may not be, but 'handsome is as handsome does' and it seems likely that even with the advent of the C-17, the C-141B will remain in service for some time.

***With side-facing canvas seats in place, the C-141B can carry 168 fully-equipped paratroops. The clamshell rear cargo doors open outwards for maximum clearance.***

# Lockheed C-5 Galaxy
## Development

**The world's largest operational aircraft at its time of introduction, the C-5 Galaxy has been the workhorse of US strategic airlifting for nearly 30 years.**

Although the introduction of the C-141 Starlifter had markedly increased Military Air Transport Service's airlifting capability, it was not capable of airlifting larger combat weapons in the US inventory such as main battle tanks and troop-carrying helicopters. To address this shortfall, the USAF began design studies in 1963, under the CX-4 requirement, for an aircraft weighing in the order of 600,000 lb (272160 kg).

By mid-1964 the programme had been defined, in a more ambitious form, as the CX-HLS (Cargo Experimental-Heavy Logistics System) which specified that the aircraft should be capable of hauling a payload of 125,000 lb (56700 kg) over 8,000 miles (12875 km) and have the ability to operate from semi-prepared airstrips. Contracts for design studies were issued to three manufacturers (Boeing, Douglas and Lockheed) and two engine

***Above: Seen in formation with a Lockheed T-33 chase aircraft, the first prototype C-5 undergoes Research, Development, Test and Evaluation (RDT&E) flight trials. An instrument probe was fitted to the nose of the aircraft for the tests.***

***Below: General Electric fought off Pratt & Whitney to win the engine contract for the C-5A. Generating 41,100 lb (183 kN) of thrust, its TF39-GE-1 engine was then the most powerful high-bypass turbofan engine to be fitted to a military aircraft.***

***Above: Rolled out on March 2 1968 before President and Mrs Johnson, the C-5 was a source of great pride to Lockheed before cost over-runs and structural problems brought the whole project into jeopardy.***

***Right: The first five C-5As underwent successful RDT&E tests in 1968/1969. The most serious incident during this phase occurred when a wheel fell off on landing at the end of an early test flight.***

companies (General Electric and Pratt & Whitney).

Lockheed won the airframe competition with the lowest bid of $1.9 billion (although this price was later proved to be wildly optimistic as total costs eventually rose to over $5.2 billion) with power to be provided by the General Electric TF39, the world's first high-bypass-ratio turbofan in the 40,000-lb (178-kN) plus thrust class.

## Structural shortfall

The demands of the CX-HLS requirement proved to be unrealistic and were never even remotely approached by the Lockheed design, by then named Galaxy. In an attempt to save weight, which could be translated into payload, Lockheed compromised on design strength, a decision which would come back to haunt the company soon after the type entered service.

Rolled out on 2 March 1968, the C-5A bore a distinct family resemblance to the smaller C-141 Starlifter, with four podded engines suspended beneath a shoulder-mounted wing, a T-tail and an upswept aft fuselage section incorporating loading doors and a ramp. There the similarity ended, for the Galaxy introduced a much revised forward fuselage with the flight deck situated above the forward part of the hold allowing the fitment of an upward-hinging 'visor' for loading/unloading at the front of the aircraft.

Directly behind the flight desk a cabin area could accommodate 15 passengers, while a second larger cabin (located in the upper fuselage aft of the wing) could take up to 75 troops. The main cargo hold was designed with a volumetric capacity of 34,795 cu ft (985.29 m³) for cargo operations and could be reconfigured to carry up to 270 fully-equipped troops.

## Flight restrictions

The C-5A first flew on 30 June 1968 and the initial tests were relatively trouble-free. However, in the summer of 1969, the appearance of wing cracks in a fatigue test airframe revealed a major shortcoming which was to plague the Galaxy for nearly a decade. In the quest to reduce weight, the strength of the wing box had been compromised. As a result, the Galaxy was only likely to achieve 25 per cent of the intended design life of 30,000 hours. These problems, along with the escalating costs, proved a major embarrassment to both Lockheed and the USAF and in November 1969 the procurement was reduced to just 81 aircraft. To help extend operational life a peacetime payload restriction of 50,000 lb (22680 kg) was implemented, which was less than 20 per cent of the maximum payload. The retrofitting of active ailerons and reinforcement of the wing box helped alleviate some of the flight restrictions imposed but were at best only a partial palliative. In 1977 the USAF eventually elected to 'bite the bullet' and institute a re-winging programme to ensure that the aircraft would achieve their design life of 30,000 hours.

Lockheed designed two new types of wing, which employed as far as possible, the existing moving control surfaces but featuring a totally new primary structure of aluminium alloy offering much increased strength and corrosion resistance. A total of 77 C-5As was put through a re-winging programme between 1981 and 1987 at a cost of over $1.5 billion.

In the mid-1980s, the production line was reopened to meet an urgent USAF demand for additional heavy airlift capacity. Fifty C-5Bs with the new wing were built, essentially similar to the C-5A but incorporating modifications resulting from experience of operations with the C-5A, including an improved automated flight control system. Deliveries began in January 1986 and the USAF accepted the final C-5B in April 1989.

***Four of the first five C-5As are seen lined up at Lockheed's base at Marietta, Georgia, in July 1969 during flying trials. The fifth example conducted joint USAF-Lockheed trials at Edwards AFB, California, where it set an unofficial world record by flying at an all-up weight of 762,000 lb (345636 kg).***

***Below: In March 1970 the fifth C-5A underwent successful cold conditions trials at Eielson AFB, Alaska. Flying tests were only conducted when temperatures were below 20°F (-7°C).***

***The C-5 was designed to carry main battle tanks like this M1 Abrams, or troop-carrying helicopters. The hinged nose section greatly decreased loading/unloading time providing a roll-on/roll-off capability.***

# C-5 Galaxy
## Service history

**In operational service with the USAF for over 30 years, the C-5 Galaxy has evolved from being a troubled and overpriced failure to a world-beating airlifter. The value of the Galaxy was graphically illustrated in the Vietnam and Gulf Wars.**

Rolled out on 2 March 1968, the first C-5A made its maiden flight in June of that year before undergoing a series of successful trials at Dobbins AFB. Four more examples joined the RDT&E under the Total Package Procurement (TPP) concept. This involved Lockheed being responsible for research, development, testing, evaluation and production under a single fixed-priced contract.

Although the evaluation and test flights proved successful, static tests showed the C-5A to have early wing cracking, giving the aircraft a design life of less than 25 per cent of what was expected.

However, so pressing were requirements for heavy lift capability in Southeast Asia that the C-5A was rushed into service barely three months after Category II testing had started.

The first unit to receive the C-5A was the Transitional Training Unit (TTU), 443rd Military Airlift Wing, Training at Altus AFB, Oklahoma. Established to rapidly provide crews for operational units, the TTU gradually received more C-5As during the spring of 1970.

### Into service

On 6 June the 3rd Military Airlift Squadron, 437th MAW became the first operational unit based at Charleston AFB. This was one of three Aerial Port of Embarkations (APOEs) established for the C-5 support flights to Vietnam. The other two bases were Dover AFB (9th MAS) on the east coast and Travis AFB (75th MAS) on the west coast. It was this latter unit which became the first to attain initial operational capability (IOC), flying its first mission to Vietnam in April 1971.

The C-5A had an immediate effect on the massive supply effort to Southeast Asia. At last, vital equipment could reach the theatre in a timescale measured in hours rather than the days or weeks required by seaborne transport. Its value was exemplified during the siege at Da Nang in 1972, when 10 Galaxy flights carried tanks, helicopters and other vital pieces of hardware to a total of 1,650,000 lb (748400 kg), with a turnaround time of less than 35 minutes.

*Above: The Galaxy has been invaluable to the USAF as the only aircraft capable of transferring large items, such as this US Navy H-53, to potential combat zones.*

*Top: On its introduction into service, the C-5 was the world's largest and heaviest aircraft. Thirty-three years later, the type is still the largest in the US inventory.*

The C-5A was also a vital component of Operational Enhance Plus – the final delivery of aircraft to the Vietnamese Air Force before the Paris Agreement brought an end to US combat activities.

In October 1973 the C-5's unique airlifting abilities were again typified during the Yom Kippur War. Unwilling to let Israel fall to Egyptian/Syrian attack, the US sought to supply arms and ammunition. However, with European allies unwilling to let their air bases be used for refuelling, the C-5 (with its inflight refuelling capability) was the only aircraft capable of carrying heavy and bulky equipment to Israel. During Operation Nickel Grass, MAC's C-5As flew 145 missions in 31 days, carrying 10,800 tons of equipment at an average of 74 tons per flight. Among vital equipment delivered was ammunition, ECM pods and Shrike anti-radiation missiles.

The Galaxy's successes during Operation Nickel Grass were overshadowed by a much publicised crash in April 1975. The Galaxy had been selected to evacuate Vietnamese orphans for an operation named Babylift. The very first flight ended in disaster when C-5A 68-0218 crashed during an attempted emergency landing after the aft door complex blew out. Many infants were among the 155 killed, out of a total of 314 people on board. This incident

*Galaxies played an instrumental role in supplying arms and equipment during the first Bright Star exercise which was held in Egypt during 1982.*

***During the mid- to late 1980s, a study programme was implemented for the aerial launch of Minuteman ICBMs (Intercontinental Ballistic Missiles) from C-5s. The tactic was designed to deprive Soviet intelligence forces of details of fixed missile launch sites and was never put into regular service.***

***In the 1980s, the C-5 fleet adopted the 'European One' camouflage scheme. Although the scheme was successful internal heat problems occurred when operating in hot climates.***

did, however, prompt the US government to fund the much-needed structural improvements to the Galaxy fleet.

The peacetime operations of the C-5A were limited due to the structural weakness of the wings and wing box. The decision to rewing the existing C-5As to C-5B standard, along with 50 new-build examples greatly increased the capability of the Galaxy fleet. Modification of the original C-5As was completed between 1981 and 1987 and in 1986 the first four new-build C-5Bs were delivered to the 443rd MAW, Training at Altus AFB.

The availability of the C-5Bs to supplement C-5As in active and associate reserve squadrons allowed a number of C-5As to be released for two AFRes and one ANG squadron. During the 1980s and early 1990s, C-5As and Bs flown by active and reserve crews participated in a number of US military operations. These included supporting US operations in Grenada in 1983 and Operation Just Cause in Panama in 1989.

The Galaxy has also proved invaluable in relief operations in the wake of natural disasters. Vital medical supplies and rescue equipment arrived via Galaxies after earthquakes in Mexico (1985) and Armenia (1988) and hurricanes Hugo (1989) and Andrew (1992). However, the C-5's greatest achievements occurred during Operations Desert Shield and Desert Storm.

The huge logistical effort of transporting US personnel, arms and equipment to Saudi Arabia was successful largely thanks to the C-5. Of the 17,341 missions flown by strategic airlifters between August 1990 and 17 March 1991, 22.4 per cent were flown by Galaxies; the aircraft were responsible for transporting 16.8 per cent of passengers and 41.5 per cent of the 563,048 tons of cargo.

## Record breaker

As well as being the world's largest and heaviest aircraft for many years, the Galaxy has held a number of other world records during its service life. In 1969 a C-5A set a new record take-off weight of 798,200 lb (362060 kg) (which was later improved on by the C-5B), and in 1984 a rewinged C-5A flew at a gross weight of 920,836 lb (417691 kg) after being refuelled in mid-air. In 1989, at a demonstration at Fort Bragg, North Carolina, a C-5B set a new air drop record of 190,493 lb (86406 kg) consisting of four Sheridan tanks and 73 paratroopers.

With the likelihood of C-5s having to operate into potentially hostile territory, modifications have recently been made for the fleet to carry the Pacer Snow defensive system consisting of AN/ALE-40 flare dispensers and an AN/AAR-47 missile-warning system; these will greatly increase the aircraft's survivability.

Air Mobility Command currently operates four C-5 squadrons – the 3rd and 9th AS, 436th Airlift Wing from Dover AFB and the 21st and 22nd AS, 60th Air Mobility Wing from Travis AFB. The latter squadron also operates two C-5Cs which have had their upper deck removed to allow loads for the Space Shuttle to be airlifted. With regular, Air Force Reserve Command and ANG squadrons all equipped with the type, the C-5 is a vital part of the USAF's heavylift resources and will remain so well into the next century.

***Left: USAF C-5s are currently painted in Air Mobility Command grey. This example is operated by the 436th Airlift Wing from Dover AFB, Delaware.***

***Below: The key to successful resupply operations is the ability to carry vital large, heavy and bulky equipment, frequently over long distances. Air-to-air refuelling capability makes the C-5 possibly the best aircraft in the world at accomplishing these missions.***

# Lockheed F-104 Starfighter
## Introduction

**Designed in the 1950s, in the aftermath of the Korean War, as the ultimate clear-air dogfighter – lightweight, simple and with breathtaking performance – Lockheed's F-104 was eventually developed into a sophisticated all-weather interdictor. Today, the F-104 remains in limited front-line use, following upgrades that will see it survive until, perhaps, 2010.**

Few aircraft have attracted such passionate feelings of love and hate, or excitement and fear, as the F-104 Starfighter. Setting out to create a brilliant world-beating air-combat fighter, its talented designers failed utterly. But the result turned out to be quite good at low-level attack and reconnaissance, and Lockheed sold an improved version to such good effect that it was, for more than 20 years, the leading tactical aircraft of the European NATO air forces and Japan, despite the fact that the US Air Force's only interest was to assist sales to others!

### Lessons from Korea

It all began with a visit to Korea in 1952 by Clarence L. ('Kelly') Johnson, the chief engineer of Lockheed Aircraft. He found even the F-86 squadrons depressed, because they were unable to outclimb or outmanoeuvre the MiG-15 'Fagots'. They pressed Johnson for a fighter with the highest possible performance, even at the cost of reduced endurance and armament. Johnson returned determined to achieve superior performance at almost any price.

Lockheed made an unsolicited proposal of the Model 83 to the

*High over San Francisco harbour, a pair of F-104As from the 337th Fighter Interceptor Squadron pass the Bay Bridge. The type proved less than ideal in the defence of the continental United States and enjoyed only a brief career with the USAF.*

***Despite the operation of the Tornado and the introduction of the AMX, the Italian air force still has front-line squadrons equipped with the F-104. For combat air patrol missions, the aircraft operate in conjunction with Tornado F.Mk 3s, which provide the Starfighters with extra radar information for interception work.***

USAF in November 1952. On 11 March 1953, the USAF issued a letter contract for two XF-104s, numbered 53-7786/7. The first, powered by a J65 rated at 8,000 lb (35.6 kN), flew on 28 February 1954. The second, with an afterburning J65 rated at 11,500 lb (51.16 kN), followed on 5 October 1954. The J65 was envisaged only as an interim engine, pending availability of the more powerful General Electric J79 but, despite this, a speed of Mach 1.7 and height of 60,000 ft (18288 m) were soon reached. The bad news was that, predictably, the XF-104 was a real handful, requiring constant accurate flying. These demanding flight characteristics would soon reappear as the F-104 entered operational service, and many Starfighter pilots would lose their lives as a result.

In July 1954, a cautious USAF ordered 17 YF-104As; these were intended to be very close to production F-104As with a J79-GE-3 engine. The aircraft entered service in a test/development capacity with the 83rd Fighter Interceptor Squadron at Hamilton AFB near San Francisco. A total of 610 F-104As had been requested, but only 153 were actually built. They were phased out of USAF service in 1960, but were recalled by the Berlin and Cuban crises of 1961-62. Likewise, instead of the planned 112 F-104B tandem-trainers, the USAF received only 26. At this point, Lockheed's Starfighter seemed to have been a failure, but Lockheed recognised that the USAF would not be a customer, except very peripherally. It therefore started to organise a powerful sales team to try to persuade foreign customers that, even if the USAF did not want the F-104, the improved Starfighter (now available) would be the greatest aircraft in the sky. The so-called Super Starfighter (F-104G) was equipped with an uprated powerplant, NASARR radar, strengthened fuselage and new mission equipment.

NATO allies were quick to adopt the F-104 Starfighter into service, with no fewer than nine NATO air forces operating the the F-104: Canada, West Germany, the Netherlands, Belgium, Italy, Turkey, Greece, Norway and Denmark. The aircraft was built under licence by consortia of Belgium, Dutch, Italian and German companies, and by Canadair.

## Unjust reputation

Many air forces had problems operating the Starfighter, but in West Germany, both in the Luftwaffe and Marineflieger, the F-104G losses reached crisis levels. By 1969, West Germany had lost more than 100 Starfighters in 10 years. This state of affairs needs to be looked at in context, however. West Germany was the world's major Starfighter operator, having taken delivery of 917 aircraft – the United States, by comparison, had 294 examples of the F-104G, Canada had 239 and Italy 149. When the German losses were viewed as a percentage of the number of aircraft operated, they were no greater than those of other F-104 operators.

Outside Europe, the major operator was Japan, which produced 200 F-104J single-seat and DJ two-seat Starfighters under licence, entering service with the JASDF in 1964. Ex-USAF Starfighters were supplied to Pakistan, Nationalist China and Jordan, while Spain received 21 F-104Gs and TF-104G trainers from the United States in 1965, in return for the American use of Spanish air bases.

The Starfighter did not see extensive combat during its service life, although Chinese Nationalist Air Force examples participated in numerous combats with Chinese Communist fighters, scoring few victories. During the Indo-Pakistan War of 1965, the Pakistan air force's single Starfighter squadron scored several victories for the loss of at least one fighter in combat.

## Stars in their eyes

Despite its unjust reputation the F-104 Starfighter remains in front-line service, although in a much modified form, with the Italian air force. Known as the F-104S, what the Starfighter initially lacked when it first entered service was solved in the 'S' variant. With extra fuselage missile pylons and an improved radar (with a 'look-down' capability enabling the aircraft to locate and shoot down at targets), the F-104S underwent a further upgrade programme during 1997 to emerge as the F-104S-ASA M.

With delivery of the Eurofighter delayed, Kelly Johnson's 'missile with a man in it' will be a constant sight in the skies over Europe well into the next century. By this time, Lockheed's Starfighter will have become the longest-serving operational fighter in history.

***With its high speed, climb performance and high-altitude capability, the Starfighter was a natural choice for NASA's test fleet. Operating from Dryden's Flight Research facility at Edwards AFB, the Starfighter served until 1983, when it was replaced by the F/A-18 Hornet. This was an ironic move since the F-104 served as a chase aircraft during the Hornet's development.***

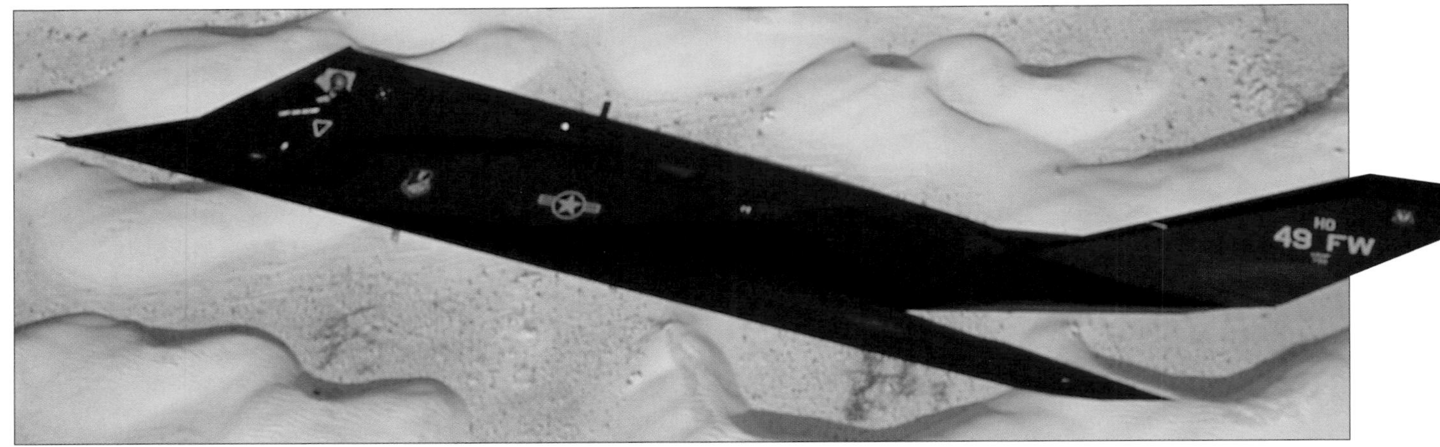


# Lockheed F-117 Nighthawk

## Introduction

**The extraordinary shape, revolutionary radar-defeating features and a top secret, yet highly glamorous development have combined with a star appearance in Desert Storm to make the Lockheed F-117 the best-known warplane in the world. It is able to penetrate hostile airspace and strike vital targets without being detected by radar defences.**

The F-117 was a mystery, and to some a miracle, when revealed to the public a decade ago. Now, it is an aging warplane with a specialised purpose.

When it emerged from a shroud of secrecy, the F-117 was hailed as marking a scientific breakthrough because of its ability to do just one thing. Today, critics are insisting that this once-revolutionary warplane is old, slow, and costly, given its ability to do only that one task. But even though it has little versatility, the F-117 performs its one mission with such drama, and so superbly, that the retirement talk is almost certainly highly premature.

The F-117 is the first operational warplane to employ low observable (LO), or stealth, technology to reduce its vulnerability to radar detection. Though called a fighter, the F-117 is not intended for air-to-air combat. Its purpose is to deliver ordnance in a dense threat environment against targets of extremely high value. The Lockheed F-117 emerged from a Cold War 'black' program where it was developed in conditions of unprecedented secrecy.

The mission of the F-117 is unique: to attack small, well-protected targets which are, in Pentagon jargon, highly leveraged. This means that their destruction will damage an enemy out of proportion to their intrinsic value. A typical assignment would be to 'decapitate' an enemy's command, control, communications and intelligence ($C^3I$) structure by attacking it by surprise with precision-guided bombs. Other F-117 targets might be nuclear storage sites, critical bridges and tunnels, or key leadership headquarters.

*Above: A 49th FW 'Black Jet' cruises serenely over the White Sands National Monument near the unit's headquarters at Holloman AFB, New Mexico.*

*Right: Stealth pilots are viewed as elite aviators, many having already accomplished thousands of hours on older attack types, such as F-111s, A-7s and A-10s. Many comment about the lack of visibility from the cockpit because of the F-117's heavy canopy framing.*

The wedge-shaped, V-tailed F-117 employs radar absorbent composite materials on its external surfaces. In addition, it has angular features which contribute to its low-observable characteristics by reducing the aircraft's radar cross-section (RCS). Use of radar absorbent materials should make the aircraft appear dim to a radar while the angular shape should cause it to 'glitter' irregularly

*Viewed from directly ahead, the F-117A is often described as looking like something from 'Star Wars'. Displayed in this view is the heavily framed cockpit canopy and underneath, the twin trapezes which extend from the weapons bay for loading.*

without giving any solid return signal as its aspect angle varies.

The angular shape results from a technique known as faceting which applies computer technology to aircraft design and, in this instance, produced radical use of 'chisel-edge' leading surfaces and sharp fuselage angles, eliminating curved surfaces in order to diffuse radar returns. The skin panels of the airframe are divided into many small, perfectly flat surfaces, which reflect at a variety of angles all signals from probing hostile ground or airborne radars.

The stealth qualities of the aircraft are enhanced by engine exhaust nozzles located atop the fuselage along the wing root just ahead of the tail surfaces. The exhaust bleeds over the aft fuselage to screen the heat emissions from detection below.

### Stealth pilot

The pilot of an F-117 occupies a small cockpit which features a windshield arrangement with a separate panel in front and two different-sized windows on each side. The pilot has a conventional head-up display for flight information and infra-red imagery, with an up-front control panel beneath it for radio and display mode selections. On the main panel are, standard MFDs (multifunction displays) installed either side of a large monochrome CRT screen. Four protruding spikes on the aircraft's nose are air data probes for air speed and altitude sensing. The F-117 has quadruple redundant fly-by-wire flight controls.

During the 1970s, low observables technology was studied in great secrecy by the Defence Advanced Research Projects Agency (DARPA) and the USAF with a goal no less ambitious than to alter aerial warfare by producing a warplane invisible to radar. Test flights of the Have Blue proof-of-concept aircraft were followed by Project Senior Trend which produced the similar but larger F-117.

In 1978 a decision was made to proceed with full-scale development and low-level production, making use of numerous components from other aircraft types to minimise potential risk.

Operating under the tightest security, the aircraft flew for almost eight years before its existence was ever publicly acknowledged. The USAF finally released some limited information and a poor quality photograph in November 1988. Flying was initially done at Groom Lake, Nevada and later at Tonopah.

During Operation Just Cause in December 1989, two F-117As flew nonstop from Nevada with air refuelling to attack the Rio Hato barracks in Panama using BLU-109B 2,000-lb (907-kg) bombs. The accuracy of the attack has been the subject of debate but overall the F-117A and its systems worked as Lockheed intended.

### Desert Storm

The Gulf War of January-February 1991 effectively began when an F-117 bombed an air defence control centre in Baghdad. USAF after-action reports on this and other missions found that Iraqi forces could not detect an F-117 approaching and often would not start shooting until its bombs exploded. The USAF concluded that the F-117 had amply demonstrated its ability to cruise to a target at around 580 mph (933 km/h), identify it before surface threats became active, and hit it with precision. During Desert Storm, the F-117's 'stealth' properties enabled it to fly 1,271 sorties in the 42-day war without a scratch.

***Inflight refuelling is a vital element in the Nighthawk's mission if it is to strike targets at great distances. Radio-silent refuellings are regularly practised, and at night the only illumination used in such manoeuvres comes from the small light above the cockpit.***

***The immediate future of the F-117A is assured, but the of the F-117B will not be built. This was a much-improved new-build model with far greater bomb-carrying potential and better systems. A projected naval version, the A/F-117X, was also based on this aircraft.***

# F-117 Development: Have Blue

**Developed and flown within the so-called 'Black World', Have Blue's remarkable capabilities remained highly classified for years.**

Predecessor to the Lockheed F-117A stealth attack aircraft, the technology demonstrator Have Blue remained classified deep within America's Black World, even after the 'Stealth Fighter' was being publicly displayed at airshows across America.

## Stealth is everything

Have Blue was like nothing that had ever flown. Restrictions imposed on its designers dictated that Have Blue's development and subsequent flight-testing would call for one of the most secretive Air Force programmes undertaken since the Lockheed SR-71 Blackbird.

In August 1975, Lockheed and Northrop were invited to develop and test an aircraft known as the Experimental Survivable Testbed (XST). Both manufacturers designed small, single-seat aircraft. Northrop's XST air vehicle used a combination of rounded and angular surfaces to achieve its lowered radar cross-section. This design was often referred to as 'Shamu' because it resembled the famous orca whale at San Diego's Sea World amusement park.

Lockheed's design however utilised a rather more dramatic approach. Their design adopted flat panels and facets which helped deflect radar waves, leading to the design being dubbed 'the hopeless diamond.' The results of radar tests gave Lockheed victory in the Have Blue demonstration programme in April 1976.

## Design features

In addition to the shaping of the demonstrator, the external surfaces of the aircraft were covered with radar-absorbent material (RAM). Later the aircraft would have canopy windows with special coatings to make the panels appear as metallic surfaces to radar.

Lockheed built two Have Blue sub-scale proof-of-concept demonstrator aircraft which, were completed at Burbank within months. Have Blue was a subsonic, single-place aircraft so ugly that it was disturbing to look at. Power was provided by two General Electric J85-GE-4A engines borrowed from a T-2B Buckeye trainer.

Have Blue was longer than many fighters but otherwise extremely small. Gross weight of the bizarre new aircraft ranged from 9,200 to 12,500 lb (4173 to 5669 kg). This lightweight design allowed the Have Blue to utilise the landing gear of an F-5 Freedom Fighter.

Initial engine runs were accomplished on Have Blue on 4 November 1977 at the Lockheed Burbank facility. To maintain security, the aircraft was parked between two semi-tractor trailers over which a camouflage net had been drawn. The runs were performed at night after the airport was closed. A local resident complained about the noise, but Have Blue's secret remained completely intact. From here the aircraft was securely covered and transported to a classified and remote test facility in the Nevada desert. This barren airfield had been specially prepared for the development of stealth aircraft and large sums of money had been invested in new hangars and runway improvements.

## Desert secrets

Flying for the first time on 1 December 1977, just 20 months from contract award,

***A rare in-flight photograph of HB 1002 shows the aircraft's extraordinary shape, highlighting the dramatic sweepback of the leading edge. Note the faceted elevons, moving platypus tail surfaces and the retractable lower blade aerial.***

***Below: The unusual shape of the sub-scale Have Blue models resulted from the need to ensure that the aircraft would present as small a radar cross section as possible to enemy air defence systems. The models were used in wind tunnel tests.***

***Below: With rumours and leaks from the USAF, the aviation community was eager to discover the secrets of stealth technology in the late 1980s. Aviation artists produced sketches and images of the secret aircraft. All proved to be unrealistic once the F-117 had been declassified.***

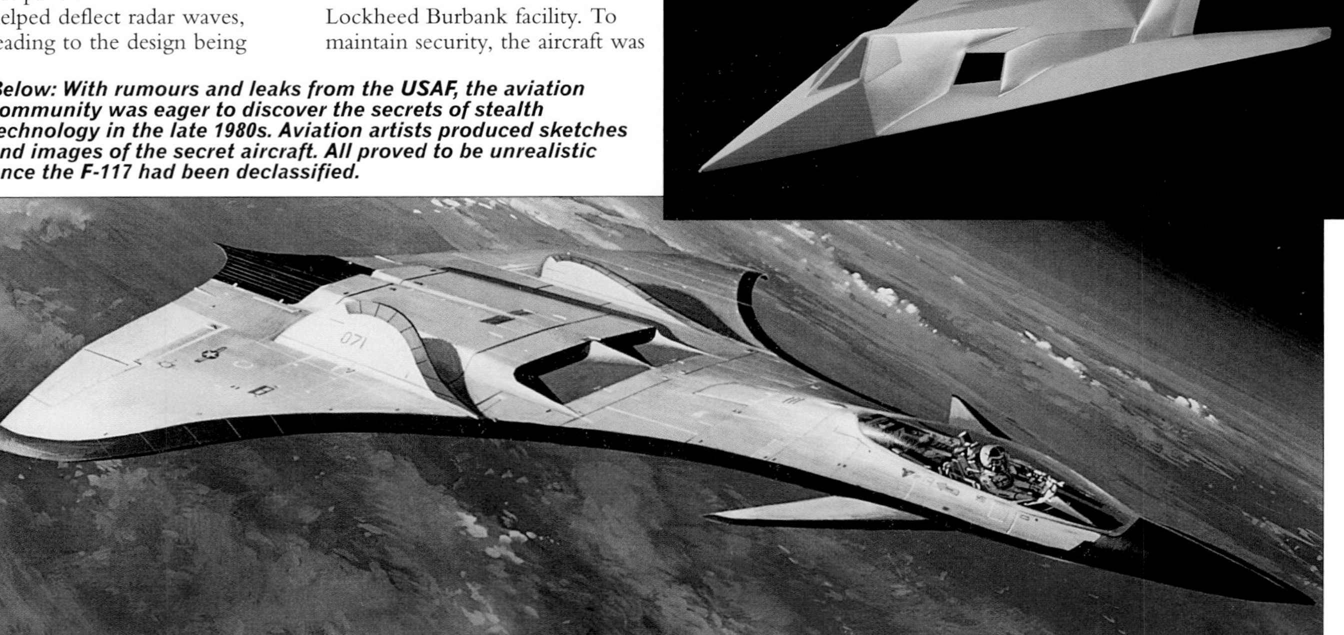

XST-1, as it was known, accomplished 35 flights, but on its 36th while attempting a landing, undercarriage failure forced the test pilot Bill Park, to abandon the aircraft. In the process Park sustained injuries that would see his retirement from further fast jet flying.

The second Have Blue first flew on 20 July 1978. It was modified to incorporate nose-wheel steering and had the anti-spin parachute of its predecessor removed. Following these modifications HB 1002 accomplished 52 flights in the following 12 months.

Having accomplished numerous test-flights a mock defence radar set-up was established in July 1979 to give final vindication of the stealth concept.

Unfortunately, prior to this HB 1002 experienced an in-flight engine fire forcing the pilot to eject from the aircraft, after having exhausted all attempts to save it.

With HB 1002 lost, both airframes were taken to a remote desert location and buried deep beneath Nevada's sagebrush.

Despite their dramatic demise the Have Blue's opened the door for further stealth designs. And the undoubted success of the F-117A 'Stealth Fighter' owes a lot to the humble Have Blue.

***Right:* The Have Blue aircraft were fundamental in the production of the five Full Scale Development (FSD) aircraft which were often known as YF-117As. The test fleet wore this overall grey paint scheme until the USAF decreed that all F-117As would be painted in the now familiar overall black scheme.**

***Above:* Seen on the ramp at Groom Lake, an early FSD 'Stealth Fighter' prepares for a test flight. This developmental model wore a three-tone camouflage scheme to conceal the aircraft when in the open.**

## Have Blue HB 1001

**This three-view depicts the first of the two Have Blue experimental aircraft, which paved the way for the design of the full-scale 'Stealth Fighter'. It wore this strange scheme to hide its unique faceted surface, although the second Have Blue was finished in an all-over grey. HB 1001 also differed by having a large instrumentation boom attached to its nose.**

### Pole testing

The flying of the HB 1002 against real radars in an operational environment was the culmination of a long RCS trials programme, which began with the testing of small, third-scale and full-scale models on poles. These tests showed the radar 'flare-spots' - areas of too much radar reflectivity.

### Systems

Have Blue utilised many off-the-shelf systems from other aircraft, including the fly-by-wire system from the F-16. The aircraft also had the F-16's sidestick controller, while the undercarriage came from the Northrop F-5. The two engines came from a Rockwell T-2B Buckeye.

### Flight control systems

Flight control systems were served by three static pressure sensors on the forward fuselage, and three total pressure probes, one on the nose and two on the cockpit windscreen post. HB 1001 also had the instrumentation boom which correlated data from the primary systems.

### Configuration

Have Blue validated the faceting concept, and the basic aircraft shape. Key differences were the inward-canting of the fins, which were mounted on the outside of the main fuselage body and much further forward than on the production aircraft. The leading edge was set at a very sharp 72.5°.

### Stealthy exhaust

The exhaust slot for the Have Blue had a greater extension on its lower lip than was featured on the F-117, with its two exhaust slots meeting at a common point on the centreline. The lower portion of the nozzle formed a two-position plate which automatically deflected downwards when angle of attack exceeded 12°.

# Out of the black

## 'Stealth' operations

*When the veil of secrecy surrounding the 'Stealth Fighter' was eventually lifted in 1988, it finally allowed the USAF to integrate the aircraft into its regular day-to-day operations.*

**During the Gulf War, the F-117 Nighthawk became a media star, presenting to the world an image of laser-guided bombs falling precisely on target. At the time, few people realised that this was not the combat debut of this revolutionary aircraft.**

With the entire development of the F-117 Nighthawk hidden from public view deep within the Nevada Desert, the USAF found itself in a unique position. In its possession was an aircraft that rendered practically all aerial defences ineffective, but the very existence of which still had to remain a closely-guarded secret. Not only was the very nature of the fledgling operational squadron continually denied, but the radar-deflecting facets of the F-117 had to be concealed from those outside the world of 'black programmes'. These extraordinary security requirements dictated that the early operational career of the 'Stealth Fighter' would place huge demands on both logistics and, more importantly, on pilots coming to grips with learning the fine art of flying the highly demanding aircraft.

Having searched the ranks for suitable candidates who had a minimum of at least 1,000 hours on either the F-111, F-4 Phantom II or A-10 Thunderbolt II, suitable pilots were then interviewed.

### New opportunities

Having the barest of details regarding their new posting, the pilots were given five minutes to decide if they were interested. Few turned down the opportunity of embarking on such a highly classified operation. Having passed this initial hurdle, the successful pilots were returned to their squadron to await further instructions, as the logistical side of the operational programme now took centre stage.

Of primary concern was the establishment of a secure base from which to fly Lockheed's new aircraft. With security now becoming difficult at the highly-classified Groom Lake facility, mainly due to the fact that those involved in the F–117 stealth programme would regularly catch glimpses of other secret aircraft, a relocation to the Tonopah Test Range (TTR) airfield, 140 miles (225 km) north-west of Las Vegas, was begun in May 1982 and completed by August 1983.

Now designated an operational unit, rather than a test and developmental squadron, Colonel James S. Allen assumed command of the first 'stealth' unit (to be known as the 4450th Tactical Group) in May 1982. He personally took delivery of the initial aircraft on 23 August 1983.

With support facilities complete at the TTR, a host of security procedures was soon

*Before 1988, all F-117 operations, including training missions, were flown at night. This caused unavoidable pilot fatigue, resulting in the loss of two or three F-117s including that of Major Ross E. Mulhare, which crashed into Sequoia National Forest in July 1986.*

*At a press conference on 10 November 1988, the US Assistant Secretary of Defense publicly revealed the F-117 with this poor quality photograph. The carefully chosen image disguised many key aspects of the aircraft's design.*

***Left:* A great deal of disinformation emerged concerning the true configuration and capabilities of the F-117. Misinformed press releases discussed the aircraft's poor flying qualities, while plastic kit manufacturers produced a plethora of fanciful and highly inaccurate models. The eventual revelation of the F-117 programme served only to show how successful the USAF's attempts to hide its revolutionary new weapons system had been.**

***Below:* In-flight refuelling plays a vital role in any F-117 mission. Seen during a daytime training flight, this F-117 refuels from a KC-10 Extender. An expanded and much safer training syllabus, conducted in daylight hours, is now in operation.**

implemented, involving patrolling UH-1N helicopters and a detachment of Special Forces guards. Now the main problem facing the new pilots of the 4450th was the lack of sufficient examples of F-117s in which to gain flight experience. Despite this, the group was declared operational on 28 October 1983, having received less than a squadron of the new aircraft.

## Cover story

To maintain the necessary flying hours, the 4450th Tactical Group was allocated a number of A-7Ds, although these were based at the nearby Nellis air base. The new stealth pilots used the aircraft as training tools, enabling a cover story to be devised. Later, they were replaced by T-38 Talons, as the A-7D cover story was no longer needed and the T-38s were cheaper to operate.

The flight characteristics of the F-117 were found to be similar to those of the A-7D. This enabled pilots to get used to the handling characteristics of the aircraft in daytime training missions, without compromising the security of the programme. An added bonus was that, to any interested party, the 4450th could now be passed off as an A-7 test unit, until enough examples of the F-117 could be delivered. Later, the A-7s were used as chase planes, flying alongside the fledgling stealth pilot during his initial series of training flights.

The F-117 was regarded by US war planners as a 'silver bullet'. In other words, only a few existed and they were to be used against high-value assets (HVAs), the Pentagon's term for the enemy's leadership structure, communications and transportation assets.

With its clandestine 'Stealth Fighter' operational, the USAF now had a warplane which had settled into service and was beginning to mature, although few people outside the programme knew of the F-117.

**No two-seat training version of the F-117 was ever built. At one stage, the conversion of a crashed single-seat example was debated, but no work was completed. Instead, the USAF relied on A-7Ds to provide flight time to prospective F-117 pilots, all of whom were high-hour fast jet pilots.**

Throughout the free-spending 1980s, the 4450th Tactical Group continued to thrive. This was also the decade when terrorism came to dominate world events. Lebanon became the focus of US attention when a car bomb destroyed a barracks housing a US Marines expeditionary force. Colonel Oliver North, later involved in the Irangate scandal, devised a plan for the F-117 to be utilised against terrorist strongholds. A similar operation was devised against Libya's capital, Tripoli, in 1986, but a more conventional plan involving British-based F-111 'Aardvarks', and USN carrier-based F/A-18 Hornets, with F-14 Tomcats flying combat air patrols (CAPs), was implemented.

In December 1989, US Forces were deployed in Operation Just Cause, the combined arms assault on Panama aimed at ousting its leader Manuel Noriega, who had offended the US by becoming a dictator with close ties to the drug cartels. Eager to show the potential of its 'silver bullet', the Pentagon's joint staff devised a mission that was both inventive and which would also silence the critics of the 'stealth' programme once and for all.

On the night of 19 December 1989, two F-117s were launched to support a Special Operations 'snatch' of Noriega. The 'snatch' was later called off as the aircraft approached Panamanian airspace, and the nature of the target was changed. Two more F-117s flew a bombing mission intended to 'stun and confuse' Panamanian Defence Forces (PDF) at Rio Hato, with another two F-117s flown as back-ups. Their target was a large, open field alongside a barracks housing 200 elite PDF troops, rather than the barracks itself.

The six F-117s flew from Tonopah and refuelled five times during the round trip to Panama. The two Rio Hato F-117s dropped two 2,000-lb (907-kg) GBU-27A/B bombs with BLU-109B/I-2000 warheads, both of which exploded several hundred feet away from their intended target. Lead pilot for this attack was Major Greg Feest, who later dropped the first bomb on Baghdad. Four of the six F-117s returned to Tonopah with their bombs on board.

The mission was viewed as a failure in Congress, with critics unleashing scathing attacks on the capabilities of the high-tech aircraft. The press referred to the F-117 as the 'Wobblin' Goblin', a term never used by those associated with the aircraft. Despite the press furore that followed the Just Cause missions, two years later the world's media would 'clearly see', or at least hear about, the real capability of the F-117, as demonstrated in the skies over Iraq.

# Lockheed P-3 Orion

## Son of Neptune

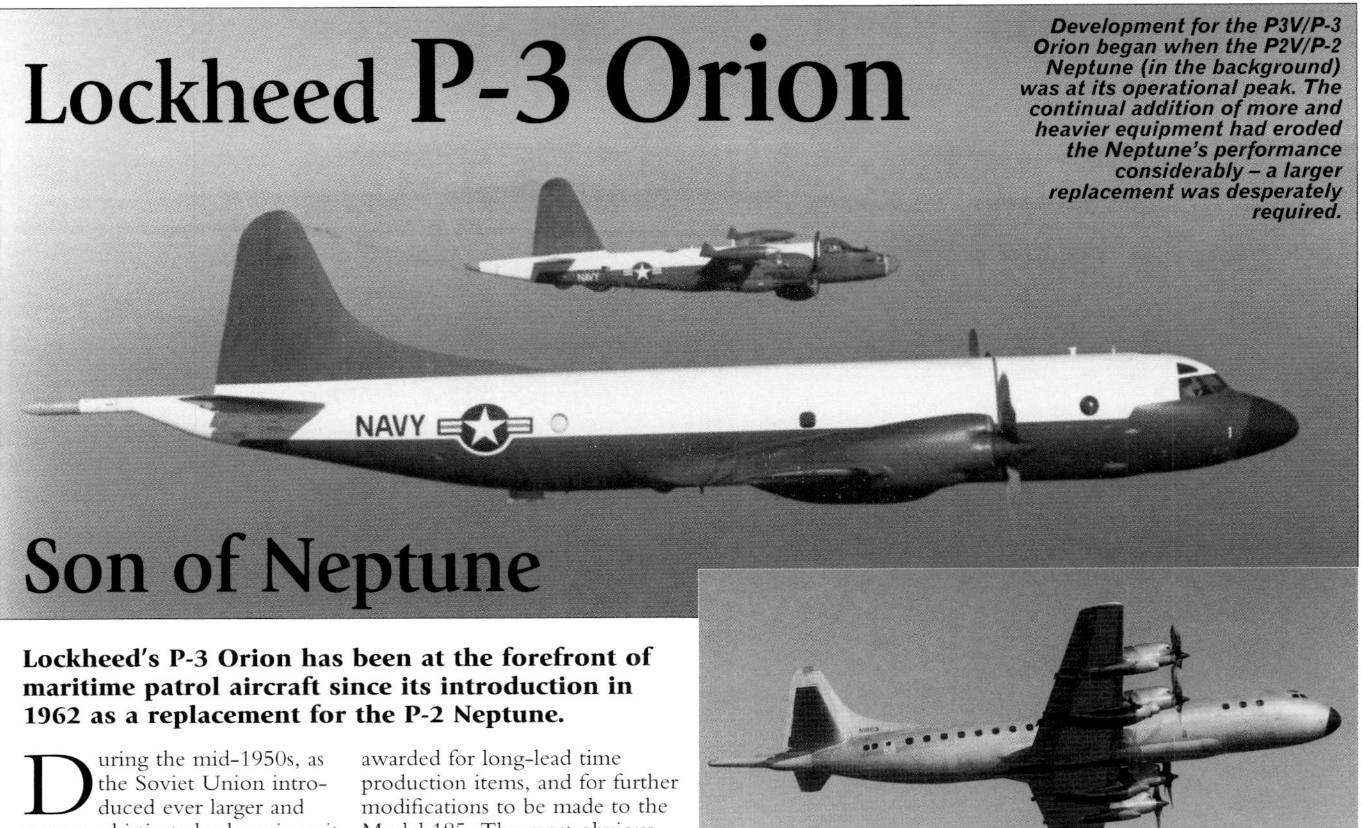

*Development for the P3V/P-3 Orion began when the P2V/P-2 Neptune (in the background) was at its operational peak. The continual addition of more and heavier equipment had eroded the Neptune's performance considerably – a larger replacement was desperately required.*

*The Orion prototype, N1883, had previously been used as a static test airframe for the L-188 Electra airliner. It was modified with representative weapon bay and MAD boom, first flying with these on 19 August 1958. Successful trials led to further modifications, such as the shortening of the forward fuselage.*

**Lockheed's P-3 Orion has been at the forefront of maritime patrol aircraft since its introduction in 1962 as a replacement for the P-2 Neptune.**

During the mid-1950s, as the Soviet Union introduced ever larger and more sophisticated submarines, it was clear to the US Navy that a replacement was needed for the Lockheed P2V Neptune. Although the Neptune had been a great success, its size and growing weight severely limited its operational effectiveness. Accordingly, Naval Type Specification 146 was issued in August 1957.

In terms of delivery schedule and cost, NTS 146 dictated an off-the-shelf approach. Lockheed's response was based on the L-188 Electra airliner, suitably modified to perform the ASW and patrol missions. Lockheed's proposal was the only one to meet all NTS 146 requirements, while the company's long history of patrol aircraft (Hudson, Ventura, Harpoon and Neptune) engendered confidence in the Navy. On 8 May 1958, the company was formally announced as the winner.

Work started immediately on turning the third Electra airframe into a mock-up of the NTS 146 patroller. A MAD boom and representative weapons bay fairing were fitted. The Model 185, as the aircraft was known in-house, took to the air in August 1958, and sufficiently impressed the Navy for contracts to be awarded for long-lead time production items, and for further modifications to be made to the Model 185. The most obvious was the shortening of the forward fuselage by 7 ft (2.13 m), but just as significant was the fitment of production T56-A-10 powerplants and most of the mission equipment. Now designated YP3V-1, and given BuNo. 148276, the aircraft flew again as the true prototype on 25 November 1959.

### Orion go-ahead

Trials in early 1960 led to the award of a contract for seven P3V-1 aircraft, the first of which (BuNo. 148883) flew on 15 April 1961. Exhaustive tests through 1961 and early 1962 proved that the new aircraft was an admirable replacement for the P2V. It offered vastly increased load-carrying ability, combined with long endurance and increased dash speed thanks to the Allison T56 turboprops. Its low-speed handling was excellent for so large a machine, while its systems were state-of-the-art. The most important of these were the Julie/Jezebel acoustic system and the APS-80 radar system, which had antennas in both the nose radome and an aft radome under the tail, providing 360° coverage. A crew of 12 manned the aircraft.

ASW weaponry comprised the Mk 44 torpedo and various depth bomb/destructors (including the B57 nuclear depth bomb). Zuni rockets could be carried on outer wing pylons for surface attack.

In September 1962 the P3V-1 was redesignated as the P-3A (often referred to as the 'Alpha'), by which time the name Orion (son of Neptune) had been bestowed on the type. Service entry occurred in June 1962, the first recipient being the East Coast Fleet Replenishment Squadron, VP-30. The following month VP-8 received P3V-1s to become the first front-line Orion squadron, followed by VP-44 in August. Both squadrons flew their aircraft on blockade patrols during the Cuban Missile Crisis in October. Orions joined the Pacific Fleet in January 1963 with VP-46. The variant was deployed to Southeast Asia from 1964, flying patrols around the Vietnamese coasts, helping to stem the supply of materiel to the Viet Cong by sea.

During its career the P-3A was updated to meet the changing needs of the ASW mission. The most important of these upgrades was the adoption of the DELTIC (DELayed TIme Compression) acoustic system from 1965 which greatly enhanced the ability to detect

*Distinguished by its chisel-shaped nose and just-visible stepped MAD boom, the YP3V-1 overflies a submarine during ASW tests in 1960. These trials led to an initial production order, placed in October.*

***The three 'Black' Orions were fitted with a plethora of intelligence-gathering equipment, and could also drop leaflets or agents. They were fitted with Sidewinder launchers, and are reputed to have shot down a Chinese MiG. The aircraft also flew briefly over Vietnam.***

### Covert reconnaissance – 'Black' Orions and Bat Rack

The range and load-carrying ability of the Orion made it a natural for reconnaissance missions. Three P-3As were converted from 1963 to operate from Taiwan on behalf of the CIA, flying missions over and around China. As well as reconnaissance missions, the aircraft undertook psywar sorties, with leaflet-dropping a routine task. The 'Black Orions' operated until 1967, whereupon two of them were converted to EP-3B Bat Rack configuration for the US Navy's VQ-1. Operational from 1969, the two Orions operated alongside Douglas EA-3B Skywarriors as signals intelligence (Sigint) collection platforms, using many of the systems initially used during their operations by the CIA. Initial successes with these machines led to an order for 10 similar aircraft which were known as the EP-3E Aries.

***This is one of the two EP-3B Bat Rack machines, displaying the underfuselage 'M&M™' radome which housed a large steerable direction-finder. The radome was extended for use. The aircraft inherited lengthened exhausts (for reduced IR signature) from its days as one of the 'Black' Orions.***

submarines. A minelaying capability was also added, as was an APU (auxiliary power unit) which allowed operations from austere bases.

P-3A production ended in December 1965, by which time 157 had been built. 'Alpha' service ended in the active-duty fleet in November 1978, although P-3As survived in the Naval Air Reserve until October 1990.

Immediately following the 'Alpha' down the line was the P-3B 'Bravo', which introduced uprated T56-A-14 engines, each rated at 4,500 eshp (3357 kW). The operational system was based on that installed in upgraded P-3As, including DELTIC. Mid-way through P-3B production, the structure was enhanced to cater for ever-growing mission weights. The new aircraft became known as Heavy Weight P-3Bs, while the first aircraft were christened Light Weight 'Bravos'. During early production the P-3B was given the capability to carry and launch the AGM-12 Bullpup radio-guided missile. Bullpup capability was retrofitted to early P-3Bs and to most P-3As.

Production of the 'Bravo' began in 1965 (with BuNo. 152718) and totalled 125 aircraft. Deliveries were made first to the West Coast FRS, VP-31, on 13 December 1965, the first front-line squadron being VP-9 which acquired its first machine in January 1966. On the East Coast, VP-26 was the first recipient, in the same month.

Intended as an interim variant pending delivery of the much-improved P-3C, the 'Bravo' enjoyed a long and productive career, leaving the Fleet in 1979, and Naval Reserve in the 1990s.

### TACNAVMOD upgrade

From 1979 surviving P-3A/Bs serving with Naval Air Reserve units underwent the TACNAVMOD, a programme which gave the aircraft a new digital processing system (AQA-5 DIFAR), as employed by the P-3C. These aircraft became known as Block I machines. Further P-3Bs were upgraded to TACNAVMOD Block II status (dubbed 'SuperBees') with further improved systems, infra-red turret and Harpoon missile capability. Yet another programme in the early 1990s produced a few TACNAVMOD Block III 'KillerBees', with ALR-66 ESM, satellite communications, and colour weather radar.

As the earlier Orions became surplus to Fleet requirements, many were reworked to perform other missions, usually with ASW equipment (including MAD boom) removed.

The list of sub-variants includes many special mission and one-off test aircraft under the following designations: EP-3A (electronic trials, ECM aggressor and missile test/range support aircraft), EP-3B (electronic intelligence platforms), EP-3E Aries (10 electronic intelligence platforms), EP-3J (two electronic aggressors), NP-3A/B (trials/test aircraft), RP-3A/D (oceanographic/geomagnetic/ice research platforms), TP-3A ('bounce-bird' pilot trainers), UP-3A/B (logistics transports/general test), VP-3A (staff/VIP transports) and WP-3A (four weather reconnaissance aircraft).

***Right: The P-3B was a rationalisation of the many improvements applied to the 'Alpha'. Its main new feature was the introduction of the uprated T56-A-14 engine.***

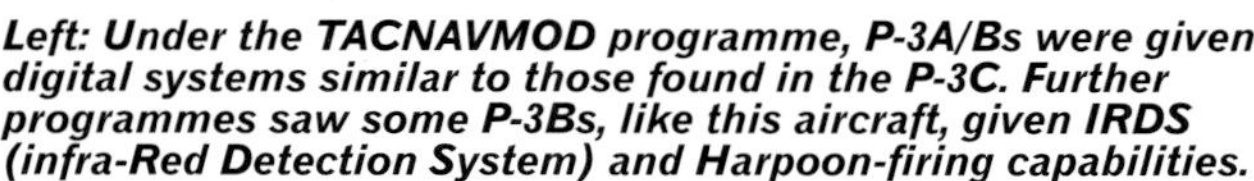

***Left: Under the TACNAVMOD programme, P-3A/Bs were given digital systems similar to those found in the P-3C. Further programmes saw some P-3Bs, like this aircraft, given IRDS (infra-Red Detection System) and Harpoon-firing capabilities.***

***Below: For attacking small surface targets the 5-in (12.7-cm) Zuni rocket was an important weapon. Precision surface attack, in the form of the AGM-12 Bullpup guided missile, came with the P-3B.***

# CP-140 Aurora and CP-140A Arcturus

**Above:** *Wearing a temporary US civil registration, the first Aurora (140101) is seen during manufacturer's tests, wearing the high-visibility scheme in which the aircraft was delivered.*

**Left:** *Eighteen Auroras were purchased to replace 33 of its predecessor, the Canadair CP-107 Argus. The apparent shortfall was more than offset by the new type's additional capabilities.*

**Canada's requirements for a new long-range maritime patroller led to a unique variant of the Orion. The airframe was unmistakeably P-3, but the surveillance system was that used by the S-3 Viking.**

In 1969 the newly unified Canadian Armed Forces began the leisurely process of finding a replacement for their Canadair CP-107 Argus maritime patrollers. Canada not only needed a new ASW aircraft to cope with the Soviet submarine threat, which was increasing in terms of numbers and sophistication, but also to handle a variety of unique national commitments such as ice reconnaissance, fishery patrol and sovereignty flights over the vast Arctic and sub-Arctic territories.

Under the acronym LRPA (Long-Range Patrol Aircraft), an RFP (request for proposal) was issued in August 1971. Submissions included the Nimrod, Atlantic, a refurbished Argus and maritime patrol versions of the Boeing 707 (which Canada operated in the transport role) and the Douglas DC-10. Lockheed submitted several Orion-based proposals, ranging from a US Navy-standard P-3C Update I or II to a special 'Canadianised' version.

Eventually the competition narrowed to just two airframes: the 707 and the P-3C. The outcome was largely dependent on the amount of offsets which could be offered to Canadian industry. Lockheed was the winner, an order being placed for 18 aircraft on 27 November 1975. A Canadian team went to Burbank to work with Lockheed on detailed design of what was to become the CP-140 Aurora. The aircraft flew from Burbank on 22 March 1979. Initial crew training was undertaken by Lockheed in California.

## Aurora anatomy

The Canadian Orion was based on the P-3C airframe and, as such, featured sonobuoy launch tubes in the lower rear fuselage. However, the number was cut from the P-3's 48 to 36. The space saved allowed the fitment of a Zeiss KS-501A camera system. This is a vertical panoramic camera which can use either daylight or infra-red film, the latter working in conjunction with an IR illuminator.

More importantly, the CP-140 dispensed with the P-3's central system in favour of a new suite based on that of the S-3A Viking. At the heart of this is the AYK-10 (Canadian designation AYK-502) digital central data processing computer, OL-82 (OL-5004) acoustic processor, ARR-76 sonobuoy receiver and ARS-501 sonobuoy reference system. The AYK-502 integrates all onboard operational functions, such as sonobuoy release and weapons management. It can fly the aircraft 'hands-off' to fly-to points generated by the TACCO (tactical co-ordinator) and automatically release sonobuoys. The radar is the APS-116 (APS-506).

Much of the new equipment

*Although the submarine threat has reduced in recent years, the Aurora fleet provides a vital ASW asset in the far North. The force is also heavily tasked with national missions along one of the world's longest coastlines.*

***Left: CP-140s participate in the Fincastle maritime patrol competitions which involve aircraft from Australia, Canada, New Zealand and the UK. In 1997 this 407 Squadron Aurora was specially painted for the competition.***

***Below: To celebrate the 75th anniversary of the Royal Canadian Air Force on 1 April 1999, several aircraft adopted wartime-style codes and roundels. This Aurora is from Greenwood-based 415 'Swordfish' Squadron.***

was unique to the Aurora, notably the CAE Electronics ASQ-502 magnetic anomaly detector (MAD) and wingtip-mounted electronic support measures (ESM) system.

From the mission crew's point of view, the most important difference is the internal layout. Unlike the P-3C, in which the TACCO, nav/comm operator and sensor operators are dispersed around the cabin, the CP-140 has a 'U'-shaped tactical compartment with two stations facing forward, two facing outwards and two facing aft. The close proximity of the operators promotes close crew co-ordination, a feature recognised by Lockheed and Raytheon in its recent P-3 upgrade proposals.

The CP-140 was also fitted with a retractable OR-5008 FLIR turret and an improved environmental control system, both features adopted by the US Navy for its P-3Cs. A feature unique to the Aurora is the capability to fit palletised sensors in the weapons bay, with suitable wiring. One system which was tested was the APD-10 side-looking imaging radar. Many of the bay-mounted sensors are used in conjunction with agencies such as Environmental Canada, which uses the Auroras for pollution control/surveillance and animal censuses. The Department of Fisheries and Ocean calls on the Aurora for spotting illegal fishing vessels, while the Royal Canadian Mounted Police, working with Canadian Customs, uses the CP-140 for tracking suspected drug shipments. Ice reconnaissance is performed on behalf of the Department of Transport, while the CP-140 also has a long-range SAR commitment, for which the SKAD (survival kit, air droppable) is carried.

In the mid-1990s the CP-140 fleet was fitted with the WX-1000 Stormscope weather reconnaissance radar. Previously, in 1992, the DND had initiated the ALEP (Aurora Life Extension Programme) which, when completed, will bring the Aurora up to fully modern standards. A modification to the radar, known as Spotlight, adds a SAR imaging mode, while new ESM, MAD and sonobuoy reference systems are incorporated. New navigation and comms suites are being fitted, along with new work-stations. An under-nose turret will house a FLIR, laser and LLLTV.

### CP-140A Arcturus

In 1989 the Canadian Department of National Defence ordered three Orion airframes from Lockheed – the last three aircraft built at the Burbank plant. The aircraft had two intended functions: to relieve the hard-pressed operational fleet of its pilot trainer duties, and to cover a shortfall in fishery/ice/sovereignty patrol assets which would occur with the impending retirement of the CP-121 Tracker fleet.

Under the AMSA (Arctic Maritime Surveillance Aircraft) project, the three aircraft (140119, '20 and '21) were delivered with minimal equipment to IMP Aerospace at Halifax, Nova Scotia, for fitting out to CP-140A Arcturus standard. Described as 'austere' versions of the Aurora, the CP-140As had none of the CP-140's ASW equipment, but retained the APS-507 radar and long-range navigation equipment. They were based on the P-3C airframe, and were completed with MAD boom and 48 sonobuoy launch tubes in the underside of the fuselage, although they are non-functional. The aircraft retained the Aurora's 'U'-shaped work-station cluster, although only the radar and nav/comm stations were equipped.

The first CP-140A was delivered to the BAMEO at Greenwood on 30 November 1992, the remaining pair following in April 1993. Their delivery allowed one CP-140 to be sent to Comox to strengthen 407 Squadron, which had increased ASW commitments.

As well as pilot training and fishery patrols, the three operational Arcturus aircraft undertake ice reconnaissance and sovereignty patrols. The aircraft are also used on anti-drug trafficking tasks. An update is planned for the fleet, along the lines of the Aurora's ALEP programme (of course, without the ASW system improvements).

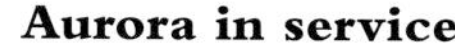

### Aurora in service

The first aircraft was delivered to CFB Greenwood, Nova Scotia, on 29 May 1980. Later that year, in November, 405 Squadron (also known, US Navy-style, as VP 405) became the first unit to equip with the type, flying its first operational mission in March 1981. VP 404 became the training squadron, while VP 415 completed Air Group 28 at Greenwood. By the end of 1981, VP 407 at CFB Comox, British Columbia, had also equipped with the type.

As well as its standard national and NATO missions, the CP-140 formed part of Canada's contributions to UN peacekeeping efforts over former Yugoslavia. Detached to the US Navy base at Sigonella, Italy, the CP-140s took part in Operation Sharp Guard, a surveillance of the Adriatic to enforce a UN embargo on prohibited goods entering Yugoslavia. This work began in September 1993.

In 2004 the Canadian Armed Forces had around 18 CP-140s on first-line strength, with an upgrade programme planned to ensure their continued service.

# International operators

**As the West's standard maritime patroller, the P-3 serves around the world. Of the overseas operators, Japan is the largest, also building the type under licence.**

## Australia

Australia received 10 P-3B aircraft in 1968 for No. 11 Squadron, followed by 10 P-3C Update II.5s for No. 10 Squadron in the mid-1970s. Ten more 'Charlies' were acquired to replace the 'Bravos' in 1982. In the 1990s the aircraft were upgraded to AP-3C standard, with revised equipment including an Elta search radar. One aircraft was modified to perform the Sigint-gathering mission. Three P-3Bs were bought in the 1990s to act as TAP-3 pilot trainers.

## Argentina

In order to replace elderly L-188 Electras in the maritime patrol mission, the Comando de Aviación Naval Argentina (COAN) received seven ex-US Navy P-3Bs, of which one was earmarked for spares recovery. Assigned to the Escuadrilla Aeronaval de Exploración at Trelew, the aircraft arrived between December 1997 and July 1999. The five-aircraft operational fleet is being repainted in the smart dark grey scheme illustrated below.

## Brazil

Brazil has purchased 12 P-3A/Bs, of which eight will be operational in the maritime patrol role (the remaining four being used for training/spares recovery). They are to be updated to P-3C Update II equivalent by EADS CASA.

## Chile

The Chilean navy acquired eight ex-US Navy UP/P-3As, the first of which was delivered in March 1993. Four P-3As serve in operational roles with VP-1 (illustrated), having been equipped with Chile-specific equipment, some of it of Israeli origin. They fly alongside EMB-111AN Bandeirantes. Two UP-3As serve with VC-1 on training and general patrol duties. Both squadrons fly from Concón, Vina del Mar.

## Greece

In May 1996 the Elliniko Polimiko Naftikon (Greek naval aviation) received the first of six P-3B TACNAVMODs for service with 353 Mira Naftikis Aeroporikis Sinergasias at Elefsis. These followed four P-3As acquired for spares (two) and to act as ground trainers (two). As in Pakistan, Portugal and Spain, the Orions are flown and maintained by the air force but tasked by the navy, which also supplies the mission crew personnel.

## Iran

The Imperial Iranian Air Force ordered six Orions in 1973. Designated P-3Fs, the aircraft were essentially P-3C airframes with P-3A/B systems. The first was delivered in 1975. After the fall of the Shah, the Orions remained operational with the Islamic Republic of Iran Air Force (IRIAF, illustrated). One aircraft crashed and, of the five remaining, perhaps three are maintained in an airworthy condition. Originally operated from Tactical Air Base 9 at Bandar Abbas, it is likely that the P-3s have moved to TAB 7 at Shiraz.

## Japan

On 29 December 1977 Japan announced the choice of the P-3C Update II.5 for its maritime patrol requirement, the majority of the 101 ordered to be built locally by Kawasaki. Later in the production run, Update III avionics were included, as were GPS and SATCOMs. These systems are being slowly retrofitted across the fleet. Regular P-3C squadrons are: Dai 1 Koku-tai (VP-1) and VP-7 at Kanoya, VPs-2 and -4 at Hachinohe, VPs-3 and -6 at Atsugi, VPs-5 and -9 at Naha, and VP-8 at Iwakuni. P-3Cs also serve with the training unit (Dai 203 Kyoiko Koku-tai) at Shimofusa, and the JMSDF's dedicated test and trials unit (Dai 51 Koku-tai) at Atsugi.

Kawasaki has also built a number of special variants. The first was the EP-3, an electronic reconnaissance variant characterised by large radomes along the fuselage, which serves with Dai 81 Koku-tai at Iwakuni. Very similar in appearance is the UP-3D, an ECM trainer/wartime jammer of which three have been ordered for use by Dai 81 Koku-tai. The OP-3 is an imagery intelligence platform, of which five are planned, while the single UP-3C is a dedicated trials platform serving with Dai 51 Koku-tai at Atsugi.

*Above: The EP-3 is a naval Elint platform, performing a similar task to the US Navy's EP-3E ARIES II.*

*Right: Many JMSDF P-3Cs (VP-2 illustrated) carry a dorsal radome for SATCOMs.*

## Republic of Korea

The first Orions to be built at Marietta were eight P-3C Update IIIs (with some equipment differences) for the Republic of Korea Navy's 613 ASW Squadron at Pohang. The first flew on 12 December 1994, and was delivered in April 1995. Nine ex-US Navy P-3B aircraft have also been purchased.

## Netherlands

Thirteen P-3C Update II.5s were ordered in December 1978 for service with the MLD. Centrally maintained by the MARPAT (Maritime Patrol Group) at Valkenburg, the Orions are flown operationally by 320 Squadron, and for training by 321 Squadron. A three-aircraft detachment is maintained at Hato, Curaçao, for Caribbean anti-drug patrols. The fleet underwent a CUP (Capabilities Upgrade Programme) which added among other systems, imaging radar, new ESM and FLIR turret, but is now for sale.

## New Zealand

The RNZAF was the first export customer for the Orion, receiving five P-3B DELTIC aircraft for service with No. 5 Squadron at Whenuapai in 1966 to replace Sunderlands. In the 1980s the fleet was enhanced under the Rigel programme, resulting in the P-3K variant with APS-134 imaging radar and an infra-red turret. Another upgrade programme, known as Sirius, was cancelled in 2000, but further upgrade proposals were sought in 2002.

## Norway

From 1968 Norway received five P-3Bs for service with 333 Skvadron, later augmented by two more in 1980. In 1989, five Bs were sold to help pay for four new P-3C Update IIIs. The two remaining P-3Bs were modified to P-3N standard for training and coast guard duties. The P-3Cs were then updated under the UIP (Upgrade Improvement program) with new central computer and other systems.

## Pakistan

Pakistan ordered three P-3Cs in 1988 for service with No. 29 Squadron at Drigh Road. The aircraft were Update II.75 hybrid aircraft. Delivery was held up until 1997 owing to an embargo placed because of US concerns over Pakistani nuclear weapons development.

## Portugal

Portugal acquired the Orion in 1985, with an order for six P-3Ps. These aircraft were ex-RAAF P-3Bs, upgraded by Lockheed with various new systems, including APS-134 non-imaging ISAR radar, a modified ALR-66(V)3 ESM system, Harpoon capability and an AAS-36 Infra-Red Detection System. Five of the aircraft were modified in-country by OGMA. The Orions have served with Esquadra 601 at Montijo since 1988, operating in a unique 'Orca' two-tone grey scheme. A modification programme has been approved for the fleet.

## Spain

Spain's first Orions were three ex-US Navy P-3A DELTIC aircraft, acquired in 1973. Subsequently, four similar aircraft were leased from the US Navy. These were replaced by five ex-Norwegian P-3Bs in 1988/89, although two of the original P-3As remained on Spanish strength. The Orions now serve with Escuadrón 221 at Morón, flown by the air force but with navy mission crew.

## Thailand

101 Squadron, within the Royal Thai Naval Air Division, received the first of two P-3A Orions in December 1993. In February 1995 they were joined by two P-3Ts – ex-US Navy P-3A TACNVAMODs with some upgraded equipment. A fifth aircraft, designated UP-3T, was delivered in November 1995 to act as a trainer, and general surveillance platform. The fleet operates from U-Tapao.

# US Navy today

The Orion has always had a limited surface attack capability through the use of rockets. In recent times precision-guided weapons such as Maverick, Harpoon and SLAM have become available, although the P-3 can still employ unguided weapons. Such a capability is demonstrated here by a pair of VP-45 Orions firing 5-in (12.7-cm) Zuni rockets.

**In the post-Cold War era, the Orion has been adapted to perform a number of new missions, mostly concerned with war in the 'littorals'.**

A series of modification programmes has been applied to the P-3C Update III fleet to improve its capabilities, especially in the non-USW (undersea warfare) world. Although traditional 'blue-water' USW is still an important part of the Orion's operations, the decrease in Russian submarine activity (and changed political situation) has lessened the emphasis in this area. However, a concurrent rise in operations in the littoral ('white-water') regions has seen a whole new range of sensors and systems developed for the Orion, culminating in the current AIP/AIMS modification, which is being applied to most of the fleet.

In the late 1980s the Orion underwent the Command Survivability Program, which added a host of defensive measures, the most obvious of which was a change to the TPS (Tactical Paint Scheme), a low-visibility grey camouflage. IR detectors and chaff/flare dispensers were added.

Under the Outlaw Hunter programme, a single Orion was fitted with APS-137 inverse synthetic aperture radar (ISAR) which could image vessels or submarine periscopes. The aircraft also received GPS navigation and a new, highly accurate ESM suite. This turned the P-3 into a capable stand-off over-the-horizon targeting system. Outlaw Hunter was extremely successful in the 1991 Gulf War, guiding US Navy attack aircraft on numerous occasions. Three more Orions were subsequently updated, the programme having been rechristened OASIS (Over-the-horizon Airborne Sensor Information System).

## Anti-drug operations

Another role which became an important task for the Orion community was fighting drug smugglers in the Caribbean, for which detachments were, and are, maintained at a number of locations such as Hato, Curaçāo and Roosevelt Roads, Puerto Rico. A special sensor package, dubbed CDU (Counter Drug Update) was developed, consisting of a roll-on, roll-off system including an APG-66 fire-control radar (from the F-16) for tracking small airborne targets, and a Cluster Ranger long-range electro-optical sensor.

Thirty P-3s were modified to take the CDU package, and are widely used in tracking boats and aircraft used by smugglers.

During Operation Allied Force, P-3C AIPs fired AGM-84E SLAM missiles against Yugoslav targets. The SLAM requires a podded datalink system to be carried under a centre-section pylon. The AIP variant is distinguished by its ventral radome for the ESM system, and by having extra 'bat-wing' antennas for the Satcoms equipment. This example, from VP-5, flies past Mount Etna.

### P-7 – cancelled successor

In October 1988 Lockheed was awarded a development contract for the P-7A (originally designated P-3G). This was a successor to the P-3C, but based on the same airframe. Engines (in the form of General Electric GE-38s) and mission system were all new, while weapon load and performance were significantly enhanced. However, the programme was cancelled in July 1990.

***Above: During operations against former Yugoslavia, US Navy P-3Cs operated from Sigonella, where this aircraft is seen taxiing for a mission during Allied Force. This VP-5 Orion, an AIP aircraft, carries AGM-65 missiles under the wings for attacks against vessels which may have attempted to beat the NATO blockade. Although routinely carried, no Mavericks were fired in anger.***

***Carrying a battery of cameras to record weapon separation, a P-3C from the Naval Air Warfare Center test-fires an AGM-65F Maverick. This missile gives a useful attack capability against small vessels operating in littoral waters. The pimple under the nose is the retractable turret for the AAS-36 IRDS (Infra-Red Detection System), a steerable imaging FLIR.***

Cluster Ranger imagery can be transmitted in real time to intercepting agencies. Further EO systems have been used, including Cast Glance. These early systems peered out from the rear observer station, requiring the port outer engine to be shut down during use so that the jet efflux would not interfere with the sensor. A partial solution was found with the AVX-1 camera, which is mounted in the port forward (Tacco) station. However, this makes the station very cramped.

## AIP

Elements of the CDU and OASIS improvements were incorporated into the AIP (Anti-surface warfare Improvement Program), which is being applied to most Orions. This brings together the GPS and ISAR of the OASIS with the AVX-1 camera of the CDU, plus new equipment such as ALR-66C(V)5 ESM (with underfuselage radome), new displays, new mission computer and additional Satcoms. Weapons capability includes AGM-65 Maverick, AGM-84 Harpoon, AGM-84E SLAM, AGM-84H SLAM-ER and, in the future, may include JASSM.

From 1999 AIP P-3s began to appear with the Wescam AIMS turret under the nose, which includes a long-range electro-optical sensor to replace the cumbersome AVX-1 system, and freeing space at the Tacco station. AIPs went to war during the Kosovo campaign, in the course of which a number of SLAMs were fired at coastal targets, and numerous coastal reconnaissance/battle damage assessment missions were flown.

With AIP/AIMS, the Orion is fully equipped for the missions it faces in the first part of the 21st century, many of which are aimed at coastal patrol. However, the airframes are getting old, and a SLAP (Service Life Assessment Program) is under way which may lead to structural improvements. In the longer term, a replacement is sought under a programme dubbed MMA (Multi-mission Maritime Aircraft). While some potential competitors work on airliner derivatives, Lockheed Martin and Raytheon are working on new patrollers based on an updated Orion airframe. New engines would be fitted, and an all-new mission suite

# P-3C Update III

**This aircraft served with VP-4 'Skinny Dragons' at Kaneohe Bay, Hawaii. All of the Orion units previously operating at MCAS Barber's Point transferred to their new location in July 1999. VP-4 was active during Desert Storm, flying from Masirah.**

**Crew**
The standard Orion crew is 10. There are two pilots and a flight engineer on the flight deck, while in the forward part of the 'tube' (as the cabin is known) are the tactical co-ordinator (Tacco), navigator/communictions operator (Nav/comm) and three sensor operators (Senso 1, 2 and 3). In the rear of the cabin are the ordnanceman and inflight technician, who double as observers.

**Sonobuoy launch tubes**
The P-3C's 52 SLTs are angled backwards to negate the effects of the aircraft's inertia, so that the store lands directly beneath the point where it was dropped. Buoy release is accomplished from the 48 ground-loadable tubes by explosive charge, while the three air-loadable tubes employ pressurisation. The final tube is a free-fall chute.

**Radar**
The standard P-3C radar is the I-band, frequency-agile Texas Instruments APS-115. To provide 360° coverage there are two antennas, one located in the nose radome and another facing aft from the tailcone. Under AIP (Anti-surface Improvement Program) selected P-3Cs are being fitted with the APS-137(V)5 radar, a version of the sensor introduced by the S-3B Viking. As well as offering standard MPA modes such as long-range surface vessel plotting and submarine periscope detection, APS-137 has two ISAR (Inverse Synthetic Aperture Radar) modes in which the radar produces two-dimensional imaging of surface targets to allow classification and battle damage assessment. Whereas SAR radars exploit the Doppler shift inherent in the relative movement of the radar (aircraft) to a fixed target, ISAR exploits the motion of the target relative to the radar. Locking on to a central point on the ship, the radar then analyses the small Doppler shifts associated with the vessel's movement relative to that point. A yawing vessel allows the radar to compile a plan view image, while pitching produces a profile image. Both are displayed on screen to allow the operator to classify the vessel. APS-137 imagery is usually combined with ESM footprints for positive non-visual identification. The APS-137 can even image the periscopes of snorkelling submarines.

**Powerplant**
The Orion is powered by four Rolls-Royce North America (formerly Allison) T56-A-14 turboprops, each developing 4,910 ehp (3661 ekW).

**Weapons bay**
The internal bay can carry up to eight 500-lb (227-kg) bombs/depth charges/mines, eight Mk 46 torpedoes or six Mk 50 Barracudas.

**Harpoon**
This P-3 carries a pair of AGM-84 Harpoons on its outer wing pylons. Up to eight AGM-84s can theoretically be carried, but two or four is a more usual load.

*Left: Lockheed hoped to sell S-3s to West Germany and Japan; in the event the former retained its Atlantics and Japan bought P-3s.*

*Below: Three Viking variants were planned initially – the S-3A (nearest the camera, 179 built), the US-3A COD aircraft (centre, six converted from S-3As) and a dedicated KS-3A tanker (furthest from the camera, not proceeded with).*

# Lockheed S-3 Viking

## Cold War sub-hunter

**The US Navy's primary carrierborne, fixed-wing ASW aircraft since 1974, the S-3 Viking has been re-roled in the post-Cold War era as a sea control type, charged with anti-surface warfare, land-attack and tanking roles.**

Lockheed Palmdale's S-3 Viking was the US Navy's carrier-based, fixed-wing ASW aircraft from the 1970s until the early 1990s and, though still in service in 2001, is in the twilight of its career. Designed to meet the US Navy's 1964 VSX (carrier-based ASW aircraft) requirement, the first service-test YS-3A (of eight built) made its maiden flight on 21 January 1972 at Palmdale, California. Conventional in design for a carrier-based warplane, the Viking is a high-wing, twin-jet aircraft with hydraulically-folding wings, retractable tricycle landing gear and pressurised accommodation for its crew of four (comprising pilot, co-pilot, tactical co-ordinator and acoustic sensor operator). Based on an August 1969 contract, Lockheed manufactured the Viking in partnership with Vought, which built wings, tail unit, landing gear and engine pods.

The original production S-3A variant was equipped with a Univac AN/AYK-10 digital computer, Texas Instruments AN/APS-116 radar and Texas Instruments OR-89 FLIR. The heart of the Viking's ASW suite is a Texas Instruments AN/ASQ-81 magnetic anomaly detector sensor in a retractable tailboom. The S-3A carried 60 sonobuoys in its aft fuselage and had a ventral bomb bay and wing stations to house bombs, torpedoes or depth charges.

### Service entry

The first S-3A Viking went to VS-41 'Shamrocks', the first FRS for the type, located at North Island, California, and was received in February 1974. VS-21 'Fighting Redtails', also at North Island, became the first fleet squadron to operate the type in July 1974. Lockheed built a total of 179 production S-3As, delivering the last aircraft in August 1978.

The improved S-3B variant was the result of a weapons system improvement programme launched in 1981, which retained the Viking airframe and engines but added improved acoustic processing, expanded ESM coverage, increased radar processing capabilities, a new sonobuoy receiver system, and provision for AGM-84 Harpoon anti-ship missiles. All but identical in outward appearance to the S-3A, the S-3B could be distinguished by a small chaff dispenser located on its aft fuselage. By the early 1990s nearly all existing S-3As had been upgraded to S-3B status at naval air depots.

### COD variant

The seventh YS-3A was modified to become the US-3A carrier onboard delivery aircraft, envisioned as a replacement for the piston-engined Grumman C-1 Trader and first flown on

*Right: Seen here in NATC colours, the first S-3B poses for Lockheed's photographer after its first flight in 1984. An important advance was a Harpoon AShM capability.*

*Below: VS-41 'Shamrocks', based at NAS North Island, was the first Viking Fleet Readiness Squadron (FRS) and was later joined by VS-27 (disestablished in 1994) on the east coast.*

***As originally deployed, an air wing's S-3 complement numbered 10 aircraft. Later reduced to six, this has since been increased to eight to cover the tanking role. These VS-29 S-3As are seen aboard USS* Enterprise *sometime in the 1970s.***

2 July 1976. In all, six US-3A Vikings, stripped of ASW equipment and transformed into 'people haulers', have been used to complement the turbine-powered Grumman C-2A Greyhound. Lockheed also modified the fifth YS-3A to test the aircraft as the KS-3A tanker. The dedicated tanker variant has not been produced, although operational Vikings have been adapted as part-time tankers with the same 'buddy' refuelling store.

Developed to meet the Cold War threat posed by the Soviet fleet of quiet, deep-diving nuclear submarines, the Viking fought in Operation Desert Storm against an enemy which possessed no submarines. The S-3A/B Viking proved an exceedingly effective conventional bomber when employed against Iraqi radar stations, anti-aircraft batteries, small vessels in the Persian Gulf and other targets.

## Special variants

Several special mission variants of the S-3B have seen service. The Outlaw Viking was modified with OASIS III equipment to provide an over-the-horizon targeting and theatre control mini platform. The Gray Wolf S-3B featured a Norden APG-76 multi-mode radar, laser ranger, digital camera system and infra-red detector. This is intended for littoral surveillance and tracking of 'Scud'-type missile launches. Orca is the name of one Viking used for testing advanced ASW systems such as the Interim Extended Echo Ranger (IEER) and an ASW laser ranger integrated with some of the Gray Wolf's equipment, including a wing-mounted synthetic aperture radar pod. Orca is believed to be able to detect minefields.

Several Vikings have been involved in anti-drug trafficking duties in the Caribbean, using camera systems, FLIR and hand-held sensors. Finally it has been reported that under the code-name Aladdin, so-called 'Brown Buoy' Vikings were used, it is believed, to drop acoustic sensors to monitor ground movements in Bosnia, similar to the use of such sensors in the Igloo White programme in South East Asia. No official comment on Aladdin has been forthcoming.

With the end of the Cold War, the S-3's mission emphasis shifted away from ASW and towards anti-surface warfare and land-attack missions. In addition, with the retirement of the Navy's KA-6Ds, A-6Es and, from 2000, the ES-3A Shadows, the surviving Vikings are also expected to provide the USN's sole carrier-based air-to-air refuelling facility. In 1998 the ASW mission was formally deleted; 114 S-3Bs remained in service. During the following year a Service Life Extension Program was being examined to extend the Viking's service until 2015. Four of the eight deployed in each carrier air wing in 2004 are assigned a permanent tanker role.

# S-3B Viking

**This S-3B CAG-bird of VS-24 'Scouts' is depicted as it appeared during its 1997 cruise aboard USS *John F. Kennedy* (CV-67), as part of Carrier Air Wing Eight. VS-24 was the first unit to employ the S-3B in combat, during Operation Desert Storm.**

### Powerplant
Power for the Viking is provided by a pair of General Electric TF34-GE-400 high-bypass turbofan engines rated at 9,275 lb (41.25 kN) thrust at sea level.

### Aerial refuelling
When fulfilling its tanker mission, the S-3B uses an ARS 31-301 'buddy' pod mounted on the left wing station. Almost all Viking missions are flown with the 'buddy' pod affixed. Internal fuel capacity totals 1,900 US gal (7190 litres).

### Weapons
A typical flexible 'swing-mission' load consists of one AGM-84D (Block 1C) Harpoon AShM and a refuelling pod, with two Mk 82 bombs and two Mk 46 torpedoes in the aircraft's weapons bays. This aircraft carries a 300-US gal (1136-litre) drop tank in place of the Harpoon.

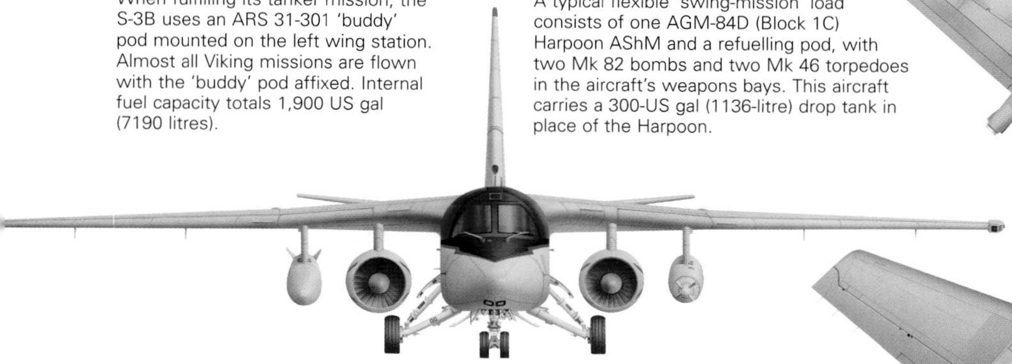

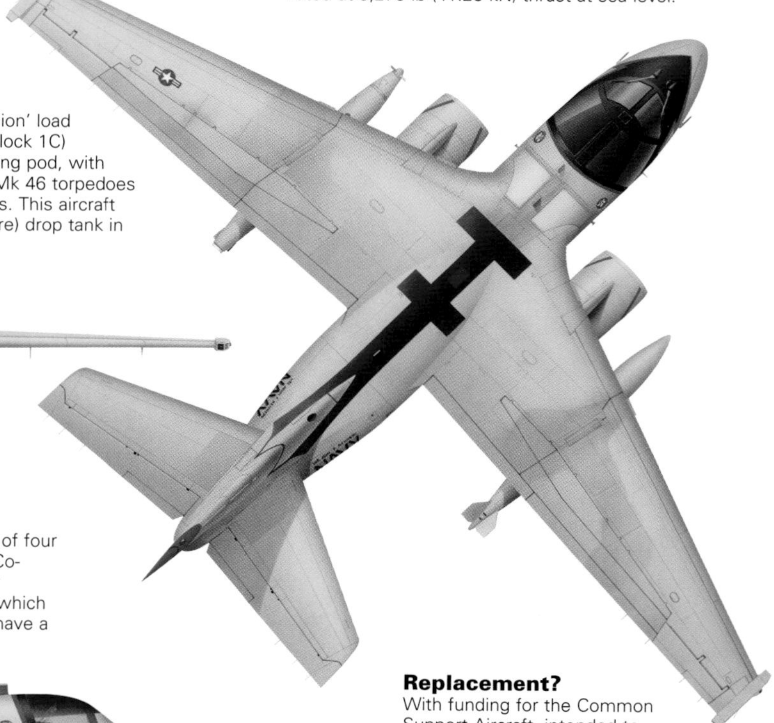

### Crew
For most of its career, the Viking flew with a crew of four in the ASW role, comprising two pilots, a Tactical Co-ordinator ('Tacco') and an enlisted Sensor Operator ('Senso'). S-3Bs converted as permanent tankers (which will be redesignated as such, possibly KS-3B) will have a crew of just two – a pilot and a naval flight officer.

### Replacement?
With funding for the Common Support Aircraft, intended to replace the E-2C, S-3B, ES-3A and C-2A, looking far from guaranteed, the S-3B may be retired without replacement. Given that the new F/A-18E/F Super Hornet has a tanker capability, this course of action looks even more likely.

8873
NAVY
VS-24
700

***The U-2R/U-2S has been in service since late 1967, at first augmenting and then totally supplanting the earlier U-2 versions.***

# Lockheed U-2

## Introduction

**Since the 1950s the mysterious shape of the Lockheed U-2 has sailed serenely over hot spots all round the Earth, recording the activity beneath it from vantage points far above the clouds. Undergoing a complete redesign in the mid-1960s to become the bigger and better U-2R, this covert observer has remained one of America's key intelligence gathering assets to the present day.**

Lockheed's graceful yet purposeful U-2 first took to the air on 1 August 1955. It had been designed and built in secret for the Central Intelligence Agency, and it was used to provide the organisation with photographic imagery of installations deep within the Soviet Union. Early-generation U-2s were also acquired by the US Air Force, and these were employed on reconnaissance tasks which included the collection of nuclear particles from Soviet A-bomb tests. In 1962 USAF U-2s were highly active over Cuba during the Missile Crisis.

The early U-2A to U-2G models went on to compile a remarkable service record, performing thousands of missions over and around hostile territory to provide the USA with important air intelligence throughout the late 1950s and early 1960s, while also gathering a mass of scientific data on high-altitude flight, re-entry vehicle performance and nuclear fall-out. From 1964 the type was used over war-torn Vietnam.

By the mid-1960s the ranks of the early U-2 variants had been severely depleted by losses, while the intelligence requirement had increased. Lockheed had meanwhile been investigating ways of updating the design and had come up with an enlarged version, with far greater payload and range. Following a request from the CIA, a major U-2 operator, the first six aircraft went to the agency, a further six following for the US Air Force.

The new aircraft entered service soon after its first flight in August 1967, and quickly showed itself to be superior in virtually all departments to the earlier variants. As well as the very considerable improvement in payload, range and operational ceiling, landing was far easier, correcting a problem that had dogged the early aircraft throughout their careers.

***When they first entered service, the U-2As were left unpainted. Because of the care taken in assembly by the 'Skunk Works' personnel the aircraft were truly magnificent to see. By the early 1960s, however, aircraft operated by the the CIA had already adopted the type's better known all-black scheme.***

### Agency aircraft

Aircraft belonging to the CIA were soon active from bases in many parts of the world, especially in Taiwan, where two aircraft were sent in 1968, to operate in Nationalist Chinese markings. This programme ended in 1974, and with it the CIA use of the aircraft, all examples then passing to the Air Force. Air Force U-2Rs saw much action during the Vietnam War, mainly from U-Tapao RTAFB in Thailand. As well as missions flown in support of the operations in Vietnam, especially the Linebacker raids (coded Olympic Torch), Senior Book covert missions were flown against mainland China.

### Carrier trials

In November 1969 Lockheed test pilot Bill Park and four CIA pilots deployed to the NASA base at Wallops Island to begin

***With his U-2 in the background, this reconnaissance pilot poses with the portable air conditioning and oxygen system which he will carry until he is connected to the aircraft's own systems.***

development of a new capability. USS *America* was waiting off the coast as Park prepared to make the first U-2 aircraft-carrier landing. He approached the carrier's flight deck at 72 kt (83 mph/ 133 km/h). With a wind over the deck of 20 kt (23 mph/ 37 km/h) the aircraft trapped easily; however, the U-2Rs carrier capability was never used operationally because of the disruption that the U-2 operations caused to the carrier air wing, although CIA pilots remained carrier-qualified for several years.

By 1975 operational losses of U-2Rs had reduced the fleet down to 10 examples. Against this background, USAF and US Army officers were re-examining how reconnaissance resources should gather and distribute intelligence during future operations. Conclusions from this study resulted in the USAF announcing a programme for a 'new' tactical reconnaissance aircraft in 1978 and in 1979 U-2R production resumed.

In an effort to break from the aircraft's dubious past some of the 'new U-2s' were renamed TR-1s – TR standing for Tactical Reconnaissance. This was largely to appease the government in the UK, where the majority of these aircraft would be based. The remainder retained the U-2R designation, and made good the attrition suffered by the earlier batch of 12 aircraft. The first aircraft from the line was a demilitarised ER-2 for the NASA Ames high-altitude research centre. The ER-2 first flew on 11 May 1981 from Lockheed's Palmdale facility. The aircraft began research flights a year later, subsequently being joined by a second example. Most tests are now connected with monitoring the Earth's ozone layer. The first TR-1A (80-1066) flew on 1 August 1981, with the first TR-1B trainer following on 23 February 1983. Visually, the second-batch aircraft differed little from the originals, but featured updated secondary systems such as communications. It was also slightly lighter, thanks to the advances made in electronic components. The surviving first-batch machines were later upgraded to the new standard.

## European deployment

Early U-2 models had much earlier operated covertly from RAF bases within the UK, on low-profile sensitive operations.

It therefore came as no surprise that a permanent U-2R unit was established at Mildenhall, Suffolk, in 1979. U-2R and SR-71 Blackbird operations commenced in April that year and continued until February 1983. By this time the new 17th Reconnaissance Wing at RAF Alconbury had been established to operate the TR-1A. This formation received its first aircraft on 12 February 1983 and three more examples followed in March 1985 building to an eventual total of 14.

European TR-1s were often found high over central Europe at 75,000 ft (22860 m) looking across the Warsaw Pact borders. These flights provided NATO commanders with a wealth of new intelligence material that often resulted in complete threat re-assessment.

The final TR-1A (80-1099), the last of the new-build aircraft, was accepted by the USAF on 3 October 1989. The final production total for the second-batch U-2R/TR-1/ER-2 was 37 examples, adding to the 12 U-2Rs built previously.

U-2Rs and TR-1As played a major part in Operations Desert Shield and Desert Storm. In October 1991 the TR-1 designation was dropped, the entire fleet reverting to U-2R or U-2RT (later TU-2R). Even though costs have spiralled, the U-2R fleet has been undergoing a major upgrading programme since 1994, the most significant aspect of which has been the installation of General Electric F118-GE-101 turbofans. The re-engined aircraft are redesignated U-2S or TU-2S (two-seater). With the final upgraded aircraft, featuring an all-new cockpit, emerging from overhaul in 2002, the U-2S will continue the remarkable service record of its forebears.

***Above: NASA flew the first-generation U-2C (above, background) on many high-altitude experiments. The larger U-2R airframe offered far greater load-carrying capability and NASA procured two aircraft as ER-2s, bolstered by a third example (illustrated) which was built as a TR-1A for the Air Force but subsequently operated by NASA on long-term loan.***

***Right: The U-2's ability to remain on station for many hours makes it a highly useful surveillance platform to cover ongoing United Nations operations like those in Bosnia.***

# Secret development

**One of the biggest problems facing military planners in the Cold War was obtaining reliable intelligence from the other side of the Iron Curtain. Produced in the utmost secrecy, the U-2 was the vehicle which provided the US with crucial photographic intelligence.**

Development of what became the most controversial aircraft of the Cold War can be traced back to 1952, when the idea of an ultra high-altitude photographic platform first gained momentum. USAF study contracts were issued to Bell, Fairchild and Martin, leading eventually to procurement of the Martin RB-57D, but Lockheed submitted an unsolicited bid with its CL-282 design. This was turned down by the Air Force, so the Lockheed Skunk Works boss, Clarence L. 'Kelly' Johnson, courted the CIA.

***While CIA U-2As were involved in overflight operations over the Soviet Union and China, the aircraft of the USAF were tasked with the High-Altitude Sampling Program (HASP) to monitor nuclear fall-out around the world. For this mission, the aircraft were fitted with a particle-collecting 'sniffer' pod on the port side.***

***The long wings of the U-2A could lift it to extreme altitude – in excess of 75,000 ft (22860 m). At this height it was immune from interception throughout the late 1950s, although the Soviets were working hard on SAM development to bring an end to the U-2's overflight days.***

After considerable political manoeuvring, Lockheed was rewarded with a contract to build a batch of 20 aircraft to be known as the U-2, the 'Utility' designation covering its true role. The CIA codename was Aquatone, and the project was conducted with the utmost secrecy, using the USAF to provide cover for the purchase of some items, notably the Pratt & Whitney J57 engines.

In concept, the CL-282 was a powered glider, utilising the basic fuselage structure of the F-104 Starfighter mated to high-aspect ratio wings. A large compartment behind the cockpit could house the huge cameras, also being developed in secret. A single main undercarriage unit supported most of the aircraft's weight, augmented by a solid-tyre tailwheel and jettisonable outrigger 'pogo' wheels.

One of the driving forces of the Aquatone project was the urgent need to assess the states of the Soviet bomber force (the US was convinced that there was a numerical 'bomber gap' between itself and the Soviets) and ICBM development. Anxious to get the U-2 into operation as swiftly as possible, Lockheed wasted no time in freezing the design (in December 1954) and commenced production. By late July 1955, the completed prototype was ready for transportation by C-124 Globemaster II to its secret test-site.

***Below: USAF U-2As were operated by the 4028th Strategic Reconnaissance Squadron, part of the 4080th SRW at Laughlin AFB, Texas. The wing also flew the Martin RB-57D.***

## Secret base

This site was Groom Dry Lake, deep in the high desert of Nevada, north of Las Vegas. It had been chosen by the test pilot for the U-2, Tony LeVier, and offered a wide expanse of lakebed and a high degree of security. The latter was enhanced by the proximity of the main US atomic weapon test site to the west. After reassembly and taxi tests, the 'Angel', as the first U-2 was nicknamed, took to the air on 4 August 1955 at the start of a successful flight test programme.

All subsequent first-generation U-2s were flown from Groom Lake, which was known as the 'Ranch' to Lockheed and CIA employees. Most of the aircraft were not built in the main

*Left: The prototype U-2R, wearing the civilian CIA registration N803X, soars over Edwards North Base on its first flight on 28 August 1967. Despite its overall similarity to the U-2C, it shared only the powerplant and configuration with its predecessor.*

*Below: Article 351, the first U-2R, takes shape in the Skunk Works Burbank factory. By the time of its development, the fanatical secrecy which had surrounded the initial U-2 had slackened, but the U-2R was nevertheless flown from the little-known and relatively secure North Base.*

*Bottom: A U-2R and U-2C of the CIA at North Base illustrate the considerable difference in size between the two aircraft. The CIA moved its operation out of Groom Lake as the secret Nevada test base had been required for the development of other classified aircraft, notably the Lockheed A-12.*

Skunk Works plant at Burbank, but in a small secret factory in Oildale which was disguised as a tyre depot.

While flight tests continued, CIA pilots began to train on the new type at Groom Lake, preparing for their first deployment to Europe. The first operational mission, a short-range flight over East Germany and Poland, was flown on 19 June 1956 and, on 4 July, the U-2 penetrated Soviet airspace for the first time. Completed in total secrecy, the U-2 programme had been brought from final approval to full operational status in just 20 months.

## U-2 development

Subsequent development of the U-2 involved considerable improvements to the sensor equipment and, in December 1958, the first U-2C took to the air. This version employed the more powerful J75 engine, which gave a considerable increase in operational ceiling to over 75,000 ft (22860 m). U-2s later sprouted arrester hooks for carrier operations, refuelling receptacles and a plethora of operational equipment.

Secret studies had continued to provide a successor to the U-2, but by 1965 'Kelly' Johnson was convinced that the best answer was to return to the basic design, but increase its size by approximately one-third. The extra power of the J75 engine had resulted in the original U-2 becoming airframe-limited, with weights ever on the increase and altitude performance being eroded. The resulting aircraft was the CL-351, at times designated U-2N or WU-2C, but which entered service as the U-2R. This restored the altitude performance of the first aircraft, but could carry a vastly increased sensor load over a greater range.

Although it was the USAF which ordered the U-2R, the CIA was included in the deal. Indeed, the first six aircraft were delivered to the Agency, and the development flying took place largely from the CIA's semi-secret U-2 operating location at Edwards North Base. Bill Park flew the first U-2R flight from there on 28 August 1967. Just over a year later, the U-2R entered operational service, flying CIA missions over Taiwan and Cuba.

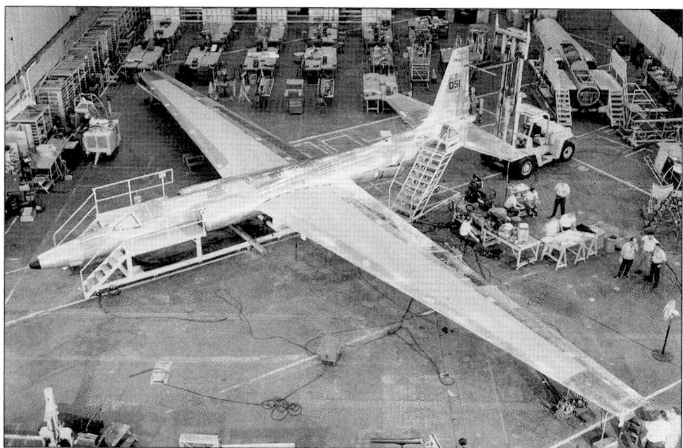

### U-2 at sea

The U-2 first went aboard a US Navy carrier in March 1964. Three first-generation aircraft were modified (as U-2Gs) with strengthened rear fuselage, arrester hook, cable guards added in front of the tailwheel and on the wingtips, overwing spoilers and a modified mainwheel for easier deck handling. Following satisfactory tests, a single aircraft was loaded aboard USS Ranger, and was used in May 1964 to gather intelligence from the French nuclear tests at Mururoa Atoll. One aircraft subsequently had a refuelling receptacle added to become a U-2H. The U-2R was also qualified for carrier operations (illustrated), the trials being undertaken aboard USS America by Bill Park in late 1969. No operational missions were ever flown from carriers, as the U-2R's great range could cover any eventuality from existing land bases.

# Recent operations

**Constant development of its systems has kept the U-2 at the forefront of the US intelligence-gathering effort. With the Cold War over, the U-2 fleet has remained highly active in support of the United States' global watch.**

***Above: For operations over former Yugoslavia the 9th Reconnaissance Wing established a detachment at Istres (OL-FR) in southern France. This aircraft is seen outside the giant hangar from which the aircraft operate. It is fitted with the Senior Spear Comint system, and probably carries an optical camera in the Q-bay behind the cockpit.***

***Left: U-2 pilots wear full pressure suits to protect them if they have to eject at high altitude, where blood would boil in the veins of an unprotected body. The suit incorporates a front strap to restrain the head during the rapid inflation of the suit.***

Few aircraft epitomised the Cold War more than the U-2. For years it had kept watch on the Soviet Union and its allies from around the borders of what President Reagan called the 'evil empire'. The U-2 had also been heavily involved in other operations at various times, notably in Vietnam, Central America and during the Arab-Israeli conflicts. When the Cold War came to an end and the 'new world order' was established, the peculiar talents of the U-2 remained just as invaluable as they had been at the height of the superpower stand-off.

One of the first responses by the US to the invasion of Kuwait by Iraq in 1990 was the dispatch of two U-2Rs to Saudi Arabia. These arrived at their new home-from-home on 17 August 1990, and began flying missions just two days later. One of the aircraft was configured with the Senior Span satellite uplink pod to allow real-time global transfer of gathered Sigint data: the other carried the new SYERS electro-optical backed camera. By the end of August the pair had been joined by two TR-1As from the 17th Reconnaissance Wing in England, both configured with ASARS-2 radar. A second SYERS aircraft completed the initial deployment in October.

Initially, the U-2 detachment was known as OL-CH (Operating Location-Camel Hump) although was later redesignated as the 1704th Reconnaissance Squadron (Provisional). The aircraft operated from Taif AB in the west of Saudi Arabia, where they were relatively safe from Iraqi attack.

## Desert Shield

During Desert Shield, the five U-2/TR-1s maintained a constant vigil of Iraq, allowing the coalition commanders to draw up a detailed picture of Iraq's military forces. All

***Among the latest U-2 sensor configurations is Senior Spur, which features a satellite datalink for the transmission of ASARS-2 radar imagery. This aircraft also carries Senior Ruby wing pods.***

***U-2R/TR-1As played a critical part in Desert Storm, providing a regular appraisal of Iraqi force dispositions through radar imagery. This trio of ASARS-2-equipped aircraft is seen immediately after Desert Storm, having returned to the Palmdale maintenance facility after a long stint in the desert.***

missions were flown in Saudi airspace, the sensors relaying their 'take' to ground stations by datalink. It was not uncommon for the U-2's progress along the border to be shadowed by Iraqi MiG-25s. In the last days of 1990 more aircraft arrived from the 9th RW at Beale, equipped with IRIS III and H-cameras to provide hard-copy photographs.

When war broke out, the U-2s flew intensive operations, and most operations were conducted in Iraqi/Kuwaiti airspace, although their flight-paths were carefully planned to keep them away from known SAM sites. An important initial task was the accurate location of the fixed 'Scud' launching sites. This was accomplished very successfully, leading to the rapid destruction of the sites by coalition aircraft. In one instance 10 sites were hit less than one hour after the TR-1 had imaged them with its ASARS-2 radar. Locating the mobile sites proved more difficult, a U-2 flying a nightly patrol with F-15Es on call. At least one mobile 'Scud' launcher was destroyed in this fashion.

For most of Desert Storm the 1704th RS(P) had 12 aircraft at Taif, and these flew up to eight missions a day, most lasting eight to 11 hours. The U-2/TR-1 system often operated as a high-altitude FAC, locating target positions which could be relayed to airborne strike aircraft. During the brief ground war ASARS-2 aircraft provided ground commanders with an hourly update on precise Iraqi armour dispositions. Desert Storm missions totalled 260, involving more than 2,000 hours of flying.

## Iraqi vigil

Since the end of the Gulf War, U-2Rs have remained in Saudi Arabia and have been one of the key elements in maintaining watch over Iraq. Codenamed Olive Branch, the mission concentrates on monitoring any significant troop moves within Iraq while keeping watch on the disposition of air defence radars and similar potential targets. The deployment also put the U-2S fleet in an ideal position for later operations against Iraq from late 2002/early 2003.

The 9th Reconnaissance Wing also continues to man two long-standing detachments in Korea and Cyprus. From Osan AB the 5th Reconnaissance Squadron keeps a vigil over the volatile Korean peninsula, while also venturing further afield in the Far East. At RAF Akrotiri on Cyprus the 9th RW's Det 1 monitors compliance with UN resolutions on the island itself, while also flying other operations in the eastern Mediterranean.

Another major area of operations has been former Yugoslavia. When the crisis first erupted, 95th RS U-2Rs (the designation TR-1A was dropped in October 1991) began flying missions from their base at Alconbury in England. This detachment was downgraded to OL status (OL-UK) and moved to Fairford. In December 1995 the U-2Rs moved to Istres in southern France (OL-FR) to lessen the transit time to Bosnia.

***The 9th RW is headquartered at Beale AFB, California, from where the wing supplies aircraft and personnel for the operational detachments. The unit's 1st Reconnaissance Squadron handles U-2 training, and counts four TU-2S trainers among its complement.***

## Modernisation

In the short time since the end of the Gulf War the U-2R fleet has undergone a major updating programme, much of it as a direct result of experience over Iraq. The Senior Span satellite uplink system has been extended to Senior Spur standard, which allows the transmission of ASARS-2 radar imagery in addition to Sigint data. The ASARS radar itself has had an all-important moving target indicator function added, while the SYERS camera now has dual-band capability, allowing it to operate using either infra-red or visible light. Ground systems have also been improved and rendered more deployable. Above all, the fleet has been re-engined with the economical F118 turbofan offering significantly improved reliability and additional power.

To reinforce the faith that US commanders place in the U-2 as one of their chief intelligence-gathering tools, it was announced in June 1998 that the fleet would be subject to another major improvement programme, centred on replacement of cockpit systems and enhanced avionics. Although the Cold War has ended, the U-2 fleet's commitments in the Middle East, Far East and southern Europe make it busier than ever.

***The Senior Span configuration – using a satellite datalink to transmit intelligence from the Senior Glass Sigint suite – saw extensive use over Bosnia.***

*Trailing the rival YF-23 by a month and two days due to delays associated with the General Electric YF120 engines, the first YF-22 took to the air in September 1990, with Dave Ferguson at the controls. The aircraft's distinctive planform and widely-spaced tail surfaces are clearly evident.*

# Lockheed Martin F/A-22 Raptor

## America's cutting edge

**F-15 Eagles may have ruled the skies over Iraq, but today the aircraft is ready for replacement, especially if it is to face competition from Russian types. The USAF's next-generation air dominance fighter will be the Lockheed Martin F-22 Raptor.**

In late April 1991 the USAF chose Lockheed/Boeing/General Dynamics to develop its proposal of the Advanced Tactical Fighter (ATF) over rival Northrop/McDonnell Douglas's YF-23. As a replacement for the Eagle, the ATF represents the single biggest advance in fighter performance since the first jets. It combines 'stealth' with a huge increase in supersonic endurance and manoeuvrability, and it is the first military jet to reflect the revolution in computer technology in its basic design and on-board electronics. Lockheed Martin encountered numerous design problems in its development of the YF-22, leading to significant visible changes from the original artist's impression of the aircraft. It was 29 August 1990, some three years after construction had begun on the earliest prototype, that the first aircraft (N22YF) was unveiled at Lockheed's Palmdale facility in California.

This first prototype flew for the first time on 29 September, while a second aircraft (N22XF) followed it into the air on 30 October. Each prototype received a different powerplant, both of which were still under evaluation by the USAF. Pratt & Whitney's YF119 turbofan proved to be more reliable than General Electric's similar YF120.

Following an extended flight-testing period, to allow for final engineering adjustments, the USAF announced on 23 April 1991 that the YF119/YF-22 combination had been selected and issued a contract for 11 (since reduced to nine) Engineering and Manufacturing Development (EMD) flying prototypes on 2 August (including two tandem-seat F-22Bs which will now be completed

*Above: The ATF programme was conceived in 1981. By 1985, Lockheed had produced a fanciful and misleading artist's impression of what would eventually become the F-22.*

*The YF-22 represents the third generation of Lockheed stealth design. Its stealth capability allows it to advance much closer to hostile aircraft before firing, giving a far higher kill probability. The aircraft nearest the camera is fitted with a spin parachute for high angle-of-attack manoeuvring tests.*

*Above: Restrained by heavy chains, the Pratt & Whitney YF119-powered YF-22 is seen here undergoing afterburner tests during one of the many static tests conducted during the programme.*

***Left:* In general, no external weapons are carried on the Raptor in an effort to retain the aircraft's 'stealth' characteristics. Instead, four weapons bays (two in the engine intake sides and two under the fuselage) house AAMs and/or bombs.**

***Above:* The first F-22 for Engineering and Manufacturing Development (EMD) was publicly unveiled on 4 September 1997 at Lockheed Martin's Marietta headquarters. At this time the aircraft was officially christened Raptor.**

as F-22A single-seat aircraft), plus one static and one fatigue test airframe.

### Combat reassessment

As construction commenced on the first two F-22A Raptors, an expansion of the aircraft's role was proposed – this will see the addition of air-to-ground attack missions, the aircraft being armed with precision-guided munitions (PGMs) and having been redesignated F/A-22.

The first production aircraft (91-4001) made its maiden flight on 7 September 1997. The F-22A incorporated noticeable design changes, among the most prominent being the broader undernose fairing and repositioned intakes. A second Raptor took to the air on 29 July 1998, with 18 development and pre-production F/A-22A aircraft flying by late 2003.

During 2004 the first USAF Raptor training squadron is due to form with a full production decision also due during the year. The first operational front-line squadron should be declared during 2005.

## YF-22 PAV No. 1

**N22YF was the first YF-22 Prototype Air Vehicle (PAV) and was powered by the General Electric YF120 engine. After the exhaustive development and test programme was completed, the rival Pratt & Whitney YF119 was selected for production F-22 Raptors.**

**Thrust-vectoring**
One of the features of the YF-22 which gave it an advantage over the YF-23 was its thrust-vectoring, which dramatically improved manoeuvrability in all flight regimes.

**Markings**
PAV No. 1 carried the General Electric logo on the intake trunk. Other badges were the Air Force Systems Command shield on the undercarriage door, the Tactical Air Command shield on the side of the fin and a small 'Skunk Works' badge at its base.

**Tailfins**
Unlike the YF-23, the YF-22 featured conventional fins with rudders, instead of all-moving units.

**Intakes**
The diamond-shaped intakes followed the same alignments in profile as the forward fuselage, so as to preserve 'stealth' characteristics

**Advanced radar**
The F-22's AN/APG-77 radar has an active-element, electronically scanned array which has long range and high resolution for the early detection of opposing fighters. It can provide detailed information about multiple threats, allowing the pilot to rapidly assimilate targets. The radar also has a low passive-detection signature.

**Missile bays**
The F-22 was designed to carry AAMs in bays underneath and to the sides of the engine intake ducts. The latter can hold four AIM-120 AMRAAM missiles, which fall away from the aircraft on launch before their motors ignite. The shorter side bays can carry AIM-7s or AIM-9 Sidewinders in pairs, the missiles being ejected sideways on launch.

*The first YF-16 wore smart General Dynamics house colours for its flight test programme. The aircraft's configuration was considered unusual at the time.*

# Falcon genesis

**Initially designed as a lightweight fighter, it quickly became apparent to pilots that the nimble F-16 would be able to accomplish far more in the future.**

*Depicted displaying its arsenal of available weapons, the F-16 soon demonstrated that it could evolve into more than a simple lightweight fighter with a limited role.*

In the mid-1960s, with US forces building up in Vietnam and air battles unfolding near Hanoi, American fighters had become heavier, costlier and more complex. The quintessential American fighter was the F-4 Phantom II, an oddly-shaped machine with bent wings, bent tail, two engines, two crew members, and a veritable host of mechanical and maintenance needs. At that time, the USAF seemed addicted to the big, the heavy, the difficult; the service was looking at a future mixed force of F-4s and F-111s, flag-bearers in a relentless march towards higher costs, greater complexity and, as a consequence, diminished numbers.

In 1965, the USAF prompted studies of an Advanced Day Fighter (ADF), a low-cost, high-performance aircraft. It was heresy for it went against the trend. The ADF was intended to have a weight of just 25,000 lb (11340 kg), with a thrust-to-weight ratio and wing loading high enough to assure a superiority of 25 per cent over the MiG-21. It would probably have been relatively easy to maintain and might have been inexpensive enough to form a large fleet.

## Money talks

This would never do, and the ADF went nowhere in the Pentagon bureaucracy. The uncloaking of the Soviet MiG-25 'Foxbat' in 1967 strengthened the hand of traditionalists who felt that American warplanes had to be costlier and more intricate.

However, more heresy came in the form of the Pentagon's first F-X fighter study of 1966-67. Here, the purpose was to rapidly bolster the tactical strength of the USAF to meet the multiplying needs of the Vietnam conflict. This study countered the trend again, calling for low cost and complexity, but it resulted in nothing more earth-shattering than the Air Force's 'off-the-shelf' purchase of the Vought A-7D for the air-to-ground role.

In 1969, a Pentagon memorandum on tactical air power suggested that both the USAF and Navy should adopt the lightweight F-XX as a substitute for the F-14 and F-15, enabling each service to double its fleet size. Both services resisted the idea, and the F-14 and F-15 moved ahead, both destined to become superb fighters but both far weightier than the F-XX or any other lightweight fighter.

## New beginnings

Deputy Defense Secretary, David Packard, who took office in 1969, was one Pentagon official interested in an austere fighter. More importantly, Packard endorsed the idea of prototyping, where warplanes would be test-flown in competition before a production machine was ordered. USAF supporters and a few industry planners kept alive the hope that Packard's

*The second YF-16 prototype wore a number of colour schemes, during its testing, including this attractive powder blue and white air superiority camouflage scheme.*

***Above: F-16As and Bs are seen in the final stages of assembly at General Dynamics' Fort Worth factory. A unique feature of this facility was its mile-long production line.***

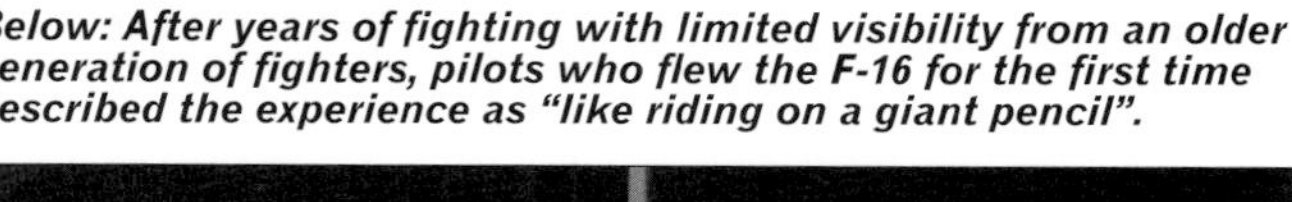

***Below: After years of fighting with limited visibility from an older generation of fighters, pilots who flew the F-16 for the first time described the experience as "like riding on a giant pencil".***

support might lead to an austere fighter design, such as Lockheed's CL-1200, Northrop's P-530 Cobra, or Vought's V-1100, entering service.

Under Packard, the Lightweight Fighter (LWF) programme came into existence and a request for proposals (RFP) was issued to industry on 6 January 1972. The RFP embodied Sprey's F-XX philosophy, calling for high thrust-to-weight ratio, a 6.5-*g* load factor, an optimum gross weight of 20,000 lb (9072 kg), and high manoeuvrability. In March 1972, after reviewing designs from five manufacturers, the Air Staff determined that the Boeing Model 908-909 was its first LWF choice, followed by General Dynamics' (GD) Model 401 and Northrop's Model P-600, a twin-engined Cobra.

After further work, the Source Selection Authority (SSA), under Lt Gen. James Stewart, rated the YF-16 and Northrop's YF-17 aeroplanes ahead of the Boeing design. This became the final decision, made by Secretary of the Air Force, Robert C. Seamans, as the LWF moved towards the full-scale prototype stage.

The GD engineering effort was overseen by designer, Harry J. Hillaker. Literally dozens of configurations for an austere fighter were examined, beginning with GD's FX-404 study of the mid-1960s and proceeding through company Models 785, 786 and 401. Today the design of the F-16 is taken for granted, although the aircraft seemed unorthodox when first seen. The production F-16C is outwardly little changed from the first YF-16, but the shape was not pre-ordained. GD's Model 401 was studied in model, mock-up and wind-tunnel forms in dozens of configurations.

## Sidestick controller

From the start, a unique feature of the F-16 Fighting Falcon was a sidestick controller located on a cockpit console to the right of the pilot. Today, pilots of other fighters still view the sidestick as discomforting, although Lt Col. John Barringer, typical of the USAF's experienced F-16 pilots, calls the transition to it "the most natural thing I've ever done". Left-handed pilots apparently use the sidestick without difficulty, and the only real problem emerged late in the F-16 programme when Israeli pilots expressed some concern over a situation in which the pilot's right arm might be seriously injured in combat.

The prototype YF-16 (72-1567) was rolled out at Fort Worth on 13 December 1973 and delivered by C-5A Galaxy transport to Edwards Air Force Base on 8 January 1974. Its first flight was an accident. During high-speed taxi testing on 20 January 1974, test pilot Phil Oestricher encountered a rolling divergent oscillation, with no solution but (as he put it) "to fly out of the situation". The first official flight with Oestricher at the controls was a 90-minute sortie on 2 February 1974.

On 13 January 1975, Air Force Secretary McLucas announced that the YF-16 had been chosen as the USAF's ADF aircraft. The cost of a production version was found to be about US$250,000 less than the YF-17. USAF officials also found that the YF-16 had lower operating costs, longer range and better manoeuvrability. Following USAF purchases, sales to a host of NATO allies would ensure the future development and success of General Dynamics' F-16 Fighting Falcon.

### Selling F-16s to the world

Eager to display to the world the capabilities of its new fighter, General Dynamics test-pilots enthralled audiences and created huge interest among future customers with their unique displays at airshows around the world. Key players in the aerial demonstration team were pilots, Neil Anderson (far left), and James McKinney (left). The unique seating position and the use of 'fly-by-wire' and sidestick controls aroused scepticism among military fast jet pilots. Upon examining the aircraft at close-quarters, however, most were suitably impressed with the Fighting Falcon. Front-line pilots were now able to fly an aircraft that was strong enough to handle more *g* than could be borne by the human body. For the first time, pilots encountered *g*-loc (gravity-induced loss of consciousness) wherein abrupt *g* forces, in certain manoeuvre regimes, could cause a pilot to black out and, in the worst case, result in a crash. Neil Anderson would lose his life to *g*-loc later in his test flying career.

By opting to purchase F-16As, the four European countries were now equipped with a fighter which could outfly and beat the latest generation of Russian fighters. The F-16A introduced a quantum leap in capability for pilots converting to it from obsolete equipment such as the F-104 Starfighter.

# F-16A/B Briefing

**Having proved to be an extremely capable aircraft during testing, the Fighting Falcon became one of the West's leading fighters. Early variants have since achieved record-breaking sales to the USAF and foreign operators.**

General Dynamics' (now Lockheed Martin's) F-16 continues to undergo constant evolution. A complicated series of modifications has led to a number of distinct variants and blocks within variants, all with their own unique capabilities and recognition features.

## FSD F-16A/B

General Dynamics built eight full-scale development (FSD) F-16A/B airframes. The first FSD F-16A flew at Fort Worth on 8 December 1976, while the first two-seat FSD F-16B flew on 8 August 1977. These FSD machines could be identified by their black radomes and black RWR (radar warning receivers) on either side of the fuselage. The FSD F-16 introduced Westinghouse AN/APG-66 radar, an increased fuselage length of 49 ft 6 in (15.09 m) and fin height of 16 ft 8 in (5.08 m). As with all subsequent variants, the addition of a second seat to produce the two FSD F-16Bs did not change the aircraft's dimensions or weight, and added no aerodynamic drag. Some 1,500 lb (580 kg) of fuel tankage was lost, however.

Most of the FSD aircraft served useful test roles, with the third and fifth FSD F-16As being modified to F-16XL standard.

## F-16A/B Block 1

The F-16A/B Block 1 retains the black radome and RWR covers. Power is provided by the Pratt & Whitney F100-PW-200 turbofan engine.

A complicated system of F-16 identification was created at an early stage. First, a change in model letter suffix is used to distinguish a single-seat F-16A from a two-seat F-16B. Thus, the first batch of F-16As and F-16Bs are both Block 1 aircraft.

Surviving F-16A/B Block 1 aircraft, together with Block 5s, were retrofitted with minor equipment changes and brought to F-16A/B Block 10 standard in 1982-84.

## F-16A/B Block 5

F-16A/B Block 5 aircraft introduced the grey radome and nose RWR cover which became standard. Powerplant is the P&W F100-PW-200 turbofan.

## F-16A/B Block 10

Block 10 aircraft introduced minor internal changes.

Twenty-four F-16A/B Block 10s were modified for the close air support role with the 339-lb (154-kg) General Electric GPU-5/A centreline pod. Developed as the Pave Claw, this houses a GAU-13/A four-barrelled derivative of the seven-barrelled GAU-8/A cannon used in the A-10A. The gun pod was never satisfactorily integrated with the aircraft, and the gun pod-capable aircraft are in storage.

Some Block 10 aircraft have become GF-16A ground instructional airframes.

## F-16A/B Block 15

F-16A/B Block 15 aircraft introduced the enlarged horizontal stabiliser, which reduces take-off rotation angle and allows flight at higher angles of attack. Block 15 machines carry two

Above: Entering testing alongside the batch of single-seat F-16s were a limited number of two-seaters. A distinguishing feature of early Fighting Falcons was their all-black radomes. One role envisaged for the two-seat F-16B was defence suppression, more widely known as 'Wild Weasel' missions.

Large numbers of F-16As were supplied to four European nations – Belgium, Denmark, Holland and Norway – in what is often referred to as the 'sale of the century'. A USAF F-16 formates with F-16As from each of these air arms.

***Preparing for a dusk bombing mission, an F-16 taxies out with a full complement of bombs and air-to-air missiles. It was clear to General Dynamics that its F-16 would be a winner.***

parallel RWR antennas beneath the radome and no blade antenna under the intake.

Minor changes to the AN/APG-66 radar provided limited track-while-scan' capability. A Have Quick UHF secure voice radio system was also introduced, along with a new cockpit layout. Netherlands Block 15 F-16A(R) aircraft carry the Oude Delft Orpheus day/night reconnaissance pod previously employed on F-104s.

### F-16A/B Block 15 OCU

Block 15 Operational Capability Upgrade (OCU) aircraft introduced structural reinforcement, minor changes and the enlarged HUD found on F-16C/Ds. The programme updates radar and software, fire control and stores management computers and adds provision for AN/ALQ-131 jamming pods. Upgrading to the more reliable, 26,660-lb (118.32-kN) thrust F100-PW-220E is also facilitated.

### F-16A/B Block 15 MLU

Aircraft subject to the Block 15 Mid-Life Update (MLU) are refurbished with a cockpit similar to that of the F-16C/D Block 50/52. They are equipped with AN/APG-66(V2A) fire-control radar, a GPS (global positioning system) navigation system, and other features including a wide-angle HUD, night vision goggle compatibility, a modular mission computer replacing the existing three, and a digital terrain system. Most recipients of this upgrade will be offered helmet-mounted display and Hazeltine AN/APX-111 IFF interrogator/transponder. The installation of F-16A/B Block 15 MLU kits from Lockheed Fort Worth is scheduled for completion by around 2005.

Four Fighting Falcons were delivered to Fort Worth in September 1992 to serve as the prototypes for conversion under the MLU programme.

### F-16A/B Block 20

F-16A/B Block 20 aircraft are being built for Taiwan. F-16 Block numbers had previously progressed from Block 15 to Block 25 (the latter being the first F-16C/D series) and the term Block 20 was created retrospectively. Originally it applied only to the 120 F-16As and 30 F-16Bs for Taiwan, but Lockheed may eventually refer to all MLU machines as Block 20s. Taiwan's aircraft have the improved AN/APG-66(V)2 radar of MLU aircraft, but employ different IFF and use the Raytheon AN/ALQ-183 ECM pod in preference to the Westinghouse AN/ALQ-131.

## F-16A Fighting Falcon

**This F-16A wears the characteristic markings of Venezuela. Twenty-four F-16As were delivered to the two squadrons of Grupo de Caza 16 at Maracay, wearing scrambled serials to confuse observers. Air defence is their main mission although air-to-ground operations are also important, hence the camouflage.**

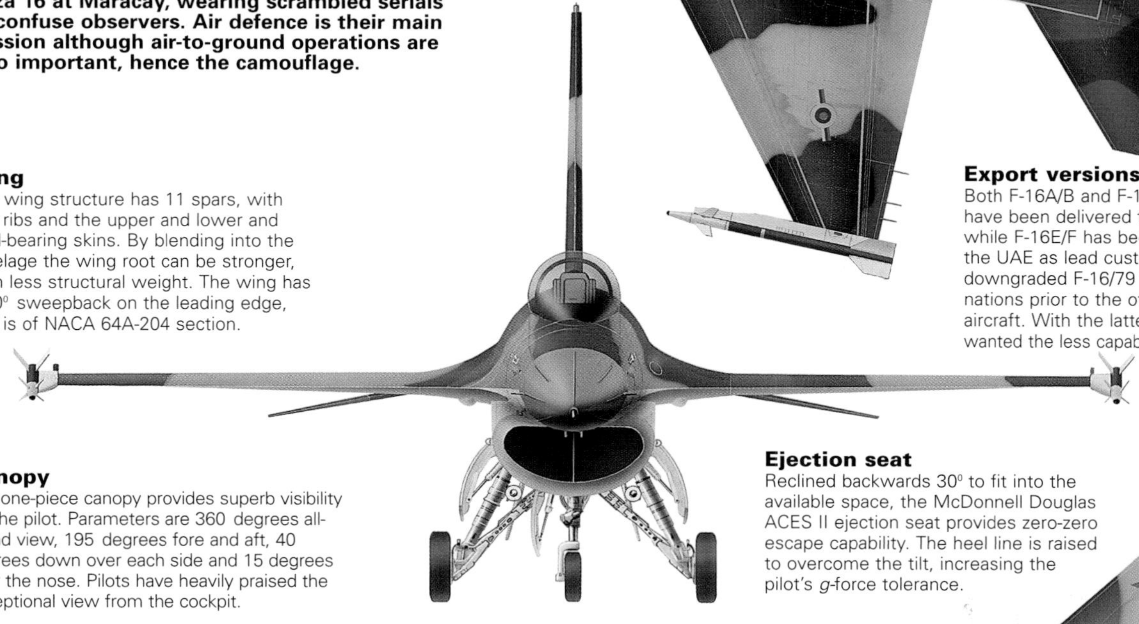

**Brake parachute**
The extended tailcone fairing fitted to Venezuelan and Norwegian F-16s houses a brake parachute for operations from short or snowy airfields. Belgian aircraft have an ECM system in a similarly extended tailcone.

**Wing**
The wing structure has 11 spars, with five ribs and the upper and lower and load-bearing skins. By blending into the fuselage the wing root can be stronger, with less structural weight. The wing has a 40° sweepback on the leading edge, and is of NACA 64A-204 section.

**Export versions**
Both F-16A/B and F-16C/D generations have been delivered to export customers, while F-16E/F has been developed with the UAE as lead customer. The downgraded F-16/79 was offered to many nations prior to the offer of full-standard aircraft. With the latter available, no nation wanted the less capable aircraft.

**Canopy**
The one-piece canopy provides superb visibility for the pilot. Parameters are 360 degrees all-round view, 195 degrees fore and aft, 40 degrees down over each side and 15 degrees over the nose. Pilots have heavily praised the exceptional view from the cockpit.

**Ejection seat**
Reclined backwards 30° to fit into the available space, the McDonnell Douglas ACES II ejection seat provides zero-zero escape capability. The heel line is raised to overcome the tilt, increasing the pilot's *g*-force tolerance.

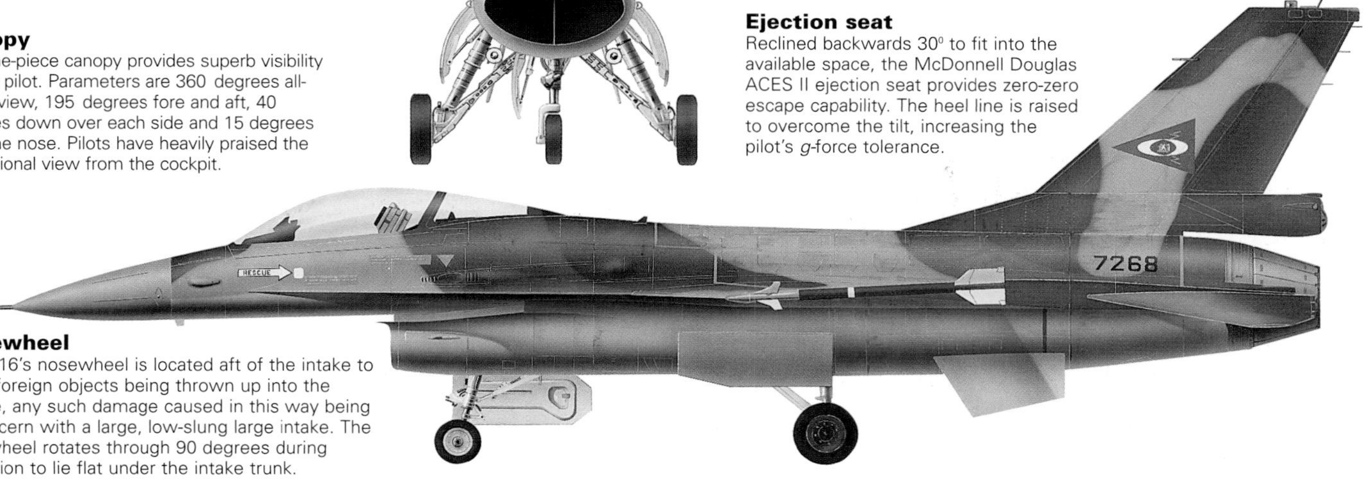

**Nosewheel**
The F-16's nosewheel is located aft of the intake to avoid foreign objects being thrown up into the engine, any such damage caused in this way being of concern with a large, low-slung large intake. The nosewheel rotates through 90 degrees during retraction to lie flat under the intake trunk.

*Along with its improved capabilities came a host of new roles for the F-16. None was more important than that of SEAD. For this role, these PACAF examples are each fitted with two AGM-88 HARMs on their inner pylons.*

# F-16C/D

## Variant briefing

**The F-16 has far outgrown its lightweight fighter origins and has become today's benchmark multi-role fighter. Radical revisions of the basic design have introduced a host of new capabilities that were out of the F-16's reach as recently as the last decade.**

The Lockheed (General Dynamics) F-16C first flew on 19 June 1984. F-16C and two-seat F-16D models are distinguished by an enlarged base or 'island' leading up to the vertical fin, from which protrudes a small blade antenna. This space was intended for the internal airborne self-protecting jammer (ASPJ), which the USAF abandoned in favour of the continuing use of external ECM pods.

Compared with earlier versions, the F-16C/D gives the pilot a GEC HUD, at the base of which is a function keyboard control (located in a console to his/her left in earlier variants). The pilot also has an improved data display, with key items of information located at 'design eye' level for HOTAS flying.

*The 86th TFW (USAFE) at Ramstein AB, West Germany became the first American base overseas to operate the F-16C and D (illustrated), on 21 December 1985. The aircraft were tasked with flying fighter and day attack missions until the wing moved to Aviano in support of NATO's 4th ATAF.*

*Operated as part of the 432nd FW of the Pacific Air Forces, these F-16C Block 30s were tasked with delivering the AGM-84A Harpoon anti-ship missile as well as carrying out local air defence over Japan.*

F-16C/Ds employ a Hughes APG-88 multi-mode radar with increased range, sharper resolution and expanded operating modes, and have a weapon interface for the AGM-65D Maverick and the new generation of AMRAAM missiles.

F-16C single-seat and F-16D two-seat fighters introduced progressive changes, some installed at the factory and others as part of the Multi-Stage Improvement Programme (MSIP) (avionics and cockpit and airframe changes) and MSIP III (further systems installation), aimed at enhancing the F-16 Fighting Falcon's ability to fly and fight at night.

### F-16C/D Block 25

F-16C/D aircraft retain the unique low-slung intake configuration of earlier Fighting Falcon variants. They have fuselage-wing 'blending', fly-by-wire controls and a blown polycarbonate canopy which, in these later versions, has a gold tint due to a lining of radar-reflecting materials. F-16C/D models also keep the General Electric M61A1 Vulcan 20-mm cannon with 511 rounds and retain the ability to carry up to 16,700 lb (7575 kg) of ordnance, including most bombs and missiles in the USAF inventory. Block 25 aircraft entered production in

### Navy aggressor

The decision by the US Navy to acquire Fighting Falcons arose from the desire to match the expanding capabilities of the new generation of Soviet warplanes in the adversary arena. Basically similar to the USAF F-16C, the Navy F-16Ns were powered by a GE F110 turbofan. To improve performance, the aircraft had their stores pylons and M61cannon deleted. However, unforeseen fatigue-induced problems, associated with DACT, resulted in the entire fleet being grounded, and eventually retired in 1991.

***Egypt is an important F-16 customer. In June 1988 it signed a deal for 41 F110-powered Block 40s, to join the 82 earlier-model F-16s already in service. Block 40 deliveries began in October 1991, followed by 52 additional aircraft in 1994/95. Another batch of 21 Block 40s was ordered in May 1996 and yet another, for 24 machines, in 1999.***

### F-16 reconnaissance pods

In an effort to increase the capabilities of its early model F-16s, the Royal Danish Air Force (RDAF) launched a development programme to find a tactical reconnaissance system – RDAF F-16As currently operate with the Red Baron camera pods salvaged from Drakens. The result was the Per Udsen Modular Reconnaissance Pod (MRP), which can house a variety of sensors. The MRP has been certified for service, and is likely in service with the Belgian (as seen here), Danish, and Dutch air forces.

July 1984 and totalled 319 – 289 F-16Cs and 30 F-16Ds. With Block 30/32 came the reconfigured engine bay, with options for the GE F110-GE-100 (Block 30) – offering 28,984 lb st (128.9 kN) – or P&W F100-PW-220 (Block 32) – offering 28,840 lb st (106.05 kN).

F-16C Block 40 is also powered by the General Electric F110-GE-100, while F-16C Block 42 Falcons are fitted with the Pratt & Whitney F100-PW-220.

The change to -220 power in Block 32/42 aircraft, brought a need to alter the contours of the F-16's air intake to accommodate the larger amount of air ingested. Because the change was not made initially, early F-16C/D Block 30s are 'small inlet' aircraft, the 1-ft (0.30-m) wider air intake having become standard for GE power on 'big inlet' models after delivery began. The USAF slightly favours the GE aircraft.

In addition, Blocks 30/32 aircraft have the ability to carry AGM-45 Shrike and AGM-88A HARM anti-radiation missiles, and AIM-120 AMRAAM. Avionics hardware changes were also introduced to the Block 30/32, which total 501 aircraft, comprising 446 F-16Cs and 55 F-16Ds.

## F-16C/D Block 40/42 Night Falcons

Night Falcons began to come off the production line in December 1988. This version introduces LANTIRN navigation and targeting pods, Navstar GPS navigation receiver, AGM-88 HARM II, APG-68V radar, digital flight controls, automatic terrain-following and, as a consequence, increased take-off weight. Greater structural strength raises the Night Falcon's 9*g* capability from 26,000 lb (12201 kg) to 28,500 lb (12928 kg). The heavier all-up weight and the need to accommodate LANTIRN has resulted in larger landing gear, bulged landing gear doors and the relocation of landing lights to the nose gear door.

Block 40/42 Night Falcons have been delivered to the USAF, Israel, Egypt, Turkey and Bahrain. A Block 42 F-16D equipped with AMRAAMs became the first USAF F-16 to score an air-to-air victory by downing an Iraqi MiG-25 on 27 December 1992.

In December 1991 General Dynamics began delivering F-16 C/D Block 50 and 52 aircraft. The first flight date for Block 50 was 22 October 1991. The first Block 50s went to the 388th Fighter Wing at Hill AFB, Utah, in 1992, followed by delivery to USAFE's 52nd FW. Block 50/52 Falcons introduced the Westinghouse AN/APG-68 (V) 5 radar with improved avionics computer.

Other additions to Block 50/52 included a Tracor AN/ALE-47 chaff/flare dispenser, ALR-56M radar warning receiver, Have Quick IIA radio, Have Sync anti-jam VHF, full HARM integration and a wide-angle HUD.

These latest F-16s are powered by the Improved Performance Engine (IPE) versions of GE and P&W engines, the 29,588-lb st (131.6-kN) F110-GE-129 and 29,100-lb st (129.4-kN) F100-PW-229, respectively. Problems arose with developmental test aircraft for the Block 52 programme in July 1991, and these had to be refitted with older F100 variants until the P&W IPE's fourth fan stage could be redesigned. Since that time, both Pratt & Whitney and General Electric have also offered engines in the 32,000-lb (142.32-kN) thrust class.

Around 100 USAF F-16C/D Block 50/52 aircraft are being raised to Block 50/52D standard, with provision for the ASQ-213 pod carried under the starboard side of the intake. This pod is known as the HARM Targeting System, and provides the F-16 with a limited 'Wild Weasel' defence-suppression capability

By far the most radical modification yet adopted by the F-16, has been Israel's 'big spine' conversion to Block 30 and Block 40 F-16D aircraft, housing avionics associated with the SEAD role. A number of aircraft modified to 'big spine' configuration have also been delivered to the Republic of Singapore Air Force within its order for 18 Block 52s.

## Block 60 and beyond

In an effort to increase the long-range striking ability of the F-16, Lockheed Martin developed the Block 60 variant. Potential customers for this avionics-laden all-weather attack variant were seen as Greece, Israel and Norway, while Israel was known to favour the F-15I. In the event, the UAE emerged as the first customer for the redically upgraded F-16E/F Block 60, with its first aircraft due in 2004. Ironically, Israel has comitted to a somewhat similar machine, as the F-16I, initialy ordering 50 aircraft, before also taking up 52 of 60 options. Despite the lack of USAF interest in the Block 60 model, it offers a cheaper, but slightly less capable night/adverse-weather, alternative to the Strike Eagle.

With delays in JSF development, improved F-16 variants look set to remain a potent force with the USAF and its allies.

***Above: Greek F-16s are unusually configured. Hellenic air force Block 50 aircraft are the only F-16Cs with a searchlight for night interception, located on the starboard front fuselage.***

***Left: The Block 60 configuration that has received the most publicity is that derived from the F-16ES, integrating conformal fuel tanks with a mass of new electronic systems. This version forms the basis of the UAE's 80-aircraft F-16E/F order. Conformal fuel tanks are also a feature of the 102 F-16I aircraft so far ordered by Israel, all of which should have been delivered by 2008, with upgraded systems.***

# ADF variant briefing

**Equipping Air National Guard units during the final years of the Cold War, the F-16A ADF was responsible for the air defence of the northern United States. However, with the enemy no longer on its doorstep, ex-USAF ADFs are now available for foreign operators.**

*Top: As well as standard F-16s, the ANG received two specialised variants. The first, intended for the ground-attack role, carried the GPU-5/A gun pod. The second, more specialised variant is the ADF (illustrated), dedicated to North American air defence.*

*Left: Portuguese F-16s have a primary air defence tasking, but can be armed with AGM-65 Mavericks for secondary ground-attack duties. Clearly visible is the bulged fin base housing the relocated rudder actuators.*

The Lockheed (General Dynamics) F-16A ADF (Air Defense Fighter) Block 15 was assigned to the air defence of the North American continent during the last years of the Cold War, but most of its operators have now transitioned to other F-16 variants.

The US Air Force announced in October 1986 the conversion of 270 (later changed to 241, consisting of 217 Model As and 24 Model Bs) F-16A/B Block 15 Fighting Falcons to ADF standard. The Cold War drove military plans, which called for 14 ANG (Air National Guard) squadrons to receive the ADF to defend North America from bombers and cruise missiles, operating under the control of NORAD. This interceptor role had not been foreseen when the Fighting Falcon was developed and no American unit had operated the F-16 with a radar-guided missile or on a long-range intercept mission.

The ADF conversion was centered primarily on upgrading the existing AN/APG-66 radar to improve small target detection and to provide continuous-wave illumination (thus giving the ability to launch AIM-7 Sparrow BVR missiles).

## Other changes

Further modifications included a night identification light in the port forward fuselage, advanced IFF, high frequency, single side-band radio, improved ECCM and provision for GPS and AIM-120 AMRAAM missile datalink. The F-16 ADF can carry up to six AIM-7 Sparrow or AIM-9 Sidewinder missiles and retains the internal 20-mm M61 cannon of the F-16A. The first successful launch of a Sparrow took place in February 1989.

Actual conversion of the F-16 ADFs (completed in early 1992) was undertaken by the USAF's Ogden Air Logistics Center (OALC) at Hill AFB, Utah, with General Dynamics-sourced modification kits. Development of the F-16 ADF was conducted at Edwards AFB in 1990 and was followed by operational test and evaluation with the 57th Fighter Weapons Wing at Nellis AFB, Nevada. The first service aircraft were assigned to the 114th Fighter Squadron, Oregon ANG, at Kingsley Field in Klamath Falls, which trained F-16A/B ADF interceptor pilots. Operational ANG squadrons which flew the ADF were the 194th FS/CA, 159th FS/FL, 169th FS/IL, 171st FS/MI, 179th FS/MN, 186th FS/MT, 178th FS/ND, 119th FS/NJ, 136th FS/NY, 198th FS/PR, 111th FS/TX and 134th FS/VT.

## Cold War changes

Changes brought about by the collapse of the Soviet Union led to a wave of drastic military cuts throughout the US armed forces. Among the ranks of the USAF, the ADF-equipped squadrons were to suffer heavily. From a front-line strength of 11 interceptor squadrons, the ADF variant now equips just three ANG fighter squadrons (178th, 179th and 186th).

The large quantities of surplus USAF ADF airframes have resulted in the aircraft being heavily marketed to foreign operators as an 'off-the-shelf' cheap alternative to the F/A-18 Hornet and MiG-29 'Fulcrum'.

First among the foreign operators to acquire the interceptor was Portugal. A total of 17 F-16As and three F-16Bs was delivered to ADF standard to 201 Esquadra under the Peace Atlantis programme. Intended originally for the air defence mission, they are armed with AIM-7Fs. Recently however, these Portuguese aircraft have adopted a secondary ground attack role, resulting in participation in NATO operations over the former Yugoslavia. Portugal is expected to purchase a second batch of 25 aircraft in view of the future retirement of the A-7P Corsair from the ground-attack role.

Jordan, a new customer for the F-16, received 25 ADF variants, along with other Fighting Falcon models, under the Peace Falcon (lease) agreement. Further examples look likely to be acquired if funding permits.

## RAF Falcons?

Surplus ADFs were offered on lease to Britain, Spain and Italy in 1995-96, as a stop-gap until the Eurofighter entered service. However, BAe and its allies within the RAF and MoD fiercely opposed the lease, fearing that Lockheed Martin's long-term goal was to undermine the Eurofighter, and sell F-16s and F-22s to the UK. An assessment of the costs of the F-16 lease concluded that the programme would be unaffordable anyway. A further blow to the ADF came when Italy chose to lease Tornado F.Mk 3s from the RAF, and Spain acquired additional stop-gap F/A-18s. This, however, did not halt interest in surplus ADF aircraft, with Italy no due to take leased machines imminently, although it seems likely that most customers will be from former Warsaw Pact countries. Looking to replace their Soviet-supplied aircraft, these countries view the F-16, and in particular, the ADF variant, with great interest, although no firm deal has yet been agreed.

*Not all the ADFs were dedicated fighters. Those of the Puerto Rico (illustrated) and Illinois Guard units had a battlefield assignment role, and were often seen carrying bombs. In contrast to other ADF squadrons, these two units were not operated under the control of NORAD, hence the TAC-style two-letter tailcode.*

# F-16A ADF 178th Fighter Squadron 119th Fighter Group North Dakota ANG

**The ADF (Air Defense Fighter) version of the Fighting Falcon was specially developed to provide the Air National Guard with a replacement for the F-4D and F-106A, which equipped most of its interceptor units.**

**ADF recognition features**
Three external features identified the single-seat ADF version of the Fighting Falcon: the 150,000-candlepower night identification spotlight on the port side of the nose; the Mk XII IFF antennas forward of the windshield and below the air intake; and the fairings over the relocated rudder servo actuators.

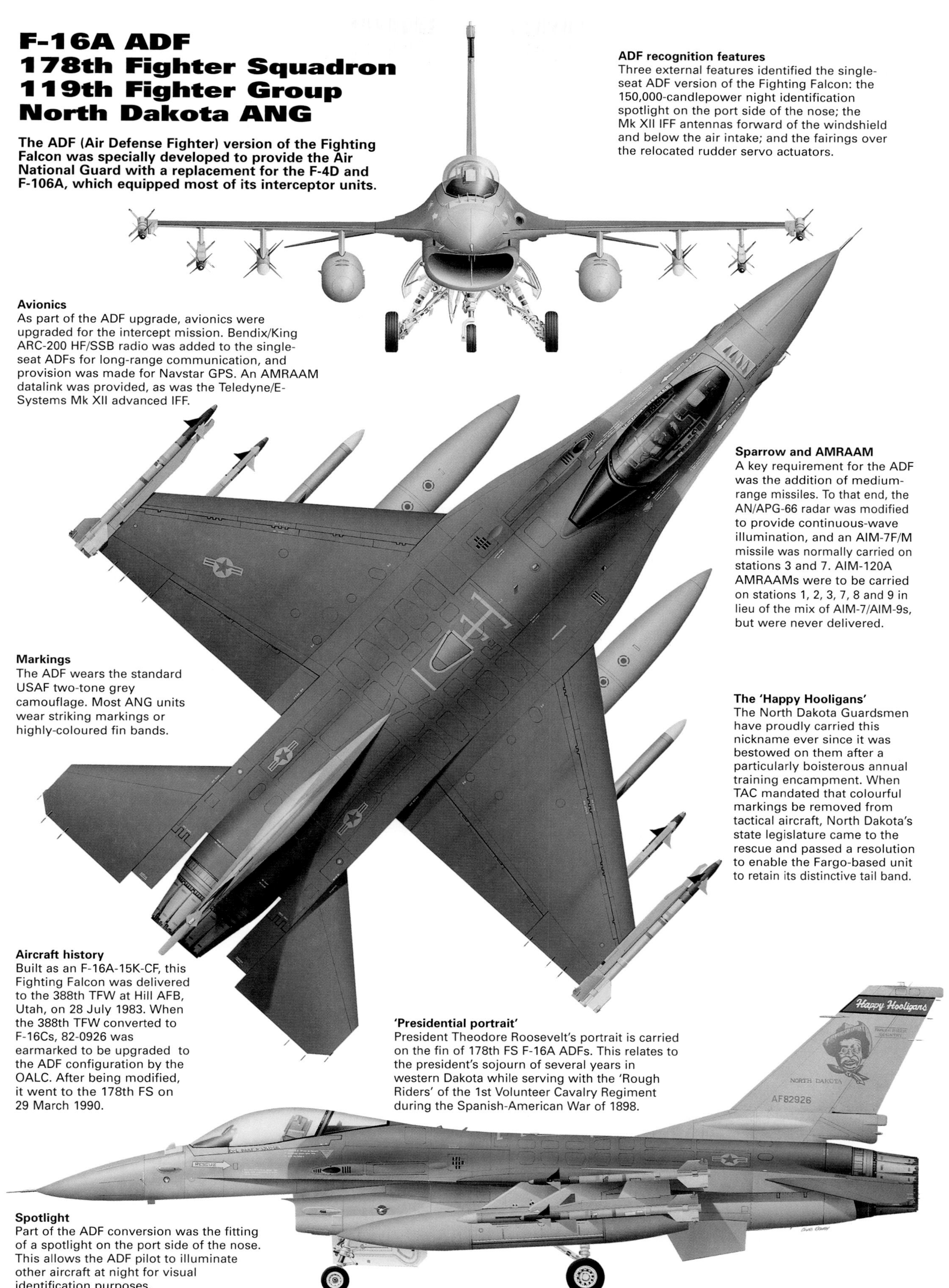


**Avionics**
As part of the ADF upgrade, avionics were upgraded for the intercept mission. Bendix/King ARC-200 HF/SSB radio was added to the single-seat ADFs for long-range communication, and provision was made for Navstar GPS. An AMRAAM datalink was provided, as was the Teledyne/E-Systems Mk XII advanced IFF.

**Sparrow and AMRAAM**
A key requirement for the ADF was the addition of medium-range missiles. To that end, the AN/APG-66 radar was modified to provide continuous-wave illumination, and an AIM-7F/M missile was normally carried on stations 3 and 7. AIM-120A AMRAAMs were to be carried on stations 1, 2, 3, 7, 8 and 9 in lieu of the mix of AIM-7/AIM-9s, but were never delivered.

**Markings**
The ADF wears the standard USAF two-tone grey camouflage. Most ANG units wear striking markings or highly-coloured fin bands.

**The 'Happy Hooligans'**
The North Dakota Guardsmen have proudly carried this nickname ever since it was bestowed on them after a particularly boisterous annual training encampment. When TAC mandated that colourful markings be removed from tactical aircraft, North Dakota's state legislature came to the rescue and passed a resolution to enable the Fargo-based unit to retain its distinctive tail band.

**Aircraft history**
Built as an F-16A-15K-CF, this Fighting Falcon was delivered to the 388th TFW at Hill AFB, Utah, on 28 July 1983. When the 388th TFW converted to F-16Cs, 82-0926 was earmarked to be upgraded to the ADF configuration by the OALC. After being modified, it went to the 178th FS on 29 March 1990.

**'Presidential portrait'**
President Theodore Roosevelt's portrait is carried on the fin of 178th FS F-16A ADFs. This relates to the president's sojourn of several years in western Dakota while serving with the 'Rough Riders' of the 1st Volunteer Cavalry Regiment during the Spanish-American War of 1898.

**Spotlight**
Part of the ADF conversion was the fitting of a spotlight on the port side of the nose. This allows the ADF pilot to illuminate other aircraft at night for visual identification purposes.

*Complete with arrester hook, the X-35C is the demonstrator for the US Navy's CV carrierborne JSF version. Although the larger surfaces alter the aerodynamics when compared with the X-35A, Lockheed Martin engineers have 'tweaked' the flight control system so that the two aircraft feel very similar in the cockpit.*

# Lockheed Martin F-35

## F-16 successor

**Although the threat of cancellation hangs over it, the US Joint Strike Fighter programme is the most important military aircraft venture in the world. Lockheed Martin's proposal is based on the X-35 technology demonstrator.**

Deemed by some to be the low-risk approach to the JSF requirement, Lockheed Martin's X-35 aircraft nevertheless employs a host of features which make it a generation ahead of today's fighters. Furthermore, advances in technology have allowed the two JSF competitors to offer F-22 stealth characteristics and avionics at F-16 prices, with unprecedented predicted savings in maintenance.

In November 1996 Lockheed Martin and Boeing were awarded contracts to develop their JSF proposals further. Part of the contract involved the construction of two Concept Demonstration Aircraft (CDAs) with which to prove the technologies the teams aimed to employ in their Preferred Weapon System Concept (PWSC) proposals. Based on the PWSC submission, actual data from the CDAs, computer predictions and a host of supporting proposals concerning manufacture, reliability and ease of maintenance, the Pentagon aims to 'down-select' to one team some time in 2001/02, which will proceed to the Engineering and Manufacturing Development (EMD) phase.

Lockheed had been a front-runner in pre-JSF competitions (CALF, JAST) and continued to refine its design throughout. As its name implies, JSF is a multi-service programme which aims to provide a land-based fighter for the USAF, carrierborne aircraft for the US Navy and, most technically difficult, a STOVL platform for the USMC. Demonstrating the necessary attributes for these differing requirements with two CDAs meant that one would have to 'double-up' its tasks.

Owing to the nature of Lockheed Martin's overall design concept, it was natural to build a conventional take-off and landing (CTOL) demonstrator – which was designated X-35A – to display the 'up and away' performance of the design, before fitting it with the STOVL equipment to become the X-35B. The second aircraft (X-35C) was built to test elements of the carrier-borne (CV) variant, although it was constructed with the ability to accommodate the STOVL lift-fan as an insurance measure should the first aircraft be lost or damaged.

*The USAF has a stated requirement for 1,763 JSFs, most of which will replace the F-16 (right), with which the X-35A is seen here. Other JSFs will replace A-10s as the USAF moves to a two-fighter force.*

*In preparation for a first flight, Tom Morgenfeld runs up the F119-611C engine of the X-35A to full power. For production JSFs the General Electric F120 is an alternative powerplant.*

### X-35 configuration

Design of the CDAs was frozen long before that of the PWSC final submission, yet Lockheed Martin's Model 220 (X-35) is much closer in configuration to the final Model 235 design than the Boeing CDAs. The aircraft resembles a scaled-down F-22, with twin, outward-canted fins, all-moving tailerons set well back, angular intakes and a stealthy, chined nose. Power in the CTOL/CV versions is provided by a single Pratt & Whitney F119-611C turbofan. An unusual feature of the X-35 is the divert-erless intakes, which have a bulge on the fuselage side to spill turbulent boundary layer either side of the intake lip. The intake is serpentine to trap radar energy, and there is a radar blocker downstream. Weapons can be housed in bays in the underside, and standard weaponry consists of two AIM-120 AMRAAMs and two JDAMs. Additional weapons can be carried externally, although these greatly increase the radar cross-section.

With Chief Test Pilot Tom Morgenfeld at the controls, the X-35A CTOL demonstrator took off for the first time on 24 October 2000. Built in the famous Skunk Works at Palmdale, the aircraft transferred to Edwards to undertake an intensive period of trials which involved high-speed manoeuvring, inflight refuelling and supersonic flight. The programme continued without any major hitches, and the X-35A completed its test programme on 22 November, having logged 27 flights. It was returned to Palmdale, where it went into the shop for conversion into the STOVL X-35B.

***On its 10th flight the X-35A demonstrated refuelling, hooking up to a 412th Test Wing NKC-135E. Both X-35s have USAF-style boom receptacles, whereas Boeing's X-32s had Navy-style probes.***

## CV demonstrator

On 16 December 2000, Joe Sweeney took the X-35C aloft for the first time. This aircraft represented the carrier variant intended for the US Navy. In order to cope with the demanding approach handling requirements, the aircraft has substantially larger wings and tails. In order to preserve the commonality of the basic design, Lockheed Martin achieved this by 'picture-framing' – that is, adding area around the basic CTOL design's surfaces without dramatically affecting the internal structure. The team accepted a slight reduction in permissible *g* loads (from +9 to +7.33) but this is within the Navy's requirements.

The primary aim of the X-35C test programme was to validate the aircraft's low-speed handling qualities. A series of mock carrier approaches was made on a dummy deck at Edwards, before the X-35C undertook a two-hop transcontinental flight from Edwards to the Navy's test establishment at Patuxent River, Maryland (with an overnight stop at Fort Worth, where, if chosen, the Lockheed Martin JSF would be built).

An exhaustive series of mock FCLPs (Field Carrier Landing Practices) proved the X-35C's excellent handling on the approach at sea level, and involved many 'off-nominal' scenarios during which the aircraft's ability to recover rapidly and safely were tested.

X-35C testing came to an end on 11 March, by which time it had racked up 58 hours in 73 flights. Apart from the 250 FCLPs flown, it also found time to continue some of the X-35A's 'up and away' testing, and flew supersonically. It also validated refuelling procedures with the KC-10 Extender.

## Production JSF

Having been chosen for production in October 2001, Lockheed Martin's JSF aircraft, to be known as F-35, will have a number of astonishing features. Among these is the AESA (Advanced Electronically-Scanned Array) radar, which can also act passively as a radar receiver, and the Distributed Infra-Red System (DIRS). The latter consists of six infra-red sensors located around the airframe, all providing imagery on the pilot's helmet visor. By moving his head the pilot will be able to see an infra-red image from all around him, including through the cockpit floor. This has obvious benefits to the STOVL pilot making a hover landing.

Many of the systems are being tested on Northrop Grumman's BAC One-Eleven trials aircraft, known as the Co-operative Avionics Test Bed (CATB). This also has a trial installation of the Model 235's proposed cockpit, which has a single contiguous 7.9-in x 19.7-in (20-cm x 50-cm) projected display stretching across the full width of the instrument panel. There is no head-up display, all relevant information being displayed on the pilot's helmet visor. Both X-35 demonstrators have been flown with a more conventional cockpit and are fitted with standard HUDs.

While commonality between variants remains a key goal, there are notable differences between them. Apart from the 'picture-framing', the CV version of the Model 235 also has much stronger undercarriage and folding wings. The aircraft has also been designed with bulged bomb bay doors to take the 2,000-lb GBU-31 JDAM and future munitions.

***Above: Tom Morgenfeld brings the X-35A in close for the camera. This veteran of many Skunk Works programmes, including F-117 and YF-22, described the control of the aircraft as superb, noting especially the crispness with which the aircraft reacted to control inputs, and stopped without any trace of 'wallow' when control commands were relaxed.***

***Left: For FCLPs at Edwards, a Fresnel lens landing system was brought in to mimic that of a carrier. Under current plans the US Navy will not get JSFs until the last of the F/A-18E/Fs have been delivered. JSFs will then start to replace F/A-18C/Ds on carrier decks. A total of 480 CV aircraft is currently planned.***

# STOVL F-35B

**For both JSF teams, the STOVL (Short Take-off, Vertical Landing) configuration intended for the US Marine Corps was the hardest challenge. Lockheed Martin chose an unproven lift-fan arrangement for its successful X-35B demonstrator.**

It is interesting to note that the three pre-1996 JSF competitors had chosen three different propulsion concepts for their STOVL aircraft. Boeing employed the direct-lift concept, as proven in the Harrier family, while the rejected Northrop/ McDonnell Douglas design employed the lift-plus-lift/cruise (LPLC) concept, as used by the Yak-38 and VAK 191. Lockheed Martin opted for a completely different tack, and one which had not hitherto been employed – the lift fan.

This concept uses the vectored thrust from the engine combined with that from a cold air fan, itself driven by power from the engine. The main disadvantage of this scheme is the same as that for LPLC: when not used for STOVL flight the lift fan (or lift engines) become 'dead' weight. In the LM design, though, there are hidden benefits. The space occupied by the lift fan in the STOVL version can be used for fuel in the CV (US Navy) and CTOL (USAF) variants. Both services have greater range requirements than the USMC.

However, the lift fan has two major advantages over the direct-lift concept employed by Boeing on its X-32B: firstly, it greatly improves the thrust recovery from the engine, and secondly it avoids many of the problems caused by hot exhaust gases re-entering the engine.

***Top and above: Lockheed Martin's STOVL concept employs a large number of moving parts which must function correctly. As well as the doors which open on the aircraft's spine and undersides, these photos highlight the vectoring engine nozzle, which is angled slightly downwards in the top photograph, and nearly vertically in the lower picture. The thrust from the cold air fan in the front fuselage is also vectored.***

Lockheed Martin designers calculated that the lift fan would blow a cushion of cold air under the hovering aircraft, preventing most hot exhaust gases, which could seriously degrade engine performance, from reaching the intakes. The theory works: in hover tests intake temperatures rose just 5°F (3°C).

## Fan installation

In Lockheed Martin's JSF proposal the STOVL version was aerodynamically similar to the CTOL USAF aircraft, for which the X-35A acted as the flying test-bed. When its programme of demonstrating 'up-and-away' performance came to an end on 22 November 2000, the X-35A returned to the Skunk Works at Palmdale to be fitted with the Allison-designed STOVL lift-fan arrangement and to re-emerge as the X-35B.

Essentially the lift fan is a large-diameter two-stage counter-rotating fan mounted in a

***Both X-35 CDAs were built with the characteristic bulge behind the cockpit necessary to accommodate the lift fan. Production CV and CTOL aircraft would not have the bulge, and would have larger cockpit canopies.***

***On 24 June 2001, the X-35B completed its first sustained hover: 35 seconds at 25 ft altitude. During its flight test programme it made 18 vertical take offs and 27 hover landings.***

bay behind the cockpit. Doors open in the forward spine to admit cold air for the fan, while doors open below to allow the accelerated air through. This air can be vectored to allow a smooth transition from pure jetborne flight (i.e. hovering) to wingborne flight. In the X-35B the air is blown through a vectoring D-section nozzle, but in the proposed production version this would be replaced by a cascade of moveable vanes.

Power for the fan comes via a drive shaft from the compressor face of the engine, which has a clutch (using a form of carbon brake technology) to provide controllable torque power to the shaft. The shaft ends in a single gear, which drives the two stages of the fan. At full power the lift fan provides around 18,000 lb (80 kN) of thrust.

Of course, this thrust is provided at the front of the aircraft, and to balance it the normal engine exhaust is vectored downwards through a three-section articulating exhaust nozzle, developed by Rolls-Royce and drawing on the experience of Yakovlev, which employed a similar device in its Yak-41 carrierborne fighter prototypes. The nozzle can be swivelled to 15° beyond the vertical to allow the aircraft to move backwards while hovering. Pratt &Whitney's engine for the X-35B is the F119-611S. The amount of thrust from the engine, and from the lift fan, can be controlled either simultaneously or differentially to control pitch and climb/descent rates.

Additional air is drawn from the engine's fan to two 'roll posts' under the aircraft's wings. The flow to these outlets is variable, providing roll control in the hover. Together, the four nozzles provide around 40,000 lb (178 kN) of thrust.

## STOVL conversion

When the X-35B transitions from wingborne to jetborne flight, a complex sequence takes place, although the transition appears seamless to the pilot thanks to computer control. Four sets of doors open: two sets cover the inlet and outlet for the lift fan, one set covers an auxiliary intake for the engine mounted immediately aft of the lift fan upper doors, and another set opens under the rear fuselage to allow the main nozzle to swivel downwards. All these doors have to fit precisely to preserve the X-35's stealth characteristics.

For take-off a short roll is standard practice, the propulsion system set in STOVL mode but with the thrust angled obliquely backwards. The aircraft lifts off at around 60 kt (69 km/h) after about 500 ft (152 m) of runway, then climbs and accelerates away to full wingborne flight. The propulsion system is configured and reconfigured automatically during the process.

With the X-35B complete, Lockheed Martin moved cautiously to a first flight. Unlike Boeing, which chose a 'fly, then hover' approach, LM elected to begin flight tests with vertical take-offs. Tests first got under way over a hover pit. This consists of a metal grate under which is a chamber, which draws off exhaust gases (and cold fan air). This allows the aircraft to mimic hovering without leaving the ground. The hover pit outlet doors can be opened or closed to simulate hovering in and out of ground effect. Initial trials began with the X-35B firmly rooted to the grate by means of special undercarriage boots, which not only restrained the aircraft, but also measured the lift forces.

Further hover testing without the restraints culminated with the first full hover on 23 July 2001. At the controls was Simon Hargreaves of BAE Systems, a Sea Harrier veteran who had seen action in the Falklands War. After additional hovering flights, the X-35B took off conventionally on 3 July for the trip to Edwards, from where the remainder of the flight test programme took place.

It should be noted that Edwards and Palmdale are about 2,500 ft (762 m) up in the desert and some tests took place in air temperatures of 96°F (36°C). Even in these hot-and-high conditions the X-35B hovered easily on less than full throttle. During the tests the X-35B was successfully hover-landed at 34,000 lb (15422 kg), twice the weight of a 'legacy' STOVL aircraft such as the AV-8B.

While hovering and wingborne flight had been mastered, the big test came on 9 July, when the first airborne transition from STOVL to CTOL mode was undertaken. On 16 July Hargreaves brought the aircraft in from wingborne flight to a vertical landing, a feat performed three days later by fellow Briton Squadron Leader Justin Paines of the RAF.

## 'Mission X'

On 20 July the Lockheed Martin team achieved its primary goal – 'Mission X'. This demonstrated the standard *modus operandi* of the aircraft, beginning with a STOVL-mode short running take-off, transition to CTOL mode for a supersonic dash, and then transition to STOVL for a vertical landing. USMC Major Art 'Turbo' Tomasetti flew the mission. Another 'Mission X' was flown on 26 July by Hargreaves, who also added a refuelling to the mission. On 30 July the X-35B completed its flight programme and in the middle of August the final bids and test data were submitted to the programme office. With Lockheed Martin now chosen over Boeing, the USMC is expecting the first F-35Bs in service around 2012.

***Above: Driven by a shaft from the engine, the lift fan provides nearly half the thrust in the hover. Behind are auxiliary engine intake doors, required to provide the necessary mass flow.***

***Left: The moment of truth – Simon Hargreaves lifts the X-35B into the air for its first free flight on 23 June 2001. Previously, the aircraft had been tested with physical or weight restraints.***

# F-4 Phantom – USMC Vietnam ops

**Flying mostly from land bases under the most austere of conditions, the Marine Corps Phantoms had an important CAS and photo-reconnaissance role throughout the Vietnam War.**

*This VMFA-323 F-4B is armed with AIM-7 Sparrows as well as a huge load of Mk 82 bombs. The Marines had little opportunity to use the AIM-7 over Vietnam, but expended huge amounts of ordnance in CAS operations.*

In 1962 the US Marine Corps began receiving the first of its new McDonnell Douglas F-4B Phantom IIs. By 1963, the Corps had enough aircraft to equip three F-4 squadrons as part of Marine Air Group-11. MAG-11 and its Phantom units – VMFA-314 'Black Knights', VMFA-531 'Gray Ghosts' and VMFA-542 'Bengals' – moved to NAS Atsugi, Japan, later that year and were perfectly placed for a quick move in theatre when the conflict in South East Asia erupted.

## Into Vietnam

On 10 May 1965, some 15 VMFA-531 F-4Bs arrived at Da Nang on South Vietnam's north east coast. As the first land-based USMC jets in Vietnam, the Phantoms were initially assigned to providing air defence for USMC operations in the region, but it was soon realised that the aircraft would be more useful on close-air-support (CAS) duties.

As such, VMFA-531 began flying bombing missions under radar guidance, night attacks under flare illumination and standard CAS sorties in support of Marines on the ground. VMFA-314 soon joined the 'Gray Ghosts' at Da Nang, as did VMFA-323 'Death Rattlers' and with VMFA-542. VMFA-513 'Flying Nightmares' also flew a tour at Da Nang, arriving in June 1965 and leaving in October for the US.

Conditions at Da Nang were primitive during these early days of operations. The problems arising from this lack of facilities were compounded by how busy the base became. As the only jet-capable base in South Vietnam during these early stages of the war, both Da Nang and its surrounding airspace became impossibly congested. This congestion affected the Marine Phantoms in two major ways.

The first of these was the establishment of a second Marine Corps base. Employing the Short Airfield Tactical Support (SATS) system, the Marines built a new airfield at Chu Lai, south of Da Nang. SATS was equivalent to a carrier deck on land, and used pierced aluminium sheeting to produce a short runway which was serviced by mobile catapulting and arresting (MOREST) gear. Chu Lai allowed two extra F-4 squadrons to be deployed, as well as relieving Da Nang.

The second major event was a horrific mid-air collision. A VMFA-342 F-4B collided head-on with a VMGR-152 KC-130F. Ironically, the USMC F-4s were routinely tasked with the protection of these tanker aircraft, as well as relying on them for refuelling services. On this occasion the tanker had a pair of VMFA-314 jets trailing on its hoses. The -342 machine hit the right wing of the tanker, destroying both aircraft and killing both crews – a total of eight men. Of the refuelling F-4s, one crashed in the sea after its crew ejected, while the second force-landed at Chu Lai.

*Photographed in 1972 as it dropped a load of Mk 82 LDGP bombs, VMFA-115 F-4B has its fuselage-side chaff dispenser door open. VMFA-115 flew tours at all three USMC land bases in SEA.*

Conditions at Chu Lai were probably more primitive than those at Da Nang. Both bases boasted problems with dust and humidity that plagued the F-4's sensitive avionics systems. Both bases were also prone to mortar attack by the Viet Cong.

## Base defence

In order to combat VC units in the immediate vicinity of Da Nang, the Marines flew their F-4s without drop tanks on very short-range missions with each aircraft carrying as many as 24 500-lb (227-kg) Mk 82s. During VC attacks, the Phantoms launched as frequently as one every ten minutes.

At Chu Lai the VC problem was even more acute. The possibility of attack was present from the very beginning of construction, and once the base had been completed, a permanent pres-

*For the crews flying unarmed RF-4B missions, speed over the target was even more important than it was for the attack crews. Photo-runs had to be flown with the aircraft held steady and usually at around 600 kt (691 mph; 1112 km/h) at 3,500 ft (1067 m).*

***This VMFA-115 F-4B has Mk 82 Snakeyes on TERs (Triple Ejector Racks) on each wing pylon, with pairs of Zunis mounted on the inboard Sidewinder rails on the pylon shoulders. It is also about to receive at least one napalm tank under the fuselage.***

ence of some 3,000 VC troops was established around the base. Similar tactics were employed by the USMC Phantoms defending Chu Lai, but now they were bombing almost as soon as they had left the runway.

By 1969 only the RF-4B Phantoms of VMCJ-1 remained at Da Nang, while four squadrons of F-4Bs were flying out of Chu Lai with the newly-formed MAG-32. This arrangement remained until 1972, when a third Marine corps base was established at Nam Phong, Thailand.

The photo-recce Phantoms of VMCJ-1 flew their first operations from Da Nang on 3 November 1966. The unit remained at the base until 1970, suffering no losses, although one aircraft was hit by AAA.

One other base was called home by USMC Phantoms during the Vietnam War, the aircraft-carrier USS *America*. VMFA-333 'Shamrocks' flew alongside the US Navy's VF-74 from the carrier between 5 June 1972 and 24 March 1973. The squadron scored the first Marine Corps MiG kill in a Marine Corps Phantom on 10 September 1972. A pair of F-4Js took on three MiG-21s near Hanoi, downing one at the expense of four Sparrows and two Sidewinders. A second MiG was damaged by a further 'Winder. Almost immediately after the combat, both Phantoms were damaged by a SAM, obliging their crews to eject over the sea. An earlier USMC MiG kill had been notched up by a Marine Corps exchange pilot flying a USAF F-4D, while a further MiG was destroyed by a USAF F-4E being flown by a USMC pilot with a Navy RIO.

## Ordnance and tactics

Standard USMC Phantom weapons were napalm tanks, Mk 80-series bombs and unguided rockets. Of the latter, the 5-in (127-mm) Zuni was the weapon of choice, while Mk 81 and Mk 82 bombs were frequently carried. In the earliest days of Da Nang operations, the Marines often 'borrowed' ordnance from the Navy, this including Mk 82 Snakeyes, which were not part of the USMC inventory. Although they had not been trained to deliver Snakeyes, the Marines soon developed their own tactics for their use, although they officially became part of the USMC armoury late in 1967.

In keeping with the unusual situations in which they found themselves, the Phantom crews soon began adapting old tactics, or developing new ones as appropriate. Since the primary mission was CAS, the F-4s were always being flown into the engagement zones of enemy AAA. The tactic developed to minimise the risk of being hit – more USMC Phantoms were lost to AAA than any other cause – was to attack at very high speed. Often these attacks were also flown at minimum altitudes, VMFA-122 reportedly making attacks at 600 kt (691 mph; 1112 km/h) from altitudes as low as 25 ft (7.62 m).

Where a group of aircraft was attacking a single target, the Phantoms would pair off and fly orbits at different altitudes around the circumference of an imaginary cone. The apex of the cone was placed on the target, with the pairs of Phantoms stepping down the sides of the cone to ever lower altitudes each time the bottom pair pressed home its attack.

The slope of the cone's sides generally equated to the diving angle of the attack. One USMC pilot reported that the AAA surrounding the attacking aircraft was often so intense that there seemed no possibility of them pulling out. He recalled however, that as soon as he was pressing home his own attacks he never once noticed any AAA, such was the concentration required to hit the target.

***Above:* *This F-4J was flying with VMFA-333 off USS* America *in 1972. Several land-based USMC squadrons also flew the F-4J, including those at Nam Phong. In 1973, F-4Js at the latter base became the last US combat aircraft to leave SEA, after flying bombing missions against Khmer Rouge forces in Cambodia.***

***Right: This F-4J was at Nam Phong in 1972. It hailed from VMFA-232, whose squadron badge is represented on the shed behind. Note the folded outer-wing panels.***

# US Navy and Marine Corps variants

## F-4A (F4H-1/F4H-1F/Model 98AM)

Following on from the two Phantom prototypes were 45 aircraft initially designated F4H-1, but later redesignated F4H-1F. In September 1962 they became F-4As. As the first 21 aircraft were considered as pre-production aircraft, configurations varied wildly. The first aircraft retained the small radome and low canopy of the prototypes but, from aircraft no. 19, the enlarged canopy and large radome were introduced. Powerplant was the J79-GE-2A or J79-GE-8 in late aircraft, as exemplified by the aircraft shown here, the eighth from last F-4A. None was issued to a front-line squadron, most seeing service with test or training units.

## RF-4B (F4H-1P/Model 98DH)

The RF-4B followed the USAF's RF-4C, and was generally similar in appearance. It was procured for the Marine Corps, which required an organic tactical reconnaissance capability (the Navy deemed it had sufficient recce assets in the RA-5C and RF-8A/G). First flying on 12 March 1965 with Irving Burrows at the controls, the RF-4B was based on the F-4B airframe with a recce nose housing cameras, IR linescan and a SLAR. The last 12 (of 46 total) had the thick wing of the F-4J. The final three had the rounded undernose bulge seen on many RF-4Cs (below). The Marine photo-Phantom went into service with VMCJ-2 and VMCJ-3, both of which provided aircraft for VMCJ-1 (above) operating in Vietnam, beginning in 1966. RF-4Bs occasionally operated from carriers in small detachments and were progressively updated. In 1975 all RF-4Bs were concentrated in VMFP-3 at El Toro, where the type was retired in August 1990.

## F-4B (F4H-1/Model 98AM)

Initially procured under the F4H-1 designation (with surviving earlier aircraft being retrospectively christened F4H-1F), the F-4B (after September 1962) was the first definitive production version and accounted for 649 aircraft, the first of which was flown on 25 March 1961 by Thomas Harris. The first F-4Bs were virtually identical to the last of the F-4As but were regarded as being in full operational configuration, with APQ-72 radar, AJB-3 nuclear bombing system, ASA-32 Automatic Flight Control System and a full set of hardpoints. Power came from the J79-GE-8 or -8A, and the APR-30 radar homing and warning system appeared from the 19th F-4B (and retrofitted to earlier machines). Deliveries to the US Navy began in the spring of 1961, the first unit to receive the F-4B being VF-121 'Pacemakers' at Miramar, which acted as the West Coast training unit. The East Coast unit, VF-101 'Grim Reapers', followed soon after. The Atlantic Fleet's VF-74 'Bedevilers' was the first front-line unit, deploying aboard the Navy's showpiece carrier USS *Forrestal*. It was F-4Bs that recorded the Phantom's first combat action on 5 August 1964 in the Gulf of Tonkin Incident, and again a B scored the Phantom's first air-to-air kill on 9 April 1965 when a VF-96 aircraft shot down a Chinese MiG-17. F-4Bs had a long service career with both Navy and Marine Corps, the last being retired from the Marine Reserve in January 1978. Many were converted to F-4N or for special purposes as NF-4Bs (test) or QF-4Bs (drone).

## F-4G

Twelve conversions of F-4Bs were made to F-4G status, this variant featuring an ASW-13 datalink which was intended to allow automatic control of the aircraft for airborne intercepts, and hands-off landings. The latter function required the aircraft to have a retractable radar reflector ahead of the nosewheel. Ten of the aircraft saw service in Vietnam, with VF-213, from October 1965. During this cruise they acquired experimental dark green camouflage. The aircraft were 'de-modded' to F-4B status in 1966/67, although some elements of the system were incorporated into the F-4B and F-4J.

***Visible just ahead of the nosewheel door of this VF-213 F-4G is the retractable radar reflector which, combined with the shipboard SPN-10 radar, allowed the variant to make automatic carrier landings.***

***This illustration shows one of the VF-213 F-4Gs during its 1965/66 combat cruise in USS Kitty Hawk.***

## Navy/Marine Corps variants

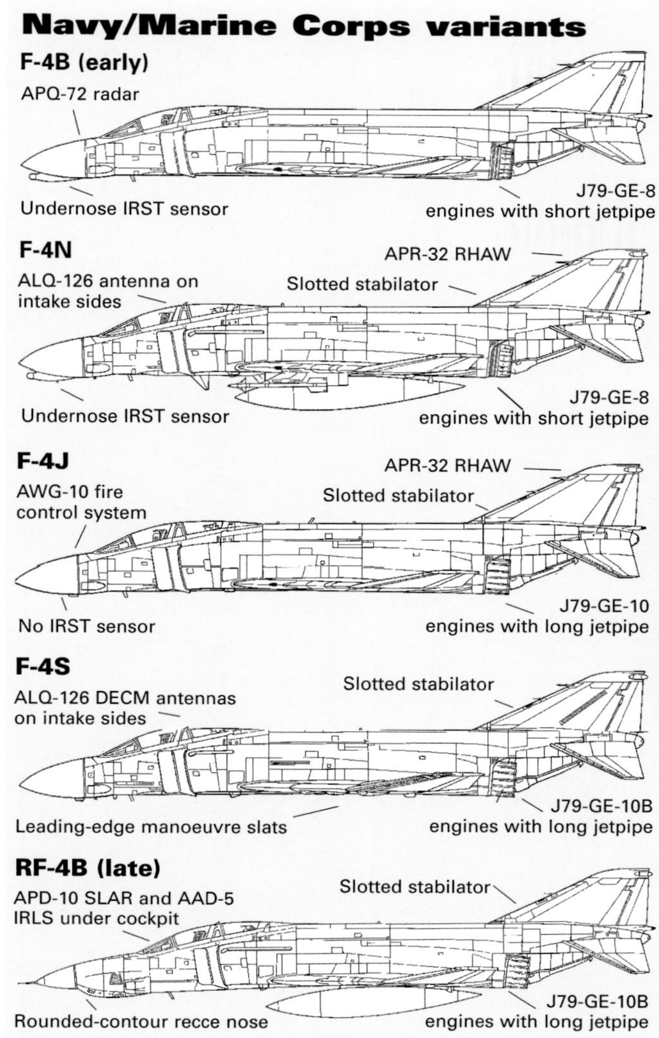


### F-4J (Model 98EV)

Second of the major Navy/Marine production versions, the F-4J introduced a host of new features. J79-GE-10 engines were fitted, characterised by longer jetpipes, while a slotted stabilator was installed to provide greater down-force on launch, and drooping ailerons used to reduce approach speed. The undercarriage was strengthened and enlarged, requiring bulges above and below the wings to accommodate the larger units. In avionics terms, the F-4J introduced the AWG-10 fire control system with APG-59 radar among other items, including a one-way datalink. The undernose IRST was dispensed with, and the RHAWS upgraded to APR-32 standard, with neater antenna installations. During the F-4J's career there were several upgrade programmes, notably that which added ALQ-126 ECM in fairings on the intake sides. 522 were built, the first flying on 27 May 1966. Deliveries began in December 1966 (to VF-101) and the variant was soon in action in Vietnam. Fifteen surplus aircraft were purchased by the RAF as the F-4J(UK). Others were converted to F-4S standard.

### F-4N

Under Project Bee Line the US Navy upgraded 228 F-4Bs to F-4N standard, the first conversion flying on 4 June 1972. The programme extended the aircraft's structural life and modified the avionics, including a new mission computer and the addition of ALQ-126 Deceptive ECM antennas on the intake sides. As the aircraft retained the undernose IRST and J79-GE-8 engines of its F-4B origins, this was the best recognition feature for the F-4N. During Bee Line, the aircraft all received the slotted stabilator of the F-4J (some F-4Bs already had this) and had their inboard leading-edge flaps locked shut, as this had proven to give greater lift and stabilator authority. Redeliveries began in 1973, and the F-4N remained in service until the mid-1980s. Shown below are aircraft from VMFA-321.

### Special-purpose variants

In addition to the main fighter variants, there have been several special-purpose conversions. One F-4B became an EF-4B for use as an electronic warfare aggressor with VAQ-33, the squadron later employing two EF-4J conversions. Two F-4Bs were used for trials as NF-4Bs, while an F-4B previously converted to YF-4J (prototype F-4J) standard now serves as an ejection seat testbed. Considerable numbers of Phantoms have been converted to drone status for missile and other tests under the QF-4B and QF-4N designations, joined by a single prototype QF-4S. At least one F-4J was converted to DF-4J standard to act as a drone controller at NAS Point Mugu. Seven F-4Js were modified for use by the 'Blue Angels' formation display team, but the survivors were subsequently returned to operational standard.

***Point Mugu is home to much of the Navy's missile test programme. Seen at the base are a DF-4J drone controller (left) and a QF-4N drone (below).***

### F-4S

Spurred by the success of Bee Line, the Navy decided to follow up with a structural/avionics upgrade for the F-4J, resulting in the F-4S. The first of 248 conversions flew on 22 July 1977. Apart from the provision of digital AWG-10B fire control system and smokeless J79-GE-10B engines, the principal change was the addition of two-position leading-edge manoeuvre slats, which greatly enhanced turn performance. The last F-4S retired from Marine service (with VMF-112) in early 1992.

# US Air Force Variants

**Although at first reluctant to operate an aircraft initially designed for the US Navy, the USAF was unable to ignore the outstanding capabilities offered by the Phantom. At first, USAF F-4s carried minimal modifications compared to USN machines, but the Air Force eventually developed its own highly capable variants to fulfil a multitude of roles.**

## RF-4C (Model 98DF)

The RF-4C was based on the airframe of the F-4C, although extra equipment reduced its internal fuel capacity. All RF-4Cs retained nuclear capability and late-service aircraft were often fitted with Sidewinders for self-defence. The F-4C's AN/APQ-72 radar was replaced by the much smaller Texas Instruments AN/APQ-99 for mapping, and terrain collision avoidance. Intended for day and night photographic reconnaissance, the RF-4C was fitted with two pairs of photoflash ejectors on the upper rear fuselage. The RF-4C could carry a single forward oblique camera, or vertical camera; behind this was a low-altitude camera although this was often replaced with a trio of vertical, left and right oblique models. A number of other cameras was employed by the RF-4C, including a giant LOROP (LOng-Range Oblique Photography) example which was carried in a centreline pod. Initial plans called for the RF-4C to equip 14 squadrons, with the first activated in 1965. The first production RF-4C went to the 33rd TRTS, a training squadron, at Shaw AFB, South Carolina, on 24 September 1964. The first operational squadron, the 16th TRS at Shaw, AFB, was deemed combat-ready in August 1965 and deployed to Vietnam in October 1965. A small number of USAF and ANG RF-4Cs participated in Desert Storm. The RF-4C was in production for longer than any other variant except the F-4E. The last USAF unit was the 192nd RS, ANG, which finally retired its examples on 27 September 1995, delivering six of its RF-4Cs to Spain.

## F-4C (Model 98DE/DJ)

The USAF's Specific Operational Requirement requested an aircraft based on the USN F-4B, but with added ground-attack capability and dual controls for a second pilot (in the back seat). Certain naval features were retained on the aircraft such as folding wings, catapult and arrester hooks. The General Electric J79-GE-15 turbojet engines were kept, as was the self-contained cartridge starter. US Navy high-pressure tyres were replaced with larger lower-pressure examples, and a USAF-style inflight-refuelling receptacle was installed in the dorsal spine. The rear cockpit had new consoles and the AN/APQ-72 radar of the F-4B was modified to APQ-100 standard to enhance the F-4C's ground-attack capability. Provision was made for all-USAF tactical stores. Some 27 F4H-1s (F-4Bs) were delivered to the 4453rd (Combat Crew Training Wing) at MacDill AFB, Florida, in preparation for the arrival of the F-4C, the first examples of which were passed on to the 12th TFW. The USAF's first two MiG kills of the Vietnam War were accomplished by F-4Cs, which were to bear the brunt of the fighting in the early years. Following their withdrawal from USAF service, refurbished examples were delivered to Spain in 1971-72 to serve with Nos 121 and 122 Squadrons. Each squadron also operated two ex-USAF RF-4Cs. The F-4Cs were withdrawn from front-line use following the introduction of the F/A-18.

## F-4D (Model 98EN)

Although externally identical to the F-4C which preceded it into USAF service, the F-4D was, in fact, very different. It was the first purpose-designed USAF Phantom variant, incorporating all the modifications required by the USAF. Retaining the basic airframe and engines of the F-4C, the F-4D had the same fuel tankage as the RF-4C. The major differences concerned the avionics, the APQ-100 radar being replaced by the smaller, lighter AN/APQ-109 as part of the AN/APA-65 radar set, which introduced an air-to-ground ranging mode. Externally, the nose remained unchanged. Delivery of F-4Ds began in March 1966, initially to the 36th TFW at Bitburg, Germany, followed by the 4th TFW at Seymour Johnson AFB, North Carolina. The F-4Ds began replacing F-4Cs in Vietnam from the spring of 1967. The AIM-7 Sparrow capability of earlier Phantoms was retained although the AIM-9 Sidewinder was initially deleted pending the introduction of the AIM-4D Falcon AAM. Sidewinder capability was soon re-introduced, however, following the cancellation of the AIM-4D. Some 793 examples of the F-4D were delivered in total, with 36 examples going to the RoKAF (South Korea). A second customer for the type was Iran. Following the Islamic revolution, however, these aircraft suffered spares shortages which led to many being grounded. Both Iran and South Korea had operational F-4Ds in 2004.

***The F-4D remained in service with AFRes units long enough to receive 'Lizard' camouflage during the late 1980s. This example served with the 89th TFS/906th TFG at Wright-Patterson AFB, Ohio.***

## US Air Force variants

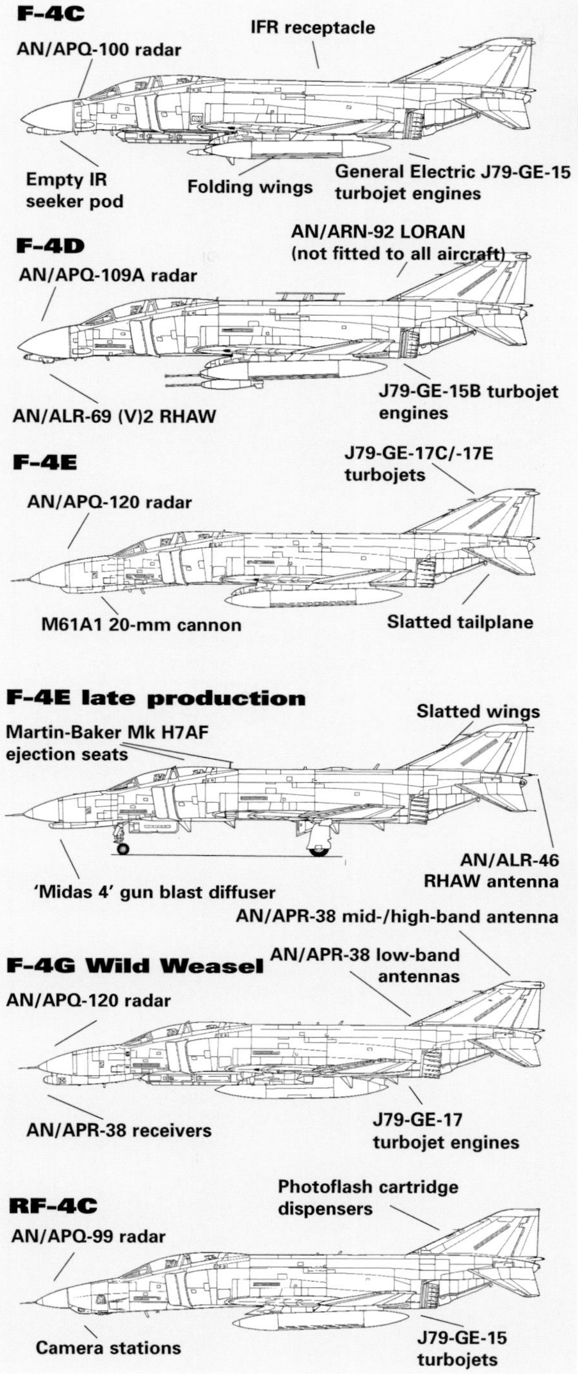

### F-4C

AN/APQ-100 radar
IFR receptacle
Empty IR seeker pod
Folding wings
General Electric J79-GE-15 turbojet engines

### F-4D

AN/APQ-109A radar
AN/ARN-92 LORAN (not fitted to all aircraft)
AN/ALR-69 (V)2 RHAW
J79-GE-15B turbojet engines

### F-4E

AN/APQ-120 radar
J79-GE-17C/-17E turbojets
M61A1 20-mm cannon
Slatted tailplane

### F-4E late production

Martin-Baker Mk H7AF ejection seats
Slatted wings
'Midas 4' gun blast diffuser
AN/ALR-46 RHAW antenna
AN/APR-38 mid-/high-band antenna

### F-4G Wild Weasel

AN/APQ-120 radar
AN/APR-38 low-band antennas
AN/APR-38 receivers
J79-GE-17 turbojet engines

### RF-4C

AN/APQ-99 radar
Photoflash cartridge dispensers
Camera stations
J79-GE-15 turbojets

### Special-purpose variants

The widespread use of the Phantom within the ranks of the USAF meant that modified examples were employed for a variety of test and evaluation duties, as well as being converted to target drones. One of the most famous test F-4s was aircraft 62-12200 (illustrated below). Built as a Navy F-4B, the aircraft was later converted to serve as the USAF RF-4C prototype. Following the completion of this trials work, -12200 was selected to serve as a fly-by-wire (FBW) control system testbed. Known as the PACT (Precision Aircraft Control Technology) demonstrator, the F-4Phantom (FBW) made its first flight on 29 April 1972. Lead ballast was added to the rear fuselage to destabilise the aircraft in pitch and te aircraft helped to pave the way for fly-by-wire controls.

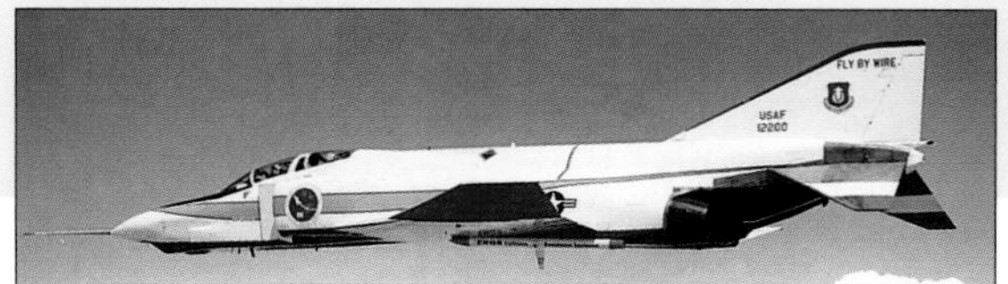

### F-4E (Model 98HO)

Combat deployment of the F-4Cs and F-4Ds in Southeast Asia from 1965 and May 1967, respectively, revealed shortcomings in these variants and in the very concept of a gunless fighter. Tests were carried out with an internal nose-mounted M61 cannon on an RF-4C, which at first attracted little interest. Then, McDD proposed an improved variant, the F-4E, which first flew on 30 June 1967, and entered service in 1968. It became the most numerous version built, with 1,397 examples manufactured. It was distinguishable from other variants by its internal centreline 20-mm M61A1 Vulcan cannon, with 640 rounds in an undernose fairing. A new AN/APQ-120 solid-state radar fire control system was housed in a longer nose. Also introduced was a seventh fuselage fuel cell and slots to increase tailplane authority, while powered wing-folding was removed. Later modifications saw the introduction of a leading-edge TISEO electro-optical sensor, and full air-to-air capability was retained with AIM-7 and AIM-9 AAMs. USAF examples were finally retired in late 1992, although the F-4E still remains one of the principal fighter aircraft of Germany (as the F-4F), South Korea and, for a short while longer, Japan.

***F-4Es served with the USAF in a variety of roles. One of the most public has been with the*** **Thunderbirds** ***Aerial Demonstration Team (right). Late model F-4Es featured slatted outer wings (below).***

### F-4G (Model 98)

Mindful of the success of the F-105G in the Wild Weasel role, the USAF decided to allocate its new F-4 to this role, also. The F-4E's cannon was deleted, and an AN/APR-38 radar and missile detection and launch homing system was installed. Westinghouse ECM underwing pods were used in conjunction with AGM-45 Shrike (later AGM-88 HARM) anti-radiation missiles for the destruction of SAM radars. All the 116 F-4Gs produced were rebuilds of existing F-4Es and, apart from the totally new avionics, the only other significant change was that made to the J79-17 engines which were modified to minimise smoke production. Self-defence weaponry was confined to a pair of AIM-7 AAMs in the rear fuselage recesses. During Desert Storm, F-4Gs played a leading part in the aerial campaign, with aircraft from the 35th TFW scything a path through Iraqi air defences with HARM missiles. Despite the succession of upgrades made to the F-4Gs in recent years, the aircraft has been replaced within the USAF by Block 50/52 F-16Cs.

# Export variants

**Based on aircraft used by the US Navy, Marines and Air Force, some Phantom variants were developed exclusively for export customers. The United Kingdom, Germany and Japan all had versions tailored to their own requirements.**

## Royal Air Force Phantom FGR.Mk 2 and F-4J(UK)

Following two prototype YF-4Ms, the RAF acquired 116 production standard F-4M Phantom FGR.Mk 2s, following the cancellation of the Hawker Siddeley P.1154 V/STOL strike/attack aircraft. Phantoms entered service first in the interdiction/strike and reconnaissance roles, carrying a wide array of stores including nuclear munitions. During the mid-1970s, when the Phantom was being replaced by the SEPECAT Jaguar in the ground-attack role in RAFG squadrons, the aircraft in turn replaced the Lightning in the air-defence role. Phantom FGR.Mk 2s served with Nos 2, 6 (the first RAF Phantom squadron), 14, 17, 19, 23, 29, 31, 41, 43, 54, 56, 64 (as a shadow squadron for 228 OCU), 74, 92 and 111 Squadrons, as well as No. 1435 Flight in the Falkland Islands. The strain on the fleet caused by basing Phantoms in the Falklands resulted in the RAF acquiring 15 surplus USN/USMC F-4Js, which served with No. 74 Sqn from August 1984 until September 1992. Only No. 56 Sqn – known as the 'Firebirds' – lasted longer, ceasing F-4 operations at the end of that year, bringing to a close RAF Phantom operations.

## Fleet Air Arm Phantom FG.Mk 1

Fifty F-4K Phantom FG.Mk 1s were ordered for the Royal Navy's Fleet Air Arm in July 1964. The use of Rolls-Royce Spey engines in British Phantoms dramatically increased the unit price of the aircraft and, while increasing range, decreased maximum speed, height and performance at altitude. The premature retirement of HMS *Victorious* and the prohibitive cost of refitting HMS *Eagle* left HMS *Ark Royal* as the only suitable carrier for the Phantom. Thus, half the order was diverted to the RAF, equipping No. 43 Squadron at Leuchars. In the Navy, the aircraft served with No. 700P Sqn at Yeovilton from April 1968 to March 1969 on trials work, No. 767 Sqn for type conversion during January 1969 to July 1972, also at Yeovilton, and operationally with No. 892 Sqn from March 1969, on various cruises on HMS *Ark Royal*, to the end of 1978. After 1978 the aircraft passed to the RAF and No. 111 Squadron.

## Japanese Air Self Defence Force F-4EJ Phantom

Japanese F-4EJs have been optimised for the air-defence mission via deletion of the F-4E's bombing system and provision for air-to-ground ordnance. A total of 140 aircraft was received by the Japanese Air Self-Defence Force (JASDF) from the McDonnell Douglas and Mitsubishi production lines, including the very last Phantom built, 17-8440, which was handed over in May 1981. Upon entering service the aircraft joined six squadrons: the 301st to 306th Hikotai. A programme from 1990 replaced the APQ-120 radar with the AN/APG-66J and extended the airframe life from 3,000 to 5,000 hours, producing the F-4EJ Kai (meaning 'extra' or 'plus'). Today, the F-4EJ Kai remains in service with the 301st Hikotai at Nyutabaru, the 302nd Hikotai at Naha and the 8th Hikotai at Misawa. They serve alongside F-15EJ Eagles in the air-interception role.

## Luftwaffe F-4F Phantom

The F-4F was a lightweight simplified F-4E for the Luftwaffe; that service ordered 175 aircraft to bridge the gap between the F-104 Starfighter and the Tornado. Ten F-4Es were also acquired for training purposes, but remained in the USA. The first F-4F was delivered on 5 September 1973, the type serving initially in two fighter-bomber wings and two interceptor wings. With the introduction of the Panavia Tornado in the early 1980s, the Phantom wings became dual-roled, but concentrated on air-defence duties from 1988 onwards. Today, the F-4Fs equip JG 71 at Hopsten, the 732 Staffel of JG 71 at Laage and JG 74 at Neuberg, as well as being part of the Taktische Ausbildungseinhiet Holloman in the USA.

# Foreign variants

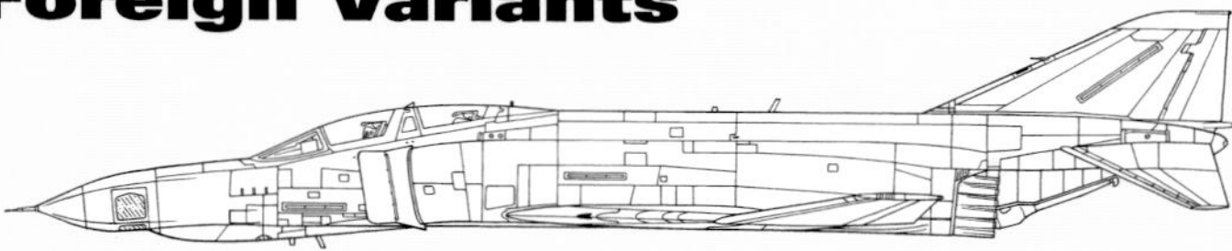

**F-4E(Special) or F-4E(S)**
Three Phantoms were converted to house the enormous HIAC-1 LOROP camera and passed to Israel. The nose featured slab-like sides and large camera windows.

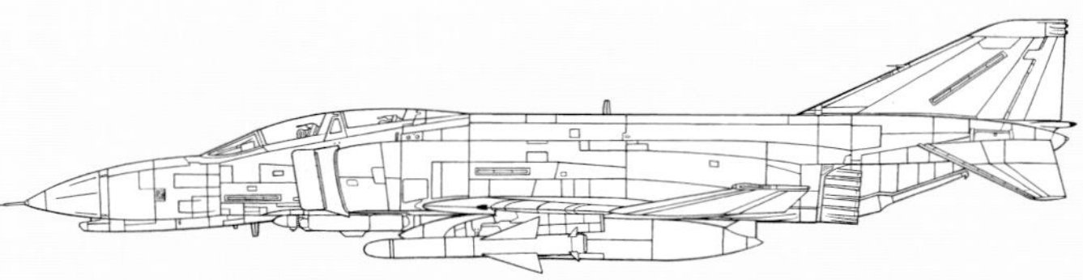

**JASDF F-4EJ Kai**
Almost identical to the F-4EJ, the upgraded F-4EJ Kai features tiny strengthening ribs on the outside of the radome, which houses the new AN/APG-66 radar.

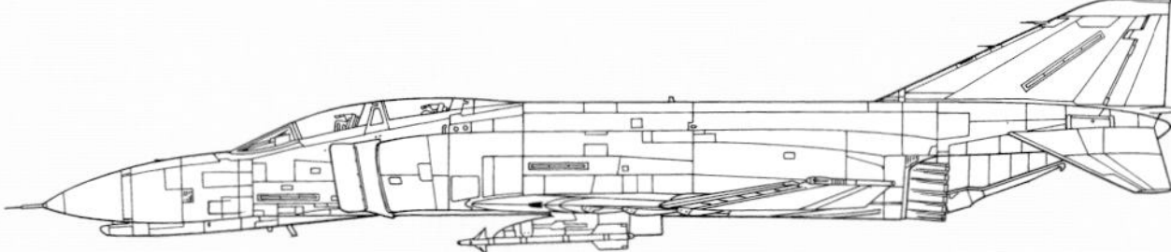

**Luftwaffe F-4F**
Differences between the F-4E and the German F-4F are not readily noticeable on the exterior of the aircraft, which was lighter and lacked Sparrow missile equipment.

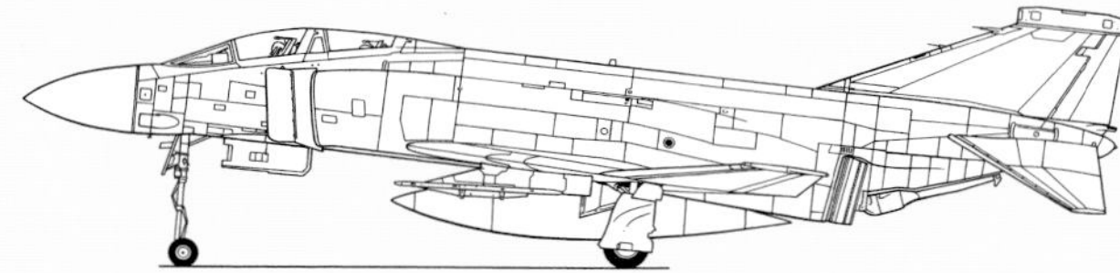

**FAA carrier-compatible F-4K Phantom FG.Mk 1**
Based on the F-4J, the F-4K had a folding radar and radome, extended nose wheel leg, a strengthened arrester hook and Spey 202/203 engines installed.

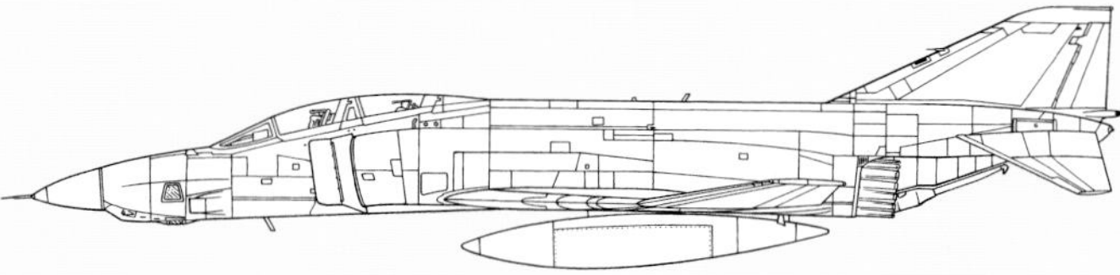

**International Export RF-4E**
The RF-4E mated the airframe and J79-GE-17 engines of the original (unslatted) F-4E with the RF-4C's nose. This Luftwaffe RF-4E has a SLAR in the fuel tank body.

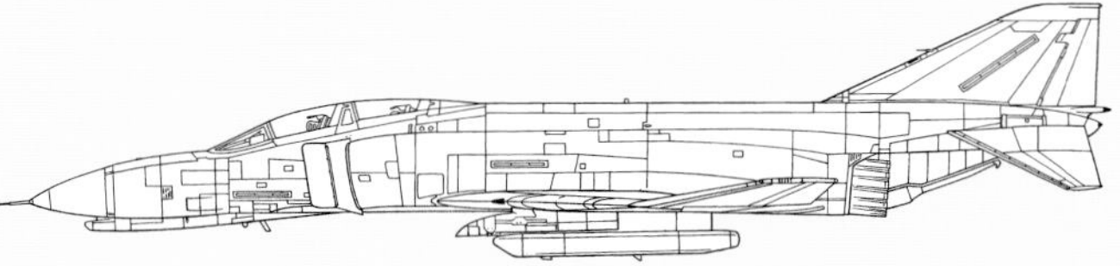

**JASDF RF-4EJ Kai (converted F-4EJ)**
The nose of the F-4EJ converted to the reconnaissance role looks very different to that of aircraft originally built as RF-4EJs (see photograph below).

## Export Reconnaissance Phantoms

First flown on 15 September 1970, the RF-4E was produced to a German specification for an RF-84F replacement. First introduced into service with AKG 51 at Bremgarten, followed by AKG 52 at Leck, a total of 88 aircraft was produced for the Luftwaffe. They were given a ground-attack capability from 1978 onwards, which they maintained until 1988. Four other nations also acquired RF-4Es from the production line, of which Iran was the second largest customer. A total of 27 aircraft was delivered to Iran prior to the Islamic revolution; 11 others were withheld. It is thought that most of the surviving RF-4Es in Iran were cannibalised for spares to keep the 'fighting Phantoms' airworthy. Israel received six RF-4Es and three RF-4E(S)s equipped with the HIAC-1 camera, requiring modified nose contours. Eight and six FY 1977 aircraft were delivered to Turkey and Greece, respectively. Turkish RF-4Es, new-built and ex-Luftwaffe, fly today from the 1 Ana Jet Us at Eskisehir, while the Greek aircraft fly with 348 MTA at Larissa.

## Japanese Reconnaissance Phantoms

Most Japanese Phantoms were built by Mitsubishi, but all the original reconnaissance-tasked RF-4EJs were assembled by McDonnell Douglas. Fourteen aircraft were produced and they differ from USAF RF-4Cs only in the deletion of some US-supplied electronics and replacement by Japanese equipment. All aircraft equipped the 501st Hikotai at Hyakuri following delivery. After being upgraded in the early 1990s, RF-4EJs were designated RF-4EJ Kais. Two of the original batch have been lost in accidents. A shortfall in reconnaissance assets is being overcome by the conversion of 17 F-4EJs to RF-4EJ Kai standard, of which 11 have been identified so far. The converted aircraft retain a limited combat capability, including the internal gun, and have no structural modifications. RF-4Es were delivered in a pale (gull) grey but later received a striking brown and two-tone green camouflage scheme.

# Phantom upgrades

**With its long projected structural lifespan, multi-mission versatility, and ability to carry large loads and a variety of weapons, the Phantom is regarded by its operators as an ideal platform for upgrading.**

## Germany – F-4F ICE

Work started in 1983, by MBB (now DaimlerChrysler Aerospace), on a Kampfwertsteigerung (KWS) or Improved Combat Effectiveness (ICE) project aimed at conferring BVR look-down/shoot-down capabilities to 110 air defence F-4Fs. A new, licence-built, Hughes APG-65GY pulse-Doppler radar was installed and Hughes AIM-120 AMRAAMs supplemented the original IR-homing AIM-9 Sidewinder capability. For ground-attack roles, another 37 German F-4Fs received similar avionics and structural improvements, but retained the original radar. Initial deliveries were made in April 1992; the last example was redelivered during 1998.

## Greece – DASA F-4E upgrade

The Phantom is planned to serve in the Greek air force until 2015. Currently, 70 F-4Es (above) are undergoing a Service-Life Extension Programme (SLEP) at Hellenic Aerospace Industries, while the air force is upgrading the first two of 39 'SLEPed' F-4Es at DASA to a similar standard as the German air force F-4F ICE. Modernisation (costing about US$8 million per aircraft), includes APG-65 radar, which is able to support AIM-120s. The remaining 37 F-4Es will undergo the modification at HAI. In the autumn of 1999 the first DASA Phantom was redelivered. Externally, the DASA F-4E can be identified by the small IFF antenna on top of the nose radome.

## Israel – Kurnass 2000 (Phantom 2000)

In the mid-1980s, the IDF/AF instigated an ambitious programme to upgrade 130 of its original F-4E Kurnass (Heavy Hammer) and RF-4E aircraft to Phantom 2000 standard for service into the next century. Airframe reinforcements were made to the fuselage and hydraulic and fuel systems were modified. The core of the Phantom 2000 avionics package is Elbit's ACE-3 mission computer (developed for the IDF/AF's F-16s), integrated with a Norden/UTC APG-76 synthetic-aperture multi-mode radar. Initial IDF/AF deliveries followed in 1989, although the new radar installations were not begun until 1992. IAI planned a re-engined Super Phantom 2000, with 20,600-lb (92-kN) thrust PW1120 turbofans, but orders were not forthcoming.

## Iran – F-4D and F-4E upgrades

Local upgrading of the IRIAF's surviving Phantoms has improved the detection range of the radars of both F-4Ds and F-4Es (above), and added defensive countermeasures. Several 'new' weapons have been integrated on the IRIAF F-4s, including the Chinese YJ-1/C-801 anti-ship missile, which was test-fired in 1997. Photographs also depict Iranian Phantoms launching what appears to be a TV-guided missile, and carrying a Standard missile (left). The latter, in its AGM-78 form, is an anti-radar missile, but Iranian weapons may have been modified to have an air-to-air or air-to-ground role. The IRIAF is expected to retain the Phantom in service as long as it can be viably supported.

### Turkey – IAI Phantom 2020

In the two-part F-4E upgrade programme, structural upgrading and the fitting of a new avionics package, broadly based on that of the Phantom 2000, were selected in 1996. IAI will upgrade 26 F-4Es in Israel and supply kits for another 28 F-4Es, to be upgraded by the THK. In some respects, including the 'glass' cockpit displays, the THK Phantom upgrade is more advanced than the IDF/AF version, with an Elta Electronics EL/M-2032 radar developed for the IAI Lavi, instead of the Norden APG-76. The prototype Phantom 2020 flew on 11 February 1999, and initial deliveries commenced in 2000.

### Spain – RF-4C SARA

'Have Quick' digital UHF/VHF communications radios, Itek AN/ARL-46 RWRs, Tracor AN/ALE-40 chaff/flare dispensers and AIM-9L Sidewinder AAM capability were standardised throughout the Spanish RF-4C fleet in the late 1980s. In late 1996, the SARA (Sistema Avanzado de Reconocimiento Aéreo) upgrade was announced, including Texas Instruments AN/APQ-172 terrain-following radar, ring laser-gyro INS and provision for an inflight-refuelling probe.

### USA – QF-4 drone conversions

Though it could not be described as an upgrade in the usual sense, the USAF's Phantom 'droning' programme is, nonetheless, another way of prolonging the useful lives of otherwise redundant airframes. Both the US Navy and USAF have, for many years, made use of retired airframes as pilotless target drones. With the retirement, in the mid-1990s, of the last F-4Gs and RF-4Cs the USAF began a new QF-4 conversion programme. Though a handful of RF-4Cs was utilised, most Phantom drones funded since 1995 have been QF-4Gs (left); options remain to keep 'production' running until 2005, bringing the QF-4G fleet to 192 aircraft.

## Japan – F-4EJ Kai

**Based at Misawa AB, this JASDF F-4EJ Kai is an aircraft of Dai 8 Hiko-tai, Dai 3 Koku-dan. This unit is charged with ground attack and anti-shipping missions and partners two other units in this role (Dai 3 and Dai 6 Hiko-tai), equipped with Mitsubishi F-1s. In 2000, Dai 8 Hiko-tai was one of four JASDF squadrons equipped with upgraded Phantoms; the other units comprised two interceptor squadrons and a reconnaissance squadron.**

**New radar**
F-4EJ Kai modifications centre around the adoption of the Northrop Grumman (Westinghouse) APG-66J radar, based on that fitted to the F-16, in place of the old Westinghouse APQ-120. The new radar is much lighter and smaller, and offers a considerable improvement in performance and reliability.

**Self-defence**
A key part of the F-4EJ Kai conversion is the upgrade of the RWR system to J/APR-6 standard, based on the J/APR-4 fitted to the F-15J. The Kai is also able to carry the AN/ALQ-131 jamming pod.

**External differences**
External additions to the Kai-modified aircraft include twin aft-facing RWR antennas on the fintip, similar forward-facing antennas on the wingtips, a large blade aerial, mounted mid-spine, for the new UHF radio, a large blade aerial on the nosewheel door and a new radome with lengthwise strengthening strips added.

**Air-to-air weapons**
F-4EJ Kais continue to have Sparrow/Sidewinder capability, using these missiles in AIM-7E/F and AIM-9P/L forms. Mitsubishi AAM-3s are now routinely carried, superseding the Sidewinder. Despite the adoption of the true look-down/shoot-down APG-66J radar, no plans to acquire a modern BVR missile have been announced, though procurement of the AMRAAM-class AAM-4 seems likely.

**F-4EJ Kai programme**
Of the 140 F-4EJs procured by the JASDF, around 90 (figures of 86, 91 and 96 have been quoted) were upgraded to F-4EJ Kai standard for service with three squadrons (301, 302 and 306), each with a unit establishment of 22 aircraft – 306 Squadron's aircraft were later transferred to Dai 8 Koku-tai. First flown in July 1984, the F-4EJ Kai entered service in December 1989. In addition to the extensive avionics update, the Kai programme also included a thorough structural SLEP to extend the Phantom's fatigue life.

**Anti-ship armament**
Officially known as an 'anti-landing craft missile' (due to the JASDF's purely defensive official role), a principal form of anti-ship missile available to the F-4EJ Kai is the ASM-2 (as seen on this aircraft). The armament has imaging infra-red guidance in the terminal phase and is powered by a small turbojet.

***During the Allied Force operations over Kosovo in 1999, the USAF assigned 24 KC-10As to the Allied Force tanker fleet, split between Moron in Spain and Rhein-Main in Germany. The example shown here was operated from the latter, as part of the 60th Air Expeditionary Wing.***

# McDonnell Douglas KC-10 Extender

## From DC-10 to Extender

**The KC-10 was ordered in the late 1970s to give fighter wings greater mobility by being able to transport support personnel, as well as refuel deployed fighters.**

The McDonnell Douglas KC-10A Extender strategic tanker/transport is based on the DC-10 Series 30CF commercial freighter/airliner and was obtained to satisfy the ATCA (Advanced Tanker Cargo Aircraft) requirement. It emerged victorious in a contest with Boeing's Model 747 in December 1977 when the USAF indicated its intention to procure 16 examples, but the number on order rose in December 1982 when the USAF placed a contract covering a further 44 aircraft. The first example of the Extender made its maiden flight on 12 July 1980 and deliveries to the Air Force commenced in March 1981, presaging a six-month period of operational testing in which all aspects were exhaustively evaluated. Just over seven years later, the 60th and last KC-10A was formally handed over on 29 November 1988. Originally allocated solely to Strategic Air Command, the KC-10A was (and still is) frequently flown by Air Force Reserve crews under the so-called 'associate' programme. The recent major USAF re-organisation that witnessed the elimination of SAC has resulted in examples of the Extender being redistributed amongst elements of Air Mobility Command and Air Combat Command.

Changes from commercial DC-10 standard include provision of an inflight-refuelling receptacle above the cockpit, improved cargo handling system and some military avionics. The most visible evidence of modification for the ATCA role is the

***Seen here in the old markings of Strategic Air Command , KC-10A 79-0434 now operates with the 305th Air Mobility Wing from McGuire AFB in New Jersey, which is broken up into the 32nd and 72nd Air Refuelling Squadrons.***

*Left: The KC-10A plays a vital role in supporting the USAF's bombers, here exemplified by a B-52. The Extender can transport 75 people and 170,000 lb (76,560 kg) of cargo a distance of 4,400 miles (7040 km). Without cargo, the KC-10A's unrefuelled range is over 11,500 miles (18507 km).*

*Below: The Aerial Refueling Operator's station on the KC-10A affords an excellent view of the refuelling aircraft. A periscopic observation system gives a wide field of vision for safe traffic management, and the station is pressurised and air-conditioned.*

McDonnell Douglas Advanced Aerial Refueling Boom (AARB) sited beneath the aft fuselage. The refuelling operator's station is equipped with a periscope observation system and rear window for wide field of view. The KC-10's boom is fitted with digital FBW control and provides greater capability than the type fitted in the KC-135. The boom is rated at a fuel transfer rate of 1,500 US gal (5678 litres) per minute.

The 'flying boom' is the preferred Air Force method of transferring fuel in flight, but the Extender is also fitted with a hose and reel unit in the starboard aft fuselage and can thus refuel Navy and Marine Corps aircraft during the same mission.

## Mid-air refuelling

Wing-mounted pods are fitted to 20 KC-10s to allow three receiver aircraft to be simultaneously refuelled with the probe-and-drogue system. Trials of this configuration were undertaken with the last KC-10 to be built, which was fitted with a pair of Flight Refuelling Ltd Mk 32B hose drum pods. Seven bladder fuel cells have been installed primarily in the lower fuselage baggage compartments, and comprise three forward and four cells aft of the wing.

The KC-10 is able to perform missions that require it to undertake aspects of both the tanker and transport functions in a single mission. As an example, accompanying and refuelling deploying fighters, at the same time as transporting technicians, administrative staff and vital ground equipment in the cabin, which can accommodate up to 75 personnel and some 17 cargo pallets.

*Right: Crew members from the 2nd Air Refuelling Squadron based at McGuire AFB in New Jersey load up a KC-10A using the upward-hinging cargo door in the forward port fuselage, at NSF Diego Garcia, British Indian Ocean Territory. A total of 60 Extenders was built for the USAF, most of which now carry the all-over charcoal grey colour scheme.*

***The introduction of the Harrier II gave the USMC a much more capable aircraft than the original AV-8A, offering greater performance and capability. This AV-8B carries a relatively light weaponload of four 500-lb (226-kg) Snakeye retarded bombs and two AIM-9 Sidewinder AAMs for self-defence.***

# Harrier II
## Development

**The original Harrier was renowned for its versatility and manoeuvrability, but was severely hampered by its lack of range and primitive avionics. Pilots' prayers were answered with the development of the McDonnell Douglas/BAe Harrier II.**

***The carbon-fibre big wing designed by McDonnell Douglas provided much greater lift, increased internal fuel capacity and two extra pylons. The prototype YAV-8B wore a patriotic red, white and blue colour scheme.***

Seeking to anticipate an RAF and USMC requirement for a Harrier follow-on even as the aircraft was entering service, Hawker Siddeley and McDonnell Douglas joined forces to consider a new airframe, while Rolls-Royce paired up with Pratt & Whitney in engine development. The US Navy was also in the market for a V/STOL combat aircraft, but expressed little interest in the design. Instead, it opted to order the Rockwell XFV-12A in 1972, but this project – of little use to the USMC – was eventually cancelled.

In March 1975, Britain withdrew from the 'Super Harrier' project, claiming that there was insufficient common ground to make the partnership viable. A little over six years later, Britain bought back into the US programme as a sub-contractor rather than the full partner it could have been and went on to order 110 of what was then called the AV-8B Harrier II.

While Britain had been indecisive about the project, McDonnell Douglas had kept the Harrier alive through the energetic support of the USMC. The St Louis designers shunned uprated engines as a quick (but expensive) way of improving the Harrier and instead devoted their attentions to doubling the aircraft's payload/range capability through modifications to the structure and the aerodynamics.

A new, larger carbon-fibre supercritical wing, together with widespread use of the same material in the forward fuselage and other areas, was combined with lift-improvement devices to boost performance, while a raised cockpit with a new nav/attack avionics suite enhanced the pilot's situational awareness. With the same engine

***The first FSD (Full Scale Development) AV-8B made its maiden flight on 5 November 1981. It featured a redesigned intake and a new forward fuselage built from carbon-fibre. A long test instrumentation boom was carried on the nose.***

***Above: McDonnell Douglas converted one AV-8B as a night-attack prototype. The aircraft was fitted with a GEC Sensors FLIR sensor in its nose which was linked to the pilot's NVGs.***

***Above: Clearly prominent on the new generation of Harriers is the increase in size of the engine intakes. Visible in this view is the GR.Mk 5's nose-mounted combined laser-and-television camera which measured slant angle and range to the target.***

power, the AV-8B was able to lift 70 per cent more external ordnance and to carry 50 per cent more internal fuel. Furthermore, the new Harrier required 60 per cent fewer maintenance personnel hours per airframe.

### Harrier II wing

The new wing was first flown on 9 November 1978, attached to the eleventh early-generation AV-8A. This was subsequently redesignated as YAV-8B as the aircraft lacked internal modifications. With a wing area of 230 sq ft (21.37 $m^2$), the machine proved to be slower than its predecessor. Three weapons pylons were mounted under either wing, and the outriggers were transferred from the tips to give a shorter wheel track for improved taxiing. One of the most significant developments from the pilot's point of view was the raised seating position, which was 12 in (30 cm) higher than before. The pilot was thus afforded a much better view, and was now able to utilise HOTAS controls in a cockpit which was far roomier and ergonomically efficient than that of its predecessor.

### Pegasus developments

The new Mk 105 Pegasus engine (known to the USMC as the Pegasus F402-RR-406A) for the AV-8B was developed from 1980 by Rolls-Royce with assistance from Smiths Industries and Dowty. First flight-tested in an early GR.Mk 3 between 1982 and 1987, an improved version of the engine was installed in Britain's first Harrier GR.Mk 5 which made its maiden flight on 23 April 1985.

A second USMC YAV-8B flew on 19 February 1979, although this was lost on 15 November when the pilot ejected following an engine flame-out. In addition to the new wing, the two USMC prototypes were fitted with the F402-RR-406A engine that featured extended forward nozzles.

Early in their development, AV-8Bs were fitted with LERXes forward of the wing roots to improve the turning radius of the aircraft and reduce wing rock when flying at low altitude. Other minor changes saw four of the seven wing pylons being plumbed for the carriage of external fuel tanks.

The vastly improved Harrier steadily gained support within the USMC, which eventually placed an initial order for 286 examples for front-line units, beginning in 1983.

### Britain's GR.Mk 5

Following the 1975 political divorce between the US and British development teams, BAe concentrated on its own Harrier schemes, without carbon-fibre technology. Most of these trials were to come to nothing, however. Britain was offered a part-share in the US project (being assigned to build 40 per cent of the AV-8B airframe), while building 50 per cent of RAF machines.

Numerous minor differences were to be found between the GR.Mk 5 and the AV-8B, some of which were responsible for the delay in the UK programme. The Pegasus Mk 105 powerplant was rated slightly differently. The cockpit was fitted with a Ferranti moving-map display, while a more sophisticated Marconi radar-warning system was installed. Other minor changes saw the adoption of Bofors chaff dispensers fitted to the rear of the AIM-9 Sidewinder launcher rails. The change in equipment resulted in the GR.Mk 5 weighing more than its US cousin.

The development of the Harrier II brought with it a change in roles. The Harrier II was no longer viewed as a close air support (CAS) aircraft; it was now seen as a 'battlefield air interdictor'.

***Flying for the first time on 21 November 1986, the TAV-8B was fitted with a taller fin and only two weapons pylons. Full tandem controls are fitted in a stepped cockpit arrangement.***

***Below: The first UK GR.Mk 5 (ZD318) flew from Dunsfold, Hampshire on 30 April 1985. The RAF's premier Harrier squadron, No. 1, was declared with the GR.Mk 5 on 2 November 1989.***

*The Harrier's Cold War role centred around deployed operations from rural and urban hides, and the aircraft's unique STOVL characteristics mean that such operations are still regularly practised.*

# GR.Mk 7 & T.Mk 10

**The Harrier is, today, arguably the most important aircraft in the RAF inventory. Versatile, flexible, deployable and extremely effective, the Harrier has played a major role in many recent operations.**

The Harrier GR.Mk 7 is the RAF equivalent of the Night-Attack AV-8B, and uses the same or similar equipment and avionics. It has the same overnose GEC Sensors FLIR, and has a fully NVG-compatible glass cockpit, although the RAF's Harrier Force uses Ferranti Night-Owl NVGs rather than the GEC Cat's Eyes NVGs favoured by the USMC. The RAF aircraft lacks the rear fuselage chaff/flare dispensers of the later AV-8Bs, but does feature the superb Marconi Zeus ECM system. Zeus consists of an indigenous RWR and a Northrop jammer which will jam both CW (continuous wave) and pulse radars. It is linked to the Plessey Missile Approach Warning System which will automatically activate appropriate countermeasures if it detects an inbound missile.

One 'traditional problem' with RAF Offensive Support aircraft has been a lack of hardpoints. The Harrier GR.Mk 7 has six underwing pylons, and a centreline station, in addition to two dedicated Sidewinder pylons. The ongoing provision of an integral BOL chaff dispenser in these pylons will finally free the aircraft from having to 'lose' a weapon station as it now does in order to carry a standard Phimat pod.

The RAF's second-generation Harrier suffered from an annoying series of teething troubles when it entered service. This included an ejection seat problem which killed a BAe test pilot, and the failure of some originally specified items of equipment to work as advertised (or sometimes even to work at all). One such item was the planned MIRLS (miniature IR linescanner) reconnaissance

*The post-Cold War world has seen carrier operations become a vital part of the Harrier force's work. RAF Harriers and RN Sea Harriers are being combined in a new 'Joint Force 2000'.*

*The Harrier T.Mk 10 is the two-seat trainer version of the RAF's 'second-generation Harrier', and has now entirely replaced the original T.Mk 4 in RAF service. It is used only for training, despite formidable operational capabilities.*

**By comparison with the original Harrier (and the RAF's ageing Jaguar), the GR.Mk 7 offers massive carrying capacity, with sufficient muscle to bear two 2,000-lb (907-kg) LGBs as well as fuel, AAMs, a chaff dispenser and even a centreline reconnaissance pod!**

system, originally intended to occupy the lower nose, and the original INS. Such problems were soon addressed, however, and by the time the GR.Mk 5 gave way to the definitive GR.Mk 7, most of the difficulties had been solved. The saddest exceptions were the twin Royal Ordnance Factory ADEN 25-mm pneumatically-cocked revolver cannon, which promised lower recoil, a faster initial rate of fire and lighter weight than the single GAU-12A fitted to US AV-8Bs. Despite intensive trials work and innovative engineering, no-one was able to solve the gun's problems, and the weapon has now been cancelled. This leaves the Harrier as the first RAF fighter-bomber not to be equipped with a gun. Confusingly, Harrier GR.Mk 7s frequently fly with empty gun pods as an aerodynamic aid.

The first GR.Mk 7s ordered as such were the 34 aircraft requested during 1988 (although earlier aircraft were rapidly converted to the later standard). Both pre-series GR.Mk 5s were adapted to accommodate the overnose FLIR and undernose Zeus antennas, serving as GR.Mk 7 prototypes. The first flew in its new guise on 20 November 1989.

The first production GR.Mk 7 was delivered in May 1990, with service deliveries beginning in August 1990 to the Strike Attack OEU at Boscombe Down. This unit has used a handful of GR.Mk 7s to develop and refine operational procedures, tactics and equipment, carrying out pioneering work with NVGs and FLIR. Production GR.Mk 7s were also delivered to No. IV Squadron (replacing first-generation GR.Mk 3s) from September 1990, and began to supplant the GR.Mk 5s of No. 3 Squadron in November 1990.

To ease the planned conversion of GR.Mk 5s to the later-standard aircraft, Nos 42-60 were completed as GR.Mk 5As with provision for GR.Mk 7 avionics (with an empty FLIR hump and Zeus antenna fairings), and were delivered straight to storage to await full conversion. Conversion of these aircraft (and of a damaged GR.Mk 5) began during December 1990, most of the former GR.Mk 5As going to Nos 1 and 20 Squadrons.

Nos 3 and IV Squadrons moved to Laarbrüch and came under the control of NATO's Rapid Reaction Force when RAF Gütersloh, Germany, closed in 1993. In 1999 the squadrons finally moved to the UK, taking up station at RAF Cottesmore.

From aircraft No. 77 (ZG506), Harrier GR.Mk 7s were fitted with the larger, so-called 100 per cent, LERX – this further delays the onset of wing rock and improves turn performance. A programme to replace the smaller, compromise, LERX on earlier aircraft was suspended due to the need for commonality, and reported difficulties in clearing the big LERX for carrier operation. Some late GR.Mk 7s have even had their 'big LERXes' removed and replaced with the original unit!

A decision to procure the Harrier T.Mk 10 (an anglicised TAV-8B, with night-attack systems) was taken in February 1990 and an order for 13 aircraft was confirmed early in 1992. This finally gave the Harrier force a trainer that was fully representative of the second-generation Harrier GR.Mk 7 in performance and capability. Powered by the Pegasus Mk 105 engine, the T.Mk 10, which first flew on 7 April 1994, is fully combat-capable, unlike its US counterpart, which can carry only training armament.

The Harrier GR.Mk 7's original, rather limited, armament of 1,000-lb (454-kg) bombs, BL755s and 2.68-in (68-mm) SNEB rocket pods has been augmented by a number of new weapons better suited for medium-level use. These include CRV-7 rockets and CBU-87 cluster bombs, as used by Jaguars during the Gulf War. The GR.Mk 7 is also compatible with Paveway II and Paveway III LGBs (both of which it dropped 'in anger' during Operation Allied Force over Kosovo). Harrier GR.Mk 7s first dropped Paveway IIs on Serb targets during operations over Bosnia in 1995, relying on TIALD-equipped Jaguars to designate their targets. Since then, TIALD has been integrated on the Harrier itself, and the aircraft can now self-designate.

To provide a reconnaissance capability for the GR.Mk 7 for Operation Warden, at least nine aircraft were rewired to carry the original GR.Mk 3 recce pod. This contained a fan of four F95 cameras with 2¾-in (70-mm) lenses and a single F135 with a 5-in (127-mm) lens. This interim solution worked well, before the Harriers received Vinten Vicon 18 Series 601 GP(1) and Series 603 LOROP pods.

Out-of-area, medium-level operations also drove the programme to improve the GR.Mk 7's navigation equipment. This finally bore fruit in late 1992 when the inertial navigation system was upgraded to FIN1075G standard, with the incorporation of GPS. This was particularly important in allowing the accurate overwater navigation required for successful carrier operation. After various trial deployments, No.1 Squadron actually deployed aboard HMS *Invincible* in November 1997, ready to participate in possible air strikes against Iraq.

The Harrier GR.Mk 7 represents a useful addition to the air wing of any RN carrier, its night- and ground-attack capabilities augmenting the superb air defence of the Sea Harrier. Following the Strategic Defence Review, the Sea Harrier and Harrier Forces are being combined, with an upgraded Harrier GR.Mk 9 due to be the only Harrier in British service from about 2008.

**Pictured during an Operation Deny Flight mission over the Balkans, this Harrier wears the current two-tone grey, 'low IR' colour scheme, with no unit markings. It carries a W. Vinten Ltd Type 18 Series 601 GP(1) reconnaissance pod on the centreline.**

# USMC Harrier IIs

*Seen unleashing an AGM-65E semi-active laser-guided missile, this AV-8B flew with VMA-223 'Bulldogs'. The squadron was formerly the last operational East Coast A-4M Skyhawk operator.*

**The Harrier's ability to operate independently of fixed bases has provided the US Marine Corps with a potent asset with which to fulfil the Corps' vital role in limited and contingency warfare situations.**

The USMC functions as a self-contained and complete force, and has a great tradition of self-sufficiency. It is a matter of pride that the USMC provides its soldiers with their own CAS (close air support), and the Harrier II plays a major part in fulfilling that 'debt of honour'. The AV-8B replaced the AV-8A and A-4M in USMC service, and equipped a training unit and seven front-line squadrons. One squadron disbanded as an economy measure, although early plans to establish two reserve Harrier squadrons were abandoned.

Administratively, the USMC is divided into two Fleet Marine Forces (FMFs), each with a geographical primary 'area of responsibility'. The Fleet Marine Force Atlantic includes the 2d (not '2nd', in USMC parlance) Marine Air Wing at MCAS Cherry Point, North Carolina, which in turn includes the AV-8B-equipped Marine Air Group 14. Cherry Point boasts four 8,500-ft (2591-m) runways, two dispersal sites and a relief landing ground at Bogue Field, which has a dummy LHA deck for shipboard qualification, and a full-size dummy carrier deck with arrester gear.

The Fleet Marine Force Pacific included the 3rd MAW at MCAS Yuma, Arizona, whose Harrier element comprised MAG 13, with a mix of AV-8Bs and AV-8B(NA)s in VMA-211, VMA-214, VMA-311 and VMA-513. During the Gulf War, MAG 13 (Forward Deployed) was based at King Abdul Aziz AB with VMA-231, VMA-311, VMA-542 and VMA-513 Det B, under the command of Colonel John 'Hunter' Bioty. More Harriers participated in the war in the form of VMA-331, which formed part of MAG 40 aboard USS *Nassau*. Another AV-8B operating unit was MAG 12, which has no Harriers or Harrier pilots of its own but maintained a constant AV-8B presence at MCAS Iwakuni through a rotational deployment of 'gun' squadrons.

*The 22-week USMC AV-8B conversion course includes 62 Harrier flights, and 60 flying hours, with 15 flights in the TAV-8B before soloing. Former AV-8A/C pilots required only 14 AV-8B flights.*

*VMA-542 'Flying Tigers' replaced its AV-8As and AV-8Cs with AV-8Bs in April 1986. The second AV-8B squadron to deploy to the Persian Gulf during Desert Shield and Desert Storm, VMA-542 left Saudi Arabia in March 1991, and subsequently became the first squadron to operate the Harrier II Plus from July 1993. The unit's aircraft wear distinctive yellow 'tiger skin' rudders.*

## MEF deployment

Marine aviation exists to deploy, usually as part of a marine air-ground task force. The largest such force is a marine expeditionary force (MEF), commanded by a two-star lieutenant general with one division and a full marine air wing, including up to 60 AV-8Bs. The forward echelon of an MEF would be provided by an MEF with an infantry regiment and a MAG, including perhaps as many as 40 AV-8Bs. They would deploy in full squadrons, and would retain their unit identities. MEFs deploy aboard the new 40,532-ton (41180-tonne) 'Wasp'-class LHDs, which can embark up to 20 Harriers and six H-60s or CH-46s.

The 'Wasp' class comprises: LHD-1 *Wasp*, LHD-2 *Essex*, LHD-3 *Kearsarge*, LHD-4 *Boxer*, LHD-5 *Bataan*, and LHD-6 *Bonhomme Richard*. A seventh example is under construction. The older 'Tarawa'-class amphibious assault ships (LHAs) are Harrier capable and can operate a standard mix of six AV-8Bs alongside CH-53Ds, CH-46D/E and AH-1Ws, as required. The 'Tarawa' class

***The tail flash on this VMA-542 Harrier II Plus is evidence of the subtle return of squadron markings to the Marines' universally grey Harrier fleet. The 'Flying Tigers' are one of the longest-standing Marine AV-8 units, having swapped their F-4Bs for AV-8As in June 1970. The aircraft pictured has just released an inert BSU-86-tailed 500-lb (227-kg) Mk 82R retarded bomb.***

***Left: Carrying an AN/ALQ-164 ECM pod on its centreline and tanking from a KC-130F, this VMA-214 AV-8B (foreground) is pictured formating with its successor, a VMA-231 Harrier II Plus.***

comprise: LHA-1 *Tarawa*, LHA-2 *Saipan*, LHA-3 *Belleau Wood*, LHA-4 *Nassau*, and LHA-5 *Peleliu*. Finally, two 'Iwo Jima'-class LPHs remain in service: LPH-9 *Guam* and LPH-11 *New Orleans*. They are Harrier capable, but have been re-roled as mine countermeasures vessels in recent years.

AV-8Bs can also deploy aboard the eight 'Whidbey Island'-class LSD deck landing vessels. Trials have been undertaken with British-type ski-jumps, but the USMC ships are considered as a means of getting to the operational area, where forward sites would be prepared, and not as routine operating platforms in their own right. Next down the scale is the marine expeditionary unit, with a reinforced infantry battalion and a reinforced helicopter squadron, usually incorporating six Harriers, which routinely wear the unit titles of the parent helicopter unit. Two Special Operations-capable MEUs are permanently deployed, each with a reinforced helicopter squadron and a reinforced infantry battalion. The aviation element usually included 12 CH-46s, four CH-53s, six AH-1s, three UH-1s and six AV-8Bs.

With its Hornets receiving radar upgrades, the USMC decided to install their now redundant APG-65 radars into some of its AV-8B Harrier II fleet. The resulting Harrier II Plus entered service with VMA-542 in 1993, with the Marine Corps subsequently converting all of its surviving 72 AV-8Bs to the new standard by the end of 2003. The AV-8B Harrier II Plus is likely to remain in service until at least 2010–2025, when it will be replaced by the F-35B.

# AV-8B Harrier II

**From the 167th AV-8B all deliveries to the USMC were of the Night Attack variant, with the first production aircraft to the new standard being delivered to the Marines on 15 September 1989. The first unit to re-equip with this version was was the Yuma-based VMA-214, the famous 'Black Sheep', previously equipped with A-4Ms. This aircraft is armed with a pair of AGM-65E Mavericks, a pair of Mk 20 Rockeye II cluster bombs and AIM-9L/M Sidewinders outboard for self-defence. Despite working up with the AV-8B during the Gulf War, the unit deployed their Harriers to Iwakuni in October 1991 – the type's first overseas deployment.**

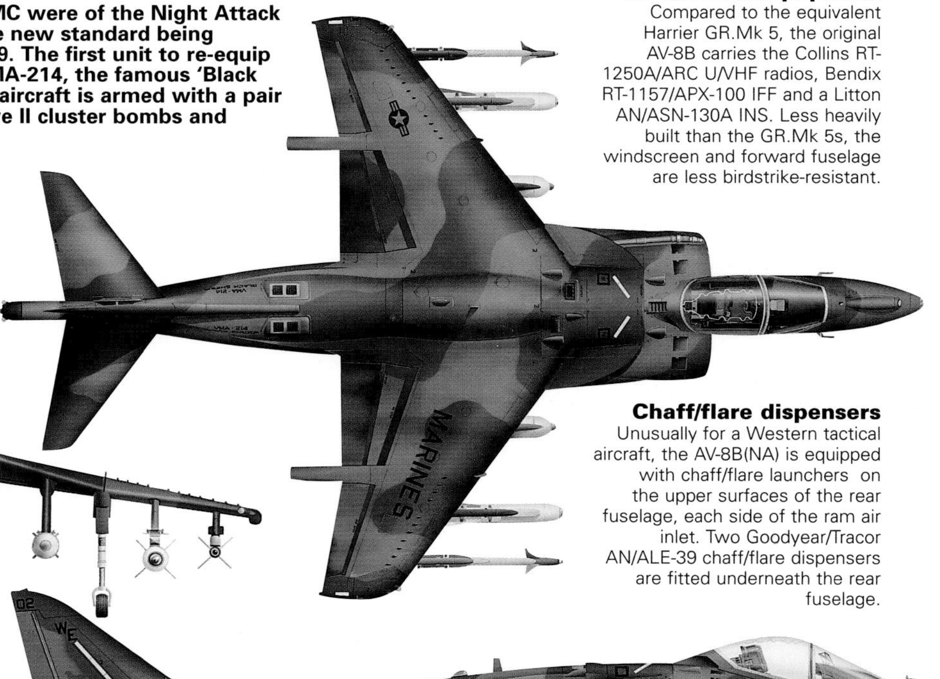

**US avionics/equipment**
Compared to the equivalent Harrier GR.Mk 5, the original AV-8B carries the Collins RT-1250A/ARC U/VHF radios, Bendix RT-1157/APX-100 IFF and a Litton AN/ASN-130A INS. Less heavily built than the GR.Mk 5s, the windscreen and forward fuselage are less birdstrike-resistant.

**Ejection seat**
The AV-8B pilot is provided with a UPC/Stencel type 10B ejection seat, located 12 in (30.5 cm) higher than the seat in the AV-8A and Harrier GR.Mk 3, The raised seat position is accomodated by the adoption of a larger, two-piece raised bubble canopy.

**Chaff/flare dispensers**
Unusually for a Western tactical aircraft, the AV-8B(NA) is equipped with chaff/flare launchers on the upper surfaces of the rear fuselage, each side of the ram air inlet. Two Goodyear/Tracor AN/ALE-39 chaff/flare dispensers are fitted underneath the rear fuselage.

**Underfuselage cannon**
The AV-8B can be fitted with a single GE GAU-12A 'Equalizer' five-barrel Gatling-type cannon. This occupies the port underfuselage pod, with 300 ammunition rounds in the starboard pod.

*Italy's two TAV-8Bs were acquired from the USMC, and Spain similarly plans to equip with TAV-8B two-seaters. Italian Harriers are operated by 1° Gruppo Aereo (1° Grupaer) based at Grottaglie, close to the Taranto naval base in southern Italy. The MMI's two TAV-8Bs were delivered in August 1991 to the newly-constructed airbase.*

# Export operators

**Italian Harrier II operational training has frequently involved co-operation with Spanish AV-8B Matadors, leading to speculation about formation of a 'Harrier Force Southern Europe'.**

Although Spain preferred to buy US-supplied AV-8S Matadors (known as VA.1s, EAV-8As or AV-8As in Spanish service) rather than British Harrier GR.Mk 1s, the aircraft's shipborne role led some to expect that the follow-on order would be for navalised, radar-equipped Sea Harriers . However, long-standing links with the USA meant that Spain procured the US version. Spain signed a contract for 12 AV-8Bs in March 1983, designating its new aircraft as VA.2 Matador IIs, although the Matador name was even less commonly used than in the AV-8S era. McDonnell Douglas refers to the aircraft as EAV-8Bs. Following initial pilot conversion in the USA, the first three aircraft were ferried to Rota on 6 October 1987.

The new EAV-8Bs were delivered in an overall matt two-tone grey colour scheme, similar to that applied to contemporary US Navy carrierborne aircraft, just as the AV-8As had worn a glossy gull-grey and white scheme which echoed that applied to US Navy carrierborne aircraft of the late 1960s and early 1970s.

The wooden-decked *Dedalo* (the former cruiser USS *Cabot*) was retired in 1988 and was replaced by the new *Príncipe de Asturias* in July 1989. AV-8Ss were cleared for operation from the new carrier's 12° ski jump by BAe test pilots Heinz Frick and Steve Thomas, and Spanish pilots were ski-jump trained at RNAS Yeovilton.

The Spanish navy leased time on the Harrier GR.Mk 3 simulator at Wittering in later years, instead of sending pilots to MCAS Cherry Point. (Subsequently, the Spanish EAV-8B simulator was used by RAF GR.Mk 5 pilots, before the RAF received its first GR.Mk 5 simulator.) EAV-8B ski jump trials were conducted later, by USMC and US Navy test pilots at Patuxent River. The smaller, older *Dedalo* had no ski jump, so such training had not hitherto been necessary. Both Spanish carriers were home-ported at Rota, close to the airfield at Rota housing the Armada Harrier squadrons.

Under the Tripartite MoU of 1990, Spain received eight new-build Harrier II Pluses and a TAV-8B two-seater, and the 10 surviving AV-8Bs will be upgraded to the same standards.

## Spanish units

8ª Escuadrilla was the original Spanish navy Matador unit, and took over responsibility for training Spanish Harrier pilots when the USMC withdrew its AV-8As. There were some expectations that 8ª Escuadrilla would eventually take the radar-equipped EAV-8Bs, but the unit decommissioned on 24 October 1996, when the surviving seven AV-8S and two TAV-8S aircraft were transferred to the Royal Thai navy. 9ª Escuadrilla was formed at Rota on 29 September 1987 to operate the Armada's EAV-8Bs, which were delivered between October 1987 and September 1988. The squadron underwent an intensive work-up prior to its first deployment in 1989. The squadron forms part of the Alpha Carrier Air Group with co-located Sea King and Bell 212 squadrons. Escuadrilla 008 continued to operate the

*Spain's AV-8Bs operate from the deck of the flagship* Príncipe de Asturias *(R-11), which is equipped with a 12° ski-jump. In total, the naval air arm acquired 12 AV-8Bs, the first of these aircraft being delivered in 1987, whilst AV-8A Matadors were passed to Thailand. In September 1990, Spain joined the Harrier II Plus programme.*

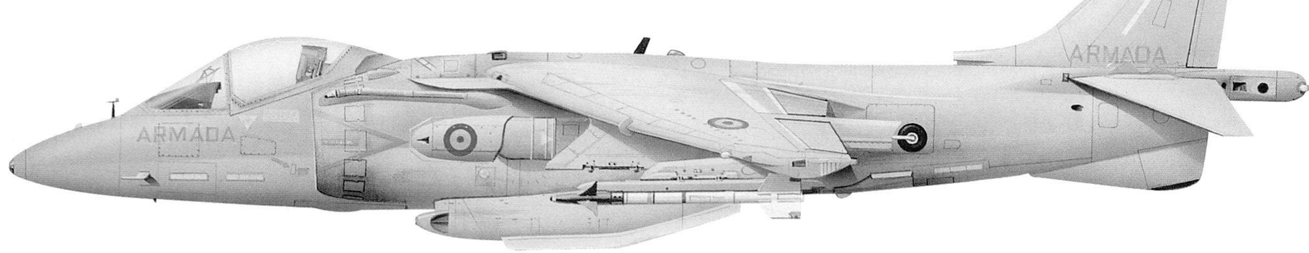

***In accordance with 1° Grupaer's wolf's head badge, this Harrier II Plus carries a wolf's paw-print fin flash. A total of 16 Harrier II Plus aircraft were ordered by Italy, whilst the TAV-8Bs were re-engined.***

EAV-8A, with a mixed complement of four AV-8As and eight 9ª Escuadrilla EAV-8Bs typically deploying aboard the *Príncipe de Asturias*. Some 9ª Escuadrilla pilots were posted to the air force from late 1994 to gain experience with the F/A-18, prior to introduction of the APG-65-equipped Harrier II Plus.

## Italian interest

Italy began looking at the possibility of acquiring Harriers in October 1967, when Hawker Siddeley test pilot Hugh Merewether landed one on the navy's helicopter-carriers, the *Andrea Doria*. A proposed buy of 24 aircraft became a planned offset deal which involved the supply of six British-built Harrier GR.Mk 50s, with 44 more to be licence-built or licence-assembled. AMI opposition and funding problems killed off the plans, although when the new helicopter-carrier *Giuseppe Garibaldi* was launched in 1983, it was clearly intended to be capable of operating fixed-wing STOVL aircraft as well as helicopters. The vessel was fitted with a 6° 30' ski-jump from the start, long before the MMI procured Harriers. The ski-jump was originally described as a device to protect the flight deck from excessive spray, to distract attention from the navy's ambitions. The ship hosted cross-deck deployments by USMC AV-8Bs and Royal Navy Sea Harriers in 1988.

After evaluation of the Sea Harrier and AV-8B, the MMI gained government approval to operate fixed-wing aircraft, and immediately ordered two TAV-8B trainers in May 1989, simultaneously dispatching a cadre of pilots to the USA for training. In 1990, construction of a runway, new hangars and other facilities began at Luni. Sixteen Harrier II Pluses were ordered (with options on eight more), and the first three of these aircraft were diverted from the USMC's allocation on 20 April 1994, being delivered to MCAS Cherry Point for training. The two TAV-8Bs were re-engined with F402-RR-408s in 1994 to improve 'hot-and-high' performance. The final single-seaters were assembled by Alenia.

## MMI two-seaters

The MMI's two TAV-8Bs were delivered in August 1991 to the new base at Grottaglie. The aircraft flew intensively, mounting many sorties from the ship and exploring co-ordinated operations with the vessel's helicopters. The first (US-built) aircraft were delivered on 3 December 1994, having been flown onto the *Giuseppe Garibaldi* off Mayport, departing for Taranto on 21 November 1994. One month later, on 18 January 1995, the *Giuseppe Garibaldi* sailed from Taranto (with the three US-built single-seaters embarked) to support UN operations in Somalia. They flew top-cover and reconnaissance sorties, proving extremely serviceable and maintainable. The APG-65 was used for ground mapping, airspace control and air traffic deconfliction. The squadron returned to Grottaglie on 22 March 1995.

# TAV-8B Harrier II

**Italy joined the Harrier club in May 1989 when it ordered two TAV-8Bs for initial pilot training, to be conducted in the United States. A front-line force of 16 Harrier II Plus aircraft followed. The TAV-8Bs were delivered in August 1991, at a reported cost of US$25 million each. This aircraft wears the markings of 1 Gruppo Aereo of the Marina Militare, based at Grottaglie.**

**Italy's aircraft-carrier**
The Marina Militare's sole CVS (light aircraft-carrier), *Giuseppe Garibaldi*, was laid down in March 1981, launched in June 1983, and commissioned in 1985. Flagship of the fleet, the 10,000-ton vessel (roughly half the size of the Royal Navy's 'Invincible'-class ships) is armed with Teseo Mk 2 anti-ship missiles, Aspide SAMs, 40-mm cannon and Mk 46 torpedoes for anti-submarine defence. An air group can comprise either 16 Harriers or 18 SH-3Ds, with a mix deployed for routine operations.

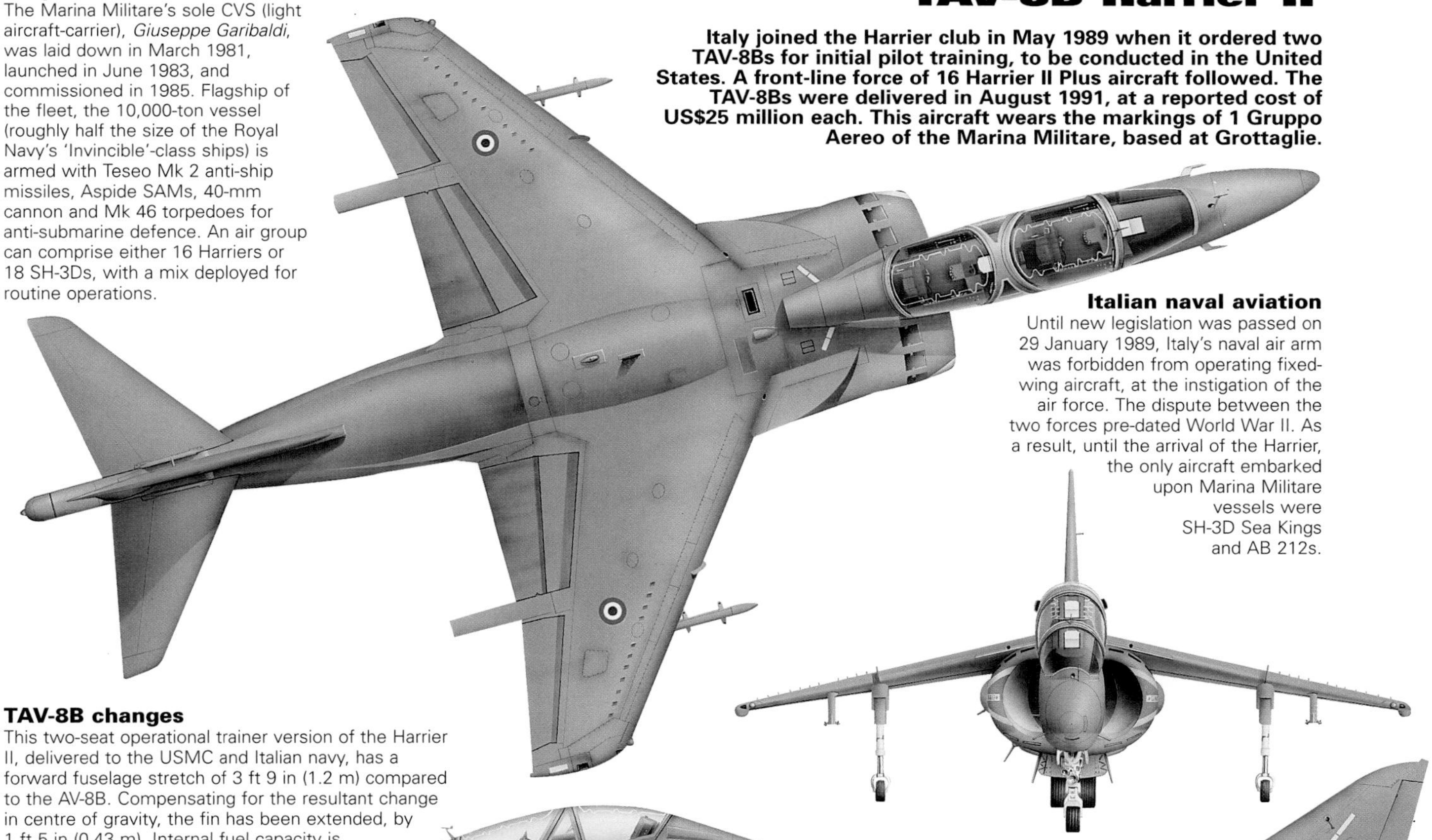

**Italian naval aviation**
Until new legislation was passed on 29 January 1989, Italy's naval air arm was forbidden from operating fixed-wing aircraft, at the instigation of the air force. The dispute between the two forces pre-dated World War II. As a result, until the arrival of the Harrier, the only aircraft embarked upon Marina Militare vessels were SH-3D Sea Kings and AB 212s.

**TAV-8B changes**
This two-seat operational trainer version of the Harrier II, delivered to the USMC and Italian navy, has a forward fuselage stretch of 3 ft 9 in (1.2 m) compared to the AV-8B. Compensating for the resultant change in centre of gravity, the fin has been extended, by 1 ft 5 in (0.43 m). Internal fuel capacity is unchanged, but underwing pylons are reduced to two hardpoints under each wing.

*Despite being introduced in the late 1950s, the MiG-21 continues to serve in some numbers. This example is a MiG-21UM of the Slovak Air and Air Defence Force.*

# Mikoyan-Gurevich MiG-21 'Fishbed'
## Introduction

*Egypt's MiG-21s saw combat against Israeli fighters during the 1960s and 1970s. They generally fared badly, scoring few kills against their better-trained opponents, although downed aircraft were soon replaced by the Soviet Union.*

**Produced in immense numbers, the MiG-21's success has helped to make MiG virtually a household name. In service with the Soviet Union and its client states during the Cold War, the aircraft remains on the strength of air forces worldwide.**

It would be fair to claim that the MiG-21 is one of the most famous military aircraft in the world. Since the end of World War II, no other fighter has been built in such large numbers (over 10,000 in the Soviet Union and a further 2,000 in China and India), or in so many versions (and still they keep appearing). Moreover, no other fighter has ever served with so many forces (56) – the C-130 Hercules is the only military aircraft to have seen more widespread service – or been involved in so many conflicts. What is remarkable is that the MiG-21 has always been a rather small and limited aircraft, possessing equipment of no outstanding ability. Indeed, in today's conflicts, the MiG-21 has found itself outclassed by the bigger, more sophisticated and more powerful Western fighters. Nevertheless, the MiG-21 has proved popular with those who have flown it and the fact that it is easy to maintain, reliable and cheap has meant that today's air forces are still keen to operate it.

### 'Fishbed' evolution

In 1953, the NII VVS, the scientific research institute of the Soviet air force, issued a specification for a new fighter and Mikoyan came up with a proposal for a small, supersonic aircraft, powered by a single afterburning turbojet, which would not carry heavy loads of fuel, electronics or weapons. The VVS required this new fighter purely to shoot down Century-series fighters and bombers such as the B-47, B-52 and B-58. However, it was soon accepted that this new fighter could not do everything that was asked of it and a new requirement was accordingly issued, which called for a fighter to carry out local defence in daylight, operate under close ground control and attack with guns only.

The Mikoyan OKB built two prototypes – the Ye-2 (with swept wings) and the Ye-4 (delta). Both aircraft were to be equipped with the R-11 engine, but they were designed before the engine was completed and so were fitted instead with the less powerful RD-9Ye. The Ye-2 first flew on 14 February 1955 and was well received, if considered to be a little underpowered, with the delta-winged Ye-4 flying a few days later. Over the following two years, a number of modifications were made to both designs and, in a final fly-off in 1957, the delta-winged variant was picked by Mikoyan and the NII VVS. The next two years saw a number of further changes to the initial design, which resulted in the Ye-6/3. Flown in December 1958, it led

*China first manufactured the MiG-21 in 1961, naming its domestic aircraft J-7s, and those for its export customers F-7s. This example is an F-7MG with upgraded weapons capabilities, allowing the carriage of AIM-9 Sidewinders and R.550 Magic AAMs.*

***The Czech Republic has retained a number of MiG-21MF 'Fishbed-Js' for air defence and attack purposes, and these equip three squadrons of the Czech air force.***

straight into a series of 30 production aircraft, designated MiG-21F. While the Soviets used a Ye-6/3 to gain a number of records including the world speed record, Mikoyan was building the first true series version, the MiG-21F-13, which had new armament. Hundreds of these aircraft were constructed, including aircraft designated S-106 which were made in Czechoslovakia, and unlicensed copies in China.

## Multi-variant MiG

From the outset, the MiG-21 was constantly upgraded and it has gone through three generational changes which have resulted in an aircraft far removed from the prototype. After the MiG-21F-13 came the -21P, which dispensed with the cannon and was only armed with two missiles. This was followed by the -21PF which had a new radar, the FL for export purposes, and the PFM with a new canopy, avionics, weapons and equipment.

Later-generation models moved away from the original lightweight fighter concept, gradually becoming heavier and more sophisticated. There was the -21R recce aircraft with reconnaissance and IR pods, TV cameras and laser sensors; the -21S fighter variant of the R; the -21SM with increased manoeuvrability; the -21MF with a more powerful engine, radar and weapons fit; and the -21SMT which was capable of carrying a greater fuel load.

The third generation MiG-21bis is by far the most advanced and capable variant, although a lack of BVR missile capability, limited radar and poor endurance limit its usefulness. It was developed as a multi-role fighter for Soviet Frontier Aviation and has a greater weapons capability than earlier variants. The bis model has served with a number of nations and, alongside earlier models, continues in front-line service although it is being replaced with more modern Western aircraft by a few countries.

The end of the Cold War did not therefore mean the end of the MiG-21, and several companies have made efforts to upgrade the surviving aircraft. IAI has produced the MiG-21-2000, Tracor has built a drone conversion named the 'QMiG-21', while the Mikoyan OKB itself has constructed the MiG-21-93. A host of other companies have offered upgrades, new avionics and fresh weapons fits.

## MiG at war

With its wide range of operators, it was inevitable that the MiG-21 would see combat. The first true conflict in which the aircraft appeared was that between India and Pakistan in 1965, its main opponents being the F-86F and F-104A. However, combat was limited and it was not until the resumption of hostilities in 1971 that the MiG-21 really found itself at war. The first kill was a PAF F-6, although F-104s were soon added to the kill lists. Other MiG-21s were used in the air-to-ground role.

The next major area of conflict for the MiG-21 was in the Middle East, where Egyptian, Syrian and Iraqi aircraft found themselves attacking Israel. Here, the MiG-21 was less than successful and many fell prey to Israeli Mirage IIICJs. In the Yom Kippur war of 1973, the Arab coalition's air forces again found themselves outclassed by Israeli F-4Es, Mirages and Neshers.

In Africa, Cuban-piloted Angolan MiG-21s were used against the UNITA and FNLA opposition parties, with two falling prey to South African Mirage F1s. Iraqi MiG-21s held their own against Iranian F-4s and F-5s while Somalian MiG-21s fared badly against Ethiopian F-5s.

During Vietnam, the agile MiG-21s performed well against the heavier, more sophisticated American aircraft in close combat when under tight ground control, although they suffered when fighting at greater distances. Despite American propaganda that the MiG forces were not a threat, Operation Linebacker II involved many strikes on MiG-21 bases. Since then, MiG-21s have been involved in a number of conflicts around Israel and Syria (including one over the Lebanon in 1982 in which over 80 MiG-21/23s were shot down), and in the localised conflicts across Africa. The aircraft's most recent combat appearance was during Desert Storm where the few MiG-21s that managed to get into the air were downed by the superior Coalition forces.

The MiG-21 is likely to continue in service into the next century. The air forces of poorer countries where the majority of MiG-21s remain on the front-line, regard upgrading existing aircraft as a preferred alternative to buying new machines. Types such as the F-16 or MiG-29, would be far more expensive than a MiG-21 upgrade.

It is unlikely that any fighter will ever again match the sales success of the MiG-21. In a world of shrinking defence budgets, few nations have the finances to spend great sums on squadrons of aircraft. Instead, the trend now seems to be to equip squadrons with small numbers of powerful, high-tech multi-purpose aircraft – the opposite of the original MiG-21 ideal.

***Above: Pictured is an engineering ground demonstrator of IAI's MiG-21-2000. IAI has completely refurbished the MiG-21, giving it enhanced capabilities, a totally redesigned cockpit and new radar. The Royal Cambodian air force was to have been the initial recipient of this type.***

***This symbol of the Cold War – a pair of MiG-21s launching for another interception or training mission – was a common occurrence for over 30 years.***

# Production variants

## Early MiG-21s

The original concept of the MiG-21 was for a simple, lightweight fighter, in which sophistication and considerations of endurance and firepower were sacrificed for outright performance. The production MiG-21 was preceded by a series of prototypes. Some had swept wings, while others had the delta-wing planform which was eventually chosen. The 40 pre-production MIG-21F (Ye-6T or Type 72) fighters, which attained limited service in 1959, were allocated the ASCC/NATO reporting name 'Fishbed-B', but the first full production version was the MIG-21F-13 'Fishbed-C', or Type 74 (above). Initial operational capability came in January 1963, with the 28th Regiment based at Odessa, with the first export sales being made to Finland. The first 114 MiG-21F-13s had a narrow-chord vertical tail, but all had their armament reduced from two to one NR-30 cannon, on the starboard side, with underwing pylons for two AA-2 'Atoll' heat-seeking AAMs or rocket pods. Fuel capacity was increased from 602 US gal (2280 litres) to 674 US gal (2550 litres). China built a copy as the Shenyang J-7 (below, in export F-7 form).

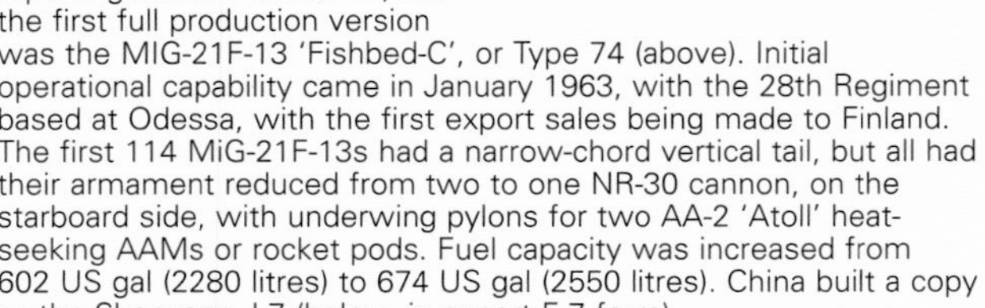

## Early radar-equipped MiG-21s

The MiG-21P 'Fishbed-D' dispensed with cannon altogether. The large inlet centrebody housed a TsD-30T R1L 'Spin Scan' radar. The canopy and spine were modified, with a bulge immediately aft of the cockpit. Internal fuel was increased to 726 US gal (2750 litres). The MiG-21P was followed by the R11F2-300-engined MiG-21PF (Type 76), which had the pitot probe relocated to the top of the nose and was equipped with the improved RP-21 Sapfir radar. NATO allocated these aircraft the reporting name 'Fishbed-E'. The MiG-21FL was externally identical to the late MiG-21PF. Intended for export, it had less powerful R-2L radar and the original engine. Approximately 200 were built under licence in India. The Type 94 sub-variants, the MiG-21PFS and the MiG-21PFM 'Fishbed-F' had two-piece canopies with fixed windscreens, blown flaps, a cruciform brake 'chute, R-11F2S-300 engines and RP-21M radar. They could fire semi-active radar-homing RS-2US (K-5M) missiles.

## Second-generation MiG-21s

Later MiG-21s gained heavier armament and increasingly sophisticated avionics. All had R-11F2S-300 or R-13-300 engines, blown flaps, pitot probes offset to the right of the centreline, two-piece canopies and broad-chord tailfins. The first of the new generation was the reconnaissance MiG-21R (Type 94R), based on the MIG-21PFM but with an enlarged dorsal fairing. The MiG-21S (Type 95) was the fighter version, with new radar and with a belly gun pod. It was followed by the MiG-21SM (Type 15), which also introduced a high-*g* combat gunsight and a GSh-23L cannon recessed into the belly. The MIG-21M (Type 96) (below and right) was an export version of the SM, also built under licence in India. The MiG-21MF 'Fishbed-J' (Type 96F) was a MiG-21M derivative for VVS use. It introduced AAM capability on all four underwing pylons.

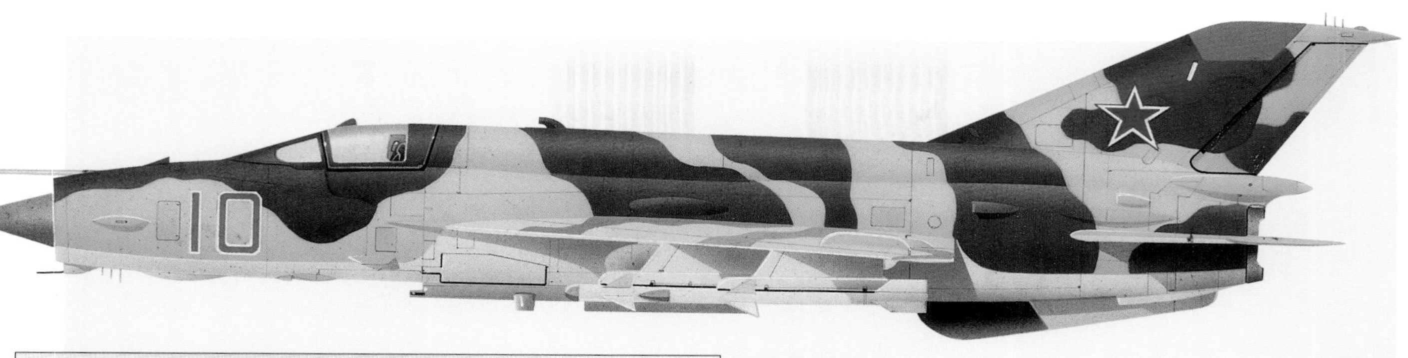

## MiG-21bis

The third-generation MiG-21bis was the most advanced and most capable production 'Fishbed' variant, although by modern standards its lack of BVR missile capability, limited radar range, mediocre low-speed handling and poor endurance limit its usefulness. The ASCC/NATO reporting name 'Fishbed-L' was allocated to the first version, which entered service in February 1972. 'Fishbed-N' was applied to later production aircraft which had an undernose 'Swift Rod' ILS antenna and improved avionics. The MiG-21bis was developed as a multirole fighter for Frontal Aviation, with better close combat capability through improved avionics and the ability to carry the new R-60 (AA-8 'Aphid') AAM. It was optimised for air combat at lower altitudes against more agile opponents, and also had an enhanced ground attack capability. It can carry four UV-16-57 rocket pods, or four 9½-in (240-mm) rockets, or two 1,102-lb (500-kg) and two 551-lb (250-kg) bombs. Equipped with improved Sapfir-21 radar and powered by the 15,653-lb (69.65-kN) Tumanskii R-25-300 engine, the MiG-21bis features a completely redesigned dorsal spine which hardly looks little different from that fitted to most second-generation 'Fishbeds', but which holds twice as much fuel. The 'Fishbed-N' was built under licence in India between 1980 and 1987. Another version of the MiG-21bis was optimised for nuclear strike. The reconnaissance version of the MiG-21bis remained in Soviet and Russian service into the 1990s. Elsewhere, the MiG-21bis still serves in large numbers with many operators.

## MiG-21U and MiG-21US

Proposed two-seat trainer versions of the MiG-17 'Fresco' and MiG-19 'Farmer' were never produced, and it soon became apparent that the subsonic MiG-15UTI would be inadequate for the conversion training of pilots expected to fly the Mach-2 MiG-21. Mikoyan accordingly designed a two-seat trainer based on the MiG-21F-13 'Fishbed-C'. Armament and radar were deleted, although provision was made for a ventral gun pack, and the aircraft also had two underwing pylons. It was fitted with a one-piece airbrake below the forward fuselage and the pitot boom was repositioned above the nose. The instructor's cockpit was added behind the normal cockpit, and both were covered by separate sideways-hingeing canopies. Internal fuel was reduced to 620 US gal (23150 litres).The new trainer first flew, as the Ye-6U, on 17 October 1960, and entered production as the MiG-21U (Type 66). Early production aircraft had the original narrow-chord fin and had a brake 'chute at the rear of the ventral fin. The basic MiG-21U received the NATO reporting name 'Mongol-A' and was built by Znamya Truda between 1964 and 1968. From the start, the more capable MIG-21US 'Mongol-B' (Type 68) had the increased-chord tailfin fitted to later fighter versions of the MiG-21. Built at Tbilisi between 1966 and 1970, it had improved ejection seats, a bigger spine raising internal fuel capacity to 647 US gal (2450 litres), a retractable periscope and blown flaps. The MIG-21UM (Type 69) introduced updated instruments, autopilot and avionics (as fitted to the MiG-21R and subsequent single-seaters), and was fitted with an angle-of-attack sensor on the starboard side of the nose. It was built at Tbilisi from 1971. MiG-21 trainers have served with most operators of single-seat 'Fishbeds', primarily as conversion or continuation trainers. However, in the former USSR and still in India, two-seat MiG-21 trainers were and are used as dedicated advanced trainers, introducing new pilots to the special challenges of supersonic flight.

# MiG-21 upgrades

**Cost-effective MiG-21 upgrades, typified by that offered by Romania's Aerostar in collaboration with Israel, provide a solution to the problems of modernising an otherwise aging 'Fishbed' force.**

*Seen during its maiden flight on 24 May 1995, the MiG-21-2000 conversion, developed by IAI's Lahav division, has suffered an uncertain fate after the collapse of a deal with Cambodia.*

Israel was an early aircraft upgrader, as arms embargoes forced the nation towards self-sufficiency. Israel's aviation industry developed integrated structural, avionics, weapons, and cockpit upgrade packages for Israeli combat aircraft and marketed upgrades to types already in Israeli service. It soon became clear that the company's landmark F-4 upgrade could form the basis of a MiG-21 modernisation.

IAI's Lavi- and F-4E-2000 based MiG-21-2000 upgrade included a MIL STD 1553B digital databus, a one-piece wrap-round windscreen, a Martin-Baker ejection seat, a wide-angle HUD, and a modernised semi-glass cockpit, with HOTAS controls. IAI also offered to improve the existing Sapfir radar, or to install a new Elta EL/M-2032 multi-mode pulse-Doppler radar.

But IAI's first MiG-21 upgrade contract was for the more modest modernisation of eight Cambodian MiG-21s, restoring the aircraft to airworthiness, without adding many new systems, and hopes that it would gain the lucrative contract to upgrade Romania's MiG-21s were dashed.

When Romania finalised plans for an upgrade of 110 MiG-21s, Elbit was awarded the contract, providing programme management and supplying and integrating the avionics, while Aerostar refurbished the aircraft and installed the new equipment.

Upgraded Romanian MiG-21 Lancers feature a MIL STD 1553B avionics system, with full HOTAS controls and multi-function display screens, a new HUD and provision for the DASH (Display and Sight Helmet) as well as modern navigation, RWR and self defence systems. The 75 close air support aircraft and the ten trainers have an Elta ranging radar, while the 25 air defence-configured aircraft have an Elta EL/M-2032 multi-mode pulse-Doppler radar. The prototype Lancer flew on 23 August 1995, two months ahead of schedule, and has now re-entered Romanian service. Several squadrons are fully operational, using weapons of Western and Soviet origin.

Romania's Lancers were all converted from MiG-21MF and MiG-21UM/US airframes, but it was soon decided that the same upgrade should be available for the MiG-21bis (widely used outside Romania), and Elbit and Aerostar modified a newly acquired bis as the prototype 'Lancer III', which made a maiden flight in October 1998.

### Croatian upgrade?

The 'Lancer III' may serve as the prototype for an upgrade to Croatian MiG-21bis fighters. These aircraft were obtained as interim equipment while an international arms embargo was in place. Hopes that they would be replaced by refurbished second-hand F-16s faded, and the aircraft are now expected to be modernised and upgraded instead, under a deal signed with Aerostar in 2002.

The MiG-21's original manufacturer was a late entrant to the upgrade market. Russian OKBs and factories were unused to refurbishing and modifying old aircraft rather than building new ones, while the major weakness of even the latest Russian fighters lay in their poor cockpit ergonomics, primitive displays, lack of processing speed and capacity, and fire control system software design, the very areas which would have to be upgraded on the MiG-21. This gave Western companies greater credibility as upgrade providers.

When it became clear that foreign companies were earning money from MiG-21 upgrades, MiG OKB teamed with Sokol to offer the MiG-21-93 upgrade. The Sokol GAZ-21 factory had been the source of most of the MiG-21s built, and thus the Russian team had an unrivalled knowledge of the aircraft's structure, aerodynamics and systems as well as jigs and tools for building new parts and components.

The MiG-21-93 featured a Kopyo radar, a new one-piece windscreen, a helmet-mounted sighting system, a modernised cockpit, provision for advanced weapons (including fire-and-

***Undertaking operational conversion training for the Romanian Lancer fleet, the ten Lancer Bs (ex-MiG-21UM/US aircraft) have a secondary combat role and front-line standard defensive aids.***

***The 25 Lancer C air defence versions represent the ultimate evolution of the upgraded MiG-21 in Romanian service, and are capable of carrying both Russian R-73 and Israeli Python III AAMs.***

forget BVR AAMs) and enhanced defensive systems. It soon became clear that there was some customer resistance to Russian avionics equipment, especially in India, and the company began to offer a number of Western avionics system options.

India is the world's largest remaining MiG-21 operator, having received more than 830 examples (580 of which had been locally assembled or built). Although some early MiG-21s were replaced by new types, large numbers of later MiG-21M, MF and bis (modified) versions remained active. India placed a US$428 million contract with Mikoyan and Sokol on 3 May 1994, covering the upgrade of 100 MiG-21bis fighters to MiG-21-93 standards (initially under the designation MiG-21I). In March 1996 the contract was expanded to cover the upgrade of 125 Indian MiG-21bis airframes, but the first 12 of these aircraft did not become operational until 2002, with 'production' some years behind schedule.

India demanded certain Western systems, including MIL STD 1553 architecture, a Sextant Avionique Totem 221G ring laser gyro INS, Israeli flare dispensers and indigenous active jammer, radios, radio altimeter, radio compass, and IFF transponder. Mikoyan offered a number of alternative engines, including the 15,657-lb (69.65-kN) TJR-25-300, a derivative of the RD-33 used by the MiG-29.

The first Indian MiG-21-93 flew on 3 October 1998 and the second followed in February 1999. Deliveries of upgrade kits began after the 14 December 2000 hand-over of the prototypes. HAL's modernisation of 123 IAF MiG-21s will give it useful experience, and the Indian company has reportedly already offered its own upgrade to Laos, Egypt and Syria.

In 1998 MiG-MAPO identified some 4,500 MiG-21s and F-7s in service with 32 air arms, and shortlisted 18 potential upgrade customers, rejecting any operator with less than 18 aircraft, and omitting India, Cambodia and Romania whose upgrade plans were decided. Since then Mikoyan and Sokol offered the MiG-21-93 upgrade to Ethiopia, and to meet Vietnam's upgrade requirement, introduced a new upgrade configuration, known as the MiG-21-98, applicable to older MiG-21 variants. This configuration includes a glass cockpit with colour LCD displays and offers a choice of compact radars. During the 1980s, Western fighter pilots could safely assume that any MiG-21 he encountered would be equipped with only the most rudimentary fire control radar, that it would lack BVR armament, and would be wholly reliant on GCI control. All these weaknesses have been addressed in the available MiG-21 upgrade packages, and a hostile MiG-21 could represent a real and potent threat. It would be no exaggeration to say that upgraded MiG-21s probably offer a more dangerous threat than early generation Lockheed Martin F-16 Fighting Falcons or Mikoyan MiG-29 'Fulcrums'.

**Rafael Python III**
The Python III is based upon the earlier Shafrir I/II missiles and was the baseline AAM in Israeli service during the 1980s and early 1990s. Now replaced by the Python IV, it remains an effective weapon. Python III has a 24-lb (11-kg) HE warhead, triggered by a contact or radar proximity fuse. Its all-aspect IR seeker can be slaved to the radar and has an off-boresight launch capability of 30°

## MiG-21 Lancer A

**Romania's Lancer A force is currently concentrated in two units, Grupul 95 based at Bacau, and Grupul 86, based at Festesti. Aircraft do not wear individual group or squadron markings, but large white titles have been applied to some aircraft, particularly those involved with PfP (Partnership for Peace) exercises. All MiG-21M/MFs considered for upgrade by Aerostar were built post-1975, and so represent the most modern 'new-build' MiG-21s of that version.**

**Opher IR-guided bomb**
Elbit's Oher terminal guidance system is typically fitted to a 500-lb (227-kg) Mk 82 bomb. It resembles a Paveway II LGB, but uses an IR seeker rather than laser guidance. Developed as an anti-armour weapon, it is nevertheless capable of engaging a range of static and mobile targets. The sensitive seeker is able to differentiate between attacked (burning) targets and unattacked ones. Typical employment range is 4.3 miles (7 km). The seeker acquires its target at about 3,280 ft (1000 m). The Mk 82 bomb version has a 192-lb (97-kg) HE warhead.

# MiG-21 today

*During over 35 years in Indian service, the MiG-21F and FL have been progressively replaced by the M series and definitive bis. Flying a tight echelon starboard at low level, this pair of MiG-21bis 'Fishbeds' serving with the IAF's No. 4 'Orioles' Squadron continued to fly from Jaisalmer in 1999.*

**The success of the MiG-21 concept has been proven by the type's continued existence in the front-line inventories of numerous air forces, and dedicated 'Fishbed' operators have now initiated upgrades.**

Russian production of the Mikoyan-Gurevich MiG-21 totalled 10,158 aircraft. There were also 194 Czech-built MiG-21F-13s, and about 574 Indian MiG-21s produced under licence by HAL, while more than 2,500 MiG-21 derivatives were also built in China, where low-rate production continues. More than 13,432 MiG-21s have been delivered since 1958 (more than twice the F-4 Phantom II's production tally) equipping more than 50 air forces.

Despite its limited combat radius and basic weapons system, the MiG-21 proved extraordinarily successful in combat situations in Vietnam and in the Middle East. The MiG-21's small size made it hard to acquire visually or on radar, while it was fast, agile, and packed an impressive punch. It was also simple to maintain, and fairly easy to fly.

Before the fall of the Berlin Wall, most Warsaw Pact air forces had received MiG-23s and MiG-29s, which formed the spearhead of their frontline forces, but large numbers of late-model MiG-21s remained in use in the tactical fighter and reconnaissance roles, providing weight of numbers.

Relatively large numbers of MiG-21s therefore remained in use at the end of 1990. The end of the Cold War saw massive reductions in air force strengths on both sides of the Iron Curtain, however, older aircraft types naturally bore the brunt of the cutbacks, as nations rebuilt smaller air arms around their most modern aircraft types.

By 2004, the MiG-21 was disappearing from Europe. Finland and Hungary had already discarded the type, and elsewhere, numbers in use had been cut back dramatically. Albania had 22 Chengdu F-7As (Chinese built MiG-21F-13s constituting that air force's most modern aircraft), Croatia had around 32 assorted MiG-21s, the Czech Republic had about 36 MiG-21MFs (twelve being assigned to NATO and deputising fighter duties for the retired MiG-23ML) and 20 UMs, and Slovakia had 12 MiG-21MFs and four UMs.

*313. Stihaci Letka at Sliac operates the MiG-21MF in the air defence of Slovakia, with training undertaken by the -21UM/US. Aircraft were formerly based at the Malacky fighter-bomber base.*

Four nations did retain the type in larger numbers. Poland had as many as 130 MiG-21s (18 of these with Naval Aviation), including MiG-21Ms, MiG-21MFs, MiG-21PFMs and MiG-21UMs, though these were being slowly withdrawn from use. In Bulgaria, the MiG-21 fleet had stabilised at 36 MiG-21bis, MiG-21MFRs (former MiG-21MFs adapted to carry the MiG-21R's underfuselage reconnaissance pod, following the withdrawal of the latter in late 1995) and MiG-21UM two-seaters, while Romania's upgraded Lancers included 92 A-model fighter bombers and fighter Lancer Bs and 14 two-seat Lancer Cs.

Elsewhere, MiG-21s served in Algeria, Angola, Cambodia, Congo, Cuba, Egypt, Ethiopia, Guinea, Laos, Libya, Mali, Nigeria, North Korea, Syria, Vietnam, Yemen and Zambia and a host of smaller former Soviet States, and in much larger numbers in India, where the type continues to equip more squadrons than any other single type. Chinese-built aircraft are believed to have served with the air arms of Albania, Bangladesh, China, Egypt, Iran, Iraq, Myanmar, Pakistan, Sri Lanka, Sudan, Tanzania, Yemen and Zimbabwe.

At one time, it seemed as though the very high cost of the latest superfighters would force some operators to modernise their MiG-21s, adding modern avionics, sensors and weapons.

The potential market for a MiG-21 upgrade was radically over-stated, however. Many MiG-21 operators are third world nations who could never afford to upgrade their aircraft, while ancient MiG-21s are an embarrassment to operators who are bent on modernising and westernising their air forces. Other potential upgrades have been prevented by international arms embargoes. As post-Cold War defence cutbacks continued, newer aircraft types including MiG-29s and early-model F-16s, were retired by their original operators and became available at extremely low cost, and other

*Prospective Vietnamese People's Air Force MiG-21bis pilots undertake conversion training on the MiG-21UM 'Mongol-Bs' of the 920 Trung Doan, Air Force Academy, based at Phu Cat.*

***Pictured at Krzesiny in April 2000, this 3 PLM 'Poznan' MiG-21MF is unorthodoxly armed with a pair of R-55 (upgraded RS-1U) 'Alkali' AAMs. Poland retains a substantial MiG-21PFM/MF/bis/R/US/UM fleet.***

operators have chosen to retire and replace, rather than upgrade their MiG-21s. Choosing to upgrade existing aircraft can be extremely cost-effective, however, and ambitious MiG-21 upgrades have been undertaken for Romania and India, and these are described separately.

Generally, MiG-21 upgrades have been fairly modest, and have provided only a short-term life extension. Egypt had been the first operator to upgrade its MiG-21s with Western avionics systems, following the country's break with the Soviet Union. Some 75-100 aircraft were fitted with a new HUD, air data computer and new ECM, RWR, IFF, and chaff/flare dispensers and were also armed with Western missiles, including the MATRA R.550 Magic, and AIM-9P-3 and AIM-9L Sidewinders.

An ambitious plan to upgrade 24 of the Czech Republic's newer MiG-21s, to give improved capability and maximum commonality with the Aero L-159 light attack aircraft, was soon dramatically reduced in scope and Czech attention turned to the purchase of new (or second hand) Western fighters. As an interim measure the MiG-21s received a new Western (NATO-compatible) IFF, a GPS-based navigation system and NATO-compatible radios. In Hungary, 20 of the air force's ageing MiG-21bis fighters received a similarly modest upgrade, receiving Western IFF equipment to allow them to remain viable while longer-term plans were finalised. In China, locally-built MiG-21 derivatives for the PLA retained indigenous avionics, but some 200 export Chengdu F-7Ms and F-7Ps were fitted with a GEC Type 226 Skyranger I-band ranging radar, and a Type 956 HUD/WAC (Head-Up Display/Weapons Aiming Computer) with a Western radar altimeter, air data computer and other systems. These aircraft went mainly to Pakistan, which subsequently contracted to refit its aircraft with FIAR Grifo-L multi-mode I/J-band pulse-Doppler radars.

Plans for an even more radically upgraded version (to be developed with US partner Grumman) with AN/APG-66 radar in a new solid nose were abandoned following the Tiananmen Square massacre of 1989. China has also developed a new arrow-winged variant known as the J-7E (F-7MG for export), and an aircraft with a new radar nose and underslung chin intake, known as the J-7FS.

There are a number of other potential upgrade providers for the MiG-21. Bulgaria's TEREM organisation, already highly experienced in MiG-21 overhaul, repair and modernisation work, was formally licensed to upgrade MiG-21s to MiG-21-93 standards by Mikoyan in 1994. With its high engineering standards and low labour costs, TEREM was considered by Mikoyan to be an ideal partner for its own upgrade, and has been spoken of as a potential upgrade provider for Syrian, North Korean and even Iraqi MiG-21s.

From the early 1990s, many MiG-21s became museum pieces, privately owned jet warbirds, or even unmanned target drones. The Russian air force has converted a number of different variants to M-21 Mishen drone configuration, and further MiG-21 drones have been produced by the US company Tracor.

### Chinese 'Fishbeds' in service

Chinese MiG-21 production was initially undertaken by Shenyang, and later Chengdu and Guizhou (two-seaters). Different versions of the same aircraft can thus bear different manufacturer's names, although the designation Jianjiji 7 ('Fighter Aircraft Number Seven', exported as the F-7) remains constant. Pictured clockwise from right are examples of F-7s from four of a total of 13 operators. Zimbabwe's two-seat FT-7BZs of No. 5 Sqn provide the air force with a supersonic training capability. Sri Lanka's fleet of Chengdu F-7BS fighters (in Chinese-style gloss white paint scheme) and Guizhou FT-7 trainers supplemented, and eventually replaced FT-5 fighter-trainers, and are operated by No. 5 Jet Sqn at Katunayake, near Colombo. Armed with AIM-9P Sidewinders, the Pakistan Air Force F-7P serves with No. 20 Sqn at Rafiqi. A further F-7 operator within the Indian Sub-continent is Bangladesh, whose F-7Ms and FT-7s of Nos. 5 'Supersonics' and 35 'Thundercats' Sqns constitute one of the force's most potent assets.

# Mikoyan MiG-23/27 'Flogger'

*The West's first view of the 'Flogger' came in 1978, when six MiG-23MLs visited Finland and France. As a measure of security, the Soviets had sanitised the aircraft by removing the under-nose IRST sensor, gun pods and AAMs.*

## Development

**In service in huge numbers with the Russian air forces and with virtually all of its former client states, the MiG-23/27 is one of the most widely-operated jet fighters ever. The key to its enduring success lies in its basic design configuration, which offers a unique blend of robustness, performance and versatility.**

Development of the MiG-23 began in the early 1960s, when the Mikoyan-Gurevich OKB began studies for a replacement for its MiG-21 'Fishbed' tactical fighter. Aware of the shortcomings of the MiG-21, the Design Bureau wanted to produce a fighter with greater payload, range and fire-power, and with more sensors to give freedom from the constraints of tight ground-controlled interception (GCI). The new aircraft was to be faster, and able to climb more rapidly than the 'Fishbed'. The new fighter would therefore have to be larger and heavier, but this would result in the aircraft having an exceptionally long take-off run. Mikoyan engineers studied many alternative approaches to the problem of producing a STOL fighter.

### Variable geometry

The variable-geometry (VG) wing had been recognised by MiG OKB as the best way of overcoming the primary short-comings of the 'Fishbed' i.e. short range and a small weapons load. Fully spread, the VG wing offered a shorter take-off/landing roll while enabling the aircraft to carry a heavier weaponload. In the fully-swept position, the wing allowed for a high top speed and good super-sonic handling characteristics. There were disadvantages to the VG wing, however, as the construction of the wing sweep mechanism required a larger fuselage and was relatively heavy. These factors, together with the importance of the position to be held by the new aircraft within the Soviet air force, resulted in two parallel designs being developed simultaneously by Mikoyan.

Although both designs utilised similar fuselages, the first design, designated 23-01 (and later MiG-23PD), utilised a fixed delta wing and was powered by a single main engine (a Tumanskii R-27-300), with two lift 'sustainer' engines (actually Koliesov RD-36-35s) located in the centre fuselage for take-off and landing. The aircraft accomplished its first flight on 3 April 1967 and was exhibited at the Domododevo air show in July of that year, where the new design was designated 'Faithless' by Western observers.

Having accomplished only 14 flights, Mikoyan realised that the lift-jet concept was flawed and the programme was quickly terminated. While this design was being developed, a second design team were constructing 23-11, which was intended to be a VG version of the 23-01. However, only the nose section, empennage design and turbojet powerplant (Tumanskii's R-27F-300) were common to the two aircraft. Following the failure of the earlier design, the 23-11 was given the highest priority within the Soviet government, with the result that the aircraft accomplished its first flight on 10 April 1967, a little over two years since the VG design had first been studied. Within weeks of its maiden flight, the new design was displayed to the public at Domododevo, where NATO assigned it the name 'Flogger'. Basic flight trials ended in July 1968, after 98 highly successful flights, resulting in the 'Flogger' being quickly ordered for front-line squadrons.

### Fledgling 'Floggers'

The first variant to enter operational squadron service was the MiG-23S, which was intended to utilise the advanced Sapfir radar (hence the 'S' suffix) and a more powerful variant of the Tumanskii turbojet. However, development of the radar was not completed by the time the aircraft entered service, resulting in early 'Floggers' being equipped with the far less capable 'Jay Bird' radar adopted from the MiG-21S. In a single stroke, the capabilities of the new aircraft were compromised, for the 'Flogger' completely lacked any BVR capability.

Aware of the operating limita-

*The Mikoyan-Gurevich Model 23-11 – the first variable-geometry member of the MiG-23 family – was designed when it became apparent that the lift-jet-equipped Model 23-01 would not be practical. The 23-11 wore a striking colour scheme, consisting of a grey fuselage with bright red wings.*

***Above: Seen flying high over the Gulf, this is one of the less sophisticated variants of the 'Flogger' (MiG-23MS) supplied to Libya. The variant lacked any BVR capability and served only in the visual dogfight arena, thus running contrary to US Navy reports on the shooting down of two 'Floggers' on 4 January 1989 by F-14 Tomcats. The reports claimed that the aircraft had posed a threat to the carrier battle fleet.***

***Left: Serving among the many units based in East Germany during the 1980s, this MiG-27K was capable of bad weather blind-bombing with laser-guided air-to-surface missiles.***

tions of the MiG-23S, a new model was quickly introduced, the MiG-23M (the suffix stood merely for 'Modified'). Equipped with the intended pulse-Doppler Sapfir radar, the 'Flogger' was at last free from the constraints of tight GCI. This meant that, coupled with the newly developed AA-7 'Apex' AAM, the 'Flogger' had emerged as a highly competent interceptor.

Rapid technological developments spawned a host of 'Flogger' variants of the MiG-23S, many the result of a an uprated powerplant or improvements to the radar. For many client states, the prestige of operating one of the first generations of VG aircraft was too good to miss, but Mikoyan was reluctant to offer the highly sophisticated models to Third World clients. This resulted in sanitised variants which lacked the sophisticated avionics – these models were designated the MiG-23MS or MiG-23MF.

## Ground attack

The 'Flogger' design had already provided the Soviet air force and its customers with highly capable variants when the additional role of ground-attack was added. This initially took the form of the MiG-23B/Bk/BM/BN family, based on the MiG-23S airframe but with a radarless nose of steeper-sloping profile, providing better forward visibility. These were followed by the definitive MiG-27 family, which dispensed with the variable-geometry intakes and jetpipe, in addition to other changes. Ordered straight off the drawing board by the Soviet air force, the MiG-27 only served to increase the reputation of its elder cousin, the MiG-23. A host of client states adopted the new aircraft, resulting in many operating both 'Flogger' variants at the same time. Throughout its operational career, the MiG-27 has undergone continual upgrading, with no fewer than four models, each of which has spawned a host of sub-variants.

***Mikoyan continues to improve the 'Flogger'. One potential upgrade is illustrated on this MiG-23MLD, which is equipped with R-77 AAMs.***

## 'Flogger' at war

**This MiG-23MLD 'Flogger-K' was used by Major Anatoly Stipanjk during his squadron's deployment to Afghanistan in 1986. The aircraft carried mission markings in the form of small white stars below the cockpit. Sometimes, individual stars were initialled by the pilot responsible for each mission.**

**Missile threat**
'Flogger-Gs' in Afghanistan carried flare/chaff launchers mounted on the upper fuselage. These were used to decoy IR-guided, shoulder-launched anti-aircraft missiles, such as the American Stinger, fired by rebel forces.

**Hero of the Soviet Union**
'Flogger' pilot Col Anatolij Levchenko flew 188 missions during the war in Afghanistan, his last being on 27 December 1986. Having attacked traffic on the Salang Pass, his aircraft was hit by AAA. Unable to eject, he dived into the enemy gun position, subsequently destroying it, and enabling the rest of his squadron to escape. Levchenko was posthumously awarded Russia's highest honour.

**Air-to-air combat**
With the Mujahideen lacking any air force, most 'Floggers' served as ground-attack aircraft. However, when attacking rebel camps in Pakistan, aerial engagements with PAF F-16s resulted in in the loss of at least two examples.

# MiG-23/27

## Variants

**Widely dismissed in the West as an obsolete and ineffective aircraft, the MiG-23/27 family has proved to be remarkably versatile and robust, and has spawned a number of variants.**

### MiG-23S/M/MF/MS 'Flogger-A/B/E'

During the 1960s, the need for a MiG-21 replacement was conceived and Mikoyan-Gurevich began design work on the MiG-23. The authorities were determined that the increased size and weight of the new fighter would not impose longer take-off distances. A series of trials confirmed that the variable-geometry Model 23-11 represented the most effective configuration, and this was ordered into production as the MiG-23S with a powerful 22,046-lb st (98.1-kN) R-27F2M-300 engine. Initially, an RP-22 'Jay Bird' radar (like that of the MiG-21S) was installed, giving a very recognisable short radome and removing BVR capability. The aircraft was also fitted with a TP-23 IRST. Fifty were built between mid-1969 and the end of 1970 and were used for operational trials before production switched to the MiG-23M, dubbed 'Flogger-B' by NATO. This featured the pulse-Doppler Sapfir-23 ('High Lark') radar and new fire control system and autopilot. The MiG-23M could fire the R-23 (AA-7 'Apex') semi-active radar-homing missile. A new 27,557-lb st (122.63-kN) Soyuz (Tumanskii) R-29-300 (with shorter jetpipe) was fitted, while at the same time the aircraft's horizontal tail surfaces were moved aft, giving a very different appearance. A fourth fuel tank was added in the rear fuselage. A new Type 1 wing, with an extended leading edge, was introduced, having a pronounced 'dogtooth' inboard. Leading-edge slats were deleted ( Type 2 wing), then reintroduced in 1973 with the Type 3 wing.

MiG-23Ms were delivered to Frontal Aviation as MiG-21 replacements, operating mainly in the battlefield air superiority role, but with an important secondary ground attack capability. Others went to the IA-PVO, where they augmented MiG-21s, Su-9s, Su-11s and Su-15s in the air defence role. Two downgraded export versions of the MiG-23M were produced, the second gaining the new reporting name 'Flogger-E'. The MiG-23MS was a substantially downgraded version with MiG-21-type 'Jay Bird' radar in a short radome, with no BVR missile capability. The MiG-23MF was less radically sanitised and retained the 'High Lark' fire control radar, AA-7 'Apex' missile capability and 'Flogger-B' reporting name of the MiG-23M, and was delivered to Russia's Warsaw Pact allies, then later to Syria, Angola, Iraq, India and Libya.

### MiG-23ML/P/MLD 'Flogger-G/K'

The MiG-23ML 'Flogger-G' (allocated the OKB designation 23-12) has improved handling, especially at high angles of attack, enhanced manoeuvrability and higher *g* limits. It features a lightened airframe, with the fourth fuselage fuel tank removed and the dorsal fin fillet deleted. More power was provided by installing the Soyuz (Tumanskii) R-35-300 engine. A very similar aircraft, designated MiG-23P (23-14), was used by the PVO and has a new digital computer that allows the aircraft to be automatically steered onto its target from the ground, cueing the pilot to engage afterburner and launch weapons. The MiG-23ML also served as the basis for the MiG-23MLD (23-18), codenamed 'Flogger-K' by NATO. The new version, reportedly produced by conversion of MiG-23ML airframes, incorporates vortex generators on the pitot probe and notches in its vestigial leading-edge root extensions. Large chaff/flare dispensers can be fitted above the rear fuselage, linked to the new RWR system. A new IFF system is fitted, and a missile-firing simulator allows economic training. Further modifications include swivelling pylons under the outboard wing panels, which move to remain aligned with the airflow even when the wings are swept.

## MiG-23ML 'Flogger-G'

**This MiG-23 wears the colours of the Syrian Air Force, which acquired large numbers of the type. For many years, the MiG-23ML was thought to be a sound but basic aircraft, but, with the end of the Cold War, Western analysts found that it was a surprisingly effective aircraft able to outperform many supposedly 'superior' Western types, notably in terms of straight-line acceleration.**

**Radar**
The MiG-23ML's radar marks a major improvement over that of the MiG-23MF, with a range of 56 miles (90 km) rather than 37 miles (60 km) and improved look-down and jamming capabilities. The radar 'picture' is displayed in the pilot's head-up display.

**Engine intakes**
The rectangular-section air intakes incorporate huge variable intake ramps which also act as splitter plates. They stand proud from the fuselage and its sluggish boundary layer airflow.

**Armament**
This MiG-23ML carries a pair of R-23 (AA-7 'Apex') missiles under the wing glove and two pairs of IR-homing R-60 AA-8 'Aphids' under the fuselage. A GSh-23L twin-barrelled cannon is housed in a GP-9 gun pack under the fuselage.

**Cockpit**
Giving the pilot a good view of his 'six' was not a priority when the MiG-23 was designed. Rear-view mirrors remedy some of the problems, but nothing can alter the poor view downwards.

## MiG-23UB 'Flogger-C'

The handling characteristics of the MiG-23 were very different from those of other aircraft in the Soviet inventory, so development of a two-seat trainer version was authorised in May 1968, six months after the the go-ahead had been given for the single-seat aircraft. The MiG-23UB(23-51) prototype or 'Flogger-C' made its maiden flight in May 1969. The MiG-23UB was always supposed to be used for both pilot conversion and weapons training, and even to have a restricted combat capability. Accordingly, a separate guidance and illuminator pod for the AA-7 'Apex' missile was fitted in a conical fairing on the starboard wingroot. Production aircraft all have the 'clawed' No. 3 wing (compatible with the carriage of outboard underwing fuel tanks on non-swivelling pylons), and the two tandem cockpits are covered by separate upward-hinging canopies. The instructor is provided with a retractable periscope to give a better view forward on approach. MiG-23UBs are fitted with an AoA limiter or an AoA warning system, together with a comprehensive avionics suite featuring a sophisticated system which allows the backseater to simulate emergencies and threats for the student pilot in the front cockpit. All MiG-23 and MiG-27 operators also use the MiG-23UB, and the type, which was phased out of production in 1978, is stored in large numbers in Russia.

## MiG-23B/BK/BM/BN 'Flogger-F/H'

In 1969, Mikoyan began studies of a cheap, mass-produced attack aircraft. However, instead of a new aircraft, economic constraints forced Mikoyan to examine the possibility of using a derivative of the MiG-23S, whose supersonic dash capability was felt to be a useful bonus. Mikoyan allocated a new designation (Model 32) but the air force – perhaps feeling that funding for a new aircraft would be harder to obtain – retained the MiG-23 designation.

The original MiG-23 had been developed as a multi-role tactical fighter and, with its rugged airframe, strong undercarriage, powerful engine and variable-geometry wing, it has the ability to operate from primitive, semi-prepared airstrips. It was extremely suitable for conversion or adaptation to the fighter-bomber role. The basic MiG-23B (32-24) was based on the airframe of the MiG-23S, but with a new, more sloping nose that gave the pilot an improved view forward and downward, and with a 112.78-kN (25,353-lb st) Lyul'ka AL-21F-300 powerplant in a shortened rear fuselage. Also like the MiG-23M, the new ground attack variant featured the No. 2 wing and was later fitted with the No. 3 wing. The new aircraft received a PrNK Sokol 23S nav/attack system. Armour was scabbed on to the sides of the forward fuselage to protect the pilot, and the fuel tanks were fitted with an inert gas-injection fire protection system. A missile illuminator and a TV camera were housed in bullet-like fairings on the wingroot gloves. Some 24 MiG-23Bs were built before production switched to an improved variant. The MiG-23BN (32-23) featured an upgraded PrNK Sokol 23N nav/attack system and was powered by a slightly derated version of the Soyuz (Tumanskii) R-29B-300 engine. The MiG-23BN was intended to have been the first attack version, but was delayed by equipment and engine problems. It introduced the leading-edge bullet fairings on the fixed wing gloves that are usually associated with the AS-7 'Kerry' ASM. The MiG-23B and MiG-23BN share the NATO reporting name 'Flogger-F'.

The MiG-23B and MiG-23BN proved disappointing in service, and many were subsequently upgraded to MiG-23BK (32-26) or MiG-23BM (32-25) standards, or exported. Improved avionics were desperately needed, and two new fighter-bombers were quickly developed, both sharing the name 'Flogger-H'. This was assigned because they had new RWR fairings on the lower 'corners' of the fuselage, just ahead of the nosewheel bay. Cuban attack MiG-23s are 'Flogger-Fs', without the intake-mounted RWR fairings, for example, while German and Czech aircraft had these fairings and are thus 'Flogger-Hs'. The first of the new variants was the MiG-23BK, which had the same nav/attack system and laser rangefinder as the MiG-27K. The MiG-23BM was similar, but with the same PrNK Sokol 23M nav/ attack system as the MiG-27D. Confusingly, the MiG-23BN designation seems to have been adopted as an overall service designation, sometimes being applied to aircraft designated BM or BK by the OKB. Many export 'Flogger-Hs' are usually described as MiG-23BNs, and were perhaps built as such, but are actually to MiG-23BK standards. Such aircraft include East Germany's MiG-23BKs, whose documentation described them as MiG-24BNs. Bulgarian, Czech, Indian and Iraqi 'Flogger-Hs' look identical, although many of the latter have fixed inflight-refuelling probes above the nose.

## MiG-27D/J/J2/K/L/M 'Flogger-D/J'

The MiG-27 designation was originally applied to a number of designs drawn up by the Mikoyan OKB for the requirement eventually filled by the Su-25. After Vietnam, the need for subsonic aircraft which could provide conventional close air support/battlefield air interdiction was realised. The original MiG-27 and similar MiG-27K 'Flogger-D' were ordered into production directly off the drawing board, and the prototype made its maiden flight during 1972. Early examples were soon in service with the Group of Soviet Forces in Germany. The 'straight' MiG-27 was very soon replaced by the MiG-27K, equipped with the PrNK-23K nav/attack system and a Fone laser rangefinder/target tracker mounted behind a small window in the nose. The MiG-27K was capable of night or bad weather blind bombing with a very high degree of accuracy. RWR and ECM equipment is highly automated, and a new stores management system gives the pilot greater flexibility in selecting and using weapons.

There are several sub-variants of the aircraft known to NATO as 'Flogger-J'. All have wing glove bullet fairings removed and extended wing leading-edge root extensions. The latter were added to serve as a location for the forward hemisphere RWR antennas, but also have the beneficial side effect of improving high-Alpha handling. All 'Flogger-Js' have a new Klen laser rangefinder in place of the MiG-27K's Fone unit. The 'Swift Rod' ILS antenna was moved from below the nose to the port side of the nose, opposite the pitot.

There is some confusion regarding Soviet designations of some of the aircraft. The first of the 'Flogger-Js' was the new-build MiG-27M, which has an enlarged laser window in the nose. Some externally identical aircraft allegedly bore the Soviet air force designation MiG-27D. This variant incorporates the RSBN-6S navigation system, which is associated with the nuclear strike role. The twin pitot probes which serve the nav/attack system are mounted high on the nose, providing the main recognition features between the basic MiG-27D/MiG-27K 'Flogger-J' and the MiG-27K 'Flogger-J2'. The latter variant was produced as a new-build aircraft, and by conversion of MiG-27s, MiG-27Ds and perhaps MiG-27Ms. It has a noticeable fairing below the nose, with a broad rectangular window for a FLIR system, and an upper window for the laser target designator which is a new system and a member of the Kaira family. The twin pitots are mounted low on the nose and the 'pimple' radome is enlarged.

The Soviet Union exported its most capable aircraft only to a handful of highly-trusted Warsaw Pact allies and a few favoured client states, so the MiG-27 has not been made widely available to foreign customers. The only exception so far has been India, which builds the MiG-27 under licence, operating a version named the MiG-27M, but which Mikoyan refers to as the MiG-27L. The aircraft has the same nose contours as the MiG-27M/D, with only a single window in the undernose fairing, and shares the same 'Flogger-J' reporting name. Soviet MiG-27s first saw combat in Afghanistan where a regiment of MiG-27Ds was deployed to Shindand for offensive operations against Mujahideen guerrilla positions. Sri Lanka has a handful of ex-Ukrainian MiG-27s in service.

# Mikoyan MiG-25 'Foxbat'

## Soviet Superfighter

**The MiG-25 'Foxbat' became a great symbol of the Soviet Cold War threat. The large family of variants remains a potent force within the former Soviet Union, despite the aircraft's 30-year old design.**

The MiG-25 was developed as a panic response to the American North American XB-70 Valkyrie strategic bomber, whose Mach 3 performance and very high-altitude capability threatened to present Soviet air defences with almost insoluble problems. When development of the Valkyrie was halted in 1961, work on the MiG-25 was well advanced, and the USSR continued with the project, perhaps knowing that a Mach-3 capable reconnaissance aircraft, the Lockheed A-12 (later SR-71), was about to begin flight tests.

In designing an aircraft for sustained flight at Mach 3, the biggest problem facing the design bureau was the so-called heat barrier. Those parts of the airframe that had to withstand the greatest heat, such as the nose and leading edges, had to be of titanium construction, but many other areas that could theoretically have been made of riveted aluminium – such as the wing skins – had to be of welded steel because no suitable heat-resistant sealant could be found, and because there was a shortage of skilled riveters. Eventually, 80 per cent of the aircraft was of tempered steel, 11 per cent of aluminium alloys and nine per cent of titanium.

Development of the Ye-155P (the original MiG-25 designation) interceptor was approved in February 1962, and the prototype made its maiden flight on 9 September 1964. The aircraft was powered by a pair of 22,500-lb (100-kN) Mikulin (later Tumanskii) R-15B-300 turbojets with a life of 150 hours, and was fitted with a Smertch-A radar, known to NATO as 'Fox Fire'; the radar had a detection range of 54 nm (62 miles; 100 km). The aircraft carried two R-40 air-to-air missiles, in mixed pairs of R-40R and R-40T semi-active radar- and IR-homing versions. Look-down capability was virtually non-existent.

Performance was up to expectations and, in March 1965 – under the cover designation Ye-266 – an early aircraft was used to establish several performance records which were countered by the US YF-12 in May 1965. Between 1965 and 1977, the Ye-266 and another early variant, the Ye-266M, eventually made 21 FAI-notified record-breaking flights, setting nine records which remained unbroken until 1994.

Production began in 1969, but the aircraft did not enter full air force service until 1973, having been plagued by engine problems. Even in service the MiG-25 was subject to severe operating limitations, which strictly constrained the amount

***Above: During the Cold War years, grainy black and white images such as this were the only views of the 'Foxbat' that could be obtained by Western intelligence agencies. However, on 6 September 1976, Soviet pilot Victor Belenko defected in a MiG-25P from Sakharovka air base to Hakodate Airport, northern Japan. A US intelligence team was quickly on site to examine his aircraft.***

***Top: The imposing size and boxy shape of the MiG-25 set it apart from other combat aircraft. The 'Foxbat' is built from a unique mix of steel, aluminium and titanium that give it the structural strength to survive in its high-speed, high-altitude operational environment – yet the design is robust enough to be maintained on a flight line, even in poor weather conditions.***

***Above: Mikoyan employed models to explore numerous configurations that would allow a fighter to travel at Mach 3. Prior to the aircraft entering service, the six design team members were awarded the Lenin Prize for their achievements.***

***Right: The MiG-25PU 'Foxbat-C' is a highly valued type. Serving as trainers, familiarisation aircraft and weather recce ships, the two-seaters see more flying hours than any other MiG-25 version.***

**The camera provision of earlier RB variants was omitted from the MiG-25RBF. Instead, the nose was fitted with two pairs of dielectric panels for its Shar-25 Elint system. This particular example wears an 'outstanding unit citation' badge just below the cockpit, in reflection of the squadron's excellent operating record.**

of time that could be spent at very high speeds, which limited the use of full engine power.

The ultimate MiG-25PD 'Foxbat-E' fighter variant entered production in 1978, and featured a new RP-25 look-down/shoot-down radar, an undernose IRST and more powerful engines. Surviving Soviet 'Foxbat-As' were brought up to the same standard from 1979, under the designation MiG-25PDS. Normal armament comprises two R-40 (AA-6 'Acrid') and four R-60 (AA-8 'Aphid') AAMs. The PD/PDS upgrade has restored the MiG-25's viability and some are expected to serve on into the next millennium.

### Pilot trainer

The MiG-25PU 'Foxbat-C' two-seat conversion trainer was rolled out in 1968. It lacks the radar and has no combat capability. The type features a new forward cockpit for the instructor, stepped down in front of the standard single-seat cockpit.

The MiG-25PU and the MiG-25P fighter have been exported to Algeria, Iraq, Libya and Syria. An Iraqi MiG-25P shot down a USN F/A-18 during the Gulf War.

### Mach 3 spyplane

Although the MiG-25 was originally designed as an interceptor, it had obvious potential as a reconnaissance platform.

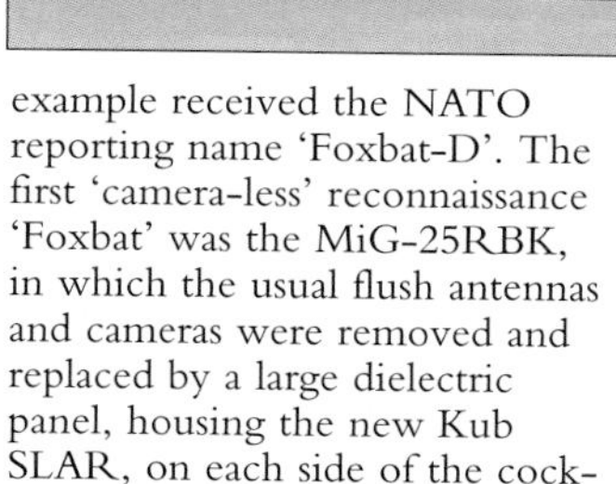

**Right: This Swedish air force photo of a MiG-25BM over the Baltic harks back to the days when 'Foxbats' were regular photo subjects for Flygvapnet Drakens and Viggens. Today, intercepts of Russian aircraft are virtually nil.**

The prototype recce aircraft, the Ye-155R-1, made its maiden flight six months before the prototype fighter, on 6 March 1964.

As the MiG-25R, the reconnaissance version passed its state acceptance tests in 1969, and series production began in April of that year. The MiG-25R had five camera ports in the nose (one vertical and four oblique), with small square flush antennas further forward on the nose.

The original MiG-25R was replaced on the production line by the MiG-25RB 'Foxbat-B' in 1970, this type remaining in production until 1982. The MiG-25RB was a dual-role reconnaissance bomber, with a Peeling automatic bombing system, as well as having the Soviet Union's first operational inertial navigation system. Camera-equipped MiG-25RBs were exported to Algeria, Bulgaria, India, Iraq, Libya and Syria.

The basic MiG-25RB also formed the basis of a model dedicated to Elint duties, with its optical sensors replaced by a variety of passive receivers and active SLAR systems. This example received the NATO reporting name 'Foxbat-D'. The first 'camera-less' reconnaissance 'Foxbat' was the MiG-25RBK, in which the usual flush antennas and cameras were removed and replaced by a large dielectric panel, housing the new Kub SLAR, on each side of the cockpit. The MiG-25RBK entered service in 1972 and remained in production until 1980.

The final reconnaissance variant was the MiG-25RBF, which is described either as an RB brought up to RBK standards, or as a new production aircraft which replaced the RBK on the production line; it has expanded jamming capability.

Unusually, the reconnaissance 'Foxbat' has its own dedicated two-seat trainer, designated MiG-25RU – this variant has no operational equipment.

### SAM suppression

Having closely followed the development of dedicated 'Wild Weasel' aircraft by the US in the final stages of the Vietnam War and in the immediate post-war period, Mikoyan developed the MiG-25BM. Developed in 1972 and known as the 'Foxbat-F' by NATO, the MiG-25BM was adapted to carry four Kh-85 (AS-11 'Kilter') anti-radiation missiles. The aircraft are believed to be equipped with a sophisticated avionics package including a Sych-M ('Little Owl') radar. The MiG-25BMs observed in service have their noses painted to represent the radomes of the fighter MiG-25s.

Fewer than 100 MiG-25BMs were built between 1982 and 1985 and all were delivered to Frontal Aviation units in East Germany and Poland; the aircraft has not been offered for export and remains extremely secret.

**Above: Pictured wearing full-pressure suits (required for high-altitude operations), these two Frontal Aviation pilots are seen in front of a 'Foxbat-F'. Changes to the cockpit are limited to the addition of revised mission equipment panels.**

**Left: The Indian air force took delivery of six MiG-25RBs and all wore the stylised eagle badge of No. 102 Sqn. One of the IAF's 'Foxbat-Bs' was written off in a crash, but all the others are believed to remain operational.**

# Development and prototypes

**Although superficially similar to the prototype MiG-29 which first flew on 6 October 1977, today's MiG-29SMT is effectively a completely new aircraft type. 'Fulcrum' develoment has encompassed two-seat, naval, export and various advanced variants.**

The first prototype MiG-29 (company designation 9-12) lacked many of the features of later development aircraft. Development delays lead to the omission of the radar, as well as the OEPrNK-29 electro-optical complex at the time of Alexander Fedotov's maiden flight of the type at Zhukovskii.

The first prototype was followed by three more 9-12 prototypes (902, 903 and 904). Bort '02', the first of these, first flew in November 1979, and introduced redesigned nosegear (the nose oleo was shortened and moved aft, necessitated by the tendency of the twin nosewheels to kick up spray and debris into the intakes), and definitive GTDE-117 APU and single-barrel GSh-30-1 30-mm cannon.

A shorter overall wheelbase improved the turning circle on the ground, and all three under-carriage units were shod with significantly larger tyres than the first prototype. The intended engine testbed, 903, was lost in a crash days after its first flight, and replaced by another aircraft, 908. Nine further 'pre-production' 9-12s were built, externally differing little from the last prototype, 904. The pre-production batch carried out extended high-Alpha and handling testing, at the instigation of deput chief test pilot Valerii Menitskii.

These trials proved the MiG-29's unrivalled ability to fly beyond the limits of the 'normal' flight envelope. By the time the MiG-29 entered service in June 1983, these aircraft had flown in excess of 3,000 hours.

## Early production

Initial batches of production 9-12 MiG-29 'Fulcrum-As' were identical in appearance to pre-production aircraft, but differ from later production 'Fulcrum-As' by their retention of ventral fins and lack of overwing chaff/flare dispensers.

Early in its career, the MiG-29 gained a secondary nuclear strike capability, with the left inner wing pylon reinforced to carry the 30-kT RN-40 free-fall device. Perhaps fourteen Frontal Aviation regiments equipped with the MiG-29, and the first of eight 16th Air Army MiG-29 regiments in East Germany (the 33rd IAP) received the type at Wittstock in January 1986.

Early production aircraft remaining in service retain ventral fins, but have been retro-fitted with with extended-chord rudders, pitot-mounted strakes and flight control system modifi-cations. A small number have lost their ventral fins and received chaff/flare dispensers, redering them indistinguishable from later production examples.

The bulk of MiG-29s deliv-ered lacked ventral fins, but instead featured new long-chord shallow strakes above the wing-roots, leading forward from the tailfin roots, each strake accomo-dating a BVP-30-26M ECM dispenser. The basic MiG-29 received a number of upgrades in service, including modified flight control surface actuators, improved flight control system to expand Alpha limits, nose strakes to generate vortices during high AoA flight and increased area broad-chord

***Above: 904, the fourth prototype 9-12 MiG-29 was used for structural loads analysis, testing the limits of combat manoeuvrability, and later air-to-ground weapons testing.***

***Top: The company's MiG-29SD was used as an inflight-refuelling test aircraft, with the bolt-on retractable IFR probe that is carried by Malaysia's MiG-29N as well as 'new generation' SMT/UBTs.***

***The first prototype 9-12 was a one-off, with longer nose gear located further forward than on subsequent aircraft, and twin ports for a GSh-23-2 twin-barrel 23-mm cannon. Later in its career 901 received ventral fins.***

***Above: Only two examples of the multi-role 9-31 MiG-29K were built, sharing commonality with the loand-based 9-15 MiG-29M. The first prototype, 911, bore the brunt of carrier trials on* Tbilisi.**

***Right: Had the MiG-29K been procured by the AV-MF, Mikoyan proposed the radarless 9-62 MiG-29KU two-seat trainer, shown in wind-tunnel mock-up form, intended for carrier landing practice.***

rudders. A small number were mofified to accept underwing fuel tanks, and to be able to fire their cannon whilst carrying a standard centreline tank.

The 9-12 MiG-29 was exported to Warsaw Pact allies as the 9-12A MiG-29A, lacking nuclear strike capability, and perhaps carrying a modified IFF system. These export aircraft were equivalent to later standard Frontal Aviation 9-12s with extended-chord rudders. The 9-12B MiG-29B was a further downgraded export variant, intended for non-WarPac clients. When the Wasaw Pact was dissolved, however, many 9-12As were effectively modified to 9-12B standard. Former East German 9-12As had SRO IFF and Laszlo datalink removed, prior to being handed over to the Luftwaffe. The Luftwaffe currently operates NATO-compatible MiG-29Gs and two-seat MiG-29GTs. The 9-12SD MiG-29N is essentially a standard 'Fulcrum-A' for Malaysian service. In 1997 Malaysia signed up for an upgrade, with IFR probe (trialled by the MiG-29SD) and the Topaz-M radar of the dual-target capability MiG-29SM.

## The 'second generation'

The MiG-29SM is categorised by the OKB as a multi-role tactical fighter. Planned as a version of the 'fat-backed' 9-13 'Fulcrum-C', the 9-13SM MiG-29SM prototypes in fact tended to be modified 9-12s, lacking the bulged spine of the 'Fulcrum-C'. Bort '331' is an exception, in that it is based on a 9-13 airframe. As yet, no definitive MiG-29SM has been built.

As the 'all new' multi-role MiG-29M (and its MiG-29K naval equivalent) have seemingly fallen victim to political intrigue and cuts in funding, Mikoyan has pursued development of the MiG-29SMT/UBT upgrades. Serving as a substitute for the earlier 9-15 MiG-29M, development of the 9-17 MiG-29SMT has been informed by the MiG-29M project, and MiG-29M prototypes remain active as avionics and systems testbeds for current projects.

One 9-13 airframe (916 Bort '16') was modified as early as 1986 to serve as a testbed for the MiG-29E, a secretive secon-generation MiG-29 programme which resluted in the 'definitive' MiG-29M. Aircraft 916 was probably equipped with thrust-vectoring nozzles, or even thrust-vectoring engines of am entirely new design. The existence of thrust-vectoring MiG-29s, however, is an official secret, and it remains unclear whether this will be incorporated into the MiG-29SMT/UBT programme during the future.

***This anonymous looking light glossy grey painted 9-13 'Fulcrum-C' at Zhukovskii reportedly carries a new 'anti-radar coating', and thus serves as a testbed for a 'stealthy' second generation MiG-29.***

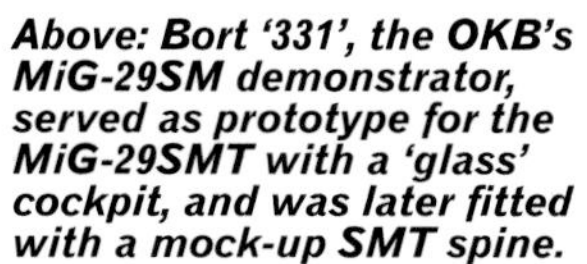

***Above: Bort '331', the OKB's MiG-29SM demonstrator, served as prototype for the MiG-29SMT with a 'glass' cockpit, and was later fitted with a mock-up SMT spine.***

***Right: Bort '304', the first prototype 9-51T MiG-29UBT (with R-60 and R-73 AAMs underwing) was converted from an existing MiG-29UB. The type is optimised for 'pathfinder' and strike duties.***

# 'Fulcrum-A/B' Description

**Following the commencement of Mikoyan's 1971 *logiky* (lightweight) fighter project, the resulting MiG-29 was hurried through development and entered service in the early 1980s.**

Compared to the Su-27 'Flanker', the development of the MiG-29 was relatively untroubled; the aircraft began to enter service in 1982, becoming widely operational by 1986. In the same year, East German regiments began to re-equip with the new fighter, Indian deliveries began, and production had reached a high rate.

### First 'Fulcrum'

The first production single-seat MiG-29s were known to NATO as the 'Fulcrum-A', and to the factory as 9-12. Externally identical to the nine pre-production aircraft, they differed from later MiG-29s by their retention of ventral fins, and lack of overwing chaff/flare dispensers.

Following the formation of the first MiG-29 regiment, the 234th 'Proskuroskii' GvIAP at Kubina, followed by the 'Combat Leader' regiment at Ros in the Ukraine, some 250 early production MiG-29s entered service, going on to form a total of 14 Frontal Aviation regiments. During the early 1990s, when the Soviet airborne presence in Eastern Europe was at its peak, more than 30 early production MiG-29s were in service in East Germany alone.

Former Warsaw Pact allies received the MiG-29A sub-variant and the standard two-seat MiG-29UB. This example of the latter is one of six serving with Hungary's 59th Tactical Fighter Regiment.

Above: The MiG-29 was 'officially' unveiled to Western onlookers when six Kubinka-based examples mounted a goodwill visit to Finland in August 1986. Early models still retain ventral fins.

Top: India received 70 baseline single-seat 'Fulcrums' in 1986. Designated MiG-29B by the manufacturer, they lack Soviet model IFF and datalink, and serve with Nos 28, 47 and 233 Squadrons.

Today, remaining early production, ventral-finned MiG-29 'Fulcrum-As' have been retrofitted with the extended chord rudders and updated flight control system of later variants. A few others have lost their ventral fins and received chaff/flare dispensers, rendering them identical to later aircraft.

### Afghanistan experience

In addition to lacking the ventral fin, another feature of the principal production 9-12 'Fulcrum-A' was the fitting of the long-chord wingroot strakes containing the BVP-30-26M chaff and flare dispenser, with 30 cartridges. The dispenser was a direct result of Soviet experience gained in Afghanistan.

In service, the main production 'Fulcrum-A' gained further refinements, including an improved flight control system (expanding Alpha limits), modified flight control surface actuators, nose-mounted vortex generator strakes and increased-area rudders, the latter also being retrofitted to early production examples. A small number of main production 'Fulcrum-As' were given the capability to carry underwing fuel tanks, and to fire their refined-muzzle

***Left:* The outstanding manoeuvrability and power-to-weight ratio of the MiG-29 led to it being an obvious mount for the Russian Swifts display team, equipped with the 9-12 and two-seat 9-51.**

***Below:* Wearing an all-over 'stars' display scheme, this MiG-29A (9-12A) 'Fulcrum-A' serves with the Hungarian Air Force's 59 HRE unit. Hungary's fleet of 'Fulcrums' is based at Kecskemét.**

cannon when carrying a centre-line fuel tank.

Reflecting the tactical role envisaged for the MiG-29 in future European air wars, the 'Fulcrum-A' was given a nuclear capability early in its service life, adopting the 30-kT RN-40 free-fall nuclear bomb.

The break-up of the USSR left some 486 9-12 'Fulcrum-As' in Russian service, 245 in the Ukraine, 80 in Belarus, 36 in Uzbekistan, 34 in Moldova, and 22 in Kazakhstan.

## Export aircraft

The air forces of Warsaw Pact nations (except the non-WarPac Yugoslavia and possibly Romania) were supplied with 9-12 'Fulcrum-As', which were of a very similar standard to Soviet service aircraft. Designated MiG-29A or 9-12A, these export aircraft lacked nuclear capability and carried a slightly different Laszlo IFF system. Reports suggest that German MiG-29As had only three radar modes, compared to the five modes of the Soviet aircraft.

The MiG-29B (9-12B) was an export variant intended for use by less close allies, including Yugoslavia, Cuba, Syria, North Korea, India, Iran and Iraq. The MiG-29B was further downgraded compared to the standard Soviet 'Fulcrum-A', lacking Soviet IFF and datalink, and perhaps fitted with the downgraded N-019E radar. Following the dissolution of the Warsaw Pact, it seems likely that East European MiG-29As were effectively reduced to MiG-29B standard.

Although downgraded MiG-29 versions (9-12A and 9-12B) were specifically tailored for export, ex-Frontal Aviation machines have also, more recently, been exported second-hand. Peru, for example, purchased 12 MiG-29s from Belarus. In addition, Moldova provided Yemen with 12 of its 34 MiG-29s, one of which was shot down, and seven of which were captured in Yemeni service. More surprisingly, the USAF took at least 21 MiG-29s in 1997.

## 'Fulcrum-B'

The 9-51 MiG-29UB (*Uchebno-Boevoi*, Trainer-Combat) two-seat trainer was always planned, although the Soviets introduced the aircraft only slowly into front-line units, continuing to rely on the MiG-23UB into the 1990s. A dedicated trainer, the 'Fulcrum-B' lacks radar and BVR missile capability, unlike the Su-27UB. An advanced training system, however, provides synthetic targets for the front cockpit displays.

## Maiden flight

The first MiG-29UB/9-51, based on a ventral fin-equipped single-seater airframe, made its maiden flight in April 1981. Entering service in 1986, and built at a separate plant at Gorkii (now Nizhny Novgorod), the production 'Fulcrum-B' lacks the ventral fins of the early 'Fulcrum-A' and the chaff/flare dispensers of later single-seat MiG-29s.

There is no difference between former Soviet MiG-29UBs and those intended for export, except in the case of the MiG-29N-compatible, English-instrumented two-seaters delivered to Malaysia, which are designated MiG-29NUB.

***Above:* Wearing unconventional 'sharkmouth' nose art, as well as non-standard two-digit and inner tailfin codes, this Russian air force MiG-29UB may be used in a dissimilar or 'aggressor' training role.**

***Left:* Trailing a single brake-chute, this Hungarian 59 HRE MiG-29A (9-12A) taxies in at its Kecskemet base. Export MiG-29As came from the same production line as standard Frontal Aviation 'Fulcrums'.**

# 'Hunchbacks'

**Offering a modest increase in internal fuel, the 'Fulcrum-C' spearheaded Soviet tactical aviation elements in East Germany, and has since been developed into a plethora of upgraded sub-types.**

When the MiG-29 'Fulcrum-C' (company designation 9-13) first appeared, Western analysts assumed that the aircraft's swollen spine incorporated a significantly increased internal fuel tankage. In reality, the increase in fuel was minimal, but the redesigned spine did house a Gardeniya active jammer: as a result the variant was not exported to Warsaw Pact clients or overseas operators, with the exception of Romania, which surprisingly received a single example to serve alongside existing 9-12A MiG-29As.

The 9-13's revised EW suite also resulted in a revised wingtip fairing, lengthened and shifted back, so that its rear end was adjacent to the wing trailing edge, and with a rear hemisphere Gardeniya antenna in the fairing supporting the starboard tailfin. Intended solely for Soviet forces, the 9-13 probably has wiring for the nuclear strike role.

In terms of internal fuel capacity, the 9-13 can now carry 890 litres in its No. 1 tank, representing an increase of 110-180 litres (24-40 Imp gal) depending on the reliability of official figures.

The prototype 9-13 (c/n 1616 Bort '26') first flew in 1986, preceded by a number of converted 9-12s, which first flew in this form in 1984. The 9-13 received no new Soviet air force designation, but was allocated the 'Fulcrum-C' reporting name by NATO's ASCC. The type began to appear in front-line units in 1986-87, with production based upon the airframe of the main production series 9-12 'Fulcrum-A', with the later cannon muzzle, increased-chord rudders and nose strakes. None were fitted with ventral fins.

The 'Fulcrum-C' was particularly common among fighter regiments within the 16th Air Army in East Germany, and in service the type picked up the nickname 'Gorbatov' (hunchback) on account of its distinctive new bulged spine.

Production of the 'Fulcrum-C' reached around 200 aircraft, which were built alongside the standard 9-12 at the MPO factory, and often served alongside the earlier variant in Frontal Aviation regiments, though usually within different squadrons.

***Above: Armed with live AAMs, including a pair of R-27s, a 787th IAP 'Fulcrum-C' sits outside its shelter on QRA at Eberswalde in November 1990, soon after the reunification of Germany.***

***Top: Most 9-13 'Fulcrum-Cs' were assigned to the 16th Air Army in East Germany. This aircraft is now in use at the weapons training school at Lipetsk, with white markings for high visibility.***

A great deal of confusion surrounds the (sometimes shifting) MiG-29S (9-13S), SD, SE and SM designations. These are applied principally to a number of upgrade configurations, sharing a common baseline but differing in detail.

## Upgraded variant

Although associated with recent export efforts, the original MiG-29S configuration was the result of a Soviet requirement. The MiG-29S appears to have originated after 1985, when it was discovered that a Phazotron employee had sold secrets to the West, compromising the radar systems of the A-50, MiG-29 and MiG-31. A crash programme was thus initiated in order to improve and upgrade compromised equipment, in particular producing new algorithms for jamming and automated jamming.

The original package of MiG-29S modifications included a 'modified sighting system' (presumably a reference to the radar being updated to N-019M Topaz standard), improvements to the active jammer, modifications to allow the gun to be fired when carrying a centreline tank, provision for underwing tanks and expanded *g* and Alpha limits. The original MiG-29S programme remains shrouded in secrecy, but it seems that fewer than 20 full-standard examples were built for Soviet surface. However, large numbers of Frontal Aviation MiG-29s were upgraded to carry underwing tanks, and some may have received other 9-13S upgrades.

***Ukraine inherited a large number of 9-13 'Fulcrum-Cs'. The type is flown by the 'Ukrainian Falcons' aerobatic team, as well as with the 138 IAD and 6 IAD combat regiments, headquartered at Mirgorod and Ivano-Frankovsk.***

# MiG-29SMT/UBT

***Armed with Kh-31, R-77 and R-73 missiles, Bort '917', the first full-standard 9-17 MiG-29SMT was previously the MiG-29SE demonstrator Bort '555', the multi-tone blue/grey camouflaged company 'hack'.***

**After the end of the potentially world-beating MiG-29M programme after mid-1990s funding difficulties, and the virtual abandonment of the 1.42, Mikoyan has invested its future in the MiG-29SMT and UBT.**

The 9-17 or MiG-29SMT is intended to substitute the MiG-29M as a MiG-29 replacement in the Frontal fighter role, and like the MiG-29M will also give capabilities once offered by dedicated fighter-bombers like the MiG-27 and Su-17M.

Some evidence suggests that the MiG-29SMT began life as an attempt to transform existing Russian MiG-29s into fighter-bombers to replace the MiG-27 and Su-17M when they themselves were supplanted by the MiG-29M. The lightweight new-build MiG-29M has now effectively been shelved in favour of the MiG-29SMT upgrade. Production of the SMT could be possible on existing production tooling, or through modification or upgrade of existing airframes, as the type retains a high level of commonality with earlier versions.

The SMT addresses the original aircraft's range/endurance deficiency, introduces a modern 'glass' cockpit and a true multi-role capability. Using the basic 'Fulcrum' airframe as the basis for a radical upgrade, the SMT carries new avionics, massive new internal fuel tanks and other refinements. The programme has been funded by the Russian air forces as an upgrade package for its in-service MiG-29s. Reflecting the type's links to the 9-13SM MiG-29SM multi-role tactical fighter development, the new aircraft's designation signifies *Toplivo*, or fuel. An initial SMT mock-up, based on a pre-production airframe, displayed a MiG-29M-derived 'glass' cockpit, with HOTAS functionality, and two large full-colour MFDs each side of the panel, augmented by smaller monochrome MFPU LCD displays at the front of each console. The aircraft also featured a revised spine, different to that ultimately fitted to the definitive SMT.

The first MiG-29SMT demonstrator, Bort '331', first flew on 29 November 1997, in the hands of Marat Alykov, and flew with a new 9-17 spine in April 1998. The first full-standard SMT was Bort '917', which was first flown as an SMT by Vladimir Gorbunov on 14 July 1998. This aircraft introduced a new spine profile, extending further aft into a 'beaver' tail similar to that of the MiG-29M.

Total fuel tankage is increased to 10,526 lb (4775 kg) giving a range of 1,370 miles (2200 km) without refuelling. The first production SMT carries the bolt-on IFR probe that was trialled by the MiG-29SD and is fitted to Malaysia's MiG-29Ns.

Russia would ideally wish to upgrade all 400-500 MiG-29s that remain in service, but funding difficulties dictate that the current requirement covers only around 180 aircraft.

## Two-seat upgrade

The 9-51T MiG-29UBT is a private venture by MIG-MAPO, and is not currently understood to be part of the SMT upgrade programme for the Russian air forces. However, they are interested in the new variant, which offers a 'pathfinder' role for use in conjunction with the single-seat SMT. The UBT incorporates the same 'glass' cockpit, enhanced avionics and increased fuel capacity of the UBT, and the first example was converted from the company's existing MiG-29UB 'Fulcrum-B' demonstrator.

As well as offering the expanded capabilities of a twin-seat multi-role fighter, the UBT can also operate as a useful trainer, with expanded training modes and new capabilities for the airborne simulation of using different weapons. The rear cockpit is intended to accommodate a WSO on combat operations, and carries a large CRT in place of the pilot's HUD, for the display of FLIR or video imagery. According to company sources, a production version of the UBT would carry an 'internally mounted' reconnaissance SLAR.

***Right: The second MiG-29UBT at Zhukovskii. Seen as a possible replacement for the Su-24, the type provides a rival to Sukhoi's Su-30 family.***

***The first production MiG-29SMT, fitted with bolt-on IFR probe, carrying Kh-31P passive radar homing 75-mile (120-km) range ASMs and R-73s.***

# MiG-29M briefing

*Although outwardly the MiG-29M closely resembles the basic 'Fulcrum', it has far more versatility and range.*

**In order to improve the baseline MiG-29A 'Fulcrum', Mikoyan set out to produce a MiG-29 derivative. With greater range and better radar than the MiG-29A, the MiG-29M has the potential to become a world-beating fighter, but has yet to enter production.**

The shortcomings of the original, baseline MiG-29 were apparent from an early stage. The aircraft was handicapped by its relatively poor range/endurance characteristics, and by a lack of multi-role versatility. It was arguably the best short-range point defence interceptor of its era, but had only the most rudimentary air-to-ground capability.

Initially developed as a private venture to replace the MiG-29, the MiG-29M married the former's highly successful aerodynamic configuration with more powerful engines, a new multi-role avionics and weapons system, genuine all-weather autonomous precision attack capability, a structurally redesigned airframe of reduced weight, and a massive increase in internal fuel capacity.

*One of the least obvious changes to the MiG-29M is its reprofiled canopy. As well as having an ARK radio compass antenna embedded in the rear section, the whole canopy has been both lengthened and raised, allowing a higher seating position, and thereby giving the pilot a better all-round view, particularly over the nose.*

### Finer 'Fulcrum'

Six prototypes were built, as well as two prototypes of a similar navalised variant, the MiG-29K. With the first prototype flying on 25 April 1986, these improved variants quickly demonstrated that the MiG-29's fundamental shortcomings had been convincingly addressed, and the way seemed clear for development to be completed, and production to begin. But then the Cold War ended, and development of the MiG-29M and MiG-29K was halted, falling victim to fierce spending cuts.

The present status of the MiG-29M programme is uncertain, and a trickle of funding for the project seems to be turned on and then off again with monotonous regularity. When the post Cold War spending cuts bit deep, development of the MiG-29M had reached a more advanced stage than that of the Su-27M, but it was the MiG fighter that was halted, while Su-27M development continued. If there was only sufficient funding for one programme, the Su-27M was, in many respects, a surprising choice. The smaller, lighter and cheaper MiG-29M was a better post Cold War aircraft than the Su-27M, and promised to be a superior performer on the export market. Existing MiG-29 customers could be expected to purchase the new MiG-29 variant, which enjoyed some commonality with the original aircraft, and used much of the same support equipment. As far as Russia was concerned, the MiG-29M also formed the basis of the carrier-borne MiG-29K, which was more versatile and useful than its Sukhoi competitor, the Su-27K.

*Above: Later 'Fulcrums' are able to carry an impressive warload. The medium-range Vympel R-77 air-to-air missile is one of the MiG-29M's primary weapons, although integration of this missile with the aircraft's systems has proved troublesome.*

### Superior Sukhoi?

Instead, the Su-27M and Su-27K continued while the advanced MiG-29s were suspended. Since then, there have been periodic attempts to provide the relatively small amount of funding needed to complete development of the MiG-29M, but the task remains incomplete.

A further complicating factor lies in the fact that the aircraft's manufacturer has a vested interest in selling off its stock of unsold baseline MiG-29s before making any production investment in the MiG-29M. Thus, potential customers for the 'full-spec' MiG-29M are being directed towards 'warmed over', upgraded versions of the basic MiG-29 'Fulcrum'.

Only fairly recently has an upgrade been available offering anything like the potential and sophistication of the MiG-29M, but this version – the MiG-29SMT – retains the heavyweight airframe of the original MiG-29 and is flying only in prototype form.

At one time, it was expected that the MiG-29M would form the basis of the advanced MiG-35, but this is dependent on economics, which will play a significant factor in future Russian fighter development.

*Before its cancellation, the MiG-29M was exhibited at both the Farnborough and Paris airshows. Although cheaper than the American F-16 Fighting Falcon and F/A-18 Hornet, no foreign orders for the new 'Fulcrum' were forthcoming.*

# MiG-29M

**All six MiG-29M prototypes were newly built, and wore standard camouflage. False over-wing intake louvres (now removed) were painted on several of the prototypes in order to fool US spy satellites into thinking that they were ordinary MiG-29As.**

### Fuel
The MiG-29 has traditionally been handicapped by its short range. The use of space-saving welded aluminium lithium alloys and the deletion of the auxiliary intakes has provided much extra internal volume for fuel in the MiG-29M. Fuel capacity has been increased by approximately 3,300 lb (1500 kg).

### Weapons
A wide variety of ordnance has been displayed on the MiG-29M. In addition to its primary role of ground-attack, the MiG-29M is also able to undertake air-to-air missions. This example is seen carrying a mixed load of air-to-air and air-to-surface weapons, with R-73 (AA-11 'Archer') and R-77 (AA-12 'Adder') AAMs outboard and Kh-31 anti-radiation missiles inboard. This wide-ranging weapons capability is made possible by the provision of an extra pair of underwing hardpoints compared to the standard MiG-29. All the pylons are restressed for the carriage of heavier stores.

### Powerplant
Powered by a pair of increased-thrust Leningrad/Klimov (Isotov) RD-33K afterburning turbofans, the MiG-29M requires greater power due to its increase in operational weight. Although externally indistinguishable to the early RD-33 engines, the new Isotov powerplants are capable of increasing the afterburning thrust from 18,298 lb (81.42 kN) to 19,400 lb (86.33 kN). Improvements are incorporated in the intake lips to accommodate these changes.

### Spine
The MiG-29M has an increased-volume fuselage spine containing extra fuel and avionics, displaced by other internal changes. This is of a less obvious profile than the big spine fitted to the 'Fulcrum-C', although it is of greater volume.

### Air-to-ground radar
Whereas the basic MiG-29 had a dedicated air-to-air radar in the shape of its N-019 (RLPK–29) 'Slot Back', the MiG-29M has a more versatile, modern multi-mode radar with multiple air-to-air and air-to-ground modes. The latter include terrain following and avoidance, real-beam or synthetic aperture mapping, target designation for air-to-surface missiles (ASMs), and a range of navigation options.

### Tailplane
The MiG-29M has an increased-area horizontal tailplane, giving greater control authority in pitch (when both tailplanes are used symmetrically) and in roll (when used differentially). An inboard dogtooth discontinuity generates a vortex which keeps flow attached at high deflection angles.

### Fly-by-wire
The MiG-29M uses an analog system, with four channels for pitch and three for roll/yaw, supplemented by a mechanical back-up. Analog signalling is claimed to improve reliability and reduce vulnerability to interference at the cost of slightly higher weight, although this claim has yet to be vindicated.

### Radome
The new flat plate antenna of the N-010 multi-mode pulse-Doppler radar allows the radome shape to be refined, omitting the prominent bulge which was previously necessary on the MiG-29A to accommodate the bulky front element of the N-019's twist cassegrain antenna.

# MiG-29K

## Carrierborne 'Fulcrum'

**To provide a multi-role fighter for the Russian navy, Mikoyan expended much effort on the MiG-29K, a thorough reworking of the basic design for carrier deployment. In the event, it lost out to the Su-27K.**

The origins of the MiG-29K remain shrouded in some mystery. Most sources suggest that the project was launched to provide a multi-role strike fighter to complement the single-role Su-27K interceptor, to equip the air wings of the planned four STOBAR (short take-off but arrested landing) carriers intended to enter Soviet navy service during the 1990s. A handful of analysts maintain that the MiG-29K was only ever planned as a fall-back, in case the Su-27K proved too heavy to operate from the new carriers. They believe that the Soviet carriers were planned as pure fleet air defence vessels, with no power-projection role, and thus with no requirement for fighter-bomber or strike/attack capabilities.

Trials with the hooked MiG-29KVP proved that the MiG-29 could be operated safely from a ski-jump, and that arrested landings were possible at operationally useful weights. Although the MiG-29KVP could have formed the basis of a practical carrierborne fighter, it was decided that the ideal carrierborne MiG-29 would require both additional wing area and additional thrust. Further, improved high-lift devices might produce a useful reduction in approach speed, without unacceptably raising the angle of attack on touch-down.

Since a new variant of the MiG-29 would be required, Mikoyan took the courageous decision to adapt it from the new multi-role MiG-29M, with its lightweight airframe, multi-mode/multi-role radar and PGM capability. Detail design began in 1985, one year before the MiG-29M made its maiden flight.

### Uprated engines

There was a degree of cross-fertilisation between the MiG-29M and the MiG-29K, with the uprated RD-33K engines developed for the carrier aircraft eventually being adopted for the -29M, too. The new engine had an exceptional regime (ChR or Chrezvychainii Regim) giving 20,725 lb st (92.17 kN) thrust for a limited period, useful on launch and in the event of a missed approach or go-around. It also had FADEC (full-authority digital engine control), advanced materials and single-crystal turbine blades. They allowed the engine to operate at higher temperatures, and the basic maximum thrust figure was increased from 18,298 lb st (81.42 kN) to 19,400 lb st (86.33 kN). Engine

***Above and top: The first MiG-29K, Bort '311', is seen during trials aboard* Tbilisi*. These included landing aboard with R-73 and R-77 missiles, the main air-to-air weapons of the type. The aircraft bore the brunt of the carrier trials, carrying photo-calibration marks on the nose. The extended and bulged wingtips housed electronic warfare equipment.***

### MiG-29KVP – carrier trials testbed

Although Mikoyan sources once insisted that there had been 'several' MiG-29KVPs, it now appears that the type was a one-off, converted from pre-production aircraft 918 and fitted with an arrester hook for carrier landing and ski-jump trials at the Nitka complex at Saki in the Crimea. The new Russian carriers were originally intended to incorporate steam catapults, but development problems prompted a change to the use of ski-jumps. The aircraft did not have the folding wings or double-slotted flaps of the definitive MiG-29K, nor was it given a 'beefed-up' landing gear. This meant that later in its career it was able to fly approaches onto the carrier *Tbilisi*, but was not cleared for the very high sink rates which can occur in a real carrier landing at sea. The MiG-29KVP began work on ski-jump take-offs on 21 August 1982. It is now on display in the museum at Monino.

*Left: For the first series of carrier trials on board* **Tbilisi**, *the MiG-29K deployed alongside a Sukhoi Su-27K (T10K) prototype. Rescue cover was provided by a Kamov Ka-27PS 'Helix-D'.*

*Below: This view of the second MiG-29K highlights the main navalised features: folding wings and arrester hook. This aircraft, seen armed with active-radar R-77 missiles (AA-12 'Adder'), also has the refuelling probe extended.*

life was claimed to be 1,400 hours, with a TBO (time between overhauls) of 350 hours.

The quintessence of the MiG-29K lay in its new wing, designed with power-folding at roughly one-third span. The wing was fitted with broader-chord double-slotted trailing-edge flaps, and featured the extended-span ailerons of the MiG-29M, though they were modified to droop (as flaperons) at low speed. The tip was moved further outboard, and increased in chord and depth, housing new defensive EW systems. The leading edge was of reduced sweep-back, giving only slightly greater chord at the root. The leading-edge flaps were redesigned.

In addition to the new wing, the MiG-29K introduced a new, strengthened long-stroke undercarriage, and had a tailhook with a light (so that the LSO could confirm that the tailhook was down at night). The aircraft also had a vertical row of red, green and amber lights on the nose oleo, designed to allow the LSO to assess the aircraft's position relative to the planned glideslope. The MiG-29K prototypes introduced a neat, fully-retractable inflight-refuelling probe below the forward edge of the port side of the windscreen. On Bort '311', the first prototype, this pushed up past a door hinged on its lower side, with the rear part of the door attached to the probe head itself. On the second machine, Bort '312', the forward part of the door was deleted entirely, and the probe tip was visible in its receptacle even when retracted.

Production MiG-29Ks would have had a fully automatic carrier landing system, in addition to the Uzel beacon homing system. The prototypes used a system derived from that fitted to the Yak-38. This was sufficient to guarantee that the aircraft would touch down within a 20-ft (6-m) circle on the deck, within tight airspeed and vertical speed limits – not quite enough to guarantee getting a wire, and not quite enough to guarantee being on the centreline.

### Carrier trials

Commonality with the MiG-29M meant that only two prototypes of the MiG-29K would be required, to prove the carrier-specific items. The radar and weapons system would be proved by the six MiG-29Ms. The first prototype was flown by Takhtar Aubakirov at Saki on 23 June 1988, and was subsequently used for extensive trials aboard the *Tbilisi* beginning on 1 November 1989. The second prototype was used mainly for weapons and avionics trials, and made only six carrier landings aboard *Tbilisi*.

The end of the Cold War and the break-up of the USSR led to the abandonment of the *Tbilisi*'s planned sister ships. *Ulyanovsk* was scrapped where it lay, partially complete, and the almost-finished *Varyag* (formerly *Riga*) became the subject of legal wrangling between Russia and the newly independent Ukraine, before increasingly desperate attempts were made to sell the vessel. Even the *Tbilisi* (already renamed before launch and official christening, having started life as the *Leonid Brezhnev*) was affected. The first thing to change was its name, the capital of the newly independent and troublesome Georgia giving way to the name of a famous Russian admiral – *Kuznetsov*.

The next thing to change was the planned composition of the carrier's air wing. With only one carrier, the dedicated Yak-44 AEW aircraft ('Hawkeye-ski') was abandoned, replaced by a hasty conversion of the Ka-29, known as the Ka-29RLD or Ka-31. Similarly, procurement of two separate fighter aircraft types for its air wing seemed unmanageably extravagant, and it became obvious that a competition was emerging between the Su-27K and MiG-29K.

When the time came to select the aircraft for Russia's one remaining carrier, the choice was made in favour of the Su-27K. This could have been largely due to Sukhoi's political influence, or perhaps the Russian navy genuinely hoped that the small batch of Su-27Ks would eventually be augmented by multi-role MiG-29s when funding permitted. The two MiG-29K prototypes remained active (though 311 was subsequently grounded, then resurrected as a MiG-29M support aircraft) and have contributed to India signing a deal for 42 MiG-29Ks in 2004, for service from 2008.

*While the first MiG-29K was finished in a standard light-grey scheme, the second aircraft, Bort '312', sported this slate-grey paint. Additional markings were MiG and MAPO (Moscow Aircraft Production Organisation) badges, and the St Andrew's Cross ensign of the Russian navy. The aircraft was still active in 2004.*

# MiG-29S Briefing

*In Russia, approximately two squadrons are equipped with the much improved MiG-29S. The aircraft wear this distinctive three-tone camouflage scheme and are compatible with the full range of Russian ordnance.*

**Viewed initially as an interim upgrade of the MiG-29A while Russian pilots awaited delivery of the MiG-29M, the MiG-29S has proved to be the only variant of the highly capable later 'Fulcrums' to enter front-line service.**

The baseline MiG-29 'Fulcrum-A' was handicapped by its lack of range, and by its relative inflexibility. The later MiG-29 'Fulcrum-C' (not built for export) added some extra internal fuel and a powerful new ECM jammer, but did little to remedy the aircraft's basic faults.

Work on the definitive MiG-29M began in the early 1980s, this aircraft transforming the 'Fulcrum' through the provision of extra internal fuel and an entirely new weapons system. At the same time, the MiG-29M kept weight increase to a minimum through the use of new materials and a structural redesign. The weight escalation that did occur was compensated for by the addition of more powerful engines. It had originally been proposed that the MiG-29M would carry its new weapons system externally, in a pod, but the weight and drag penalty was unacceptable. Although a prototype 9-14 with a representative pod was flown, it was soon decided that a redesign could provide sufficient internal volume for the new system, and for fuel, while also saving weight.

But the MiG-29M was an ambitious programme, which would clearly take many years to develop fully, and there was an obvious need for an interim improved 'MiG-29 Plus' to meet the needs of the Russian air forces and export customers.

### Limited development

At an early stage, the decision was taken to limit the scope of any improvements in order to speed up development and to allow existing MiG-29s to be retrofitted to the new, upgraded MiG-29S standard.

The MiG-29S was initially viewed as an upgrade for Soviet MiG-29s and, as such, the initial MiG-29S was based on the 9-13 'Fulcrum-C' airframe, with its humped back housing active jammer and fuel. A prototype flew during 1984, at much the same time as the 9-14. The OKB had a clear view of what the total modification package should contain but, in order to put the aircraft into service quickly, produced the modification as a multi-stage upgrade.

### Improved handling

The first MiG-29S aircraft for the Russian air force featured a revised flight control system, with four new computers for stability augmentation allowing higher *g*- and Alpha-limits, and enabling greater angular deflection of the control surfaces. The aircraft also had provision for two 253-Imp gal (1150-litre) underwing fuel tanks and strengthened pylons to allow the carriage of up to 8,818 lb (4000 kg) of air-to-ground ordnance, with tandem pairs of side-by-side 1,102-lb (500-kg) bombs under each wing. This represented a doubling of the aircraft's warload. Modifications were also made which allowed the cannon to be fired even with the centreline fuel tank in place,

*Despite the improved fuel capacity of the MiG-29S series, an IFR probe is offered as one part of the upgrade package. Holding station behind an IL-78M 'Midas' tanker is this MiG-29S on a test flight from the Russian Flight Test Centre at Akhtubinsk.*

***Above: The improved N-019M 'Topaz' radar of the MiG-29S enables it to engage two targets simultaneously, and fire the R-77/AA-12 'Adder' AAM (known unofficially as the 'AMRAAMski').***

***Left: The MiG-29SE development aircraft was first displayed at Russia's Test Centre, Zhukhovskii. The type was rumoured to be the aircraft of choice for Malaysia.***

which had hitherto been impossible. Finally, the first phase of the MiG-29S upgrade included a revised sighting system (allowing the simulation of IR and radar targets for training purposes) and improved built-in test equipment. By the time Russian MiG-29s left East Germany, many clearly had the ability to carry underwing tanks, presumably indicating that they had been brought up to full MiG-29S standard.

## Dogfight double

The second phase of the MiG≠29S upgrade included software modifications to the N-019M 'Topaz' radar, and greater processing capacity, which allowed better simultaneous target tracking. Subsequent improvements brought with them compatibility with the R-77 (AA-12 'Adder') missile, and even simultaneous dual target engagement capability.

At this stage, it became apparent that the MiG-29S upgrade would be of interest to MiG-29 export customers, and that the new variant's enhanced capabilities might even bring new foreign customers.

Accordingly, the MiG-29S was offered with Western navigation and communications equipment (TACAN, ILS, GPS and radios), with a Western-compatible IFF, and with instruments and displays placarded in English. With the aircraft being marketed seriously for export, Mikoyan also added a bolt-on retractable refuelling probe package.

## Fulcrums for sale

The standard export MiG-29S was known as the MiG-29SD (or as the MiG-29SE when based on the 9-13 airframe). The Malaysian MiG-29Ns were effectively MiG-29SDs but, during the 800-hour overhaul, the aircraft were given a 6,613-lb (3000-kg) weapon load capability, Cossor IFF, English instruments and other avionics changes, R-77 capability, and an inflight refuelling probe.

With the MiG-29SM came compatibility with TV- and laser-guided air-to-surface weapons, a radar mapping mode and simultaneous dual target engagement capability. The demonstrator was based on the 'Fulcrum-A' airframe, but the actual variant could be based on either the 9-12 or the 9-13 airframe.

The latest MiG-29 'Fulcrum' export version is the MiG-29SMT, which first flew during 1997. This had an enlarged spine housing extra fuel, with further fuel in the wing LERXes, replacing the auxiliary intakes. The new version also has a modernised glass cockpit and other improvements, and marks an attempt to give a level of capability consistent with that of the MiG-29M, in an upgraded MiG-29 'Fulcrum' airframe.

***Developed during the Cold War, the 'Fulcrum' marked a turning point in Russian fighter design, being both highly manoeuvrable and able to carry a vast array of weapons. Undergoing a series of upgrades in recent years, the fact that these variants have failed to achieve their full potential can be attributed more to political interference than to their lack of performance.***

*Large and equipped with extremely powerful engines, the MiG-31 'Foxhound' is typical of Russian design philosophy.*

# Mikoyan MiG-31 'Foxhound'

## Development

**Dismissed in the West as a crude, brutish adaptation of the MiG-25, the MiG-31 is in fact one of the world's most sophisticated interceptors.**

By the 1970s, Soviet air defences were in a pitiful state. Russia's Tu-114 'Moss' AWACS platform was available only in very small numbers, and was of limited capability, while the vast network of SAMs had progressed little since the U-2 of Francis Gary Powers had been blasted from the sky over Sverdlovsk on 1 May 1960. The huge IA-PVO interceptor force was equipped with a variety of aircraft, from ageing Sukhoi Su-11 'Fishpots' and MiG-21 'Fishbeds' to newer MiG-25 'Foxbats'. None of the types in service was capable of meeting the threat posed by low-level NATO strike aircraft, by new long-range stand-off missiles or by the new generation of agile Western fighters. Many of the types in use, particularly the lumbering Tupolev Tu-28 'Fiddlers' and Yak-28 'Firebars', were beginning to show their age.

Work on overhauling Soviet air defences was accorded a high priority, and development began on two new AWACS platforms (the A-50 'Mainstay' and An-74 'Madcap'), an array of new SAMs, and various new fighters. The most ambitious of these were the MiG-29 'Fulcrum' (intended as a tactical fighter for Frontal Aviation) and the Sukhoi Su-27 'Flanker' (a long-range agile interceptor and escort fighter for the IA-PVO and Frontal Aviation). Both of these aircraft were single-seaters, and neither promised to be in service before 1985, so a number of interim fighter projects were instituted. New lookdown/ shootdown radar was fitted to the existing Su-15 to produce the Su-15 'Flagon-F', while a similar process produced the MiG-25 'Foxbat-E'. The IA-PVO also took delivery of large numbers of MiG-23 'Floggers', which had a limited lookdown/shootdown capability.

### New design

Although often assumed to have originated as an interim aircraft, or at best as an insurance policy in case of the failure of the Su-27, the MiG-31 actually represented an attempt to produce a long-range interceptor which would be capable of operating independently of ground control, and whose two crew members would also enhance mission performance in a hostile electronic warfare environment, and not just a low-risk, quick-to-develop Su-27 alternative.

The MiG-31 airframe seems to have originated from that of the Ye-155M, a research derivative of the MiG-25 intended to explore ways of increasing the speed and range of the MiG-25 family. It had been intended to undertake a two-stage programme, first fitting new 29,761-lb (132-kN) R-15BF-2-300 engines (with 7,253 lb/ 32 kN more thrust than the R-15B-300 of the standard MiG-25) and then revising the aircraft structure to raise the limiting Mach number (which was then thermally limited to Mach 2.83). With the new engines, service ceiling was raised to 79,396 ft (24200 m), and range increased to 1,193 miles (1920 km) or 1,559 miles (2510 km) with a 1,166-Imp gal (5300-litre) external fuel tank. Unfortunately, engine development took longer than anticipated, and the second stage of the programme, covering structural and material changes, was shelved. The two Ye-155M prototypes still had a role to play, however. They were converted to serve as testbeds for the new 34,170-lb (152-kN) Soloviev D-30F6 dual rotor turbojets being developed for the MiG-31, after a competition between Soloviev and Tumanskii.

### Record breaker

Under the 'cover' designation Ye-266M the re-engined Ye-155M shattered a number of world records. On 17 May 1975 OKB Chief Test Pilot Alexander Fedotov set time-to-height records of 2 minutes 34.28 seconds to 8,202 ft (2500 m), and 4 minutes 11.78 seconds to 13,123 ft (4000 m). His deputy, Ostapenko, took the 9,843-ft (3000-m) record with a time of 3 minutes 9.8 seconds. On 22 July 1977, Fedotov took two more records, those for altitude (achieving 121,653 ft/37080 m)

*Aware of the limitations of the single-seat MiG-25 'Foxbat', Mikoyan developed a two-seat variant. Though constructed in complete secrecy, the cover of the 'Foxhound' was blown when defecting 'Foxbat' pilot Lt Victor Belenko landed in Japan. He revealed that the Russian Air Force was about to receive a two-seat model with a much improved radar.*

**Right: The first MiG-31s seen by the West were encountered by Norwegian fighters during 1985, and included this aircraft. It appeared to have one 'segmented' afterburner nozzle and one plain, and led to much head-scratching among Western analysts. Operating from bases on the Kola Peninsula, these aircraft were often intercepted by F-16s.**

with 2,204 and 4,409 lb (1000 and 2000 kg) payloads. The Ye-266M's final record, set by Alexander Fedotov on 31 August 1977, was an absolute altitude of 123,524 ft (37650 m).

The MiG-31 (which bore the internal designation Project 83) was so closely based on the experimental Ye-155M that it was originally designated Ye-155MP, and was expected to gain the service designation MiG-25MP. The first prototype, bearing the code 831 (indicating the first example of project 83), first flew on 16 September 1975, in the hands of Fedotov.

## Western worries

In the West, the first indication that a 'Super MiG-25' was under development came in September 1976, when Lieutenant Victor Belenko defected to Japan in an early-model MiG-25. He described a MiG-25 with a stronger airframe for supersonic flight at low altitude (the MiG-25 was limited to 575 mph/925 km/h at sea level), with uprated engines, new avionics and new fuselage pylons for six examples of a new long-range missile. He also revealed that the new aircraft would have an internal gun, advanced look-down/shootdown radar and a genuine anti-cruise missile capability. His description provided the inspiration for Craig Thomas' novel *Firefox*, but was taken with a pinch of salt by many experts and, apparently, many intelligence agencies.

The West began to refer to the new aircraft as the MiG-31 in 1977, and began to sit up and take notice when a MiG-31 prototype was observed by a satellite destroying a target at below 200 ft (61 m), at some 12 miles (20 km) range, while itself at 20,000 ft (6096 m). In a later test a MiG-31 at 55,000 ft (16765 m) destroyed a UR-1 RPV flying at 70,000 ft (21336 m). The reporting name 'Foxhound' was announced in mid-1982, and examples of the new type started to be intercepted by Norwegian air force fighters from 1985. At one stage, Western experts were happily stating that a single-seat version had been flown, and that 24 examples of a strategic reconnaissance version were in service. Both reports seem to have been mistaken. The West was, however, taking the MiG-31 seriously, and some began to overestimate the new interceptor. US Assistant Secretary of State for Defense Donald Latham went as far as to describe the MiG-31 as being superior to any existing US fighter, including the F-15.

**At least one MiG-31 (the seventh) was fitted with streamlined cylindrical ESM pods. These were later replaced by anti-flutter weights. The large 'winglets' are thought to be related to some form of MiG-31 aerodynamic development.**

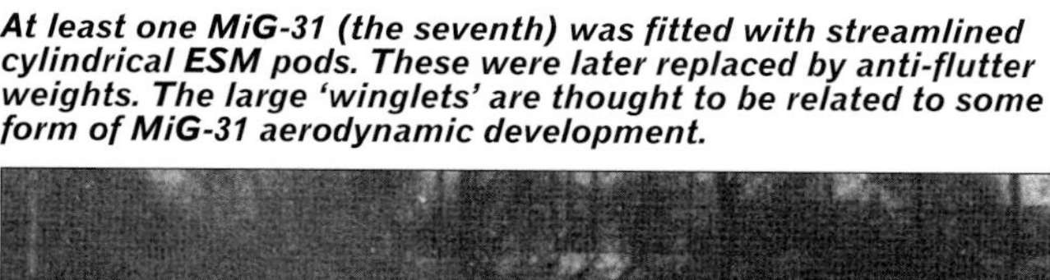

## Series production

Production of the MiG-31 commenced at Gorky (now Nizhny Novograd) in 1979, after intensive trials. These were not without incident, and numerous modifications were incorporated into the production aircraft. One of the major improvements was the repositioning of the airbrakes underneath the intake duct, rather than on the 'shoulders' of the intake ducts.

By comparison with the MiG-25, the MiG-31 has larger and more complex engine intakes, and these have been tailored to reduce airflow problems and reduce fuel consumption during missions.

Initial trials revealed the need for inflight refuelling, and a crude semi-retractable probe was added to the port forward fuselage. This was not fitted to early production aircraft, but is now standard equipment. At the time inflight refuelling was fairly uncommon in the Soviet Union outside the long-range bomber force. 'Foxhound' pilots had to master and develop techniques for fighter inflight refuellings.

Once mastered, the capabilities of the MiG-31 soon became apparent to the Soviet Union. Flights of more than five hours were now possible coupled with a highly sophisticated radar. Capabilities such as these saw that the early MiG-31s were quickly deployed to Russia's frontline interceptor bases.

**Below: Most early developmental 'Foxhounds' were eventually retired to the Russian air museum at Monio near Moscow.**

# MiG-31M 'Foxhound-B'

## Briefing

**As the latest incarnation of the 'Foxhound', the MiG-31M is one of the most effective interceptors ever built, even though it seems unlikely to ever enter service.**

*An imposing aircraft from any angle, MiG-31M '057' displays the redesigned nosewheel doors, repositioned landing/taxiing lights and wingtip ECM pods that help to identify this latest variant.*

*Right: External differences between the MiG-31M and earlier variants are not easy to spot. One noticeable feature of the MiG-31M is its larger dorsal spine, believed to house both avionics and fuel.*

With the passage of time, the shortcomings of the original MiG-31 became more evident. An improved variant, the MiG-31M, had been planned from the start, and work on this aircraft began around 1978. Designed under the direction of Edward Kostrubskii, the new variant (designated 'Product 5') introduced avionics and aerodynamic changes. Little is known about the MiG-31M's early history, although the first prototype was lost on 9 August 1991, while being flown from the Zhukhovskii flight research centre. Both crew ejected safely.

Information on the MiG-31M first appeared in 1990, as an offshoot of the CFE talks. Better photographs became available in early-1992, after the aerospace display at Minsk-Maschulische, where the seventh MiG-31M, '057', made its public debut.

This aircraft displayed many of the features previously attributed to the MiG-31M. The fuselage spine was completely recontoured, with a higher horizontal top line and wider cross-section, presumably containing both avionics and fuel. Extended chord, curved, leading-edge root extensions had been added in an effort to improve the aircraft's poor high Alpha handling, as was an angle of attack meter, with a probe on the side of the nose.

Although never intended as a dogfighter, the high angle of attack handling did present a serious problem, sufficient to be openly criticised by Russian test pilots, and was responsible for several accidents. Mikoyan clearly believes that agility is the future and has described the aircraft as its last aerodynamically stable fighter.

The MiG-31M's hydraulically boosted flight controls are backed up by a 'clever' autopilot which enhances stability and handling. Visibility for the pilot was improved by adding a single-piece curved windscreen. The backseater's side windows have been reconfigured and the windows between the cockpits have been deleted.

One significant area where the MiG-31's capabilities were significantly enhanced was its air-to-air missile (AAM) armament. The MiG-31M introduced two new AAM types: the R-77 and the R-37. The medium-range R-77 (originally RVV-AE, NATO designation AA-12 'Adder', and dubbed 'AMRAAMski') has terminal active radar homing and is described as a 'launch-and-forget' weapon. Developed to replace the MiG-31's R-33 (NATO AA-9 'Amos') for long-range engagements, the R-37 features an active seeker and extends range from around 62 miles (100 km) to 93 miles (150 km).

MiG-31Ms have never been seen carrying the MiG-31's distinctive 30-mm gun pod on the starboard rear fuselage.

### Uncertain future

Despite its systems upgrades, the MiG-31M has not been described as a 'core programme', and production funding seems unlikely. India is a possible production partner for a 'private venture', if security regarding the new weapons system permits. Whatever the future of the MiG-31M, the 'basic' MiG-31 will remain a vital link in Russia's air defences for many years to come.

*Above: Visibility from the MiG-31M's cockpits has been greatly improved to overcome a major MiG-31 drawback. The MiG-31M features a new single-piece, curved windscreen and new transparencies in the rear cockpit.*

*Left: The MiG-31M adds two new missiles to the armoury of the MiG-31. Four R-77 medium-range weapons are carried underwing, while up to six R-37 long-range AAMs can be carried semi-recessed under the fuselage.*

# MiG-31M 'Foxhound'

**This aircraft, '057', was the seventh MiG-31M built and was first seen by Western sources in 1992. Little is known about the MiG-31M programme, which remains shrouded in secrecy. One prototype appears to have been destroyed in 1991. Both China and India have expressed interest in the project, but development has been delayed by serious funding problems. At present it appears unlikely that the MiG-31M will enter operational service with Russian forces.**

### R-77 medium-range AAM

The MiG-31M's medium-range armament comprises four R-77 missiles carried underwing. R-77 (NATO designation AA-12 'Adder') has a range of 80 miles (50 km) and has inertial guidance and terminal active radar homing. The missile was quickly dubbed 'AMRAAMski' due to its appearance and perceived likely similarity in performance to the West's AIM-120 AMRAAM. Designed to attack manoeuvring targets, the R-77 features unusual rear control fins (dubbed 'potato mashers'). The missile has also been seen on MiG-29 and Su-27 fighters.

### Undercarriage

Early MiG-31s featured three-piece nosewheel doors, with the landing/taxiing lights incorporated into the front door. The MiG-31M has dispensed with this layout in favour of simpler, two-piece doors. As a result, the landing lights are now mounted on the undercarriage oleo itself.

### R-37 long-range missile

Designed to replace the MiG-31's R-33 weapon, the R-37 is built by the Spetztekhnika Vympel NPO missile design bureau. Similar to the AIM-54C Phoenix AAM, it has a range of around 93 miles (150 km) and uses inertial guidance for mid-course with an active radar seeker for the terminal phase of the engagement. The MiG-31M carries six of these massive weapons in staggered semi-recessed trios under the fuselage. The missiles' rear control fins fold to ease clearance during loading.

### SPECIFICATION

**MiG-31B 'Foxhound-A'; MiG-31M generally similar to MiG-31B except where noted**

**Dimensions:** wing span 44 ft 2 in (13.464 m); overall length, including probe 74 ft 5¼ in (22.688 m); overall height 20 ft 2¼ in (6.15 m); wing aspect ratio 2.94; wing area 663 sq ft (61.6 $m^2$)

**Powerplant:** two Aviadvigatel D-30F6 turbofans, each rated at 34,170 lb st (151.9 kN) with afterburning

**Weights:** empty 48,115 lb (21825 kg); internal fuel 36,045 lb (16350 kg); maximum take-off weight on internal fuel 90,390 lb (41000 kg); maximum take-off weight with twin underwing tanks 101,850 lb (46200 kg); maximum take-off weight (MiG-31M) 114,640 lb (52,000 kg)

**Performance:** maximum permitted Mach No. 2.3 at altitude; maximum level speed at 57,400 ft (17500 m) 1,865 mph (3000 km/h); maximum speed at sea level 932 mph (1500 km/h); economic cruising speed Mach 0.85; service ceiling 67,600 ft (20600 m)

**Range:** radius of action with maximum internal fuel and four R-33 missiles at Mach 2.35 447 miles (720 km); ferry range on maximum internal fuel and without armament 2,050 miles (3300 km); maximum endurance (unrefuelled) 3 h 36 min

### 'Sabre' LERXes

Never a particularly easy aircraft to fly, the MiG-31 suffered from poor handling qualities, especially at high angles of attack. This has been rectified somewhat on the MiG-31M by the addition of large LERXes (leading-edge root extensions, dubbed 'Sabre' in Russian) just aft of the huge air intakes.

### Wingtip pods

Aircraft '057' carried these rather large pods on its wingtips. They are believed to house ECM/ESM equipment, and feature large vertical fins and dielectric panels on the front, centre and rear, plus a number of other small protuberances. They are similar in design to those seen on the Su-30M attack 'Flanker'.

### Weapons stations

Original MiG-31s had a total of six weapons stations (four under the fuselage and two under the wings). The MiG-31M has two extra stations semi-recessed under the fuselage, plus an additional pair of hardpoints under the wings, and these may be 'plumbed' for the carriage of external fuel tanks.

### Inflight-refuelling probe

In an effort to extend range and endurance, MiG-31s were retrofitted with a semi-retractable inflight-refuelling probe mounted below the front cockpit on the port side. On the MiG-31M, this has been made fully retractable and relocated to starboard.

Above: About 157 Mil Mi-8/17 'Hips' remain in the Indian Air Force's inventory, equipping some 15 units. This Mi-8, of No. 115 Helicopter Unit from Jodhpur, is seen overflying the Umaid Bhawan Palace.

# Mil Mi-8/9/14/17 'Hip'/'Haze'

## Mi-8 into service

**The most numerous and important helicopter possessed by the Soviet forces in the latter part of the Cold War, the Mi-8 'Hip' remains in widespread service with air arms in Russia and around the world in a wide variety of roles.**

Above: The first prototype Mi-8 (V-8) made its maiden flight during 1961 and was demonstrated to members of the Soviet government in September 1962.

The Mi-8 came from the design bureau of the brilliant Soviet helicopter pioneer Mikhail Leontyevich Mil, who died in 1970. A string of mass-produced and record-breaking helicopters remains the testament to his engineering and design skills. The Mi-8, a turbine-powered development of the Mi-4 'Hound' (itself a shock to the West), was first seen in public at Tushino in 1961 and was powered by a single 2,700-shp (2013-kW) Soloviev turbine mounted above the cabin roof. Although the fuselage was new, with the pilots' seats at the front instead of over the cabin, the helicopter employed the rotor hub, rotor blades, transmission and boom of the Mi-4. The second prototype, which flew in September 1962, was powered by two 1,400-shp (1044-kW) Isotov TV2 turboshafts, and the production version was given a five-bladed main rotor in place of the four-bladed rotor inherited from the 'Hound'.

### 'Hip' structure

The Mi-8's fuselage is a conventional all-metal semi-monocoque structure of the pod and boom type. The tricycle landing gear is non-retractable, with a steerable twin-wheel nose unit which is locked in flight, and a single wheel on each main unit. Two pilots sit side-by-side in the cockpit, which also has provision for a flight engineer's seat. The standard passenger version has 28 four-abreast tip-up seats with a centre aisle, a wardrobe and luggage compartment, or 32 seats and bulkheads that are removable for the carriage of cargo. The Mi-8T has cargo tie-down rings on the floor, a winch of 441-lb (200-kg) capacity, an external cargo sling system with a capacity of 6,614 lb (3000 kg), and 24 tip-up seats along the side walls of the cabin. Clamshell freight doors and hook-on ramps facilitate vehicle-loading, while a passenger airstair is standard on the commercial version. The Mi-8 Salon (a VIP version for 11 passengers) was demonstrated at the Paris air show in 1971.

NATO allocated the reporting names 'Hip-A' and 'Hip-B' to

Right: An East German 'Hip-C' demonstrates the Mi-8's ability to lift heavy artillery in the field. This example is also carrying four UV-32-57 pods containing 2.17-in (55-mm) rockets for light attack duties.

**Left: The Egyptian air force equipped many of its 'Hips' with distinctive squared-off sand filters, manufactured by APME (Aircraft Porous Media Equipment) in Britain. They dramatically increase serviceability and prolong engine life.**

**Above: The Mi-8 'Hip-C' was the first major production version and was built in large numbers for both civilian and military customers. This example features the early-style Doppler box beneath the tailboom.**

the Mi-8 prototypes, and at the spectacular 1967 Domodedovo air display the 'Hip' appeared in military colours. Military production was under way, and no time was lost in taking advantage of the Americans' hard-won experience in Vietnam. The 'Hip' became the standard Soviet utility/assault helicopter (able to carry 24 armed troops) and was well to the fore in the Soviet development of the airmobile concept.

## Armament

Outriggers with two pylons were added on each side of the cabin to carry four UV-32-57 packs, each containing 32 2.17-in (55-mm) S-5 air-to-surface rockets. This version was designated Mi-8T 'Hip-C', but by 1979 a more potent variant, the 'Hip-E', had become the world's most heavily-armed helicopter with six UV-32-57 packs housing 192 rockets, four AT-2 'Swatter' anti-tank guided missiles on rails above the rocket packs, and a nose-mounted 0.5-in (12.7-mm) machine-gun. Even when fully fuelled and armed, the 'Hip-E' can still lift 12-14 troops, though operations at maximum gross weight allow little power for manoeuvring at low speed and in the hover.

Other military versions in use include the 'Hip-D' and 'Hip-G', which have been developed for command and control duties. The 'Hip-D' is similar to the 'Hip-C', but features canisters on the outer stores racks and added antennas for the battlefield communications-relay role, while the 'Hip-G' has rearwards-inclined antennas projecting from the rear of the cabin and from the undersurface of the tailboom, though intended for the same task as the 'Hip-C'. The 'Hip-F' is an export version of the 'Hip-E' and is equipped with six AT-3 'Saggers' in place of the four 'Swatters'. This version first entered service with the East German 'Adolf von Lotzow' Combat Helicopter Regiment. The 'Hip-J' is an ECM version identifiable by additional small boxes on the sides of the fuselage, fore and aft of the main landing-gear legs. The 'Hip-K' is a communications-jamming ECM version with a large antenna array on each side of the cabin.

Over 1,600 Mi-8s served with the USSR's Frontal Aviation, 900 with Transport Aviation and a further 100 with Naval Aviation, many of which remain in service today with Russia and former Soviet states. Mi-8s were also exported to 39 other countries and have tasted combat in several theatres of action. During the first evening of the Yom Kippur War in 1973 a force of about 100 'Hips', carrying crack 18-man Egyptian commando teams, crossed the Suez Canal to attack Israeli oilfields and to hinder the movement of reinforcements. The commandos were supported by 'Hips' armed with rockets and bombs, while others were modified to carry two fixed heavy machine-guns and up to six light machine-guns to provide suppressive fire around LZs. Napalm bombs were also reported to have been rolled out through the clamshell doors on to Israeli positions along the Canal. Egyptian Mi-8s were additionally used for resupply and medevac duties. The Syrians employed about a dozen 'Hips' to deliver commandos 8,000 ft (2440 m) up Mount Hermon to capture an Israeli observation post.

In the bitter Ogaden war, the Soviet commander of the Ethiopian forces used Mi-8s to airlift troops and light armoured vehicles over a mountain and place them behind forward Somali positions. And earlier, in 1974, two Soviet 'Hips' operated from the deck of the ASW helicopter cruiser *Leningrad* as they helped to sweep mines from the southern end of the Suez Canal. The Soviet Union also widely operated the Mi-8 for both troop transport and as gunships in the protracted Afghanistan conflict. More recently, Russia has utilised the 'Hip' in two hard-fought campaigns in Chechnya.

Like the Huey 'slicks' and 'hogs' of the Vietnam War, troop-carrying 'Hips' are usually escorted by the more heavily-armed Mi-24 'Hind' gunships. It has been claimed in the USA that both these helicopters were used to wage chemical and biological warfare against the Afghan guerrillas, with loads generally fired in 2.17-in (55-mm) rocket rounds.

## Humanitarian role

Mi-8s have also been put to humanitarian use. During 1985, for instance, Soviet and Polish 'Hips' took part in famine-relief operations in drought-stricken Ethiopia. The Polish Relief Helicopter Squadron arrived at Assab aboard the MV *Wislica* with 100 tons of food and equipment. Three days later, the Mi-8Ts were assembled and began airlifting supplies for distribution to the starving people in the desert. In Finland, the Mi-8s of the Finnish air force (Suomen Ilmavoimat) and the Frontier Guard (Rajavartiolaitos) have added a useful dimension to the country's communications network, particularly through the long, hard winters when overland routes are blocked by snow or floods. Other military air arms use the Mi-8 as dedicated SAR aircraft fitted with radar and specialised rescue equipment.

**Above: A Border Guards patrol disembarks from a hovering Mi-8TB. The machine-gun-armed 'Hip-E' has three pylons on each outrigger for rockets or bombs and 'overwing' launch rails for 'Swatter' ATMs.**

**Left: Seen in 1991, while operating with the Mixed Transport Aircraft Brigade of the Hungarian air force, this Mi-8T wears the standard Hungarian tactical camouflage scheme.**

# Mi-17 variants

**The Mi-17 expanded the capabilities offered by the basic Mi-8 'Hip' and has been built in almost as many variants. The latest upgrades offer enhanced all-weather capabilities and modernised avionics.**

## Mi-8MT 'Hip-H'

In Russian military service the Mi-17 is known as the Mi-8MT. An updated version of the Mi-8T, the aircraft is powered by two Klimov 1,874-shp (1397-kW) TV3-117MT engines, equipped with dust filters.

## Mi-8AMTSh (Mi-171Sh)

Armed with eight 9M114 *Shturm* or *Igla*-V missiles, the Mi-8AMTSh is built at Ulan-Ude. Crew positions are protected with armour plating, and state tests began in April 2000. Note the chin-mounted EO pod.

## EW derivatives

The Mi-17Z-2 (below) is a Czech electronic warfare ECM conversion of the 'Hip-H', currently in service with Slovakia. A further EW derivative is the Mi-17PP (Mi-8MTPB) ECM platform, with complex antenna arrays.

## Mi-8MTO

The Mi-8MTO (*ochki nochnogo videniya*, night vision optics) is a dedicated nocturnal attack conversion of the MT/MTV which has been tested in Chechnya by the Combat Experimental Group at Mozdok.

## Mi-8MTV 'Hip-H'

The MTV (*visotnyi*, or high altitude) is equipped with 2,190-shp (1633-kW) TV3-117VM engines for 'hot-and-high' operations. The military version is also available as the radar-equipped MTV-1 (a Croatian example is pictured opposite), while the the Mi-8MTV-2 offers a six-hardpoint stub wing. The export equivalent is the Mi-17-1V, which can be equipped for fire-fighting.

## Mi-8AMT

Unarmed 'civilian' Mi-17s carry the designation Mi-8AMT in Russia, and are also operated in limited numbers by the armed forces. The illustrated example has the square windows of the original Mi-8S *salon* version.

## Mi-17MD

Kazan offers the Mi-17MD upgrade with a radar housed in a reprofiled nose, a partial 'glass' cockpit, increased capacity hold and a large rear-loading ramp. India ordered 40 examples in May 2000. The Mi-17KF variant introduces a Canadian supplied avionics and electrical system.

## AEFT modification

Aeroton's AEFT (Auxiliary External Fuel Tanks) conversion adds a further 418 Imp gal (1900 litres) of fuel in internal tanks, as well as six external tanks providing a further 626 Imp gal (2850 litres). Operational range with all additional tanks in use is 807 miles (1300 km).

# Mi-14 'Haze'

*The Mi-14BT lacks a towed MAD 'bird', the aft fuselage instead housing mine countermeasures towing equipment. Only 25-30 examples were built, including six for East Germany's Marineflieger and a pair for Bulgaria's Naval Air Arm (illustrated).*

**Developed to counter the threat of nuclear submarines, the Mi-14 inherited the airframe and rotor system of the Mi-8, and was followed by search-and-rescue and mine countermeasures variants.**

The Soviet AVMF favoured helicopters over fixed-wing aircraft for in-shore ASW operations, and deployed the Mi-4PL in this role from 1956. Preliminary design for a replacement was derived from the Mi-8 and began in 1959, and a full-scale development followed the first flight of the V-8A prototype in 1962.

The resulting V-14 was powered by two navalised 2,225-shp (1660-kW) Isotov TV3-117MT turboshafts, and carried operational equipment based on that of the Ka-25PL. A retractable undercarriage was incorporated and an amphibious airframe allowed the aircraft to remain afloat following an engine failure. A weapons bay could accommodate eight 260-lb (120-kg) PLAB-250-120 *Lastochka* depth charges or a single guided torpedo: the definitive 1,265-lb (575-kg) APR-2 *Orlan* weapon was introduced into AVMF service in the early 1980s.

## First flight

The first prototype, converted from an Mi-8 airframe and powered by interim TV2-117 engines, made its first flight on 1 August 1967, and flew with the production turboshafts in 1969. After a protracted development period for the *Kalmar* ASW suite, itself based around the *Initsiativa*-2M search radar, *Oka*-2 dipping sonar and *Orsha* MAD, production aircraft entered service with the Baltic Fleet at Donskoye in 1974. Production Mi-14PLs entered operational service two years later. A small number of aircraft were retrofitted with the improved *Osminog* ASW suite after 1979.

Export customers for the ASW variant included East Germany, Poland, Bulgaria, Yugoslavia, Syria, Cuba, Libya, North Korea and Vietnam.

*The boat hull of the 'Haze' allows operations in Sea States 3-4, or planing at up to 37 mph (60 km/h). Note the sponson-mounted flotation bags and tail float of this Russian navy Mi-14PS.*

A minesweeping variant, was developed in 1973, the resulting Mi-14BT was capable of towing a variety of mine countermeasures (MCM) rafts as well as life rafts and assault vessels. Precise mine 'sweeps' are conducted using an SAU-14 autopilot. Additional fuselage windows allow the countermeasures operator to monitor the sled. The Mi-14BT entered AVMF service in 1979, and a handful were exported.

Development of a SAR helicopter was initiated in 1970, and the prototype Mi-14PS was converted from an early ASW version. Equipped with an additional SAR operator/diver, a retractable rescue hoist and basket with a three-person capacity and searchlights, the Mi-14PS also entered service in 1979, and three examples were delivered to Poland in addition to approximately 25 for the Soviet Union. The Mi-14PS is capable of accommodating six life rafts and up to 19 survivors within its cabin, and is capable of towing additional life rafts.

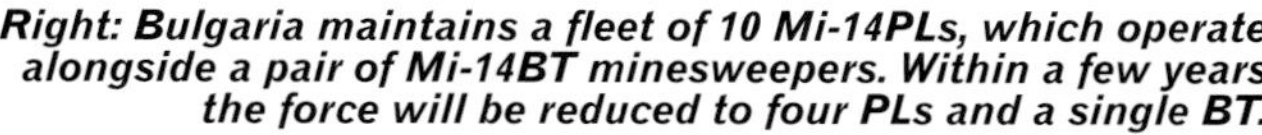

*Right: Bulgaria maintains a fleet of 10 Mi-14PLs, which operate alongside a pair of Mi-14BT minesweepers. Within a few years the force will be reduced to four PLs and a single BT.*

*Below: Russia and Ukraine have withdrawn most of their ASW variants from service. Weapons are carried in a large lower mid-fuselage bay and in Soviet service included the 1-kT Scalp nuclear depth charge, weighing in at 3,520 lb (1600 kg). Pictured is a Mi-14PL from the Ukrainian navy.*

# Mil Mi-24/25/35 'Hind'

## Introduction

**The ferocious-looking Mi-24 'Hind' became the symbol of the Soviet Union's involvement in the Afghanistan war, performing countless ground-support missions. The type was also exported to a host of client states, seeing extensive combat throughout Asia and the Middle East.**

*Above: The Indian air force operates the export sub-variants of the Mi-24, known as the Mi-25 and Mi-35. They serve with No. 104, No. 116 and No. 125 Units at Pathankot in northern India.*

*Below: Now retired from front-line service with the Russian army, this Mi-24 'Hind-A' is on show at the Monino Air Museum outside Moscow. It is displayed fully-armed with rocket pods and wingtip AT-2 'Swatter' ATGMs.*

The Mil Mi-24 'Hind' has become one of the most widely-known assault helicopter gunships in the world. Its impressive firepower and the vast numbers available meant that it was the backbone of first-line assault helicopter regiments of the former Warsaw Pact nations. It was therefore of major concern to NATO planners who estimated that, in the event of war, Allied forces would encounter hundreds of 'Hinds' over the European front lines during the opening stages of an armoured assault.

Although now regarded as an assault helicopter, the 'Hind' entered service with the Soviet armed forces as the 'Hind-A', which was viewed by Western analysts as no more than an armed transport. Soviet interest in armed helicopters had really been kindled as a result of watching US involvement in Vietnam, when the advantages of such a machine in the assault role became clear. Mil Mi-4 'Hounds' were hastily modified with racks for rocket pods and air-to-surface missiles, or were fitted with machine-guns. The development of dedicated attack and escort helicopters by the Americans was watched with great interest and, in the late 1960s, the Mil Design Bureau was told to develop a similar machine. The project commenced under the leadership of Mikhail Mil himself.

The Mil Mi-24 was developed from the tried and tested, combat-proven Mil Mi-8 'Hip' assault transport. The 'Hind' utilised the basic power-train and dynamic system of the 'Hip', its five-bladed main rotor redesigned with a smaller diameter, and the tail rotor moved to the port side of the tail boom. A new fuselage was designed, with a narrower cross-section which minimised drag and the target area presented to enemy air defences.

The new helicopter was first seen by the West at East German airfields in 1974. It was dubbed the 'Hind', but it was then realised that there was a pre-production version with simpler horizontal wings without the missile launchers, so the standard version was called the 'Hind-A' and the pre-production type was termed the 'Hind-B'. The name 'Hind-C' was then given to a supposed model without the nose gun and chin sight. Only a few of these early 'Hinds', if any, remain in service, and those that do serve as trainers or squadron hacks. Few examples were exported, but those operated by Afghanistan, Algeria, Libya and Vietnam undertook combat patrol missions along each nation's borders.

Operational experience with the initial Mi-24s soon showed that the original concept was slightly flawed. The type's ground-attack potential was clearly reduced when carrying troops, and it was realised that this role was better suited to less agile helicopters like the Mil Mi-8. As the Mi-24's transport role declined, its attack capability became progressively more important. It soon became apparent that the greenhouse canopy of the 'Hind-A' gave less than perfect all-round visibility, and offered the crew little

*Seen undergoing maintenance at the Syrzan Air Force Academy, Volga Military District, are these 'Hind-D' trainers. The nose gun and ammunition doors are faired over and the air data sensor boom is deleted. The majority of training 'Hinds' were converted from standard attack 'Hind-Ds' and 'Hind-Es'.*

**A pair of East German 'Hind-Ds' on patrol. East Germany used its 'Hinds' on border patrols, especially along the Berlin Wall. In the event of a European war, NATO planners foresaw hundreds of Mi-24s being used in the initial opening assault.**

**Below: Recent reductions in defence spending by the Russian armed forces have forced Mil to adapt its Mi-24 to the civilian role. This Mi-24PS is operated by the Russian Ministry of Internal Affairs (police) as a law enforcement helicopter. The Mi-24PS is suitably equipped with searchlights, loudspeakers and a FLIR turret.**

protection. The solution was to redesign the Mi-24 with an entirely new nose, with heavily-armoured tandem cockpits for the pilot (rear) and gunner (front). These were covered by bubble canopies, with bullet-proof armoured glass windscreens. The pilot's cockpit canopy incorporated a large door which opened to starboard, while the front canopy hinged sideways to port. The new arrangement gave a much smaller frontal area, improved visibility and reduced drag.

Under the nose was fitted a stabilised turret housing a completely new four-barrelled YakB 0.5-in (12.7-mm) Gatling gun. Beside the new gun turret were a missile guidance pod and a laser rangefinder. The cabin itself retained its seats, but came to be regarded as a space for stowing AT-2 'Swatter' anti-tank missiles. Designated 'Hind-D' by NATO, the new gunship model was produced at a rate of 15 examples per month at its peak, with hundreds being exported to the Warsaw Pact and client states.

But it was the Soviet army that first undertook combat operations with the new gunship model, in Afghanistan. Operating alongside the Sukhoi Su-25 'Frogfoot', the 'Hind-Ds' quickly became one of the Soviet weapons most feared by the *mujaheddin*. Providing close air support and convoy escort capabilities, the 'Hinds' were able to pursue the enemy to their hide-outs. Only the introduction of the American shoulder-launched Stinger SAM by the CIA affected the abilities of the Mi-24. Other operators were quick to exploit the capabilities of Mil's new attack helicopter; the war between Iran and Iraq saw 'Hinds' engaging in air-to-air combat, with Iraqi examples downing Iranian Bell AH-1 Cobra gunships and even McDonnell Douglas F-4 Phantom IIs.

Spurred on by combat experience in Afghanistan, the 'Hind-F' saw the introduction of a larger-calibre cannon. With the nose turret deleted and a GSh-30-2 twin-barrelled 30-mm cannon mounted on the starboard side of the forward fuselage, this improved attack variant was supplied to Angola and Iraq in limited quantities.

In recent years, at least two 'Hind' reconnaissance variants have been produced for the Russian army. Identified by NATO as the 'Hind-G', the Mil-24RKR is charged with NBC reconnaissance, picking up soil samples to ascertain the spread of nuclear fallout. The other reconnaissance variant, the Mi-24K or 'Hind-G2', serves as an artillery fire correction platform. Equipped with a large camera mounted in the cabin, it serves only in limited numbers with the Soviet armed forces.

The abolition of the Warsaw Pact has meant that examples of the Mi-24 have found their way into NATO hands, with examples being operated by the US army and the RAF. The reunification of Germany saw large numbers of former East German Mi-24s being absorbed into the air force but, after being thoroughly evaluated, all examples were retired to comply with limits set by the CFE (Conventional Forces in Europe) Treaty.

More recent developments have been the formation of Russian and Czech 'Hind' display teams. Shrinking Russian defence budgets have led to the production of de-militarised 'Hind' variants for service with Russia's police force. Despite the many innovations brought about by the 'Hinds', the concept looks set not to be repeated as Russian army aviation awaits the introduction of a truly dedicated attack helicopter such as the Kamov Ka-50 'Hokum' or Mil Mi-28 'Havoc'.

**To celebrate the 20th anniversary of the Czech Air Force's 51st Helicopter Regiment at Prostejov (which disbanded in October 1994), a Mi-24 'Hind-D' from the 1st Letka was painted in a smart 'tiger' colour scheme. It appeared at a number of air shows throughout Europe as one half of the unit's two-ship display team.**

# Mi-24 'Hind' Early variants

**The awesome 'Hind', once so feared by NATO ground forces, has progressed steadily since its conception. The original variants bear little resemblance to their descendants, which are in operational service with forces worldwide.**

## Mil V-24 Prototype ('Hind-B')

The Mi-24 prototypes were powered by a pair of 1,700-shp TV2-117A turboshaft engines, as used on the Mil Mi-8 'Hip'. The aircraft were fitted with a modified version of the Mi-8's five-bladed main rotor, and a three-bladed pusher tail rotor mounted to starboard. The V-24s had provision for detachable stub wings which may have had underslung weapons pylons. No nose gun was fitted and no provision was made for missile guidance. It is believed that the cabin doors were split vertically and hinged outwards, instead of being split horizontally and opening upwards and downwards.

## Mil Mi-24B 'Hind-A'

As the Mi-24A entered production, the Mil OKB continued improving the helicopter's armament. The Mi-24B, or izdeliye 241, featured a USPU-24 powered chin turret with a 12.7-mm Yakoushev/Borzov YakB-12.7 four-barrelled Gatling-type machine-gun. This was slaved to a KPS-53AV sighting system which automatically made corrections for the helicopter's movement. The system featured an analog computer receiving input from the helicopter's air data sensors.

The manually-guided 9M17M Falanga-M anti-tank missiles gave way to an upgraded version, the 9M17P Falanga-P. The missiles were controlled by the Raduga-F SACLOS guidance system which increased kill probability three to four times. The targeting part of the system comprised low light-level television (LLLTV) and forward-looking infra-red (FLIR) sensors in a slab-sided ventral housing offset to starboard ahead of the nose gear, with twin protective metal doors covering the sensor window. The system was gyro-stabilised, enabling the helicopter to manoeuvre vigorously to avoid ground fire while targeting. The guidance part of the system (the command link antenna) was located symmetrically in a small egg-shaped fairing offset to port which could traverse as the missile manoeuvred, since the antenna dish was fixed.

The Mi-24B full-scale mock-up was probably rebuilt from the original 'Hind-B' mock-up, since it had no wing anhedral and featured the tested-and-failed detachable missile launchers on the fuselage sides. The real thing, however, was converted from several early-production Mi-24As with starboard-side tail rotor. The Mi-24B successfully passed the manufacturer's trials in 1971-72 but was eventually abandoned.

## Mil A-10

During 1975, it was revealed that a Soviet helicopter designated A-10 had captured eight world records. Powered by Isotov TV-2-117A engines, the aircraft was a stripped-down early 'Hind-B', with its stub wings removed and was flown by a female civilian crew. The record-breaking flights, conducted between 16 July 1975 and 26 August 1975, included a record 212.9 mph (342.6km/h) over 15 and 25 km (9.32 and 15.53 miles), 207.82 mph (334.44 km/h) over a 100-km (62.13-mile) closed circuit, 206.69 mph (332.62 km) over 1000 km (621.40 miles), a time to climb record of 3000 m (9,843 ft) in two minutes and 33.5 seconds and an altitude record of 6000 m (19,685 ft) (achieved in 7 minutes and 43 seconds).

## Mil Mi-24A 'Hind-A'

Testing of the 'Hind-B' revealed it was too cramped to accommodate the Raduga-F semi-automatic command line-of-sight (SACLOS) guidance system and the fast-firing machine-gun installation. Thus, two prototypes were converted by cutting off the cockpit section and grafting on a new forward fuselage. The new nose was slightly longer and had a more pointed profile, with more sharply raked upper windshield segments to reduce drag. The car-type pilot's door was replaced by a sliding bubble window to give the pilot some downward vision, and the A-12.7 machine-gun was fitted. A small teardrop fairing for the command link transmitter antenna was located immediately forward of the nose gear.

In this form, the helicopter entered production in Arsen'yev in 1970 as the Mi-24A, aka izdeliye 245. It was in this form that the Mi-24 was seen by NATO for the first time, resulting in the reporting designation designation 'Hind-A' being allocated to this more developed model. Early-production Mi-24As had the tail rotor on the starboard side, as on the Mi-8; when seen from the hub, the tail rotor turned clockwise so that the forward blade went with the main rotor downwash. However, due to poor directional control in some flight modes, in 1972 the tail rotor was relocated to port. The tail rotor still turned clockwise, meaning that the forward blade now went against the main rotor downwash, increasing tail rotor efficiency dramatically. The APU exhaust was also extended and angled downwards to prevent rain getting in.

More than 240 Mi-24As had been built when production ended in 1974. Once again, the seemingly illogical Soviet practice of launching full-scale production even before the aircraft had been officially phased in had paid off, allowing flight and ground crews to familiarise themselves with the helicopter by the time the thumbs-up from the Air Force came. Initially, the Mi-24A was operated by independent helicopter regiments but, later, the helicopter equipped independent combat control helicopter regiments. When the Army Aviation was formed within the Soviet armed forces, Mi-24s equipped independent helicopter squadrons within mechanised infantry divisions. The Mi-24A was also exported (e.g., to Afghanistan, Libya and Vietnam) and has seen action in the Afghan war and various African conflicts.

## Mil Mi-24U 'Hind-C'

The Mil Mi-24U was a dedicated trainer version of the 'Hind-A' stripped of all armament but retaining stub wings and equipped with dual controls. Small numbers were supplied to Soviet forces (mainly to second-line training units) and a handful may have been exported alongside 'Hind-As', to Afghanistan, Algeria, Libya and Vietnam. No Mi-24Us are believed to currently be in service.

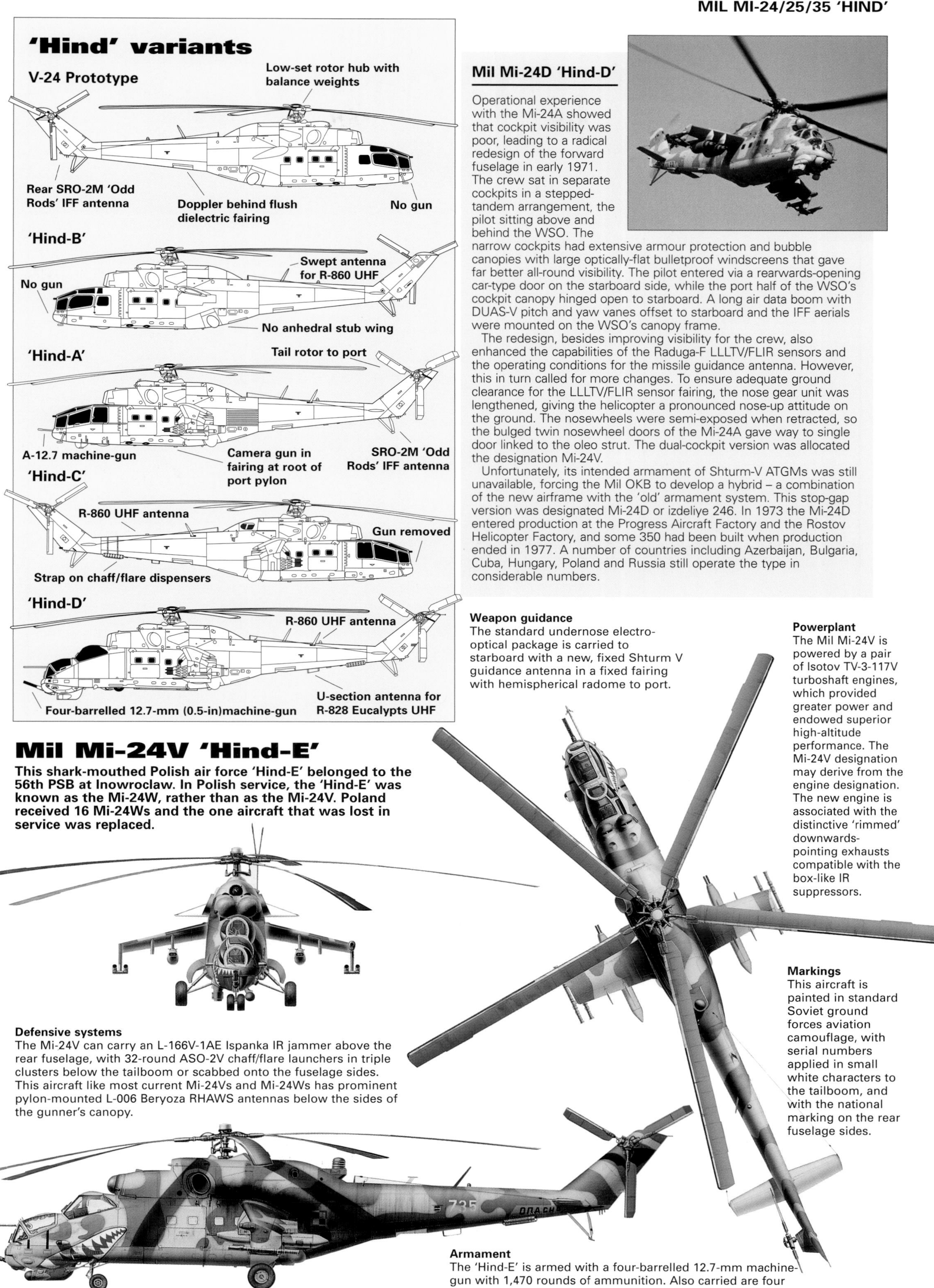


## 'Hind' variants

### Mil Mi-24D 'Hind-D'

Operational experience with the Mi-24A showed that cockpit visibility was poor, leading to a radical redesign of the forward fuselage in early 1971. The crew sat in separate cockpits in a stepped-tandem arrangement, the pilot sitting above and behind the WSO. The narrow cockpits had extensive armour protection and bubble canopies with large optically-flat bulletproof windscreens that gave far better all-round visibility. The pilot entered via a rearwards-opening car-type door on the starboard side, while the port half of the WSO's cockpit canopy hinged open to starboard. A long air data boom with DUAS-V pitch and yaw vanes offset to starboard and the IFF aerials were mounted on the WSO's canopy frame.

The redesign, besides improving visibility for the crew, also enhanced the capabilities of the Raduga-F LLLTV/FLIR sensors and the operating conditions for the missile guidance antenna. However, this in turn called for more changes. To ensure adequate ground clearance for the LLLTV/FLIR sensor fairing, the nose gear unit was lengthened, giving the helicopter a pronounced nose-up attitude on the ground. The nosewheels were semi-exposed when retracted, so the bulged twin nosewheel doors of the Mi-24A gave way to single door linked to the oleo strut. The dual-cockpit version was allocated the designation Mi-24V.

Unfortunately, its intended armament of Shturm-V ATGMs was still unavailable, forcing the Mil OKB to develop a hybrid – a combination of the new airframe with the 'old' armament system. This stop-gap version was designated Mi-24D or izdeliye 246. In 1973 the Mi-24D entered production at the Progress Aircraft Factory and the Rostov Helicopter Factory, and some 350 had been built when production ended in 1977. A number of countries including Azerbaijan, Bulgaria, Cuba, Hungary, Poland and Russia still operate the type in considerable numbers.

## Mil Mi-24V 'Hind-E'

**This shark-mouthed Polish air force 'Hind-E' belonged to the 56th PSB at Inowroclaw. In Polish service, the 'Hind-E' was known as the Mi-24W, rather than as the Mi-24V. Poland received 16 Mi-24Ws and the one aircraft that was lost in service was replaced.**

**Weapon guidance**
The standard undernose electro-optical package is carried to starboard with a new, fixed Shturm V guidance antenna in a fixed fairing with hemispherical radome to port.

**Powerplant**
The Mil Mi-24V is powered by a pair of Isotov TV-3-117V turboshaft engines, which provided greater power and endowed superior high-altitude performance. The Mi-24V designation may derive from the engine designation. The new engine is associated with the distinctive 'rimmed' downwards-pointing exhausts compatible with the box-like IR suppressors.

**Markings**
This aircraft is painted in standard Soviet ground forces aviation camouflage, with serial numbers applied in small white characters to the tailboom, and with the national marking on the rear fuselage sides.

**Defensive systems**
The Mi-24V can carry an L-166V-1AE Ispanka IR jammer above the rear fuselage, with 32-round ASO-2V chaff/flare launchers in triple clusters below the tailboom or scabbed onto the fuselage sides. This aircraft like most current Mi-24Vs and Mi-24Ws has prominent pylon-mounted L-006 Beryoza RHAWS antennas below the sides of the gunner's canopy.

**Armament**
The 'Hind-E' is armed with a four-barrelled 12.7-mm machine-gun with 1,470 rounds of ammunition. Also carried are four AT-6 'Spiral' launch tubes in pairs on the endplate pylons, with gun pods on the inboard underwing pylons. These gun pods each contain a GSh-23L 23-mm cannon.

# Late 'Hind' variants

**The later Mi-24 variants, beginning with the Mi-24V, introduced new engines and improved anti-tank missiles in the light of operational experience.**

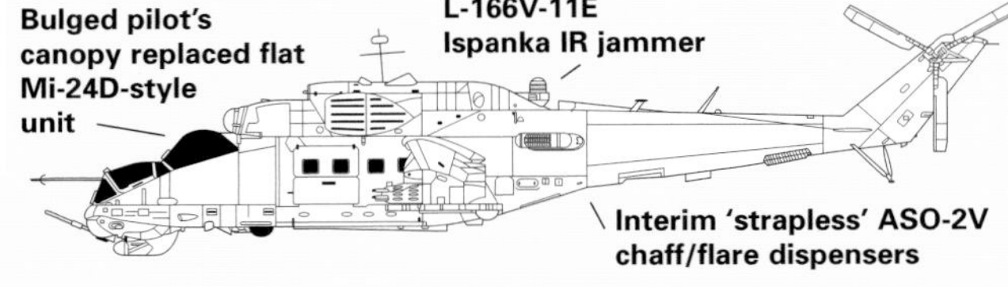


## Mi-24V 'Hind-E'

Developed in parallel with the Mi-24D, the Mi-24V features the definitive airframe/engine/missile combination. The Mi-24V first flew in 1976, but Shturm missile development problems delayed service introduction until 1979 (two years after the Mi-24D). Early Mi-24Vs differed little from the Mi-24D, lacking PZU engine intake filters and having much the same avionics fit and antenna configuration. The only visible changes were the new fixed Shturm-V guidance antenna pod for the 9M114 Shturm (AT-6 'Spiral') missile, and the addition of attachment points for the new missile's launch rails. The Mi-24V rapidly began to replace the Mi-24D in Soviet service, and it is possible that some of the earlier versions were recycled through the factory prior to export, or for upgrade to the later standard. As the major Soviet service variant, the Mi-24V was subjected to many improvements. It is believed that the first Mil Mi-24Vs retained the same engines as the Mi-24D, and that the improved TV-3-117V was introduced during production. New downward-pointing engine exhausts and associated IR suppressors were almost certainly developed for later production batches of the new variant, and then applied to the earlier Mi-24D and later Mi-24Ps. From 1985, reports emerged of Mi-24Vs carrying extra 9M114 launch tubes under the outboard underwing pylons, bringing the total number of missiles carried to eight. The Mi-24V introduced provision for carrying external fuel tanks underwing, all four pylons being 'plumbed' for the carriage of PTB-450 110-Imp gal (500-litre) drop tanks. New weapons for the Mi-24V included the B-8V20A rocket pod, containing 20 unguided S-8 80-mm (3.15-in) rockets, the KMGU-2 sub-munitions dispenser, and the UPK-23/250 23-mm cannon pod (with 250 rounds of ammunition). Weapons cleared for use on the Mi-24V as a result of Afghanistan war experience included the 9-A-669 GUV universal gun pod containing a 0.5-in (12.7-mm) four-barrelled machine-gun with 750 rounds, flanked by two four-barrelled 0.3-in (7.62-mm) machine-guns with 3,400 rounds. The same pod could be configured with a 213-PA grenade launcher and 300 30-mm rounds. Later 'Hind-Es' introduced new defensive avionics, with L-006 Beryoza RHAWS antennas. The original SRO-2 IFF set was replaced by the 62-01, a triangular blade antenna replacing the old 'Odd Rods'.

## Mi-35 'Hind-E'

For many years the 'Hind-E' was simply unavailable for export, except to selected Warsaw Pact allies. Eventually the 9M114 Shturm missile and its associated guidance equipment were cleared for wider export, as were some of the Mil Mi-24V's advanced defensive systems. As a result, the Mil Mi-35 was born as a slightly downgraded export variant. Confirmed Mil Mi-35 operators have included Afghanistan, Angola, and India (illustrated).

## Mi-35 'Hind-E' trainer version

Trainer versions of frontline Mi-24 variants exist, even though operationally capable aircraft can themselves be used for training, with rudimentary 'foldaway' flying controls in the front cockpit. The Mi-24U 'Hind-C' and Mi-24DU 'Hind-D' were dedicated trainers, with full dual controls and minus gun armament. Trainer versions of the 'Hind-E' also exist, albeit only for the export market. Whether the Indian aircraft illustrated was built as a trainer or converted remains uncertain.

## Mi-24P 'Hind-F'

Early experience in Afghanistan revealed that there were targets against which a 0.5-in (12.7-mm) machine-gun was ineffective, but against which unguided rockets or guided missiles were too expensive. Mil began work on two 'Hind' variants (derivatives of the Mi-24V) armed with different calibre cannon. One of these was the Mi-24P. This was designed around the twin-barrelled 30-mm GSh-30-2. Since this weapon was too large to be housed in the existing nose turret, the weapon was fitted to the starboard forward fuselage, aimed simply by pointing the helicopter itself. The type was first identified in the West during late 1982. Mi-24Ps were exported to East Germany. Like the 'Hind-E', the Mi-24P front cockpit is fitted with an emergency control column. This can be used by the gunner if the pilot is incapacitated, or by an instructor supervising a pupil in the rear seat. The front cockpit also has a fold-away collective lever and yaw pedals.

## Mi-35P 'Hind-F'

The Mi-35P designation is applied to export versions of the 'Hind-F', and was unknown until a Mi-35P visited the Helitech exhibition at Redhill during 1989, the first public appearance in the West of the 'Hind'. This aircraft's H-370 code was assumed to be a Paris air show code, but may in fact have been an Angolan air force serial number. Angola and Iraq are believed to be the only current export customers of the Mi-35P, since Germany's aircraft were understood to retain the Mi-24P designation, and Afghan Mi-35Ps (if they were Mi-35Ps and not Mi-24Ps borrowed from the Soviet air force) are now out of service.

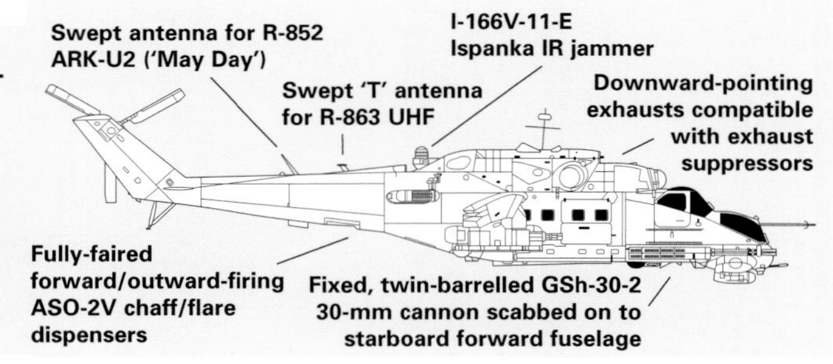

## Mi-24VP

As a means of increasing the Mi-24's firepower, a need dramatically demonstrated by combat experience in Afghanistan, the Mi-24VP was designed as an alternative to the Mi-24P. A derivative of the Mi-24V, it used a turret-mounted twin-barrelled GSh-23L 23-mm cannon instead of the Mi-24P's fuselage-mounted, fixed 30-mm cannon. The larger size of 23-mm rounds compared to (0.5-in) 12.7-mm rounds means that the number of rounds carried is much reduced, and that the ammunition stowage and carriage system (which has to fit into the same space) has had to be completely redesigned. There are reports that an experimental Mi-24VP was flown with a fenestron tail rotor, and that another flew with a narrow 'X' (delta H) tail rotor like that fitted to the Mi-28 and AH-64 Apache. Production of the Mi-24VP was limited, the new ammunition feed system proving troublesome and unreliable. The *Berkuty* (Eagles) display team, drawn from the helicopter training centre at Torjok, included at least one Mi-24VP (illustrated), which was painted with the logo of an English sponsor.

**Pitch/yaw vanes retained**

**No camera gun on endplate/wing junction**

**Unidentified 'letterbox'-type aperture**

**'Clutching hand' mechanisms on endplates consist of three finger 'buckets' on the end of a downward-hinging arm**

## Mi-24RCh Hind-G1'

The Mil Mi-24RCh (RCh for Razvedchik, or reconnaissance/chemical) is a dedicated NBC detection/reconnaissance aircraft, optimised for the gathering of soil and air samples for analysis. The variant is believed to be a production version, and not produced by conversion of Mi-24Vs, though this cannot be entirely discounted. The cockpits and cabin are hermetically sealed, and a huge air filter is installed in the cabin floor, projecting below the port lower fuselage ahead of the cabin door. Despite this, all four crew (pilot, gunner, flight engineer and analyst) normally wear full NBC kit in flight. Soil samples are gathered using 'grabs', three of which are carried in a claw-like fitting below the endplate pylon. Some Mi-24RCh helicopters have also been seen with a further fitting mounted on the tail bumper. This may be a device for dropping or firing some kind of ground marker. Air samples are sucked through an aperture behind the port cabin door, and fed via a prominent orange-coloured pipe to the analysis equipment. A massive datalink console occupies most of the front of the cabin, allowing the analyst to pass preliminary results to the tasking authority.

The Mi-24RCh cannot carry ATGMs, so has no underfuselage guidance pod. The underfuselage optical sighting system housing is also deleted, leaving only the gun turret, which is retained, although the front cockpit also includes dual flying controls. Operational Mi-24RCh aircraft are often seen carrying underwing rocket pods. The cabin window arrangement is changed slightly, with the twin windows in the starboard entry door replaced by a single blown observation window. Some aircraft have the late-standard fully faired-in chaff/flare dispensers, and others have the cruder framework-mounted units. PZU intake filters and late-style downward exhausts seem to be standard.

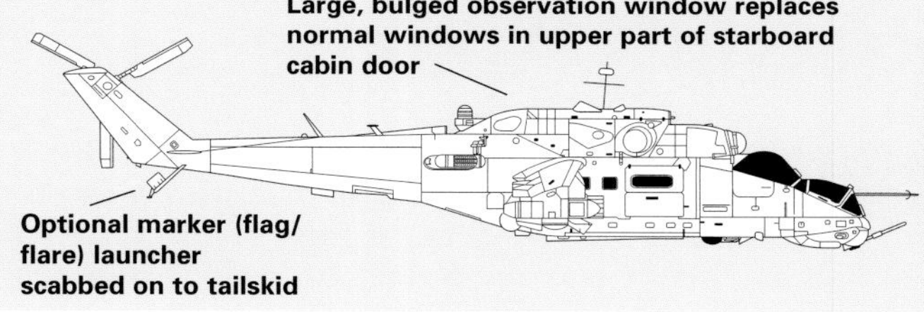


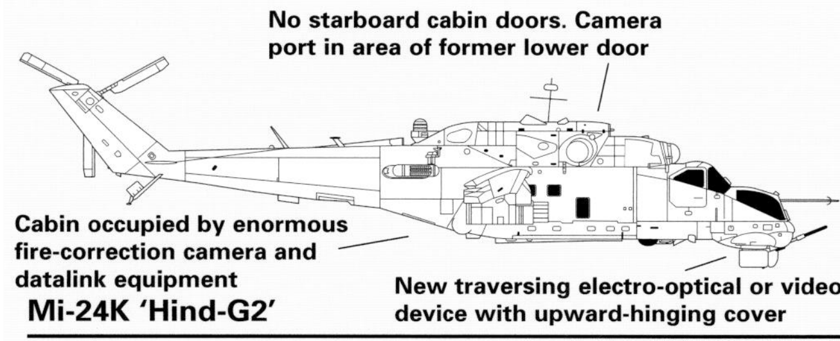


## Mi-24K 'Hind-G2'

The Mi-24K (K for Korrektirovchik, or correction) is a dedicated fire-correction helicopter, a modern equivalent to the artillery spotter. It uses a massive fully automated camera installed in the cabin, with a 1300-mm/f8 lens for observing the fall of shot. Access to the film magazine is through the port cabin doors, while the starboard cabin door is sealed, its windows removed and replaced by a single lower window through which the lens points. Beside this is a smaller aperture for the exposure meter. It is reported that the Mi-24K does not have dual controls. Like the Mi-24RCh, the Mi-24K cannot carry ATGMs and lacks the command/guidance pod under the port forward fuselage. It does, however, have a fairing below the starboard side of the nose, beside the gun turret. This appears to be a swivelling device whose forward end can be covered by a hinged fairing when pointing forward. When this is hinged out of the way, a circular aperture is revealed. Whether this serves a video camera or an electro-optical or infra-red sensor is uncertain. The aircraft can be armed with underwing rocket pods. Some Mi-24Ks have the late-standard fully faired-in chaff/flare dispensers; others have the cruder framework-mounted units.

## Mi-24 environmental research version

A 'Hind-E/F' sub-variant was shown at an international ecology and earth resources exhibition at Nizhny Novgorod (now renamed Gorky). Reportedly designed for monitoring surface oil pollution, flooding, air pollution and the like, the aircraft was fitted with comprehensive data processing equipment, and a datalink to relay information to ground stations. The aircraft had an unusual sensor in the nose (possibly retractable) taking the form of a broad, flat 'tongue' projecting horizontally forward from the base of the gunner's windscreen. Apart from this, the aircraft had a box-like pod on the starboard outboard underwing pylon. This pod was reportedly developed by the 'Polet' scientific production association and the scientific research radiophysics institute.

**Unidentified, possibly semi-retractable 'tongue' fairing in place of gun turret**

**Unidentified pod similar to those sometimes carried by 'Hind-G' but larger**

**Based on Mi-24V airframe without Ispanka IR jammer, chaff/flare dispensers and missile rails**

## Mi-35M

An upgraded, night-capable, version of the Mi-24/35, the Mi-35M is an export equivalent of the Mi-24M offered to the Russian Army (now proposed in the form of the more modestly upgraded Mi-24VP). The Mi-35M features the main and tail rotor assembles and transmission of the Mi-28, and 2,194-shp (1,636-kW) Klimov TV3-117VMA engines. The production Mi-35M will feature reduced empty weight as a result of a new titanium main rotor head, composite rotor blades, shortened stub wings and non-retractable landing gear. A twin-barrelled 23-mm gun is fitted in the nose turret. Missile options include up to 16 Shturms, or more modern 9M120s, with 9A-220 Ataka AAMs for self-defence. A Night Operation Capable Avionics System (NOCAS) produced by Sextant Avionique/Thomson Optronic provides night vision for target acquisition and identification, missile guidance and gun aiming.

*Despite its reported defeat by the Kamov Ka-50 'Hokum', the Mi-28 'Havoc' has been chosen as Russia's next attack helicopter, albeit without funding.*

# Mil Mi-28 'Havoc'

## Russia's Apache

*Right: Rolling slowly out of the cargo hold of an Aeroflot An-124 'Condor', Mil's latest attack helicopter made its British debut at Helitech '89 at Redhill, Surrey.*

**The Mil Mi-28 'Havoc' made its public debut at the Paris Air Salon in 1989, before the first photograph had been published. The general impression created was that the Mi-28 was the Soviet Union's response to the American AH-64A Apache, with some improvements. However, future development of the 'Havoc' is now in doubt.**

Development of the Mil Mi-28 was undoubtedly driven by the US Army's Advanced Attack Helicopter programme and the Hughes AH-64 Apache – which flew as early as September 1975. Building on its experience with the Mi-24 'Hind' gunship/transport, the Mil Design Bureau began working on a much smaller, dedicated anti-tank helicopter under the leadership of Marat Tischenko. Progress was rapid and the first of four prototypes (012) flew on 10 November 1982 – almost a year before the first AH-64A was handed over to the US Army. Given the NATO codename 'Havoc', the compact and boxy Mi-28 followed what has become the conventional helicopter gunship configuration, with an undernose cannon, and stepped armoured cockpits accommodating pilot (rear) and gunner (forward). The Mi-28 sits on a tricycle undercarriage, with large single main wheels, and a castoring tail wheel.

The main rotor is built around a titanium head, with five composite blades attached by a single Elastomeric bearing. The blades have swept-back tips and a cambered, high-lift section. The first prototype was fitted with a conventional three-bladed tail rotor, which was replaced on the second and third prototypes by a four-bladed 'scissors'-type GFRP tail rotor. The blades are set at approximately 35° to each other and form a narrow 'X' shape. Power is provided by two Klimov (Isotov) TV3-117VMA turboshafts each rated at 2,225 shp (1659 kW). The engines are mounted in pods high on the fuselage sides, and a range of exhaust suppressors has been tested on each prototype. The latest configuration uses three downward-pointing nozzles housed in an IR-suppressing shroud.

Stub wings, with four pylons for weapons carriage, are attached to the engine pods. Each hardpoint can carry 1,058 lb (480 kg), typically consisting of four tube-launched 9M114 Shturm C (AT-6 'Spiral') or 9M120 Vikhr anti-tank missiles or 9M39 Igla V air-to-air missiles plus a variety of 3.15-in (80-mm)/4.80-in (122-mm) rocket pods and gun pods. Each wingtip is fitted with an unusual podded chaff/flare dispenser, with provision for radar and laser warning receivers. The Mi-28 is also armed with a single-barrelled 2A42 30-mm cannon under the nose, with twin 150-round ammunition boxes co-mounted to traverse, elevate and depress with the gun itself, reducing the likelihood of jamming. The gun traverses through 110° on each side of the centreline, elevates to 13° and depresses through 40°. Two rates

*Both engines are fitted with a (composite) downward-facing shroud that would appear to direct the Mi-28's exhaust plume directly at ground-based IR SAMs. An upwards-facing shroud has reportedly been tested on an earlier prototype.*

*Left: Both the 2A42 cannon and stub-wing mounted guided weapons are normally fired from the front cockpit, although when fixed in position the cannon may also be fired from the aft crew position. A new cannon, specially designed for use by the Mi-28 is under development.*

***The Mi-28's crew sit in armoured surrounds, reported variously as titanium bathtubs or composite armour panels. The 50-mm windows are stated to be resistant to 7.62-mm fire, and to provide some protection against 12-mm fire.***

***Above: The fourth prototype of the Mi-28 was demonstrated at Asian Aerospace '94 in an effort to achieve sales in the Far East. At present, no orders have been placed for the early model 'Havoc'.***

of fire are available: 300 rpm for air-to-ground use, and 900 rpm for air-to-air. The nose is tipped with a radome for missile guidance, while under the nose is provision for a daylight optical weapons sight and laser rangefinder.

The cockpit is covered by flat, non-glint panels of armoured glass, and is protected by titanium and ceramic armour. Vital components are heavily protected and duplicated, and shielded by less important items. In the event of a catastrophic hit, the crew are protected by energy-absorbing seats, which can withstand a 40 ft (12 m) per second crash landing. An emergency escape system is installed which blows off the doors and inflates air bladders on the fuselage sides. The crew members roll over these before pulling their parachute ripcords.

A hatch in the port side, aft of the wing, gives access to the avionics compartment and to an area large enough to accommodate two or three people (in some discomfort). This is intended to allow an Mi-28 to pick up the crew of a downed helicopter in combat.

## Kamov's challenger

The Mi-28 has been competing with the Kamov Ka-50/ Ka-52 for government orders and has reportedly lost out to its rival in the crucial battle to be Russia's next attack helicopter and Mi-24 replacement. The Ka-50 was officially adopted by the Russian army in October 1994, but despite entering service in limited numbers, its funding and production status remain unknown.

Mil has pressed ahead with what will be the definitive Mi-28 version, the Mi-28N (Nochnoy, night) – also referred to unofficially as 'Havoc-B'. Mil has referred to this aircraft as the 'Night Pirate' and 'Night Hunter', and it owes its new all-weather/night-attack capability to the addition of a mast-mounted millimetre-wave radar. This is claimed to be equivalent to the AH-64D's Longbow radar, although it is unclear whether the Russian radar even exists yet. A new sensor suite has been added, including the Zenit TV/FLIR, and laser spot tracker in a ball turret under the nose radome.

The prototype Mi-28N ('White 014') was rolled out at the Mil factory near Moscow on 16 August 1996. The aircraft had previously been exhibited at the 1995 Moscow air show, but without any avionics. It first flew on 14 November 1996 and has since entered flight trials. The Mi-28N has received positive assessments from the Russian authorities, but no substantial funding commitments.

## Foreign interest

In October 1995, an evaluation of the basic Mi-28 was made 'in-country' by the Swedish Army Aviation Centre. The intention was to evaluate the Mi-28 against the AH-64 as part of Sweden's ongoing requirement for a dedicated attack helicopter. Three pilots (two Swedish and one Russian) flew tactical mission profiles and undertook live weapons firings with a single Mi-28 (042). While reservations were expressed about the modernity (and safety) of some of the onboard systems – and the lack of supporting technical documentation and certification standards – the Swedes were impressed with the aircraft's tough construction, man/ machine interface and its very reliable performance. Weapons accuracy was described as "good and astonishingly repeatable". The greatest weakness of the Mi-28 was its lack of night capability, a flaw to be corrected in the Mi-28N. The Swedish evaluation remains the only independent assessment of the Mi-28 and it was generally positive – in some fields the 'Havoc' performed better than the AH-64A Apache. However, the Mi-28, and the Mi-28N in particular, remains an immature design that may never be fielded by Russian forces and this almost certainly denies it the chance of export sales.

***Left: For ground attack missions the 'Havoc' can be equipped with 9M114 Shturm C (AT-6 'Spiral') anti-tank missiles and 20-round UV-20 rocket pods (for 80-mm C-8 rockets), as illustrated.***

***Below: The development of the Mi-28N was a natural evolution of Mil's only current production combat helicopter. Combat experience in Desert Storm and, more importantly (for Russian forces), in Chechnya underlined the real need for night/adverse weather-capable combat aircraft.***

# Mitsubishi F-1/T-2

## F-1: Ship-killing Samurai

***A Mitsubishi F-1 of 3 Hikotai roars into the air from its base at Misawa AB. By the time it is retired, the type will have seen almost 30 years service with the JASDF.***

**A derivative of the T-2 trainer, the Mitsubishi F-1 was Japan's first major post-war combat aircraft and has performed a vital anti-shipping role for the JASDF since the late 1970s.**

***From most angles the similarities between the F-1 and the Anglo-French Jaguar are obvious. Note also the F-1's pronounced 'humped back', a legacy of its origins in the T-2 two-seater.***

A populous and highly industrialised island nation with dwindling natural resources, Japan is utterly dependent on foreign trade. Its raw materials generally come from overseas, while markets are also chiefly found outside Japan. All of this brings with it a heavy reliance on the sea, and defence of the sea lanes is accorded a high priority. Nevertheless, for many years Japan was unable to equip its armed forces with equipment capable of defending against invasion or against interdiction of the sea lanes. After Japan lost World War II, the victorious Allies ensured that the defeated nation remained militarily weak. Allied strictures, combined with the humiliation of the old military class and the growth of a culture of anti-militarism, made it inevitable that Japan's new armed forces would be overtly defensive in nature. The three arms were even named as 'Self-Defence Forces' and were equipped with defensive weapons and systems.

Thus the anti-shipping role is known as the 'anti-landing craft' role, and fighter-bombers are known as support fighters.

### Dual requirement

By the 1970s the Japan Air Self-Defense Force was keen to acquire a dedicated support fighter – a type it had never operated – and also had an outstanding need for a supersonic trainer to better prepare pilots for its F-104J Starfighters. Thus it was decided to combine the SF-X and T-X requirements in a single type.

Initially Japan looked abroad, the Northrop F-5 and SEPECAT Jaguar being obvious candidates. In fact, the latter was intensively evaluated and licence production was discussed, but negotiations foundered on the level of royalties to be paid and the locally-built 'Jag' was not to be. However, Japan's enthusiasm for the Jaguar should not be underestimated; as will be seen, it had a major influence on the configuration and detail design of the eventual F-1/T-2 design.

### Indigenous solution

In the event, a decision to proceed with an entirely indigenous trainer was taken in November 1966, after intensive lobbying by Japanese aircraft manufacturers, and in September 1967 Mitsubishi was awarded a development contract for the T-2, with a basic design contract following on 30 March 1968.

The T-2 (T-X) prototype made its maiden flight on 20 July 1971 and became Japan's first supersonic trainer on its 30th flight. The new trainer was developed from the start with a view to providing the basis for a fighter-bomber, and Mitsubishi continued feasibility studies of a fighter-bomber version of the aircraft.

For a while the future of the SF-X derivative looked in doubt, the Japanese Ministry of Finance favouring the purchase of a batch of F-5A fighter-bombers and the diversion of local resources towards the development of a replacement for the P-2J maritime patrol aircraft (P-XL). Eventually Prime Minister Kakuei Tanaka cancelled the P-XL programme, and, in 1972, the government decided to fund the development of an indigenous fighter-bomber based on the T-2.

A prototype development contract was placed by the Defense Agency in 1973. Mitsubishi was commissioned to take the sixth and seventh T-2s from the Komaki production line, and to rebuild them as single-seat fighter-bombers. These two aircraft were initially known as Special Spec T-2s, and

***The JASDF shares its Misawa Air Base with the F-16s of the 35th Fighter Wing (formerly the 432nd FW) of the USAF's Pacific Air Forces. The 35th Wing eventually adopted the 'WW' tailcode.***

***Above: Despite many weaknesses and encroaching obsolescence, the F-1 remains extremely popular with its pilots, who are proud to fly what is still Japan's only indigenous frontline fighter.***

***Above right: The inner pair of underwing pylons and the centreline station are each 'plumbed' to carry a 220-US gal (821-litre) drop tank.***

then as T-2(FS)s, before taking the designation FS-T2 Kai.

Changes from the T-2 were kept to an absolute minimum, in order to minimise cost and delay. The fuselage shape and cross section was maintained, even though drag could have been reduced by getting rid of the bulge where the rear cockpit used to be. Instead the rear cockpit was adapted as an avionics bay, and was covered by a simple access hatch, which followed the shape of the old rear canopy. Because virtually all of the changes were internal, this meant that T-2 flight test results remained largely valid, and FS-T2 Kai flight tests could be limited mainly to exploring the effect of carrying various external stores, and to proving the new avionics and systems.

The seventh T-2 (59-5107) was the first of the two aircraft to fly in single-seat form on 3 June 1975, with the sixth (59-5106) following on 7 June. At the conclusion of the test programme the JASDF placed its first order for 18 of the new aircraft. The JASDF had wanted to place an initial order for 50 aircraft in Fiscal Year 1976, but was unable to do so because of the deteriorating financial situation, and was forced to 'drip-feed' the order over several fiscal years. A large single order would have allowed more rapid re-equipment of the three-squadron fighter-bomber force, whereas limiting the original order to only 18 aircraft delayed formation of the second and third units by one and two years, respectively.

The first true F-1 prototype, 70-8201, was rolled out at Komaki on 25 February 1977, and made its maiden flight on 16 June 1977. After brief manufacturer's flight trials, it was handed over to the JASDF on 16 September 1977.

### First unit

The first JASDF unit to convert to the Mitsubishi F-1 was 3 Hikotai at Misawa, which began re-equipment in September 1977, transferring to the control of the 3 Kokudan on 1 March 1978 when conversion was complete. 3 Kokudan's second squadron, the 8 Hikotai, began conversion to the F-1 on 30 June 1979, and when this was complete the 6 Hikotai began transitioning to the new type, on 11 March 1980. This was the sole F-1 unit assigned to the 8 Kokudan at Tsuiki. Squadrons originally formed with 18 aircraft each (plus attrition replacements), but this was felt to be too small a number, and the JASDF pushed for squadrons with 25 aircraft each. This prompted a move by the Japanese defence ministry to cut the number of squadrons to two, and the JASDF rapidly decided that three 18-aircraft squadrons were ideal, or at least better than two 25-aircraft units.

### Delayed replacement

The search for a replacement fighter support aircraft began as long ago as 1982 and culminated in the FS-X programme which, in turn, spawned the Mitsubishi F-2. This much-modified derivative of the Lockheed Martin F-16 was first delivered for operational trials in 2000, initially at Misawa AB. It is scheduled to re-equip 6 Hikotai in 2006, followed by 8 Hikotai in 2007.

By 2004, the 37 or so surviving F-1s equipped two squadrons, one of the Misawa-based units (Dai 8 Hiko-tai) having re-equipped with the F-4EJ Kai pending the arrival of the F-2.

## Mitsubishi F-1

**This aircraft, 70-8203, was the 3rd of 77 production F-1s delivered to the JASDF. It carries the black panther badge of 8 Hikotai (8th Sqn), 3 Kokudan (3rd Air Wing) based at Misawa AB on the island of Honshu.**

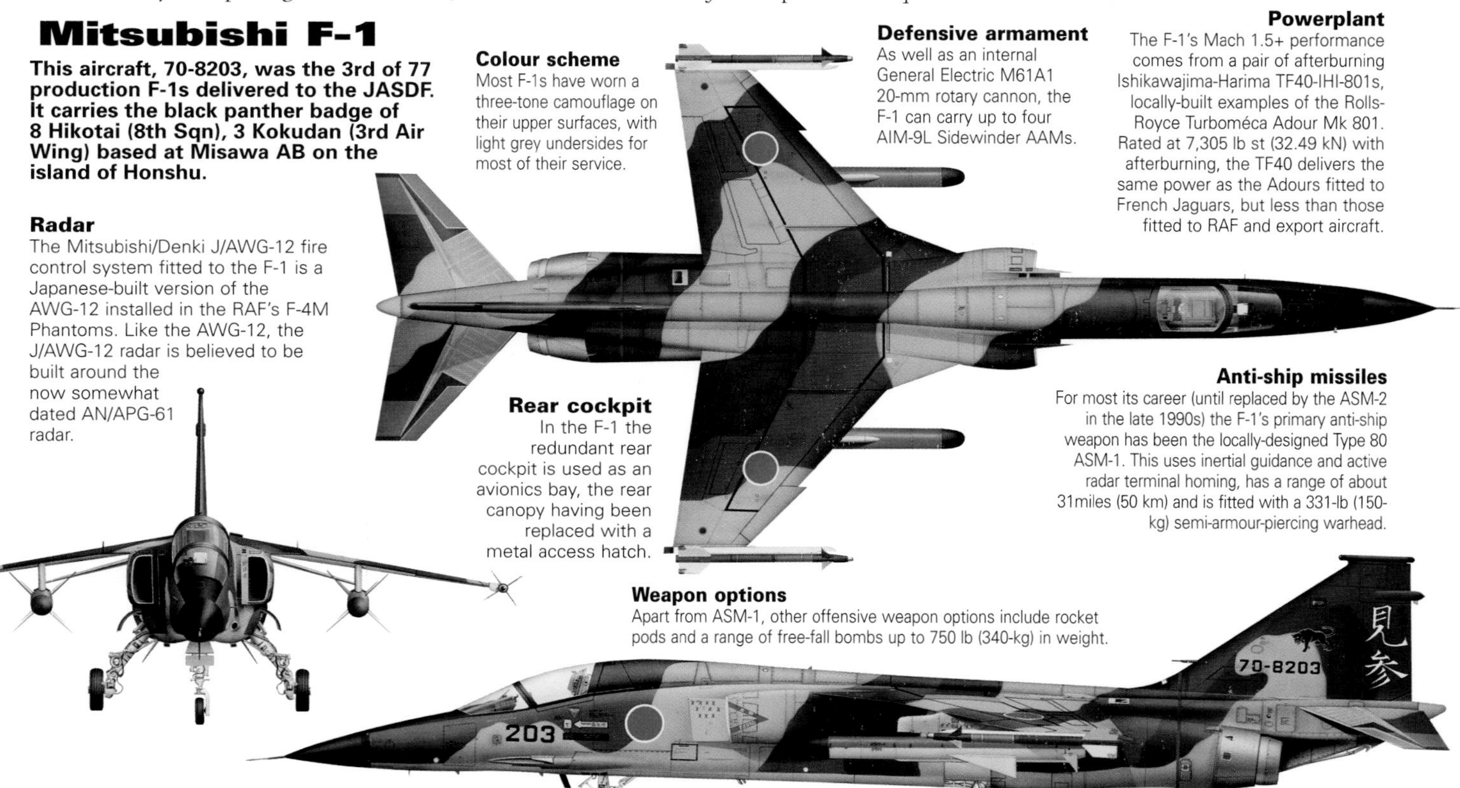


**Radar**
The Mitsubishi/Denki J/AWG-12 fire control system fitted to the F-1 is a Japanese-built version of the AWG-12 installed in the RAF's F-4M Phantoms. Like the AWG-12, the J/AWG-12 radar is believed to be built around the now somewhat dated AN/APG-61 radar.

**Colour scheme**
Most F-1s have worn a three-tone camouflage on their upper surfaces, with light grey undersides for most of their service.

**Defensive armament**
As well as an internal General Electric M61A1 20-mm rotary cannon, the F-1 can carry up to four AIM-9L Sidewinder AAMs.

**Powerplant**
The F-1's Mach 1.5+ performance comes from a pair of afterburning Ishikawajima-Harima TF40-IHI-801s, locally-built examples of the Rolls-Royce Turboméca Adour Mk 801. Rated at 7,305 lb st (32.49 kN) with afterburning, the TF40 delivers the same power as the Adours fitted to French Jaguars, but less than those fitted to RAF and export aircraft.

**Anti-ship missiles**
For most its career (until replaced by the ASM-2 in the late 1990s) the F-1's primary anti-ship weapon has been the locally-designed Type 80 ASM-1. This uses inertial guidance and active radar terminal homing, has a range of about 31miles (50 km) and is fitted with a 331-lb (150-kg) semi-armour-piercing warhead.

**Rear cockpit**
In the F-1 the redundant rear cockpit is used as an avionics bay, the rear canopy having been replaced with a metal access hatch.

**Weapon options**
Apart from ASM-1, other offensive weapon options include rocket pods and a range of free-fall bombs up to 750 lb (340-kg) in weight.

# Mitsubishi T-2

## Supersonic Samurai

**Japan's first indigenously-designed military aircraft, Mitsubishi's T-2 was intended to replace the venerable Lockheed T-33 Shooting Star and North American F-86 Sabre as an advanced trainer for Japan's Air Self Defence Force. Remarkably similar to the European SEPECAT Jaguar that Japan nearly purchased and using the same Adour turbofans, the aircraft later spawned a dedicated attack derivative. Today, the T-2 is still in service and used for advanced training and, until 1996, was also the mount of Japan's famous *Blue Impulse* national aerobatic team.**

*A T-2(Z) of Dai 21 Hikotai (21st Squadron) which is part of Koku Kyoiku Shudan (Air Training Command) on a solo pilot training sortie. This squadron is part of 4 Kokudan (4th Air Wing) and its stylised '4' insignia is clear on the tail. While the aircraft of 21 Hikotai wear a red four outlined in white, the Dai 22 Hikotai T-2s sport a blue four with a white outline.*

The first Japanese-designed supersonic military aircraft took to the air on 20 July 1971. The T-2 was a two-seat combat trainer, that was designed to double as an aircraft in which Japanese Air Self Defence Force (JASDF) pilots could be trained for both the F-104J Starfighter and F-4EJ Phantom fighters and which would provide valuable design experience for a subsequent indigenous fighter. Ultimately, the Mitsubishi T-2 was so successful that it itself proved readily adaptable to become that fighter, the F-1.

## Jaguar influences

During the 1960s, studies began in Japan to find a new trainer to replace the F-86, T-33 and T-1A. Some in the JASDF favoured an entirely foreign solution with T-38s and F-5s being used. Licence production of the SEPECAT Jaguar was also considered but negotiations broke down because of financial wrangles. However, the Jaguar's popularity was apparent and its design played a major part in the eventual configuration of the T-2.

After it was realised that the F-86s would remain in JASDF service longer than had previously been thought, it was decided that the time was available an indigenously-designed trainer to be built. The Jaguar's Rolls-Royce/Turboméca Adour turbofan was selected over a General Electric type, and Fuji, Kawasaki and Mitsubishi all submitted airframe designs. The Japanese government then also requested that the manufacturers provide a modified ground attack version. Mitsubishi's XT-2 design was selected as winner of the competition on 5 September 1967 and a basic design contract was issued in March 1968.

## Service entry

The first prototype, which closely resembled the SEPECAT Jaguar, flew on 20 July 1971 and reached Mach 1.03 on its 30th flight, thus making it Japan's first indigenous supersonic aircraft. After two years of tests, the XT-2 was officially redesignated the T-2 and production began. A total of 96 T-2s was delivered in two standards, the unarmed T-2(Z) and the cannon-equipped T-2(K). The T-2 first entered operational service with the 21st Hikotai at Matsushima on 25 March 1976. It soon began to replace the T-33 and F-86 and also went on to see service with Japan's aerobatic display team, *Blue Impulse*. A few T-2s also saw front-line service, operating with F-1 Squadrons. On 17 December 1982, six T-2s and a pair of T-33s formed the Hiko Kyodotai (Aggressor Squadron) to give dissimilar air combat training to F-4EJ, F-15J and F-104 pilots. T-2s still operate as trainers but were replaced by the more manoeuvrable T-4 in the *Blue Impulse* team in 1996.

***Six T-2(K)s of the 21st Hikotai fly in close formation. The arrival of the T-2 had a huge impact on JASDF training. The retirement of the T-33 and the F-86 cut 100 hours from the previous 600-hour programme of pilot training.***

## *Blue Impulse* T-2(K)

**This Mitsubishi T-2 wears the colourful markings of the *Sengi Kenkyuhan (Blue Impulse)* formation display team which comes under the control of the 4th Kokudan at Matsushima. The team's aircraft wore a complex and attractive colour scheme that was designed by a Japanese schoolgirl in a competition. The T-2s were replaced by Kawasaki T-4s.**

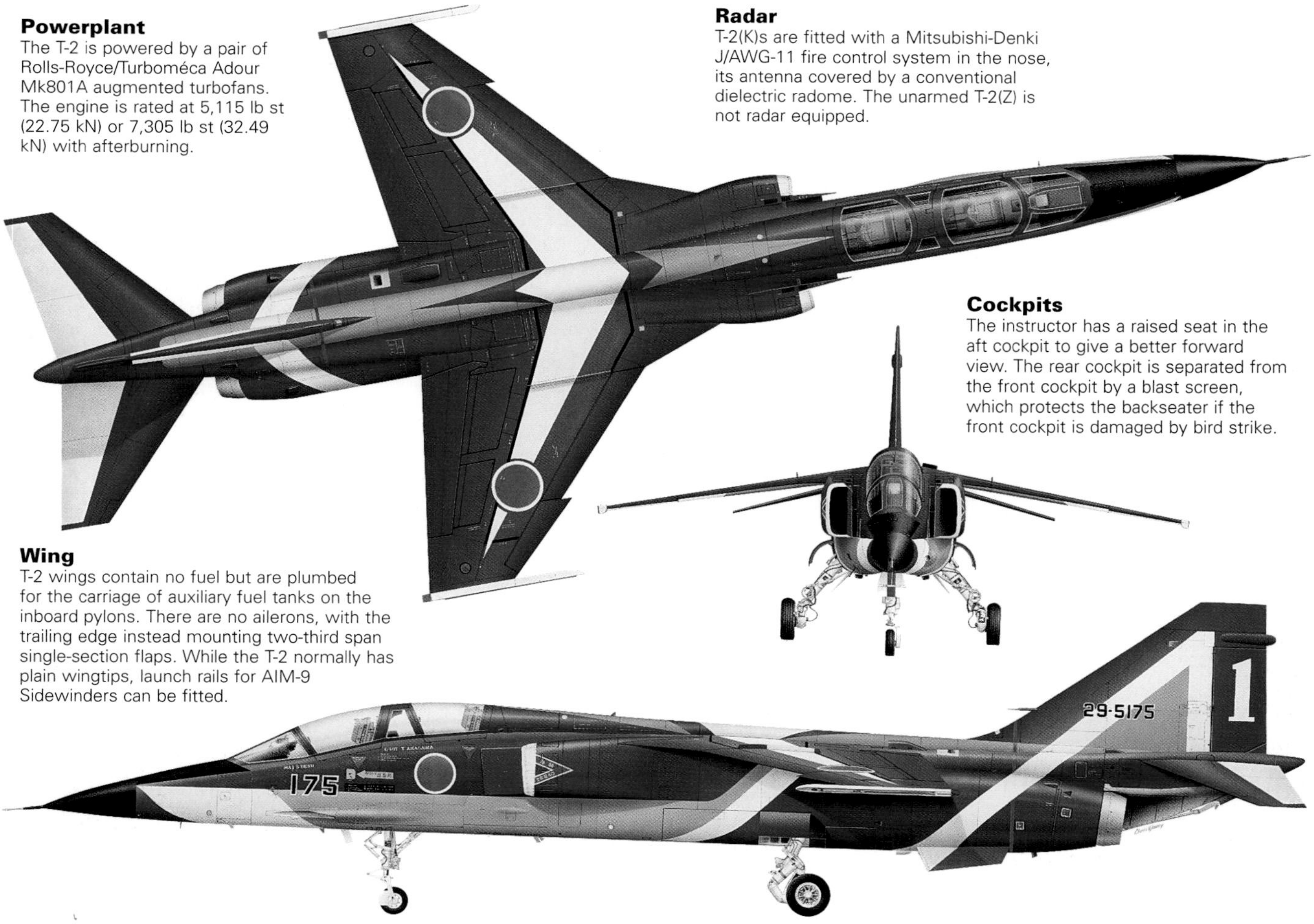

**Powerplant**
The T-2 is powered by a pair of Rolls-Royce/Turboméca Adour Mk801A augmented turbofans. The engine is rated at 5,115 lb st (22.75 kN) or 7,305 lb st (32.49 kN) with afterburning.

**Radar**
T-2(K)s are fitted with a Mitsubishi-Denki J/AWG-11 fire control system in the nose, its antenna covered by a conventional dielectric radome. The unarmed T-2(Z) is not radar equipped.

**Cockpits**
The instructor has a raised seat in the aft cockpit to give a better forward view. The rear cockpit is separated from the front cockpit by a blast screen, which protects the backseater if the front cockpit is damaged by bird strike.

**Wing**
T-2 wings contain no fuel but are plumbed for the carriage of auxiliary fuel tanks on the inboard pylons. There are no ailerons, with the trailing edge instead mounting two-third span single-section flaps. While the T-2 normally has plain wingtips, launch rails for AIM-9 Sidewinders can be fitted.

29-5175

1

175

A Q-5III displays a typical attack weapons load, comprising four 551-lb (250-kg) bombs on the fuselage pylons, underwing rocket pods and external fuel tanks. The outboard pylons are optimised for carriage of the PL-7 self-defence AAM.

# Nanchang Q-5/A-5 'Fantan'

**Despite being based on the ancient MiG-19, the Nanchang Q-5 (*Qiang*-5, known to export customers as the A-5, or Attack-5) remains in widespread service, and indeed forms the backbone of the PLA Air Force and PLA Navy's fighter-bomber forces.**

A PL-7-equipped Q-5III demonstrates the wing planform it inherited from the MiG-19. The 167-Imp gal (760-litre) drop tanks are an almost permanent fixture, as the Q-5 is not blessed with outstanding range when carrying weapons.

The Shenyang Aircraft Design Department presented a preliminary design concept for a new supersonic attack aircraft in early 1958. But the Shenyang factory was already heavily engaged in licence manufacture of the MiG-17 and MiG-19, re-building and overhauling MiG-15s and was also working on an advanced air defence/interceptor fighter. Accordingly, the Aviation Industry Bureau directed that the new attack aircraft should be undertaken by the Nanchang Aircraft Factory, albeit with considerable assistance from the Shenyang factory, since Nanchang had previously concentrated on the production of piston engined trainers and light transports, and had undertaken only limited licence assembly of the MiG-19P and MiG-19PM.

Design of the Q-5 attack aircraft began in August 1958, when Nanchang sent ten senior design engineers to the Shenyang Aircraft Design Department to work on the layout. Such operational analysis as was conducted suggested that supersonic performance would be important, and Shenyang naturally chose to base the aircraft quite closely on the airframe and powerplant of the Russian MiG-19, which it was then building under licence as the Shenyang J-6.

The aircraft's intakes were moved to the fuselage sides, giving shorter, more efficient inlet ducts and leaving the nose free for a radar or new ground attack avionics. The nose gear was also redesigned, rotating to lie flat in the bottom of the nose as it retracted. The fuselage was refined and area-ruled, while the canopy was redesigned to open upwards and backwards. The wing was also redesigned, with reduced sweep and increased area, and the aircraft gained a larger tailplane. The full-scale mock-up of the Q-5, incorporating these features, was completed at Shenyang and was shipped to Beijing in October 1958.

## Drawing revisions

Because work on the Q-5 began during the so-called 'Great Leap Forward', extreme efforts were made to fly the new aircraft in the shortest possible time, and as a direct result, the design had to be constantly refined in the light of wind-tunnel testing, and the design drawings had to be completely revised four times.

The prototype programme was cancelled in 1961 due to severe economic problems, and the production line was dismantled and the design team was dismissed. The programme was kept alive by 15 of the 300-strong team, working in what was virtually their spare time, and prototype construction continued, albeit at a slow pace.

Work on the Q-5 officially resumed in 1963, and on 4 June 1965, Tuo Feng Ming made the type's maiden flight. The aircraft's preliminary design certificate was awarded at the end of the year, following rectification of minor problems, and construction of a pre-production batch was authorised. Further modifications were made to the hydraulics, braking, fire control and fuel systems, and two modified prototypes were flown from October 1969. These demonstrated improved performance, being supersonic at medium

Right: Broadly similar to the Q-5III, the cost of the 'westernised' A-5C is a quarter that of SEPECAT's Jaguar.

Far right: The 'Fantan' is manufactured on sizeable production lines at Nanchang, in the province of Jiangxi in south-east China.

level and transonic at very low level, while handling characteristics and take-off and landing performance was also improved. Series production of the Q-5 was approved at the end of 1969, and deliveries to the PLA Air Force began at the start of 1970.

Because it achieved success after encountering significant technical difficulties the Q-5 was awarded a State Special Prize for scientific and technical progress.

### Nuclear bomber version

The basic Q-5 formed the basis of a new nuclear weapon carrier version, with a recess for a small tactical bomb under the belly. Relatively small numbers were produced, and one was used for China's 13th nuclear test, on 7 January 1972, lofting an atomic bomb onto the test target. The basic Q-5 was hampered by its short range, and in 1976 Nanchang proposed the development of an extended range version, with the original internal bomb bay being replaced by increased internal fuel tankage, and with all weapons carried on external pylons.

Five Q-5Is were built, and the first of these was flown at the end of 1980. The new variant also introduced a revised landing gear, Wopen WP-6A engines, and a Type I rocket-powered ejection seat, while the brake parachute was moved from the ventral fin to the base of the tailfin trailing edge. Further improvements (with a 360° coverage RWR, new ECM equipment, a new gunsight and pressure refuelling) resulted in the Q-5IA, which became the main production variant for the PLA Air Force, accounting for about 600 of the approximately 1,000 aircraft built. This version had a 35 per cent improvement in low level radius of action, and a 26 per cent increase in maximum range, yet could carry 1,102 lb (500 kg) more weapons and could land in 427 ft (130 m) less than the basic aircraft. Had any Q-5IA aircraft been exported, they would have used the designation A-5A.

A torpedo-bomber version was built for the PLA Navy as the Q-5II, and this aircraft featured a raised cockpit and a drooping radar nose. Any export version of the Q-5II would have used the designation A-5B. Some have suggested that the Q-5II designation applied to a version of the Q-5IA fitted with a new RWR, but this seems to be untrue.

### Q-5IA and Q-5III

The Q-5IA formed the basis of the modernised Q-5III, which had improved avionics and revised weapons pylons, designed to be compatible with a range of Chinese and Western weapons. A development contract for the Q-5III was signed in April 1981, and the new variant was certificated in January 1983, following flight testing of three prototypes. The Q-5III was produced only for export, as the A-5C, and was delivered to the air forces of Pakistan, Bangladesh, Myanmar and North Korea, with the first deliveries taking place in January 1983. Pakistani and Bangladeshi A-5s at least used a Martin Baker Mk 10 zero-zero ejection seat.

Plans to upgrade the Q-5 resulted in two further derivatives of the aircraft. An agreement was signed with Aeritalia on 1 August 1986, and this led to the development of the Q-5M/A-5M, with two extra underwing pylons and a new avionics suite, including a Western INS, IFF, HUD and RWRs, and a new ranging radar. The first of two prototypes made its maiden flight on 30 August 1988, but was destroyed in an accident on 17 October.

The Italian upgrade was evaluated against the Q-5K Kong Yun (Cloud), which was the result of a similar agreement with the French Thomson-CSF company. The Q-5K had a new avionics system, again with INS and a modern HUD, but with a nose-mounted laser rangefinder rather than a ranging radar. The first of two prototypes made its maiden flight on 17 September 1988.

In the event, arms embargoes which followed the Tienanmen Square massacre killed off both Western upgrade configurations, and it was not until 2000 that another upgrade configuration emerged.

This was the A-5D, which featured an indigenous ALR-1 laser rangefinder in a small undernose fairing for improved bombing accuracy.

## Q-5 III 'Fantan'

**The 'Fantan' has a poor range and load-carrying ability by modern standards, yet remains a useful ground-attack aircraft on account of its high speed at low level and immense sturdiness. This Q-5 wears export-style three-tone tactical camouflage: most PLAAF examples wear all-white schemes.**

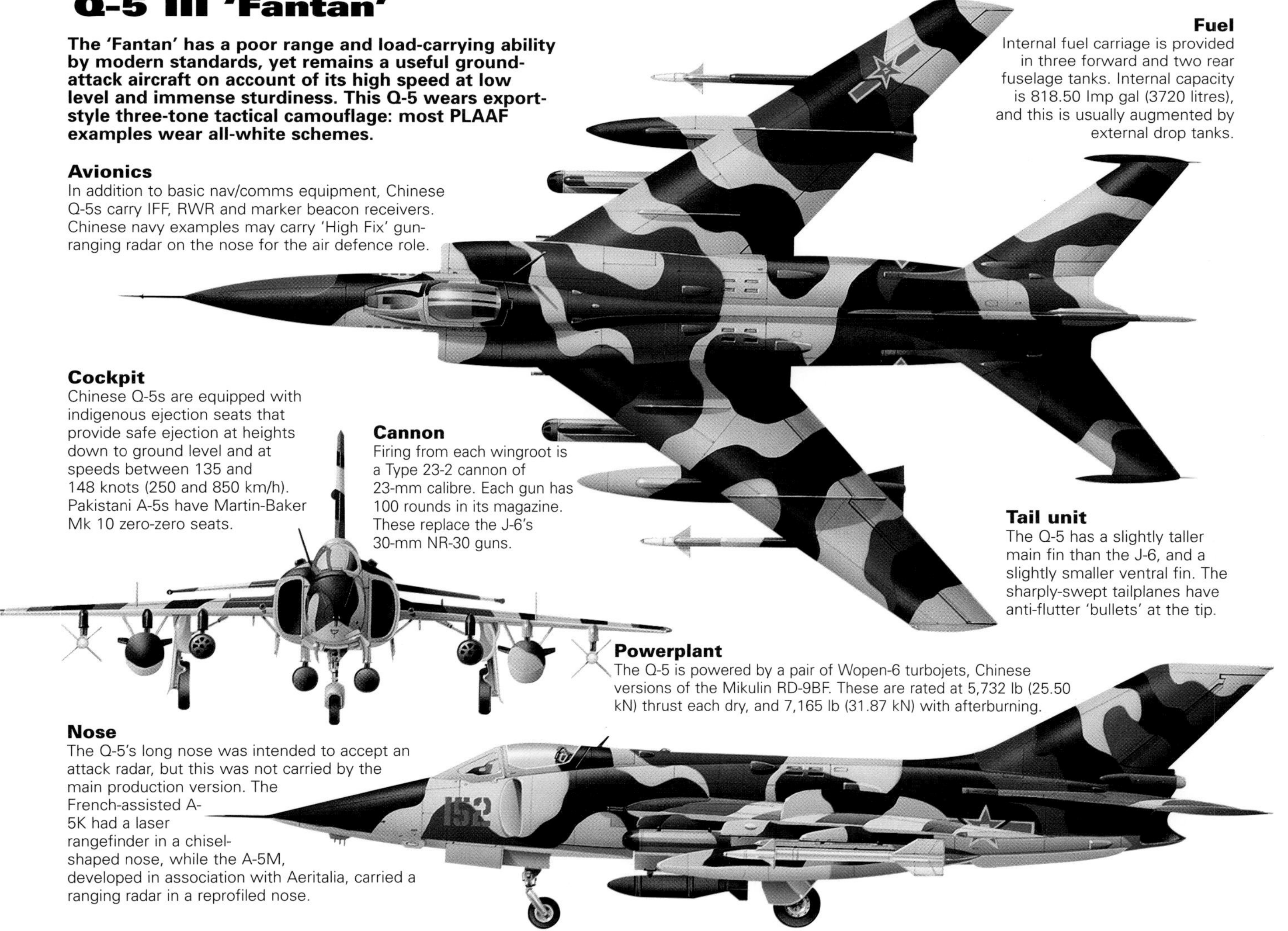

**Avionics**
In addition to basic nav/comms equipment, Chinese Q-5s carry IFF, RWR and marker beacon receivers. Chinese navy examples may carry 'High Fix' gun-ranging radar on the nose for the air defence role.

**Fuel**
Internal fuel carriage is provided in three forward and two rear fuselage tanks. Internal capacity is 818.50 Imp gal (3720 litres), and this is usually augmented by external drop tanks.

**Cockpit**
Chinese Q-5s are equipped with indigenous ejection seats that provide safe ejection at heights down to ground level and at speeds between 135 and 148 knots (250 and 850 km/h). Pakistani A-5s have Martin-Baker Mk 10 zero-zero seats.

**Cannon**
Firing from each wingroot is a Type 23-2 cannon of 23-mm calibre. Each gun has 100 rounds in its magazine. These replace the J-6's 30-mm NR-30 guns.

**Tail unit**
The Q-5 has a slightly taller main fin than the J-6, and a slightly smaller ventral fin. The sharply-swept tailplanes have anti-flutter 'bullets' at the tip.

**Powerplant**
The Q-5 is powered by a pair of Wopen-6 turbojets, Chinese versions of the Mikulin RD-9BF. These are rated at 5,732 lb (25.50 kN) thrust each dry, and 7,165 lb (31.87 kN) with afterburning.

**Nose**
The Q-5's long nose was intended to accept an attack radar, but this was not carried by the main production version. The French-assisted A-5K had a laser rangefinder in a chisel-shaped nose, while the A-5M, developed in association with Aeritalia, carried a ranging radar in a reprofiled nose.

***Three anonymous-looking F-5As from the USAF's 4441st CCTS at Williams AFB fly a neat formation for the camera. The Williams-based F-5s briefly wore unit markings in the shape of a yellow lightning flash, but the markings were short-lived due to the high aircraft turnover.***

# Northrop F-5 family

## Introduction

**The F-5 was developed as a lightweight fighter for use by nations too poor to afford the latest hardware. Its combination of performance and economy proved powerful, however, and the aircraft was refined and improved, and widely exported.**

At the height of the Cold War, military spending was exorbitant and, while major powers such as the US were able to re-equip with increasingly expensive and sophisticated 'Century Series' fighters, other nations needed a reasonably priced combat aircraft that could be deployed in large numbers. They would also need to be able to operate from less lavishly equipped airfields and would require less extravagant logistical networks.

Northrop was one of the first companies to take up the challenge and commissioned a study to examine what kind of fighter was needed by the Free World. It discovered that reducing operating costs was the best way of producing an affordable fighter. It also correctly deduced that operating costs were directly proportional to size, weight and complexity, and set about designing a lightweight fighter, the N-102. Reliance on powerplants in the class of the General Electric J79, Pratt & Whitney J57 and Wright J65 ensured that the N-102 (later named 'Fang') would never be a true lightweight; the design had spiralled upwards in weight and cost and was cancelled in favour of a lighter aircraft.

### Fang to Freedom Fighter

The design of such a fighter began in 1955, using the designation N-156. The availability of General Electric's miniature J85 made possible the development of a smaller, lighter aircraft. After a series of abortive examples, the final design chose for aerodynamic wind-tunnel testing was tested in two closely related forms – the single seat N-156F and two-seat N-156T.

The J85 engines were installed side-by-side in the rear fuselage, hanging from rails. They could be accessed and removed by taking off the lower part of the rear fuselage. The two engines were so light that they could actually be removed and refitted using manpower alone.

The aircraft was designed for a maximum speed of Mach 1.5, leading it to be referred to as a 'slow fighter'. The wingtips incorporated launch rails originally intended for Sidewinder, Falcon or Sparrow missiles.

Internally, there were few surprises. The quest to save weight brought machined and chemically milled skins, and the extensive use of sandwich construction. All fuel was carried in fuselage tanks, the wing remaining dry. The tanks were divided into fore and aft groups and full cross-feed between the tanks was provided. The cockpit was typically American, which is to say it was large, roomy and well appointed, with a remarkably good all-round view through the massive canopy.

In November 1955 Welko Gasisch, head of preliminary design, was told to concentrate on the two-seater as this seemed to have the greatest chance of finding a customer. The N-156T was therefore quickly developed to fulfil the USAF's 1955 General

***Liberally applied with Dayglo and with its nose painted black to resemble an enormous radome, the Sidewinder-equipped N-156F takes to the sky during early flight-testing.***

***Below: Shortly after being shipped to Edwards AFB (but still unflown), the first N-156F is seen in company with the first two YT-38 Talons. Northrop's J. D. Wells and Hank Chouteau are seen with Captains Swart Nelson and Norvin Evans, respective USAF pilots of the T-38 and N-156F.***

*Above: The F-5B prototype made its maiden flight on 24 February 1964. The first production model was accepted by the USAF within a month and the type entered service on 30 April 1964.*

*Right: Three Norwegian F-5A(G)s (in the foreground) and a single F-5B(G) are seen on a pre-delivery test-flight. Due to Norway's adverse weather conditions, Norwegian F-5s had provision for JATO bottles, arrester hooks and windscreen de-icing.*

Operational Requirement SS-240L for a supersonic basic trainer. The aircraft was selected for purchase in June 1956, and the USAF authorised the construction of three prototypes under the designation YT-38, the third to be a static test airframe.

Development of the N-156F fighter was not abandoned, and was resumed at full speed once the T-38 was underway. The work carried out was an invaluable windfall for the N-156F team, who soon had access to reams of wind-tunnel data and also expected to benefit from flight-test results.

## N-156F go-ahead

The N-156F retained maximum commonality with the T-38, and the T-38 mock-up was rapidly rebuilt to serve as the fighter mock-up. The aircraft, quickly dubbed 'Freedom Fighter', was still a private venture and Northrop was gambling with its own money, so it was important to limit changes as far as was possible.

The N-156F was rolled out on 31 May 1959 and shipped to Edwards AFB, where it made its maiden flight on 30 July 1959 in the capable hands of Lew Nelson, four months after the first flight of the YT-38. The company quickly completed and flew the second prototype, but suspended work on the third when the USAF decided that planned testing could be achieved with the two aircraft already completed.

With the two flying aircraft turning in unprecedented levels of reliability and availability, Northrop completed far more testing than it had expected. However, despite tests and studies demonstrating the effectiveness of the N-156F, the USAF decided in August 1960 that there was no immediate requirement for 'this class of airplane' and the programme was cancelled. The N-156F was dead. Or so it seemed.

## Freedom Fighter reborn

The USAF always remained sceptical about the N-156, preferring stripped-down versions of the F-104G already sold to Japan and several NATO countries. However, the US Army took a closer interest in the aircraft, borrowing a prototype for evaluation in its fixed-wing close support aircraft trials. The US Army evaluated a pair of Fiat G91s, the A4D-2N Skyhawk and the N-156F in a series of comparative trials held mainly at Edwards AFB. However, the USAF did not want the army to operate its own close-support aircraft and pressed for the competition to be cancelled.

The army went on to use helicopters in the fire support role, but USAF interest in the N-156F had been reawakened and the type was examined once more. USAF selection of the N-156F to meet the FX requirement was formally approved by the Secretary of Defense on 23 April 1962, and resulted in an immediate flurry of interest, much of which translated into orders. The designation F-5 was allocated on 9 August. A $20 million fixed-price contract was signed in October 1962, initiating production. This called for a mix of single-seat F-5As and two-seat F-5B operational trainers, in a ratio of 9:1. The third N-156F was completed to the production configuration under the designation YF-5A, powered by a pair of J85-GE-13 engines. Most importantly, it had a strengthened wing to allow the fitting of an extra pair of hardpoints (bringing the total to seven), and also had a strengthened undercarriage. With the flight-test programme well under way, a second contract followed on 27 August 1963, bringing the total number of aircraft to 170.

Norway announced its order for F-5As on 28 February 1964, part-funding the 64 aircraft by replacement of one of the planned squadrons of F-104Gs. The first F-5A was accepted by the USAF during January 1964, but it lacked nose cannon and the type did not enter service until August 1964, with the 4441st Combat Crew Training School at Williams AFB.

## The first twin-sticker

The two-seat F-5B combined the tandem two-seat cockpit of the T-38 with the airframe of the F-5A, retaining the single-seater's underwing hardpoints, wing and bigger engine intakes. Only the two 20-mm cannon were missing. On the day on which the F-5B entered service – 30 April 1964 – the TAC's F-5 training programme was initiated with the 4441st CCTS, which was soon equipped with seven single-seat F-5As and five two-seat F-5Bs.

The first operational F-5 squadron was an Iranian unit based at the First Fighter Base at Tehran-Mehrabad. This was declared combat-ready in June 1965. Greek F-5As were declared operational with 341 Mira in July 1965, while the first Norwegian aircraft were declared operational the same month.

*Above: Despite its flimsy-looking undercarriage, the F-5's performance from semi-prepared dirt strips was impressive. This early F-5A is fitted with a test instrumentation boom and carries 1,000-lb (454-kg) bombs underwing for rough runway trials.*

*Right: This F-5A from the 4441st CCTS wears a TAC badge on its tail, superimposed over the yellow lightning flash. The type entered service with the 4441st in August 1964.*

# Foreign 'Fives'

***The Netherlands ordered 75 NF-5As and 30 NF-5Bs in 1967 to meet its requirement for an F-84F Thunderstreak replacement, and deliveries finally finished in 1972. F-5s had a long and successful career with the KLu, with the last NF-5 unit transitioning to the F-16 in 1991.***

**Although not built in quite the numbers enjoyed by the F-4 and F-104, the F-5 proved to be one of the most successful products of the US aircraft industry in the post-war era. Reliable, effective and easy to maintain, the early variants of the Freedom Fighter remain in service to this day.**

As early as 1959, Northrop was able to announce that it was discussing licence-production of the (then still) N-156F with a consortium of European countries plus Australia and the UK. Ultimately, the F-104G won the licence contract in Europe, with production in Italy, Germany, Holland and Belgium, as well as Canada and Japan. While several nations operated both the F-5 and the F-104, it was to be Canada that was unique in manufacturing both aircraft.

In Canada, licence production was undertaken by Canadair for the CF-5A/D versions of the F-5A/B (Canadian Armed Forces designation CF-116) and for versions designated NF-5A/B for the Royal Netherlands air force. The CF-5A differed in some respects from contemporary F-5s, most notably with the inclusion of the J85-CAN-15 engine, rather than the J85-GE-13.

During the 1960s and 1970s, Canada underwent a period of demilitarisation, and the cut-price CF-5 represented a major saving. Nevertheless, the inauguration of the Liberal government in 1968 saw further cuts and CF-5 production was reduced from 118 to 54 aircraft.

Some CF-5As could be fitted with a Vinten 70-mm camera nose and were then designated CF-5A(R). The CF-5As could also be fitted with refuelling probes, but neither these nor the reconnaissance nose could be carried by the two-seat CF-5Ds. The Freedom Fighters enjoyed an active service life with the Canadian Armed Forces, even when squadron strength was reduced to two units. With the purchase of the F-188, Canada's F-5s were reduced in role to that of a lead-in fighter trainer, a mission they enjoyed until retirement in the mid-1990s.

In order to help finance the purchase of new-build CF-5Ds, 20 CF-5As and CF-5Ds were sold to Venezuela in 1972, these being locally known as VF-5As and VF-5Bs.

Despite opposition from Northrop, Canadair set about licence-production of the CF-5 for resale to other nations. Holland's first NF-5A flew on 24 March 1969 and the type equipped three operational units until the last examples were retired in 1991.

Northrop had a stake in the Spanish company CASA and this led to a licence-building agreement after Spain selected the F-5A in 1966. The remaining two squadrons of CF-5Bs in Spanish service are designated AE.9 and equip the 231 and 232 Squadrons at Talavera, providing advanced flying training.

## Other operators

As part of a US-led re-equipment programme, a large force of F-104s and F-5s was supplied to Greece by the USA between 1960 and 1965. A decade later, 12 F-5As and Bs, acquired from

***Turkey is still a major operator of the F-5A/B, with 139 examples on strength in 2004. Operated in the attack, reconnaissance and lead-in fighter trainer roles, they are a useful complement for the Turkish F-16 force.***

***CASA-assembled SF-5Bs continue to be used in the lead-in fighter training role by the Spanish air force. Of the 34 two-seaters built, just over 20 survive in service with Ala 23, based at Talavera.***

***As a result of its considerable oil-derived wealth, Venezuela has long operated a highly competent air force. In 1972, a total of 27 Canadair VF-5A/Bs was purchased from Canada. Today, just 17 aircraft, including upgraded VF-5A aircraft remain.***

Iranian surplus stock, was supplied and in 1983 Jordan supplied 13 F-5As and six F-5Bs. Over the next decade, Norway, Jordan and the Netherlands all supplied further aircraft. Today, however, only 29 F-5s remain in service, a mixture of Northrop- and Canadair-built single- and twin-seaters.

Iran was the first true export operator of the F-5A and pilots of the Imperial Iranian Air Force were trained at Williams AFB in the USA. The first Iranian F-5 unit became operational in 1965 and ultimately 104 F-5As and F-5Bs were supplied from the US. However, from 1974, the F-5As were gradually replaced by F-5Es, though a number of F-5Bs were retained for training.

With Iran's retirement of the earlier models, a number of aircraft was passed on to Jordan, which has also since retired its early Freedom Fighters in exchange for F-5Es.

South Korea was another early recipient of the F-5A/B and the initial batch of 20 was delivered to the 105th Fighter Squadron in 1965. By 1971, 87 F-5As, eight RF-5As and 35 F-5Bs had been delivered to the RoKAF.

However, the following year, 36 F-5As and all the RF-5As were transferred to the desperate South Vietnamese government, to which the Americans began supplying more modern types. The USA supplied 18 F-5As to Morocco in 1966 and these were later supplemented by further F-5As, RF-5As and F-5Bs. Today, eight F-5As and a handful of F-5Bs and RF-5As remain, though the type has been mostly replaced by the F-5E and Mirage F1C/E.

Norway was another F-16 operator which relied on its F-5s as lead-in fighter trainers. A total of 78 F-5As, 16 RF-5As and 14 F-5Bs was received, but as in so many countries, the appearance of the F-16 spelt the end for all but a squadron of F-5s.

With the retirement of the F-8, the F-5 became the Philippines' sole jet combat aircraft, though the few that do remain have a questionable service record.

During the late 1960s, some 92 F-5As and 23 F-5Bs were acquired by Taiwan, the majority with US financial assistance. During the 1970s, most of these aircraft were transferred to South Vietnam, though two squadrons of F-5As were retained for training purposes.

Thailand received its first F-5s in 1967 as part of an agreement that would see Thai soldiers fight with the South Vietnamese during the Vietnam War. The initial aircraft were all ground attack variants and it was only with the purchase of Northrop F-5E Tiger IIs that an air defence capability was achieved.

## F-5A Freedom Fighter

**This Kongelige Norske Luförsvaret/Royal Norwegian Air Force F-5A was not actually a Tiger-PAWS aircraft, but despite this, it carried the banner for 336 Skv and its NATO Tiger credentials since it made its public debut outside Norway at the 1994 Battle of Britain air show, at RAF Leuchars. It has now been retired.**

**Powerplants**

Production F-5As were fitted with 4,080-lb st (18.10-kN) J85-GE-13 turbojets. Higher-powered (4,300-lb st/ 19.10-kN) J85-GE-15 engines were offered to the USAF for its initial F-5As. The louvre doors on the intakes, situated towards the rear of the fuselage, provided additional air for the engines during take-off and low-speed flight (below 329 mph/530 km/h).

**F-5 Tiger-PAWS**

At the hands of New York's Sierra Technologies, 15 KNL F-5s underwent the Tiger-PAWS upgrade during 1993 and 1994. Tiger-PAWS (Programme for Avionics and Weapons Systems) was intended to allow the F-5 to act as a lead-in fighter trainer for the F-16, and so added a comprehensive avionics upgrade and new MIL-STD 1553B databus to the elderly Freedom Fighters.

**Arrester hook**

Norway's F-5s were specially modified to cope with the extreme climatic conditions they encountered and, as a result, were referred to by Northrop as F-5A/B(G)s. An arrester hook was an essential piece of equipment for operations on icy runways.

**External fuel**

One of the obvious recognition features of the early-model F-5A/B was its 'coke-bottle' area-ruled tiptanks. Each of these integral tanks could hold 50 US gal (189 litres) of fuel. The jettisonable centreline tank could carry 150 US gal (568 litres).

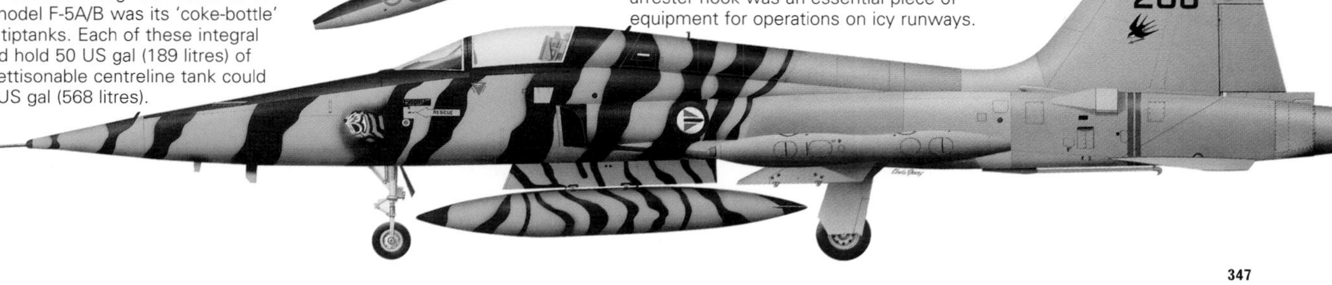

208

# F-5E/F Tiger II

F-5Es and Fs and locally-converted RF-5Es have served the Republic of Singapore Air Force for more than 20 years. These examples bear the kite badge of No. 144 Sqn. Initially used for air defence, the type took on a tactical fighter role in the wake of F-16 Fighting Falcon deliveries.

## F-5s for the world

**While the F-5A was agile and nippy, it lacked even the most basic tools for air-to-air combat, with no radar and no lead-computing gunsight. Northrop hoped to demonstrate a second-generation F-5, with a larger wing and more powerful engines to increase performance and agility, and with radar and other avionics improvements to enhance operational capability.**

General Electric had launched a J85 growth programme in 1962, and had tested a larger compressor in 1963. However, neither the Secretary of Defense nor the USAF were prepared to endorse Northrop's unsolicited proposal for a more powerful F-5 without demonstration of the advantages of a re-engined F-5.

Accordingly, the sixth F-5B was leased to General Electric to serve as an engine development testbed. The aircraft was fitted with enlarged intakes and intake ducts and the engine bays themselves were modified, while extra wingroot sections extended wingspan and area. The aircraft was soon fitted with a pair of experimental YJ85-GE-21 engines, and in this form was known as the YF-5B-21. The new engine conferred a useful increase in thrust and, so equipped, the YF-5B-21 flew for the first time on 28 March 1969.

Congress required that the Advanced International Fighter follow-on to the Freedom Fighter should be selected competitively, and on 26 February 1970 the USAF asked eight companies for proposals. The competition took six months, at the end of which the Secretary of Defense approved production of the Northrop design. The USAF selected the Northrop aircraft to meet its International Fighter Aircraft requirement (as the Advanced International Fighter requirement had been renamed), and its decision was announced on 20 November 1970. An initial fixed-price plus incentive contract was signed on 8 December 1970, for 325 aircraft. The single-seat F-5A-21 was formally designated F-5E on 28 December.

The first F-5E was rolled out at Hawthorne on 23 June 1972, making its maiden flight on 11 August 1972, four months before the target date (which had been set in November 1970). Development did not proceed without a hitch. In order to reduce weight, Northrop redesigned the aft fuselage and was forced to use expensive titanium in the new engine/exhaust shroud. This increased costs and imposed delays. Aggressive marketing of the new aircraft led to higher than expected orders, which helped reduce the losses, much to the surprise of the USAF.

Unfortunately, the J85-GE-21 engine proved less reliable than had been hoped, and malfunctions were experienced during August, leading to a suspension of flight trials between 21 September and 16 December. Even though flight testing was then resumed, the engine was not formally re-approved until 25 April 1973.

Of the 13 F-5Es accepted by the air force during FY73, six were used for testing and seven went to equip TAC's training

The Tiger II has sold well in the Middle East, to such countries as Bahrain, Iran, Saudi Arabia and Jordan. F-5Es and Fs (pictured) of the RJAF equipped no fewer than five squadrons.

This Sidewinder-armed F-5E is one of a large number delivered to the Republic of Korea Air Force. Korean Air Lines assembled 68 of these machines, known locally as the Chegoong-ho (Skymaster). Note the flattened nose radome, the oval cross-section of which eliminated directional stability problems, especially at high angles of attack. This was fitted, in the main, to late production F-5E/Fs.

## RF-5E TigerEye – Tiger II camera ships

Northrop originally intended to provide a limited reconnaissance capability for the F-5E by installing an RF-5A-type nose containing four KS-121A cameras in six different configurations. Such a nose was fitted to a handful of Saudi F-5Es, which were used in the tactical reconnaissance role pending the availability of the dedicated RF-5E TigerEye. By the mid-1970s this original nose offered inadequate volume for a modern reconnaissance suite. The F-5E was too small to carry a high-drag recce pod, and had only limited ground clearance with its short-stroke undercarriage. The answer was to redesign the nose to provide integral bays which would provide increased volume. Northrop went back to the drawing board and designed an entirely new nose section (8 in/20 cm longer than that of the basic fighter) with 26 cu ft (0.74 m$^3$) of capacity, nine times the space available in the RF-5A. The dedicated RF-5E TigerEye offered virtually the same level of capability as the RF-4E but in a smaller, cheaper airframe which was compatible with existing F-5E fighter fleets. A variety of camera fits were available, Northrop claiming 90 per cent of the capability of the RF-4E at about 60 per cent of the life cycle cost. The aircraft was optimised to appeal to existing F-5E operators who could not justify procuring a separate dedicated type for the reconnaissance mission. The launch customer was Malaysia, who took two aircraft (one pictured above), while Saudi Arabia took 10 more. Singapore also converted six of its own F-5E fighters to RF-5E configuration.

unit, which was intended to work up to an initial establishment of 20 F-5Es, in addition to its twin-stick F-5Bs. The first F-5E entered service with the 425th TFTS on 4 April 1973. The 425th TFTS fulfilled the same role as the 4441st CCTS had done, of providing crew training for F-5 customer nations.

### F-5F – the Twin Tiger

Production tooling for the F-5E was 75 per cent common with F-5A tooling, while the aircraft parts inventory was 40 per cent the same. Despite its higher performance and different avionics fit, Northrop had not initially anticipated any requirement for a two-seat version of the Tiger II. However, initial operational experience soon showed that a two-seater based on the F-5E would be a worthwhile development, since the performance differential between the F-5B and the F-5E was a wide one, and there were appreciable operating differences. On 15 May 1973, the USAF gained Congressional approval to examine a Northrop proposal to develop a two-seat Tiger II.

Instead of simply building a trainer aircraft with the nose of the F-5B, Northrop chose to produce an entirely new two-seat forward fuselage. This was stretched by 42 in (107 cm) to accommodate the second cockpit, instead of locating the front cockpit further forward in the nose avionics and cannon bays, as had been done in the T-38 and F-5B. This allowed the F-5F to retain one of the F-5E's 20-mm cannon (the port cannon), with a half-sized 140-round ammunition tank. The rear seat was raised 10 in (25 cm) above the front seat (as in the T-38 and F-5B) to give the instructor an adequate forward view. The rear cockpit contained a radar display, in addition to the full dual controls.

The F-5F flew for the first time on 25 September 1974. Unusually, the second F-5F made its first flight on the same day as the first. These two aircraft joined the F-5E/F-5F Joint Test Force at Edwards, where development proved swift and trouble free. The F-5F was slightly heavier than the F-5E and had slightly inferior take-off performance.

## F-5E Tiger II

**Once a renowned Hawker Hunter display team, *La Patrouille Suisse* swapped its elderly, but much-loved Hunters for the F-5E in 1994. Concurrently, a radically new colour scheme was introduced, incorporating the Swiss flag.**

**Airframe changes**
To accommodate the new engines the fuselage was lengthened by 15 in (38 cm) and widened by 16 in (40 cm). This allowed the internal fuel tanks to be enlarged, giving an extra 570 lb (258 kg) of fuel. The increase in width also increased overall wingspan and wing area. The wingroot leading-edge extensions were refined and enlarged until they represented 4.4 per cent of the total wing area.

**Tiger II operators**
As well as about 100 F-5E/Fs operated in the aggressor role by the USAF, US Navy and USMC, the Tiger II was exported widely and has served with the air arms of Bahrain, Brazil, Chile, Honduras, Indonesia, Iran, Jordan, Kenya, Malaysia, Mexico, Morocco, Saudi Arabia, Singapore, South Korea, Sudan, Switzerland, Taiwan, Thailand, Tunisia and Yemen.

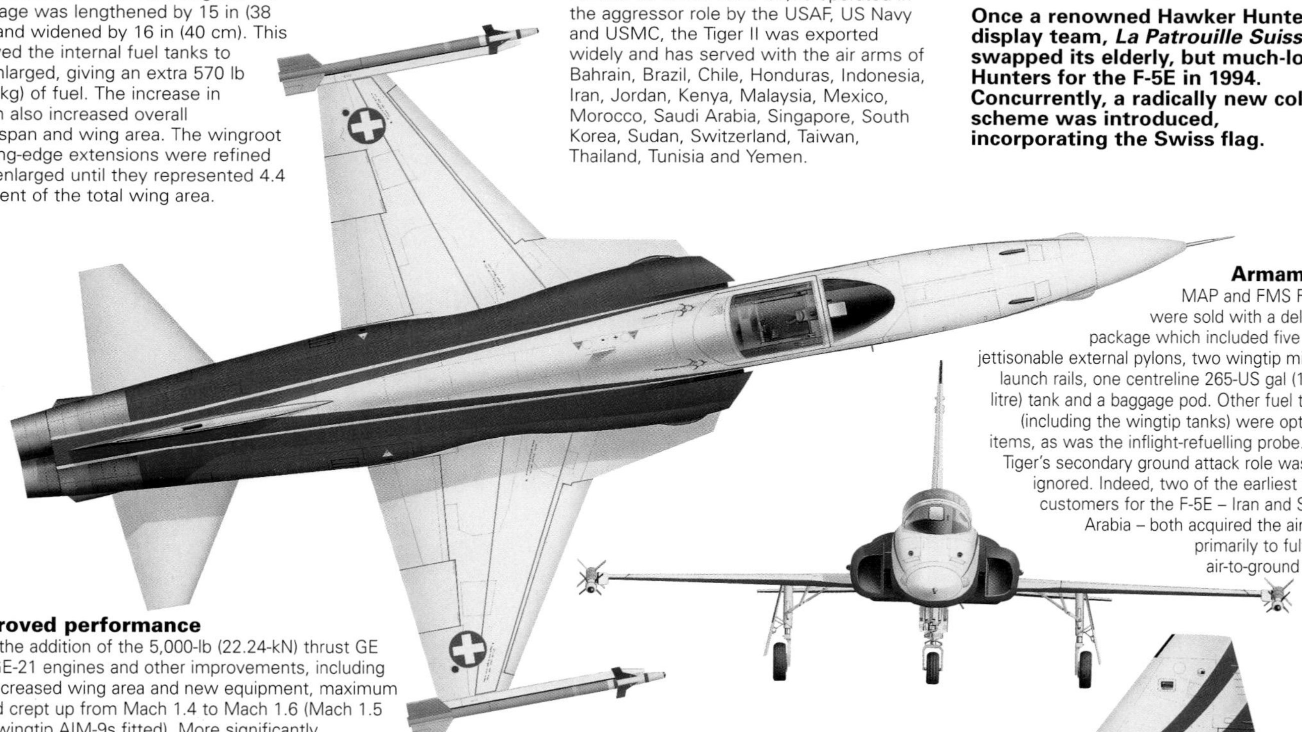

**Armament**
MAP and FMS F-5Es were sold with a delivery package which included five non-jettisonable external pylons, two wingtip missile launch rails, one centreline 265-US gal (1003-litre) tank and a baggage pod. Other fuel tanks (including the wingtip tanks) were optional items, as was the inflight-refuelling probe. The Tiger's secondary ground attack role was not ignored. Indeed, two of the earliest FMS customers for the F-5E – Iran and Saudi Arabia – both acquired the aircraft primarily to fulfil an air-to-ground role.

**Improved performance**
With the addition of the 5,000-lb (22.24-kN) thrust GE J85-GE-21 engines and other improvements, including the increased wing area and new equipment, maximum speed crept up from Mach 1.4 to Mach 1.6 (Mach 1.5 with wingtip AIM-9s fitted). More significantly, maximum cruise went up from Mach 1.2 to Mach 1.45. The new engines allowed even a heavily-laden aircraft to attain more economic cruising altitudes, thereby increasing radius of action and endurance.

**Radar**
The radar chosen for the F-5E was the Emerson AN/APQ-159(V). It provided limited air-to-air search and tracking capabilities, in-range envelope computation for the Sidewinders and ranging for the guns.

**Fuel system**
Unlike the F-5A, which had tip tanks, the F-5E's wing was completely dry. Two internal fuel cells in the fuselage have a capacity of 671 US gal (2540 litres).

# Northrop Grumman B-2 Spirit

## 'Stealth bomber'

*Now that its teething troubles are being solved, the B-2 is proving its huge potential in regular USAF squadron service.*

**An aircraft like no other, the B-2 was designed to penetrate Soviet airspace and destroy the ballistic forces of the Soviet Strategic Rocket Forces.**

Developed in great secrecy, the Northrop Grumman B-2 flying wing was designed as a 'stealthy', or radar-evading bomber for the Cold War mission of attacking Soviet strategic targets with nuclear bombs and stand-off weapons. The B-2 began as a 'black' programme, known in its infancy as Project Senior C. J. and later as the ATB (Advanced Technology Bomber). In its early days, USAF leaders believed that the service's top priority was the B-1B bomber, and only a handful even knew of the B-2 project. To the latter group, the B-1B was an 'interim' weapon awaiting the B-2; at the height of the Cold War, the USAF expected to procure no fewer than 132 examples of the B-2.

Drawing heavily on its previous flying wing designs, Northrop was aided extensively by Boeing, Vought and General Electric, using a three-dimensional computer-aided design and manufacturing system to create the B-2's unique 'blended wing/double-W' shape. More than 100,000 radar cross-section images of B-2 models and components were analysed to assess their 'stealth' properties, followed by a total of 550,000 hours of wind tunnel tests. Nine hundred new manufacturing processes had to be developed for the programme as well as the use of rugged, high-temperature composite materials, ultrasonic cutting machinery, automated tooling via the 3D database and laser sheraography inspection. Northrop is responsible for building the forward and mid-fuselage sections, aluminium, titanium and composite parts and the cockpit, while Boeing builds the aft centre and outboard sections.

Graphite/epoxy composites are extensively used on the B-2 to provide a radar-absorbent honeycomb structure. To reduce infra-red signature, the four

***Above:** Seen here alongside airframe AV-6 at Edwards is one of the original Northrop N-9MB flying wings. It was restored to airworthy condition in November 1994 for the 50th anniversary of its first flight.*

***Left:** One of a series of early ATB models from Northrop gives some idea of the configuration changes undergone by the B-2 during its design phase. Although the 'notched' flying wing shape was quickly decided upon, further refinements took more time. This model has inward cantered vertical fins at the extreme rear of the centrebody, which was longer than that of the ultimate configuration.*

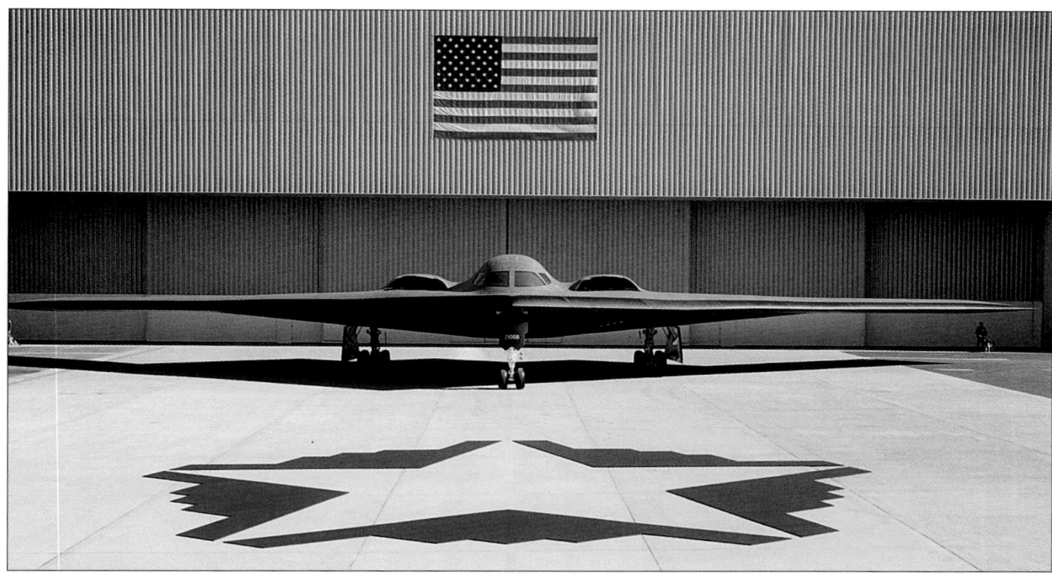

***The B-2 is taking the USAF into a new era of warfare. An enormous undertaking, its value has been the source of constant debate in the House and the Senate.***

General Electric F118-GE-110 turbofans exhaust through V-shaped outlets set back and above the trailing edges to hide these heat sources from the ground. Chloro-fluorosulphonic acid is injected into the exhaust plume to suppress the formation of contrails.

## Avionics

The B-2's swept (33°) leading edge and saw-tooth trailing edge configuration trap radar energy. Further low-observables (LO) measures include 'S'-curved engine intakes and stealthy dielectric panels covering the AN/APQ-181 J-band radar that hide its antenna from reflecting hostile radar waves while allowing it to function normally. The cockpit is equipped for two, with upward-firing McDonnell Douglas/Weber ACES II ejection seats, and there is room for a third crew member. The pilot has charge of the mission computer, which handles target tasking (or retasking in flight). Navigation and weapons delivery is the responsibility of the WSO, in the right-hand seat. The two primary positions have four multi-function colour displays. The aircraft has a quadruply-redundant digital fly-by-wire system, actuating movable surfaces on the wing trailing edges, the latter combining aileron, elevator and flap functions and occupying 15 per cent of the wing area. A beaver tail acts as a pitch-axis trimming surface and, along with the elevons, helps in gust alleviation.

To verify targets at the last moment, the B-2 will briefly turn on its AN/APQ-181, spotlighting only a small area, and then attack. Since 1987, the unit has been under test in a specially-modified USAF C-135 and, although radar was installed on some of the prototype (now production) B-2s, all radar testing has been done on the C-135. The B-2 will be equipped with an electronic warfare system, comprising the IBM Federal Systems AN/APR-50 (ZSR-63) RWR and the secret ZSR-62 defensive aids system.

The B-2 was originally envisaged as a high-level penetrator but, by the time its design was frozen in 1983, a low-level role had been assumed. Modifications needed to adapt the original ATB design to this new role included moving the cockpit and engine inlets, adding inboard elevons (resulting in the distinctive 'double-W' planform), modifying the leading edge and making substantial internal changes, including new bulkheads.

***Above:* Spirit of Missouri *was the first operational B-2 'stealth bomber' and can be seen here returning to Whiteman AFB. Development of the B-2 was fraught with problems, not least of which was the fact that every worker had to undergo a security vetting process. This increased the cost of the programme by some 10-15 per cent.***

***Left: Seen coming in to land at Vandenberg AFB is aircraft AV-4 which is wearing white markers on its leading edges for icing tests. The drag rudders are also noticeable as they are opened to 45° to help slow down the aircraft.***

***Inset: When viewed from the rear, the B-2's shape becomes dramatically altered. The thin structure further enhances the B-2's survivability by making it harder to see visually as well as electronically.***

***Left: Ahead of each engine inlet is a small auxiliary inlet which removes the turbulent boundary layer that might otherwise impede engine performance. It also provides cool air to mix with the exhaust efflux to reduce the bomber's infra-red signature.***

# Spirit in the sky

**Despite a host of detractors, the B-2 finally made it into service, though in somewhat limited numbers. While secrecy is still tight, the aircraft has made a small number of official flights abroad.**

In a surprise move in April 1988, the USAF released an artist's impression of the B-2, an aircraft which had previously been shrouded in total secrecy. Six prototypes (five for the USAF) were funded in 1982, the first (82-1066) being rolled out at USAF Plant 42, Palmdale, on 22 November 1988. Northrop carefully managed the ceremony so as to hide details of the aircraft's wing design, and the 500 assembled guests had only a limited front view of the B-2 from ground level. An enterprising photographer discovered that Northrop had not blocked off the airspace above the plant, and so obtained the first complete photographs of the aircraft after a quick sortie in a Cessna.

The B-2's first flight took place on 17 July 1990 (originally planned for 1987), when the first aircraft (also referred to as AV-1/Air Vehicle One) was delivered to the USAF at Edwards AFB to begin the test programme. This date had been delayed from 15 July due to a fuel system malfunction, and had been preceded by a series of high-speed taxi runs on 13 July, when the nose wheel was lifted briefly. AV-1 was joined by 82-1067 on 19 October 1990.

***In recent conflicts, the US's enemies have faced the problem of having to cope with the B-2A as well as the F-117A. The B-2A has achieve results as least as good as those attained by the F-117A in the Gulf.***

A test schedule of 3,600 hours was set out, commencing with 16 flights (67 hours) of airworthiness and handling trials. Completed in mid-June 1991, these flights also included the first air-to-air refuelling, with a KC-10A, on 8 November 1989. Block 2 testing had begun in October 1990, investigating the low observable (LO) characteristics of the 'real thing'. These flights revealed the first signs that all was not as advertised with the 'stealthy' B-2, and subsequent flights were halted while modifications were carried out on 82-1066. 'Stealth' testing continued into 1993, while 82-1067 was engaged on further performance and load trials. The third aircraft (82-1068) made its maiden flight on 18 June 1991 and was the first to carry the full avionics mission fit, with the Hughes AN/APQ-181 LPI (low-probability of intercept) radar. The first weapons drop by a B-2 was made by the fourth aircraft (82-1069), which initially took to the air on 17 April 1992. A single inert Mk 84 2,000-lb (908-kg) bomb was dropped by this aircraft on 4 September 1992.

Earmarked for further weapons, LO and climatic testing, the fifth B-2 (82-1070) made its first flight on 5 October 1992, followed by 82-1071 on 2 February 1993. By the end of 1993, the programme had chalked up 1,500 flying hours.

## Early problems

In July 1991, deficiencies were revealed in the B-2's 'stealth' profile. It has been admitted that the aircraft can be detected by some high-powered, land-based, early warning radars. However, comment has not been passed on Russian claims that the bomber is vulnerable to its new-generation SAM systems, such as the S-300PMU (SA-10/A 'Grumble') and S-300V-9M83/82 (SA-12A/B 'Gladiator'/'Giant'). The USAF is implementing a 'set of treatments' to the leading edges and flying surfaces to reduce the aircraft's signature across a range of frequencies.

Problems with the B-2's performance have not helped in the battle for funding on Capitol Hill. The original target was for a fleet of 133 airframes, including

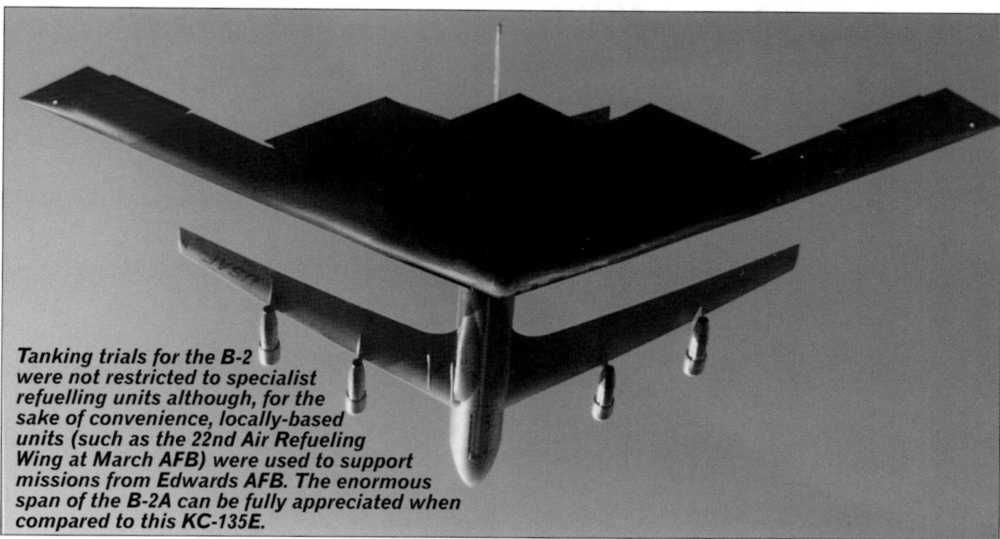

***Tanking trials for the B-2 were not restricted to specialist refuelling units although, for the sake of convenience, locally-based units (such as the 22nd Air Refueling Wing at March AFB) were used to support missions from Edwards AFB. The enormous span of the B-2A can be fully appreciated when compared to this KC-135E.***

prototypes but, by 1991, this had been cut back to 76 aircraft. After the original six aircraft were ordered in 1982, three more were funded while the B-2 was still a 'black' project. In 1989, money was allocated for a further three, followed by two in 1990 and two in 1991. Congress then froze acquisition at 16 (15 for the USAF). The USAF claimed that it could not provide effective operational capability with fewer than 20 aircraft, and five more were subsequently approved by 1993. This approval came with the caveat that the type's LO problems should be rectified before any production occurred. Original 1987 estimates for a 75-aircraft programme stood at $64,700 million (in total), although it is not beyond the bounds of possibility that some of the huge budget dedicated to the B-2 had been spent on other 'black' projects. Hopes for even more B-2s appeared in May 1995 when $500 million was added to the FY96 defence budget to build two more B-2s, and Northrop Grumman offered to build 20 more B-2s at a flyaway cost of $566 million each. However, in recent years, the USAF has opposed the purchasing of more aircraft on the grounds that they are costly to maintain and operate. The dissolving of Strategic Air Command and the development of UAVs (Unmanned Aerial Vehicles) – which could theoretically replace manned bombers – have not helped the B-2's cause either.

## Into service

The first aircraft for the USAF (88-0329/'WM', *Spirit of Missouri*) was delivered to the 509th BW at Whiteman AFB, MO, on 17 December 1993, exactly 90 years to the day after the Wright brothers' first flight. This was the eighth B-2 (AV-8), the first aircraft to production standard. It preceded into the air AV-7, which was still undergoing extensive electromagnetic and emission-control tests.

Currently, work is being done to ensure that the 394th Bomb Squadron will be fully equipped with eight aircraft for operational duties; the 394th will join the already operational 393rd Bomb Squadron. At present, the USAF operates 19 B-2As, which include aircraft assigned to training, operations, testing and maintenance, as well as those in reserve or under modification.

## Unstealthy B-2?

In August 1997, a highly publicised report by the General Accounting Office (GAO) highlighted a number of shortcomings in the B-2. Most notable of these was the fact that the B-2's 'stealthy' qualities were degraded by excessive moisture, and thus the aircraft required extensive field maintenance. In short, the B-2 could not operate in the rain as it should do. The maintenance time for each flight hour has also risen from the projected 50 hours to 124 hours. All B-2s will now have to fly operational missions from Whiteman AFB, generally on a non-stop basis, and supported by tankers.

Another, less critical, problem encountered with the B-2 was its lack of a name. In accordance with USAF tradition, the official name of Spirit is never heard around the aircraft. The name 'Beak' (in a similar vein to the one-syllable 'Buff' for the B-52, and 'Bone' for the B-1) is used by some as a nickname due to the B-2's beak-like nose, but this has not achieved universal status. Neither has '*Voron*' (Russian for raven), the callsign for B-2 test flights. Many crews simply refer to it as 'the jet' and there is no doubt to those at Whiteman as to what that means.

### B-2 artwork

One question facing the B-2 has been the matter of where to place artwork. Bright badges would be impossible on a 'stealth' warplane and so the decision was made to place artwork on the nosewheel door. Test aircraft received artwork that symbolised the virtues of the B-2; *The Ghost* badge (above) relates to the 'stealthy' abilities of the aircraft, while *Christine* displays the links with Stephen King's supernatural car. The badge *Fire & Ice* (left) relates to the all-weather testing phase of the B-2. In-service aircraft, such as *Spirit of California* or *Spirit of Texas*, have been named after US states, while the thirteenth production aircraft was named *Spirit of Kitty Hawk* in honour of the first sustained powered flight.

***The uniqueness of the B-2 has given rise to a host of rumours about its capabilities, one of which is that it can hover. It has also been claimed by Ben E. Rich, Skunk Works chief of the F-117 project, that the B-2 project was named Aurora during competition for funding and that the near-mystical Aurora hypersonic spyplane does not, in fact, exist.***

# Northrop Grumman E-2 Hawkeye

## Eyes of the fleet

**Already serving for over 30 years and scheduled to serve for another 20, the Hawkeye remains a vital part of any US Navy carrier air wing. Though undergoing few exterior changes, the aircraft's systems have been progressively updated, ensuring that it remains in the forefront of its field.**

*Inset: Three systems operators occupy the main cabin of the Hawkeye. Foremost among them is the CICO (Combat Information Center Officer), who instructs the pilots on the altitude and flight direction required for the operation in hand.*

*Main picture: Apart from the very similar unflown Yak-44 'Russian copy', the E-2 remains the only aircraft ever designed from the start for the AEW mission, a role in which it still dominates.*

***The original E-2A (and E-2B) Hawkeyes are recognisable by their rounded nose, which was modified in the E-2C to house antennas for the ALR-59 PDS (passive detection system).***

Since 1964 the Hawkeye has protected US Navy carrier battle groups and shepherded their aircraft, tasks which it still performs today and is likely to carry out for some time yet. It has been used operationally in numerous conflicts, and has outlasted all of its contemporaries. At the time of writing, the envisioned replacement (the Common Support Aircraft) cannot realistically be expected to enter service until 2020.

The Hawkeye's strange configuration was a result of dramatically conflicting requirements: aerodynamic efficiency for long range/endurance, the need to carry a very large radar in a position where it had a relatively unobstructed 360° view, low carrier approach speed, and the ability to fit onto carrier decks and lifts.

As a result, the aircraft features high aspect ratio (9.27) wings with high-lift devices for long range and low approach speed, a dorsally-mounted rotodome to house the radar, a pressurised cabin to house the operators, and efficient T56 turboprop engines. To fit the confines of the hangar deck, the rotodome can be lowered by around 2 ft (0.61 m) when not in use. The height restriction also dictated the use of four vertical fins as a means of providing sufficient keel area and yaw authority during an asymmetric take-off, without the height exceeding that of the hangar roof; the E-2's height is a remarkable 18 ft 3¾ in (5.58 m). The slender wings were fitted with a folding system which hinged the wings back while rotating them through 90° so that they lay parallel to the fuselage. With wings folded, the E-2 has a span (across the propeller blades) of 35 ft ½ in (10.68 m), compared to 80 ft 7 in (24.56 m) with the wings spread.

Fully equipped for life on board a carrier, the Hawkeye was tailored for its role with a host of new features, which included an advanced autopilot for flying precise orbits, and an unusual rudder-only turn feature which made good use of the widely-spaced fins and was employed to keep the radar level during orbits.

E-2As entered service with the Pacific Fleet's VAW-11, and in late 1965 undertook their first Southeast Asia combat cruise. In 1969 the first E-2B conversion was flown, representing a major improvement over the -2A by virtue of its Litton L-304 digital mission computer. This was swiftly followed by the E-2C, which was dubbed Hawkeye II, so wide-ranging were its improvements. All subsequent US Navy production aircraft have been designated E-2C, but the latest aircraft are very different from the aircraft which first entered service with VAW-123 in November 1973. Today, this initial batch is known as the Basic E-2C.

## Basic 'Charlies'

Basic 'Charlies' were readily identifiable by a lengthened, reprofiled nose and a large airscoop added aft of the flight deck, necessary to increase cooling for the new mission equipment. Basic E-2Cs were the mainstay of the fleet until 1980, when an improved version of the Hawkeye started to enter service. When further upgraded variants began to appear in a two-stage programme in the late 1980s (known as Group I and Group II), the 1980-standard Hawkeye was retrospectively christened the Group 0.

In 1988 the first of 18 Group I aircraft appeared, and this type entered service with VAW-112 in August 1989. The Group I had new engine flight deck instruments and revised lighting, a cooling system with 12-ton (as opposed to 10-ton) capacity, an SCADC (standard central air data computer) and improved APS-139 radar. For the pilots, however, the main difference was the installation of the T56-A-427 engines. Although the new engines had been flown in a Hawkeye as early as 1986, it was not until 17-19 December 1991 that they were given an impressive public outing when a Group I Hawkeye was used to set a series of 20 time-to-height, closed-circuit speed and altitude records.

Significant though the improvements introduced by Group I were, they merely provided a springboard for a far more advanced Hawkeye – the Group II. This entered service in June 1992 with VAW-113 and consists of both new-build aircraft and conversions from 12 Group I aircraft. Having initially equipped the Pacific Fleet with Group IIs (leaving the Atlantic Fleet with Group 0s), the US Navy is progressing rapidly towards an all-Group II fleet.

New to the Group II is the phenomenal Lockheed Martin APS-145 ARPS (advanced radar processing system) with its fan beam antenna. The radar provides fully automated operation with continuous coverage from the surface to high altitude. Furthermore, the rotodome can operate at variable speeds from 5-6 rpm (it previously operated at a fixed 6 rpm) for greater flexibility.

***Left: Arguably the least glamorous aircraft on the US Navy's carrier decks, the E-2 nevertheless has a vital role to perform, one which is central to the carrier battle group's ability to project power on a global basis. No air wing operation could be conceived without the 'Hummer' acting as an airborne sentinel, looking for hostile action, while directing friendly aircraft.***

***Below: VAW-112 was one of several Pacific Fleet Hawkeye squadrons established on 20 April 1967 from the various detachments of VAW-11. The squadron is currently serving on the carrier*** **John C. Stennis** ***(CVN 74).***

More often than not, the Hawkeye is the first aircraft to launch and the last to recover, co-ordinating other carrier air elements over a dual or even a triple cycle of operations.

# Seaborne sentinel

**With a service record dating back to the 1960s and a projected future ensuring its survival to 2020, the E-2 remains a constant bastion on the decks of the US Navy's carriers, keeping a watchful eye on those who dare to challenge American ships or territory.**

A crew of five operates the Hawkeye, comprising two pilots and three weapon systems operators. The three systems operators occupy the main cabin, seated side-by-side facing to port. With the operator consoles installed, together with seats and the racks of electronic equipment, there is little spare room. In Hawkeye parlance the cabin is known as the CIC (Combat Information Center) and has three consoles. At the centre console sits the CICO (Combat Information Center Officer). To the CICO's right sits the RO (Radar Operator), whose initial task is to turn the equipment on, usually before the aircraft has taken off. He/she then acts as an airborne controller, albeit junior to the other two operators.

On the CICO's left is the ACO (Air Control Officer). The initial task in this seat is to establish communications links with other air defence elements such as interceptors and the carrier's CIC. Again, this is accomplished on deck or land. When 'on task', the ACO joins the RO and CICO in monitoring aircraft and controlling friendlies.

## New displays

In Hawkeyes up to and including Group I, each WSO had a round monochrome main display, but in the Group II this has been changed for an 11-in (27.94-cm) square screen with colour symbology, known as the EMDU (Enhanced Main Display Unit). This provides a graphic representation of the main computer's processed data. Each operator can choose which information is displayed to suit particular tasks.

## Individual controls

At the central console, the CICO has main control of the voice communications suite, and his/her console is flanked by UHF/VHF radio controls, although any of the three WSOs can access the radios once they have been tuned to the correct frequencies. Further to the right are the controls for the radar and IFF, traditional responsibilities of the RO. To the left of the CICO's console are the HF and datalink controls, operated by the ACO. Included in them is the new MFCDU (Multi-Function Control Display Unit), which is the dual Link-16 JTIDS and GPS display. Another MFCDU is installed on the flight deck, and the pilots have the use of one of the three UHF/VHF radios carried.

Unlike that of the E-3 AWACS, the E-2C's system is fully operational at take-off, and the aircraft can be 'on task' as soon as it is airborne. In the defensive role, the primary reason for having an AEW aircraft in the first place is to extend the radar horizon, so that low-flying (less than 100 ft/30 m) aircraft can be detected a long way from the carrier. Within three minutes of take-off, the Hawkeye can reach 10,000 ft (3048 m), from where the radar horizon is already 125 nm (143 miles; 231 km). After eight minutes it has reached 20,000 ft (6097 m) with a horizon of around 180 nm (207 miles; 333 km), and after 18 minutes reaches its initial operational cruise height of 30,000 ft (9146 m), from where the horizon is 220 nm (253 miles; 407 km) away. A standard patrol can last for six hours, during which time the aircraft slowly climbs as it burns off fuel. A six-hour mission will 'reach the top' at about 37,000 ft (11280 m), by which time a second E-2 will be on station during continuous operations. A defensive patrol close to base could be extended to 10 hours with a single inflight refuelling, although at present the US Navy has only a trials aircraft fitted for receiving.

For offensive operations, or defensive patrols further from base/carrier, the E-2 has an unrefuelled time on station of four hours at 300 nm (345 miles; 555 km) from base or just over one hour at a 600-nm (690-mile; 1111-km) radius, these figures rising to 7½ hours and 4½ hours respectively with one refuelling. At extreme range, a refuelled one-hour station can be undertaken at a 1,000-nm (1,151-mile; 1852-km) radius. During maximum intensity operations, the E-2 can be turned round and airborne

*The E-2's flight deck has not changed dramatically over the years, apart from the substitution of strip-type engine instruments in place of dials, which accompanied the new Dash 427 engines. Mission equipment will be added to the co-pilot's position, in a new glass cockpit on Hawkeye 2000-derived aircraft.*

again in under 15 minutes, including a crew change and refuelling.

### Far-sighted radar

At its operating altitude the Group II Hawkeye has an impressive reach. Low-flying, fighter-size aircraft can be detected at more than 220 nm (253 miles; 407 km) distance (the effective horizon), while aircraft at altitude can be seen at about 300 nm (345 miles; 555 km). Low-flying cruise missiles show up at more than 120 nm (138 miles; 222 km), while helicopters can be tracked from about 100 nm (115 miles; 185 km) distance. In the simultaneous maritime surveillance role, detection range for small patrol boats is more than 125 nm (143 miles; 231 km).

This capability can be put to effective use in a number of ways, many of which can be performed simultaneously. The primary role is defensive – providing early warning of approaching aircraft using radar, IFF and the Passive Detection System (PDS). The Hawkeye system can then be used to direct appropriate reactions, being able to vector interceptors accordingly. A datalink can be maintained with a ground/ carrier-based command centre and a real-time picture can be presented to commanders.

Production of the E-2C at the old Grumman plant at Calverton, New Jersey came to a halt in 1994, with a total of 139 aircraft being built. However, work continued at the Fort Augustine plant in Florida where retrofits from Group I to Group II were undertaken. In 2000, low-rate production has been restarted at Fort Augustine and the plant expects to turn out four aircraft a year for the US and future export orders.

Capable though the Group II is, evaluations are currently being made of Hawkeye 2000 – the next-generation E-2. New systems include a navigation system, an improved Raytheon Model 940 computer, improved workstations and increased ability in the Theatre Missile Defence role.

Another improvement is the incorporation of the CEC (Co-operative Engagement Capability) sensor fusion system. This allows vessels to share sensor information about threats from a variety of platforms.

Currently, the US Navy's E-2C squadrons are equally spread between Atlantic and Pacific fleets,with a number equipping Reserve and test units. Six other Navy squadrons were retired in the mid-1990s in cost-cutting exercises.

***Although it is a relatively large aircraft, the Hawkeye is very manoeuvrable on deck. Furthermore, the Hawkeye's wing-fold mechanism allows it to assume a relatively compact shape for deck operations and stowage.***

Overseas, the Hawkeye equips several nations, all but France using their aircraft for land-based operations. Japan, Singapore, Egypt, Taiwan and France still operate the type, while Israel's aircraft are currently in storage, Mexico taking three of these after upgrade by IAI.

Numerous other nations are currently studying the procurement of an AEW platform, with Italy, Malaysia, South Korea, Spain, Thailand and a combined Gulf Co-operation Council force being eyed as potential Hawkeye customers. With the replacement of the US Navy fleet by Group II aircraft, numbers of Group 0 aircraft have become available for modification and export at noticeably less cost than all-new machines.

The E-2 many more years of service to offer and, by 2020, the Hawkeye will have notched up over 60 years of front-line service. With new-build Advanced Hawkeyes – based on the upgraded Hawkeye 2000 package – on order for the US Navy and due in service from 2010, the Hawkeye of the future will doubtless be as radically different in its capabilities compared to today's service machines, as the latter are when compared with the first E-2As.

## E-2C Hawkeye

**The E-2 fleet lagged behind the rest of the US Navy in adopting low-visibility schemes and still today, many aircraft, especially CAG birds, wear colourful markings. This example is from VAW-126 'Seahawks,' and is illustrated as it appeared when operating from USS *Kennedy*.**

**Radar**

The APS-145 radar is the latest in a long series of E-2 radars, all improvements of the same basic design. The radar sweeps a 3-million cubic mile envelope of airspace, while simultaneously plotting the positions of surface vessels. Up to 2,000 targets can be tracked at one time, thanks to high-speed processing and long-range automatic track initiation, and 40 separate intercepts handled. Compared to the previous APS-139, the APS-145 has better overland performance with less ground clutter.

**Configuration**

The E-2's strange layout is a product of two conflicting requirements. The airframe needs to be large to contain the equipment, operators and fuel for the long-range AEW mission, yet the aircraft must still fit a carrier hangar deck. The wings are designed to fold and rotate through 90° to lie parallel to the rear fuselage.

**Rotodome**

The Randtron APA-171 rotodome houses a large rotating antenna array for the main radar system, with associated IFF equipment. The radar antenna is designated TRAC-A (Total Radiation Aperture Control-Antenna) and features very small sidelobes. The rotodome rotates at 6 rpm, and retracts vertically to fit the hangar deck.

**Tail**

The unusual fin arrangement of the Hawkeye results from the requirement to provide sufficient keel area yet still fit the aircraft into the cramped confines of the carrier hangar. The port inner fin is the only one of the four not to have a double-hinged rudder.

# Tornado takes shape

**Once derided by critics as being a jack of all trades but a master of none, the Tornado is, today, the king of low-level, all-weather strike aircraft.**

***Above: Tornado prototype 06, one of the British pre-production aircraft, can be seen carrying eight 610-lb (277-kg) cluster bombs, two fuel tanks and Skyshadow ECM pods. This aircraft was the first of the prototypes to test fire the Mauser 27-mm cannon.***

In January 1968, a meeting was held by the air force chiefs of Belgium, West Germany, Italy and the Netherlands. The aim was to replace the Lockheed F-104G Starfighter, and the result was the planning of the Multi-Role Combat Aircraft (MRCA). A Joint Working Group was commissioned, which took effect from 3 March and, over the next few months, the group was joined by Canada (which also flew the Starfighter) and Great Britain, which had suffered from a number of disastrous programme cancellations in the 1960s, including those of the Hawker P.1154 and the BAC TSR-2.

In July 1968, the six governments launched the first phase of the MRCA programme. By October, the MRCA's requirements had been defined, but Belgium and Canada withdrew from the programme, leaving BAC (Britain), MBB (West Germany), Fiat (Italy) and Fokker (the Netherlands). These companies formed Panavia Aircraft, based in Munich, while the four customers – the Luftwaffe, Marineflieger, Aeronautica Militare and the Royal Air Force – established NAMMA (NATO MRCA Management Agency). This enabled them to act as a single body to transmit their requirements to Panavia. Equally important in keeping the MRCA on cost and on target was the adoption of Memoranda of Understanding (MoUs) which described the goals to be achieved and which had to be regularly signed by the members' governments at each interval in production. Despite the progress being made, the Netherlands withdrew from the project in July 1969; this failed to harm the programme, Fokker's workshare being shared among the remaining Panavia companies.

In their challenging specifications, members of the programme required the aircraft to be capable of a number of roles despite the fact that some of the operators would not have a need for all of them. The roles consisted of: interdiction; counter-air attack; battlefield air interdiction; close air support; reconnaissance; maritime strike/attack; and point interception. Some new weapons would be designed for the MRCA, but the aircraft had to be compatible with the in-service weaponry of the four prospective operators.

***Above: The prototype MRCA was rolled out at Manching, West Germany, on 8 April 1974. Designated P. 01, it wore the Panavia company colours and was serialled D-9591.***

***Below: The first British MRCA prototype is pictured with another product of a joint European venture, the Anglo-French SEPECAT Jaguar. The Jaguar entered service in 1973, some seven years before the Tornado.***

***Right: When P.02/XX946 completed its maiden flight from Warton on 31 October 1974, it became the first of the prototypes to fly under the name 'Tornado'. Here P.02 refuels from a Victor K.Mk 2. Tornado refuelling trials were also conducted with the aircraft acting as a tanker – these trials were in response to a specific German and Italian requirement.***

***Left: P.02's duties included performance trials, the carriage of external stores and in-flight refuelling. The MRCA had to be compatible with a broad range of existing equipment – not only did it have to fulfil a wide variety of tasks, but it also had to be capable of carrying the weapons and stores of four different air forces.***

Development of the MRCA was covered by an MoU of 22 July 1970 calling for, among other things, nine flying airframes and a static test airframe. At this stage, West Germany ordered 700 aircraft although, with the purchase of a number of F-4 Phantoms, this number was reduced to 324. Great Britain ordered 385 aircraft and the Italians ordered 100, making a total of 809 Tornados.

Of the 16 prototype and pre-production aircraft, P.01, 04, 07, 11, 13 and 16 were to be completed in West Germany, P.02, 03, 06, 08, 12 and 15 in Britain, and P.05, 09 and 14 in Italy, leaving P.10 as the static airframe in the test rig at Warton. P.01/D-9591 first became airborne on 14 August 1974 and, in the same month, the name Tornado was chosen. Two months later, P.02/XX946 became the first aircraft to fly under the official name.

The remaining 13 aircraft flew over the next few years to complete the batch trials. These aircraft became increasingly complex, starting with a mere flying shell and progressing to the full production standard – the only aerodynamic changes made to later models reflected the search for a more aerodynamic tailfin root fairing. A near definitive fairing was applied to P.06/XX948, the duties of which included trials for the Mauser 27-mm cannon, which was developed specifically for the forward fuselage of production aircraft. P.07 majored in autopilot and terrain-following trials, P.08 was a second dual-control machine, and P.09 was dedicated to weapons development. Two of the nine – P.08 and P.04 – were lost in accidents which killed all four of the crewmen. However, the first of these crashes did not occur until June 1979, by which time the Tornado prototypes had already accumulated 2,750 hours.

## Production batches

Moves toward quantity manufacture gathered momentum in July 1976 when Batch 1 was authorised in the form of 23 RAF and 17 West German Tornados. The initial RAF production Tornado ZA319 flew on 10 July from Warton, while the first West German aircraft, 4301, flew seven days later. Italy was not planning to introduce the Tornado into service until a later date than its partners – its first aircraft did not fly until 25 September 1981 at Turin. The RAF aircraft were designated Tornado GR.Mk 1 to indicate ground-attack and reconnaissance roles, while the other air forces merely used the name 'Tornado' although, to Panavia, the aircraft is always the IDS (Interdictor/ Strike) variant. Batch 2, signed in May 1977, covered 113 aircraft, and Batch 3 was signed in June 1979. Another four batches were delivered between then and 1992.

Unlike many arms procurement programmes (notably that of the Eurofighter), the Tornado IDS deserves great credit for the fact that its costs were kept down. Design changes did occur that increased the aircraft's cost, but these were due to NAMMA's requests for extra refinements, such as Electronic Counter Measures (ECM), after the price had been fixed. There were some complaints about the aircraft which, being technical, failed to gain public attention such as the fact that the R.B.199 Mk 101 reheated turbofans failed to reach their targets, but later aircraft rectified this problem. Despite these early teething problems, the Tornado proved a success when it entered service and represented a major leap forward in attack capability for the three nations involved.

***P.12 was the second of the six pre-production aircraft, making its first flight on 14 March 1977. Flying from Boscombe Down, it participated in British trials that were designed to take the Tornado into squadron service.***

# Tornado GR.Mk 1

**Since entering service in 1982, the Tornado GR.Mk 1 has served as the RAF's premier strike/attack platform. In recent years it has adopted additional roles such as defence suppression, reconnaissance and anti-ship attack. In 1998, it relinquished its nuclear role.**

Production of GR.Mk 1 aircraft, for the Royal Air Force, totalled 229 aircraft. They were built in different batches, which had small but important differences. Batch 1 aircraft numbered 23 and were not fitted with the undernose LRMTS (laser rangefinder/marked target seeker). Today these aircraft are used for basic Tornado conversion training by the TTTE.

Batch 2 production contained 55 aircraft for the RAF, again without LRMTS. These were the first operational aircraft, being assigned to No. IX Squadron and the Tornado Weapons Conversion Unit. Batch 3 included 68 RAF aircraft and represented a considerable increase in capability over the earliest machines. LRMTS was fitted from the beginning, the engines were the more powerful RB 199 Mk 103, with a rating in afterburner of 16,900-lb (75.26-kN) thrust. Most of this batch began the re-equipment of RAF Germany, being based at Laarburch.

RAF GR.Mk 1s accounted for 53 aircraft in Batch 4 and these equipped the second wing in Germany, at RAF Bruggen.

Unconfirmed reports suggest that these were the first RAF aircraft to be fitted with nuclear weapon delivery systems, for use with the 600-lb (272-kg) WE 177B tactical laydown weapon. The final RAF GR.Mk 1 block (not including those built as GR.Mk 1As) was Batch 7, which included 27 RAF aircraft.

## Into service

No. IX squadron was chosen as the first RAF Tornado squadron and it began trading in its Vulcans in spring 1982. Two more UK-based squadrons, Nos 27 and 617, began transitioning soon after. Conversion to the new aircraft was undertaken rapidly, although it took some time to explore new tactics for the type and bring them into operational use, a task which occupied No. IX Squadron for some time.

At a time when the Cold War was still 'hot', it was imperative that RAF Germany should receive the new type, beginning with Nos XV, 16 and 20

***Above: No. XV Squadron was the first in RAF Germany to receive Tornados, acquiring its first aircraft in July 1983. The type replaced the Buccaneer.***

***Below: No. 27 Squadron was one of the three UK-based units to acquire the Tornado GR.Mk 1. All three had been Vulcan users.***

***This immaculate four-ship is from No. 31 Squadron, a Bruggen-based unit. During the Cold War era, the Bruggen Wing had an important nuclear mission.***

***RAF Tornados have been regulars at US exercises, where they have been highly successful in both medium- and low-level bombing. Here a GR.Mk 1 awaits its next mission as a B-52 gets airborne.***

Squadrons at RAF Laarbruch. The Bruggen wing (Nos 14, 17 and 31 Squadrons) followed soon after and were joined by No. IX from the UK. RAF Germany Tornados took over the important nuclear alert mission from Jaguars, although they retained a potent overland attack role, with conventional weapons.

In the early years of its service, the Tornado GR.Mk 1 had four main conventional weapons at its disposal. For general-purpose bombing the 1,000-lb (454-kg) bomb was used, usually carried in fours. An alternative load was the Hunting BL755 cluster bomb, while for precision attack the CPU-123 1,000-lb (454-kg) laser-guided bomb could be employed ≠ although until 1991 the Tornado relied on designation from another source (either a ground FAC, or a Buccaneer carrying a Pave Spike laser designator). Lastly, the Hunting JP233 dispenser pod was carried in pairs under the fuselage pylons. This dispensed cratering munitions and minelets. It was primarily designed for use against airfields, although it could also be used to great effect against railways. With the exception of BL755, these weapons were all employed by RAF Tornado GR.Mk 1s during the 1991 Gulf War, which marked the Tornado's combat debut.

## 'Mini-fleets'

From the outset of Tornado development, it was always intended that the aircraft should fulfil a number of roles. Having established the aircraft in the overland strike/attack role, further developments in weapon systems and changes in international politics (notably the end of the Cold War) have seen the RAF's Tornado force restructured into four 'mini-fleets'. Each 'mini-fleet' retains full overland capability and continues to practise the delivery of standard conventional ordnance. However, each has a speciality role. Two of the 'mini-fleets' fly the GR.Mk 1A (reconnaissance and, until 31 March 1998, nuclear strike) and GR.Mk 1B (anti-surface unit warfare), which are described elsewhere, but two retain the GR.Mk 1.

Both are based at Bruggen. Nos IX and 31 Squadrons fly Batch 4 Tornados modified to carry the BAe ALARM anti-radiation missile on lethal SEAD missions. It was originally intended that No. IX Squadron should become a dedicated SEAD/'Pathfinder' unit, but these plans were shelved. The remainder of the Bruggen Wing, Nos 14 and 17 Squadrons, are TIALD specialists, using the GEC-Marconi targeting pod for delivery of LGBs, including the recently-acquired GBU-24 Paveway III 2,000-lb (907-kg) weapon.

The remainder of the RAF's GR.Mk 1 fleet remained in the training role, with the Trinational Tornado Training Establishment and No. XV (Reserve) Squadron, the latter absorbing the RAF portion of the TTTE when it closed. By late 2003, no front-line Tornado GR.Mk 1s remained operational.

### Laser-bomber

Previously reliant on Buccaneers to provide laser designation, the Tornado desperately required an autonomous designation capability. This came courtesy of the GEC-Marconi TIALD (Thermal Imaging Airborne Laser Designator) pod, of which two prototypes made a high-profile combat debut in the Gulf War. The TIALD consists of a TV, thermal imager and laser designator, mounted in a swivelling turret, itself mounted on an articulated head to provide complete freedom of movement. TIALD was initially brought into service by a No. 617 Squadron detachment, but has subsequently been the speciality of Nos 14 and 17 Squadrons.

***In 1998 RAF Tornados deployed to Kuwait as part of Operation Bolton, in response to the Iraqi refusal to allow UN inspection teams access to suspected weapons-producing sites. This aircraft is from No. 14 Squadron, seen carrying a TIALD pod.***

### Defence suppression

To provide the Tornado with a hard-kill capability against radars, the BAe ALARM was developed. The missile has a programmable search function which allows it to prioritise targets and to be launched in various modes. The most common is 'loiter' mode, whereby the weapon climbs under the power of its Nuthatch motor to anything up to 70,000 ft (21336 m) before deploying a parachute. As it hangs under the 'chute, it searches for a target. When one is found, it 'slips the leash', starts its motor and homes straight on to the radar. Two or three ALARMs is a standard load and the weapon is chiefly employed by Nos IX and 31 Squadrons.

***No. 20 Squadron was initially responsible for flying SEAD missions with the ALARM missile, its crews undertook the weapon's first firings during the Gulf War. Most GR.Mk 1s could carry F.Mk 3-style 495-Imp gal (2250-litre) 'Big Jug' tanks.***

*Clutching a pair of Sea Eagle missiles to its belly, a No. 617 Squadron GR.Mk 1B flies over the Orkneys from its base at Lossiemouth. The 'Grib', as it is colloquially known, replaced the redoubtable Buccaneer in the anti-shipping role.*

# GR.Mk 1A/1B and GR.Mk 4

**Having established itself as the RAF's prime strike/attack platform, the Tornado subsequently adopted the roles of reconnaissance and anti-shipping attack. In the late 1990s the whole fleet is undergoing a major update programme.**

First flying on 11 July 1985 in prototype form, the GR.Mk 1A was a tactical reconnaissance variant of the Tornado although, apart from the loss of the internal cannon, it retains full overland strike/attack capability. A total of 14 was produced by conversion of existing GR.Mk 1s (mostly for No. II Squadron) while a further 16 were new-build aircraft (mostly for No. 13 Squadron).

Easily identified by the side window for the sensor, the upgraded GR.Mk 4A is fitted with TIRRS (Tornado Infra-Red Reconnaissance System), this comprising a panoramic infra-red linescan in an under-fuselage fairing, and two SLIR (side-looking infra-red) systems peering either side through gold-tinted windows. The system works solely in infra-red and records on to video tapes, making it the first filmless airborne reconnaissance system. The benefits of this are enormous: inflight editing and the ability to view recorded imagery without the need for prior processing make TIRRS intelligence available to commanders much more quickly than traditional methods.

TIRRS, however, is essentially a low-level system, so to cater for medium/high-level work, GR.Mk 4As can carry the Vinten GP1 pod, which has a general-purpose camera. This uses traditional film in its Tornado application.

Another role adopted by the Tornado was that of ASUW (anti-surface unit warfare), or anti-shipping strike. The availability of Tornados after the end of the Cold War allowed the

*Above: No. 12 Squadron also flew the GR.Mk 1B, this unit having earlier flown the Buccaneer in the same anti-shipping role. The Sea Eagle missile was designed for open-ocean attacks against large warships, and has little application in today's world. Accordingly, Nos 12 and 617 Squadron have transitioned to a precision attack role with TIALD and laser-guided bombs.*

*Left: Two development aircraft for the GR.Mk 4 upgrade model display the additional undernose FLIR fairing that distinguishes modified aircraft.*

***Left: 142 aircraft have been converted to GR.Mk 4 standard, including the reconnaissance aircraft (which became GR.Mk 4As). The GR.Mk 4 has a much expanded weapons repertoire, with the Brimstone anti-armour missile, Storm Shadow stand-off weapon and GBU-24 laser-guided bomb eventually adding to existing weapons.***

***Below: The Marham Reconnaissance Wing consists of two Tornado GR.Mk 4A squadrons (Nos II and 13) and a single Canberra unit. Despite their recce tasking, the Marham Tornados were the last in the RAF to have a nuclear role with the WE177 bomb.***

type to replace the Buccaneer in this role. Twenty-six aircraft were converted to GR.Mk 1B standard, although the modifications were relatively minor. A new cockpit display and dedicated pylons allowed the GR.Mk 1B to launch the BAe Sea Eagle anti-ship missile.

## Mid-life update

While the Cold War was still raging, the RAF drew up plans to enhance the survivability and effectiveness of its Tornado fleet, resulting in the GR.Mk 4 programme. This was initially an ambitious upgrade which included some 'stealth' features, a fuselage stretch and a Terprom covert terrain-matching navigation system, but was considerably reduced to save costs. The current GR.Mk 4 has a fixed FLIR mounted under the port side of the nose, wide-angle HUD, new cockpit displays and night-vision goggles, Mil Std 1553 databus, and Mil Std 1760 weapons architecture, the latter allowing it to easily carry all weapons designed to this common NATO standard. A fully-embedded GPS is provided. A total of 142 aircraft was covered by the GR.Mk 4 programme, of which several are GR.Mk 4A reconnaissance platforms. In addition to TIRRS, these aircraft can carry the new RAPTOR long-range oblique infra-red/visible light sensor for high-altitude reconnaissance at long stand-off ranges. The first GR.Mk 4 conversion flew on 29 May 1993, with first squadron deliveries made in 1998 and the programme completed, somewhat late, in June 2003. A GR.Mk 4 was lost to US fire during Operation Iraqi Freedom.

## Tornado GR.Mk 1A

**Utilising the world's first filmless reconnaissance system, the GR.Mk 1A ushered in a new era of rapid-response intelligence-gathering. The aircraft has been in service since 1988, and was used with distinction in the Gulf War, being employed to hunt for mobile 'Scud' launchers in the wide expanses of the Iraqi desert.**

**Reconnaissance sensors**
The GR.Mk 1A has a three-sensor infra-red system, known as TIRRS, which provides horizon-to-horizon coverage. The central IRLS is the principal sensor, the two SLIRs filling in coverage near the horizon. The latter can be set to be either roll-stabilised or locked in one position as the aircraft banks.

**TREF**
Data from the TIRRS is analysed in the Transportable Reconnaissance Exploitation Facility (TREF), a mobile ground station. Operators feed in the video tapes and can fast-forward quickly to 'events' previously marked by the navigator. The TREF equipment allows the interpreter to zoom in on specific features and to swap the image between black-hot and black-cold for better interpretation. The final result is usually a written report rather than hard-copy prints.

**Imagery recording**
Data from the three sensors is recorded on to six video tapes. The navigator has a control panel to allow inflight editing of the tapes during the flight back to base.

**External pods**
In addition to its internal TIRRS, the recce Tornado can carry the Vinten GP1 or Hughes Danbury RAPTOR pod for high-altitude stand-off work.

# Tornado IDS/ECR – Italy

**Since the mid-1980s, Italy's Tornado force has been a powerful asset on NATO's southern flank, especially in the nuclear strike and anti-shipping roles. The employment and development of the fleet has closely matched that of the German Tornado squadrons.**

***Top: Italy sent eight Tornados to participate in Desert Storm. These aircraft were assigned low-level missions against Iraqi airfields; one was lost on the first night of the war.***

***Above: A yellow lightning flash on the tail identifies that this Tornado is from 36° Stormo at Gioia del Colle in southern Italy. The aircraft is armed with two Kormoran anti-ship missiles.***

The Aeronautica Militare Italiana (AMI) received 100 Tornado IDS aircraft, of which one was a refurbished pre-production aircraft, 15 were from Batch 2 production, 28 from Batch 3, 27 from Batch 4 and 29 from Batch 5. Of the total, 12 were twin-stickers, which were assigned serials in the MM55000–55011 range, while the fully operational aircraft were coded MM7001–7088.

Service deliveries began on 17 May 1982 when the first aircraft arrived at the central maintenance unit. Later that year 154° Gruppo/6° Stormo stood up at Ghedi to become the first operational unit. Italian Tornado crews converted to the type at the Trinational Tornado Training Establishment at RAF Cottesmore, before progressing to Ghedi for operational conversion with 154° Gruppo. This unit operates the majority of the twin-stick aircraft. It also has an important overland strike commitment. Although there was a ready pool of suitable pilots for the initial conversion courses, there were insufficient prospective navigators, and conversion of full crews progressed slowly. Most of the early back-seaters were F-104 pilots, who had rapidly to acquire rear-seat experience in TF-104s or Luftwaffe Phantoms.

Two further operational units formed in 1984/85: 156° Gruppo/36° Stormo at Gioia del Colle and 155° Gruppo/6° Stormo at Ghedi, to form a front-line force of 54 aircraft plus 12 trainers. The remaining 34 aircraft were considered as reserves, but were not stored instead being distributed among the three front-line units. They were later used to form a fourth squadron in the shape of 102° Gruppo, which stood up at Ghedi in 1993 as part of 6° Stormo. Ghedi had earlier (in 1990) lost 155° Gruppo to 50° Stormo at Piacenza.

From the outset the Italian Tornados operated in a similar fashion to those of Germany, employing many of the same weapons and systems. The standard free-fall weapon is the Mk 83 1,000-lb (454-kg) bomb, usually carried in fives on the underfuselage pylons with AIM-9 Sidewinders on the wing pylons for self defence. Cerberus and BOZ pods are carried to provide electronic and mechanical countermeasures. The bulky MW-1 munitions dispenser was acquired for operations against airfields and other area targets, while the British-built BL755 cluster bomb is also employed. In the nuclear role, the aircraft are armed with US-owned B61 tactical weapons held on a dual-key basis. Ghedi is believed to be the only nuclear base.

With its key position in the Mediterranean and lack of a land border with the Warsaw Pact, Italy placed a heavy emphasis on anti-ship operations, and from an early date the Tornado force was equipped with MBB Kormoran 1 missiles, usually carried in pairs. The principal maritime attack unit is 156° Gruppo at Gioia del Colle, which also has a secondary overland role. To extend the Tornado's reach in the maritime (and other) roles, use is made of the Sargent Fletcher 28-300 buddy-buddy refuelling pod.

Another role undertaken by the AMI Tornado fleet is that of reconnaissance, using the MBB/Aeritalia multi-sensor reconnaissance pod. Initially these were allocated to all of the operational units, although some specialisation among units has since crept in, with 102° Gruppo becoming the main reconnaissance squadron. 155° Gruppo has become the AMI's principal SEAD unit, acquiring HARM missiles in 1994 after the missile had been deployed on an interim basis to other units in 1991/92.

***Following their poor performance in Desert Storm, Italy's Tornados have been regular participants in NATO exercises where inflight refuelling with USAF KC-135s is practiced. Here a desert camouflaged example, carrying a CLDP laser designator on the port fuselage station, eases in behind the boom operator.***

## Gulf War

Italian Tornados first saw action during Operation Locusta, the codename for the AMI participation in Desert Storm. A dozen aircraft were deployed to Al Dhafra in Abu Dhabi, from where they conducted 226 sorties in 32 missions, dropping 565 Mk 83 bombs. Unfamiliar with refuelling from USAF KC-135s, the AMI employed some of the force on buddy tanking missions following a disastrous first mission during which only one aircraft successfully took on fuel. This aircraft continued to the target but was shot down, its crew (Major Mario Betlini and Captain Maurizio Cocciolone) becoming PoWs. Subsequently the AMI has employed its aircraft over Bosnia and Albania, 6° Stormo Tornados flying their first mission on 2 September 1995 from Gioia del Colle. Five days later bombs were dropped in anger for the first time, Mk 83s being released against Serbian targets. Reconnaissance and tanking missions have also been flown over Bosnia.

***The latest Tornado variant to enter Italian service is the ITECR. The aircraft fly with 155° Gruppo in the SEAD role, employing the American developed AGM-88 HARM. Unlike the attack variants the ITECRs adopted an overall pale grey camouflage.***

## SAM suppression

The Italian Tornado fleet has benefitted from two upgrade programmes. The first is ITECR (Italian Electronic Combat and Reconnaissance), under which 16 IDS aircraft have been converted to a similar standard to the German ECR defence suppression aircraft, albeit with a greater content of Italian equipment, including an Elettronica RHAWS. The prototype conversion first flew in July 1992, equipped with an Imaging Infrared System (IIS) recording on to videotape rather than the film used in the German ECR. The production aircraft, now in service with 155° Gruppo, are not thought to be fitted with the IIS, however.

For the remaining IDS fleet the AMI is pursuing a mid-life update programme which enhances the central computer, adds a microwave landing system and active ECM, and provides precision-guided munition capability. The first step was the modification of six aircraft to carry the Thomson-CSF CLDP laser designator pod for use in conjunction with GBU-16 Paveway II 1,000-lb (454-kg) laser-guided bombs. The CLDP/GBU-16 combination has been carried operationally over Bosnia. At least 14 more aircraft will be so-modified and new LGBs (such as Paveway III or the Israeli-built Griffin and Opher) are to be acquired.

***Italy ordered 100 Tornados, 34 of which were to serve as in-use reserves. This example operates with 154° Gruppo which previously flew F-104G Starfighters. It carries the MBB/Aeritalia multi-sensor pod, which provides the AMI Tornado fleet with a reconnaissance capability.***

*Wheeling over the German forest, for which its dark 'lizard' camouflage was specifically developed, this JBG 31 Tornado lugs the bulky MW-1 dispenser. Like the JP233 employed by the RAF's Tornados, MW-1 required the aircraft to overfly its target. This is less than ideal above today's battlefield, and development of a stand-off successor, the Taurus has proceeded.*

# Luftwaffe Tornados

**With a requirement to replace its huge fleet of Starfighters, the Luftwaffe became the largest operator of the Tornado IDS. It has developed the type for service in a number of roles, and belatedly introduced the type to operations over Bosnia.**

*Right: The development of the ECR version resulted in the Luftwaffe possessing arguably the best defence suppression platform in Europe.*

Originally intended as a one-for-one replacement of the F-104 Starfighter, with an initial requirement for around 700 aircraft, the Tornado finally equipped four front-line Luftwaffe squadrons (and one training wing) for a total of 247 new-build aircraft. These came from production Batches 1 to 7. Subsequently, the Luftwaffe acquired 40 ex-Marineflieger aircraft in order to establish a tactical reconnaissance wing.

The first Luftwaffe aircraft to enter service were assigned to the Trinational Tornado Training Establishment at RAF Cottesmore, England which handled type conversion. Germany-based JBG 38, the operational training unit at Jever, acquired its first aircraft in November 1981 (at which time it was known as the Waffenausbildungs-komponente, or WaKo). JBG 31 at Norvenich began conversion from the F-104 in July 1983 to become the first front-line unit, followed by JBG 32 at Lechfeld (July 1984), JBG 33 at Büchel (August 1985) and JBG 34 at Memmingen (October 1987). Plans to form a fifth geschwader, JBG 37, were abandoned when the Luftwaffe cancelled its 35-aircraft Batch 8 order for more ECRs. With the draw-down in forces at the end of the Cold War, a number of Luftwaffe Tornados are held in storage at MADC at Davis-Monthan AFB, Arizona.

Training began at Holloman AFB, New Mexico, in 1996 as a means of overcoming low-level flying restrictions and poor weather in Germany, while the ranges around Goose Bay, Labrador, are extensively used in the summer months for low-level operational training. The initial type conversion will also be transferred to Holloman upon the closure of the TTTE in 1999.

## Strike/attack

When it first entered service, the Luftwaffe Tornado was dedicated to the overland strike/attack role, armed with 1,000-lb (453-kg) Mk 83 bombs or nuclear weapons – the latter being US-owned B57/B61s. The nuclear capability is retained, JBG 33 at Büchel being the strike-assigned unit. Another important weapon developed for the Tornado was the MW-1, a cumbersome dispenser system carried under the fuselage which could deliver a variety of sub-munitions for anti-armour, anti-runway and other area denial missions.

For self defence, Luftwaffe aircraft carry a pair of AIM-9L Sidewinders on the inner wing shoulder pylon, while outboard wing pylons are used for carrying BOZ chaff/flare dispensers and Cerberus ECM jamming pods.

The Luftwaffe Tornado fleet has been gradually updated, beginning with the modification of early aircraft to Batch 5 standards with Mil Std 1553 databus and limited HARM missile capability. Thirty-five new-build aircraft were completed to ECR (Electronic Combat and Reconnaissance) standard, fitted with an infra-red linescan system, forward-looking infra-red and an emitter location system. In the event, the linescan system proved troublesome and was removed, although the underfuselage fairing is retained. The ECR aircraft, which all fly with JBG 32, are now used almost exclusively in the Wild Weasel defence suppression role.

For reconnaissance, the Luftwaffe has replaced its RF-4Es

*Displaying the first camouflage scheme applied to Luftwaffe Tornados, this aircraft served with the TTTE at RAF Cottesmore, which provided type conversion for Italian, German and UK crews.*

***Left:* This ECR is shown carrying four AGM-88 HARM missiles, the type's principal weapon for anti-radar operations. ECRs flew operational missions over Bosnia until November 1996, when they withdrew to leave only reconnaissance aircraft based in Italy.**

***Below:* The Luftwaffe's reconnaissance-dedicated aircraft are standard IDS machines modified to carry the MBB/Aeritalia pod under the centreline. The pod contains two cameras and an infra-red linescan system.**

with the 40 ex-navy Tornados now assigned to Aufklärungsgeschwader 51 at Schleswig-Jagel. These aircraft use the MBB/Aeritalia multi-sensor pod as used by Italy and the Germany's Marineflieger, but are in the process of acquiring a new camera pod which includes the linescan unit taken out of the ECRs. The new pod combines traditional wet film sensors with a video recording system for the IRLS. A new long-range oblique camera pod is also under development for deployment with AG 51.

Both ECRs and reconnaissance aircraft have been active over former Yugoslavia with Einsatzgeschwader 1, a composite unit based at Piacenza in Italy. The first mission was flown on 31 August 1995 and represented the first operational mission by a German aircraft outside of its home nation since the end of World War II.

For the immediate future, the Luftwaffe Tornado fleet is undergoing an update programme, which provides a thorough reworking of the aircraft's systems and adds a Mil Std 1760 weapons interface, steerable FLIR, integrated GPS and a host of other features. The Rafael Litening pod has been procured to provide laser designation capability, while new weapons under development are the Aramis anti-radiation missile and the KEPD-350 Taurus stand-off dispenser.

## Tornado IDS

**This Tornado wears the badge of Jagdbombergeschwader 33, which consists of a Tornado plan-view superimposed on a stylised diving eagle. Based at Büchel, JBG 33 has an overland role which includes the use of B61 nuclear weapons. Most of its aircraft are from Batch 5 production. This aircraft is depicted carrying the bulky MW-1 dispenser which could be used against a variety of area targets.**

### Defences
Active jamming is provided by the Elta/DASA Cerberus pod, the latest version being Cerberus IV. On the opposite outboard wing pylon is the BOZ-100 pod, which provides mechanical countermeasures (chaff and flares). Antennas for the Elettronica ARI 23284 radar warning receiver are mounted in the fin tip.

### Camouflage
The first Luftwaffe Tornados wore a three-tone pattern of greys and greens, but most deliveries were made in a much darker three-tone green scheme. This was ideal camouflage against enemy fighters over Central Europe. In the mid-1990s it was replaced by a light grey scheme although this has not been adopted fleet wide.

### MW-1 dispenser
The MW-1 ejected its sub-munitions sideways in a variety of patterns. Sub-munition options are the MUSA fragmentation bomblet, KB 44 anti-armour bomblet, MIFF delayed action mine and the STABO runway cratering bomb.

### Radar
The AEG-Telefunken radome covers the Texas Instruments radar set. This, in effect, is two radars: one for ground mapping functions to feed the nav/attack system and one for terrain-following. The latter has a small antenna mounted below the main attack radar antenna.

### Cannon
The IDS (and Luftwaffe reconnaissance version) has a pair of IWKA-Mauser 27-mm cannon, each armed with 180 rounds. The ECR version has the cannon removed to make room for internal equipment.

### Fuel
German Tornados do not have the fin tank specified for RAF machines. Total internal capacity is 1,285 Imp gal (5842 litres), usually augmented by two 330-Imp gal (1500-litre) drop tanks on the inner wing pylons. A further pair of tanks can be carried under the fuselage.

*Marineflieger Tornados were originally finished with sea-grey upper surfaces and white undersides, with a relatively high demarcation line. They represented a huge improvement over the F-104.*

# Marineflieger Tornados

**In German naval service, the Tornado has proved a supremely capable maritime attack and reconnaissance aircraft. The fleet remains a potent weapon, although it has been reduced in numbers.**

The Marineflieger acquired the Tornado to replace 135 ageing Starfighters operating in the strike, attack, anti-shipping and reconnaissance roles. Some 112 examples of the more effective (and expensive) Tornado were eventually ordered, including 12 twin-stickers. This allowed each wing to have a nominal strength of 48 aircraft, plus reserves. Few dual-control aircraft were required, since Marineflieger crews were trained as part of the Luftwaffe arrangements at the TTTE.

When it became clear that the Tornado would not be available to replace the first F-104Gs in 1975, the Luftwaffe turned to an interim buy of F-4 Phantoms, but the Marineflieger soldiered on with its F-104Gs, and was thus accorded a high priority when the time came to receive Tornados. MFG 1 became a Tornado unit before the first Luftwaffe wing, JBG 31, converted to the type. Marineflieger training and conversion to the Tornado was remarkably rapid, despite the fact that the air arm had never had any fast-jet backseaters.

The Marineflieger took 16 aircraft from Batch 2 (five twin-stickers), 32 from Batch 3 (no trainers), 48 from Batch 5 (five with dual controls), and 24 from Batch 6 (two trainers). All of the Batch 5 aircraft, and the majority from Batch 6, went to MFG 2.

## Weapons options

Marineflieger F-104Gs were equipped with AS30 ASMs, and a similar, but more modern, missile was required for the new Tornados. The AS34 Kormoran was selected, and a DM469 million order for 350 missiles was placed. Installation of the Kormoran is remarkably straightforward, and the missile was integrated on the last F-104s in service, and on all Marineflieger Tornados. A total of 174 Kormoran Mk 2s was delivered from 1989, together with AGM-88 HARMs. Some 96 Marineflieger Tornados were equipped to carry Sargent Fletcher 28-300 buddy inflight-refuelling pods, 73 of which are believed to have been delivered.

## MFG 1

MFG 1 was originally classed as the 'naval Tornado conversion and weapon training wing' and

*Above: MFG 2's two Staffeln are based at Eggebek. When MFG 1 deactivated, its aircraft were transferred to the Luftwaffe's AG 51, which immediately moved into MFG 1's former base at Schleswig-Jagel.*

*Right: Surprise was expressed in some quarters that MFG 1's identity had not been preserved by redesignating the surviving MFG 2 (illustrated), but in fact both units had formed in the same year (1958) and had enjoyed very similar histories.*

***MFG 1 had flown its final F-104 mission on 29 October 1981, and stood down while aircrew underwent training with the TTTE at Cottesmore. Today, with the disestablishment of MFG 1, MFG 2 has adopted the badge of the former unit.***

formally recommissioned on 2 July 1982, with the delivery of the first four naval Tornados. The Marineflieger's Tornados were externally identical to those delivered to the Luftwaffe, although they wore an entirely different colour scheme, similar to that applied to naval F-104s and even to the Sea Hawks before them.

MFG 1 was declared operational on 1 January 1984, and soon proved that the Tornado was a highly effective replacement for the Starfighter in the maritime environment. Its two-man crew and sophisticated radar made it better in adverse weather or at night, while the advanced navigation system eased the task of finding targets (and indeed the way home) over the featureless sea. The Tornado's long-range, overwater navigation capabilities were demonstrated on 20 July 1984 when two MFG 1 Tornados flew the 980 miles (1580 km) to the Azores, landing with a navigation system error of only 6 ft (1.8 m).

The first naval Tornado wing was initially armed with BL755 CBUs, Kormorans and a range of bombs. Later, it began integration of the AGM-88.

The end of the Cold War forced the navy to sacrifice one of its units and MFG 1 deactivated on 1 January 1994.

## MFG 2

MFG 2 was the fifth and penultimate front-line German Tornado wing, flying its last Starfighter sortie during May 1987, after receiving its first Tornado on 11 September 1986. MFG 2 was equipped with the 48 HARM-capable Batch 5 Tornados, the AGM-88 being supplied to the unit's second Staffel for use in the anti-shipping role. The Batch 5 naval Tornados were delivered in a new, two-tone wraparound disruptive camouflage. The first Staffel continues to have a reconnaissance role, using 26 MBB Aeritalia reconnaissance pods. This task formerly included flying a daily 'Eastern Express' reconnaissance run around the Baltic to monitor and photograph shipping.

That MFG 2 survived subsequent defence cuts was hardly surprising. The unit fulfilled the same anti-shipping role as MFG 1, and its two Staffeln respectively performed the additional roles of tactical reconnaissance and HARM-shooting, making the wing considerably more versatile than the previous unit.

# Tornado IDS

**'Eastern Express' sorties provided MFG 2 with many opportunities to see 'enemy' aircraft, since they were sometimes intercepted over international waters by Poland-based Russian Su-27s, and by MiG-29s based in East Germany. With the dissolution of MFG 1, MFG 2 was increased in size, but subsequent force draw downs have reduced it to about 49 Tornados.**

**HARM capability**
Fifth-batch Tornados feature a number of avionics upgrades, not least the capability to employ AGM-88 HARMs. The upgrades also include a MIL-1553B databus, improved RWR and active ECM. HARM is employed by MFG 2's second Staffel, alongside the Kormoran 2, while the first Staffel concentrates on combining tactical reconnaissance with Kormoran 2 AShM operations.

**MBB Kormoran 2**
Kormoran 2 is a digital version of the missile, with increased internal volume allowing a heavier warhead compared to the original, which weighed 364 lb (165 kg). A slightly larger-boost motor increases range from 18 to 22 miles (30 to 35 km), while the improved electronics give better ECCM capabilities and allow simpler launch procedures, making multiple missile launches a viable proposition.

**Geschwader badges**
The MFG 2 badge initially consisted of a weapons sight, overlaid with the numeral '2', as shown on this aircraft. MFG 2 now uses the former MFG 1 badge of a sea eagle striking the water.

**Inflight refuelling**
The Tornado IDS can be equipped with a retractable inflight-refuelling probe, faired into the starboard side of the fuselage alongside the cockpit. The probe allows Marineflieger aircraft to 'buddy' refuel from other Tornados or, alternatively, from hose-equipped tankers.

**Outer pylons**
Marineflieger aircraft follow the standard Tornado outer pylon fit, with a chaff/flare pod to port, in this case BOZ-100, and an ECM pod to starboard, here a Cerberus pod.

# Tornado ADV Development

A fully-armed F.Mk 2 poses for the photographer, demonstrating the clean lines that helped to make the Tornado ADV, Britain's choice for a long-range 'bomber destroyer'. It will, however, eventually be replaced by the Eurofighter.

**Designed to defend Britain from unescorted Soviet bombers such as the Tu-22M, the Tornado ADV has acquitted itself well. However, with the end of the Cold War and the advent of long-range bomber-escorts, this Tornado variant now finds itself to be overspecialised for its changing role.**

Although an interception capability was one of the requirements put forward for the MRCA, no air force contemplated using the ground attack Tornado IDS for point defence. It was the UK alone which elected to proceed with the development of an Air Defence Variant (ADV) optimised for air-to-air combat. Whereas in continental Europe the onus was on fast, agile interceptors to operate on a central European battlefield, Britain being an island required another type of aircraft. The main danger to Britain was seen as coming from long-range bombers attacking UK targets with cruise missiles and so an all-weather interceptor, able to track and engage multiple targets, was needed. The use of beyond visual range air-to-air missiles was deemed to be the most appropriate way of downing Soviet aircraft.

It was vitally important that the UK operated a fighter capable of stopping the Soviets far away from British shores as it was estimated that, in the event of war, 40 per cent of NATO's air power would congregate in the UK. RAF Strike Command decided upon a policy of all-round, far-reaching air defence with long-legged interceptors, tankers to further increase range, AEW aircraft to cover the Iceland-Faroes-UK gap and ground radars on the western coast. Central to all these factors would be the Tornado ADV.

During 1976 it was announced that 165 of the 385 Tornados required by the RAF would be of the ADV version, having 80 per cent commonality with the IDS. One of the main changes was a 4-ft 5½-in (1.36-m) longer fuselage, partly resulting from a more pointed radome, but mainly due to an extra bay added forward of the wings. With its new length, the aircraft could accommodate four BAe SkyFlash radar-guided AAMs under the fuselage (the front pair semi-recessed). Two (and later four) AIM-9L Sidewinders were to be attached to the sides of the inboard wing pylons, although the outer hardpoints were not used.

*Aircraft A01 is seen here, unpainted, at the Warton factory, just prior to roll-out in August 1979. The aircraft flew soon after, performing well in testing and in a number of mock sorties.*

Three prototype Tornado ADVs were added to the first batch of Tornado IDSs and the first (ZA254) flew at Warton on 27 October 1979. The aircraft was fitted with dummy SkyFlashes from the outset and managed to reach Mach 1 on its first flight. Within a week, the aircraft had accumulated 8¼ flying hours, including an airborne refuelling and a night landing. Supersonic acceleration was found to be better than in the IDS due to the improved shape of the fuselage, but the more forward centre of gravity demanded extra elevator angle at lift-off.

ZA267 joined the programme on 18 July 1980, introducing a main computer and associated cockpit TV displays. Assigned to weapons development, '267 was a dual-control Tornado. The third aircraft to fly was ZA283, on 18 November 1980.

Assisted by earlier trials of IDS Tornados, ZA254 had, by mid-

***ZA283, the third Tornado ADV prototype, was the first to receive the overall grey scheme, similar to that of RAF Phantoms and Lightnings. It was also the first aircraft to receive the Foxhunter radar and flew with it on 17 June 1981. It then went on to fly test missions against Lightnings and other Tornado targets.***

*Aircraft ZA254 spent many years undergoing flight-testing before it was placed as a gate guardian at RAF Coningsby. Here, it can be seen carrying a pair of instrumentation-filled Sky Shadow pods for use in association with SkyFlash firing trials.*

*The Tornado ADV was designed to be compatible with BAe's SkyFlash missile, a derivative of the AIM-7E-2 Sparrow, but with improved seeker and fuse. The weapon entered service on the Phantom in 1978 and has a range of 31 miles (50 km). Aircraft ZA283 was the first ADV to fire the SkyFlash.*

1980, been able to demonstrate an IAS (indicated air speed) of 800 kt (920 mph; 1480 km/h) at 2,000 ft (610 m). This was of significance as the speed of most other modern combat aircraft reduces to 700-750 kt (806-864 mph; 1297-1390 km/h) at this height, therefore giving the ADV an edge over a potential opponent. Early in 1982, the same aircraft flew a simulated CAP sortie involving a 2-hour 20-minute loiter at a distance of 375 miles (604 km) from base. This feat was achieved with an extra pair of 330-Imp gal (1500-litre) tanks as used on the IDS, and not the 495-Imp gal (2250-litre) drop tanks as fitted to the definitive interceptor Tornado. West German and Italian Tornados (until Italy's recent loan of RAF ADVs) were unable to emulate this feat for two reasons: RAF IDS and ADV Tornados have an extra fuel tank inside the fin, holding 121 Imp gal (551 litres), and the additional fuselage length of the ADV enables it to be fitted with an extra internal tank holding 165 Imp gal (750 litres). The standard internal fuel capacity of German and Italian IDS aircraft is 1,340 Imp gal (6092 litres).

## Early problems

The Tornado's turbofan engines are fuel-efficient at low level, but the trade-off is that, at medium and high levels, thrust is reduced in comparison with a turbojet. Similarly, if forced into close combat, a mission for which it was not designed, the ADV finds itself somewhat outclassed by aircraft which have been designed for the task. Off the coast of Iceland, such a possibility seemed remote until the advent of the long-range bomber escort Su-27 'Flanker' family.

Realising that the Tornado might well have to 'mix it' with highly capable opponents, the RAF commissioned a twin-dome combat simulator which became operational at the main ADV base of Coningsby. BAe also developed a new control column grip containing all the switches necessary for close combat.

Fighter Tornados have the same wing sweep range as their bomber compatriots (25-67°), except that later production aircraft introduced automatic sweep selection to suit flight conditions. This facility was retrofitted to the software of earlier machines.

Because of the fact that the centre of gravity was further forward, the 'nibs' (inboard, non-moving leading edges) of the wings have their sweep increased from 60 to 67°. Additionally, they include the forward antennas for a Marconi radar warning receiver, the rear component of which is mounted on the tailfin trailing edge. In contrast to the 'clip-on' refuelling probe on the starboard side of the IDS's forward fuselage, the ADV has a fully retractable unit on the port side.

## Into service

The first of the ADVs reached the RAF in 1984 when 16 F.Mk 2s, as they were now designated, served with No. 229 OCU. These aircraft only flew an average of 250 hours each and were initially delivered without radar, with steel ballast instead making up the weight. They were eventually placed in storage and cannibalised for spares. There was a plan to upgrade these ADVs to F.Mk 2A standard, which would have given the aircraft F.Mk 3 capability, but without that aircraft's new engine.

First flying on 20 November 1985, the F.Mk 3 replaced the F.Mk 2 on the production line and introduced a host of improvements, most notably the incorporation of the new RB.199 Mk 104 engine. This had a 14-in (36 cm) extension to the afterburner section and incorporated a DECU 500 digital engine control. This was the world's first example of a full-authority digital engine control (FADEC) unit and gave precise computer controls to the engines, while also offering improved fault diagnosis and engine monitoring. These modifications gave a 10 per cent increase in combat thrust and reduced afterburning fuel consumption by 4 per cent. The new engine installation can be noted by the fact that the trailing edge of the fin below the rudder was extended aft, following the line of the rudder's trailing edge down to the jetpipes. On earlier aircraft, it cut forward in a scallop.

Several avionics upgrades including those to the inertial navigation system, and new systems such as the Automatic Manoeuvre Device System (AMDS) were also added, as was provision for two more AIM-9 Sidewinders. The F.Mk 3 became operational in 1989 and, since then, has undergone a series of further upgrades.

*This Tornado F.Mk 3 demonstrates the extended jetpipe associated with the more powerful Mk 104 engine and the filled-in finroot fairing, both of which distinguish it from its Tornado F.Mk 2 predecessor.*

*This classic view of one of the RAF's initial Tornado F.Mk 2s was taken from the rear ramp of an RAF Hercules. The semi-recessed positioning of the forward BAe SkyFlash missiles is well demonstrated.*

*Aircraft from the Coningsby Wing pose for the camera. In the foreground is an aircraft from the F.3 OEU trials unit, while behind is a Tornado from the OCU, No. 56(R) Squadron. With the disbandment of No. 29 Squadron, the only front-line resident became now No. 5 Squadron (background).*

# ADV operators

**Apart from its parent service – the RAF – the ADV has only been sold to Saudi Arabia and leased by Italy. Oman ordered eight, but cancelled the purchase in favour of cheaper Hawks.**

## United Kingdom – Royal Air Force

After the three Tornado ADV prototypes, BAe Warton assembled 18 F.Mk 2s and 152 F.Mk 3s for the RAF, including eight aircraft ordered by Oman but not delivered. They equipped a training unit and seven front-line squadrons, while a handful were allocated to trials establishments.

**229 OCU/No. 65 Squadron/ No. 56 (Reserve Squadron):**
In November 1984, 229 Operational Conversion Unit at RAF Coningsby received the first of a batch of 16 Tornado F.Mk 2s to begin the task of training crews (far right). F.Mk 2s served with the unit until 1988, by which time the F.Mk 3 was in full OCU service, having first arrived in late 1986. On 1 January 1987, the OCU assumed the 'shadow' identity of No. 65 Squadron, and on 1 July 1992 was renumbered as No. 56 (Reserve) Squadron. The unit continues to train ADV crews, including those of Italy. In preparation for Eurofighter deliveries to Coningsby, the OCU has moved to Leuchars.

**Coningsby Wing:**
No. 29 Squadron was the first front-line unit, officially reforming on 1 April 1987 as an F.Mk 3 squadron. Completing the Coningsby line-up was No. 5 Squadron (below right), which formally stood up in its new guise on 1 January 1988. When budget cuts demanded that one unit be lost, No. 29 was chosen, disbanding on 31 March 1999, No. 5 following in 2003.

**Leeming Wing:**
The North Yorkshire base was the second to receive Tornado F.Mk 3s, beginning with No. 11 Squadron (below, officially formed 1 July 1988). On 1 November 1988, No. 23 Squadron was formed, and No. 25 Squadron completed the wing on 1 October 1989. As part of the Options for Change defence review, No. 23 was disbanded on 28 February 1994.

**Leuchars Wing:**
On 23 September 1989, No. 43 Squadron officially completed its transition from the Phantom, followed by No. 111 Squadron on 1 May 1990. Leuchars is due to be the final base to transition to the Eurofighter.

**No. 1435 Flight:**
Four Tornado F.Mk 3s took over the Falklands air defence commitment from Phantoms in July 1992. The tasking is manned on rotation from UK-based squadrons.

**Other units:**
A number of Tornado F.Mk 2/3s has been used for test purposes. Four are assigned to the Coningsby-based F.3 Operational Evaluation Unit, which was formed on 1 April 1987 and carries out test work in support of the front-line force. More academic work has been undertaken by aircraft assigned to DERA, the most notable being F.Mk 2 ZD902 – known as TIARA – which tests new fighter technology. Between 1988 and 1990 the Empire Test Pilots School operated a single F.Mk 2.

## Saudi Arabia – Royal Saudi Air Force

When Oman cancelled its order for eight Tornado ADVs (placed on 14 August 1985), it was left to Saudi Arabia to become the only overseas customer for the type. The order was placed on 26 September 1985, soon after the Omani deal was struck, and covered 24 ADVs to equip two fighter squadrons. The ADV buy was part of the massive Al Yamamah acquisition programme which also covered the Tornado IDS, Hawk, PC-9 and Jetstream. To ensure delivery within the specified timescale, the Saudi aircraft were taken from RAF production (made good in later production batches), and the first was delivered to Dhahran on 9 February 1989 to begin the equipment of No. 29 Squadron. This unit formally stood up with its new type on 20 March, and all 12 allocated aircraft were delivered by 20 September.

Deliveries of the second batch of 12 ADVs allowed the formation of No. 34 Squadron, also at Dhahran. The first aircraft was received on 14 November 1989, and all had been delivered by mid-1990. However, attempts to operate two squadrons with just 12 aircraft each and no spares proved to be too ambitious, and No. 34 Squadron was absorbed into No. 29, although the numberplate remained as a cadre in the senior unit. No. 29 Squadron was active in Operation Desert Storm, joining RAF Tornado F.Mk 3s in flying combat air patrols along Saudi Arabia's borders with Kuwait and Iraq.

***Saudi Tornado crews trained alongside those of the RAF at Coningsby. Included in the Saudi buy were six twin-stick aircraft. These retain full combat capability but have rudimentary flying controls in the rear cockpit.***

A further batch of 36 Tornado ADVs formed part of the follow-on Al Yamamah II deal at the time of its initial agreement in July 1988. However, by the time the contract was signed in May 1993 the ADV had been dropped from the shopping list, although 48 more IDS aircraft were supplied. The main factor in the deletion of the ADV was the ready availability of F-15C Eagles, which proved to be far better suited to Saudi Arabia's air defence needs than the long-range, maritime air defence optimised ADV.

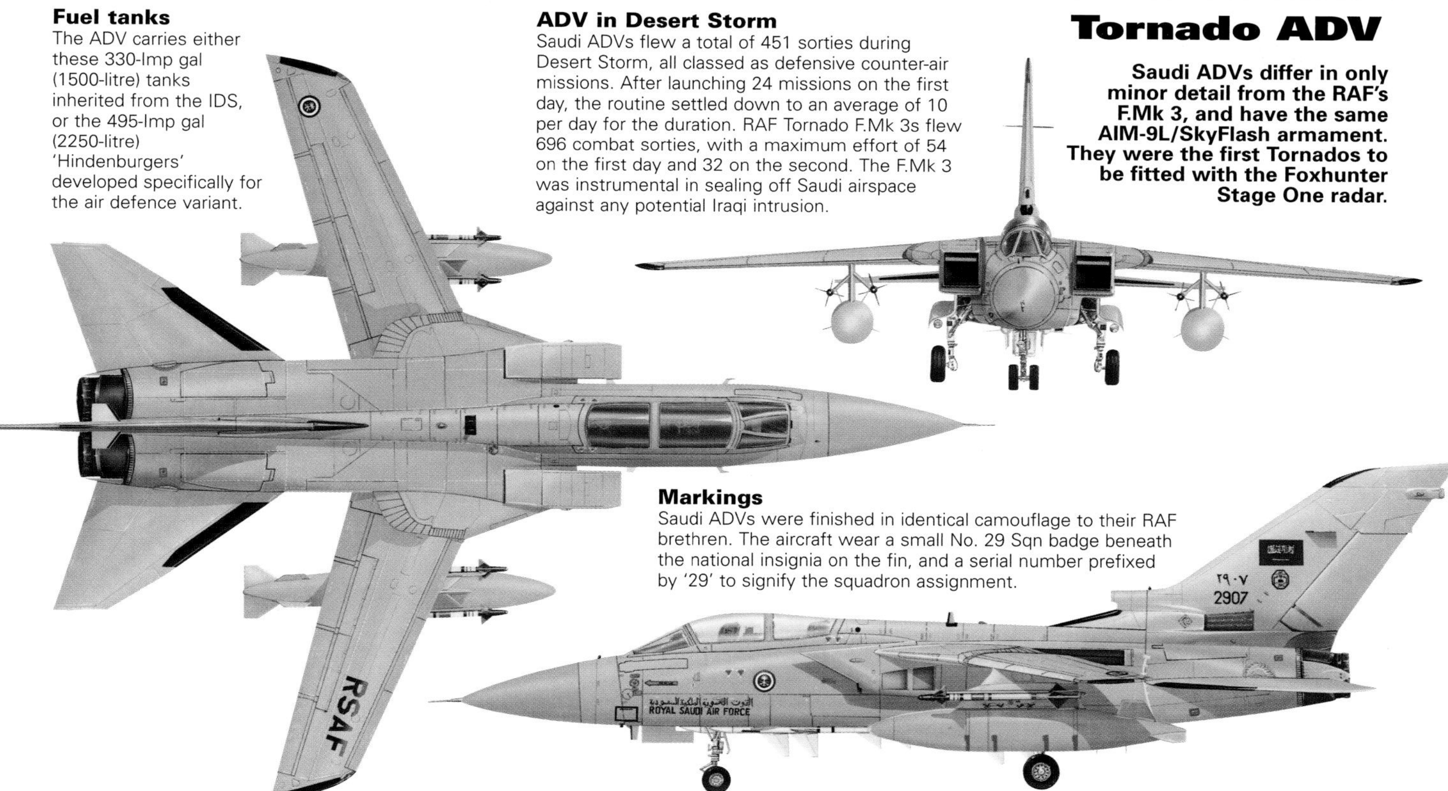


## Tornado ADV

**Saudi ADVs differ in only minor detail from the RAF's F.Mk 3, and have the same AIM-9L/SkyFlash armament. They were the first Tornados to be fitted with the Foxhunter Stage One radar.**

**Fuel tanks**
The ADV carries either these 330-Imp gal (1500-litre) tanks inherited from the IDS, or the 495-Imp gal (2250-litre) 'Hindenburgers' developed specifically for the air defence variant.

**ADV in Desert Storm**
Saudi ADVs flew a total of 451 sorties during Desert Storm, all classed as defensive counter-air missions. After launching 24 missions on the first day, the routine settled down to an average of 10 per day for the duration. RAF Tornado F.Mk 3s flew 696 combat sorties, with a maximum effort of 54 on the first day and 32 on the second. The F.Mk 3 was instrumental in sealing off Saudi airspace against any potential Iraqi intrusion.

**Markings**
Saudi ADVs were finished in identical camouflage to their RAF brethren. The aircraft wear a small No. 29 Sqn badge beneath the national insignia on the fin, and a serial number prefixed by '29' to signify the squadron assignment.

## Italy – Aeronautica Militare Italiana (AMI)

As its F-104S interceptor force grew more obsolete, and introduction of the Eurofighter replacement slipped, Italy faced a yawning 'fighter gap'. To partially bridge this deficiency, the AMI signed on 17 November 1993 to lease 24 surplus RAF F.Mk 3s for five years (with a further five-year option). Under the agreement the aircraft remained RAF property and, if required, could be recalled to UK service at short notice. The first 12 aircraft were handed over from July 1995, and were used to replace the F-104S Starfighters of the 12° Gruppo Caccia Intercettori, part of the 36° Stormo at Gioia del Colle. The second batch went to the 21° Gruppo Caccia Intercettori at Novara/Cameri, another former F-104S squadron and part of the 53° Stormo. The 21° Gruppo was subsequently moved to Gioia and became part of the 36° Stormo to group all the F.Mk 3s at one base (which also accommodates IDS aircraft). The Italian F.Mk 3s flew from this base during Allied Force (illustrated). They will return to the UK at the end of the lease, to be replaced by leased F-16s.

# Rockwell B-1

## The early 'Bones'

**One of the most controversial modern warplanes, the B-1A was set to give the USAF an unprecedented strike capability. Despite its prowess, political wranglings ensured its untimely cancellation.**

***Above:** 74-0158 touches down at Edwards AFB at the end of its inaugural flight. It was to be exactly one month before the aircraft flew again, on 23 January 1975. The first aircraft was the general aerodynamic and performance test vehicle.*

***Top:** The four B-1As continued to fly on the Bomber Penetration Evaluation programme until April 1981. The No. 3 aircraft, shown here, retired from flying on 15 April, having logged more than 829 hours in 138 sorties, the greatest number of all the four prototypes.*

The B-52 was developed in a great hurry in the early 1950s for service with what was then Strategic Air Command. The aircraft was expected to be progressively withdrawn from service from 1961 or 1962. The replacement was planned to be either the WS (Weapon System)-110 CPB or the WS-125 NPB. The CPB was to be a Chemically-Powered Bomber, so-called because it was to burn not ordinary kerosene, but higher-energy 'zip fuel' in order to cruise at Mach 3 at very high altitudes. The NPB was to be a Nuclear-Powered Bomber, slow but with essentially unlimited range and thus able to attack any target from any direction.

In the event, the NPB was never built, the high-energy fuel was abandoned, and all that was left on the drawing board were two giant 2,000-mph (3220-km/h) prototype XB-70 Valkyries, the first of which flew in 1964.

Undeniably impressive, these aircraft were no longer viable when it was recognised that ICBMs could hit fixed targets with greater speed and reliability. Aircraft deemed as suitable successors included modified B-52s, the B-58 and the FB-111, but all failed to make the grade.Many unclassified sources are available describing the 50-plus projects proposed by 14 US aerospace firms from 1960 to fill the need for a new long-range bomber. By 1964, the requirement had been formalised as the Advanced Manned Strategic Aircraft (AMSA).

### B-1 genesis

Despite arguments over the need, and fights over the budget, in April 1969 AMSA crystallised into a USAF programme as the B-1. RFPs (Requests for Proposals) were issued seven months later, and on 5 June 1970, Secretary of the USAF Robert C. Seamans Jr announced that the B-1 would be built by North American Rockwell. The engine award went to General Electric, with an augmented turbofan designated F101-100.

The original programme comprised one ground- and three flight-test aircraft, plus 27 engines. A fourth prototype was ordered in the FY1976 budget, built virtually to production standard. Some 240 production aircraft were planned, with initial operational capability with SAC scheduled for 1979.

The programme slipped slightly. First flight had been due in April 1974, but in fact the first B-1 flight article (74-0158) was rolled out from USAF Plant 42 at Palmdale, California, on 26 October of that year. It made its first flight on 23 December and landed at Edwards AFB, home of the Air Force Flight Test Center. The crew comprised Rockwell test pilot Charlie C. Bock Jr, Colonel Emil 'Ted' Sturmthal and engineer Richard Abrams. The No. 3 aircraft (74-0160, the avionics testbed) flew on 26 March 1976. The second B-1 (74-0159) was initially used for static structural testing, and so did not fly until 14 June 1976. The considerably modified No. 4 aircraft (76-0174) first flew on 14 February 1979.

Even though it was calculated that the B-1 would a heat-soak at Mach 2 temperatures, the ruling material throughout the structure could be aluminium, just as in Concorde. Originally, it had been hoped that Mach 1.2 could be sustained during low-level penetration, but this target was lowered to about 650 mph (1046 km/h), or Mach 0.85, in order to give the crew more time to identify targets. This greatly eased the problem of turbulence, and also enabled the proportion of aluminium alloys to be increased.

About 150,000 lb (68 tonnes) of fuel could be housed in eight integral tanks, one in each outer

*SAC's bomber trio formates off the boom of a KC-135 tanker. The B-1A featured the speed and terrain-following ability of the FB-111, while exhibiting load-carrying capability and range performance similar to those of the B-52.*

*Left: The fourth aircraft differed from the first three in being fitted with ejection seats in place of the escape module, a fact denoted by the lack of 'elephant ears'. Inflight refuelling formed an important part of the trials programme.*

*Below left: The B-1A's only appearance outside the USA was in September 1982 when the No. 4 aircraft attended the air show at Farnborough, UK.*

wing and the rest in the fuselage. Weapons were to be carried in three 15-ft (4.6-m) fuselage bays; each could house about 25,000 lb (11340 kg) of nuclear or conventional weapons, or eight AGM-69A SRAMs (Short-Range Attack Missiles) on a rotary launcher. No provision was made for defensive armament, apart from comprehensive electronic warfare systems managed by the DSO.

On the whole, the B-1 flight test programme went according to plan. Numerous modifications and additional equipment were introduced, and throughout the programme the avionics integration contractor, Boeing Aerospace, strove to resolve problems in what was probably the most complex avionics installation ever to fly at that time.

One of the B-1's major hurdles, an IOT&E (Initial Operational Test & Evaluation) that simulated SAC combat missions, was successfully passed in September 1976. The Phase I flight test programme was completed on 30 September 1976, with all test objectives met. On 2 December 1976 the DoD and USAF jointly announced that the B-1 would go into production. Contracts had been placed for the first three aircraft and for eight Block 2 aircraft, and funds were authorised for production tooling.

Apart from the largely unresolved question of the avionics, the only cloud on the horizon appeared to be that of cost escalation. In 1970 the unit price was $40 million and, by 1972, allowing for RDT&E (research, development, test and engineering), this had reached $45.6 million. By 1975, however, the unit figure had risen to just over $70 million.

These figures clearly worried the new president, Jimmy Carter, who took office on 20 January 1977. On 30 June 1977, the last day of FY77, in his regular press conference, he announced, "My decision is that we should not continue with deployment of the B-1, and I am directing that we discontinue plans for production of this weapons system." He expressed the view that ICBMs, SLBMs (Submarine-Launched Ballistic Missiles) and modernised B-52s armed with ALCMs would provide adequate defence capability.

The decision to cancel the B-1A was made by the new president based on principle (Carter genuinely hoped to reduce the arms race) and on cost (then, as now, the price tag on a new bomber was an easy target for those in all areas of society who wanted resources directed elsewhere).

## Resurrection

Despite the cancellation of the production programme, the Carter administration permitted flight-testing to continue, together with many related RDT&E efforts. The greatest effort continued to be focused on the avionics, particularly the defensive system, but GE never ceased to develop the F101 engine, many other contractors kept their engineering teams intact and working on the B-1, and USAF facilities continued to give direct B-1 support.

The need to reduce RCS (radar cross-section) became increasingly important, achieved by paying the most careful attention to achieving a smooth unbroken external surface without cracks or badly-fitting joints, and by covering the exterior skin with RAM (radar-absorbent material), of which several varieties were giving promising results. What became known as 'stealth' design grew rapidly in importance, and in 1978, formal work began on a 'black' (highly classified) programme, loosely called the ATB (Advanced Technology Bomber). This programme eventually resulted in the B-2.

Cancellation of the production B-1 did not terminate flying of the prototypes. Less than a month after the decision was taken, on 28 July 1977, the No. 3 aircraft became the first to launch a SRAM. This prototype was later modified with an advanced ECM system and with DBS (Doppler-Beam Sharpening) added to the forward-looking radar. The second aircraft, which only began flying in June 1976, continued with No. 1 to push up the Mach scale. The first aircraft had reached Mach 2 in April 1976, and after completing its tests, was placed in storage in 1978. The No. 2 prototype continued with air-loads testing and engine/inlet evaluation, and on 5 October 1978 reached Mach 2.22, the highest speed attained by any B-1. The No. 4 aircraft flew for the first time long after the cancellation of the B-1, and in 70 flights (totalling 378 hours) carried out many valuable tests on both offensive and defensive avionics before closing the prototype flight programme on 30 April 1981. The four aircraft were stored at Edwards in a near-airworthy condition, having logged 1,895 hours in 347 flights.

*Seen at Edwards AFB in 1976 are the first three B-1A prototypes during Phase 1 of flight-testing. This included evaluation of flying qualities, structural loading and ECM equipment.*

# B-1B Lancer

At the heart of the re-roling of the B-1B was the Conventional Munitions Upgrade Program (CMUP). This B-1B from the 28th Air Expeditionary Wing was heading out on a combat mission against al Qaeda and Taliban forces in Afghanistan, in support of Operation Enduring Freedom during December 2001.

**In recent years the B-1B has moved to the forefront of conventional warfare. Its ability to carry unrivalled internal ordnance gives an added flexibility to combat operations never before seen.**

Following the end of the Cold War, military planners began to appreciate that there was a need for platforms capable of responding to smaller, and perhaps multiple, regional conflicts, as opposed to a major European war. Furthermore, it was apparent that the conventional bomber force was ill- prepared to meet all the current contingencies.

To better suit the B-1B to the conventional role, the Air Force initiated the Conventional Munitions Upgrade Program (CMUP), in 1993, designed to expand the B-1's lethality, survivability and maintainability as a conventional bomber.

Over the past few years, conventional B-1Bs have played a major role in quick-response deployments to Korea, Guam and the Persian Gulf, not to mention the recent NATO Yugoslavian operations and the US attacks on Afghanistan.

While seeing its combat debut in Operation Desert Fox in December 1998, the B-1B's true value as a conventional bomber was demonstrated in Operation Allied Force, during which B-1Bs of the 37th BS and 77th BS deployed to RAF Fairford, England, flew over 100 combat sorties and dropped more than 5,000 Mk 82 500-lb (227-kg) general purpose iron bombs against a variety of Yugoslavian targets. These B-1Bs were all part of the Block D upgrade currently being fielded by the Air Force, which brings to the platform improved communications, a much-needed GBU-31 Joint Direct Attack Munition (JDAM) capability and improved self-defence measures with the addition of the ALE-50 towed decoy.

## Conventional munitions

All B-1Bs existing prior to the CMUP were designated as Block A models. Block B saw the addition of an improved synthetic aperture radar and minor modifications to the Defensive Countermeasures System. The Block B upgrade was completed and fielded in 1995.

The next modification came in the Block C, upgrading the B-1B to deliver cluster bombs such as the CBU-87B/B Combined Effects Munitions, the CBU-89 area denial munition and the CBU-97 Sensor Fuzed Weapons. Conversion of the first Block C began in October 1996 and full operational capability (FOC) followed in September 1997. Using all three bays, the Block C configuration can carry a total of 30 CBUs per bomber.

The Block D upgrade, which began development in 1995, integrates a near-precision conventional munitions delivery capability for guided weapons such as the GBU-31 JDAM. JDAMs are carried by the B-1B's eight-capacity Conventional Rotary Launcher, one launcher per bay, for a total of 24 JDAMs. The first operational Block D versions reached Ellsworth AFB in November 1998. Key to this Block upgrade was the addition of the MIL STD 1760 electrical interconnect system (a standard 'smart weapons' interface), a communications upgrade to enhance security, and a Global

Above: A 184th Bomb Wing B-1B refuels over France. During Allied Force all B-1B missions involved tanking. The decision to forward-deploy the B-1B was welcomed by crews who still undertook seven-hour missions, most of which were at night.

Below: Most B-1B missions are flown by two-ship formations, although a number of four-ship formations were employed during Allied Force, with each aircraft striking multiple targets.

*Left: B-1Bs continue to employ weapons and defensive systems in new and innovative ways, while also learning to operate in two-ship formations and with other Air Force and Navy assets.*

*Below: The B-1B stood down from its nuclear role on 27 July 1991. What little remains of the USAF nuclear mission is now solely performed by the B-52H Stratofortress and the B-2A Spirit.*

Positioning System (GPS) for both aircraft and weapons navigation. Another enhancement of the Block D upgrade is the addition of the ALE-50 Towed Decoy System. This provides protection against RF threats by 'seducing' RF-guided missiles away from the host aircraft. The ALE-50 is deemed an interim capability until the full-up Block F capability can be fielded with the improved ALE-55. Block D initial operational capability (IOC) was achieved in December 1998, but not in time for Block D B-1Bs to participate in Desert Fox. All B-1Bs were modified to the Block D JDAM standard by early 2001, with the TDS installation to be completed by 2004.

### Block E Upgrades

The Block E upgrade will modify the existing Avionics Control Units for controls and displays, guidance and navigation, weapons delivery, critical resources and terrain-following. A primary objective is to allow the B-1B to employ up to three different weapons systems (one per bay) on a single sortie. Two weapons modifications included in the Block E configuration will further enhance the B-1B's conventional lethality. Wind Corrected Munitions Dispensers (WCMDs) will improve high-altitude accuracy of cluster bomb units by using GPS position updates to provide inertial guidance corrections for ballistic and wind errors after release. The B-1B's suite of weapons will also see the addition of stand-off precision weapons capability through the deployment of the 1,000-lb (454-kg) AGM-154 Joint Stand-Off Weapon (JSOW) and the stealthy AGM-158A Joint Air-to-Surface Strike Missile (JASSM). These long-range precision strike capabilities are significant because they add a 'built-in' self-defence capability since the B-1Bs are launching from well outside the enemy threat envelope. IOC for Block E B-1B capability was slated for 2003.

Block F represents the defensive systems upgrade. For this, all but nine of the ALQ-161A's 109 Line Replacement Units will be removed, with the remaining units re-used for the Band C/D antenna and flare/chaff dispenser system. To enhance situational awareness, the ALR-56M RWR will be added, as well as an upgraded processor. Also added as part of the Block F upgrade will be the Integrated Defense Electronic Countermeasures/RF Countermeasures System which includes the ALQ-214 radio frequency countermeasures subsystem, the Integrated Multi-Platform Launch Controller and dual-capable launcher, and the ALE-55 Fibre-Optic Towed Decoy. The Block F upgrade will reduce the weight of the B-1B by approximately 4,000 lb (1814 kg). With EMD approved in 1997, a final production decision was expected in March 2002. While IOC was scheduled for 2003, modification of the entire fleet to Block F standards is not expected until 2009 and not all aircraft may be modified. From August 2002, despite its proven capabilities, the B-1B fleet began to retire aircraft, heading towards a planned total of 60 aircraft. However, by early 2004 there were calls to bring some of the 33 retired aircraft back into service.

### 'Bone' at war

Although deployed and ready to support the near-attack against Iraq in November 1998, the B-1B would have to wait another month for its chance to enter combat. Forward-deployed in Oman in November were four B-1Bs, two each from Ellsworth AFB and Dyess AFB; two additional B-1Bs were diverted inflight at the last minute when President Clinton cancelled the strikes.

Operation Desert Fox saw the B-1B make its combat debut on 17 December 1998, when two of the six deployed Block C B-1Bs attacked Iraqi targets with Mk 82 bombs from approximately 20,000 ft (6100 m). Flying six-hour, night-time missions, each B-1B carried a total of 63 bombs. B-1Bs flying in Desert Fox flew a total of six missions and dropped some 126,000 lb (57154 kg) of ordnance, all in the form of Mk 82s.

Operation Allied Force began on 24 March 1999, with B-1Bs flying their first missions out of RAF Fairford, beginning 1 April, just 14 hours after the first bombers arrived in theatre. Initial strikes were against Serbian army staging areas in Kosovo. All B-1Bs participating originated from Ellsworth AFB's 28th BW. In total, B-1Bs launched over 100 combat sorties and amassed over 700 flight hours in Allied Force, with all missions seeing the bomber loaded with 84 Mk 82 bombs and some CBUs, although the latter were not dropped. Mission Capable rates were in the range of 91 per cent.

During the initial phase of Operation Enduring Freedom, directed against the Taliban and al Qaeda terrorist networks, and unleashed upon Afghanistan on the night of 7 October 2001, Diego Garcia-based B-1Bs and B-52Hs accounted for the greatest amount of tonnage dropped.

With the onset of Operation Iraqi Freedom in 2003, the B-1B again returned tocombat, once more achieving excellent results, with individual aircraft attacking multiple targets and even loitering while being assigned new targets by other platforms.

*Above: The ALE-55 Fibre-Optic Towed Decoy, also slated for the Boeing Super Hornet, became operational very recently. The Block F upgrade will reduce the number of defensive system 'black boxes' from 120 to 34.*

*Right: A 28th Air Expeditionary Wing B-1B formates on a KC-10A on its way to Afghanistan. The 'Bone' spearheaded attacks against Afghan air defences and command and control centres.*

# Saab Draken Development

**Sweden's double-delta Draken was a revolutionary concept, and typical of Saab's bold and independent approach to fighter design. First flown in the mid-1950s, the aircraft remains in front-line service with Austria and Finland more than 40 years later.**

*Above: A pair of J 35Ds of F13 wing, Swedish air force, presents the characteristic side-view and wing planform of the Draken. The 35D introduced the more powerful licence-built RM6C (Avon 300 series), with a Flygmotor afterburner.*

*Right: This line-up comprises the three prototypes, identifiable by a tiny square window behind the main canopy, and the unique tailcone/nozzle arrangement of the imported Avon 200 series engine. The third aircraft in the line-up is the first J 35A.*

There can be little doubt that if (for example) a British manufacturer had designed the Draken, production would have been numbered in thousands rather than hundreds, and it would have seen widespread service as the ideal, low-cost Hawker Hunter replacement. In reality, Sweden's restrictive export policy limited overseas marketing to a few trusted countries.

The fact is that, in the mid-1950s, the Swedish air force (like that of France) saw the air defence problem in proper perspective, and demanded large numbers of affordable fighters, whereas the UK planned massive aircraft to carry heavy, long-range guided missiles that never materialised. While the UK fell back on the twin-engined English Electric Lightning, an operational derivative of the P.1 aerodynamic research aircraft, Sweden took afterburner development to new limits and demonstrated to the world what could be achieved with a well-designed single-engined fighter. If only around 600 were built, this was no reflection on the merits of the basic concept: in terms of an effective, affordable multi-role fighter, Sweden had undoubtedly got it right. Only politics stood in the way of the type's success in the marketplace.

## Draken origins

The story of the Draken (dragon) dates back to 1949, when the Flygvapen (Swedish air force) issued a draft operational requirement for an interceptor to succeed the Saab J29 'Flying Barrel' and provide air defence against bombers flying at near-sonic speeds. It was felt at that stage that it would be sufficient if the new fighter had a level flight speed of Mach 1.4-1.5, although this requirement was later increased to Mach 1.7-1.8. To put this early work into perspective, the J29 – Europe's first swept-wing fighter – had flown only in the previous year (the maiden flight took place on 1 September 1948) and there was no swept-wing fighter in full operational service anywhere in the world. The North American F-86 Sabre and Mikoyan-Gurevich MiG-15 were just beginning to be delivered to their first units and here was the Swedish air force demanding a speed increase of no less than 50 per cent over these types.

*Right: Seen at their Norrköping base, these J 35As of F13 were photographed shortly after the wing became the first to become operational on the Draken in March 1960.*

*Below: The development of the two-seat trainer, Sk 35C, was undertaken at an early stage. Space for the second cockpit was made available by reducing the size of the forward fuel cell.*

*Above: Delivery of the dedicated photo-reconnaissance S 35E began in mid-August 1965. Three squadrons from F11 and F21 wings operated this variant before it was withdrawn in June 1979.*

*Right: The first export order for the Draken occurred in 1968, when Denmark ordered 20 single-seat A 35XDs (fundamentally similar to the J 35F) and three two-seat TF 35s.*

In addition to genuine supersonic performance (far in advance of that possessed by the North American F-100 Super Sabre, which did not fly until 25 May 1953), the new fighter was required to have a very high climb rate, and to be operable from the same sites as the J29. This implied that, in addition to using conventional airfields, it would also have to be able to take off and land from straight stretches of highway around 6,560 ft (2000 m) long, some of which were a mere 42 ft 8 in (13 m) across. Such operations demanded moderate take-off and touchdown speeds, and excellent directional handling on the ground.

Faced with the basic problem of achieving a major advance in speed, the Saab project team combined a single afterburning Rolls-Royce Avon with an airframe of very low drag. Minimising drag meant reducing the maximum cross-section of the aircraft, and the use of aerofoil surfaces that were as thin as possible, consistent with relatively conventional construction techniques.

The minimising of the cross-section area was achieved in effect by 'hiding' one object behind another. Thus, the engine was placed behind the pilot, while the fuel and main landing-gear units were behind the air intakes. At this stage, the aircraft looked rather like a Dassault Mirage III, with a simple delta wing, but with flattened pitot intakes blending into a thickened root chord.

## Double-delta

At the end of this preliminary stage, the team thus had a plain delta wing that was fixed in area by ceiling and fuel capacity. However, a check on landing performance showed that this area was larger than necessary from a stall speed viewpoint. The obvious solution was to reduce the wing chord. This could not be done at the root, where stowage volume was required, so it was done farther outboard by cranking the leading edge. In this way, the distinctive double-delta or cranked delta was produced.

Since there was very little data available on the handling characteristics of delta-wing aircraft, and none whatever on the double-delta, Saab tested the planform firstly with a one-eighth scale model in a conventional wind tunnel, then with a 0.7-scale manned aircraft, the Saab 210 Lilldraken (Little Dragon). Powered by a 1,050-lb (4.7-kN) thrust Armstrong Siddeley Adder turbojet, the Lilldraken had a wing planform similar to the full-scale Draken, which at that time had its intakes forward toward the nose. The cockpit was naturally disproportionately large and, since the Lilldraken was only to investigate low-speed handling, the landing gear was only semi-retractable. Approximately 1,000 flights were made with this technology demonstrator, proving that there were no special handling problems associated with the new planform.

As confidence in the new concept grew, the Swedish authorities first ordered a mock-up of the proposed J 35 fighter in March 1952. Then, in August 1953, a contract was signed for three prototypes and three pre-series aircraft. The first prototype of the Saab 35 made its maiden flight on 25 October 1955. The three prototypes were powered by imported Rolls-Royce Avons, the second and third aircraft joining the flight test programme during January and March 1956, respectively. Subsequent Drakens were built with Avons made under licence by Svenska Flygmotor (now Volvo Flygmotor); the company also developed an afterburner to produce far more thrust than the British design. Aside from its wing planform, the Draken was relatively conventional, with fully-powered flying controls. Construction was conventional, although some aluminium honeycomb was used. Fuel was stored in a combination of bag and integral tanks. Two unusual features are that the Draken has a trio of small wing fences underneath the outer panel on each side, and that the nosewheel doors open to lie flat against the front fuselage, to minimise the reduction in directional stability with the landing gear down.

The prototypes proved the soundness of the basic design, and demonstrated speeds of around Mach 1.4. The first pre-series aircraft flew on 15 February 1958, differing mainly in having the locally-manufactured RM6B engine with Model 65 afterburner. Although the J 35A was only an interim version, 65 were ordered in a contract signed in August 1956, this number including the three pre-series aircraft.

*Left: Austria received 24 ex-Swedish air force J 35Ds in the late 1980s. The aircraft were redesignated J 35Ö and were modified to incorporate J 35F-type bulged canopies.*

*The J 35F could carry two licence-built derivatives of the Hughes Falcon air-to-air missile as well as Sidewinders.*

*The last Flygvapen Draken unit was F10 at Ängelholm, which finally traded its J 35s for JAS 39 Gripens during 1999. In later years, Swedish Drakens wore an overall grey air superiority colour scheme.*

# In Swedish service

**Between 1960 and 1999, the Draken equipped 26 Divisioner (squadrons) organised within 11 regional Flygflotilljer (wings), serving in the air defence, ground attack and reconnaissance roles.**

There can be little doubt that Saab's design engineers came up with a winner when they designed the J 35 Draken.

Production continued for more than 20 years, resulting in a production tally of 615 – respectable by any standards, let alone for tiny, neutral Sweden. The Draken proved to be effective and efficient, and attracted orders from Finland, Denmark and Austria – all in the face of fierce competition.

The aircraft probably deserved more success than it gained. It offered the performance of the Lightning on half the engine thrust, and was capable of genuine STOL (short take-off and landing) operation, allowing it to operate from short highway strips.

Design of the Draken began in 1949, with project manager Erik Bratt selecting a then-unconventional double-Delta configuration to combine very low drag with low-speed handling and manoeuvrability. The first Draken prototype flew on 25 October 1955, with the production standard J 35A following on 15 February 1958 – fairly rapid progress by European standards at the time. When the J 35A entered service with F13 in March 1960, it had beaten the Lightning into front-line service (the British aircraft had entered service with the Central Fighter Establishment in 1959), as well as the Mirage IIIC and probably the MiG-21F. Nor was this a reflection of European backwardness – the marginally useful F-104A only beat the Draken into front-line service by two years, and the F-106 by just over one year.

## Ongoing changes

Although the J 35 Draken would undergo major improvements throughout the course of its production life, the basic design was sound – even the first production version was operationally useful.

Saab built some 90 J 35As (including prototypes), which entered service with F16 at Uppsala. They also functioned as the Draken OCU (operational conversion unit) and served with F13 at Norrköping. The aircraft were equipped with an Ericsson PS-02 PN793/A radar, which was based on the French CSF Cyrano used in the Mirage III. Ferranti's AIRPASS system for the Lightning was better, but Ericsson's radar was still relatively effective and reliable, and complemented the aircraft's armament of four IR-homing Rb 24 (licence-built AIM-9B Sidewinders) and two internal 30-mm ADEN cannon. In the air-to-ground role (the J 35A was a genuinely multi-role aeroplane) the aircraft could carry air-to-ground rockets below the wings. This range and weight of armament marked a significant edge over many of the Draken's

*Four J 35Fs of F13 are seen during a training sortie from their Norrköping base during 1968. The J 35F formed the backbone of Sweden's fighter defences until the arrival of the Saab Viggen during the 1970s.*

*Until the end, F10 operated a handful of Sk 35C two-seat trainers for conversion, continuation and standardisation training and instrument checks. These wore an overall silver scheme.*

*Extra pylons below the intake duct identify this aircraft as a J 35J, despite its mid-period camouflage. The aircraft wears the markings of F10, the last Swedish Draken operator.*

rivals, not least the Lightning, which never carried more than two missiles. In any case, the J 35A proved to be an interim type, and some 25 of the aircraft were subsequently converted to two-seat trainer configuration as Sk 35Cs.

Meanwhile, Saab delivered 73 J 35Bs from 1962-1963, and these aircraft re-equipped F16 and allowed the re-formation of F18 at Tullinge, which later incorporated an aerobatic team, known as the Acro Deltas.

A new Ericsson X-band radar with much improved performance was used on the J 35B and it was coupled to a new Saab-developed S-7 collision course sighting system.

But even before the J 35B could enter service, the next Draken model was already in flight test. The J 35D introduced the more powerful Avon 300-series engine (in licence-built Flygmotor RM6C form) and featured aerodynamic and avionics improvements.

Saab built 120 J 35Ds that supplanted F13's J 35As and allowed the conversion of F3 at Malmslätt, F4 at Östersund, F10 at Ängelholm and F21 at Luleå. 28 J 35Ds were converted to recce configuration as S35Es; 32 of which were also newly built. The S35E featured a camera nose accommodating five OMERA/Segid SKa 24 cameras, with four more in the wing roots, replacing the cannon. S35Es served with recce Divisions attached to several of the front-line Draken fighter wings (including F11, F13, F17 and F21).

Even the J 35D was an interim type, and development work on the 'definitive' J 35F actually began in 1959, even before the Flygvapen had taken delivery of a single J 35A. The J 35F entered full front-line service in 1966. It marked a major improvement over earlier versions, and became the most numerous Draken sub-type in Swedish service.

### New weapons

Introducing Hughes AIM-4 Falcon missiles (built under licence as Rb 27s and Rb 28s), the J 35F had a new PS-01 radar and other avionics improvements, including links with the new STRIL 60 air defence system. F10 and F13 received the 230 J 35Fs, which replaced J 35Ds, to F16 replacing J 35Bs and were also delivered to F1 at Västerå, and to F12, and F17. Some of the aircraft were actually J 35F-2s, with an undernose IRST (Infra-red Search and Track) system. The Draken force wound down rapidly after the introduction of the Viggen in 1979, eventually leaving only F10 at Ängelholm. F10 did at least receive 66 J 35F-2s modernised, refurbished and upgraded under the System 35 Ny programme as J 35Js. Apart from a structural re-work and life extension, the J 35Js received PS-011 radar, with ECCM (electronic counter-countermeasures) improvements, IRST refinements and an additional pair of pylons under each inner wing/intake duct. The first J 35Js were handed over in 1987, and the programme was completed in late August 1991. After the upgrade, J 35Js were re-painted in an overall air superiority grey colour scheme similar to that worn by JA37s. In 1994 the first of F10's Divisions was converted to the AJS 37 and the third disbanded in March 1997 – the second Division converted to the JAS39 in 1999-2000.

## J 35J Draken

**This J 35J was specially painted to celebrate a squadron anniversary, receiving the 3rd Division's swordfish badge above and below each wing, with a nose and fin band in that squadron's yellow colours. The aircraft was then used as the Division's aerobatic display aircraft. This aircraft wears the original disruptive camouflage, which was replaced by overall two-tone grey on most J 35Js during the 1990s.**

**Configuration**
The Draken's distinctive and dramatic 'double Delta' planform still looks modern today, and combined the low drag of the Delta wing with an astonishing low-speed manoeuvrability.

**Internal armament**
The J 35F and J 35J only have a single internal ADEN M/55 30-mm belt-fed cannon, fitted well aft on the starboard wing root. Earlier variants had twin ADEN cannon.

**Upgrade**
Selected J 35F-2s (some of which had begun life as J 35F-1s) were delivered to FFV at Linköping, split into sections, refurbished and refitted (front sections by Saab) before assembly and flight test.

**IRST**
The J 35J had a modified version of the J 35F-2's S71N IRST (infra-red search and track), refined to give better performance at low level.

**External armament**
Even after upgrade to J 35J standards, Swedish Drakens continued to use the Falcon-based Rb 27 (semi-active version) and Rb 28 (IR version), as well as the AIM-9 Sidewinder.

**Powerplant**
The J 35J retains the same Svenska Flygmotor RM6C (Avon 300-series) engine as the J 35F, with a Model 67 afterburner, which is rated at 17,637 lb st (79.36 kN) with afterburning.

# Foreign operators

**In all, 615 Drakens were built, including prototypes and trials airframes, most of them for the Swedish air force, the Flygvapnet. Export sales amounted to 63 new-build aircraft – 12 for Finland and 51 for Denmark. Both countries also took delivery of secondhand ex-Swedish aircraft, as did Austria, in 2002 the last operator of Saab's '35 system'.**

## Finland (Ilmavoimat)

The Drakens of the Ilmavoimat (Finnish air force) were a mixture of aircraft built under license in Finland and ex-Flygvapnet aircraft acquired later. After much political wrangling Finland ordered 12 brand new Saab 35S aircraft (known in some sources as the 35XS: X for export, S for Suomi) in April 1970, the package including weapons and spares. The 35S (pictured above right) was based on the Flygvapnet's J 35F and was armed with SARH-guided Rb 27 (AIM-26B) and IR-guided Rb 28 (AIM-4D) Falcon AAMs. The Volvo RM 6C-powered aircraft were assembled at the AB Valmet plant in Finland and entered service during 1974/75. Although it was the first variant to be ordered by Finland, it was not the first to enter service. Before these aircraft were delivered, Finland leased six former Flygvapnet J 35Bs (known locally as 35BSs, pictured below right) for training purposes; these entered service with HävLLv 11 at Rovaniemi in May 1972. All weather avionics and missile armament was deleted prior to delivery and training of an initial batch of personnel was undertaken at Tullinge in Sweden. All were purchased outright in 1976 along with a batch of six refurbished J 35F1s (35FS, pictured bottom) and three two-seat SK 35C (35CS, pictured below) trainers. In 1984 a second Draken unit – HävLLv 21 – was established at Tampere-Pirkkala with a mixed fleet of 35S and 35FS aircraft; a follow-on batch of 18 'zero-timed' FSs and two CSs was acquired from Sweden over the next two years to equip the new unit. Another 35BS was also purchased to replace one of the original six machines of this type which had suffered fire damage. In 1990 the search for a replacement for the Draken began, the McDonnell Douglas (Boeing) F/A-18C/D 'getting the nod' in 1992. By 1997 HävLLv 21 had re-equipped with Hornets, the squadron's remaining Drakens passing to HävLLv 11, with which they remained in service until the type was finally retired by the Ilmavoimat in August 2000.

## Denmark (Flyvevåbnet)

Aware of Denmark's requirement for a new multi-role aircraft, Saab began the development of a fighter-bomber version of the 35X in 1967. The sixth Draken prototype, which had also served a test aircraft during the development of the J 35D and F for the Flygvapnet, was equipped with a strengthened wing and extra hardpoints. A pair of 280-Imp gal (1275-litre) drop tanks were also provided, increasing range to 1,864 miles (3000 km). The Draken faced competition from the Northrop F-5 and Dassault Mirage III, but both were eventually discounted on the grounds of cost and a contract for the supply of 20 Saab 35XDs (right), designated F-35 by the Flyvevåbnet and three two-seat variants (above) with full combat capability (TF-35) was signed in March 1968. Deliveries began in 1970, the new aircraft replacing F-100 Super Sabres and equipping Esk 725 at Karup. An option on 20 single-seat RF-35 tactical reconnaissance aircraft was converted to a firm order within a matter of months; these aircraft were delivered during 1971/72 (with another three TF-35s) and issued to Esk 729, also at Karup, as a replacement for the RF-84F Thunderflash. An all-weather capability was added to the fleet in 1975 with the introduction of Red Baron IR pods on outboard underwing pylons. The TF-35 conversion trainer fleet was boosted with a further order for five aircraft; these were delivered during 1976/77 and issued to both squadrons. Like other operators, the Flyvevåbnet has continually upgraded its Drakens. In the mid 1980s an extensive upgrade dubbed WDNS (Weapon Delivery and Navigation System) was introduced. This included the installation of a new INS and weapon delivery computer, a HUD, a nose-mounted LRMTS (laser range-finder and marked target seeker), an ECM suite and a new RWR. The complete package gave the aircraft an attack capability close to that of Denmark's F-16s. The first upgraded aircraft was completed in 1981, the last of 43 F-35 and TF-35s being re-delivered in 1986. Defence budget cuts forced the disbandment of Esk 725 in 1991 and the concentration of Draken operations with Esk 729. The remaining aircraft remained in use until early 1994 when the Draken was finally retired.

## Austria (Österreichische Luftstreitkräfte)

In 2002, the Austrian air force is the last operator of the Draken and is expected to retain the type until 2005. Austria first considered the purchase of 24 Drakens in 1967 but it was 18 years before an order was finally placed, in order to make good a lack of supersonic fighter aircraft in the Austrian air arm. Twenty-four ex-Flygvapnet J 35Ds were extensively refurbished by Saab to 35ÖE standard (pictured) and delivered between 1987 and 1989, entering service with 1. Staffel, Fliegerregiment 2 at Zeltweg and 2. Staffel, Fliegerregiment 2 at Graz-Thalehof. Initially the aircraft carried no missile armament, but the border violations by the Yugoslav air force during the 1991 fight for Slovenian independence led to the purchase of a batch of AIM-9P-3 Sidewinder AAMs with which to equip the aircraft. After Denmark retired its Drakens, purchased their RWRs and chaff/flare dispensers, which were fitted with the aid of Valmet. The 35ÖEs were scheduled for retirement in 1996, a number of new types being considered, including the F-16, F-18, Mirage 2000-5, JA39 Gripen and MiG-29SE, but public debate over the future of the Austrian fighter force caused a reappraisal of these plans. The Draken is now expected to soldier on until at least 2005, when it will be replaced by a force of 18 Eurofighter Typhoon fighters.

By comparison with the earlier Draken, the Viggen marked a massive improvement in capability, and proved to have more docile handling characteristics into the bargain.

# Saab 37 Viggen

## Thor's hammer

**A unique shape in European skies, Sweden's SAAB Viggen was a product of its country's fervent desire to remain neutral in a world dominated by the East-West conflicts of the Cold War.**

Reflecting Sweden's desire to remain non-aligned, even in the face of the enormous costs that come with designing an aircraft indigenously, the Saab Viggen was produced as the successor to the revolutionary Saab Draken, and is still in service despite its age and the encroachment on its territory by the new Saab JAS 39 Gripen.

Design programmes first commenced in 1952 when a number of attack designs were studied. Svenska Flygvapnet (Swedish air force or Fv) wanted an aircraft to replace the Saab Lansen for attack duties and, at a later date, the Draken in the interception role.

The new aircraft was designated Fpl 37, and the powerplant was the first feature that was decided upon. After a number of options were studied, the Pratt & Whitney JT8D-22, which had been designed for the Boeing 727 airliner, was chosen and Svenska Flygmotor soon obtained a license to build the engine for the new aircraft. However, the JT8D-22 was not designed to be used with an afterburner and so a number of modifications had to be made.

Working on a scaled-up earlier design, the double-delta Spey-powered 1504B, Saab submitted their resultant model 1534 for official approval in February 1962, and was rewarded on 28 September by its formal acceptance as the next combat aircraft for the Swedish air force.

*The Viggen prototype seen in flight. The aircraft wore a Viggen (thunderbolt) badge on the air intake and was fitted with a long test instrument boom on the nose.*

The Fpl 37 was first made public in December 1962 when its novel wing configuration generated huge interest. As the first canard-equipped military aircraft to enter production, the Fpl 37 was clearly an innovation. The flaps on the canards' trailing edges, acting in unison with, or

*The Saab test fleet, minus aircraft 37-5, is pictured together at the FMV test centre, at Malmen. The unpainted No. 37-4 crashed a month later on 7 May 1969.*

in opposition to, flaps and elevons at the rear of the wing, allowed the Viggen to avoid the high landing and take-off speeds which characterised contemporary deltas such as the Dassault Mirage III.

This ability to be able to operate from 1,640 ft (500 m) runways was one of the chief specifications laid down by the Swedish government to the designers and this performance was virtually unrivalled by any contemporary attack jets.

The hefty outward appearance of the Viggen belies the fact that the aircraft is commendably light for one stressed to +12*g*. This is because of the imaginative use of honeycomb panels and metal bonding in the airframe.

Care was also taken to ensure that the Viggen was easy to service between flights, so that a high sortie rate can be maintained during hostilities. Easy servicing is essential because half of the personnel in the Fv are conscripts with only 10 months of training and in wartime, 80 per cent of military personnel would be reservists.

It was soon realised that the Fpl 37 aircraft would need to perform a number of duties and so a number of different variants was planned. The AJ 37 would be an attack aircraft, the SF 37 would replace the Draken in the reconnaissance role, the SH 37 would perform maritime reconnaissance and patrol and the SK 37 would be used for two seat training.

## Prototypes

AJ 37 Viggen mock-up '37-0' was revealed to the press on 4 April 1965 and the first prototype '37-1' was rolled out on 24 November 1966. In natural metal, with national insignia on the nose, Thor's thunderbolt (the Viggen) on the intakes and SAAB37-1 in black on the fin, '37-1' first flew on 8 February 1967. The aircraft was described as 'being as simple to fly as a sportsplane' by its test pilot Eric Dahlstrom, though even he was caught out by the high nose-up attitude adopted for short landings resulting in the occasional scraped jet-pipe. Tragically, another pilot was killed when he accidentally fired the ejector seat while sitting on the runway and his parachute failed to open. By 1979, 37-1 had flown some 800 hours or 1,133 flights, and the aircraft was then placed in a Swedish air force museum.

***The second and third prototypes pose during trials. No. 2 is unarmed, while No. 3 carries ECM pods inboard and chaff and flare dispensers.***

Prototype 37-2 first took to the air in September 1967 with another two aircraft flying over the next year. 37-2 and 37-3 were used for weapon carrying tests, -3 being the first aircraft fitted with radar and the complete avionics suite. To improve longitudinal stability when carrying external stores, 37-4 had a saw-tooth in the wing. No. 37-5, which was first flown on 15 April 1969, was used for military trials, and 37-6 conducted tests on a series of systems and weapons. It was also the first Viggen to fly at an airshow – Paris in 1969. The final prototype to fly was the SK 37 two-seat trainer which first took to the air on 2 July 1970. Deliveries first began in 1971 with four Swedish air force attack squadrons becoming operational by 1975.

## Saab SF 37 Viggen

**This SF 37 (Spanings Foto) Viggen wears the markings of F13 at Norrköping-Bråvalla, whose first squadron (1 Spaningsflygdivision) was a reconnaissance unit equipped with both SF 37s and SH 37s. The unit's second squadron flew the JA 37 fighter. In 1993 the Viggen force was radically reorganised. F13 disbanded and 1 Spaningsflygdivision moved to F10, replacing the Drakens previously flown by that unit.**

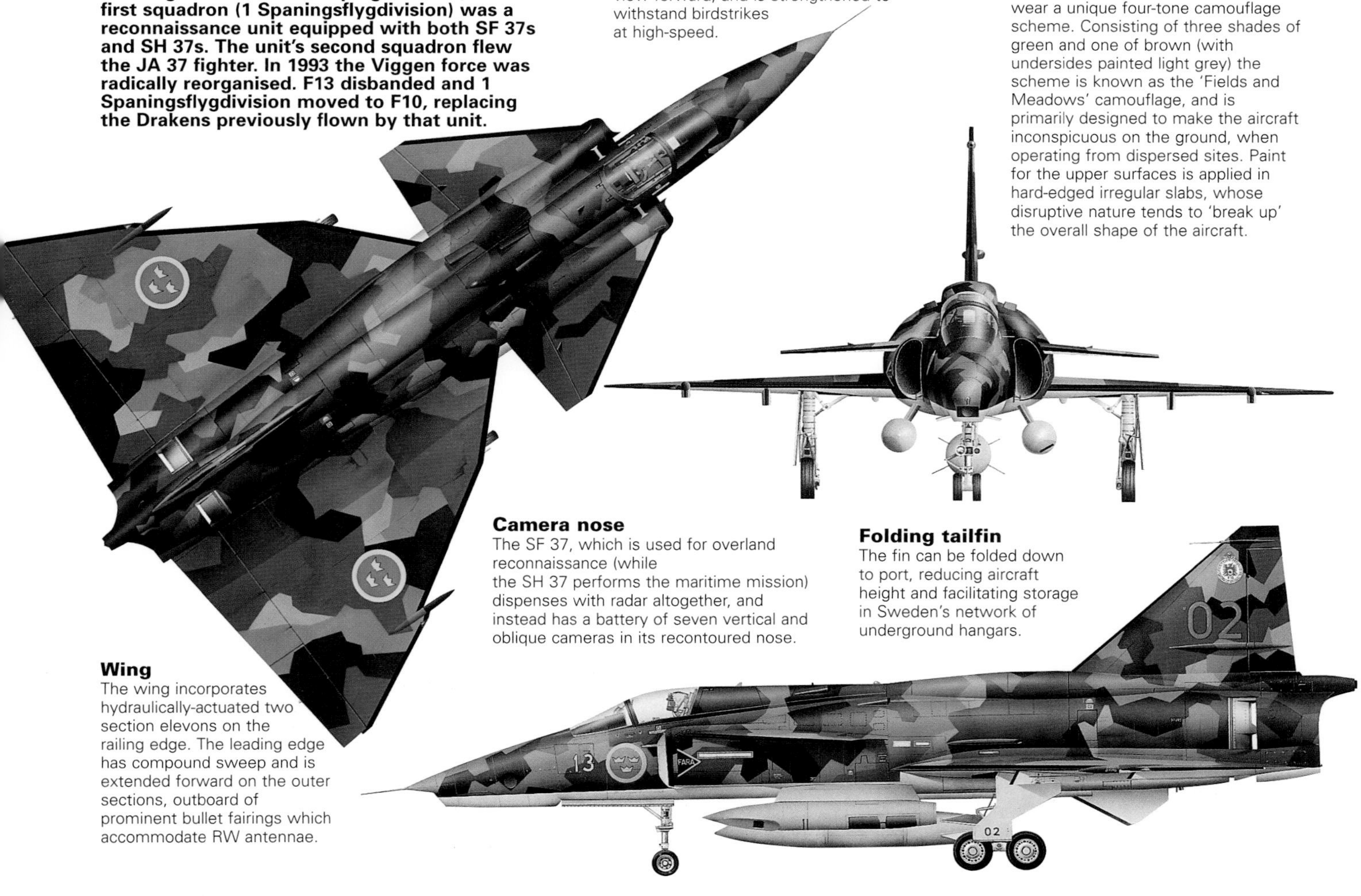

**Windscreen**
The Viggen's wraparound single-piece windscreen gives the pilot an excellent view forward, and is strengthened to withstand birdstrikes at high-speed.

**Camouflage**
All attack, reconnaissance and trainer Viggens, and many JA 37 fighters, wear a unique four-tone camouflage scheme. Consisting of three shades of green and one of brown (with undersides painted light grey) the scheme is known as the 'Fields and Meadows' camouflage, and is primarily designed to make the aircraft inconspicuous on the ground, when operating from dispersed sites. Paint for the upper surfaces is applied in hard-edged irregular slabs, whose disruptive nature tends to 'break up' the overall shape of the aircraft.

**Camera nose**
The SF 37, which is used for overland reconnaissance (while the SH 37 performs the maritime mission) dispenses with radar altogether, and instead has a battery of seven vertical and oblique cameras in its recontoured nose.

**Folding tailfin**
The fin can be folded down to port, reducing aircraft height and facilitating storage in Sweden's network of underground hangars.

**Wing**
The wing incorporates hydraulically-actuated two section elevons on the railing edge. The leading edge has compound sweep and is extended forward on the outer sections, outboard of prominent bullet fairings which accommodate RW antennae.

# Viggen variants and operators

## Saab AJ 37 Viggen

In the early 1960s, Saab studied a low-cost, single-seat, single-engined fighter capable of supersonic flight at low altitude and Mach 2 at height, but able to take off and land in 1,640 ft (500 m) to replace the multi-role J 32. This demanding specification was necessary if the new aircraft was to operate in the SAF's STRIL 60 integrated air defence system and BASE 90 concept dispersed airstrips. For good short-field performance, Saab pioneered the use of flap-equipped canard foreplanes with a delta-wing configuration, in conjunction with an integral thrust-reverser for the RM8 turbofan.

For reliability, the powerplant was based on the 14,771-lb st (65.7-kN) commercial Pratt & Whitney JT8D-22 turbofan, developed and built by Svenska Flygmotor for supersonic flight, and with a Swedish afterburner providing a thrust increase of more than 70 per cent to around 26,014 lb (115.7 kN) for take-off. An autoland technique for minimum landing distance involved automatic approach speed control and selection of reverse thrust in a no-flare touchdown with a 16.4 ft (5 m) per second compression of the main undercarriage oleos. The initial AJ 37 attack aircraft, soon named Viggen (Thunderbolt), incorporated many other features novel for its time, including a Saab CK-37 miniaturised digital air data and nav/attack computer, SRA head-up display for primary flight data, and a Cutler-Hammer AIL microwave beam landing-guidance system. A rocket-boosted Saab ejection seat provided zero-zero escape capabilities.

On 5 April 1968, the Swedish government authorised the air force to order 175 AJ/SF/SH 37s for delivery from 1971, and by April 1969 all six single-seat prototypes were flying, the last fully representative of the initial production attack variants. The first of these became airborne on 23 February 1971, deliveries starting soon afterwards, in June, to F7 at Satenas to replace A 32A Lansens; four attack wings became operational with AJ 37s by mid-1975. No first-generation AJ 37s remain in service today; they have either been replaced by the upgraded AJS 37 or by the new JAS 39 Gripen.

## JA 37 Viggen

For the dedicated interception role, with a secondary ground-attack capability, Saab developed the JA 37 Viggen. Although externally similar to the attack variant, the interceptor introduces fundamental changes under the skin, with avionics, armament, engine and structural modifications. The JA 37's primary sensor is the Ericsson PS-46/A medium-PRF multi-mode X-band pulse-Doppler look-down/shoot-down radar, which has four air-to-air modes and a look-down range in excess of 30 miles (48 km). New avionics include an upgraded and higher-capacity Singer-Kearfott SKC-2037 central digital computer and KT-70L INS, Decca Doppler Type 72 nav radar, Garrett AiResearch LD-5 digital air data computer, Saab-Honeywell SA07 digital AFCS, Svenska Radio integrated electronic display system, and an SRA HUD. The RM8B turbofan is uprated by Volvo to develop 16,600 lb (73.84 kN) maximum dry thrust and 28,109 lb (125 kN) with afterburning. This extra power allows the JA 37 to fly at Mach 1.2 at low altitude, and to exceed Mach 2 at higher altitudes. Airframe changes include a wing restressed for a higher load factor, a fuselage stretch of 4 in (10 cm) ahead of the wing to accommodate the modified powerplant, a 4-in (10-cm) fin extension similar to that of the Sk 37 trainer, and four instead of three elevator actuators under each wing. Four AJ 37 prototypes were modified to JA 37 standard for the development programme, the first making its initial flight on 27 September 1974, a few days after SAF orders for the first 30 production Viggen interceptors. In March 1980, the Swedish government authorised a third batch of 59 JA 37s, increasing overall production of this variant to 149 and the Viggen total to its final figure of 330. JA 37s were planned to replace Flygvapnet J 35 Drakens in the 1978-85 period and to arm at least eight of the 10 Draken air defence squadrons active at that time.

Today, the JA 37 is the most numerous Viggen subtype in front-line service, with around 77 on strength0.

## Sk 37 Viggen

With the Viggen fulfiling its role as the Flygvapnet's primary combat aircraft system, there was a pressing need for a trainer version. The Sk 37 Viggen (Skol, or School) tandem two-seat trainer was developed simultaneously with the AJ 37. This variant is somewhat unusual in having two separate cockpits for pilot and instructor. The stepped rear (instructor's) cockpit, fitted with a bulged canopy and twin lateral periscopes, replaces some electronics and a forward fuel tank. Fuel capacity is partially restored by a permanently-mounted ventral fuel tank. Other changes include a 4-in (10-cm) taller fin to restore stability following modification of the aircraft to produce the deeper forward fuselage. Because of its height, even the standard AJ 37 fin can be folded on the ground to allow clearance for the SAF's cavern-based hangars. Despite its radome, the Sk 37 has no radar and, therefore, no radar navigation capability, having to rely on Doppler and DME.

### SF 37/SH 37 Viggen

Designed as an S 35E Draken replacement, the SF 37 (right) adaptation of the AJ 37 is equipped for all-weather day and night overland reconnaissance, with low- and high-altitude film cameras giving complete horizon-to-horizon lateral coverage, plus a VKA 702 infra-red camera recording thermal images in place of the nose radar. Twin ventral pods also house night cameras and illumination equipment, the photoflash system operating with light just outside the visible wavelengths. A Red Baron IR line-scan system, with the standard active and passive underwing ECM pods, may also be carried, but the SF 37 has no attack capability and armament is normally confined only to defensive Rb 74 (AIM-9L) AAMs. All nine cameras have automatic exposure control and image motion compensation controlled by the aircraft's central computer.

The SH 37 (below right) was modified from the AJ 37 as a successor to the Saab S 32C Lansen for all-weather sea surveillance and patrol, with secondary maritime strike capability, and fitted with modified radar, plus ventral night reconnaissance and SKA 24D 600-mm lens long-range camera pods. Underwing ECM pods are also normally carried, as well as AAMs on the outboard wing stations. Both the SF and SH 37s normally operate with a ventral fuselage drop tank. F13 at Norköping formed the first SH 37 squadron in late 1976, and the 27 Viggens of this type built between 1977 and 1979 served alongside the SF 37s to equip the three mixed reconnaissance squadrons in F13, F17 and F21. All surviving SF/SH aircraft had been modified through the AJS 37 upgrade programme by 2004.

### AJS 37 Viggen

During 1993-1997, some of the first-generation Viggens were given new life through the AJS programme, comprising the installation of a new mission computer and digital databus to provide integrated attack, fighter and reconnaissance capabilities. Originally, the programme was very ambitious and intended to modify 115 AJ/SF/SH 37 Viggens into AJS 37 multi-role standard. However, financial limitations reduced this number to 98 and the idea of a virtually identical standard was dropped. Thus, the programme eventually resulted in the conversion of 48 AJS 37s (former AJ 37 with additional radar surveillance capability), 25 AJSH 37s (former SH 37 with additional ground-attack capability) and 25 AJSF 37s (former SF 37 with additional fighter capability). Today, only 1 Divisionen F10 (Johan Röd) and 1 Divisionen F21 (Urban Röd) continue to fly the AJS/AJSF/AJSH 37 Viggen, and many high-houred airframes have been withdrawn from use and stored, scrapped or given to museums.

The AJS 37 family of Viggens can carry a large and varied weaponload, with air-to-surface armament including Swedish-developed Rb 04E and Rb 15F radar-homing anti-ship missiles, Rb 05A radar-command-guided and Rb 75 (AGM-65 Maverick) TV-guided missiles.

# Units and bases

**From a peak of 17 Divisioner in the early 1990s, Viggens are now operational with only 10 units (F6, F13 and F15 have all been disbanded). Today, those Viggens in service will undergo upgrades, ensuring that they remain in service until at least 2006.**

### F21 Norrbottens Flygflottilj, Luleå

Based at the northernmost permanent Viggen airfield, F21 operates two squadrons of JA 37s (illustrated) plus a unit of AJS 37s, giving it a true multi-role capability. Its maritime surveillance AJSF 37s monitor activities in the Gulf of Bothnia and the Baltic Sea.

### F4 Jämtlands Flygflottilj, Östersund

Like most current Swedish Viggen wings, F4 operates two Jaktflygdivision of JA 37 'Jakt Viggens' (fighter Viggens) – illustrated below – for air defence against hostile invaders. Also at F4 are the Flygvapnet's two-seat Sk 37s. These aircraft have always been a precious commodity and are among the highest-timed Viggens still operational.

### F17 Blekinge Flygflottilj, Ronneby

Most of Sweden's airfields are in the south of the country. In the event of actual combat during the Cold War, this region would have been criss-crossed by NATO or Soviet fighters, and units such as F17 at Ronneby would have been tasked with defending Sweden's borders from hostile incursions. Pictured below are JA 37s, two divisions of which are operated by F17.

### F16 Upplands Flygflottilj, Uppsala

Two Jaktflygdivision of JA 37s are based at Uppsala, tasked with interception, like other aircraft of this unit since 1943. F16 was the fifth and last wing to receive the Jaktviggen.

### F10 Skånska Flygflottilj, Ängelholm

One of only two operators of the upgraded AJS 37, the F10 wing located at this southerly base has an attack/ jakt/ spaningsflygdivision (attack/fighter/ reconnaissance) capability. The AJS 37s were supported in this task by J 35J Drakens.

# Saab JAS 39 Gripen

## Swedish superfighter

**Although small in size, the Gripen is a giant in capability. Despite a number of setbacks, Swedish ingenuity has produced an affordable, maintainable and credible fighter which meets and, in some cases, exceeds the Swedish air force's stringent requirements. With the sale of the aircraft to South Africa and the lease of 14 Gripens to Hungary, Saab and its partners are looking forward to considerable international success.**

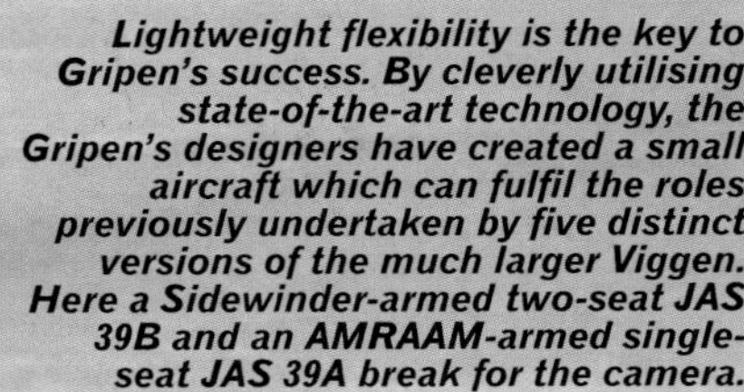

*Lightweight flexibility is the key to Gripen's success. By cleverly utilising state-of-the-art technology, the Gripen's designers have created a small aircraft which can fulfil the roles previously undertaken by five distinct versions of the much larger Viggen. Here a Sidewinder-armed two-seat JAS 39B and an AMRAAM-armed single-seat JAS 39A break for the camera.*

*The Gripen two-seater is designated JAS 39B. A total of 29 is to be built, including this prototype aircraft which replaced one of the production single-seaters in Batch 1. The final 14 are widely expected to be built as full combat aircraft, being used in a command and control function or even as 'UCAV leaders'.*

At the start of the 1980s Sweden began development of a new lightweight fighter which would eventually replace the Draken and Viggen in Flygvapnet service. Some 10 years before the end of the Cold War, the Soviet Union posed a real and quantifiable threat, and what became the Gripen was designed accordingly. However, the inherent flexibility of this state-of-the-art weapon system has allowed it to remain highly relevant to the changed world of the 21st century.

By 1981, the requirement had crystallised into the JAS (Jakt Attack Spaning – fighter, attack, reconnaissance) programme. The aim was to produce a single fighter that could undertake all the missions assigned to the five Viggen variants.

Although Saab was the principal contractor and integrator, the JAS programme encompassed many other areas of the Swedish defence industry, notably Ericsson (PS-05/A radar), Volvo-Aero (licence-built General Electric F404 powerplant) and FFV (weapons/systems). The grouping was named IG (Industri-Grupp) JAS, and submitted its Saab 2110 design in 1981, leading to a development contract being issued on 30 June 1982, covering the provision of five prototypes and 30 single-seat Batch 1 production aircraft.

Harnessing the latest technological advances, notably in computing power and avionics, the IG JAS team was able to create an aircraft which could perform all the missions required of it, but in a much smaller, lighter (and therefore cheaper) airframe. The Gripen, as the JAS 39 was named in September 1982, was a true fourth-generation fighter, with 'glass' cockpit, aerodynamic instability (with fly-by-wire controls), multi-mode radar, modern weapons and carefree-handling turbofan. Furthermore, the aircraft could easily meet the Flygvapnet's demands to be operable from the numerous highway strips that are the cornerstone of Swedish defences, and to be easily maintainable by conscript technicians.

Having dallied with the RB.199 engine in earlier studies, IG JAS settled on the F404 to power the Gripen. Volvo-Aero and GE shared the development of the Gripen's version, including a new afterburner. In the Gripen the engine is designated the RM12.

Ericsson's PS-05/A radar drew on some features of the UK's Blue Vixen, but is otherwise an indigenous product. At a very light installed weight, the PS-05/A offers astounding multi-mode performance, from sea search to beyond visual range air-to-air. The radar began flying in a converted Viggen, immediately showing a quantum leap in capability over the Viggen's standard PS-46.

## Software troubles

What became the most troublesome part of the Gripen programme was the flight control system, a simplified version of which flew from September 1982 in a modified Viggen, known as ESS JAS. Continuing software problems with the FCS kept Gripen firmly on the ground long after its 26 April 1987 roll-out, and it was not to be until 9 December 1988 that the first aircraft took to the air, piloted by Stig Holmström.

On the sixth flight, on 2 February 1989, the aircraft was lost in a landing accident caused by FCS failure. An intense period of FCS work ensued, including many flights using Calspan's modified Lockheed NT-33 variable-stability testbed. Gripen no. 2 first flew on 4 May 1990, by which time the programme had slipped three years. By the end of 1991, the remaining three prototypes had flown. Whereas nos 1 and 2 had been flight envelope expansion aircraft, with simplified systems and no 'glass' cockpit, the final three were equipped to a roughly production standard. No. 3 was used primarily for radar, avionics and ECM trials, no. 4 handled avionics and weapons, while no. 5 had a full production system test role.

The first production aircraft, 39-101, flew on 10 September 1992, but it was retained by the test team as a replacement for the lost first prototype. Therefore, the second aircraft, 39-102, became the first aircraft to be handed over to the Flygvapnet, an event occurring on 8 June 1993. Another FCS-induced accident occurred very visibly on 18 August 1993, when the second production machine crashed during an airshow over Stockholm, thankfully with no injury to pilot (the hapless Lars Rådeström, who had survived the no. 1 prototype crash) or spectators. Further work was rapidly undertaken to rectify this latest FCS problem.

Production of the 30 Batch 1 aircraft continued although, in the event, one of the aircraft was completed as the prototype two-seat JAS 39B (39-800). Adding the second cockpit required removal of the port-side Mauser BK 27 cannon and an increase in forward-fuselage length. Fuel capacity was slightly reduced. The Flygvapnet subsequently ordered 14 two-seaters in each of Batches 2 and 3, the latter aircraft almost certainly to be missionised for a combat role.

Deliveries of single-seat Batch 1 JAS 39As were initially made to F7 Wing at Såtenäs, which had previously operated AJ 37s. The first squadron to be declared operational was 2 Div. Gustaf Blå, which achieved this capability on 1 November 1997 after an evaluation exercise. 1 Div. Gustaf Röd followed on 30 December 1988, completing the conversion of F7.

At the time of their introduction, the Batch 1 Gripens were essentially 'A 39s', for they lacked the definitive AIM-120 AMRAAM capability for the air defence role, and had no reconnaissance capability.

Såtenäs has become the lead base for the Gripen programme, with the establishment of the central training centre there. Like the aircraft, this is a state-of-the-art facility, with a high degree of simulation allowing students to learn their trade with minimised use of the actual aircraft.

*The key air-to-air weapon for the Gripen is the AIM-120B AMRAAM, known locally as the Rb 99. AMRAAM was cleared operationally in mid-1999, finally allowing the Gripen to justify the 'J' in its JAS 39 designation.*

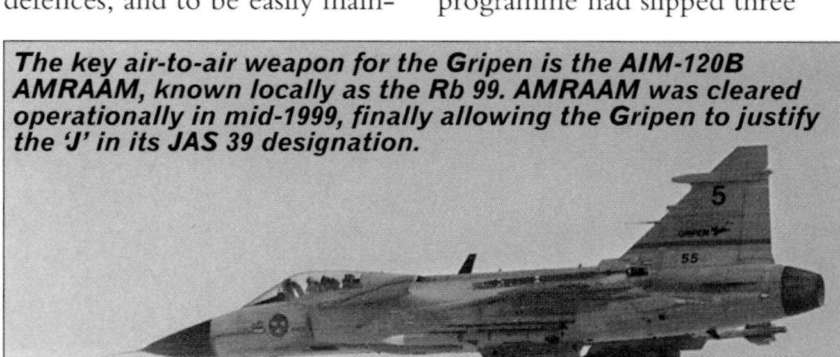

*The black-painted second prototype handled the high-alpha departure and spin tests, fitted with an anti-spin chute. Production aircraft (rear) were initially built with black radomes.*

In the air defence role Gripens carry a standard load of six missiles, a total which is adequate but hardly ideal. Future plans for the Saab aircraft incorporate the addition of multiple launchers to boost combat persistence.

# In service

**Rapidly becoming the dominant aircraft in Flygvapnet service, Saab's Gripen is being actively marketed around the world. The sales team has achieved success in South Africa, but also has its sights set on South America and eastern Europe.**

At the end of the 1980s Sweden had 26 combat squadrons, but in the post-Cold War 1990s this number fell sharply. On 13 December 1996 Sweden's parliament (the Riksdag) announced the latest in its regular Defence Decisions, one aimed at making heavy cuts to the defence budget. It was announced that the future front-line structure of Flygvapnet would comprise just 13 combat squadrons – 12 with Gripens and one flying upgraded JA 37 Mod D Viggens.

Sweden's first operational Gripen unit was F7 Skaraborgs Flygflottilj (F7 Wing) at Såtenäs, in southwestern Sweden. F7 has established a tradition as a 'lead unit', with a history that stretches back to the Caproni B16 bomber. F7 has three component squadrons, which like all Swedish squadrons are designated by colour: Röd (red, 1st squadron), Blå (blue, 2nd Squadron) and Gul (yellow, 3rd squadron).

The first Gripen squadron was Gustaf Blå, which was declared fully operational on 1 November 1997, it was followed by Gustaf Röd on 30 December 1998.

The markings and camouflage schemes applied to the Gripen force have changed several times over the years. An overall matt grey finish, with high-visibility national markings, was applied to the first few production aircraft. Most Batch One deliveries carried black unit markings on the nose and Dayglo codes on the fin. On the Gripen (unlike previous Swedish aircraft) the code always reflects the last two digits of the serial. Batch Two aircraft introduced low-vis grey markings on an overall grey finish. The black radome was eliminated as a result of radar propagation problems.

These Batch Two Gripens line the apron at F10 Skåne Wing, Ängelholm. However, with defence cutbacks, the two Gripen squadrons under operational conversion there ceased operations by 31 December 2002 and transfered to F17 Blekinge Wing.

On 30 September 1999 the first two Gripens arrived at F10 Skåne Wing, Ängelholm, to inaugurate the third of Sweden's planned Gripen squadrons. However, a shadow was already looming over the entire Swedish Defence Forces as a new Defence Decision, even more radical than the 1996 plan, was being finalised. On 30 March 2000 the Riksdag passed a new Defence Bill and confirmed that the Swedish Air Force would now have just eight Gripen squadrons, distributed over four wings. F10's home at Ängelholm, which has just completed an expensive modernisation programme to prepare it for Gripen operations, will be closed down and the unit disbanded.

The Riksdag decision brings other changes to the ongoing introduction of the Gripen system at the different wings. The previous plan called for F16 Uppland Wing, at Uppsala, to become the third Gripen wing. Indeed, by late 1999, the initial conversion training process had already begun. Now, F21 Norbotten Wing, at Luleå in northern Sweden, will become the next unit to transition to the Gripen. Conversion training for

The Gripen has been aggressively marketed in eastern Europe, with Hungary in particular being targeted as a potential customer. Substantial investment by Sweden was made in Hungarian industry and this attention eventually paid off in the form of a 14-aircraft, 10-year lease deal. As an interim measure, however, Hungary has also purchased MiG-29 'Fulcrums'.

***Early Gripens were armed only for the air defence role, and then restricted to carrying only Sidewinders. Rapid development has expanded this capability. These aircraft display two of the dominant air-to-ground weapons in the inventory, the Rb 75 Maverick and the DWS 39 (BK 90).***

the wing's technicians and pilots will start later this year, and the wing's first fighter squadron will be operational with Gripens in 2002. The reconnaissance squadron at F21 is scheduled to fly its AJSF/AJSH Viggens until the end of 2003.

The first of the two squadrons of F4 Jämtland Wing, based at Östersund, is scheduled to begin conversion during 2002. That year will also see the F10 Gripens relocating to F17 Wing at Ronneby, which means that all four Flygvapnet wings should have partially re-equipped by 2004.

Each of the eight squadrons will have approximately 25 Gripens, but F7 Wing will maintain two oversized squadrons with aircraft and personnel equivalent to three of today's squadrons, which typically operate 16 aircraft. No Gripens will be kept in storage or reserve – all will be kept flying. The new structure will come into effect on 1 July 2000 and be fully implemented by 2003/04.

### Export market

With the lack of much in the way of conflicts, the success of modern fighters is more often than not gauged by their performance on the export market and this has not traditionally been Saab's strongest field. Sweden's politically neutral stance, coupled with the unique Swedish requirements, have hindered sales. The Gripen suffers from from some of these problems coupled with the fact that some of its systems and equipment are American built and the US vetoes sales to politically undesirable countries, some of which might have been potential Gripen customers. Furthermore, the modern fighter-market is a cut-throat business and despite the fact that it is the only fourth generation fighter in service, the Gripen has to contend with the F-16 and F/A-18, Mirage 2000 and Rafale, MiG-29 and Su-27 and Eurofighter.

However, the Gripen has chalked up one major success already. On 3 December 1999, the South African Air Force announced that Saab-BAe would supply 28 Gripens and 24 Hawk 100s to be delivered between 2005 and 2012. Local companies have been selected to provide a new fully-digital radio system, power unit, communication control and display unit and multi-function weapon pylons.

In Europe, Austria and Hungary had been touted as likely customers but the former's dithering and the latter's MiG-29 acquisition has meant that attention has now turned to the Czech Republic, which is looking for 36 fighter aircraft and Poland which wants 60. In both competitions, the F-16 and Mirage 2000 are also strong contenders but, as of autumn 2000, decisions had yet to be made.

Chile, and to a lesser extent Brazil, have been strong contenders for the Gripen, though political considerations have affected both nations' decisions. At one point, Chile seemed set to agree a deal but an economic downturn put paid to that idea. The air force is currently awaiting a decision from the new President. The Netherlands, New Zealand, Nigeria, Philippines, Romania and Slovenia have also expressed interest in the Gripen.

## JAS 39A Gripen

**This aircraft, 39154, is a Batch Two Gripen and was delivered to Flygvapnet in June 1998. F7 Wing has two operational Gripen squadrons, Gustav Röd (Gustaf red, 1st squadron) and Gustav Blå (Gustaf blue, 2nd squadron).**

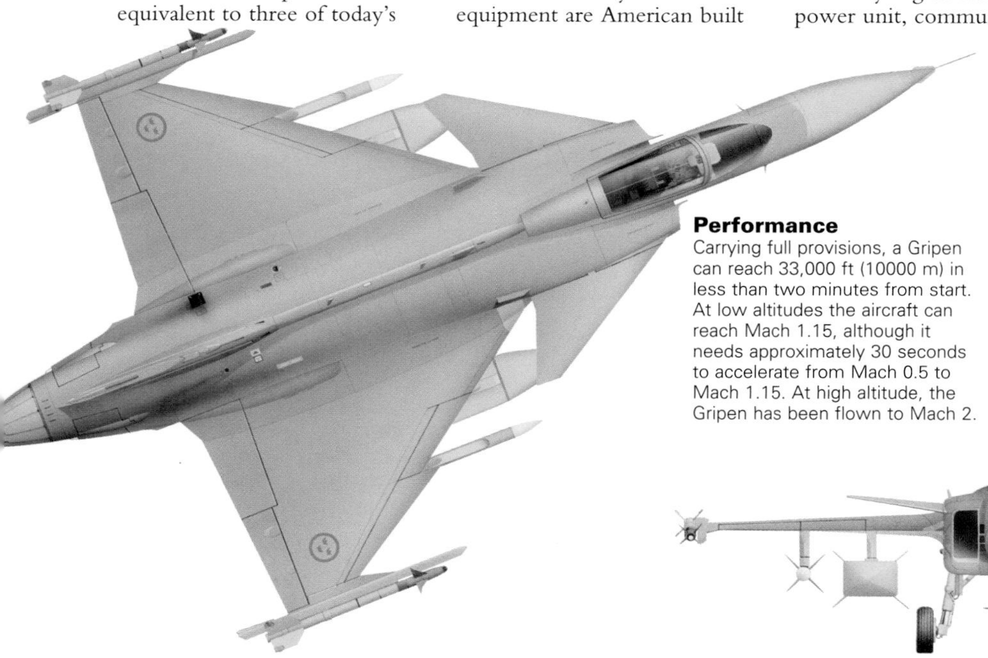

**Performance**
Carrying full provisions, a Gripen can reach 33,000 ft (10000 m) in less than two minutes from start. At low altitudes the aircraft can reach Mach 1.15, although it needs approximately 30 seconds to accelerate from Mach 0.5 to Mach 1.15. At high altitude, the Gripen has been flown to Mach 2.

**New radio fit**
Early in 2000, Saab selected Germany's Rohde & Schwarz to provide a new set of tactical radios for the Gripen, replacing the existing Swedish radios and making the aircraft more interoperable. The Rohde & Schwarz Series 6000 compact UHF/VHF radios function in the 30- to 400-MHz range and are compatible with Have Quick I/II, SECOS and SATURN encryption standards.

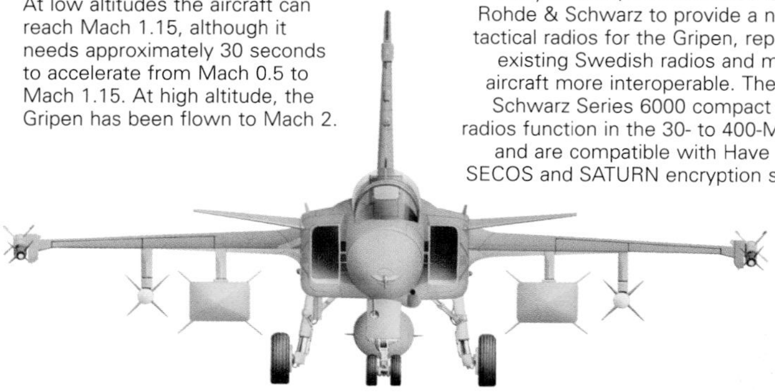

**Armament configuration**
This Gripen is seen in a mixed attack/defence loadout with two BK 90 (DWS 39) glide weapons on the inboard wing pylons and Rb 99 (AIM-120) AMRAAMs on the outboard pylons. The wingtips hold Rb 74 (AIM-9) Sidewinders. The Sidewinder is due for replacement by the IRIS-T.

**Conspicuity**
Subdued markings, a very low-vis colour scheme and the Gripen's small size all combine to make it a difficult opponent in close-in dogfighting. However, some pilots ruefully note that the holographic HUD is so big that it can produce distinctive green flashes of sun 'glint' that can sometimes betray the position of the aircraft.

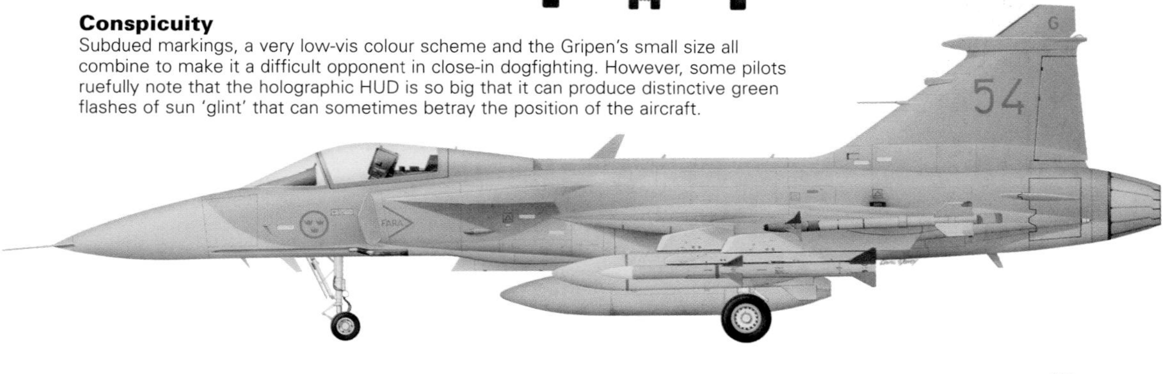

*XW563, the second British single-seater and the seventh prototype overall, turns away from the camera, lugging two 1,000-lb (454-kg) bombs on the centreline. Up to seven similarly-sized weapons could be carried when all four wing pylons were used.*

# Jaguar development

**The amalgamation of requirements put forward by the RAF and the Armée de l'Air, SEPECAT's Jaguar was a major advance over contemporary jets, but suffered in export sales against 'allied' Dassault aircraft.**

*The first Jaguar prototype (E01), a French two-seater (centre), had a shorter fin than later aircraft. It made its maiden flight on 8 September 1968 at Istres. It is seen here accompanied by the second (E02, back) and third (A03, front) prototypes.*

It was in 1962 that the United Kingdom and France found themselves separately looking for a high-performance jet trainer. The Royal Air Force wanted a replacement for the Gnat and Hunter; the Armée de l'Air desired an aircraft to bridge the gap between the Fouga Magister and the Mirage III, but which would also be capable of development into a strike/attack machine. As a result, the French specification was named ECAT – Ecole de Combat d'Appui Tactique (Tactical Combat Support Trainer). Breguet (now part of Dassault) and the British Aircraft Corporation's Warton Division (later BAe Warton) were chosen to participate, the joint company being registered in France to reflect Breguet's design leadership. It was titled SEPECAT – Société Européenne de Production de l'Avion d'Ecole de Combat et d'Appui Tactique (European Production Company for the Combat Training and Tactical Support Aircraft) – and formed in May 1966. The Jaguar was the first Anglo-French combat aircraft and the first RAF aircraft to be designed completely in metric units. The RAF intended to use its aircraft exclusively as advanced trainers, whereas French interest lay in a ground-attack aircraft with STOL performance. Eventually, both the RAF and Armée de l'Air abandoned the combat training role and used the aircraft for strike and attack in single-seat form, merely retaining a handful of two-place machines for pilot conversion duties.

Designed from the outset for close support and daytime interdiction, the Jaguar has a configuration and wing loading optimised for ease of weapon-carrying and stability as a weapon platform at low altitude. Power is provided by two Rolls-Royce/Turboméca Adour reheated turbofans that were the subject of an associated joint development programme. Engine thrust originally lagged behind progressive increases in aircraft weight, leaving the Jaguar noticeably underpowered in hot climates, although this shortcoming was eventually remedied in RAF and export aircraft. Low-speed handling was improved by double-slotted flaps along the entire wing trailing edge, ailerons being omitted in favour of outer wing spoilers.

The first of eight Jaguar prototypes was actually a French two-seat aircraft and made its maiden flight on 8 September 1968, the remaining aircraft of this batch soon displaying the significant differences between UK and French versions. Each air force agreed to buy 200 Jaguars, the RAF split being 165 single-seat and 35 two-seat machines, the former designated Jaguar S (for 'Strike') by the manufacturers and GR.Mk 1 by the RAF. GR.Mk 1s are immediately recognisable by their chisel-shaped noses and fintop pods, respectively housing a Ferranti ARI23231 LRMTS (Laser Ranging and Marked Target Seeker) and Marconi ARI18223 radar warning receiver. Internally, the GR.Mk 1 had a Marconi-GEC 920ATC NAVWASS (Navigation and Weapon-Aiming Sub-System), projecting relevant route and targeting information onto the pilot's HUD and driving a look-down moving-map display.

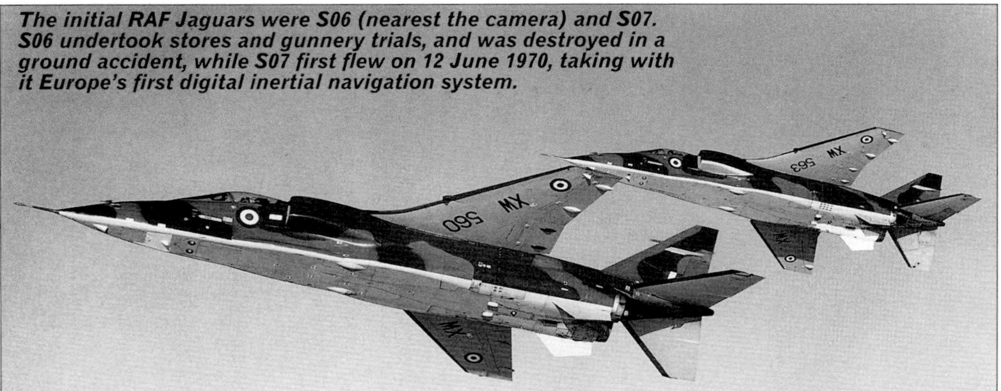


*The initial RAF Jaguars were S06 (nearest the camera) and S07. S06 undertook stores and gunnery trials, and was destroyed in a ground accident, while S07 first flew on 12 June 1970, taking with it Europe's first digital inertial navigation system.*

## Powerplant

Initial production aircraft were powered by two Adour Mk 101

***With a lick of paint, overwing MATRA Magics and a dummy chisel nose, faithful old S07/XW563 became the Jaguar International. The Union Jack/Tricolour logo soon became an ironic joke, with every Jaguar being sold outside France facing competition from Dassault, which was trying to sell the Mirage F1.***

turbofans, each developing 5,115 lb st (22.8 kN) dry and 7,304 lb (32.5 kN) with reheat. After consideration of a variable-geometry air intake for efficient engine performance well above Mach 1, it was decided to opt for a fixed system for simplicity. The Adour had never been airborne, even in a multi-engined testbed, before the first Jaguar take-off from Istres. In its early form, the Adour was less than satisfactory for, having been tailored to the Jaguar in cruising flight, it needed powerful reheat to meet take-off and supersonic requirements. Fuel efficiency was good and gave the Jaguar long legs, but additional power flexibility was required for such contingencies as engine failure on approach.

Useable internal fuel is 920 Imp gal (4182 litres) in self-sealing tanks: 200 (910) in the front fuselage, 258 (1172) in the centre fuselage, 252 (1146) in the rear and 210 (955) in the wing. The centreline pylon and inboard pair of the four wing pylons are 'wet' and able to carry a total of three drop tanks, each holding 261 Imp gal (1187 litres) of useable fuel. The Jaguar A and S variants have a retractable refuelling probe in the starboard side of the forward fuselage, while some French Jaguar Es and Omani Jaguar Bs have a fixed probe in the extreme nose.

The first British aircraft was a single-seat Jaguar (the S06 prototype XW560), which initially flew on 12 October 1969. Delivered between 1973 and 1978, RAF Jaguar GR.Mk 1s served with four nuclear strike squadrons at Brüggen, Germany (Nos 14, 17, 20 and 31), a reconnaissance squadron (No. II) at Laarbruch, Germany, and with the Coltishall Wing's Nos 6, 41 (reconnaissance) and 54 Squadrons, all three tasked with conventional support of NATO forces in Europe.

Despite its lack of radar, a navigator and air defence capability, the Jaguar marked a quantum improvement over the F-4 Phantoms it replaced, giving a genuine ability to find pinpoint targets and attack them with a hitherto unknown degree of accuracy. All-weather operation was not degraded, and the new aircraft proved much more difficult to intercept due to its high speed at very low level. It also introduced an often-practised ability to operate from motorway strips, and a rough-field capability.

The Jaguar B two-seat training variant features a 2-ft 11-in (0.9-m) fuselage stretch to accommodate a second seat, which is raised by 15 in (38 cm). The aircraft were built with the full navigation and attack avionics suite, but have limited combat capability, since they lack lasers, inflight-refuelling probes or radar warning receivers, and have only the port cannon fitted. The first British Jaguar B flew as the B08 prototype (XW566) on 30 August 1970. Britain assigned 35 Jaguar Bs to training duties. Designated T.Mk 2, they were delivered to No. 229 OCU at Lossiemouth for pilot conversion and to each squadron as continuation trainers. A total of 14 T.Mk 2s was upgraded with the more capable FIN1064 nav/attack unit, becoming T.Mk 2As, and also gaining Mk 104 engines.

## Naval version

Navalisation of the Jaguar was one chapter of the aircraft's story with a less than happy ending. The Jaguar M was a single-seat naval machine based on the A version, but having a strengthened airframe, stronger undercarriage, an extended nose wheel leg, a 5.5-*g* capable arrester hook and a laser rangefinder as standard.

M05/F-ZWRJ was the prototype and first flown at Melun/Villaroche on 14 November 1969. Transferred to Istres flight test centre on 21 November, M05 spent much of the ensuing months practising deck landings before being ferried on 20 April to the Royal Aircraft Establishment, Bedford, England, for carrier landing and take-off trials on its catapult and dummy deck.

After a detailed onboard structural examination, the Jaguar M made its first catapult launch at sea on 10 July. The trials ended on 13 July, after 12 landings and launches. M05 returned to Bedford between 24 June and 14 July 1971 to prepare for carrier operations at sea with external stores. In a second series of 20 launches and landings on the same vessel between 20 and 27 October 1971, the aircraft operated at a take-off weight of 27,170 lb (12325 kg) and landed at 20,680 lb (9380 kg). However, the navy was unhappy with Jaguar costs, which meant that it would only be able to afford half of the 100 new fighters it required to replace the Dassault Etendard IV. A study showed that the same money (FFr 1,600 million) would buy 75 A-4 Skyhawks, although the LTV A-7 Corsair was also considered.

Dassault then arrived with a Super Etendard proposal. The firm had taken over Breguet in 1971 and so had a half share in the Jaguar as well as a 100 per cent share in Etendards and Mirages. A government directive of November 1972 ordered Dassault not to promote the Super Etendard, yet two months later the Aéronavale caused consternation by announcing that the aircraft had been selected for service in place of the Jaguar.

Not for the last time did the UK partners in SEPECAT suspect that their new Dassault counterparts regarded the Jaguar as a cuckoo in the Mirage's nest and that Dassault would stop at nothing to promote its own products instead of the Jaguar, on which profits had to be shared with the British.

***Right: The one-off Jaguar M prototype for what promised to be an excellent carrierborne strike fighter is seen landing during trials aboard the carrier, Clemenceau. Dassault persuaded everyone that the twin-engined Jaguar's approach performance was mediocre, and then sold the luckless Aéronavale the single-engined Super Etendard.***

***This early RAF Jaguar (note the lack of LRMTS) carries an early warload, with 'slick' 1,000-lb (454-kg) bombs in tandem inboard, and 19 round SNEB rocket pods side-by-side outboard. A 264-Imp gal (1200-litre) fuel tank is carried on the centreline.***

At the height of Jaguar deployment, RAF Germany boasted no fewer than five squadrons flying the type. Four formed a nuclear-capable strike wing at Brüggen, while one was at Laarbruch (alongside strike Buccaneers) in the tactical reconnaissance role.

# UK operators

**In all but one case, the Jaguar replaced the Phantom in the strike/attack/recce role, equipping squadrons both at home and in Germany. The three UK-based units continue to provide valuable service today.**

## No. II (Army Co-operation) Squadron

Tasked with tactical reconnaissance in RAF Germany, No. II Sqn was resident at Laarbruch with Phantoms when it received its first Jaguar on 26 February 1976 (both types are illustrated below). The last Phantom left in July and the squadron was declared operational on the new type in October. For most sorties the Jaguars carried the BAe centreline reconnaissance pod. The Jaguar era ended in late 1988 as No. II converted to Tornado GR.Mk 1As, the final Jaguar mission being flown on 16 December.

## No. 14 Squadron

No. 14, a previous Phantom operator, became the first RAF Germany Jaguar squadron on 7 April 1975, although full conversion was not achieved until December. Based at Brüggen, the squadron was also the last Jaguar unit in Germany, flying its final mission on 14 October 1985, by which time Tornado GR.Mk 1s had been taken on strength.

## No. 6 Squadron

No. 6 converted from Phantoms on 2 October 1974 and, for its first month, was based at Lossiemouth, before moving to Coltishall, where the squadron remains today. The unit's aircraft carry the Royal Artillery 'gunner's stripe' on the fin and their unofficial 'Flying Can-openers' badge on the intake sides. During the Cold War, No. 6 would have expected to deploy to Tirstrup in Denmark in the event of hostilities. Today, the squadron is one of three Coltishall-based Jaguar units, which are in the process of converting to the updated GR.Mk 3/ T.Mk 4. Like the other remaining Jaguar squadrons, it contributed aircraft and crew during Operation Granby (Gulf War) and shares the burden of manning peacekeeping detachments in Italy and over Iraq.

## No. 17 Squadron

The black/white zig-zag markings and gauntlet badge (commemorating the squadron's use of the Gloster Gauntlet) of No. 17 Squadron first appeared on the Jaguar in June 1975. The first of the new aircraft began replacement of the Phantom FGR.Mk 2, a process completed by February 1976. Part of the Brüggen wing, the Jaguars were employed on a variety of strike/attack duties, including tactical nuclear strike. On 16 August 1984 the squadron received its first Tornado GR.Mk 1, completing the transition on 1 March 1985 when the Jaguar element was disbanded. Shown below is a squadron aircraft cavorting with a Luftwaffe F-104G.

## No. 20 Squadron

No. 20 Squadron was unique in converting to the Jaguar from the Harrier, rather than from the Phantom. Jaguars began arriving at Brüggen in January 1977 while the squadron continued to operate Harriers from Wildenrath. Conversion to the new type and new base was completed on 1 March and the unit joined the rest of the Brüggen wing on strike/attack duties. The squadron had a relatively brief Jaguar career, being disbanded on 24 June 1984. It stood up the next day as a ready-made Tornado GR.Mk 1 unit. In acquiring the Tornado, it became the only squadron to fly all three current RAF attack types.

***The RAF Germany Jaguar force operated from hardened aircraft shelters, unlike those based in the UK.***

## No. 31 Squadron

The third of the Brüggen squadrons to form, No. 31 began receiving Jaguars in January 1976 although it was not until 1 July that the final Phantom bowed out. Between 13 June and 1 November 1984, the squadron made the transition from the Jaguar to the Tornado GR.Mk 1.

## No. 41 Squadron

No. 41 is the UK-based reconnaissance unit, based at Coltishall but with a war base at Tromsö in Norway. The first aircraft arrived to replace the Phantom on 27 April 1976 and the squadron was declared operational on 1 April 1977. Generally carrying centreline multi-sensor pods (illustrated below), the squadron continues in service today, having supplied aircraft and crews for both Gulf Wars.

## No. 54 Squadron

The RAF's first front-line Jaguar unit, No. 54 officially stood up with the type at Lossiemouth on 1 July 1974, although squadron members had been training on it since March. On 8 August 1974 the squadron moved to the operational Jaguar base at Coltishall. Like No. 6 Sqn, No. 54 was a NATO-designated Regional Reinforcement Squadron with a wartime base at Tirstrup. The squadron survives today at Coltishall on the GR.Mk 3/T.Mk 4.

## JCT/226 OCU/No. 16 (Reserve) Squadron

Jaguar pilot training commenced at Lossiemouth in September 1973, initially under the auspices of the Jaguar Conversion Team. With No. 54 Sqn's pilots converted to type, the training effort was formalised as 226 Operational Conversion Unit on 1 October 1974. While Jaguar training was at its height, the OCU was split into Nos 1 and 2 Squadrons, beginning on 11 November 1974. No. 1 Squadron was disbanded shortly after. For a short while, the aircraft of No. 2 Squadron wore a leaping jaguar badge on the side of the nose. Aircraft subsequently acquired a tartan fin-band (from 1981) in addition to 226 OCU's torch and quiver markings which had first appeared on Jaguar intakes in 1977. A two-digit code was applied throughout (left). On 1 November 1991 the OCU was assigned the 'shadow' squadron number of No. 16 Sqn and that unit's 'Saint' markings began to appear. Later, the unit was formalised as No. 16 (Reserve) Squadron (below) and all vestiges of 226 OCU markings disappeared. Throughout its history, the training effort has remained at Lossiemouth, operating from a hangar/apron complex on the west side of the base.

## Trials units

Four MoD test units have operated Jaguars. The first was the Aeroplane & Armament Experimental Establishment at Boscombe Down which performed service tests on the type. Several aircraft have been assigned to the Fixed-Wing Test Squadron over the years. Two Jaguar T.Mk 2s were procured specifically for the Empire Test Pilots' School, also at Boscombe. This pair was written off in accidents, but replaced by two ex-RAF aircraft and operated in Procurement Executive 'ripple' scheme on fast-jet handling work at the school. At least four more Jaguars wore 'ripple' schemes for service with the Royal Aircraft Establishment (renamed Royal Aerospace Establishment, then Defence Research Agency and finally Defence Evaluation Research Agency) at Farnborough and other bases for a variety of systems trials and aviation medicine research. The final test unit is the Strike/Attack Operational Evaluation Unit (SAOEU), part of the Air Warfare Centre. As its name suggests, this unit undertakes the trials of weapons, systems and tactics for the RAF's attack fleet, also operating Harriers and Tornados.

***Two examples of 'raspberry ripple' Jaguar T.Mk 2s are ZB615 (right) which flies with DERA, and XX145 (below), one of two serving with the ETPS. Both are now based at Boscombe Down.***

# French Jaguars

**The Armée de l'Air has operated the Jaguar in four main roles during its 26 years of operations – pre-strategic nuclear strike, conventional tactical air support, electronic warfare and defence suppression. As well as seeing combat in Africa, the French Jaguar played a large part in the war with Iraq in 1991 and more recently in Allied Force.**

## Allied Force

The French fighter/attack force at Istrana included 12 Jaguar As (from EC 1/7, EC 2/7 and EC 3/7) in its complement, used primarily for precision strikes with laser-guided weapons. Shown below is an aircraft armed with a single MATRA BGL-1000 laser-guided bomb, aimed by the ATLIS II designation pod carried on the centreline.

*Seen shortly after taking on fuel from a C-135FR tanker, with its air-to-air refuelling probe extended on the starboard side, this Jaguar A was part of Operation Crécerelle, the French deployment of forces over Bosnia in 1995.*

In France, the Jaguar has always played 'second fiddle' to wholly indigenous aircraft types. Some would suggest that this is because the Jaguar was always 'half-English', and that exports would only ever give France half of the profits, whereas the Mirage F1 (for example) would always give 100 per cent of any profit to Dassault. Others saw the chauvinism involved as coming from Dassault who, rather than initiating the Jaguar design, inherited the aircraft when it absorbed Breguet, the French half of the Jaguar creator, SEPECAT.

***The Cross of Jerusalem in a blue pennant on the tail of this Jaguar identifies it as belonging to 2e Escadrille, Escadron de Chasse 1/7 'Provence', currently based at St Dizier. EC 1/7 is mainly tasked with anti-radar missions, using the AS37 Martel.***

## Low profile

But whatever the reason, the Jaguar has seldom been promoted by Dassault, or by the Armée de l'Air although it has, in truth, been one of the most important types in the French inventory, and has carried out a number of vital operations. But while Britain has made great efforts to sell the Jaguar overseas (with some success), and while the RAF has been pleased to trumpet the aircraft's usefulness and successes, the French Jaguar has often been accorded a low profile.

This dismissive view of the Jaguar in French service has had its effect, of course. Although the type remains in front-line service (and was heavily involved in the 1999 Allied Force air attacks against Serbia), it has never been modernised, and the aircraft remains much as it was when it first entered French service.

## Past technology

To the astonishment of RAF Jaguar pilots who experience the French Jaguar (on exchange tours, for example), the Armée de l'Air version has a very old-fashioned cockpit, drawing comparisons with 1950s fighter-bombers like the Hawker Hunter or Dassault Super Mystère. The French Jaguar was cruder than the RAF aircraft even when it entered service, lacking the RAF aircraft's HUD, projected moving map and NAVWASS navigation and weapons system. Since then, of course, the RAF has modified its Jaguars many times, while the French Jaguar cockpit is much as it always has been. Furthermore, the French Jaguar retains the original Adour Mk 102 engine. Even today, after several successive re-engining and engine upgrade programmes, most RAF pilots regard their aircraft as being underpowered. The French aircraft are, of course far worse, especially in hot-and-high conditions.

But despite this 'simplicity' and lack of power, the Jaguar remains a vital part of the Armée de l'Air inventory, and is much prized for its maintainability, versatility and ability to deploy at minimal notice and with remarkably little support. It is this deployability that has resulted in the aircraft being used in anger against the Polisario in Mauretania in 1977, against Libyan forces in Chad in 1978 and 1986, and during Operation Desert Storm in 1991. Subsequently, French Jaguars have flown combat missions in support of UN operations over Bosnia, Serbia and Kosovo. Some maintain that the ageing Jaguar is still the weapon of choice for French commanders who have to fight a real war.

The Jaguar was not always regarded as being solely an aircraft for rapid deployment and out-of-area operations, however. When it became operational in 1974, Escadre de Chasse fulfilled the nuclear strike role, using the indigenous AN 52 bomb, and this task was retained until 31 August 1991. EC 7 had three front-line escadrons (EC 1/7 'Provence', EC 3/7 'Languedoc' and EC 4/7 'Limousin' – the latter existing only between April 1980 and July 1989) and another which functioned as the Jaguar OCU (EC 2/7 'Argonne'). It was augmented by a single element of EC 3 (EC 3/3 'Ardennes' at Nancy-Ochey) between April 1977 and June 1987, and by Escadre de Chasse 11. The Toul-based EC 11, with its four escadrons (EC 1/11 'Roussillon', EC 2/11 'Vosges', EC 3/11 'Corse' and EC 4/11 'Jura'), tended to fulfill the out-of-area role.

EC 11 disbanded, escadron by escadron, and passed its commitments (and many of its aircraft) to EC 7, whose three constituent squadrons went from 15 to 20 aircraft each. EC 3/11 'Corse' finally disbanded in July 1997.

***French single-seat Jaguar As are equipped with a neat foldaway inflight-refuelling probe, while the two-seat Jaguar Es have a fixed probe on the nose. C-135FRs and KC-135Rs provide the Armée de l'Air's inflight-refuelling capability.***

## Vital role

Today, France's under-powered and simply-equipped Jaguars continue to play a vital role in France's defence, using a wide variety of weapons. In this area, the French Jaguars do have capabilities not shared by the RAF, notably with the AS30L laser-guided missile, which gives French Jaguar pilots a real stand-off PGM. Unfortunately, though, the carriage of AS30 and an ATLIS laser designator pod leaves only one pylon available for fuel, while defensive AAMs (MATRA Magics), chaff/flare dispensers and ECM pods jostle for the remaining two pylons. RAF aircraft do at least have the option of a pair of dedicated overwing missile pylons.

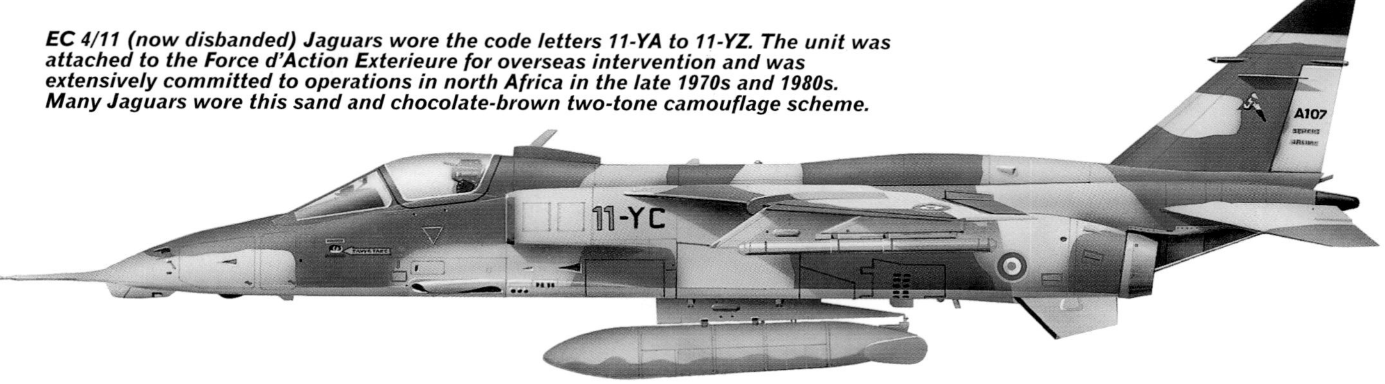


***EC 4/11 (now disbanded) Jaguars wore the code letters 11-YA to 11-YZ. The unit was attached to the Force d'Action Exterieure for overseas intervention and was extensively committed to operations in north Africa in the late 1970s and 1980s. Many Jaguars wore this sand and chocolate-brown two-tone camouflage scheme.***

# Jaguar International Operators

*Traditionally an operator of British-built aircraft, Oman ordered a squadron of 12 Jaguar Internationals in 1974 and in the mid-1980s ordered a further squadron. Two trainer aircraft were also obtained in 1982.*

**From its earliest days, several nations saw the SEPECAT Jaguar as an answer to a number of their needs. However, because of Dassault's subversive sales techniques, sales were lost to Mirage aircraft.**

Serious marketing of the Jaguar began in 1974 when BAC revealed details of export orders from undisclosed customers (in fact Ecuador and Oman). Several days later an RAF aircraft was displayed with Jaguar International titles and a mock radar nose, surrounded by weaponry appropriate to an export variant. This Jaguar was subsequently fitted with Adour Mk 104 RT-172-26 engines with 27 per cent higher thrust over the original Mk 102, and therefore became the prototype Jaguar International.

The designation Jaguar K had originally been earmarked for export S and B Jaguars, however, this was never used and each export customer instead received its own specific two letter designation. The first production Jaguar International was a two-seat aircraft for Ecuador and was officially designated Jaguar EB. The single seat Ecuador variant goes by the name Jaguar ES.

In the early years of its service the Jaguar attracted attention from several countries, and in 1974 Belgium was offered a work-sharing agreement. A UK sales team visited Kuwait the same year, followed by a team from Dassault. Kuwait's subsequent order for 50 Jaguars and 16 Mirage F1s raised a few eyebrows. Ultimately, the F1 order was confirmed but the Jaguar one was not. 1975 saw Turkey, with funding from Libya, and Egypt plan to buy 24 and 50-60 Jaguars respectively, but the Egyptians opted instead to buy the Dassault-Dornier Alpha Jet. Abu Dhabi considered the Jaguar instead of buying a second squadron of Mirage IIIs, though the Mirage was ultimately selected. Pakistan was another potential customer, and considered buying 100 Jaguars since the US had refused to supply the Pakistanis their first choice, the LTV A-7 Corsair II, because of an arms embargo. Ultimately, the Pakistanis ordered Mirage 5s.

All of the eventual Jaguar export orders were completed by British sales teams and what is more, they did so in the face of adversity from their supposed colleagues at SEPECAT, who rubbished the Jaguar to sell more Mirage aircraft.

*Ecuador was the first export customer of the Jaguar, ordering 12 – 10 single-seaters and 2 two-seaters – in 1974. These equipped one squadron of Grupo 211. The Ecuadorians operate Jaguars alongside Kfirs and Mirage F1s.*

## Global Jaguar

Ecuador was the first export customer for the Jaguar, placing an order, for ten single-seat Jaguar International ESs and two twin-stick EBs, which was announced in 1974. Deliveries began in January 1977, allowing the re-

*Nigeria ordered its 18 Jaguars in 1983, with the option to buy a further 18. The first aircraft arrived the following year and were delivered to a squadron at Makurdi under NF Strike Command, passing to Tactical Command when the former was disbanded.*

equipment of Escuadrón de Combate 2111 at Taura. Six surviving single-seaters were upgraded with over-wing missile launch rails for the Matra Magic R550 from 1994, while all eight surviving aircraft had their original NAVWASS replaced by Ferranti's FIN 1064 INAS. A further upgrade is likely, probably incorporating elements of the RAF's Jaguar 97 modification package.

Oman's first Jaguar order was one of the two (with Ecuador's) announced (anonymously) by BAC on 28 August 1974. It was soon revealed that the customer for ten Jaguar International OS single-seaters and two OB two-seaters was Oman. Delivered from March 1977, the first batch entered service with No. 8 Squadron at Masirah. A second order for another 12 aircraft (again including two trainers) was placed in mid-1980, and the air force subsequently received an ex-Indian loan RAF Jaguar T.Mk 2 and an ex-RAF GR.Mk 1. The second batch of aircraft, fitted with the more powerful Mk 811 engine and upgraded avionics, re-equipped No. 20 Squadron at Masirah from 1983. Delivered in a configuration similar to that of the original RAF GR.Mk 1 and T.Mk 2 the Omani Jaguars were subsequently brought up to GR.Mk 1A/ T.Mk 2A standards (apart from their more powerful export-standard engines), and a contract has now been signed for a further upgrade to Jaguar 97 standard.

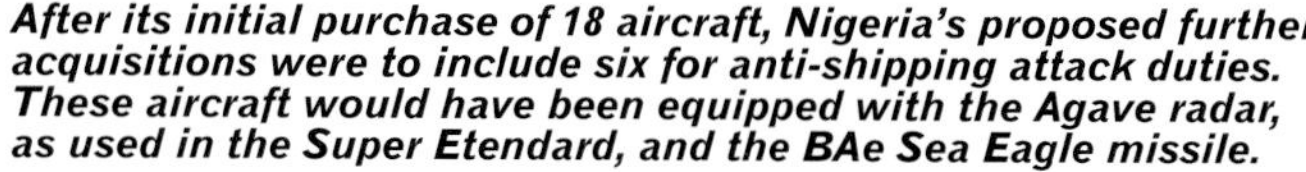

***After its initial purchase of 18 aircraft, Nigeria's proposed further acquisitions were to include six for anti-shipping attack duties. These aircraft would have been equipped with the Agave radar, as used in the Super Etendard, and the BAe Sea Eagle missile.***

Nigeria ordered 18 Jaguar Internationals (including five two-seat Jaguar BNs) in 1983. The first of these was delivered in May 1984 but was used initially for aircrew training at Warton. The first two aircraft were passed on to Makurdi on 30 October 1984. A second batch of 18 aircraft (including six maritime versions with Agave radar) was cancelled, and the type was withdrawn from use as an economy measure in 1991, when ten single-seat SNs and four BNs remained in service. Speculation as to the future for the Nigerian Jaguars remains rife. Some believe that the aircraft remain BAe or even British Government property, and rumours circulate that they were never fully paid for. The surviving aircraft have reportedly been surveyed for re-sale and most are said to be structurally sound, having accumulated relatively few flying hours.

## Japanese interest

In the 1970s, when Japan was deciding how to replace its T-33 and F-86 training aircraft, BAC and Breguet offered to lease 30 two-seat Jaguars for the period 1971-4. As the Jaguar had originally been planned as a training aircraft, this seemed a logical suggestion and the idea found some favour with Japanese military officials. The idea of licence production was also mooted, but Japan's refusal to pay more than five per cent royalties (when the norm was eight to 16 per cent) to SEPECAT meant that the deal fell through. However, the Jaguar did influence the Japanese immensely and the Mitsubishi T-2's development owed a great deal to the Jaguar's design.

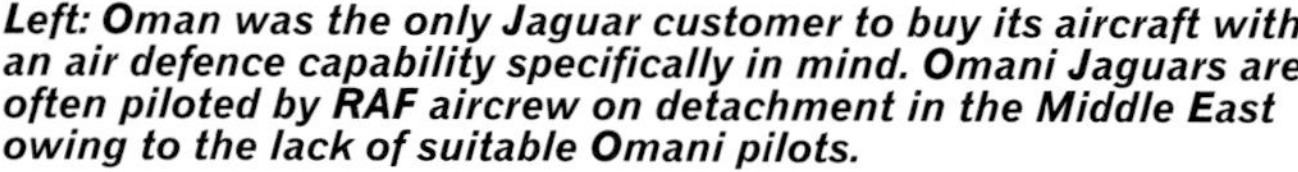

***Left: Oman was the only Jaguar customer to buy its aircraft with an air defence capability specifically in mind. Omani Jaguars are often piloted by RAF aircrew on detachment in the Middle East owing to the lack of suitable Omani pilots.***

***Below: Ecuadorian Jaguar pilots have to come to Lossiemouth in Scotland every 18 months for emergency procedure check out training as the FAE (Fuerza Aérea Ecuatoriana) does not have its own Jaguar simulator.***

*A trio of No. 14 Squadron Jaguars formates for the camera. Known as the 'Fighting Fourteenth', the squadron was declared operational on the Jaguar in September 1980, after its pilots had completed their training in the UK.*

# Indian operations

**India is the major export customer for the Jaguar International, employing the aircraft in the ground and maritime strike roles. Over 100 Jaguars remain in operation today, and various upgrades have ensured that the aircraft will remain in service for many more years.**

Having previously operated the Canberra and Hunter in the ground attack role, with great success, the Indian air force naturally looked to the UK for a successor to these important types in its inventory. The first expressions of interest in the Jaguar emerged even before the aircraft flew, in 1966, although it was to be 1978 before India placed a firm order for the aircraft, following a fierce competition with the Mirage F1 and Saab Viggen. Even then, the decision to procure Jaguars was nearly cancelled in 1980, when the incoming government attempted to overturn major procurement decisions taken by its predecessor.

## First squadron

However, the Jaguar procurement decision was based on unassailable logic, and had gone too far to be cancelled. Even before the 1978 announcement, steps had been taken to prepare for the Jaguar, and the first four Indian pilots were posted to the RAF's No. 226 OCU in February 1976, staying with No. 54 Squadron after their course. Eight more pilots followed them, four going to No. 41 Squadron to gain reconnaissance experience. These 12 pilots formed the nucleus of the first Indian Jaguar squadron, No. 14, which re-equipped with 18 loaned RAF Jaguars in July 1979. The squadron was declared operational at Ambala in September 1980.

Two of the loaned aircraft were lost in service, and two were retained for trials work, but the rest returned to the UK between 1982 and 1984, as 40 new-build Batch Two Jaguar Internationals (including five twin-stickers) were delivered. These aircraft were basically similar to the RAF GR.Mk 1, with Marconi NAVWASS, but were powered by Adour Mk 804 engines, the export equivalent to the later Adour Mk 104. The type was briefly known as the *Shamsher* ('Sword of Justice') in Indian service, and the aircraft was designated Jaguar IS or Jaguar IT (two-seaters). These early aircraft re-equipped No. 14 Squadron, and also allowed the formation of a second unit, No. 5 Squadron, which formed around a cadre provided by No. 14 and which became operational in August 1981. Thus, Nos 5 and 14 Squadrons, operating the British-built, NAVWASS-equipped Batch Two Jaguar International aircraft, made up the wing at Ambala.

The second batch of 45 new-build aircraft (confusingly known as Batch 3) was assembled in India from BAe-supplied components

*Above: No. 6 Squadron ('Dragons') uses the Jaguar IM in the maritime attack role. These aircraft are fitted with the Agave radar and can carry the BAe Sea Eagle anti-ship missile.*

*The original batch of Jaguar IMs delivered to the IAF is due to receive a radar upgrade, replacing the current Agave unit (seen here) with the new ELTA EL/M-2032 radar. An additional four new-build aircraft will also be equipped to this standard.*

and sub-assemblies. The aircraft incorporated a number of improvements, and were powered by more powerful RT172-58 Adour Mk 811 engines. The aircraft featured a MIL STD 1553B digital databus and had a new locally-integrated DARIN (Display Attack and Ranging Inertial Navigation) nav-attack system. This was built up around a Sea Harrier-type Smiths (GEC Avionics) Type 1301 HUDWAS, a GEC-Ferranti COMED 2054 (Combined Map and Electronic Display) as used in the F/A-18, and a SAGEM ULISS 82 INS, as well as locally-designed IFF, ADF, radalt, V/UHF and HF/SSB. No. 27 Squadron ('Flaming Arrows') formed with the new DARIN-equipped Jaguars at Bangalore in June 1985, moving back to Gorakhpur after conversion.

No. 16 Squadron ('Cobras') was the next unit to form, converting to the Indian-assembled DARIN aircraft at Gorakhpur in October 1986. Batch 3 included eight Jaguar IMs, dedicated maritime aircraft with nose-mounted Agave radar and provision to fire a Sea Eagle ASM from the centreline pylon.

***Part of Western Air Command, No. 14 Squadron operates the Jaguar IS in the deep strike role. The aircraft use overwing rails to carry R550 Magic air-to-air missiles for self-defence.***

The Indian maritime Jaguars equipped 'A' Flight of No. 6 Squadron ('Dragons') at Pune, operating alongside the unit's Canberras.

A total of 45 Jaguars, assembled by Hindustan Aeronautics Ltd (HAL), were to have been followed by the production of 56 more Jaguars, but instead India procured a further 31 aircraft (all single-seaters) which were again assembled largely from BAe-supplied kits. An order for 15 extra aircraft was cancelled in 1989 (having been approved in January 1988) and then resurrected in 1993. Four of these aircraft were Maritime Jaguars, fitted with the ELTA EL/M-2032 radar, which will also be fitted to the surviving Jaguar IMs already in service with No. 6 Squadron, while further Jaguars were ordered in 2000.

### Fleet upgrade

India has an outstanding requirement to upgrade its entire Jaguar fleet, and especially the original NAVWASS-equipped 'Direct Supply' aircraft, since NAVWASS must now be regarded as obsolete. A limited upgrade of a number of two-seat Jaguars to integrate the Israeli Litening laser designator pod has been reported, and a programme of 'Stealth' enhancements has been tested, and may be being adopted fleet-wide.

Some sources suggest that an Indian Jaguar upgrade would be likely to include the integration of Russian avionics systems, to ensure compatibility with other in-service platforms. This, however, seems unlikely, and reports of Indian interest in the RAF's Jaguar 97 programme seem more credible.

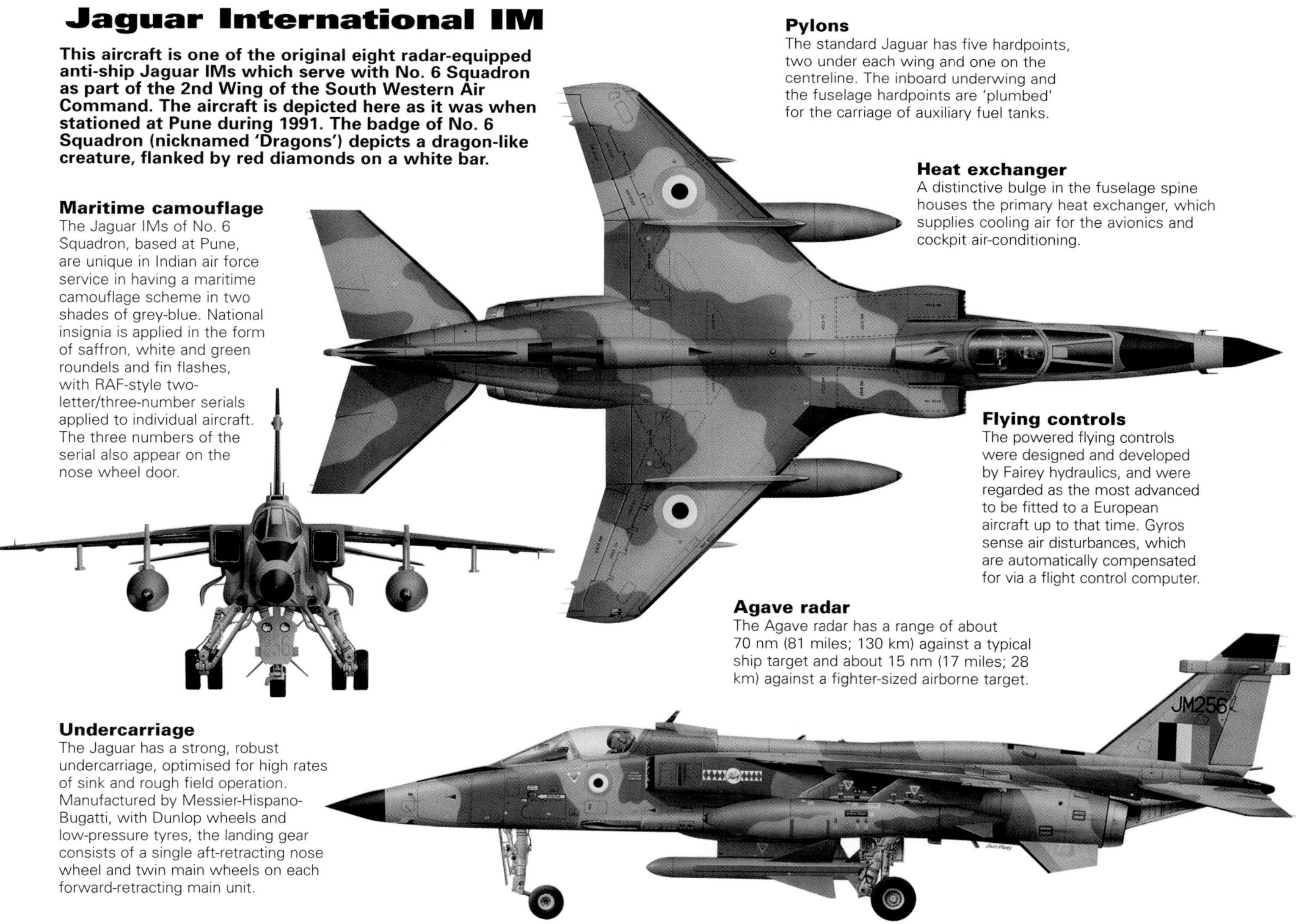


## Jaguar International IM

**This aircraft is one of the original eight radar-equipped anti-ship Jaguar IMs which serve with No. 6 Squadron as part of the 2nd Wing of the South Western Air Command. The aircraft is depicted here as it was when stationed at Pune during 1991. The badge of No. 6 Squadron (nicknamed 'Dragons') depicts a dragon-like creature, flanked by red diamonds on a white bar.**

**Maritime camouflage**
The Jaguar IMs of No. 6 Squadron, based at Pune, are unique in Indian air force service in having a maritime camouflage scheme in two shades of grey-blue. National insignia is applied in the form of saffron, white and green roundels and fin flashes, with RAF-style two-letter/three-number serials applied to individual aircraft. The three numbers of the serial also appear on the nose wheel door.

**Pylons**
The standard Jaguar has five hardpoints, two under each wing and one on the centreline. The inboard underwing and the fuselage hardpoints are 'plumbed' for the carriage of auxiliary fuel tanks.

**Heat exchanger**
A distinctive bulge in the fuselage spine houses the primary heat exchanger, which supplies cooling air for the avionics and cockpit air-conditioning.

**Flying controls**
The powered flying controls were designed and developed by Fairey hydraulics, and were regarded as the most advanced to be fitted to a European aircraft up to that time. Gyros sense air disturbances, which are automatically compensated for via a flight control computer.

**Agave radar**
The Agave radar has a range of about 70 nm (81 miles; 130 km) against a typical ship target and about 15 nm (17 miles; 28 km) against a fighter-sized airborne target.

**Undercarriage**
The Jaguar has a strong, robust undercarriage, optimised for high rates of sink and rough field operation. Manufactured by Messier-Hispano-Bugatti, with Dunlop wheels and low-pressure tyres, the landing gear consists of a single aft-retracting nose wheel and twin main wheels on each forward-retracting main unit.

# RAF Jaguar upgrades

**The RAF's ageing Jaguars are being transformed with new systems and weapons. This process will make them arguably the most capable all-rounders in the RAF's inventory, with formidable capabilities in precision attack as well as self-defence.**

***Above: This formation comprises one Jaguar from each of the Coltishall Wing's units. Their weapons represent the Jaguar's new precision attack capabilities, namely TIALD and laser-guided bombs.***

***Above: The cockpit of a Jaguar 96 shows the new digital moving map display, and the control column with stick top from the Tornado F.Mk 3. The Jaguar 97 gained a further display for imagery from TIALD and reconnaissance sensors.***

The Jaguar's performance in the Gulf War showed its inherent versatility, maintainability and deployability, and helped overcome real pressures to withdraw the type from RAF service prematurely, as an economic measure.

The aircraft's flexibility and ease of servicing, and the RAF Jaguar force's long-practised out-of-area deployment capabilities, make the Jaguar the perfect aircraft in the post-Cold War era. It became the aircraft of choice for deployment overseas in support of NATO and UN peacekeeping and ceasefire monitoring operations.

NATO operations in the former Yugoslavia revealed that the RAF had a critical shortage in its ability to deliver precision-guided munitions autonomously, and this led to a crash programme to introduce a laser designation capability into service in the shortest possible time. Work was already under way to incorporate TIALD (GEC's podded Thermal Imaging Airborne Laser Designator) onto RAF Tornados, following the emergency TIALD integration on five aircraft during Operation Desert Storm, but it was contractually difficult to speed up the process. The RAF's Harrier force, meanwhile, already had more than enough on its plate integrating other new weapons and sensors, leaving the Jaguar as the next most logical platform into which to integrate a laser designator. A DRA (Defence Research Agency) Jaguar had, in fact, already been fitted with TIALD for generic trials aimed at ascertaining the feasibility of using the pod in a single-seat fast jet. The trials were intended to prove that the pod could be used by the Harrier GR.Mk 7 (and later Eurofighter) but also had the effect of showing the Jaguar's suitability as a TIALD platform.

Accordingly, the RAF's Urgent Operational Requirement

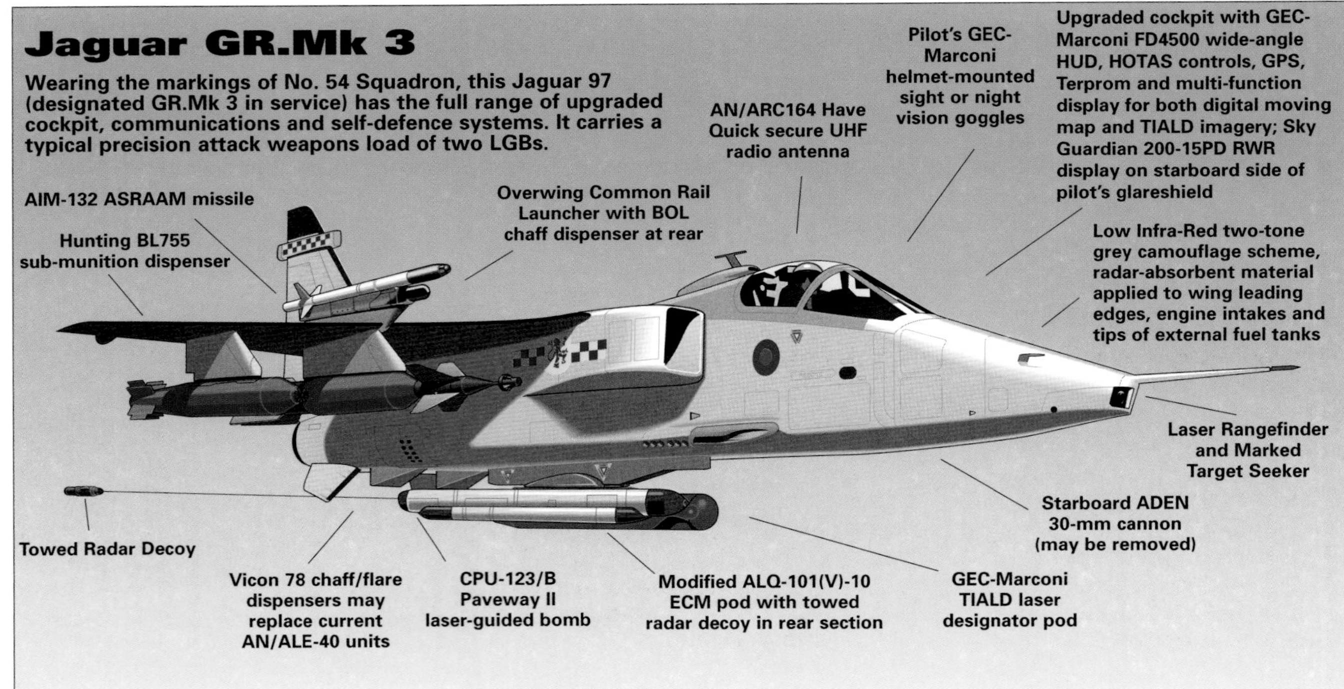


**Jaguar GR.Mk 3**

**Wearing the markings of No. 54 Squadron, this Jaguar 97 (designated GR.Mk 3 in service) has the full range of upgraded cockpit, communications and self-defence systems. It carries a typical precision attack weapons load of two LGBs.**

## Upgraded Jaguar weapons and stores

New weapons are being cleared in stages for the different Jaguar upgrades. They will retain the standard fixed internal armament of two 30-mm ADEN cannon, although the starboard gun may be removed. The upgraded Jaguar will retain several weapons which were cleared rapidly for combat operations during Desert Storm. US CBU-87 cluster bombs for medium-level bombing augmented Hunting BL755s used for low-level work, while Canadian CRV-7 2¾ in (70-mm) high-velocity rockets proved highly effective against Iraqi armoured and hardened fixed targets. They can be carried in seven- or 19-round pods. For self-defence against the Iraqi air threat, RAF Jaguars received AIM-9L Sidewinder air-to-air missiles, carried on overwing missile pylons as originally fitted to the Jaguar International. Jaguar 97s will receive Common Rail Launchers with rear BOL chaff dispensers and the AIM-132 ASRAAM short-range AAM which, when used in conjunction with the helmet-mounted cueing system, will give the Jaguar the ability to engage targets at even greater off-boresight angles than the AIM-9 Sidewinder.

However, the Jaguar will receive its most significant boost in the field of precision attack. The standard British 1,000-lb (454-kg) bomb can be modified with a Paveway II laser-guidance kit to make the CPU-123/B LGB. Greatly improved low-level capability and stand-off range will come from the US 2,000-lb (907-kg) GBU-24 Paveway III LGB, which has already been dropped from a trials Jaguar. This weapon has been recently procured by the RAF for its Tornado GR.Mk 1s and Harrier GR.Mk 7s. Currently, the Tornado IDS is the RAF's sole operational launch platform for the BAe ALARM anti-radar missile. Integration of this weapon would make Jaguar a highly capable SEAD aircraft. Other possible minimum collateral damage weapons include 500-lb (227-kg) LGBs such as the US GBU-12B/D, laser Maverick ASMs, and Hellfire or Brimstone anti-armour missiles.

***A Jaguar 96 reveals its teeth at Boscombe Down. Arrayed on the floor are ALARMs, CPU-123/Bs, 1,000-lb and BL755 bombs, CRLs, Phimat and ALQ-101 pods. CRV-7 rocket pods are also carried, with ASRAAMs overwing.***

(UOR) for a rapid TIALD integration was framed around providing TIALD integration on 12 Jaguars, 10 single-seaters (later designated GR.Mk 1B) and two two-seaters (T.Mk 2B). The UOR was raised in June 1994, and in May 1995 two aircraft flew the first TIALD missions over Bosnia. This was a remarkable achievement, especially since the GR.Mk 1B had also received a MIL STD 1553B databus, Global Positioning System (GPS) equipment, and a digital moving map. The UOR work was incorporated by RAF St Athan and DERA (Defence Equipment Research Agency) Boscombe Down, rather than by BAe, the aircraft's original manufacturer.

The Jaguar GR.Mk 1B flew over Bosnia in a self-designation configuration, with a centreline tank and with a laser-guided bomb (LGB) and TIALD carried asymmetrically underwing, but was also capable of designating ('spiking') targets for other LGB-carrying aircraft, with TIALD on the centreline and with two underwing tanks. In this configuration, Jaguars 'spiked' for Harrier GR.Mk 7s during Operation Deliberate Force. The success and relatively low cost of the UOR upgrade led to an RAF requirement to upgrade the rest of its Jaguars to a similar standard.

### Jaguar 96 upgrade

The RAF's Jaguars are thus being upgraded under an ambitious two-stage programme, leading to so-called Jaguar 96 and Jaguar 97 configurations although, when service release is obtained, all will be known as Jaguar GR.Mk 3s or T.Mk 4s. The interim Jaguar 96 features a new head-up display (HUD), provision for the digital moving map (though not all have the new display screen), GPS, and the BASE Terprom terrain reference navigation system. This gives a degree of passive terrain avoidance/warning capability, and is capable of providing accurate passive ranging for weapons delivery. Four Jaguar 96s are TIALD-compatible, and several more are capable of carrying reconnaissance sensors, principally the Vinten Series 603 GP(1). The Jaguar 96 is an interim aircraft, and all surviving Jaguars will eventually be converted to Jaguar 97 configuration. The first aircraft to be modified to Jaguar 96 standards was XX738, which took to the air in January 1996.

***XX108, an early production Jaguar, was used for various trials and test work by BAe and DRA Boscombe Down. The only fully instrumented Jaguar, it carried out aerodynamic trials to clear TIALD and the carriage of asymmetric weapons loads.***

The full-standard Jaguar 97 has a more advanced LCD screen for TIALD information and the digital moving map, and all Jaguar 97 aircraft will be compatible with both TIALD and recce pods. The Jaguar 97 will also be integrated with a helmet-mounted sight and with a new mission planner, and may gain new weapons, including ASRAAM and perhaps even systems like a towed radar decoy. The helmet sight will be able to cue the pilot's attention to pre-briefed targets or to obstacles, and will be capable of cueing the TIALD pod or air-to-air missile seeker heads, thereby giving the Jaguar a highly formidable self-defence capability.

***Remarkably, many of the improvements incorporated on the Jaguar were spend-to-save measures, actually saving money through their improved reliability, supportability and durability.***

Other possible additions to a 'Jaguar 98' configuration could include a Forward-Looking Infra-Red (FLIR), advanced ECM, an anti-radar missile such as the BAe ALARM, and even a JTIDS or MIDS tactical datalink. Even without such features, the Jaguar GR.Mk 3 will be one of the most capable fighter-bombers in service, with many of the same systems that are planned for the next-generation Eurofighter.

### Uprated engines

The Jaguar upgrade is being accompanied by a number of other programmes. Addressing the aircraft's perceived lack of thrust, the Jaguar 97 will be fitted with a new, more powerful Adour Mk 106 engine, developing 25 per cent more thrust than the Mk 104 currently fitted. Finally, all Jaguar 97s will be capable of carrying reconnaissance sensors, including the state-of-the-art GP(1) EO electro-optical reconnaissance pod. This system will make the Jaguars of No. 41(F) Squadron among the world's most capable tactical reconnaissance platforms.

# Jaguar over Bosnia

**After performing with conspicuous success during Operation Granby, the RAF's Jaguars enjoyed something of a renaissance, thanks to their blend of useful capabilities and easy and rapid deployability.**

While RAF Harriers were constrained by airfield surface and FOD considerations (proving unable to operate from bases like Cairo West), the Jaguar could go wherever there was a long enough runway, though a lack of thrust meant that 'hot-and-high' performance could be marginal. Moreover, a squadron could deploy at a moment's notice, and with minimal ground support.

With the Tornado force heavily committed to operations over Iraq, maintaining detachments in Saudi Arabia and Kuwait, the Jaguar and Harrier forces took it in turns to fulfil commitments over Northern Iraq (operating from Turkey) and the Balkans (flying from Italy).

The Jaguar force first deployed to Gioia del Colle on 16 July 1993, when No. 6 Squadron deployed 12 aircraft for participation in Operation Deny Flight. The Jaguars were among the NATO fighter bombers which were tasked with mounting standing CAPs over Bosnia, ready to respond to calls for assistance from NATO ground forces, and deterring aggression by their presence. The Jaguars were soon called upon to mount some expertly flown mock attacks, circling to keep enemy guns quiet. They also flew vital recce missions, usually using two aircraft, one carrying the original BAe-built recce pod and the other carrying a Vinten Type 18 Series 603 LOROP pod. Sometimes a recce pair would be accompanied by a bomb-toting Jaguar flying 'top-cover'. The Jaguars deployed were to full Granby standards, with Have Quick radios, overwing Sidewinder missile rails and a comprehensive defensive aids fit, including chaff/flare dispensers, and underwing AN/ALQ-101 ECM and Phimat chaff pods. They usually carried underwing fuel tanks, leaving the centreline pylon free for a recce pod or for one or two 1,000-lb (454-kg) bombs. The aircraft were painted in an overall light grey colour scheme, and had all squadron markings removed. The three Coltishall squadrons took it in turns to man the detachment.

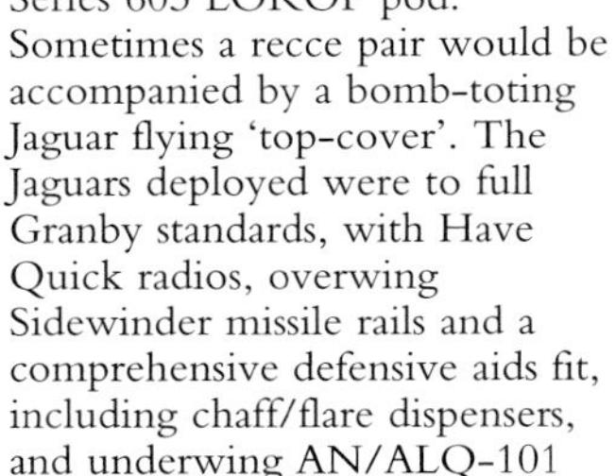

***Above: This Jaguar is fully equipped for a combat mission in the Balkans theatre, armed with a pair of live 1,000-lb (454-kg) bombs, overwing Sidewinders and a full fit of pods and tanks.***

***Top: Two Jaguars, configured as a recce machine (lead aircraft) and as a bomber, await their turn on the tanker somewhere over the Adriatic. The Jaguar's lack of power was more than made up for by its great versatility and useful 'buddy-lasing' capability.***

***Clutching a TIALD pod to its belly, this No. 54 Sqn Jaguar also provides a good view of the Phimat pod which has become a near permanent fixture on the type's starboard outer pylon. In this configuration the 'Jag' has only AIM-9 and gun armament.***

## Tank-busting

The Jaguars first went into action on 22 September 1994, when three No. 41(F) Sqn 'Jags' attacked a Serb tank which had pinned down a NATO FAC. The Serbs closed Sarajevo airport for two and a half weeks in retaliation for the attack.

Two RAF Jaguars dropped unguided 1,000-lb bombs during the NATO air raid against the Krajina Serb air base at Udbina on 21 November 1995, with two more flying post-strike reconnaissance sorties. All four aircraft were flown by pilots

***Where relatively FOD-free bases can be provided, the Harrier GR.Mk 7 is a highly capable attack platform. Working in co-operation with TIALD-equipped Jaguars, the type was able to deliver LGBs against Serbian targets.***

from No. 54 Squadron.

Even before the raid on Udbina, it had become clear that the RAF was in danger of being sidelined in Bosnia because it lacked sufficient autonomous laser designation capability. The growing need to avoid collateral damage placed increasing emphasis on the use of Laser Guided Bombs (LGBs) and other PGMs, but there was a great shortage of airborne designation capability in-theatre.

The RAF's Buccaneers had retired during 1993, together with their Pave Spike pods, and while the Panavia Tornado/TIALD combination (combat proven in prototype form during Granby) was effective enough, it was contractually difficult to speed up the process of integrating the production TIALD pod onto the aircraft.

Accordingly, in 1994, an Urgent Operational Requirement was issued to integrate TIALD onto the Jaguar. This built on a fortuitous single-seat TIALD demonstration and feasibility study which had been carried out using a DERA Jaguar. The aircraft received a new cockpit display, and an integrated INS/GPS, together with a MIL STD 1553B digital databus.

The resulting Jaguar GR.Mk 1B was produced in record time, and three aircraft were deployed to Bosnia in June 1995. The aircraft were configured in a self-designation fit, carrying TIALD pods and a Paveway II LGB, and came close to being used in anger. They were actually despatched on a multi-national mission in July 1995, but this was recalled after take off.

The Jaguars were replaced in theatre by Harriers at the end of July 1995, but two TIALD-equipped Jaguars were maintained on standby to provide laser designation for the Harriers if required.

When NATO launched Operation Deliberate Force, in an effort to force the Serbs to the negotiating table, the two TIALD-equipped Jaguars were deployed and were quickly in action. The Jaguars were flown by pilots from No. 6 Sqn, and normally flew singly, escorting packages of four LGB-armed Harrier GR.Mk 7s.

## Third party designation

RAF Harriers dropped 48 Paveway II LGBs during Operation Vulcan, all of them relying on third party designation by the Jaguars. Some 41 of these (86 percent) scored direct hits, with four more (another 7 percent) falling within 20 ft (6 m) of their aim points. This was an extremely impressive record, which has not been equalled in subsequent RAF operations using TIALD, and which was a better success rate than was achieved by USAF Lockheed F-117 Nighthawks and General Dynamics F-111s during Operation Desert Storm.

The Jaguar had certainly proved that it was still an extremely important platform for the RAF, while the upgrade which created the GR.Mk 1B version became a template for such modifications. The entire Jaguar fleet was subsequently brought up to the same standard, under the designation Jaguar 96 and Jaguar 97 (later GR.Mk 3 and GR.Mk 3A).

The Jaguar force took over the Gioia del Colle detachment again in February 1997, continuing to fly CAS and recce missions over the former Yugoslavia until April 1998, when the RAF deployment came to an end.

***Left: The Canadian-manufactured CRV-7 rocket is another Jaguar weapon of choice. This powerful weapon, carried in pods on the inboard wing pylons, was integrated with the British Jaguar during Operation Desert Storm.***

***Below: The TIALD/Jaguar combination is particularly effective. Compared to the TIALD/Tornado integration, changes were made to the Jaguar fit so that the pod could be better used by the Jaguar's single crew member.***

# ShinMaywa PS-1/US-1A

***The original PS-1 was a dedicated ASW flying boat, optimised for very long-range patrol duties. The prototype and two pre-production aircraft were followed by 20 production aircraft. The type served from 1971 to 1989, when it was replaced by land-based P-3 Orions.***

## Japan's big 'boats

**The Kawanishi company won a deserved reputation for its wartime military flying boats, and re-named as Shin Meiwa in 1949, re-entered the flying-boat business in the early 1960s. It did so with the PS-1, the first of a new generation of large, turbine-engined flying boats, a trend-breaking design which inspired similar new designs from Beriev in Russia and Harbin in China.**

As an island nation and a major maritime trading power, Japan has traditionally placed a heavy emphasis on protecting commercial shipping. In the age of the aircraft, this led to an early interest in the use of flying boats for ASW and maritime patrol duties. During World War II, Kawanishi dominated the Japanese flying-boat scene, not least with its massive H8K 'Emily', regarded by many as being the best flying boat of the war. For the first few years after World War II, the former Kawanishi company, re-named as Shin Meiwa, worked principally as a sub-contractor, producing components and sub-assemblies for other manufacturers. But the company never lost its interest in flying boats, nor its ambition to build flying boats of its own design.

Shin Meiwa began actively lobbying to build such an aircraft for the JMSDF from as early as 1952, believing that in certain key areas it could produce an aircraft which would be superior to contemporary US designs, exemplified by the Grumman UF-1 Albatross, six of which were procured for the JMSDF from 1961.

***Above: Withdrawal of the PS-1 did not mark the end of the Shin Meiwa flying boat, since an amphibious SAR derivative had already been designed, under the designation US-1.***

### UF-XS

Shin Meiwa bought a further Albatross from the USA and used this aircraft as a flying test-bed for testing its own ideas. This aircraft, designated as the UF-XS, was extensively modified by Shin Meiwa, which aimed to improve stability on the water in high seas, improve STOL performance, and reduce water ingestion by the engines. The hull was considerably modified, with a new step, a spray suppressor on the nose, and fairing back to a raked knife edge stern. The aircraft gained two additional 600-hp (447-kW) Pratt & Whitney R-1340 radial engines outboard of the usual 1,425 hp (1063-kW) Wright R-1820s, and a T58 turboshaft was installed to provide compressed air for the blown flaps and tail. The aircraft first flew in its new form on 25 December 1962, and heavily influenced the design of the all-new SS-2 flying boat.

Design of the SS-2 was well advanced in January 1966, when the JMSDF issued a development contract to meet its PX-S requirement. The first prototype was thus able to make its maiden flight on 29 October 1967. Shin Meiwa's design featured an advanced single-step planing bottom, a high-set T-tail, and four T64 turboprop engines, each driving a three-bladed Hamilton Standard 63E60-15 propellor. The wings featured powerful leading-edge slats and massive two-section flaps, and the tailplane also featured leading-edge slats. A General Electric T58 turboshaft was installed for flap blowing, and to blow along the rudder and elevators, providing greater control authority at lower speeds. The aircraft featured large, fixed stabiliser floats outboard, and had what appeared to be a retractable

***Right: A grossly-altered Grumman UF-2 Albatross, the UF-XS proved much of the SS-2's airframe design. The aircraft gained three extra engines.***

***The 71st Kokutai at Iwakuni has operated the US-1 since 1976, and the original batch of 12 aircraft was augmented by six further aircraft.***

undercarriage. In fact the latter was strong enough to support the aircraft's weight for taxiing and for beaching, but could not be used to take off or land from a conventional runway, and the PS-1 production aircraft was very much a flying boat, and not an amphibian.

## PS-1 in service

For its ASW role, the PS-1 had a powerful search radar in the nose, and was equipped with retractable MAD gear and comprehensive sonar processing equipment, together with Jezebel acoustic detection and Julie echo-ranging equipment. The two pilots and flight engineer on the raised flight deck were joined by a radio operator, a navigator, a tactical co-ordinator, MAD and radar operators, two sonar operators and two observers. Torpedoes were carried in distinctive pods slung below the wing between the engine nacelles.

The PS-1 was evaluated by a specially formed detachment of the 51st Koku-tai at Iwakuni between July 1968 and 1970, and this unit remained at Iwakuni as an operational evaluation/tactical development unit until 1983. The new type entered service with the frontline 31st Koku-tai on 1 March 1973. The prototype and two pre-production aircraft were followed by an initial batch of twelve production aircraft, and later by eight more. Six of the PS-1s were lost in service, and in 1980 it was announced that the JMSDF's ASW requirements would in future be met by land-based P-3 Orions, which were significantly cheaper to operate. Plans to form a second Kokutai (the 32nd) were abandoned. The first prototype was subsequently converted to serve as the prototype of a proposed fire-bomber variant in 1976, but was written off on 26 April 1983.

## The amphibious US-1

Even as the PS-1 was entering service, Shin Meiwa was completing the prototype of a dedicated search and rescue derivative, the US-1, to replace its small fleet of UF-2 Albatross amphibians. The new SAR version was designated as the SS-2A by Shin Meiwa, but apart from the absence of ASW role equipment, the only major change was the addition of a retractable undercarriage in place of the original beaching gear, transforming the big flying boat into a true amphibian.

## SAR role equipment

Extra rescue hatches were installed, together with a large dinghy door on the port side, and the new version was fitted out with searchlights, loud-hailers and domed observation windows. Smoke and dye markers replaced the PS-1s sonobuoys. These changes were minor however, and there was no prototype. Instead, the first of an initial twelve aircraft made its maiden flight on 18 October 1974, and entered service with the 71st Koku-tai on 1 July 1976, after evaluation by a detachment of the 51st Koku-tai.

The first seven aircraft were delivered with 3,060 ehp (2282-kW) T64-IHI-10E turpoprops, but were later retrofitted with the 3,490 ehp (2602-kW) T64-IHI-10J engines used on later aircraft, which were designated as US-1As. New US-1As were ordered in 1992, 1993, 1994 and 1995, taking the total number delivered to 16 by 1997. A further aircraft was approved in FY1999. This allowed the withdrawal of some of the older aircraft, and the frontline strength with the 71st Koku-tai remained at seven aircraft in 2001, three of them based at Atsugi, the rest at Iwakuni and by 2004 the total force strength was 10 aircraft. One US-1 was converted to fire-bomber configuration but the cost of the US-1 makes further conversions (let alone new production) most unlikely. The US-1A offers a unique very-long range SAR capability, and cannot be replaced by helicopters, so that the place of the amphibian in JMSDF service seems assured.

## Upgrade

A US-1A Kai upgrade was proposed in 1996, and funding was requested (and turned down) in the FY 1999 budget. The request has since been re-submitted. This will see the US-1As being re-engined with 4,500-ehp (3396-kW) Rolls-Royce AE2100J turboprops, driving six-bladed Dowty R414 propellors. The upgrade also includes new avionics (including Thomson-CSF/DASA Ocean Master radar) and a digital cockpit, with flight trials starting in 2003/04. ShinMaywa (as the company was renamed in 1992) has also proposed a more extensively modernised new-build derivative of the US-1A.

# US-1A

**The SAR-optimised US-1 differs from the ASW PS-1 in being an amphibian, with a robust retractable undercarriage allowing the aircraft to take off and land from conventional runways, while retaining the ability to land on the water to pick up survivors. The PS-1 had integral beaching gear but this was not stressed to allow the aircraft to take off or land.**

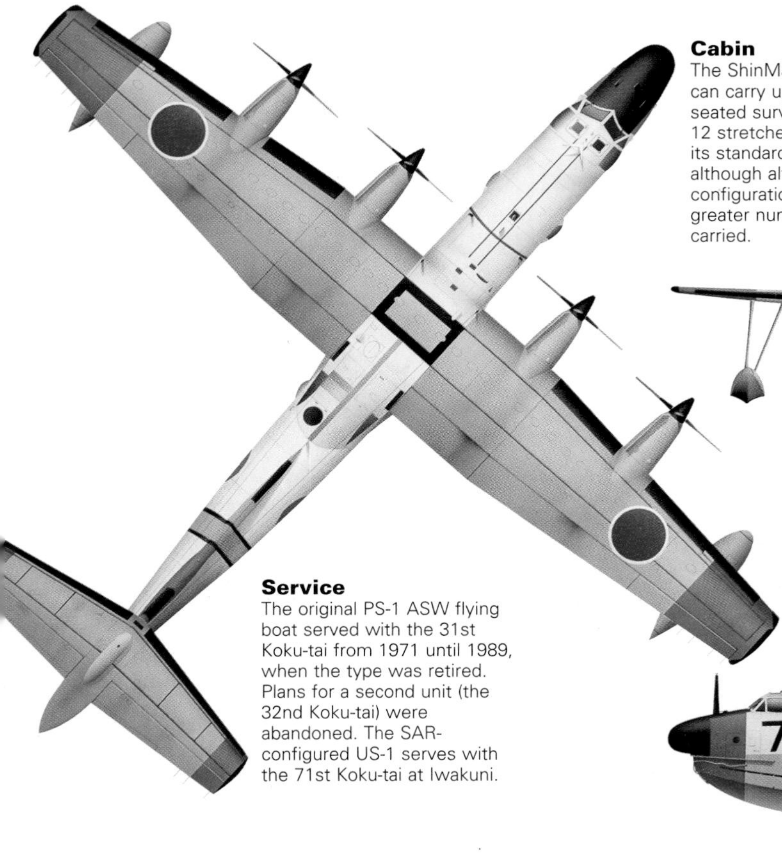

**Cabin**
The ShinMaywa US-1 can carry up to 20 seated survivors and 12 stretcher cases in its standard fit, although alternative configurations allow far greater numbers to be carried.

**Engines**
The first seven ShinMaywa US-1s were delivered with 3,060 ehp (2282-kW) T64-IHI-10E turpoprops, but were later retrofitted with the 3,490 ehp (2602-kW) -10J engines used on later aircraft. An auxiliary T58-IHI-10-M2 engine powers the boundary layer control system, blowing high pressure air to the flaps and tail surfaces.

**Service**
The original PS-1 ASW flying boat served with the 31st Koku-tai from 1971 until 1989, when the type was retired. Plans for a second unit (the 32nd Koku-tai) were abandoned. The SAR-configured US-1 serves with the 71st Koku-tai at Iwakuni.

# The Sikorsky story

*In the tri-service aircraft designation system introduced in 1962, the HSS-2 became the SH-3A. A trio of early-production SH-3As of US Navy anti-submarine unit HS-3 formate for the camera, some time in the 1960s.*

**First flown in 1959, the Sikorsky S-61 ASW design has been of the most successful medium-lift helicopters in the world and remains in service today with a number of navies.**

When the fabled Sikorsky company in Stratford, Connecticut began to manufacture the SH-3 Sea King series (a helicopter family that ultimately included international S-61s and the US Air Force's HH-3E 'Jolly Green Giant' of Vietnam combat rescue fame) for the US Navy, American military forces suddenly reaped the benefit of a quantum leap in helicopter technology. The Sea King introduced an amphibious hull, twin turbine engines located above the cabin, and an advanced flight control system.

The prototype for this series first flew on 17 March 1959. The first versions (designated HSS-2 by the US Navy, and redesignated SH-3A in 1962) had the job of carrying anti-submarine warfare (ASW) sensors. These helicopters were assigned to aircraft-carrier decks and tasked with prowling nearby waters to guard carrier battle groups from submarine attack – a job they shared with longer-ranged, fixed-wing ASW aircraft such as the Grumman S-2 Tracker and Lockheed S-3 Viking. Thirty-seven Sea Kings were assembled in Canada as CHSS-2s and most were upgraded with newer ASW gear and redesignated as CH-124s.

US Navy Sea Kings became operational in 1962. When they began hunting submarines in the early 1960s, many Sea Kings flew from the old wooden decks of specialised anti-submarine carriers like the USS *Randolph* (CVS-15). In the early to mid-1960s, subsequent Sea King variants were equipped for various transport duties, minesweeping, drone or spacecraft recovery (including those that plucked astronauts out of the sea after missions into orbit and to the Moon), electronic surveillance and other combat duties. Hunting submarines remained the primary job, however. US Navy variants included a YSH-3A service test prototype, and SH-3As, SH-3Ds, SH-3G and SH-3H models – 318 helicopters altogether, destined to serve for a quarter-century until being replaced only recently by the Sikorsky SH-60F. The ultimate Sea King was the SH-3H, packed with an 838-lb (380-kg) arsenal of weaponry, including Mk 46 or Mk 50 torpedoes.

All US Navy Sea Kings were meant, at least initially, to hunt submarines, with the exception of the nine Vietnam-era HH-3A combat rescue craft plus a few SH-3G models that were stripped of warfighting equipment and used for 'hack' or utility transport duties. Captain Edward Marsyla, who flew the HH-3A in high-risk combat rescues in Viet Cong territory, drew little comfort from the knowledge that the HH-3A model had armour around its transmission and that 'a couple' of these models had RHAW (radar homing and warning) receivers. Marsyla always worried that there was no frontal armour protection: "If you can see somebody in front of you, you're kind of screwed." Surprisingly, only one HH-3A was lost in battle.

## Marine machine

The US Marine Corps operated a small number of Sea Kings in the VIP airlift role. The VH-3A Sea King model of 1965 was replaced in 1976 by the VH-3D, operated as a presidential aircraft and known as 'MARINE ONE' when the US President is on board.

The reliable Navy and Marine Sea King helicopters all shared a common identifying feature which made them easy to distinguish from their Air Force cousins: all Navy and Marine models had a streamlined after-fuselage, with clean lines broken

*Above: 147137 was the XHSS-2 prototype. First flown on 17 March 1959, the aircraft should have been designated 'HS2S-1', but was called the HSS-2 by the US Navy as a ploy to imply parts commonality with the HSS-1 Seabat (S-58). This older design shared parts of its transmission and rotor system with the S-62, a single turbine-engined design from which the S-61 was derived. In fact, the HSS-1 and HSS-2 had nothing in common but their manufacturer.*

*Left: The USAF's first H-3s were CH-3As (ex-USN SH-3As) used for offshore radar support.*

***CH-3C 62-12577 demonstrates its upswept – and loading ramp-equipped – rear fuselage. The CH-3C was the first H-3 variant built for the USAF. Based on the unbuilt HR3S-1 proposed to the USMC, the CH-3 was tasked with drone recovery and transport duties, the design serving as the basis for the later HH-3E search-and-rescue variant.***

only by a tail wheel as part of the landing gear.

In contrast, a rear-loading ramp and a nosewheel were introduced with Sikorsky's S-61R series, which also had main wheels retracting forward into sponsons and a 2,000-lb (907-kg) winch. Powered by two 1,502-hp (1119-kW) General Electric T58-5 turboshaft engines, the S-61R family of military helicopters was externally very similar to Sikorsky's civil, land-based S-61L which first flew on 31 March 1960. The best-known US military version was the US Air Force's HH-3E (although the service also operated a CH-3C cargo model). The US Coast Guard employed this aircraft, calling it the HH-3F Pelican. Whatever its primary role, every military helicopter in the world is used sooner or later for search and rescue duties. This was a secondary duty for US Navy anti-submarine Sea Kings, but rescue is the very essence of existence for the HH-3E and for S-61s in the armed forces of many countries.

On 9 November 1967, Captain Gerald O. Young took an HH-3E 'Jolly Green Giant' on an extraordinary combat rescue mission that resulted in his helicopter being riddled with gunfire and shot down. Young came to earth hanging upside-down in the cockpit, clothing afire, the fuselage burning and riddled with bullet holes. His eventual escape and subsequent successful rescue of a survivor while under heavy fire made him the only H-3 pilot ever to be awarded the Medal of Honor.

To an imperilled survivor, no gift could seem more like a godsend than a Sea King hovering loudly overhead and letting down its survival hoist. Thousands are alive today because of an S-61 rescue. In Vietnam, HH-3Es ventured deep into enemy territory, threaded their way through hostile gunfire, and rescue downed airmen.

***Left: NH-3A 148033 was employed as a high-speed research test-bed in a joint Army/Navy programme. Note the podded turbojet engines and fixings below the main rotor for short wings.***

***Below: Nine RH-3As were used by the USN to pioneer minesweeping techniques using towed equipment, though they proved to be short on power and were replaced by RH-53s.***

## Foreign production

The Italian licence-built version of the S-61 is similar to the US Navy's SH-3 series (with tail wheel). Some users have specified the Italian-built Agusta/Sikorsky aircraft, equipped with an anti-ship weapon system including Sistel radar and AS12, Sea Killer Mk 2 or Exocet missiles. About 390 of these machines, designated ASH-3D and ASH-3H, have been built by Agusta for the Italian navy. Examples manufactured in Japan by Mitsubishi (variously designated HSS-2, -2A, -2B, S-61A and S-61AH) have filled both the ASW, search-and-rescue and Antarctic support roles.

Total production of military models of the S-61 has exceeded 770 by Sikorsky, with 400 more by its other builders, including Westland in the UK. It was only natural that the S-61 would continue a long tradition of co-operation between the American Sikorsky firm and the British manufacturer, when the Royal Navy sought an ASW helicopter to supplement the Wessex (itself based on a Sikorsky design). The Westland story added to the success already achieved by Sikorsky. Military S-61, H-3, and Sea King variants have served in 30 countries altogether, divided about evenly between those manufactured by Sikorsky and the licence-built Westland product.

# Sikorsky and licence-built variants

**The Sea King and its derivatives will go down in history as one of Sikorsky's most successful helicopters. During its long and proud service life, the basic design has been produced under licence by Mitsubishi in Japan and by Agusta in Italy, allowing a host of variants to emerge, each more capable than the last.**

## XHSS-2

The original contract for the then-unnamed Sea King called for a single prototype and six pre-production aircraft, but this was soon amended to give a trials batch of 10 aircraft. The prototype Sea King (147137) was designated XHSS-2 under the pre-1962 US Navy designation system, with 'HS' indicating helicopter, anti-submarine, and the second 'S' being Sikorsky's manufacturer's code. The 'X' prefix indicated the aircraft's experimental status. The XHSS-2 differed little from the pre-production YHSS-2s and production HSS-2s which followed it. Sikorsky's engineers had done a great job with the basic Sea King, and few changes were necessary. Visually, the XHSS-2 differed from later aircraft in having a shallow box-like fairing on the starboard fuselage side, over the front part of the door runner. This feature was unique to the first prototype. The XHSS-2 also had a very much smaller undernose fairing and no Doppler antenna, and had a small 'forehead' antenna fairing at the top of the central windscreen frame. These features were initially retained by early YHSS-2s.

## HSS-2 (SH-3A)

The aircraft was redesignated as the SH-3A under the unified tri-service designation system introduced in 1962. 'S' stood for anti-submarine, 'H' stood for helicopter, '3' indicated that it was the third type of helicopter in use (taking 1962 as a baseline, and the type making third place alphabetically after the Bell H-1 and Kaman H-2), and 'A' indicated that it was the first production variant. The first SH-3As were delivered to their squadrons in an overall midnight-blue colour scheme, with codes, serials and other markings applied in brilliant white, although three-tone camouflage (illustrated), and overall battleship-grey schemes (with black codes) were sometimes used in Vietnam. The SH-3A could carry a heavy weaponload in the ASW role, with up to four torpedoes, or a single Mk 57 or Lulu nuclear depth bomb. Bendix AN/AQS-10 sonar was fitted (though some SH-3As may have been retrofitted with AQS-13) and was the primary ASW sensor. The first SH-3As were not fitted with Doppler antenna fairings and lacked flotation bags on the sponsons, but these items were usually retrofitted. With a production total of 245 (excluding the YSH-3As), the SH-3A was the most numerous new-build Sea King. A single SH-3A (149723) was bailed to NASA (as NASA 538) for the development of blind-flying and blind-landing equipment. The aircraft was fitted with a 14-in (36-cm) TV monitor in front of the co-pilot's position, with a massive box-like fairing projecting from the windscreen. Two SH-3As (148998 and 151544) were converted to SH-3D standard, and many more (over 150) to SH-3G and SH-3H configuration. Japan's initial aircraft, and the Canadian CHSS-2s (later redesignated as CH-124s), were broadly equivalent to the SH-3A.

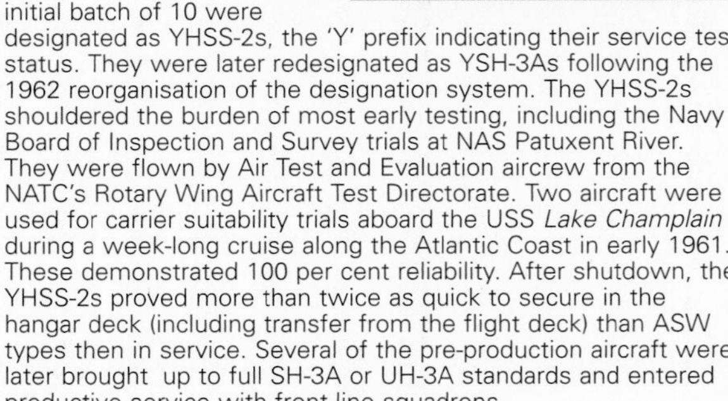


## YHSS-2

The remaining nine aircraft (147138 to 147146) from the initial batch of 10 were designated as YHSS-2s, the 'Y' prefix indicating their service test status. They were later redesignated as YSH-3As following the 1962 reorganisation of the designation system. The YHSS-2s shouldered the burden of most early testing, including the Navy Board of Inspection and Survey trials at NAS Patuxent River. They were flown by Air Test and Evaluation aircrew from the NATC's Rotary Wing Aircraft Test Directorate. Two aircraft were used for carrier suitability trials aboard the USS *Lake Champlain* during a week-long cruise along the Atlantic Coast in early 1961. These demonstrated 100 per cent reliability. After shutdown, the YHSS-2s proved more than twice as quick to secure in the hangar deck (including transfer from the flight deck) than ASW types then in service. Several of the pre-production aircraft were later brought up to full SH-3A or UH-3A standards and entered productive service with front-line squadrons.

## RH-3A

Nine SH-3As were converted to RH-3A standard for mine countermeasures duties under a contract placed by the Bureau of Naval Weapons. The RH-3A was fitted with an extra full-size cargo door on the port side, and had bubble observation windows in the rear of the cabin. A special squadron, HM-12, was formed to operate the new variant. The RH-3A was the first US Navy helicopter capable of streaming and recovering its own towed minesweeping gear. Three RH-3As of HM-12 operated from the mine countermeasures vessels USS *Ozark* (in the Atlantic) and three from the USS *Catskill* (in the Pacific). The remaining three aircraft were used for tests and training. Having proved the concept of helicopter mine countermeasures, but having also demonstrated little power margin thanks to the bulk of the minesweeping gear, the RH-3As were replaced by more powerful RH-53s in 1972.

## SH-3D

The SH-3D (illustrated) followed the SH-3A on the Stratford production line and was a refined and enhanced ASW version of the Sea King. SH-3Ds also had the new AN/APN-182 Doppler in place of the old AN/APN-130 Doppler. An AN/ASN-50 heading reference system was also fitted. Structural modifications allowed an increase in gross weight to 20,500 lb (9300 kg). Armament was reduced to a pair of torpedoes, but these were carried on variable launch rails which allowed them to be launched from a low hover as well as from forward flight. Sikorsky started to implement a service life extension programme (SLEP) on an initial group of 26 SH-3Ds during 1987. The $100 million programme stressed reliability and maintainability improvements, and modernised aircraft were redesignated as SH-3Hs. Changes were made to the main rotor head, while the main gearbox was upgraded. Changes were also made to the tail rotor gearbox, drive shaft and primary servo. Crashworthy seats were installed. The aircraft also received an emergency lighting system for use if the crew had to egress at night. Spain re-equipped with six SH-3Ds before any US Navy squadrons received the new variant. The four survivors were subsequently upgraded to SH-3G and later SH-3H configuration. A handful of redundant SH-3Ds were sold to Brazil to augment the navy's S-61Ds during the 1990s.

## VH-3D

The VH-3D entered service during 1976, when the Marines' HMX-1 at Quantico took over sole responsibility for the presidential helicopter mission. President Gerald Ford was the first president to use the VH-3D. The presidential helicopter fleet was divided into two distinct parts, white-topped aircraft being used by the president, vice-president and foreign heads of state, while green-topped aircraft were used for DoD VIP transport requirements. The VH-3s served alongside similarly modified Sea Stallions and Sea Knights, but these were primarily used for transporting the Secret Service, press and cargo, while the Sea Kings were prized for their range, room, comfort and speed, and thus the aircraft of choice for VIP transport.

## SH-3H/UH-3H

The SH-3H was originally seen as little more than a SLEP for the SH-3D, but the programme was soon widened to include the provision of new equipment as well and the SH-3H came to be viewed as the first of a new generation of ASW helicopters. The type received six key ASW improvements, new equipment for the anti-ship missile detection (ASMD) role, as well as 12 basic aircraft improvements, and the utility and convertibility features of the SH-3G. The aircraft also had an extra forward window on the port side, as fitted to a handful of SH-3As. SH-3G convertibility/ utility improvements included provision for easy sonar removal and reinstallation, the installation of 15 troop seats and 110-US gal (416-litre) underwing auxiliary fuel tanks. The SH-3H conversion programme eventually encompassed 163 aircraft, including SH-3Gs and previously unconverted SH-3As and SH-3Ds. Weapons options included two torpedoes or depth bombs, or a single heavyweight depth bomb. Some SH-3Hs were stripped of their ASW equipment and used in the utility role under the designation UH-3H.

## Mitsubishi HSS-2 (S-61A, S-61AH)

The JMSDF was a natural customer for the Sea King in light of the perceived threat from the large Soviet Pacific submarine fleet which regularly appeared off the Japanese coast. Japan's growing indigenous aircraft industry made the lure of licence-manufacture a strong one. A licence agreement between Sikorsky and Mitsubishi was signed in May 1962, and was sealed with an initial JMSDF order for 11 HSS-2s. The original Japanese licence-built Sea King was a standard S-61B, broadly equivalent to the US Navy SH-3A. Production by Mitsubishi totalled 55, the first example being delivered to the JMSDF on 24 March 1964. The HSS-2, which equipped five squadrons, had been withdrawn from use by 1986, having spent the last few years of its career in the liaison, utility and training roles. The HSS-2A (illustrated), similar to the SH-3D, was delivered from late 1974, but has now been retired. The HSS-2B was closely equivalent to the US Navy SH-3H, 83 of these advanced ASW helicopters being produced. They were fitted with extended sponsons housing MAD equipment, and had provision for search radar, with a small retractable radome on the centreline. The most obvious external feature of the HSS-2B was the unusual intake guard arrangement adopted during service. Two Mitsubishi-built S-61As were delivered in 1965, followed by a third and an S-61A-1 soon afterwards. These were procured for use aboard the icebreaker Fuji, which supported Japanese scientific/ environmental operations in the Antarctic. The S-61As and S-61A-1 went on to serve with the Yokosuka Chihotai for operations aboard the icebreaker Shirase. Twelve more locally-built S-61A-1s, equipped for SAR duties, were procured as S-61AHs from late 1983. They wore a distinctive colour scheme with brick-red undersides and medium-grey upper surfaces, and were festooned with mirrors above and below the cockpit. A searchlight (or later a FLIR sensor or TV camera) could be carried on an articulated pylon aft of the port mainwheel sponson.

## SH-3G

The SH-3G appeared in 1970 and was intended as a more versatile utility helicopter, retaining the ASW potential of the SH-3A while being able to seat up to 15 passengers, or move bulky cargo. The SH-3A's AQS-10 sonar was removed but retained on board the aircraft, moving with it and available for reinstallation if necessary. An initial batch of 11 SH-3Gs was converted from the SH-3A and these were soon joined by 94 more, bringing the total to 105. A handful of SH-3Gs was produced by the conversion of SH-3Ds, and these retained their later AQS-13 sonar. All SH-3Gs originally had the basic SH-3A-style short sponsons, without MAD or smoke-marker provision, though some aircraft later received long MAD-type sponsons. Provision was made for the installation of a pair of 175-US gal (662-litre) external fuel tanks under the stub wings, and to use the HIFR (Hover In-Flight Refuelling) system. The floor was strengthened and reinforced and a door gun could be installed. Six of the earliest SH-3Gs could mount a 7.62-mm Minigun, but most aircraft could mount only an M60 machine-gun. The SH-3Gs of Detachment 9, HC-1, were used for the recovery of the Apollo 15 astronauts, the first space recovery undertaken by the SH-3G. The SH-3Gs of HC-2 saw extensive service during the Gulf War, receiving a range of 'Duck' nicknames, including 148047 *Wild Duck*, 149731 *Desert Duck*, *Dusty Duck* and *Stealth Duck* (illustrated). Some SH-3Gs were converted to SH-3H standard, but the basic type remains in use, alongside transport conversions of redundant SH-3Hs.

## S-61D-3/4 (SH-3A/SH-3H)

Brazil (illustrated) received four S-61D-3s (broadly equivalent to the US Navy SH-3D) in 1970, later taking delivery of two more. The helicopters replaced Sikorsky HSS-1s. The six Sikorsky-built S-61Ds were augmented by four Italian-built aircraft, and later by two ex-US Navy SH-3Ds. The aircraft have all been brought up to a common standard, with undernose radar and provision for AM39 Exocet missiles. Argentina received four S-61D-4s (export versions of the US Navy's SH-3D) in early 1978, later followed by a fifth, equipped with a VIP interior. Four more SH-3Ds were delivered in February 1978, two of them equipped with radar. The later Argentine Sea Kings were all Agusta-built, and were virtually identical to the H standard.

## Agusta (AS-61)

Having watched with great interest the capabilities of the helicopter within the US Navy's Sixth Fleet, operating in the Mediterranean, Italy was keen to acquire the Sea King. The AS-61A-4 was a multi-role variant developed and built for export and suited equally to SAR, trooping and freighting. Four such helicopters are used by Venezuela, serving in the tactical transport role. The Venezuelan aircraft are augmented by a single Sikorsky-built SH-3D. Iranian aircraft were similarly designated AS-61A-4, but may have been ASW-configured, being externally similar to the batch of Italian navy ASH-3Ds. They retained a sonar cut-out below the fuselage, and had a nose-mounted search radar and undernose Doppler. Only about 10 Iranian Sea Kings are believed to be in service today with the Iranian navy. The Italian air force uses two VIP-configured AS-61s which provide transport for the Pope within Italy. Aircraft for the Italian navy were broadly analogous to the ASW-optimised Sikorsky-built SH-3D (S-61D), but had different engines and radar. The first entered service in 1968, following the 1967 order for 24 aircraft. The demonstrated success of the Sikorsky-built SH-3H in US Navy service prompted the Italian navy to upgrade the specification of the remainder of its planned Sea King buy to virtual SH-3H standard. As such, later Italian navy aircraft are sometimes referred to as ASH-3Hs. The primary ASW sensor of the ASH-3H is the AQS-18 sonar with 360° simultaneous search capability, while Italian Sea Kings are equipped to fire both Exocet and Marte Mk 2 (illustrated) ASMs. The Italian navy will replace its Sea Kings with the Anglo-Italian EHI EH101.

# US service/ CSAR

The ASW-configured HSS-2 (SH-3A) was eventually replaced by the SH-3D, illustrated here. Featuring uprated engines, new dipping sonar and additional fuel, a total of 72 SH-3D Sea Kings was eventually built for the USN.

**One of Sikorsky's most successful designs, the Sea King has proved its versatility, serving with distinction with the US Navy, Air Force, Army, Marines and Coast Guard. Flown by the USAF in Vietnam, the 'Jolly Green Giants' pioneered combat search and rescue (CSAR) operations.**

Designated XHSS-2, the prototype Sea King anti-submarine warfare helicopter made its maiden flight in March 1959, and differed little from the YHSS-2 and production HSS-2s that followed. The nine YHSS-2s, (redesignated YSH-3A in 1962) underwent early flight-testing at NAS Patuxent River in 1961.

During a week-long Atlantic coast cruise in early 1961, two YHSS-2s completed carrier suitability trials aboard the USS *Lake Champlain*. Capable of limited water landings, the Sea King was the US Navy's first all-weather service helicopter.

## Naval origins

The first production HSS-2s joined the HS-1 conversion and demonstration unit at Key West in 1961. HS-2 – another early operator – pioneered the use of the Sea King in inflight refuelling from a destroyer, for which the unit won a US Navy commendation.

The first SH-3As (as the HSS-2 became from 1962) were delivered to squadrons in an overall midnight blue scheme, with Dayglo noses and tail pylons; this was replaced by three-tone camouflage or battleship grey schemes for those helicopters in Vietnam service. The SH-3A was equipped with four Mk 46 or Mk 48 torpedoes; or a single nuclear depth bomb, including the 1,200-lb (544-kg) Lulu device. A production run of 245 aircraft made the SH-3A the most numerous H-3 production variant.

A single SH-3A was operated by NASA in the development of blind-flying techniques, and was later used with nose-mounted radar for trials with the USCG.

Minor Sea King versions to see USN service included the HH-3A Minigun-armed CSAR helicopter, deployed to HC-7 in the Philippines in 1970; the single NH-3A high-speed

The HH-3E resulted from a USAF requirement for an aircrew recovery and CSAR helicopter for Vietnam service. The above example served with USAF Alaskan Command.

Above: Landing the S-61/H-3 on water was far from routine; for such a manoeuvre, the helicopter required still water conditions, and was prone to overturning and sinking.

Right: The VH-3E designation was applied to a small number of USAF CH-3Es converted for use as VIP transports. This example served with the 1st Helicopter Squadron at Andrews AFB.

**Left: The US Navy, Air Force and Army have all used the H-3 as a drone recovery platform. At one stage, it was proposed that the H-3 should itself be used as a target drone – the QCH-3E – for AH-64 gunnery practice, but this did not materialise due to a lack of funding.**

**Below: Three ex-USN SH-3As were transferred to the USAF in April 1962. Flown by the 551st Base Flight, they supported offshore radar platforms in the Atlantic.**

research aircraft which, with fuselage-mounted turbojets, attained a speed record of 242 mph (390 km/h) in May 1965; the NSH-3A Mid-Air Recovery System (MARS) trials aircraft, used for retrieving satellite camera film capsules; and the nine RH-3A mine countermeasures helicopters, which operated minesweeping gear on behalf of HM-12, until replaced by RH-53s in 1972.

The USN Sea King ASW fleet was updated with the arrival of 72 refined SH-3Ds in 1966, and the 'new-generation' SH-3H ASW/SAR conversion helicopter from 1972. Replacement of the SH-3H with the SH-60F began in 1989, although the former still saw service in the Gulf War. The SH-3G was a versatile 15-seat utility helicopter, retaining ASW potential. The UH-3H was a dedicated utility helicopter, produced through conversion of retired SH-3Hs, and fulfilling the demand for utility helicopters that had arisen due to a lack of surplus SH-60 airframes.

## USAF variants

The USAF began its relationship with the H-3 when it acquired three ex-USN SH-3As in 1962. Known as CH-3As, they were employed in the support of Texas Tower offshore radar sites. Post-1962, these three aircraft were redesignated CH-3Bs, in common with newly-built aircraft employed for the same task. Replacing piston-engined helicopters, the radar rig-support CH-3Bs were operated by the 551st Base Flight. A single CH-3B, *Otis Falcon*, made history by flying to Paris via Labrador, Greenland, Iceland and Scotland, breaking time and distance records for a helicopter crossing of the Atlantic.

The CH-3C was the first H-3 variant to be specifically designed for USAF use, and the first to feature a rear-loading ramp. The initial USAF CH-3C was handed over in December 1963, and the type was originally used for drone recovery, geodetic survey and Minuteman ICBM site support.

A further detachment at Patrick AFB, Florida monitored Gemini launches and other space flights. The CH-3C took part in the first helicopter air-to-air refuelling trials with a USMC KC-130F, and formed the basis of the HH-3E 'Jolly Green Giant' CSAR helicopter. During the Vietnam War, USAF CH-3Cs lifted 400,000 lb (181440 kg) of supplies per month. A handful of black-painted 'Pony Express' examples flew in support of US special forces troops, while others flew reconnaissance drone recovery missions with MARS gear, retrieving 2,655 drones between 1964 and 1975.

The MH-3E, first designated in 1990, was basically an HH-3E tasked with special operations. Fitted with FLIR and GPS, the aircraft saw service in Operation Desert Storm, with appropriate sand and brown camouflage. These machines were replaced in service by the MH-60G.

## Other operators

In US Coast Guard service, the radar-equipped HH-3F Pelican extended-range SAR helicopter first flew in 1967, and remained in service for 30 years. In all, 40 were operated by the USCG, equipped with LORAN (Long-Range Aid to Navigation), and in some cases FLIR. The last HH-3Fs, with Nitesun searchlights, were used in drug enforcement operations.

The high-profile green and white VH-3D VIP transports of Marines HMX-1, which replaced earlier VIP-configured VH-3As from 1976, were used by the US President.

### 'Jolly Green Giants'

Conforming to a USAF requirement for a CSAR helicopter for the Vietnam War, the HH-3E entered service following combat evaluation by the 38th ARSS. Based on the CH-3C, the aircraft featured combat modifications to improve survivability and increase range. Around 1,000 lb (454 kg) of titanium armour plating was added, and provision was made for door guns. Long-range fuel tanks were supplemented by a telescopic inflight-refuelling probe. The first HH-3E was delivered to the 38th ARSS in Vietnam on 5 November 1965. During the type's heroic Vietnam service, the HH-3E acquired the nickname 'Jolly Green Giant', and recovered scores of downed aircrew. In one memorable incident, Technical Sergeant Donald Smith suffered enemy fire to his winch cable while attempting to pick up a downed F-100 pilot. Smith was awarded the Air Force Cross after directing in another aircraft to rescue him and his charge. Lieutenant Colonel Royal A. Brown was also recognised for the 16th save of his second combat tour, bringing his total number of rescues to 32. The HH-3E served until 1994, with the Air Force Reserve and Air National Guard, until finally replaced by the Sikorsky HH-60. The final active-duty HH-3E unit was the 1st Fighter Wing's rescue detachment, based at Patrick AFB, Florida.

# The Westland story

*In the hands of Westland's Chief Test Pilot Slim Sears, the first of four Sikorsky-supplied SH-3Ds lifts off from Avonmouth Docks for its flight to Yeovil in October 1966. It would be three more years before a Westland-built Sea King HAS.Mk 1 would make its maiden flight.*

**A mid-1960s agreement with US helicopter manufacturer Sikorsky for licence production of the S-61 resulted in four US-built examples being shipped to Westland to serve as pattern aircraft.**

The first British Sea King was an SH-3D (allocated the serial G-ATYU/ XV370), which was flown from Avonmouth docks on 11 October 1966. Three more (XV371-373) were used for British ASW systems trials as part of Sea King HAS.Mk 1 (Spec. HAS.Mk 261) development for the Royal Navy.

The first of 56 production Westland Sea King HAS.Mk 1s (XV642-677/XV695-714) began flying on 7 May 1969, followed by 13 HAS.Mk 2s (with uprated Rolls-Royce Gnome H.1400 turboshafts and six-bladed tail rotors) from mid-1976, and the first 15 HAR.Mk 3s for RAF SAR roles from September 1977. Eight more HAS.Mk 2s from early 1979 included a prototype HAS.Mk 5 ASW upgrade conversion, many of the earlier RN Sea Kings also being converted to HAS.Mk 5/6 or HAR.Mk 5 standards.

New-build HAS.Mk 5s and 6s followed from mid-1980, eventually increasing overall RN ASW Sea King deliveries to 113. The HAS.Mk 5 introduced Thorn-EMI Sea Searcher radar in a large, flat-topped radome, Racal MIR-2 Orange Crop ESM, new sonobuoy dropping equipment and a GEC-Marconi AQS902 LAPADS acoustic processing system. The cabin was enlarged to make room for the new equipment. The HAS.Mk 6 has a further enhanced ASW suite and reduced equipment weight,

*Above: The first Westland Sea King (G-ATYU/XV370) was merely a navalised Sikorsky SH-3D. The next three aircraft (XV371-373) were used in trials for Royal Navy specified anti-submarine systems, and delivery of the production-standard HAS.Mk 1s to the Royal Navy began in May 1969.*

*The result of an urgent requirement for a shipboard AEW platform, the Sea King AEW.Mk 2 has proved itself to be highly effective, able to detect hostile aircraft and missiles at distances well beyond the range of the fleet.*

**Above: Externally similar to RN HAS.Mk 1s, Germany's Sea King Mk 41s were equipped with an increased rear cabin area, with room for up to 21 passengers. The first examples entered service with Marineflieger MFG 5 at Kiel-Holtenau on 6 March 1972.**

**Above: A rarely-seen Sea King variant is the Mk 47 operated by the Egyptian air force. Comparable in equipment and role to the RN's HAS.Mk 2, it serves alongside assault variants.**

resulting in a 30-minute extension to endurance. Among other improvements, the Orange Crop ESM system is raised to Orange Reaper standard, and the dunking depth of the sonar is increased from 245 ft (75 m) to 700 ft (213 m).

The acquisition of three more HAR.Mk 3 SAR versions in 1985 brought RAF procurement to 19. This included one which had been acquired, in 1980, for the ETPS at Boscombe Down which was transferred to No. 202 and, later, No. 22 SAR Squadron. Another early-1992 RAF order added six upgraded HAR.Mk 3As, recommencing production of the Sea King and thus providing further Wessex replacements.

## Assault variant

Development of a non-amphibious Sea King (without floats) as the Commando assault, tactical and general transport began in mid-1971. The first customer deliveries were made to the Egyptian air force in early 1974. These were followed by successive RN orders, from 1979, for 41 similar HC.Mk 4 Commando helicopters. Two Mk 4X Sea Kings (ZB506/7) were built by Westland as DRA avionics, rotor and systems test aircraft for EH101 development, bringing the overall UK service procurement of all variants to 175.

Westland has supplied 147 Sea Kings (and the related Commando) to overseas customers. German Sea Kings were converted from SAR to anti-ship roles from 1986 with Ferranti Seaspray Mk 3 radar and BAeD Sea Skua AShMs (anti-ship missiles). These also arm Indian navy Mk 42Bs, while some Pakistani and Qatari Sea Kings/Commandos are equipped to launch Aérospatiale AM39 Exocet AShMs. Indian navy Mk 42Bs are Advanced Sea Kings, with 1,465-shp (1092-kW) Gnome H.1400-1T turboshafts, composite main and tail rotors, improved avionics and a 21,500-lb (9752-kg) take-off weight.

The RN's lack of airborne early-warning capability resulted in two HAS Sea Kings (XV650 and 704) being modified to AEW.Mk 2A standard with Thorn-EMI Searchwater radar and associated equipment, including anti-Exocet I-band jammers and Racal MIR-2 Orange Crop ECM. This involved fitting a large radome suspended to the starboard of the cabin and swinging back through 90° for ground stowage. Both AEW.Mk 2A development aircraft began flying in July 1982 with No. 824 Sqn. Eight other Sea Kings were modified as AEW.Mk 2As and equipped No. 849 Sqn, the FAA's historic AEW unit (shore-based at RNAS Culdrose) and RN V/STOL carrier flights from 1 November 1984.

Today, the Sea King remains an important type to the UK, not only for the Royal Navy, but also in financial terms, with Westland continuing to offer modifications and upgrades to operators. With the Royal Navy still taking delivery of the Sea King HAS.Mk 6 for service with its five ASW squadrons, and the RAF operating two squadron-strength SAR units as well as one flight from No. 78 Squadron in the Falkland Islands, the Sea King's future is secure.

However, Westland is not planning further airframe development due to the imminent introduction of the Anglo-Italian EH101.

**Broadly similar to the RAF's HAR.Mk 3, Belgian Mk 48s combined the rescue-type airframe of the German and Norwegian aircraft with the engines and tail rotor of the HAS.Mk 2. In 1983 Westland undertook an upgrade which saw the introduction of an improved navigational suite and a FLIR turret.**

# Commando variants

**The dedicated troop-carrying Commando was developed as a private venture and export customers for the aircraft were found long before the British armed forces expressed any interest in the type.**

## Sea King Mk 4X

The Sea King (and particularly the Commando-based HC.Mk 4) has proved to be a popular test and trials platform. Such experimental aircraft included two specially prepared Sea King Mk 4Xs, originally ordered for use by the RAE at Farnborough and Bedford. The two aircraft are basically standard HC.Mk 4s, but were delivered without dorsal-mounted Sea Searcher radomes. The radomes have since come and gone from the aircraft, but usually with the 'base-plate' left in place. ZB507 (seen right) gained a LORAN-type 'towel rail' antenna on the upper part of the starboard tailboom, while both aircraft have had changes to their nose contours in order to accommodate different test fittings and instrumentation packages.

## Sea King HC.Mk 4

It was not until 1978 that the Royal Navy asked Westland to produce a study of a Commando variant to replace its Wessex HU.Mk 5s in the assault transport role. The aircraft for the Royal Navy (designated Sea King HC.Mk 4) were based on the Sea King HAS.Mk 2 powerplant and dynamic system, with H.1400-1 engines and six-bladed tail rotors. Folding main rotors and tail rotor pylons were retained. The aircraft had the same extended cabin as other Commandos and rescue Sea Kings as well as the standard Commando Mk 2 fixed undercarriage, without sponsons.

The first Sea King HC.Mk 4 (ZA290) flew on 26 September 1979. Some 42 Sea King HC.Mk 4s were built, two of these (ZF115 and ZG829) being delivered to Boscombe Down for trials or test pilot training duties. The first batch of 10 aircraft (ZA290-299) was delivered by September 1981 and was available for use in the Falklands, along with some aircraft from the second batch (ZA310-ZA314). The Sea King HC.Mk 4 has seen the most action among Royal Navy Sea King variants, first in the Falklands, then in the Gulf, then in Operation Haven in Turkey and northern Iraq, and over Bosnia. NAVSTAR GPS was added for Operation Granby, along with various defences. Door guns are routinely fitted for operations.

## Commando Mk 1 (Sea King Mk 70)

A land-based transport version of the Sea King was first projected by Yeovil in 1972, and the marketing department quickly applied the name Commando. It was the Arab Republic of Egypt which was to place the first order. The Commando Mk 1 was something of an interim type, lacking several of the features which had been expected to appear on the production Commando. It was, in reality, not a Commando as such, but a basic troop-carrying version of the initial Sea King HAS.Mk 1 with sonar, radar and ASW equipment removed and with the larger cabin and increased fuel capacity of the Sea King Mk 41. The original sponsons, five-bladed tail rotor and Gnome H.1400 engines were retained. The first Commando flew initially on 12 September 1973, and the aircraft were delivered from 29 January 1974.

## Commando Mk 2 (Sea King Mk 72)

With the successful sale of Commando Mk 1s to Egypt, Westland refocused its attention on the export market for its troop-carrying Sea King derivative. The company's strongest sales prospects were in the Middle East and Far East, and it became clear that the performance of the Commando would have to be maximised to cope with 'hot-and-high' conditions. Accordingly, Westland combined the airframe of the Commando with the H.1400-1 engines and six-bladed tail rotor of the HAS.Mk 2 and Mk 50 to produce the Commando Mk 2. Weight was saved by fitting non-folding main rotor blades and a simplified fixed undercarriage, and by removing the sponsons. The integral flotation gear was replaced by easily removable flotation packs. The removal of the undercarriage sponsons also improved the aircraft's ability to carry weapons, by clearing the stub wing and providing an optional wingtip hardpoint outboard of the undercarriage. Like the Commando Mk 1, the new version retained the stretched cabin and increased-capacity fuel tankage. Westland's efforts were rewarded by a 1974 order from Egypt for 19 Commandos, including 17 utility Mk 2s. These aircraft are sometimes seen fitted with sand filters. The first Commando Mk 2 flew on 16 January 1975, and was delivered on 21 February.

## Commando Mk 2A (Sea King Mk 92)

Qatar placed an order for three Mk 2As in 1974, soon after the Egyptian order. The Mk 2A was, to all intents and purposes, identical to the Egyptian aircraft. The Commando's large cabin allows a variety of seating and stretcher layouts, with capacity for up to nine stretchers with seated attendants or 'walking wounded' casualties. A 'clip' of three vertically stacked stretchers would take up the same space as six seats. The Commando also has a formidable cargo-carrying capability, either internally or underslung. The first of the Qatari Commandos made its maiden flight on 9 August 1975 and was delivered on 10 October. The last of the trio was delivered by air from Brize Norton (like the first two) on 19 May 1976.

## Commando Mk 2B (Sea King Mk 72)

Two aircraft were delivered to Egypt specially fitted out for the VIP transport role. The aircraft differed in having an extra pair of cabin windows on the starboard side (giving a row of four windows) and a single additional window to port. Internally, the plush cabin was well appointed and well soundproofed. The first Mk 2B flew on 13 March 1975 and was delivered on 19 August. The second was delivered on 3 June 1976.

## Commando Mk 2C (Sea King Mk 92)

The Mk 2C was a VIP version of the utility Mk 2A for Qatar. There are no obvious external differences between the Mk 2C and the two VIP-configured Mk 2Bs operated in Egypt. No serial number is carried, and the words Qatar Emiri Air Force are applied to the tailboom in Arabic script. The Mk 2C made its maiden flight on 9 October 1975.

## Commando Mk 2E (Sea King Mk 73)

The Commando Mk 2E is a dedicated autonomous electronic warfare platform, equipped with the Italian Selenia/Elettronica IHS-6 integrated ESM/ECM system. Four were built for Egypt following a 1978 order. The first Mk 2E made its maiden flight on 1 September 1978. The IHS-6 integrates the RQH-5 ESM system which detects, locates and identifies hostile emissions in the 1-18 GHz frequency range, and the TQN-2 modular jamming system. It incorporates a 'wide open' instantaneous frequency measuring (IFM) antenna for monopulse direction-finding (DF). The system has an automatically accessed threat library, with a capacity in excess of 2,000 emitters, and can track 50 targets simultaneously. EW operators sit behind a sophisticated console incorporating twin CRT displays with alphanumeric and graphic presentation of threat information. The TQN-2 is a highly capable system allowing spot, barrage and hybrid jamming in four bands simultaneously, and can be used to control chaff launchers for passive countermeasures. The I- and J-band antenna is steerable but other bands are served by fixed antennas.

## Commando Mk 3 (Sea King Mk 74)

Despite their Commando designation, the final Qatari aircraft are externally almost indistinguishable from Sea Kings, since they have undercarriage sponsons housing a retractable undercarriage and a dorsal radome, as well as a folding tail rotor pylon. The undercarriage sponsons are not quite standard, however, since they do not have provision for flotation bags. Instead, the aircraft must have the disc-like Commando flotation gear attached to the outer faces of the sponsons. Like the Commando 2 series, the aircraft retains a single extra window at the rear of the stretched cabin, on the port side. This is of the domed, 'bubble' type for improved all-round visibility. The Commando Mk 3 was intended to perform utility duties and also to operate in the ASV role. The aircraft are Exocet-compatible, but can carry a range of other weapons, including 16 SURA rockets, 18 SNEB rockets or a pair of podded 50-calibre machine-guns. Exocet seems to be the standard weapon, however, and is carried routinely. The first Commando Mk 3 flew on 14 June 1982, and was delivered on 26 November 1982. Delivery of the full batch of eight aircraft was complete by 4 January 1984.

# Westland variants

**Westland's Sea King is a much improved version of the Sikorsky SH-3. The versatile UK development is a successful ASW aircraft and has also given rise to capable, dedicated AEW, ASV and SAR derivatives.**

### Westland Sea King HAS.Mk 2

The Sea King HAS.Mk 2 came about as a direct result of improvements designed for the Australian Mk 50, whose prototype flew on 30 June 1974. The Royal Navy's HAS.Mk 2 used the same uprated 1,600-shp (1200-kW) Gnome H1400-1 engines that gave better 'hot-and-high' performance. The new variant also had the new six-bladed tail rotor which improved yaw authority at high all-up weights, plus a prominent 'barn door' intake guard. Only 21 Sea King HAS.Mk 2s were built by Westland, the rest being produced by conversion of HAS.Mk 1s. The first HAS.Mk 2 (XZ570) made its maiden flight on 18 June 1976 and No. 706 Squadron re-equipped with the new version in December 1976. The avionics fit of the HAS.Mk 2 included Plessey Type 2069 Sonar, Racal Decca 71 Doppler, TANS. Several avionics upgrades and modifications were applied during the service career of the HAS.Mk 2 and most were fleet-wide.

### Westland Sea King Mk 42/42A, Mk 43 and Mk 50/50A

**Mk 41:** The first export customer for the Sea King was the West German Marineflieger, which ordered 22 Mk 41s for search and rescue. The Sea King Mk 41 was closely based on the Royal Navy's HAS.Mk 1 but lacked sonar and ASW role equipment. It introduced a lengthened cabin, achieved by moving the rear bulkhead 5 ft 8 in (1.7 m) further aft and the extra pair of bubble observation windows. Deliveries took place in 1973-1974. Twenty surviving Mk 41s were extensively modernised and updated by MBB to give an anti-surface vessel capability in a programme which ended in 1988. They gained a Ferranti Seaspray Mk 3 radar for over-the-horizon targeting of the BAe Sea Skua ASMs, and the provision of a Ferranti Link II datalink.
**Mk 42/42A:** The Indian navy received batches of twelve Sea King Mk 42s in 1971 (six) and 1973-74 (six). Basically equivalent to the HAS.Mk 1, these equipped INAS 330 and INAS 336 shore-based at INS Garuda (Cochin), but frequently deployed aboard INS *Vikrant*. The first six aircraft operated from shore bases during the 1971 war with Pakistan. At least five Sea King Mk 42s have been written off, and the survivors, together with three Sea King Mk 42As (delivered in 1980) are now concentrated within INAS 330. The Mk 42As are broadly equivalent to the Royal Navy HAS.Mk 2.
**Mk 50/50A:** The Royal Australian Navy received ten Mk 50s in 1975-76. These essentially acted as prototype for the second generation of Sea Kings although they were fitted with the US Bendix Oceanics AN/ASQ-13A dipping sonar and a winch-operated refuelling system that permitted refuelling from ships while in flight, without having to alight. Two Mk 50As were delivered in 1983 as attrition replacements. Upon replacement by the Sikorsky S-70B-2 Seahawk, the Mk 50/50As were withdrawn from the ASW role during 1990. At about the same time, they received composite main rotor blades. The seven surviving Sea Kings serve in the utility role; their tasks include military and civilian SAR, VertRep, transport and SAS support.

### Sea King HAS.Mk 1

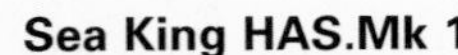

The Royal Navy placed a production order for 56 production Sea Kings in 1966. The first prototype, XV642, made its maiden flight on 7 May 1969 and the type entered service shortly after. Serialled between XV642 and XV677, and XV695 and XV714, the 56 HAS.Mk 1s were fitted with Ecko AW391 search radar (also known as the MEL ARI.5955 or MEL lightweight) with a prominent dorsal thimble radome. Most of the avionics were housed in the bottom of the nose. The aircraft also had a Marconi AD580 Doppler, a Plessey 195 dunking sonar, electronic automatic flight control system (AFCS) and a comprehensive communications fit. These made even the baseline Westland Sea King a significant improvement over the original US-built SH-3D from which it was derived. Armament consisted of four Mk 44 homing torpedoes, four Mk 11 depth charges, or a single WE177 nuclear depth bomb. Even with the sonar equipment left in place, the Sea King HAS.Mk 1 could carry 11 fully equipped troops, the number rising to 20 without sonar and 27 with the cabin stripped out. A 600-lb (272-kg) capacity variable-speed rescue hoist could be installed above the cabin door, and up to 6,000 lb (2720 kg) could be carried underslung. Most surviving HAS.Mk 1s were converted to HAS.Mk 2 standards. All HAS.Mk 1s had disappeared from RN service by the end of 1980.

### Westland Sea King. AEW Mk 2A, AEW.Mk 5 and AEW.Mk 7

The Royal Navy's lack of organic airborne early warning cover for its carriers was highlighted by the loss of HMS *Sheffield* (acting as a radar picket) on 4 May 1982 during the Falklands war. A crash programme was instituted to provide the fleet with its own AEW platform resulting in flying hardware within only 11 weeks. The AEW Sea King was produced by conversion of Sea King HAS.Mk 1s and HAS.Mk 2s, with an I-band Thorn EMI ARI 5980/3 Searchwater maritime surveillance radar forming the heart of the programme. The pulse-compression, frequency-agile search unit is the same as used in the RAF's maritime reconnaissance Nimrods. It had a proven ability to detect low-flying targets in any sea state, and with severe weather clutter, although it had been optimised for the detection of surface targets (such as submarine periscopes) and not fast-moving airborne targets. At 10,000 ft (3048 m) the radar has a range of about 125 miles (200 km) against a fighter-sized target. The antenna for the search radar is pitch and roll stabilised and offers a full 360° scan. It is housed in an unusual inflatable domed 'kettle drum' radome made of impregnated Kevlar fabric. It can be swung down to the vertical position in flight to project below the aircraft, and can swing back to the horizontal to give sufficient ground/deck clearance to allow the aircraft to land. The radar antenna is bulky, and does cause some drag, and cruising speed with the radar deployed is limited to 103 mph (166 km/h). The original radar was retained for tactical and navigation purposes, but sonar was removed. The AEW.Mk 2A also featured Racal MIR-2 'Orange Crop' ESM, but was otherwise similarly equipped to the ASW HAS.Mk 2. Nine AEW.Mk 2As were produced by conversion, the first of these flying on 23 July 1982.

## Westland Sea King HAR.Mk 3/3A and HAR.Mk 5

**HAR.Mk 3:** In 1975 the RAF placed an order for 15 Sea King HAR.Mk 3s to replace elderly Wessex and Whirlwind aircraft in the search and rescue (SAR) role. The HAR.Mk 3 featured lengthened cabins, long-reach winches, extra fuel tankage and extra bubble observation windows, as well as H.1400-1 engines and a six-bladed tail rotor. The aircraft's avionics were generally similar to those of the HAS.Mk 2, but also had a VHF radio for communications with the police, mountain rescue teams, etc. The initial batch of HAR.Mk 3s entered service in 1978 and was followed by a further four aircraft. Six aircraft were specially modified for service with No. 78 Sqn on the Falklands Islands. These have NVG-compatible cockpits, Navstar GPS and Racal RNS252 SuperTANS, as well as ARI 18228 radar warning receivers and provision for chaff/flare dispensers.
**HAR.Mk 3A:** The HAR.Mk 3A is the RAF's second-generation SAR Sea King and features a digital colour search radar, an upgraded flight control system and improved communications equipment. The first of six aircraft ordered entered service in 1993.
**HAR.Mk 5:** The Royal Navy's dedicated SAR Sea King is essentially a HAS.Mk 5 stripped of much of its ASW mission equipment. Uniquely among rescue Sea Kings presently in service, the four known HAR.Mk 5 conversions have MEL Sea Searcher radar.

## Westland Sea King Mk 42B/42C, Mk 45/45A and Mk 47

**Mk 42B/Mk 42C:** India became the first customer for the Advanced Sea King when it received 20 Mk 42Bs in batches of 12 and eight. These feature 'hot-and-high' Gnome H1400-1T engines, composite main rotor blades and a new five-bladed tail rotor. Other new equipment includes launch beams for two Sea Eagle missiles, MEL Super Searcher radar, AQS-902 sonobuoy processor, HS-12 dipping sonar and Hermes ESM. The Indian Mk 42Bs serve with INAS 336, shore-based at Cochin, but are regularly deployed aboard the carriers *Viraat* and *Vikrant*, and the indigenous 'Godavri'-class frigates. The Sea King Mk 42C is a dedicated utility transport and SAR version of the Advanced Sea King. Its avionics are similar to those of the RAF's Sea King HAR.Mk 3s, but with a nose-mounted Bendix radar. Delivery of six aircraft took place between 1987 and 1988.
**Mk 45/Mk 45A:** The Mk 45 designation applies to six ASW Sea Kings ordered by Pakistan and delivered between 1975 and 1977. These were broadly equivalent to the Royal Navy HAS.Mk 1. Five were modified for a secondary ASV role with provision for AM39 Exocet ASMs. The aircraft equip No. 111 Squadron (the 'Sharks') shore-based at Sharea Faisal. A single Mk 45A (ex-Royal Navy HAS.Mk 5) was acquired as an attrition replacement.
**Mk 47:** Saudi Arabia ordered six ASW Sea Kings on behalf of Egypt in 1974. The Sea King Mk 47 was basically similar to the Royal Navy HAS.Mk 2 and the Australian Mk 50, with virtually the same avionics and equipment fit but with the original Plessey Type 195M sonar as fitted to the HAS.Mk 1. Deliveries began in 1976. The six aircraft are based at Alexandria for ASW duties. The Egyptian Mk 47s are all winch-equipped and can perform SAR missions.

## Westland Sea King HAS.Mk 5 and HAS.Mk 6

**HAS.Mk 5:** Main features of HAS.Mk 5 upgrade were an all-digital MEL Sea Searcher X-band radar, Plessey Type 2069 dipping sonar and AQS902 LAPADS acoustic processing and display system. Thanks to LAPADS the Sea King HAS.Mk 5 could monitor signals from passive or active sonobuoys. Some HAS.Mk 5s were equipped with the USN SH-3H's AN/AQS-81 towed MAD birds purchased from Sikorsky. The majority of HAS.Mk 5s (55) were produced by conversion of existing airframes (comprising one HAS.Mk 1, 19 HAS.Mk 2s and 35 HAS.Mk 2As); these were augmented by 30 new-build aircraft. Royal Navy Sea Kings were deployed to the Gulf for mine countermeasures and ASV duties. Two were fitted with GPS, AN/ALQ-157 IRCM jammers, M-130 chaff/flare dispensers, RWRs, secure speech radios and a door-mounted 7.62-mm GPMG. Role equipment included Sandpiper FLIR, Menagerie ECM, hand-held thermal imaging equipment and Demon, a video-based mine-hunting system. Crews were expanded to include a diving supervisor and three divers. They successfully provided a rapid-reaction mine detection and destruction unit.
**HAS.Mk 6:** The HAS.Mk 6 is primarily an update of existing HAS.Mk 5 airframes. It offers a dramatic improvement in ASW capability pending the service entry of the EH101 Merlin. It features composite main rotor blades and a new fully integrated tactical mission system that includes a digital AQS-902G-DS enhanced sonar system integrating data from the sonobuoys and a new Digital Type 2069 dipping sonar with a much improved deep water capability. Other new equipment includes an internal AIMS (Advanced Integrated MAD System), improved IFF, ESM upgraded to Orange Reaper configuration, and a pair of VHF/UHF secure speech radios. The HAS.Mk 6 is 500-800 lb (227-363 kg) lighter than the HAS.Mk 5, this approximating to 30 minutes of extra fuel. The first converted HAS.Mk 6 flew in 1987 and was followed by 72 further conversions plus five new-build aircraft.

## Sea King Mk 43 and Mk 48

**Mk 43:** Between 1972-73, Norway received 10 Sea Kings to provide military and civilian SAR cover. The resulting Sea King Mk 43 was broadly equivalent to the German Mk 41, and was thus based on the RN's HAS.Mk 1 airframe and engine. The aircraft equip 330 Skvadron headquartered at Bodø with operational flights at Bodø, Banak, Ørland and Sola. The nine surviving Sea Kings have been upgraded to Mk 43B standard, and have been joined by three new-build aircraft. The Mk 43B is a unique hybrid and features MEL Sea Searcher, plus a nose-mounted Bendix/King weather radar, upgraded navigation avionics and a FLIR 2000 turret.
**Mk 48:** Belgium received five Sea Kings for SAR duties in 1976. These were broadly similar to the RAF's HAR.Mk 3. The Sea Kings were delivered to Escadrille 40 (40 Smaldeel) at Koksijde by 1976. The aircraft have secondary VIP, troop transport, parachute jumping, underslung load, medevac, organ delivery and paramilitary and police duties. They were retrofitted with composite main rotor blades during the 1980s, and also received a major navigation systems update. All five aircraft have been upgraded with a Bendix RDR1500B radar, a FLIR Systems FLIR 2000F and an improved navigation suite.

# H-53 development

*The second YCH-53A (Bureau No. 151614) made the type's first flight on 14 October 1964 from Stratford, Connecticut. Only two YCH-53As were used in flight tests before production aircraft were delivered.*

**Developed from a US Marines specification for a heavylift assault helicopter that could operate from ships, the H-53 family of helicopters has given sterling service in conflicts ranging from Vietnam to the Gulf War.**

Development of the versatile H-53 family began in October 1960 when the United States Marine Corps declared a wish to replace its Sikorsky HR2S-1s with a new ship-based heavy assault helicopter. The HR2S-1 (later redesignated CH-37C) had validated the long-standing Marines conviction that helicopters were the ideal vehicles in which to bring troops and equipment ashore during amphibious raids. However, the HR2S-1 was growing old and proving difficult to maintain and so it was decided that a replacement was needed.

Initially, the USMC joined the Army, Air Force and Navy in sponsoring the development of the medium-sized Tri-Service VTOL transport. However, the resulting Vought-Hiller-Ryan XC-142A programme became over-ambitious and ran late, and so the Marines decided to make their own request for a new heavylift helicopter.

In a requirement issued by the Bureau of Naval Weapons on 7 March 1962, the Marines called for a ship-based helicopter capable of lifting an 8,000-lb (3630-kg) payload over a radius of 100 nm (115 miles; 185 km) at a speed of 150 kt (172 mph; 278 km/h). Its missions would be ship-to-shore transport, downed aircraft recovery, personnel transport and aeromedical evacuation.

Three companies responded, Boeing Vertol with a redesign of its HC-1A, Kaman Aircraft with a development of the British-designed Fairey Rotodyne and Sikorsky indicating its intent to develop a twin-turbine S-65. Having lost a previous competition to supply the Marines with a medium-lift helicopter, Sikorsky went all-out to win the contract. It was selected as the winner in July 1962 when the S-65 was chosen as a result of technical, production capability and cost considerations. However, due to insufficient funds in the USMC budget, the anticipated contract for four prototypes could not be realised until Sikorsky lowered its R&D bid, and the revised number of two prototypes was ordered. This revised proposal gained acceptance and, on 24 September 1962, the DoD announced that Sikorsky's helicopter had been accepted – the two YCH-53A prototypes, a static test airframe and a mock-up were built in a $9,965,635 contract.

Sikorsky's design was powered by two General Electric T64 shaft turbines and incorporated many proven features of other Sikorsky designs. There was the main transmission of the S-64 (CH-54) crane helicopter and the 72-ft (22-m) diameter, six-bladed main rotor and anti-torque rotor of the S-56 (CH-37) heavylift helicopter. The winning design itself was of similar configuration to, but larger than, its S-61 (SH-3A) stablemate. First flown on 14

*A Marines CH-53A carries a CH-46 helicopter fuselage during testing at Patuxent River. This heavylift capability allowed the Sea Stallion to recover over 1,000 downed aircraft in Vietnam.*

*The HH-53C was a development of the interim HH-53B rescue helicopter. Its design meant that the internal and external fuel capacity had to be reduced but, due its telescopic refuelling probe, its combat radius was not affected. HH-53Cs of the 55th ARRS also flew in support of every Apollo space mission, ready to retrieve the manned capsules in the event of an abort after launch.*

***Above: The main mission of the RH-53D was to tow a minesweeping sled, which would drag mines to the surface. They would then be detonated by the helicopter's pair of 0.5-in (12.7-mm) machine guns.***

***Left: The simple idea of adding an extra engine to the H-53 airframe resulted in a far more powerful aircraft. This test YMH-53E (without the typical large sponsons of the MH-53E) is able to drag its anti-mine sled through the roughest seas.***

October 1964 and smoothly completing trials while encountering few problems, the initial production variant, the CH-53A, entered service with the Marine Corps in September 1965. The 141 'A' model Sea Stallions were followed on the production lines by three other heavylift transport variants (20 CH-53Cs for the USAF; 126 CH-53Ds for the USMC; and two CH-53Gs for West Germany) with more powerful T64 engines and other improvements. In addition, 20 CH-53Gs were assembled in West Germany and 90 more were built under licence.

Whether in combat or while undergoing trials, the heavylift transport variants of the twin-engined S-65 series proved highly satisfactory. This can be seen in the fact that, in Vietnam between 13 January 1967 and 18 May 1971, Marine Heavy Helicopter Squadron 463 (HMH-463) was credited with recovering a total of 1,096 fixed-wing aircraft and helicopters; the dollar amount saved far exceeded the total acquisition cost of all CH-53As and CH-53Ds. HMH-463 gained further recognition as being part of Operations Eagle Pull and Frequent Wind which saw its helicopters being used to pull American citizens and their allies out of Phnom Penh and Saigon. During the course of the war, the Marines lost 19 CH-53A/Ds to a variety of causes.

Back in America, Sea Stallions were making the headlines by establishing unofficial payload and gross weight records for a helicopter built outside the USSR. A CH-53A also became the first helicopter to be fitted with an automatic terrain clearance system.

### H-53 variants

All of these successes did not go unnoticed and the interest of the Air Force and Navy plus several foreign customers led Sikorsky to design specialised rescue and mine-countermeasure variants of its twin-engined helicopter. Development of the HH-53B, prompted by the need to provide a more powerful, better armoured and defended combat rescue aircraft, was initiated in September 1966. Sikorsky quickly developed the Super Jolly rescue helicopter and the first HH-53B flew on 15 March 1967. Sikorsky went on to build 44 HH-53Cs for the USAF, two S-65C-2s for Austria and 33 S-65C-3s for Israel.

In Vietnam, Super Jollies proved to be a highly effective combat rescue aircraft and in their first three years of combat they saved the lives of some 371 aircrew. HH-53s also gained fame for their participation in the Son Tay prison raid and the rescue of the *Mayaguez* crew from captivity in Cambodia. During the conflict, the USAF lost some 14 CH-53/HH-53s in combat, including one shot down by a MiG-21. After the war, the Super Jollies had their capabilities expanded when they were brought up to HH-53H Pave Low III and then Pave Low III Enhanced standard. This was partly due to the poor performance by the Navy RH-53Ds during the attempted rescue of American hostages in Iran in April 1980. In Pave Low III Enhanced form, the HH-53 is the most capable special operations helicopter in service with the Air Force Special Operations Command and, in 1986, its designation was changed to MH-53J to reflect its expanded special operations role.

### Minesweepers

Experiments with minesweeping helicopters led to the conclusion that only the CH-53 was powerful enough to drag the heavy minesweeping gear. However, due to the need for CH-53As to support the Marines in Vietnam, the first experiments with minesweeping Sea Stallions did not occur until winter 1970. Fifteen helicopters were given the appropriate equipment and were redesignated RH-53As prior to their assignment to Helicopter Mine Counter-measures Squadron Twelve (HM-12). They gained notoriety during Operation Endsweep, the removal of mines from North Vietnamese waters between February and July 1972. These first RH-53As were later supplemented by 30 specially-built RH-53Ds in Navy service. They have been used since in several mine-clearance operations from Nimbus Star in 1964 to Earnest Will in the 1980s. Iran also received six essentially similar mine countermeasures helicopters before the fall of the Shah. The Iranian RH-53Ds were the last S-65s built as the success achieved with military customers did not repeat itself in the civilian world.

### Three-engined S-80

By autumn 1970, the USMC's experience with the CH-53A had convinced it that a helicopter was needed that could lift 1.8 times the load that could be lifted by the Sea Stallion. The first step towards acquiring such an aircraft was the approval on 24 October 1967 of a specific requirement calling for a helicopter with an 18-ton capability, but which was small enough to operate from LPH amphibious assault ships. In addition to the Marines' needs, the Navy also wanted a new vertical re-supply helicopter, and the Army a heavylift helicopter.

Sikorsky responded to this by placing a third engine inside the CH-53 upper fuselage fairing, the additional power being delivered through a beefed-up transmission to a seven-bladed main rotor. Requiring only limited airframe development, this suggestion quickly gained the interest of the Marine Corps which lent its support to the project. The Army, however, followed its own requirement which resulted in the aborted Boeing-Vertol XCH-62. The YCH-53E first flew on 1 March 1974 but, due to a more vigorous development and testing scheme than that of its predecessor, the CH-53E did not enter service until February 1981. The new helicopter proved exceedingly popular with the Marines, fulfilling all their hopes, while the Navy adopted the three-engined minesweeping derivative, the MH-53E, in April 1988. This helicopter was also delivered to the Japanese Maritime Self Defence Force as the S-80M-1 a year later.

A VH-53F presidential transport derivative was also proposed, but was ultimately cancelled.

***Commercially, the CH-53 or S-65C was a failure. This aircraft was modified by NASA to demonstrate its commercial capabilities, but the helicopter was ultimately too expensive to operate.***

# CH/RH-53 Operations

**Offering a heavylift capability for amphibious operations, the CH-53 was quickly developed into a host of variants to fulfil roles for both the USAF and West German forces.**

After winning the HH(X) competition, Sikorsky struggled to complete the YCH-53A prototypes in the face of a shortage of design personnel, and late delivery of sub-contracted components and government-furnished equipment. Weight increases extended the proposed delivery date of the initial 16 production CH-53As. Production CH-53As, as first delivered to HMH-463 at MCAS Santa Ana, California in September 1965, were initially identical to the YCH-53As, and like these prototypes were powered by 2,500-shp (1864-kW) T64-GE-6s. Before accelerated training could commence and deployment to Southeast Asia was authorised, four developments were made to improve the usefulness of the CH-53A in combat: (1) an engine air particle separator (EAPS) filtering system was installed in front of the air intake of the engines; (2) defensive armament was provided (a pintle-mounted M60 machine-gun being added to fire from hatches on both sides of the forward fuselage); (3) 450 lb (204 kg) of amour was added to protect the crew and vital components; and (4) the CH-53A was tested in the 'flying crane' role, as combat operations in Vietnam had revealed that the Marines' most urgent need was for a helicopter capable of retrieving aircraft without the need for removing parts and equipment to reduce weight.

Trials revealed the need to increase power if the CH-53A was to be able to retrieve the CH-46A, the standard Marine medium helicopter. Accordingly, plans were made for the installation of T64-GE-1 engines that would be allowed to operate for short periods at a maximum rating of 3,080-shp (2296-kW) instead of the standard 2,850 shp (2125-kW) and for their replacement beginning in early 1968 by specially modified 3,435-shp (2561-kW) T64-GE-12s or T64-GE-16s, the retrofitting of these more powerful engines being made without the need for airframe changes.

Production CH-53As had a crew of three (pilot, co-pilot and crew chief) and were designed to carry internally either 38 assault troops, 42 litter patients and four attendants, or 8,000 lb (3630 kg) of cargo. The cabin measured 30 ft (9.14 m) in length, 6 ft 6 in (1.98 m) in height , and 7 ft 6 in (2.29 m) in width and incorporated roller conveyors and a tie-down system. Bulkier loads weighing up to 20,000 lb (9070 kg) were carried externally. Although primarily intended for use in the transport role, the CH-53As' usefulness increased when, from the 34th production machine, they were fitted with hardpoints for towed minesweeping equipment.

## Minesweeping

Fifteen CH-53As modified as RH-53As were acquired by the US Navy. All were fitted with hardpoints for towed minesweeping equipment. The Navy decided that further modification would be required, and the 15 Sea Stallions were re-engined with 3,925-shp (2926-kW) T64-GE-413 shaft turbines. They were operated by the Navy pending availability of the specialised RH-53D variant. Rear-view mirrors were fitted in tubular mounts on each side of the nose to enable the pilot and co-pilot to visually track the towed minesweeping equipment, and a rectangular frame was attached to the rear ramp to prevent the towing cable from hitting the airframe or tail rotor. Following their replacement in Navy service by RH-53Ds, the RH-53As were returned to the Marine Corps and were once again designated CH-53As.

***Above: Easing away after refuelling from a USMC KC-130, a CH-53E demonstrates the precise flying qualities of the type. Some Soviet helicopters have outstripped the -53 in terms of power and lifting capability, but the Stallion remains a true giant of the helicopter world.***

***Marine assault! The principal*** **raison d'être** ***for the Sikorsky H-53 was to provide rapid transport between ship and shore for the USMC. Although it is a very capable troop transport, the helicopter was tailored for the carriage of the heavy equipment that accompanies the Marines during amphibious assaults.***

## USAF interest

Having closely observed the progress made by the USMC with the CH-53, the USAF perceived a similar need for a heavy lift helicopter. Twenty CH-53Cs were built for the USAF, which requested a change of powerplant to the 3,925-shp (2926-kW) T-64-GE-7, and these variants differed externally from Marine CH-53As in being

*Left: Self-protection is an increasingly important part of helicopter operations. Over the battlefield, shoulder-launched heat-seeking missiles like the SA-7 'Grail' are particularly dangerous, and are best countered by the release of flares from dispensers on the rear fuselage sides. They provide a dense heat source much greater than that of the helicopter itself, thereby drawing away the missile.*

*Below: The USAF was quick to exploit the potential of inflight refuelling with the H-53 in an effort to increase the helicopter's range. Shown below is an HH-53 preparing to engage one of the trailing refuelling drogues from an HC-130P tanker.*

fitted to carry 450-US gal (1703-litre) external tanks. The CH-53C was distinguished from the HH-53C by its lack of inflight-refuelling probe. CH-53Cs first replaced CH-53As on loan from the Marines for covert operations in Laos with the 21st SOS, and were later operated by TAC and United States Air Forces Europe to airlift equipment for the Tactical Air Control System, and by MAC for pilot training. The type was gradually withdrawn from service to undergo a modernisation programme which brought the remaining seven examples up to MH-53J standard.

### More improvements

First flown on 27 January 1969, the CH-53D was to all intents and purposes nothing more than an improved version of the CH-53A, with strengthened transmission to enable early T64 variants to be replaced first by 3,695-shp (2755-kW) T64-GE-412s, then by 3,925-shp (2926-kW) T64-GE-413s and later by 3,925-shp (2926-kW) T64-GE-413s. The transmission was rated at 7,560-hp (5637-kW) single-engined operation, but the additional power enabled CH-53Ds to operate without significant limitations even under hot-and-high conditions. Other improvements incorporated during production included use of the Sikorsky Blade Inspection Method to eliminate the need for mandatory blade retirement after a specific number of operating hours. Standard fuel capacity remained at 638 US gal (2363-litre) in two sponson tanks and, as was the case with the CH-53A, one to five 330-US gal (1136-litre) ferry tanks could be installed in the fuselage.

### German giants

Seeking a replacement for the Sikorsky H-34s and Weserflug H-21s of the Heeresflieger, West Germany evaluated the Boeing Vertol CH-47 and Sikorsky CH-53 in 1966. Orders were placed in June 1968 for two Sikorsky-built CH-53Gs through USN channels and 133 CH-53Gs to be built under licence by a consortium led by VFW. Production costs soon reduced the total requirement to 110 examples, which serve with three medium transport regiments.

### Superior lifter

Seeking to improve the capabilities of the CH-53, modifications were made that included an additional centrally mounted third engine with intake and exhaust on the port side, a beefed-up transmission, and a seven-bladed main rotor with broader chord blades and increased diameter.

Designated CH-53Es, the variant differed internally from the CH-53D in having a 6-ft 2-in (1.88-m) longer fuselage, a broader tailfin, a low-mounted tailplane, longer sponson housing that enabled internal fuel capacity to be increased from 638 to 1,017 US gal (2415 to 3850 litres), and provision for 650-US gal (2460-litre) pylon-mounted tanks for an inflight-refuelling probe.

The first production CH-53E was accepted by the USMC on 13 December 1980, following operational evaluation at MCAS Quantico, MCAS Cherry Point, NAS Norfolk, Fort Bragg and aboard an LPH. The improved variant demonstrated its superior lifting capability.

By February 1981 CH-53Es equipped five Marine squadrons operating in heavylift shore operations and in support of amphibious assault operations. In August 1990, during Operation Desert Shield, ship-based CH-53Es were among the first helicopters to reach the new troublespot. They provided a lifting capability not only for the USMC but also for the US Army and other coalition forces.

In the next few years, USMC CH-53Es will begin serving alongside the delayed MV-22 Osprey and are currently undergoing a major upgrade programme which has led to the introduction of the Hughes AN/AAQ-16 FLIR, Night Vision System and the adaptation of the cockpit to NVG-compatibility.

The Sikorsky CH-53E is fulfiling a proud tradition stemming from the CH-53A, and for the present the helicopter looks set to remain a vital component within any overseas military operation by the US.

*The two principal characteristics of mine-hunting H-53s are rear-view mirrors mounted on each side of the nose for tracking the towed sled, and a ramp-frame that prevents the towing cable fouling the rear fuselage or tail rotor. Before the dedicated RH- and MH-53s became available, the US Navy used converted CH-53As, known as RH-53As, which served with HM-12 (illustrated). This unit was heavily involved in Operation Endsweep, during which mines were cleared from North Vietnamese waters such as Haiphong Harbour.*

*The addition of a refuelling probe set the HH-53 apart from its CH-53 progenitor. This fitment enables the 'Super Jolly' to loiter over potential rescue sites for longer periods of time.*

# HH-53 variants

## 'Super Jolly'

**During Vietnam, the ageing HH-3 proved insufficient to the task of combat rescue – the USAF therefore turned to Sikorsky's H-53, which offered unparalleled power and superior range.**

Development of the HH-53B began in September 1966, prompted by the urgent need of the Aerospace Rescue and Recovery Service to supplement its HH-3Es with a more powerful combat rescue helicopter. Changes from the CH-53A were kept to a minimum, but as the main requirement was additional range, a retractable flight refuelling probe was fitted. A jettisonable fuel tank, able to carry 650 US gal (2460 litres), was added to each side and braced to the fuselage by two parallel struts. Three Miniguns and 1,200 lb (544 kg) of armour were added for self-defence.

The HH-53Bs were provided with a rescue hoist, mounted externally above the main door on the starboard side of the forward fuselage. A jungle penetrator and 250 ft (76 m) of steel cable enabled downed aircrews to be recovered in dense jungle areas without the need to land.

Preceded into USAF service by a pair of CH-53As borrowed from the Marine Corps to initiate crew training, the first HH-53Bs were flown on 15 March 1967. Barely five months later, two HH-53Bs were deployed to Southeast Asia to serve with the 37th ARRS at Udorn RTAFB, Thailand. They made their first rescue before the end of 1967 and quickly demonstrated their superiority over the HH-3Es when operating under hot and high conditions. Quickly supplemented by HH-53Cs and afterwards primarily assigned to CONUS-based units, HH-53Bs were operated until the late 1980s, when the last four were modified as MH-53Js.

*Only eight HH-53Bs were built, this being the first (66-14428). Despite being available only in small numbers, the success of the HH-53B led to further development, resulting in the HH-53C.*

### Super 'Super Jolly'

After rushing up the development of the interim HH-53Bs, Sikorsky refined the design of the Super Jolly to produce 44 HH-53Cs. With delivery to the Aerospace Rescue and Recovery Service commencing in August 1968, the new Super Jolly version was distinguished externally by the absence of parallel bracing struts between the fuselage and the boom supporting the external tanks. This change was made possible after the external tanks of the HH-53Bs resulted in unsatisfactory roll-handling and forced a shift to smaller tanks, with capacity reduced from 650 to 450 US gal (2460 to 1703 litres). Fortunately, the reduction in external tank capacity had no significant impact on mission radius and endurance as the HH-53C relied routinely on inflight-refuelling. A convincing demonstration of the type's remarkable endurance was given from 15-24 August 1970, when two HH-53Cs were refuelled 13 times by a pair of HC-130Ns and, with seven intermediate stops, were flown 9,000 miles (14500 km) from Eglin AFB, USA to Da Nang AB, Vietnam.

Other improvements incorporated during production included the installation of additional armour and the fitting of a more

*A rare picture shows water rescue operations from an HH-53C, with a swimmer dropping from the ramp during a low hover. Such operations ensure that the helicopter is in a dangerous position for as little time as possible.*

**Seen here over Tower Bridge, London, this HH-53C is not in its normal combat environment. There has been a constant HH-53 presence in the UK for the past two decades, with HH-53Cs and, later, MH-53Js located at the USAF's Woodbridge, Bentwaters, Alconbury and Mildenhall bases.**

complete set of radios to facilitate communications between the 'Super Jolly' and HC-130 tanker/rescue command post aircraft, fighters providing fire support, and downed aircrews. Changes dictated by combat experience included the introduction of an experimental RHAW system during the spring of 1972 and the subsequent installation of IR countermeasures pods. The lack of RHAW (radar homing and warning) gear had come to light in 1971 when the North Vietnamese started moving SAMs and radar-guided guns near the DMZ and along portions of the Ho Chi Minh Trail.

While most HH-53Cs were operated in the combat rescue role, those of the 55th ARRS flew in support of every Apollo space mission as their external cargo hook of 20,000 lb (9072 kg) capacity would have enabled them to retrieve the manned capsule in the event of an abort shortly after launch. Others were assigned to the Air Force Flight Test Center at Edwards AFB and to three Test Squadrons (the 6512th at Edwards AFB, the 6514th at Hill AFB and the 6593rd at Hickam AFB) to recover drones and space capsules. In addition to operating its 'Super Jollies' in support of the military space programme, the Hawaii-based 6593rd Test Squadron also made good use of its HH-53Cs during rescue operations; for example, on 22 March 1979 it saved 19 Japanese fishermen from a vessel burning 80 miles (128 km) south of the island of Hawaii. HH-53Cs remained in USAF service until the late 1980s, when the last were modified as MH-53Js.

## Special Forces superlative

Before the entry into service of the HH-53B, it had already become obvious to the USAF that combat rescue helicopters would have to be provided with night/all-weather capability to be able to recover downed aircrews as quickly as possible. Accordingly, a limited-capability Pave Low I system using low-light-level television (LLLTV) was tested at Eglin AFB and was fitted in November 1969 to a 'Super Jolly' of the 40th ARRS at Udorn RTAFB. Unfortunately, Pave Low I proved ineffective and a more reliable system did not become available until 1972. Although still far from being satisfactory under certain operating conditions, the revised system did prove its worth on 21 December 1972 when it enabled the crew of an HH-53C to make the first night combat rescue (the fortunate recipient being the pilot of an F-4J from VMFA-232 that had been shot down over Laos).

After the war ended in Southeast Asia, the ARRS continued to work with the Air Force Systems Command to obtain a more capable night/all-weather system for its 'Super Jollies'. Designated Pave Low II, the improved package was fitted in June 1975 to a modified HH-53B (66-14433) which, redesignated YHH-53H, underwent system testing at Edwards AFB and operational evaluation by the 1550th ATTW at Kirtland AFB.

Successful evaluation of the YHH-53H Pave Low II led to that helicopter being upgraded to the HH-53H Pave Low III configuration and to the modification of eight HH-53Cs to the same standard. The work was performed at the Naval Air Rework Facility which had been handling overhaul and repair for all H-53s since the onset of the programme. Later, to replace two HH-53Hs lost in training accidents in 1984, two CH-53Cs were fitted with a flight refuelling probe and Pave Low III avionics to bring them up to HH-53H standard.

Delivered in 1979-80, these night/all-weather capable Pave Low III helicopters were fitted with a complex avionics fit, including a Texas Instrument AN/AAQ-10 FLIR, a Canadian Marconi Doppler navigation system, a Texas Instrument AN/APQ-158 TF radar, a Litton inertial navigation system, a computer-projected map display system, RHAW and chaff/flare dispensers. The designation of the Pave Low III helicopters was changed from HH-53H to MH-53H in 1986, when these special operations helicopters were upgraded under the Constant Green programme.

Pave Low III HH-53Hs were first assigned to the 67th ARRS at RAF Woodbridge in 1980, but were soon handed to the 20th SOS, 1st SOW, at Hurlbert Field, Florida. Transferred from TAC to MAC in March 1983, the 1st SOW began supplementing its Pave Low III MH-53H helicopters with Pave Low III Enhanced MH-53Js in late 1987. In late 1999 Pave Low IV MH-53Ms began to enter front-line service.

**Above: The 1550th Air Transport Training Wing was established at Hill AFB, Utah, in July 1971, flying this HH-53H, among others. It moved to Kirtland AFB in February 1976, and was redesignated the 1550th CCTW.**

**Left: The HH-53H Pave Low III was the USAF's first night/all-weather helicopter. Derived from the HH-53, an additional nose fairing mounted sensors for low-level penetration, the white turret visible here housing the AN/AAQ-10 FLIR.**

# Special ops and minesweeping

## MH-53E/H/J

**Representing the latest and most powerful of the venerable H-53 family is the MH-53 series of highly versatile Special Operations and mine-clearing helicopters in service with the USAF and US Navy.**

In a USAF rebuild of two CH-53Cs and eight HH-53B/Cs, the Sikorsky HH-53H Pave (precision avionics vectoring equipment) Low III was fitted with night/all-weather search and rescue equipment. This included an inertial navigation system, Doppler, projected map display, infra-red and terrain-following radar. The HH-53H was a member of a family which had been in service since 1967 and which had, in a number of variants, served so well in Vietnam. However, in 1986, under the Constant Green programme, the Special Forces role was added to this variant and so it was redesignated the MH-53H. This was the first version of the H-53 family to be fully cleared for nocturnal operations, with the crew employing NVGs (Night Vision Goggles).

It was later decided to upgrade the MH-53Hs and several CH-53Cs to MH-53J standard. This was partly due to the poor performance of the Navy RH-53D helicopters in the unsuccessful Eagle Claw American hostage rescue mission, combined with less than total satisfaction with the HH-53H version. The Pave Low III Enhanced MH-53J helicopters are Special Forces aircraft with upgraded Pave Low III night and adverse weather capabilities. They are also fitted with integrated digital avionics for increased reliability. MH-53Js further differ from their predecessors in being fitted with a strengthened transmission to absorb the power of two 4,380-shp (3266-kW) T64-GE-415s, in possessing 1,000 lb (454 kg) of additional armour, and in having their maximum take-off weight increased from 42,000 lb (19050 kg) to 50,000 lb (22680 kg). They first entered service at Hulbert Field, Florida, in 1988.

### MH-53s in combat

Since then, USAF MH-53Hs and MH-53Js of the 1st SOW took part in Operation Just Cause in Panama, dropping Navy SEALs into Panama City. Then in March 1990, they were transferred into the USAF's Special Operations Command.

During Operation Desert Storm, MH-53Js provided navigation and support for the US Army AH-64 Apaches which attacked Iraqi radar defence sites as part of Task Force Normandy on the opening night of the Gulf War. Later in the conflict, they were involved in the insertion of the SAS and US Special Forces teams which then went on to hunt the much-publicised Iraqi 'Scud' missile launchers.

At present, the USAF is planning to replace its MH-53Js with the new Bell-Boeing CV-22 Osprey tilt-rotor aircraft, although problems with congressional funding have constantly pushed

*Above: The US Navy's MH-53 performs the minesweeping role inherited from the RH-53D. The mirrors positioned forward of the cockpit allow the crew to monitor the sled as it is pulled through the water.*

*Top: A Mildenhall-based Special Forces MH-53J cruises over the English countryside. The advanced Pave Low III system allows the MH-53J to perform low-level flights, even at night or in bad weather, for covert infil/exfil missions into hostile territory.*

***A Special Operations MH-53J demonstrates the use of flares for protection against enemy infra-red missiles. Flare dispensers are mounted on the rear fuselage sides and on the wing sponsons.***

back the entry into service date for that type. Nevertheless, the MH-53J is perfectly able to remain in service until then and even beyond.

### Mine-hunter

By combining the airframe and powerplant of the three-engined CH-53E with the minesweeping gear of the RH-53D, Sikorsky created the MH-53E. The MH-53E offers a greatly improved capability as its increased power enables it to drag minesweeping gear through rougher seas than the RH-53D, and its more advanced avionics give it an all-weather capability.

Development of this variant began in 1980 and the prototype first flew a year later. Externally similar to the CH-53E, the MH-53E has been fitted with enlarged sponsons, which enable the internal fuel capacity to be raised from 1,017 US gal (3850 litres) to 3,200 US gal (12113 litres). This gives the MH-53E the ability to sweep for mines with a towed sled for some four hours, while operating 30 minutes from its base. What is more, the addition of an air-air refuelling probe enables the endurance of the helicopter to be extended even further. As with the earlier RH-53D, the MH-53E can deal with mechanical, acoustic and magnetic mines using equipment mounted on its sled.

Today, the MH-53E is in service with a number of naval units. At Norfolk, HM-14 uses the MH-53E, while at Corpus Christi NAS, Texas, the helicopter is operated by HM-15.

## MH-53J Pave Low III Enhanced

**In 1995 this MH-53J was based at RAF Mildenhall with the 21st SOS 'Dust Devils', as part of the 352nd SOG. It has adopted the new low-IR signature overall grey finish, in place of the green 'European One' camouflage carried previously by AFSOC's MH-53J fleet.**

**Main rotor**
The MH-53J has a 72-ft 3-in (22.02-m) diameter main rotor. The titanium and steel elastomeric rotor head can be folded for full shipboard capability.

**External fuel tanks**
Two 500-US gal (1893-litre) jettisonable fuel tanks are an almost permanent fixture on the MH-53J. Those MH-53Js converted from HH-53Bs retain the latter's braced external fuel tank installation.

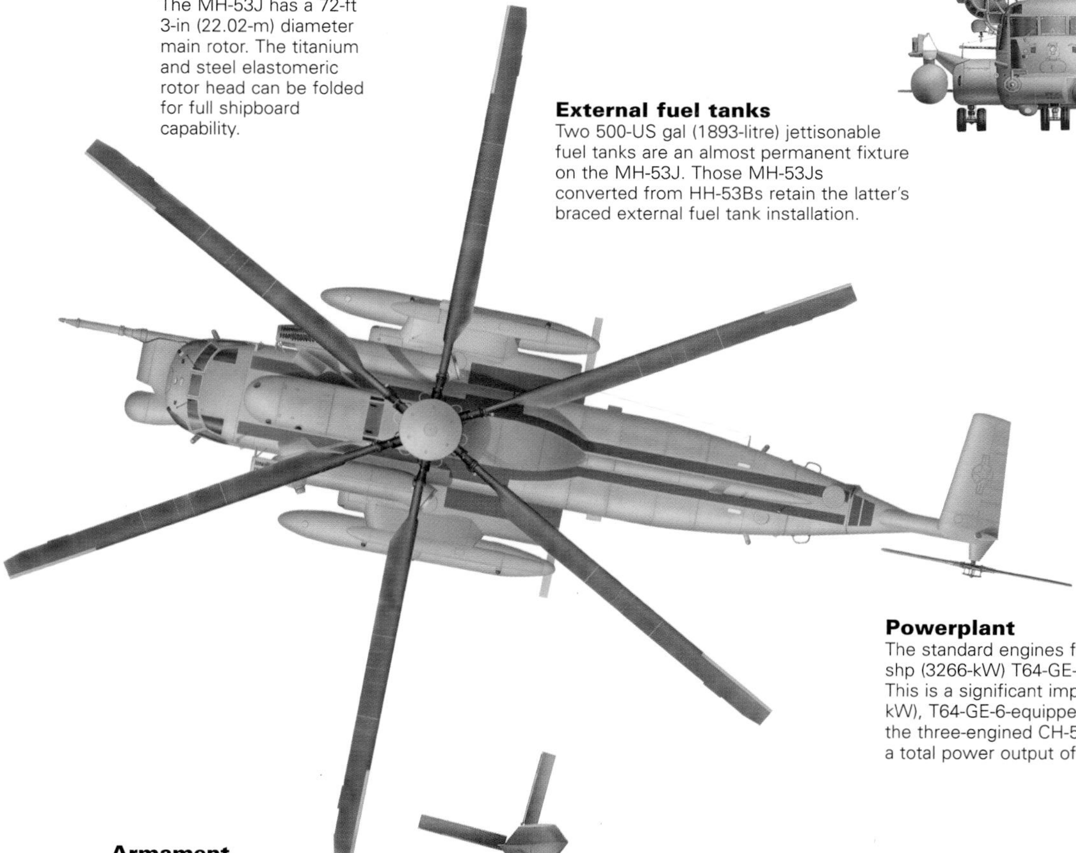

**MH-53 genesis**
The first Pave Low was the HH-53B Pave Low I, which underwent limited trials in Vietnam towards the end of the US involvement. This experience motivated the Aerospace Rescue and Recovery Service, along with AFMC, to develop the Pave Low II, which first flew as the YHH-53H in 1975. Production HH-53Hs were equipped as Pave Low IIIs, with AAQ-10 FLIR, APQ-158 terrain-following radar (TFR), refuelling probes and many of the other systems fitted to today's MH-53Js. HH-53Hs became MH-53Hs in 1986, and the MH-53J Pave Low III Enhanced upgrade was initiated in 1987.

**Powerplant**
The standard engines fitted to the MH-53J are two 4,380-shp (3266-kW) T64-GE-415s with an uprated transmission. This is a significant improvement over the 2,850-shp (2125-kW), T64-GE-6-equipped CH-53A, but is overshadowed by the three-engined CH-53E whose three T64-GE-614 provide a total power output of 13,140 shp (9789 kW).

**Armament**
The Pave Low III Enhanced carries three guns; two are 7.62-mm Miniguns which are mounted on either side of the fuselage, while mounted on the rear ramp is the tried and trusted 0.50-in (12.7-mm) heavy machine-gun. Although its rate of fire is less than that of the Minigun, the '50 cal' has a greater range and much greater weight of shot. Up to 450 rounds (including armour-piercing) can be carried.

# Far Eastern/Middle Eastern operators

### Japan (Kaijo Jieitai – Japan Maritime Self-Defence Force)

Japan is the only overseas customer for the three-engined S-80, purchasing 11 of the S-80M-1 version. This is essentially similar to the US Navy's MH-53E Sea Dragon (although it lacks a refuelling probe) and is used for mine countermeasures. The first was ordered in 1986 and was handed over to the JMSDF on 30 November 1990, having been reassembled by Mitsubishi. After trials with Dai 51 Koku-tai, the MH-53 fleet was assigned to Dai 111 Koku-tai at Iwakuni AB, replacing KV-107s which had performed the mine countermeasures role since 1974. Mission equipment consists of minesweeping 'sleds' which are towed behind the aircraft. Prominent mirrors enable the flight deck crew to monitor the progress of the 'sled', while 0.5-in (12.7-mm) machine-guns are fitted to detonate surfaced mines.

### Iran (Islamic Republic of Iran Naval Aviation)

In the 1970s Iran procured a large amount of arms from the United States. Among the purchases were six RH-53D mine-sweepers which were very similar to their US Navy counterparts, having provision for a refuelling probe (although not fitted) and the ability to use a variety of Edo mine-sweeping systems. Assigned BuNos 160099 to 160104, the six aircraft were the last two-engined S-65s built before production shifted to the S-80. The helicopters were ordered in 1975, and were allocated the Iranian serials 6-2701 to 6-2706. In Imperial Iranian Navy service they were operated by a mine countermeasures squadron based on Kharg Island. After the fall of the Shah in 1979 all US maintenance and spares support was withdrawn, but the RH-53D force received a supply from a most unexpected source when several US Navy RH-53Ds were abandoned at the 'Desert One' landing strip during the Eagle Claw hostage rescue attempt. By 1988 the active fleet was down to two, but rose to four or five, before falling back to two by 2004. Clearly, Iran has either successfully acquired spares covertly or reverse-engineered the necessary items.

*Israel's S-65 fleet has been upgraded to CH-53D-2000 standard, with an Elisra EW suite and other improvements.*

### Israel (Israel Defence Force/Air Force)

When France embargoed further Super Frelon deliveries in 1967, Israel turned to the S-65C-3, of which 33 were acquired. These had refuelling probes and were similar to the HH-53C. Impressed with the Yas'ur (albatross), as it is known in IDF/AF parlance, Israel added to its fleet through the purchase of the two S-65C-2s from Austria. After the 1991 Gulf War, Israel was given another 10 aircraft – ex-USMC CH-53As. From May 1992 42 aircraft emerged from the IAI/Mata Yas'ur 2000 upgrade programme, which not only upgraded the engines and transmission to CH-53D standard, but installed a new mission computer, EW system, new cockpit displays and new autopilot. The force is operated by 114 and 118 Tayeset at Tel Nof.

**SIKORSKY H-53**

# European operators

*In recent years Germany's CH-53s have been heavily involved in UN/NATO operations, seeing active duty in northern and southern Iraq, Somalia, Croatia, Bosnia and, most recently, Kosovo. The three front-line units are part of Heeresflieger brigade 3, which has elements placed on rapid alert status, including CH-53s. At least one of the alert aircraft is fitted out for medevac duties.*

### Germany (Heeresflieger)

Faced with replacing Piasecki H-21s and Sikorsky H-34s, the West German army opted for the S-65 in June 1968, becoming in the process the largest overseas customer. Two aircraft were supplied in complete form by Sikorsky, another 20 were assembled by VFW-Fokker at Speyer from knock-down kits, and 90 were wholly built at Speyer, for a total of 112. Designated CH-53G, the German aircraft were similar to the CH-53D, but lacked refuelling probes and sponson-mounted tanks. Assigned the heavylift transport role in support of the army, the first CH-53 entered service in March 1973. In the late 1990s, 20 aircraft were modified with a self-defence package, NVG-compatible lighting and external tanks for UN peacekeeping operations. The result is designated CH-53GS. In 2001 the fleet was serving with 1./HFR 15 at Rheine, 1./HFR 25 at Laupheim, 1./HFR 35 at Mendig and the Heeresfliegerwaffenschule (army aviation school) at Bückeburg.

### Austria (Österreichische Luftstreitkräfte)

Austria purchased two S-65C-2s (also designated S-65Ö) similar to the USAF's CH-53C. They were intended primarily to provide emergency disaster relief and were delivered in 1970. Although effective, they were too expensive for the Austrian government, and were sold to Israel, being flown out on 15 May 1981.

With over 1,000 aircraft now in service, the Black Hawk is the backbone of any US Army air assault.

# Sikorsky H-60 Black Hawk/ Seahawk

## Introduction

**Sikorsky Black Hawks and Seahawks were among the unsung heroes of the Gulf War. Combining manoeuvrability, versatility and reliability, the 'Hawks' have revolutionised the deployment of helicopters over the battlefield.**

The request for proposals (RFP) for the Utility Tactical Transport Aircraft System (UTTAS) was issued in January 1972. The new utility helicopter was required to carry squad-sized units like the UH-1 Huey, but had to be capable of doing so in high temperatures and/or at high altitude. It also had to be highly manoeuvrable, more reliable, and more easily maintainable than the UH-1. Experience gained in Vietnam emphasised improved crashworthiness and survivability, with main rotor blades capable of absorbing hits from 23-mm shells, and internal fuel tanks able to absorb hits from 12.7-mm shells. Further, the new UTTAS was required to be easily transportable, so that one could be airlifted in a C-130, two in a C-141, or six in a C-5 – preparation for air transportation was to take no more than 6½ hours.

### A winning design

For Sikorsky which, by the end of 1971, had already produced some 5,000 helicopters, winning the UTTAS competition was of the utmost importance. To do so, the Sikorsky design team adopted a strategy calling for a thorough understanding of US Army requirements and full compliance with RFP conditions; the company aggressively developed the 'right' technology, undertaking full-scale demonstrations of advanced technology systems and components. To undertake this testing, Sikorsky flew five technology demonstrators: three CH-53Ds, an S-67 and an S-61. Each was fitted with components

*The addition of the ESSS pylons to the Black Hawk allows the helicopter to carry either extra fuel or weapons. Up to 16 Hellfire missiles can be carried.*

### Black Hawks in the midst of the storm

The UH-60 saw widespread service during the Gulf War, with the US Army alone deploying approximately 400 Black Hawks to Saudi Arabia. The ground war began on 24 February 1991, the largest single lift in air assault history involving more than 300 aircraft, many of which were UH-60s. During the course of the war, three UH-60s were lost, although only one was due to ground fire. Also serving in the campaign were ship-based Seahawks from both the US and Australian navies.

***By far the most significant foreign operator in terms of sheer numbers of Black Hawks and Seahawks in service is Australia. Initially, S-70A-9s (foreground) served with the RAAF, but they were subsequently turned over to the army for the troop transport role. The S-70Bs (background) are equipped with RAN-specified equipment which includes an internally-mounted AQS-504 MAD system and other sonar-processing equipment.***

that were to be utilised on Sikorsky's design. After extensive testing, the prototype UH-60A flew for the first time on 17 October 1974, in the event beating its rival, Boeing Vertol's YUH-61A, by one month. Although problems were encountered early on in the flight-test programme, the US Army was impressed enough by the Black Hawk's performance to place an order for the helicopter on 23 December 1976. Minor structural changes were made to the Black Hawk's rear fin and rotor head to improve its handling in the hover.

### In the army now

Deliveries of the Black Hawk to the Army began on 31 October 1978 and, following service trials and initial training of crews at Fort Rucker, Alabama, and maintenance personnel at Fort Eustis, Virginia, the UH-60As entered service with the 101st Airborne Division (Air Assault) in June 1979. Four aircraft were delivered for Force Development Test and Experimentation (FDTE) at Fort Campbell, Kentucky. The UH-60A was a far more capable combat helicopter than the UH-1H in terms of crew survivability in the event of a crash, and had a much improved performance in 'hot-and-high' conditions. With the addition of the External Stores Support System (ESSS) shoulder-mounted/fuselage-braced pylons to carry either fuel tanks or weapons, the fitting of Hover Infra-Red Suppressor Subsystem (HIRSS) to cool the engine exhaust and reduce IR detectability, the advent of the more powerful UH-60L variant, and the installation of upgraded countermeasures systems, the Army Black Hawk has evolved into the world's leading utility helicopter. It has also been supplied to a host of countries, many of which – such as Australia (Hawker de Havilland) and Japan (Mitsubishi) – have obtained permission from Sikorsky to build the Black Hawk locally under licence.

Although intended to fulfil the role of a utility helicopter, the potential of the Black Hawk saw the development of a number of Special Operations variants for both the US Army and USAF, the latter being keen to find a suitable helicopter for the CSAR role. Equipped with a nose-mounted IFR probe and sophisticated avionics, these MH-60G Pave Hawks and MH-60Ks are tasked with operating deep behind enemy lines in all weathers. During the Gulf War one Black Hawk, a UH-60A, was shot down during a rescue mission while trying to retrieve an F-16 pilot from Iraqi territory. Only three of the six crew were to survive and all were made PoWs, one of them – Flight Surgeon, Maj. Rhonda L. Cornum – holding the dubious distinction of becoming America's first female PoW.

By far the most high-profile role for the Black Hawk is that carried out by the USMC's HMX-1 at Quantico. Under the designation VH-60N, the two helicopters are configured for VIP transport for the President of the United States and his immediate aides.

### Navalised variants

In response to the light airborne multi-purpose system (LAMPS) III requirement, Sikorsky proposed a navalised variant of the Black Hawk with an over-the-horizon search and strike capability for the latest ASW frigates and destroyers, partnering the Kaman SH-2 Seasprite which served on earlier vessels. Sikorsky was awarded the development contract for the Seahawk in September 1977. The Army's decision to adopt the UH-60 was seen as a major factor in influencing the Navy to choose the S-70B Seahawk.

The Seahawk retained an 83 per cent commonality with the UH-60A, but introduced some important features including anti-corrosion treatment on the airframe and engines. With these structural modifications came a host of avionics equipment dedicated to the detection of enemy submarines and, in a secondary role, a fuselage-mounted hoist for rescue operations. Entering front-line service in 1983, the Seahawk has since been steadily upgraded in parallel with the vessels it is intended to attack with its anti-ship missiles and depth charges.

A follow-on variant to the Seahawk, the SH-60F Ocean Hawk, entered service with the US Navy in 1991. Intended to operate from the US Navy's super carriers, the Ocean Hawk utilises a Bendix AQS-13F dipping sonar in place of air-dropped sonobuoys. Many of the components necessary for helicopter operations from small decks have been deleted to allow extra rescue equipment to be carried during air operations from the carrier deck.

### Foreign/civilian service

Many countries' armed forces found themselves in a similar position to the United States, in that they were looking for a suitable utility helicopter to replace their ageing fleet. Sikorsky was therefore eager to market both the Black Hawk and Seahawk globally. Under the company designation S-70, Sikorsky sold the helicopter throughout the world, with many customers electing to obtain a licence to allow them to build the helicopter locally. Some countries, such as Japan, fitted a host of indigenous equipment to the Seahawks, to enable them to operate in the anti-submarine role. Other operators, such as Colombia and the Philippines, armed their aircraft for anti-drug operations. Similarly, the USCG, a long-time operator of the HH-60J Jayhawk (a dedicated long-range rescue variant), is currently proposing to arm its fleet for anti-narcotic operations.

The Black Hawk has been adopted by a number of countries for operation by both civilian and paramilitary organisations. Brunei operates one S-70A in a VIP configuration, which is very often flown by the Sultan of Brunei himself when attending civic engagements. Other operators, such as Turkey and the Republic of Korea, have equipped their police forces with the S-70A and UH-60P, respectively. Although not armed, these variants have retained their offensive capability, which can be exercised if required.

***Above: Ordered in January 1986 to replace the Bell VH-1Ns, two VH-60Ns serve as VVIP transports for the President and his advisors. The 'Presidential Hawks' are equipped with a host of flight safety and avionics improvements.***

***Right: The HH-60J Jayhawk is a specialised variant for the USCG. Equipped with a Bendix search/weather radar and Nitesun searchlight, the Jayhawk can undertake rescue missions in all weathers, 24 hours a day.***

# Army variants

**The basic S-70/H-60 has been developed into a multitude of variants for use by both the US Army and a host of operators who are seeking a battlefield utility helicopter able to fulfil a number of roles.**

### YUH-60A (Prototypes)

Three YUH-60A prototypes were ordered during the UTTAS competition (three more were ordered after Sikorsky won the competition). The first of the three prototypes initially flew at Stratford, Connecticut, on 17 October 1974. It was fitted with a fixed stabiliser on a fuselage tail cone, but this was found to present handling problems. Other early features of the prototypes were their broad-chord cambered fin, short main rotor shaft and a fuselage fairing that incorporated the engine intakes. Other less significant changes were to the cabin windows to allow for the fitting of flexible machine-gun mounts.

### UH-60A

The main version of the Black Hawk assault transport helicopter for the US Army remained in production for 11 years, the first UH-60A having flown on 17 October 1978. The UH-60A was replaced on the production line by the more powerful UH-60L in October 1989. UH-60As differed from the prototypes by incorporating, among other features, a refined undercarriage, a redesigned upper fuselage fairing, a taller main rotor shaft, and a fixed tail wheel. Other UH-60As were test-flown with composite rear fuselages for test work relating to future H-60 versions.

### YEH-60A and EH-60A

As part of its Special Electronics Mission Aircraft (SEMA) programme, the US Army instructed TRW Electronics System Laboratories of California to integrate and install Quick Fix IIB direction-finding (DF), intercept and communications jamming equipment into a UH-60A. Designated YEH-60A, the modified Black Hawk first flew on 24 September 1981. The successful evaluation of this experimental EW helicopter led the army to formulate plans for the acquisition of 130 EH-60As. In October 1984 Tracor Aerospace Inc. was awarded the contract for the conversion of the initial batch of 40 UH-60As to EH-60A configuration. The first EH-60A conversion was delivered in July 1987. The model designation was subsequently changed to EH-60C, but budget constraints led to procurement being terminated after the conversion of only 66 examples.

### YEH-60B

A single UH-60A was modified as a prototype for a proposed battlefield surveillance version with the Stand-Off Target Acquisition System (SOTAS) under a $36.6-million contract which, when awarded in September 1979, had called for five prototypes. The YEH-60B was fitted with a Motorola sensor mounted in an an underfuselage radome which was extended in flight to rotate a full 360°, a display station in the cabin, datalink to a ground-based processing station, and extendable main undercarriage to provide clearance for the extended radome. The concept called for the EH-60B to operate behind the forward edge of the battle area (FEBA) to detect the movement of enemy forces on the battlefield and relay the information to a ground station. The YEH-60B first flew on 6 February 1981, but the planned acquisition of 78 EH-60Bs was cancelled to provide funding for the J-STARS programme.

## Battlefield rescue

**The UH-60A and UH-60L are often used in the medevac role, but the dedicated UH-60Q – which has recently finished operational testing – may be set to replace the former types in this role.**

**'Dust Off'**
Following the tradition set by UH-1 pilots during the helicopter war in Vietnam, the medevac Black Hawks have adopted the callsign of DUST OFF. For the rescue role, the UH-60A (illustrated) is equipped with cabin-mounted stretchers in place of the troop seats, and can be fitted with an external rescue hoist.

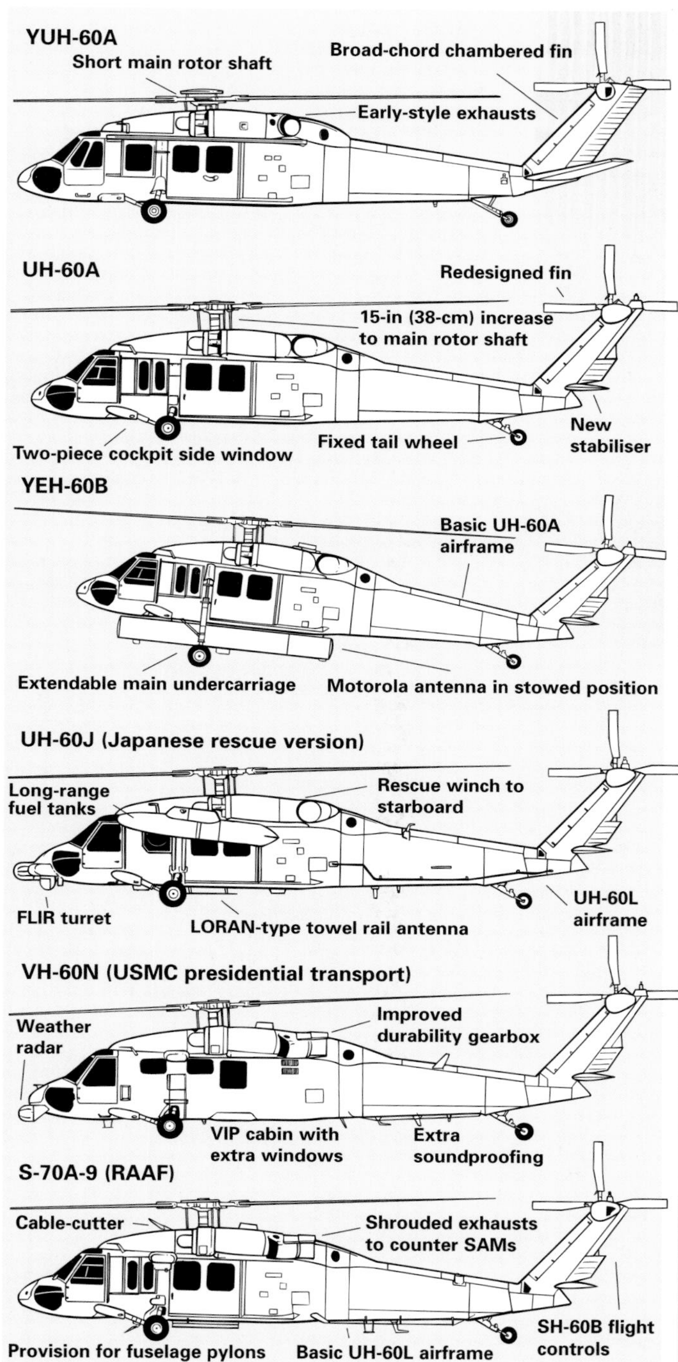


## MH-60K

Looking to expand its Special Operations forces, in 1990 the US Army initiated a series of upgrades to modify 30 UH-60As to MH-60A standard, and later to MH-60L standard through the introduction of Miniguns, auxiliary fuel tanks and a comprehensive nav/comms equipment fit. A definitive and more capable variant, the MH-60K, which is able to launch FIM-92A Stinger AAMs, was introduced into service in June 1992. Externally, the MH-60K differs little from the Air Force MH-60G, but is regarded as being far more capable for Special Operations missions.

## UH-60L

As more equipment was added to the UH-60, so its weight grew and power margins were reduced. In an effort to alleviate these problems, Sikorsky introduced the UH-60L in March 1988. The UH-60L has retained the UH-60A's flight controls, although it is fitted with the uprated T700-GE-701C engine and a new transmission that has restored the Black Hawk's performance capabilities. The increase in power enables the UH-60L to lift far greater loads. However, with ever increasing demands being placed on the UH-60 airframe, 1,200 UH-60A/L aircraft will be upgraded to further improved UH-60M standard from 2004.

## S-70A

Most military export variants of the Black Hawk have been given S-70A company designations as illustrated by these examples: S-70A-1 Saudi Arabia; S-70A-5 Philippines; S-70A-11 Jordan. Australia has the largest non-US fleet of Black Hawks, operating 36 examples. The aircraft were initially delivered to the RAAF, but have now been transferred to the Australian Army Air Corps. In addition to the RAAF Black Hawks, the RAN operates the S-70B-2 Seahawk. Other international operators of the S-70 include Bahrain; Brunei; Egypt; Hong Kong; Jordan; Mexico; Morocco; the People's Republic of China; the Philippines; Saudi Arabia, where the helicopters are known as Desert Hawks; and Turkey, which purchased 12 S-70A-17 Black Hawks (illustrated right) for its National Police. Many of these aircraft are in VIP configuration, serving as transportation for government officials. In the UK, Westland Helicopters was granted a licence to produce the Black Hawk under the designation WS-70, although only one example has been built.

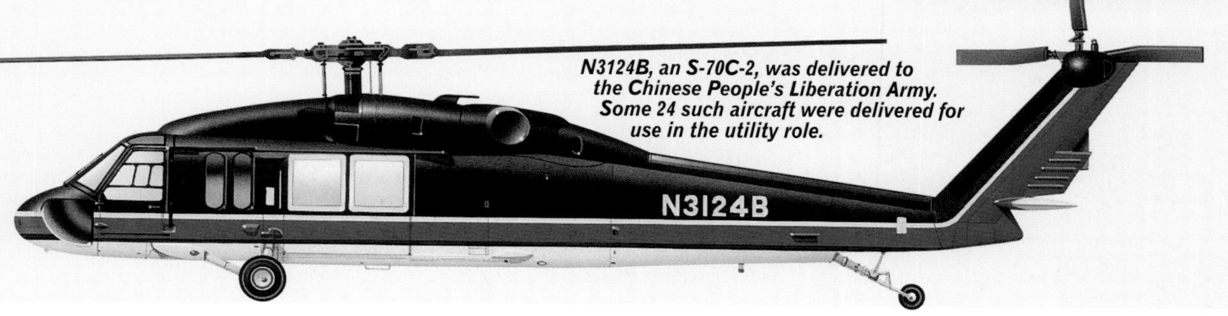


***N3124B*, an *S-70C-2*, was delivered to the Chinese People's Liberation Army. Some 24 such aircraft were delivered for use in the utility role.**

# USAF and USN variants

**When looking for a new utility helicopter, the USAF and US Navy followed the army's example in purchasing the H-60. A host of variants has been spawned and they also have a global following.**

## UH-60A Credible Hawk

In 1981, the USAF decided to order the UH-60A to replace its HH-3Es. Once the UH-60A was chosen the USAF immediately began a programme of upgrading the aircraft. This included the addition of a telescopic inflight-refuelling probe and auxiliary cabin tanks to extend range. Weaponry was also altered with the replacement of the M60 machine-guns with 0.50-in (12.7-mm) M218s. The first examples of the UH-60A entered service in 1987.

## YSH-60B Seahawk

In 1978, Sikorsky was awarded the contract for the development of the YSH-60B and the first example flew in 1979. The aircraft had empty fuselage fairings, which would be filled with electrical equipment, stores pylons on either side of the fuselage and a pylon on the starboard side for the towed magnetic anomaly detector (MAD) bird. By 28 May 1980, a fully equipped YSH-60B was able to fly a simulated ASW mission. Operational test and evaluation started in May 1981, and by the end of testing, the five YSH-60Bs had accumulated more than 3,000 flight hours.

## aHH-60G and MH-60G Pave Hawk

After the USAF completed the Credible Hawk programme, it had to upgrade the existing Credible Hawks and new-build UH-60As to one of two standards. Although both were initially designated MH-60G Pave Hawk, Sikorsky delivered the UH-60As with only some Air Force equipment installed, consisting of folding stabilator, hover infra-red supression system (HIRSS), winterisation and wire-strike kits, rescue hoist and NVG-compatible cockpit. Sikorsky Support Services then fitted a refuelling probe, auxiliary cabin tanks and hardpoints for external tank carriage, and the mission avionics were installed at the Naval Air Depot at Pensacola, Florida. MH-60 aircraft serve with the 16th Special Operations Wing (SOW) at Hurlburt Field/Eglin AFB, Florida, and there are examples at the Ogden Air Logistics Center, Hill AFB. All retain the MH-60G designation, and are fitted with a Bendix-King 1400C colour radar in a port-side nose radome, global positioning, Carousel INS, map display, Doppler, secure communications equipment and full countermeasures. Further Special Operations Forces- (SOF) dedicated equipment includes AAQ-16 forward-looking infra-red (FLIR) under the nose, pilot head-up display that projects on to one of the lenses of the night-vision goggles (NVG) system, and numerous other improvements. Since October 1991 over 80 aircraft have been designated HH-60G to reinforce the combat rescue role they undertake. These aircraft have the basic Phase Two avionics, but funding for their updating with the Phase Three equipment (FLIR, head-up display (HUD) etc.) has not yet been forthcoming. HH-60Gs are usually seen with M60 or Minigun door weapons in place of the MH-60G's usual 0.50-in (12.7-mm) guns. HH-60Gs are operated by the 57th OG Combat Rescue School at Nellis, the 85th Group at NAS Keflavik, Iceland and the 347th Wing at Moody AFB. The Pacific Air Forces (PACAF) operates HH-60Gs with the 18th Wing at Kadena, and 35th Fighter Wing, Misawa, Japan and the 51st Fighter Wing, Osan, Republic of Korea. They are also assigned to three Air Force Reserve units, comprising the 301st, 304th and 305th RQSs (Rescue Squadrons) of the 920th and 939th RQW; and two Air National Guard units (106th and 129th Rescue Groups).

## SH-60B Seahawk/MH-60R Strike Hawk

The SH-60B, which replaced the SH-2 Seasprite and first flew on 11 February 1983, functions as an extension of the shipboard weapon system of the cruiser, destroyer or frigate on which it is deployed. With radar, electronic support measures (ESM), MAD, infra-red, and sonobuoy sensors, the SH-60B can detect and track submarines and surface ships, and attack with anti-submarine warfare (ASW) torpedoes and anti-shipping missiles. For rescue and special operations missions, the SH-60B also carries a door-mounted 0.3-in (7.62-mm) machine-gun. An upgrade programme for 93 SH-60Bs, called Block I, continued through 1999, and included installing the ability to use the Mk 50 torpedo, GPS, the AAS-44 infra-red sensor and AGM-119 Penguin anti-shipping missiles. The SH-60B Seahawk Light Airborne Multi-Purpose System (LAMPS) Mark III helicopter is deployed in detachments of one or two helicopters (depending on ship capacity) on board cruisers, destroyers and frigates. These detachments provide ASW, anti-shipping, rescue, logistics and utility services for surface warships. The type is to be replaced by the new-build MH-60R Strike Hawk.

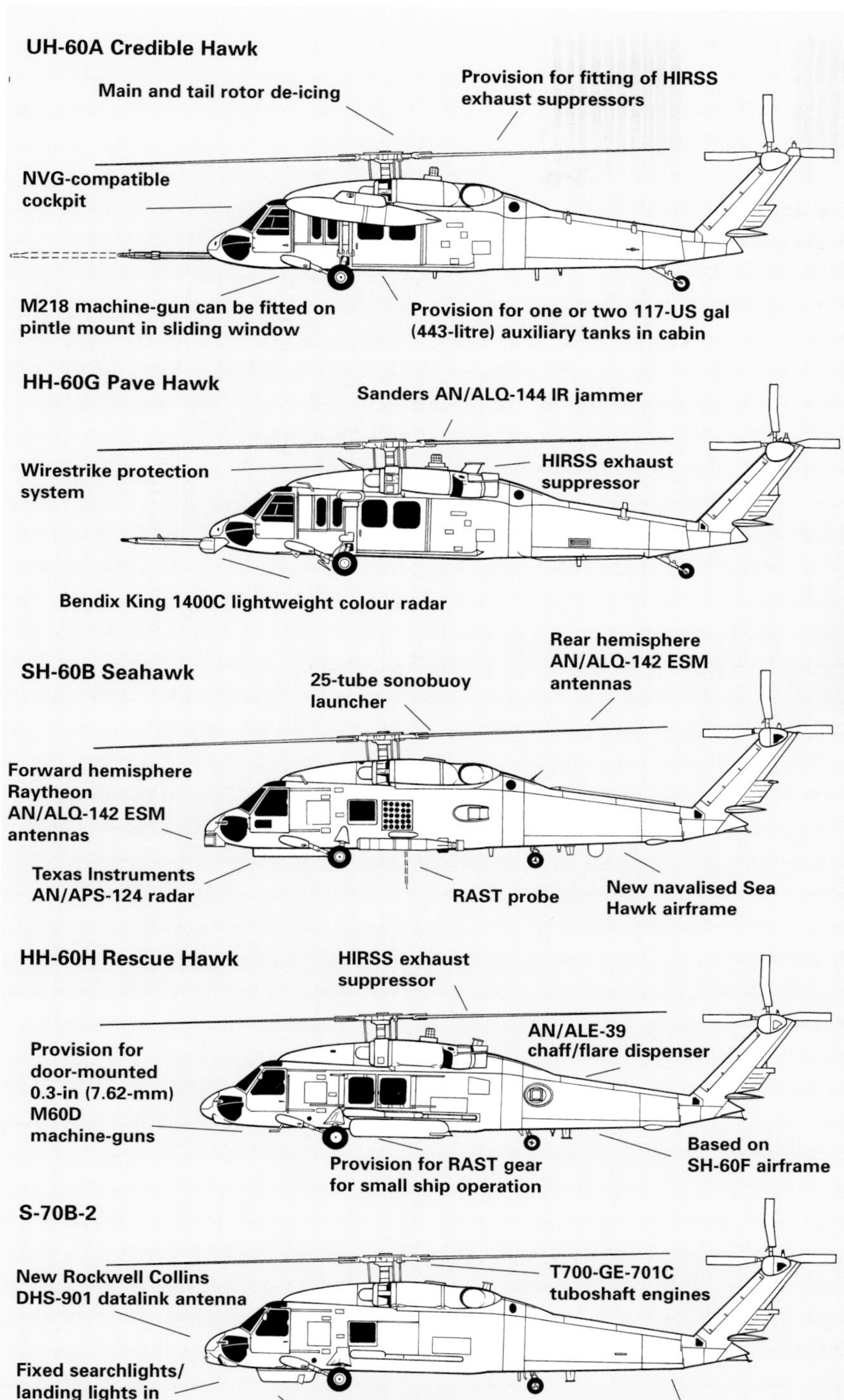


## SH-60F (MH-60R) Ocean Hawk

The SH-60F has replaced the SH-3H Sea King in all active-duty Helicopter Squadrons (HS) as the aircraft-carrier's ASW helicopter. Equipped with dipping sonar and armed with ASW torpedoes, the SH-60F provides inner-zone defence to a carrier battle group. The AQS-22 dipping sonar will replace the current AQS-13F. The SH-60F also serves in plane guard, rescue and logistics roles. The Navy is developing the SH-60R to replaceme both the SH-60B and SH-60F. A plan to remanufacture SH-60B/F and HH-60H airframes into SH-60Rs has been abandoned in favour of obtaining new-build MH-60R and MH-60S utility helicopters. The MH-60R features many improvements, including an increase in gross operating weight; two additional stores stations; improved cockpit displays; an AQS-22 dipping sonar; an upgraded ESM system; an infra-red sensor; and an integrated self-defence system. The MAD system will be deleted, but the SH-60R will retain the 0.3-in (7.62-mm) machine-gun, Penguin and Hellfire missiles, and the Mk 46 and Mk 50 torpedoes as armament.

## HH-60H Rescue Hawk

In HS squadrons, the SH-60F is augmented by the HH-60H strike rescue version, whose main role is conducting combat SAR, and insertion and extraction of special warfare forces. The HH-60H is armed with 0.3-in (7.62-mm) machine-guns and AGM-114 Hellfire air-to-ground missiles. Whereas the Navy had previously undertaken the role it called combat rescue, a reactive mission to retrieve crew, the HH-60H's role of strike rescue is intended as a proactive mission, with the Rescue Hawk an integral part of any mission-planning. A requirement to recover a four-man crew 250 nm (288 miles; 463 km) from base was the most important criterion. The secondary role of covert operations largely centres around the infil/exfil of sea/air/land (SEAL) commando teams. For this tasking the HH-60H has recovery assist, secure and traverse (RAST) gear to allow it to operate from vessels other than its parent aircraft-carrier.

## HH-60J Jay Hawk

The Sikorsky HH-60J Jay Hawk is the Coast Guard's medium-range recovery helicopter for search and rescue missions. The Jay Hawk is able to carry out a six-hour mission over a radius of 300 miles (483 km) and it employs state-of-the-art radar, radio, and navigational equipment and extends the range at which search and rescue missions are possible, enabling it to come to the aid of the distressed from greater distances than before.

## Foreign variants

The Seahawk version of the H-60 has been widely exported to nations including Australia, Japan, Greece, Spain and Taiwan. Australia's S-70B-2 (below), Japan's S-70B-3 and Spain's HS.23 are variants of the SH-60B, while Taiwan's S-70C(M)-1 Thunderhawk is an SH-60F derivative. Greece's eight S-70B-6 Aegean Hawks are a hybrid of the SH-60B and the SH-60F.

# H-60 operators

**In addition to serving US military operators, the S-70 family has achieved numerous foreign exports. Current baseline export variants comprise the S-70A (transport), S-70B (naval) and S-70C (non-FMS).**

## South Korea

South Korea signed an agreement to build the UH-60P (similar to the UH-60L) for domestic military requirements in March 1990. Following the import of seven US-built examples, Korean Air Lines UH-60P flew on 15 February 1992. The 100th aircraft was delivered in 1999, and the type serves principally with the Korean army (below, aboard USS *Essex*), with smaller numbers available to the navy and air force.

## US Air Force

Converted from Army UH-60A/L aircraft, USAF Pave Hawks were universally designated MH-60G until January 1992, when 82 in the combat rescue role were redesignated HH-60H. The remaining 16 aircraft remained as MH-60Gs for special operations service, until early 2000 when all but nine machines remaining in the inventory became HH-60Gs. The upgraded Block 152 version of the latter first flew in April 1999.

## US Navy

Production of the initial SH-60B ASW/ASST version for the USN was authorised in FY82. Construction of this variant was followed by the SH-60F CV inner zone combat helicopter, initial deployment of which took place in 1991. Used for strike-rescue and special warfare support, the HH-60H (below) entered service in 1990. The USN plans to acquire as many as 243 MH-60R helicopter, with new dipping sonar, for production from 2005. Based on the Army's UH-60L, 237 examples of the MH-60S should replace the CH/HH-46D.

## US Army

The US Army operate the Black Hawk in its initial UH-60A form, some of which have been given upgraded self-defence systems, and the EH-60A Quick Fix IIB battlefield ECM detection and jamming platform (below). MH-60K/Ls and AH-60Ls serve with the 160th SOAR, where they supplanted the initial MH-60A. Meanwhile, the improved UH-60L replaced the UH-60A in production from 1989. The UH-60Q designation covers 'Dustoff' aircraft.

## Mexico

The Mexican Air Force's 1st Combat Wing's Special Operations Squadron 216 operate a pair of S-70A-24s (similar to UH-60Ls) from Santa Lucía. These aircraft were delivered to Mexico in 1991.

**EXPORT DELIVERIES**

| | Black Hawk | Seahawk |
|---|---|---|
| Argentina | 1 | |
| Australia | 39 | 16 |
| Bahrain | 1 | |
| Brazil | 4 | |
| Brunei | 7 | |
| Chile | 1 | |
| China | 24 | |
| Colombia | 32 | |
| Egypt | 4 | |
| Greece | | 8 |
| Hong Kong | 3 | |
| Israel | 15 | |
| Japan | 1 | 2 |
| Jordan | 3 | |
| Korea: RoKAF: | 3 | |
| Korea: FMS: | 3 | |
| Korea: Co-prod.: | 7 | |
| Malaysia | 2 | |
| Mexico | 2 | |
| Morocco | 2 | |
| Philippines | 2 | |
| Saudi Arabia | 21 | |
| Spain | | 6 |
| Taiwan | 19 | 10 |
| Thailand | | 6 |
| Turkey | 79 | |
| UK | 1 | |

## Japan

Mitsubishi undertook production of both the S-70B-3 version of the SH-60B for the JMSDF (as the SH-60J, below), and the S-70A-12 SAR version for the JASDF/JMSDF (UH-60J, bottom) and JGSDF (UH-60JA). The first production SH-60J was delivered in August 1991. Development is underway of the SH-60Jkai with new rotor system and sonar. The UH-60JA adds radar and FLIR for night/adverse weather operations.

## Australia

The RAAF received 39 S-70A-9s (below) between 1987-1991 as replacements for the UH-1, the majority being assembled by Hawker de Havilland. In 1989 the aircraft were transferred to Army service. The RAN selected the S-70B-2 (bottom) in 1984 for operation from 'Adelaide' class frigates. Half of the 16 were assembled by ASTA.

## Colombia

The S-70A-41 designation covers 22 aircraft delivered to Colombia during 1994 (two), 1995 (two), 1997 (seven) and 1998 (11). Although the original requirement specified UH-60A standard aircraft, those received were to UH-60L specification. Further orders were placed in late 1999.

## Taiwan

Deliveries of the S-70C(M)-1 Thunderhawk (SH-60B standard, above) to the Taiwanese navy began in 1990. A second order, for the (M)-2 version was placed in 1997. The S-70C-2 Super Blue Hawk (below and bottom) was developed for customers not qualifying for FMS status, and was delivered to Taiwan in 1985-86, most being operated on SAR duties. A further batch of four S-70C-6s was handed over in April 1998.

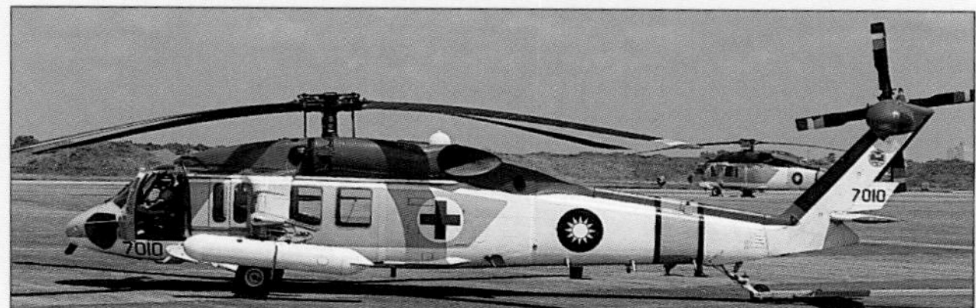

## Spain

The Spanish navy received six dipping sonar-equipped S-70B-1s (HS.23s) from December 1988. An additional batch of six was approved in 2000, with the order covering the upgrade of the earlier machines to the new standard, with AGM-114 capability.

**US DELIVERIES**

| | Black Hawk | SH-60B | SH-60F | HH-60H | HH-60J |
|---|---|---|---|---|---|
| USAF | 91 | | | | |
| Army | 1,601 | | | | |
| USN | 2 | 181 | 82 | 42 | 42 |
| DEA | 5 | | | | |
| SOA | 23 | | | | |

# Sukhoi Su-17/20/22 'Fitter'

## Soviet attacker

*The Su-17M in its latter variants formed an important part of tactical elements of the VVS prior to the collapse of the USSR. The nearest aircraft, an Su-17M-4 '43 Blue' carries a typical ground attack load of a single S-24 240-mm (9.4-in) rocket on the starboard inboard wing station, and a pair of FAB-250 250-kg (551-lb) bombs underfuselage.*

**Maintaining much similarity with its Su-7 forebear, the combat-proven Su-17 'Fitter' is capable of carrying double the bombload, from an airstrip half as long as that of its predecessor. After almost thirty years of service, it remains in the inventory of numerous air arms.**

During the mid-1960s, following the introduction of the Su-7B into service, and with design work on the improved Su-7BKL and Su-7BMK variants underway, the Sukhoi Design Bureau confronted the task of improving the take-off and landing performance of its fighter-bombers. The Su-7BKL had been equipped with solid-fuel JATO rockets and braking parachutes, but more radical approaches were to be considered for future combat aircraft. Accordingly, Sukhoi began testing of both STOL (short take-off and landing) and variable geometry aircraft, the T-58VD and the S-22I, developments of the Su-15 and Su-7, respectively.

The S-22I experimental variable geometry fighter-bomber was based on a series production Su-7BM airframe, but introduced variable sweep on the outer wing section alone, with the pivot outboard of the landing gear. This method minimised structural redesign, and reduced the effect of the shift in centre of aerodynamic pressure and centre of gravity created by the variable wing sweep. The S-22I, the Soviet Union's first variable geometry aircraft, made its first flight on 2 August 1966. In July 1967, the S-22I, wearing striking red lightning flash markings, was unveiled to the public at the Domodedovo air display.

### Su-17 into production

In comparison to the Su-7, the S-22I displayed greatly improved take-off and landing performance; meanwhile, range and endurance at low wing sweep angles were also improved, despite a reduction in fuel load, and an increase in weight over the Su-7BM. In November 1967, after governmental agreement, series production was approved.

The production version of the S-22I was known as the Su-17 (or S-32 to the Design Bureau). The Su-17 designation had been used previously for the Type 'R' swept-wing experimental fighter of 1949. Despite the new wing, the Su-17 maintained basic commonality with the Su-7BKL/BMK, incorporating the spine fairing of the Su-7U for additional equipment. Two additional stores pylons were added on the fixed wing section, making a total of six hardpoints. Hydraulic and fuel systems and electronic equipment and avionics fit was essentially duplicated from the Su-7BKL. Tactical capability was improved through the introduction of the Kh-23 (AS-7 'Kerry') ASM, and provision for up to four 253-Imp gal (1,150-litre) drop tanks. The wing-root NR-30 30-mm cannon of the Su-7B were retained, but SPPU-22 23-mm gun pods with articulated barrels could be pylon-mounted in order to increase firepower. The maximum combat load of the initial Su-17 was ultimately 6,612 lb (3,000 kg), including the newly introduced 80-mm (3.15-in) S-8 and 250-mm (9.84-in) S-25 unguided rockets.

*One of the first production Su-17s, apparently armed with four KMGU submunitions dispensers. The initial Su-17s represented only a modest advance over the Su-7B in terms of capability, with only take-off and landing performance being truly enhanced.*

The Su-17 represented a great advance in tactical capability over its predecessors, but weight increases on the production aircraft meant that in terms of performance, only the take-off and landing characteristics were actually improved over those of the Su-7BKL. Nevertheless, Su-17 series production began in 1969, initially in parallel with manufacture of the Su-7B, before the latter was phased out in 1971. Initial Su-17s equipped a single

***Right:* The Su-17M of 1971 was the first quantity-produced Su-17 version. This example is armed with 80-mm B-8M1 and 57-mm UB-32M/57 rockets pods, and UPK-23/250 23-mm cannon pods.**

***Below:* The Su-17UM, represented here in prototype form, was the first of the 'Fitter' family to introduce the characteristic revised cockpit and forward fuselage profile, improving the pilot's view.**

evaluation regiment. The first major series produced version was the Su-17M, which introduced the AL-21F-3 powerplant, increased fuel capacity and improved equipment. The new-generation AL-21F-3 turbojet developed greater thrust, but had smaller dimensions, allowing for an increased fuel load. A new hydraulic system, and cruciform brake chute were added, together with a modernised PBK-2KL bombsight. Additional underfuselage pylons increased the number of hardpoints to nine. The Su-17M was delivered to Far East elements of the Soviet air arm from 1972, and was also exported as the Su-20. Differing only minimally from the Su-17M (for example in the introduction of the R-3S/AA-2 'Atoll' self-defence AAM), the Su-20 served with the air forces of Poland, Egypt, Syria and Iraq. A fixed-wing version of the Su-20 for export was submitted for flight tests, but this promising aircraft (with the standard Su-20 fuselage coupled to the Su-7BKL wing) was cancelled after flying in 1973.

The Su-17M was followed in 1975 by the Su-17M-2, with improved ordnance delivery systems. The key to the Su-17M-2's advance in capability was the Fon laser rangefinder, combined with an ASP-17 optical sight, PBK-3 combination bomb/gunsight and KN-23 integrated navigation system. The latter could automatically fly the aircraft to a predetermined target. The characteristic feature of the Su-17M-2 and its Su-22 export equivalent, however, was the DISS-7 Doppler system fairing under the nose. The Su-17M-2 could carry Kh-25 (AS-10 'Karen') and Kh-29L (AS-14 'Kedge') ASMs, as well as R-60 (AA-8 'Aphid') AAMs. Surprisingly, the export relative of the Su-17M-2, the Su-22, was equipped with the R-29B-300 engine of the MiG-23BN/MiG-27 series, within an increased width rear fuselage. The Su-22, lacking the advanced weapons introduced on the Soviets' Su-17M-2, was delivered to Angola, Libya and Peru, all of which took it into combat.

## A radical redesign

The Sukhoi Design Bureau next addressed the cockpit layout of the Su-17 family, in order to provide the pilot with an improved view. A redesign was necessary and this first appeared on the Su-17UM tandem two-seat trainer, which featured an all-new forward fuselage angled down by six degrees and an enlarged dorsal fairing. Although single- and two-seat aircraft were requested in 1974, the two-seat Su-17UM was afforded higher priority, and first flew in 1975.

In concert with the Su-17UM, Sukhoi developed the Su-17M-3 fighter-bomber. The first new generation single-seater, the Su-17M-3 retained the redesigned forward fuselage design of the Su-17UM, with the instructor's position replaced with an additional fuel tank. Two additional underwing hardpoints, for carriage of the R-60 AAM, were added for self-defence, and the Klyen-PS laser station replaced the earlier Fon. Series production of the Su-17UM and Su-17M-3 began in 1975-76, both incorporating increased vertical tail area to combat low speed instability.

Export versions of the Su-17UM and Su-17M-3 were designated Su-22M and Su-22U, respectively, both powered by the R-29 turbojet. The down-graded Su-22M was followed by the Su-22M-3 from 1982, which incorporated the complete equipment package of the Su-17M-3.

In order to unify training, the Su-17UM with its reduced combat load was superseded by the Su-17UM-3, with the sight and other equipment of the Su-17M-3. Production began in 1978, and ultimately all Su-17UMs were brought up to definitive Su-17UM-3 standard. The Su-17UM-3 was in turn exported as the Su-22UM-3. A few of these were delivered with R-29 engines, before export versions were fitted with the AL-21F-3 as standard from 1983.

The final production version of the Su-17 was the definitive Su-17M-4 (completed for export as the Su-22M-4). Entering production in 1980, this variant is distinguished by its dorsal fairing air intake. However, the major advance over earlier models is the introduction of an integrated navigation and sight system, incorporating a computer, laser rangefinder, new navigation and sighting equipment, illumination radar and TV display. After operational experience in Afghanistan, the Su-17M-4 (together with the Su-17UM-3) was fitted with additional armour plating and IR decoy dispensers to increase survivability.

**Slovakia's Su-22M-4R fleet is tasked with tactical reconnaissance duties, for which the aircraft mount the KKR combined IR/photographic/TV pod. The aircraft were formerly operated by 47 PZLP, the Czechoslovakian tactical reconnaissance regiment.**

***Below:* Angola's Su-22s (export versions of the undernose Doppler-equipped Su-17M-2) have seen operational use. Examples were based at Menongue during the main 1986 offensive against UNITA.**

# Variants

### Su-7IG (S-22I)

The S-22I was an experimental variable geometry derivative of the Su-7BM, incorporating minimum structural change. The wing pivot was located aft of the landing gear, creating a movable outer wing section with leading edge sweep varying from 30° to 63°. The single prototype was first flown by V. I. Ilyushin on 2 August 1966. On 9 July 1967, the S-22I was flown by I. K. Kukushev at the Domodedovo air display. After the addition of the new variable-sweep, high-lift wing, empty weight was increased to 20,900 lb (9480 kg), compared to 18,447 lb (8370 kg) for the Su-7BM.

### Su-17 (S-32) 'Fitter-B Mod'

Known to the Sukhoi Design Bureau as the S-32, the pre-series aircraft received the customer designation Su-17. The production go-ahead for the aircraft, which served with a single evaluation regiment, was given in 1967, and production began in 1969. The Su-17 had a spine fairing similar to that of the Su-7U, and two prominent cable ducts on the side of the fuselage, inherited from the Su-7BKL/BMK. Two additional pylons were added to the fixed wing section to complete a total of six. The strengthened main landing gear could be fitted with skis for operations from snow-covered airstrips. Compared to the Su-7BKL, the weight of the Su-17 was increased by around 2,204 lb (1000 kg). The Su-17 cockpit was updated with a K-36 ejection seat.

### Su-17M (S-32M) 'Fitter-C' and Su-20 (S-32MK) 'Fitter-C'

The first series production aircraft was the Su-17M which flew in 1971, which introduced the new generation AL-21F-3 engine in place of the Su-17's AL-7F-1. The Su-17M (an example is pictured at the Irkutsk test facility) carried additional fuel, and the cable ducts were removed. The height of the tail fin was increased, and the forward fuselage lengthened by 8 in (0.23 m). A new cylindrical rear fuselage section was added in conjunction with the smaller AL-21F-3 powerplant, a rear-view mirror was added to the canopy, and a single cruciform brake chute was added. The total number of pylons was increased to nine, with forward fuselage and outboard wing pylons capable of carrying drop tanks. The export version of the Su-17M was the Su-20, first flown in 1972, and delivered to Poland, Egypt, Syria and Iraq.

### Su-17R and Su-20R 'Fitter-C'/Recce conversions

The Su-17R and its Su-20R export equivalent featured few internal changes, but incorporated wiring and plumbing for a choice of three Sukhoi-designed KKR multisensor reconnaissance pods on the centreline. One pod carried forward radar and Elint receivers; one a forward camera, SLAR and Elint modules; and one carried four cameras, IRLS and a photoflash cartridge battery. Pictured (right) is a Polish Su-20R of 7 PLB-R (Air Bomber-Reconnaissance Regiment) seen at Powidz in 1991. Examples of the Su-22 have also been modified to carry KKR recce packages under the designation Su-22R. More recent tactical reconnaissance versions are the Su-17M-3R (S-52R) and Su-17M-4R (S-54R). These have been exported as the Su-22M-3R and Su-22M-4R respectively. Whilst the Su-17M-3R was modified to carry the centreline KKR pod during production, the Su-17M-4R was so equipped from the beginning of its production run.

### Su-17M-2 (S-32M2) 'Fitter-D' & Su-22 (S-32M2K) 'Fitter-F'

First flown in 1973, the Su-17M-2 (a former Soviet example from the Tambov Pilot School pictured below right) was developed in order to improve ordnance delivery with the introduction of the *Fon* laser rangefinder and other equipment, including a distinctive undernose Doppler fairing. Series production took place from 1975-77, and the export version was the Su-22 (Peruvian examples from Escuadron de Caza 11 'Los Tigres' pictured below left) with R-29BS-300 engine. The Su-22, also delivered to Angola and Libya, was produced between 1976 and 1980, with a downgraded avionics fit.

## Su-17UM (S-52U) 'Fitter-E' & Su-22U (S-52UK) 'Fitter-G'

Introducing a redesigned forward fuselage and cockpit in order to improve pilot view, the Su-17UM two-seat combat trainer was the first of the 'second generation' Su-17s. The Su-17UM (and its Su-22U export equivalent with R-29BS-300 engine) also introduced a new, larger, dorsal fairing, and both were produced between 1976-81.

## Su-17M-3 (S-52) 'Fitter-H' & Su-22M (S-52K) 'Fitter-J'

The Su-17M-3 was developed in conjunction, and built in parallel with, the Su-17UM to fulfil a government requirement (a Soviet example is pictured below left, with an S-25 rocket underwing) for a new fighter-bomber version. The forward cockpit structure was inherited from the Su-17UM, with the instructor's position now used to house additional fuel. Two additional pylons for R-60 self-defence AAMs were added underwing, and the weapons system was updated with the Klyen-PS laser targetting system. The export version was the R-29BS-300-powered Su-22M (built 1979-81), a Libyan example of which is pictured, armed with R-3S AAMs, as intercepted by a US Navy aircraft over the Mediterranean in 1981.

## Su-17UM-3 (S-52UM3) 'Fitter-G' and Su-22UM-3 (S-52UM3K) 'Fitter-G'

The Su-17UM-3 unified Soviet pilot training by bringing the basic Su-17UM combat trainer to Su-17M-3 standard (a Soviet example is pictured above, with the instructor's periscope deployed). The Su-17UM-3 was produced from 1978, with the equipment of the Su-17M-3. Su-17UMs were eventually upgraded to Su-17UM-3 standard during 1979-80. The export version of the Su-17UM-3 is the Su-22UM-3. Powered by the R-29BS-300. Production of the Su-22UM-3 began in 1982. From 1983, however, all export versions were fitted with AL-21F-3 turbojets, resulting in the Su-22UM-3K (a Polish example of which is pictured above, with rear fuselage ECM dispensers).

## Su-17M-4 (S-54) 'Fitter-K' and Su-22M-4 (S-54K) 'Fitter-K'

The definitive single-seat 'Fitter' is the Su-17M-4, and its Su-22M-4 export equivalent (pictured right in East German service). The 'Fitter-K' carries an integrated navigation and weapons system, reducing pilot workload, and enhancing tactical capability. This system includes a sighting system consisting of a computer, laser rangefinder, radar and TV display. While improving the capabilities of the new variant, the system also causes some reduction in fuel capacity, since the new avionics occupy space behind the cockpit that was previously used for fuel. The M-4 can be differentiated from the M-3 by virtue of a new air intake in the dorsal fairing. Su-17M-4 production began in 1980, and the aircraft (together with Su-17UM-3s) were upgraded in 1987 following Soviet experience in Afghanistan. Both the Su-17M-4 and Su-22M-4 (series production of which began in 1984) are powered by the AL-21F-3.

***This Su-17M-4 was operated by the 20 Aviatsionnaya Polk Istrebeitelei-Bombardirovchikov (20th Fighter-Bomber Regiment), based at Gross-Dölln (Templin) in the former East Germany. '27 Yellow' is armed with UB-32-57 57-mm (2¼-in) rocket pods and R-60 self-defence missiles underwing, with Kh-25MP (AS-12 'Kegler') anti-radar missiles under the fuselage.***

*Only a handful of Su-24s have been built for export, with the bulk of production going to the Soviet VVS. When the Soviet Union disintegrated in the early 1990s, the fleet was largely divided between Russia and the Ukraine. The Ukrainian fleet contains the majority of the Su-24MP 'Fencer-F' electronic warfare platforms.*

# Sukhoi Su-24 'Fencer'

## Sukhoi's 'suitcase'

**Designed to offer the Soviet Union the same capabilities the US enjoyed with the F-111, the Su-24 offers brute force coupled with a wide-ranging payload. Even after 20 years of service, the 'Fencer' is still a vital aspect of the Russian air force.**

In the 1950s the tactical arm of the Soviet Air Force, the FA (*Frontovaya Aviahtsiya*, or Frontal Aviation), took delivery of its first Sukhoi Su-7B 'Fitter-A' short-range fighter-bombers. No replacement was forthcoming for the elderly Ilyushin Il-28 longer-range bombers until the arrival of the Yakovlev Yak-28 'Brewer' early in the next decade. The Yak-28 proved disappointing because it suffered from a short range, a small war load, and severe restrictions in the firing of its guns and in the accurate delivery of its bombs.

By the mid-1960s, two important factors had become evident. The first was the superiority of equivalent USAF designs, such as the General Dynamics F-111 'Aardvark', which had begun its flight development programme in 1964. These aircraft could outperform any current Soviet type, carry a wider range of weapons and, perhaps most important of all, they possessed outstandingly superior avionics.

The second factor made it imperative to challenge the rapid developments in surface-to-air missile capability: active radar-homing missiles were now capable of destroying any aircraft at the altitudes at which Soviet aircraft could currently attack. Ways had to be found of flying safely at supersonic speed underneath the radar screen and of locating and destroying the target from this altitude.

To meet this challenge, MiG and Sukhoi began work on new aircraft. MiG's design work resulted in the MiG-27 'Flogger-D'. Sukhoi had already started work on the Su-17 but decided to press ahead on a longer range interdiction bomber. Their goal was to emulate the performance of the F-111 but the concept of a variable geometry aircraft was initially disregarded in favour of a fixed swept wing aircraft. The resultant S-6 had a two-man tandem cockpit with side-by-side engines. Tests soon proved that the S-6 was inadequate for task it was designed to do and it was scrapped. A new design

*Above: From above the T6-1 clearly displays its aerodynamic origins in the Su-15TM 'Flagon'. Buried in the fuselage were four RD36-35 lift engines, fed with air via intakes in the upper fuselage. Barely visible are the doors that opened to act as intakes for the vertical engines.*

*The first of the swing-wing aircraft was the T6-2I. Seen here during weapon tests, it has been fitted with the undernose sighting system/ defensive antenna group and IR sensor forward of the windscreen. Immediately demonstrating outstanding performance, the aircraft first flew on 17 January 1960.*

***Su-24s based in Europe, such as these 'Fencer-Bs' (background) and 'Fencer-Cs' (foreground) at Osla in Poland, represented the powerhouse of the Soviet forces in Europe. While situated far back from the borders with the West, they were close enough to make their considerable presence felt if war ever broke out in Central Europe.***

called the T-6 was started, which had a double-delta wing, similar to that of the Su-15TM, side-by-side seating and two Tumanskii R-27F2-300 turbojets. The aircraft was intended to carry a range of air-to-air and air-to-ground weaponry. But during testing, the Air Force modified their demands for the new aircraft and the current configuration for the T6-1 proved inefficient. Once again, attention turned to the variable geometry concept. Any lasting worries about the capability of variable geometry aircraft were quickly dispelled by the impressive demonstration of the F-111 at the 1967 Paris air show. The wings were added to the old fuselage and the new aircraft was designated T6-2I. First flight was achieved on 17 January 1970.

Armament for the T6-2I was carried externally on six hardpoints with the exception of an internal Gryazev/Shipunov GSh-6-23 cannon with 500 rounds of ammunition beneath the fuselage's starboard side.

Test flying of the T6-2I continued from 1970 to 1976; it performed about 300 flights during this time. 1971 was its most active year in terms of test flying, with 73 flights taking place. At first the T6-2I was used for performance and stability tests, in particular for examining controllability at different wing sweep angles. Later, the automatic flight controls, essential to reduce pilot fatigue on high-speed operations of long duration, were put through a rigorous test programme by flying sorties at very low altitude.

At the end of 1970 the T6-2I was joined in the performance test programme by the second variable-sweep prototype: aircraft T6-3I. Ninety flights were undertaken on this aircraft in 1971, which together with the test flights of the T6-2I, imposed a heavy schedule that year for the test team. The T6-3I also completed its test programme in 1976, the final year being predominantly occupied by determining its ability to take off and land from a large variety of unpaved runways. Like the T6-2I, it made about 300 flights.

Test pilot Vladimir Ilyushin conducted the first flight of the T6-3I and the third swing-wing prototype: the T6-4I on 16 June 1971. Unfortunately, the T6-4I crashed in 1973 after only 120 test flights.

## Sukhoi Su-24

Confident in the design, and undoubtedly influenced by the T6-2I's vastly superior capabilities when compared with the Yak-28s in service, the Soviet Air Force did not wait for the test programme to be completed before ordering the T6-2I into production as the Sukhoi Su-24. Preparations for series production of the Su-24 had begun at the Novosibirsk aircraft factory No. 153. In December 1971 the first production aircraft, the seventh swing-wing airframe was taken for its maiden flight by factory test pilot Vladimir Vylomov. The aircraft was designated construction number 0115301: Batch 01 built by factory No. 153, first aircraft in batch.

The Su-24 was constantly modified during early production, as lessons learnt by the hastily-deployed service units were relayed back to the OKB (*Opytno Konstruktorskoye Byuro*), or design bureau. Many were retrofitted with later features. Pressure from the VVS to increase range was responded to at the beginning of the eighth production batch when the capacity of the number one tank was increased to 220 Imp gal (1000 litres). From the 15th batch of aircraft the rear fuselage was redesigned to reduce drag.

## Into service

When news of the introduction of the Sukhoi Su-24 into VVS service was given by Admiral Moorer, USN, in 1974, very little was known about it in the West; even the designation, quoted as 'Su-19', was incorrect and this error was not rectified until 1981. On entering service with Frontal Aviation regiments that had previously operated such types as the Yak-28 and MiG-27, the Su-24 proved to be much more demanding in maintenance and service. Considering the complexity of its systems, this was hardly surprising. Extra headaches were caused by the fact that this was the VVS's first experience with systems controlled by an onboard computer.

Alternatively one cause for satisfaction was the aircraft's ability to withstand bird strikes; a collision with a large eagle and another with 17 sparrows resulted in no serious damage – at least not to the aircraft. In spite of these difficulties, and no doubt remembering the idiosyncrasies of their previous mounts, the air crews liked the Su-24 and it was they who christened it *Chemodahn* (Suitcase), a reference to the slab-sided shape of its fuselage. They appreciated the good field of view, the well-planned cockpit and even the automatic flight systems, especially on low-level operations. Flight handling was reasonably easy, even though the Su-24 could be less forgiving in certain circumstances.

***Although most Su-24s were supplied to the VVS, a regiment was transferred in 1989 to the AVMF (Naval Aviation), to support the Baltic Fleet. The 132nd MShAD is still operational with the Su-24M, for which training is undertaken by the 240th GvSAP, at Ostrov.***

# 'Fencer' today

Lacking any self-defence capability other than R-60 AAMs, the Su-24MR is a highly effective reconnaissance aircraft. Its varied surveillance systems are datalinked to ground stations, ensuring the speedy transferral of information.

**Deficiencies in the early 'Fencers' led to the advanced M model, with its increased weapons capability. From this variant came specialised reconnaissance and electronic warfare versions that, 25 years later, still play an integral role in Russian air force operations.**

Production of the Su-24 proceeded at Novosibirsk, with improvements constantly being incorporated. Recognition of the individual production batches is complicated by many of the modifications being retrofitted to aircraft built previously. None of these alterations resulted in a new designation and it was not until 1978 that sufficient major changes took place on the factory production lines to justify the change to Su-24M (*modifitseerovannyy* meaning 'modified').

Major changes were made to the avionics, the most fundamental being the installation of a new weapons control system now known as the PNS-24M Tigr NS. To accommodate the updated equipment the forward fuselage was extended by 29.9 in (76 cm), while still retaining the nose radome.

Less obvious, but equally innovative, was the replacement of the electro-optical sighting system by the *Kayra*-24M (Grebe) day/night low-light-level TV system/laser designator. This device enabled the aircraft to carry laser- and TV-guided missiles such as the Kh-25ML, Kh-29L and the Kh-29T, dispensing with the previously necessary external designator pod.

Not only were better weapons now an option, but also the number that could be carried was increased by the addition of a ninth hardpoint. These amendments offered the Su-24M numerous extra selections from a formidable array of weaponry. A new defence system known as *Karpaty* (Carpathian mountains) was introduced, with the small hemispherical *Mak* (Poppy) infrared sensor situated amidships on the fuselage roof. Combat capability was greatly improved by the addition to all Su-24Ms of an inflight-refuelling system.

## Sukhoi Su-24MK

For many years Su-24s were manufactured exclusively for the Soviet air force, but in the mid-1980s permission was granted to export them to Arab states. In the late 1980s the Sukhoi OKB designed a version of the Su-24M for the newly-opened and potentially lucrative export market. It was a specially-modified version designated Su-24MK (*kommercheskiy* meaning 'commercial', i.e., export version), also known as *izdeliye* 44M. There were very few differences between the Su-24M and the Su-24MK and those differences were mainly in the avionics, particularly the IFF equipment and weapons options; for example, the Su-24MK could carry more bombs – 38 FAB-100s compared with 34 on the Su-24M, and four rather than two air-to-air missiles. A different computer, designated TsVM-24, was also installed. Any country now prepared to purchase this type could, no doubt, have its particular requirements met.

Export sales of the Su-24MK have been disappointing but, with hindsight, this should not be surprising as some potential customers may have decided in favour of the Su-30MK or are prepared to wait for the Su-34, rather than buy a design nearly 30 years old, albeit much updated. However, Syria and Iran will probably order more Su-24MKs. Sales reported so far are: to Iraq – 24, Libya – 15, Syria – 12 and Iran – 9. It is also believed that Algeria received 10 aircraft.

The future of the 'Fencer' is closely linked to the economic prosperity of the countries operating it. The Ukraine is unwilling to purchase further military equipment, however, Syria, Libya and Iran all continue to operate their 'Fencers' and may be interested in further purchases.

## Sukhoi Su-24MR

By the mid-1970s it had become clear that existing reconnaissance aircraft in the VVS were inadequate. Aircraft suffered from limited range and outdated equipment. The Sukhoi OKB modified two airframes, T6M-26 and T6M-34, to become T6MR-26 and T6MR-34 (R for [*samolyot-*] *razvedchik*, reconnaissance aircraft) respectively. The variant was known as Su-24MR to the VVS, T6MR to the OKB and *izdeliye* 48 to the plant. The first flight took place in September 1980.

Most of the ground-attack equipment was removed from the Su-24MR, but the basic structure and layout remained unchanged. A smaller nose radome was

A Ukrainian 'Fencer' crew boards its Su-24M for a training sortie. The aircraft's sturdy undercarriage was designed for use on various unprepared surfaces but, in practice, the Su-24 has operated solely from hard runways.

***The Ukrainian air force has around 180 'Fencers' arranged in two divisions. The 32nd BAD has 'Fencer-B/Cs' while the 289th BAD has Su-24M 'Fencer-Ds' (illustrated). Both units also have a small number of recce Su-24MRs assigned.***

complemented by a large SLAR (side-looking airborne radar) panel and two smaller dielectric panels. These covered reconnaissance equipment and were located on each side of the nose. Three underfuselage hardpoints were removed and the built-in cannon omitted. A comprehensive reconnaissance suite, known as BKR-1 *Shtyk* (BKR for *bortovoy kompleks razvedki*, meaning 'onboard reconnaissance suite'; *Shtyk* meaning 'bayonet') and claimed to be the best in the world, was developed by the Moscow Institute of Instrument Engineering. It afforded both visual and electronic reconnaissance by day or by night and could function efficiently in all weather conditions. Its constituent parts were a thermal imaging unit, a television camera and a panoramic camera which had an f3.5 lens of 3.6-in (90.5-mm) diameter. It had a *Shtyk* MR-1 synthetic aperture side-looking radar, radiation monitor, radio-monitoring pod and a laser pod providing 10-in (0.25-m) resolution from 1,315 ft (400 m) altitude. The laser scanned an area four times the height of the aircraft and gave an image of almost photographic quality.

## Sukhoi Su-24MP

Design work on the Su-24MP (*izdeliye* 46) electronic countermeasures (ECM) aircraft began in 1976. Construction of these prototypes entailed the modification of two Su-24M airframes, the T6M-25 and the T6M-35, which were then redesignated T6MP-25 and T6MP-35 respectively; the P represented *postanovschchik* [*pomekh*], indicating that it was an ECM platform. The first flight of the Su-24MP took place in December 1979.

Very little technical information relating to this variant has been released, but it is known to have a sophisticated and extensive network of systems for detecting, locating, analysing, identifying, classifying, storing and, if required, jamming all known electromagnetic emissions. Up to four R-60 or R-60M air-to-air missiles can be carried, but no air-to-ground missiles. The internal cannon is retained. It has been stated that only about 20 of this variant were built and their mission is electronic reconnaissance, intelligence-gathering and performing the invaluable service of escorting attack aircraft to their targets and neutralising hostile radars.

## 'Fencer'

When news of the introduction of the Su-24 into VVS service in 1974 broke out, very little was known of the aircraft in the West. The incorrect designation of Su-19 remained until 1981 and estimates over size and span were wildly inaccurate. When aircraft began to be stationed in West Germany in 1979, some information was gathered, but as late as 1987, commentators were disagreeing on the type of engine powering the aircraft.

For the Soviet units operating the 'Fencer', the new mount proved a vastly more demanding bird than their previous MiG-27s and Yak-28s. There were initial teething problems with the advanced avionics and new systems but in spite of these difficulties, and no doubt remembering the problems with their previous aircraft, the air crews liked the Su-24 and they soon christened it affectionately '*Chemodahn*' (suitcase), as reference to the slab-sided shape of the fuselage.

The 'Fencer' made its operational debut in 1984 during the Afghan war. Its precision bombing capability and superior weapons load made it a valuable addition to the Soviet forces in-theatre. The aircraft were located at Soviet bases in the Central Asian and Turkestan Defence Districts on the southern borders of the USSR and were predominantly used against static targets such as *mujaheddin* fortifications. Su-24 sorties were sporadic throughout the conflict as ground troops had more need for close support aircraft such as the Su-25 rather than the carpet-bombing 'Fencer'. Su-24s suffered no losses to ground fire, but there were maintenance mishaps, with several aircraft lost.

## The future

It is now more than 30 years since the first 'Fencer' flew and 25 years since it entered Soviet service. Despite many improvements, the aircraft does not incorporate much in the way of modern developments and lacks any 'stealthy' aspects. It is therefore, despite still possessing a formidable capability, clearly ready for replacement, especially as its Western counterpart, the F-111 has been retired. The Su-24M's successor is another Sukhoi product, the Su-34, also known as the Su-32FN, a side-by-side derivative of the Su-27. It is expected that, money permitting, this aircraft will also replace the remaining Su-17s and MiG-27s. However, it is thought that Su-24Ms and MRs will remain in service for another decade.

***Above: Russian sources state that nine Su-24MKs were delivered to Iran following the acquisition of 24 ex-Iraqi aircraft. By contrast, Iranian sources state that 14 were bought from Russia before 16-18 ex-Iraqi aircraft were acquired.***

***Left: Of note in this view of an Su-24M in maximum sweep configuration is the small hemispherical* Mak *IR sensor mounted on the spine behind the cockpit, and the retractable refuelling probe ahead of the windscreen.***

# Sukhoi Su-25 'Frogfoot'

## Introduction

***Far removed from its single-seat attack cousin, the* Su-25UTG *was intended to train Soviet pilots in basic carrier operations, but these were never conducted at the proper level.***

**Built in relatively small numbers, and equipping only a handful of Frontal Aviation regiments, the Su-25 is an effective and popular close air support aircraft, which has seen extensive action in Afghanistan. In recent years a host of new variants has emerged, although few have entered large-scale production.**

VVS USSR (Soviet Air Force) was a pioneer in the development and wide use of specialised ground attack aircraft to support its ground forces on the battlefield. After the end of World War II, units equipped with the well-known Il-2 Stormovik and its successor, the Il-10, were disbanded and new designs were ordered. The Soviet order of battle in the 1950s and 1960s was based on fighter-bomber units able to deliver not only conventional ordnance, but also tactical nuclear weapons. Typical of the aircraft based on this philosophy were the Su-7 'Fitter' and its variants, supplemented by the MiG-15 and MiG-17 fighter-bomber versions, equipping regiments specialised for battlefield ground support.

In the early 1960s, project discussions on the need for a new ground attack aircraft were held. The reasons behind these talks were the emergence of new data from Southeast Asia and other localised conflicts, the WarPac Dniepr '67 exercise, analyses of the new USAF A-X attack aircraft project (resulting in the development of the A-10 Thunderbolt), and the requirement for better damage resistance and survivability. General I. P. Pavlovskiy, Commander of Army, was the leading person in these discussions, and he managed to persuade the highest authorities about the necessity for new ground attack aircraft. The Ministry of Air Industry issued the official proposals to LSSh 'Stormovik' in March 1969 and four construction bureaux – Mikoyan, Yakovlev, Ilyushin and Sukhoi OKB – took part in the competition.

***As it catches the wire aboard the carrier* Admiral Kuznetsov, *one of the 10 Su-25UTGs is brought to a halt. Following the collapse of the Soviet Union, five examples were given to the Ukraine.***

The latter submitted its T8 project as a private venture by a group of designers. Its design did not comply with the thinking of the period, which had produced aircraft such as the MiG-23/27 'Flogger'. However, the design proved successful enough to win the competition, although continued development of the T8 would be needed before the aircraft could enter front-line units. Sukhoi was keen to test its new aircraft under combat conditions and two T8 prototypes took part in Operation Romb-1, which involved gun and weapon trials in Afghanistan in April/March 1980. The state acceptance trials were finished by another member of the early T8 prototype batch at air base Mary in Turkmenistan. With final trials protocol coming to an end, recommendation to put the new aircraft into production – under the designation of Su-25 – was agreed in March 1981. The new aircraft had been initially detected in the West by a US satellite in 1977, whereupon it was designated 'Frogfoot' by the ASCC.

***Repainted and fully restored, one of the early developmental T8s now resides at a Soviet air base. Clearly illustrated are the more slender nose profile and smaller intakes of the early models. During development, at least two T8s were lost, one claiming its test pilot, Y. A. Yegerov.***

## Curious design

Many in the West were puzzled that Sukhoi had adopted a thirsty turbojet instead of an economical turbofan, but designers argued that the higher thrust available with the Tumanskii R-95s offered better agility at lower altitudes. Coupled with this was the fact that the project had begun as a private venture and the development of an entirely new powerplant would have resulted in a huge increase in the cost of the programme.

The achievement of economy and simplicity in the design was the first major goal, and so systems from existing aircraft were utilised wherever possible. Manoeuvrability was the second goal, the third being that the aircraft should be able to operate fully-laden from semi-prepared airstrips close to the front line where maintenance facilities would be limited. Finally, the 'Frogfoot' had to be able to survive battle damage. To this end, the pilot sat in a 1-in (2.5-cm) thick titanium bathtub, shielded by armoured glass. Vital systems in the aircraft were protected by armour and the fuel tanks were filled with reticulated foam and surrounded by inert gas to minimise the chance of explosions.

Su-25s quickly began rolling off the production line at Tbilisi, and the VVS wasted no time in sending the vastly improved and more capable aircraft into the skies over Afghanistan again, eventually equipping the 200th Guards Independent Fighter Bomber Regiment at Bagram (north of Kabul). Twenty-three Su-25s were lost to enemy action during the war, a handful falling to Pakistani F-16s. Despite the losses, the 'Frogfoot' achieved a highly respectable combat record, although many were to return to their bases with considerable damaged inflicted by US-supplied Redeye shoulder-launched SAMs.

**_The two-seat Su-25UB 'Frogfoots' retain the full combat capability of the single-seat Su-25. The Ukraine currently operates around 60 Su-25s, including five two-seat examples which serve with the 299th ShAP naval unit at Saki._**

## Post-war service

In spite of its achievements, the Su-25 enjoyed only limited export success, the first customer being Czechoslovakia in 1984 which received 36 examples. Bulgaria followed in 1985 with an order for 36. The first non-WarPac operator was Iraq, which obtained 30, although some sources quote 84 examples. These were active during the Gulf War, but their performance was less than impressive, with 30 examples being shot down or destroyed in their hangars by Coalition forces. Thirty four examples were delivered between 1987 and 1989 to the People's Republic of Korea air force, although it is unknown at present how many are still in operation. The only African user is Angola, with 14 examples being delivered between 1988 and 1989; these have seen extensive action in the numerous bush-wars to plague this continent. Many Angolan aircraft have been lost to shoulder-launched SAMs, potentially the 'Frogfoot' pilot's greatest threat.

**_Equipped with a revised canopy, 'Blue 09' was the second Su-25T developed to improve the ground attack capability of the 'Frogfoot'. No orders have yet been received for the type._**

## Future 'Frogfoots'

Following the introduction of the single-seat Su-25K 'Frogfoot-A' and its tandem two-seat operational trainer derivative, Su-25UB 'UBK Frogfoot-B', Sukhoi has proposed a huge number of variations of these baseline models. The first of these was the Su-25BM, which utilised the basic airframe of the 'Frogfoot-A'. This model was developed as a target-tug following the attachment of a 'Kometa' (Comet) pod to the fuselage. Although successful, only 50 examples were purchased by the VVS and the type's close resemblance to the standard 'A' variant frequently resulted in this specialised aircraft being used for ordinary attack missions.

Following the development of three Russian aircraft-carriers, Sukhoi developed the Su-25UTG/UBP. This utilised the two-seat fuselage of the trainer variant and was equipped with arrester gear. The 10 examples produced underwent carrier trials using the ski-jump method for take-off; one was lost in an accident and the remaining examples are used as land-based trainers following the cancellation of the carrier programme.

By far the most capable variant yet developed utilising the Su-25 airframe is the Su-25T, which makes use of the two-seat fuselage, but is fitted for single-pilot configuration only. The rear space is used for extra avionics, the nose of the aircraft houses improved Shkval avionics, and a larger fuselage-mounted cannon is installed. The greatest improvement is seen in the cockpit, which is equipped with MFDs; the Su-25T is thus able to deliver the latest air-to-ground weapons such as the Kh-35 and Kh-58 guided missiles.

A further improvement of this variant is the Su-25TM (Su-39), of which eight have been delivered for state acceptance trials. Bulgaria and Slovakia are interested in obtaining this example.

Despite Sukhoi's introduction of other types such as the impressive Su-27, the 700 or so 'A' models built look set to remain a potent attack aircraft well into the next century.

**_In response to the ASCC designation of 'Frogfoot', a single Czech Su-25K received a highly elaborate colour scheme for its debut at Western air shows. Painted on the tail was the design of a large frog crushing a tank, although observers were keen to point out that the tank depicted was an elderly Russian World War II T-34._**

# Development

***Above:*** ***Ammong the latest developments of the 'Frogfoot' is the Su-25TM (Su-39). Utilising the two-seat fuselage of the Su-25UB, the TM dispenses with the rear seat to allow for the accommodation of extra avionics to undertake missions in all weathers. Though far more capable than the Su-25 'Frogfoot-A', only a handful of TMs has entered Russian service.***

***Left:*** ***In the search for a suitable ground-attack aircraft, both Sukhoi and Ilyushin submitted design studies. Sukhoi's winning design adopted a highly conventional layout, with the engines widely separated so that no single AAA hit could disable both.***

**The Sukhoi Su-25 'Frogfoot' utilises proven systems incorporated into a heavily armoured airframe. Originally developed purely as a battlefield day attack aircraft, the latest variants of the Su-25 are able to undertake missions in all weathers, 24 hours a day.**

The development of the 'Frogfoot' can be traced back to the late 1960s. Having observed with great interest the progress of the USAF's AX programme, which resulted in the development of the A-10 Thunderbolt II, the USSR reviewed its own existing fighter-bombers. To everyone's surprise, the elderly MiG-17s and MiG-15s proved to be more effective than the faster, but less agile, MiG-21s and Su-7s. In addition, during the Six-Day War the devastating effectiveness of 30-mm cannon-equipped Israeli fighters (including obsolete Ouragans and Mystères) against ground targets (including tanks) prompted General I. P. Pavlovskii, commander of the Red Army, to call for the development of a new ground-attack aircraft.

Sukhoi's 'Shturmovik' was designed by a group of senior personnel, including Oleg Samolovich, D. N. Gorbachev, Y .V. Ivashetchkin, V. M. Lebedyev and A. Monachev, who based the design on a configuration produced by I. V. Savchenko, commander of the air force academy. The aircraft design, known as the SPB project, was designed around a pair of 3,865-lb st (17.2-kN) Ivchenko/Lotarev AI-25T engines. It was estimated that the machine would have a maximum speed of between 310 mph and 500 mph (500 and 800 km/h) and a range of 465 miles (750 km). Sukhoi stressed the key words of 'closer, lower and quieter', rather than the contemporary VVS slogan of 'higher, faster, further'. The programme goals were the design of an aircraft with high battle damage resistance and tolerance, which would be simple and economic to produce, operate and maintain, which would have unmatched performance and agility at very low level and which could operate fully laden from a semi-prepared 390-ft (120-m) airstrip.

## Official request

Officialdom caught up with the Sukhoi bureau in March 1969, when an official request for the 'Shturmovik' aircraft was launched. Mikhail Simonov was appointed head of the design team, with the Sukhoi design now known as the T8.

The T8 mock-up was presented to the authorities at Khodinka, near Moscow. Although an official order for the prototype had not been placed, two prototypes (T8-1 and T8-2) were, in fact, already under construction, Sukhoi having authorised commencement of the work on 6 June 1972. The official order for the two prototypes (plus T8-0, a static test airframe) was finally issued on 6 May 1974. T8-1 undertook its first high-speed taxi trials on 25 December 1975. However, two days before the maiden flight (planned for 22 February 1975), one of the RD-9 powerplants suffered turbine failure, causing major damage. This, allied with many other, resulted in the decision to rebuild the entire aircraft and, after a two-year lay-up, the revised design was revealed on 26 April 1978. Designated as the T8-D, this aircraft was the first prototype to resemble the final Su-25, with long-span wings and a taller tailfin.

Prior to this, in March 1976, the aircraft had been re-engined with R95Sh engines to become the T8-2D. The navigation and

***Two VVS Su-25 units were based in East Germany as part of the 16th Air Army (Group of Soviet Forces in Germany). The small number of 'Frogfoots' is somewhat surprising. There is little doubt however, that the regiments would have been extensively reinforced in time of war.***

***Below:** Apart from the pylons furthest outboard, all of the underwing hardpoints fitted to the Su-25 are of the heavy-duty universal type. The centre pylons on each side are wired to allow the carriage of ECM jammer pods. Adaptor rails allow for the fitting of AAMs.*

***Above:** Positioned between each powerplant is a welded titanium keel. This serves to protect the opposite engine from fire damage in the event of the other being hit.*

attack suite of the Su-17M-2 had been replaced with that of the Su-17M-3. This equipment was subsequently fitted to the T8-3 and the following developmental models, which numbered 15, including two-seat variants.

During the aircraft's development, at least two T8s undertook combat testing in Afghanistan, where the aircraft acquired a highly distinguished combat record.

The first production Su-25 rolled off the production line at Tbilisi, Georgia in April 1981. Despite the Su-25's tremendous weapons and operational capability, export success was not forthcoming, with relatively few Warsaw Pact nations acquiring the aircraft. However, the Russian air force has been impressed with the Su-25's capability and is continuing to develop the 'Frogfoot'.

## Su-25 'Frogfoot'

**This 'Frogfoot', 'Red 29', was one of those based at Bagram, Afghanistan during the late 1980s (it is seen here in the markings it wore in 1988). It was during this period that Soviet operations in Afghanistan were at their peak, a fact reflected by the number of incursions made by VVS combat aircraft over the Pakistani border.**

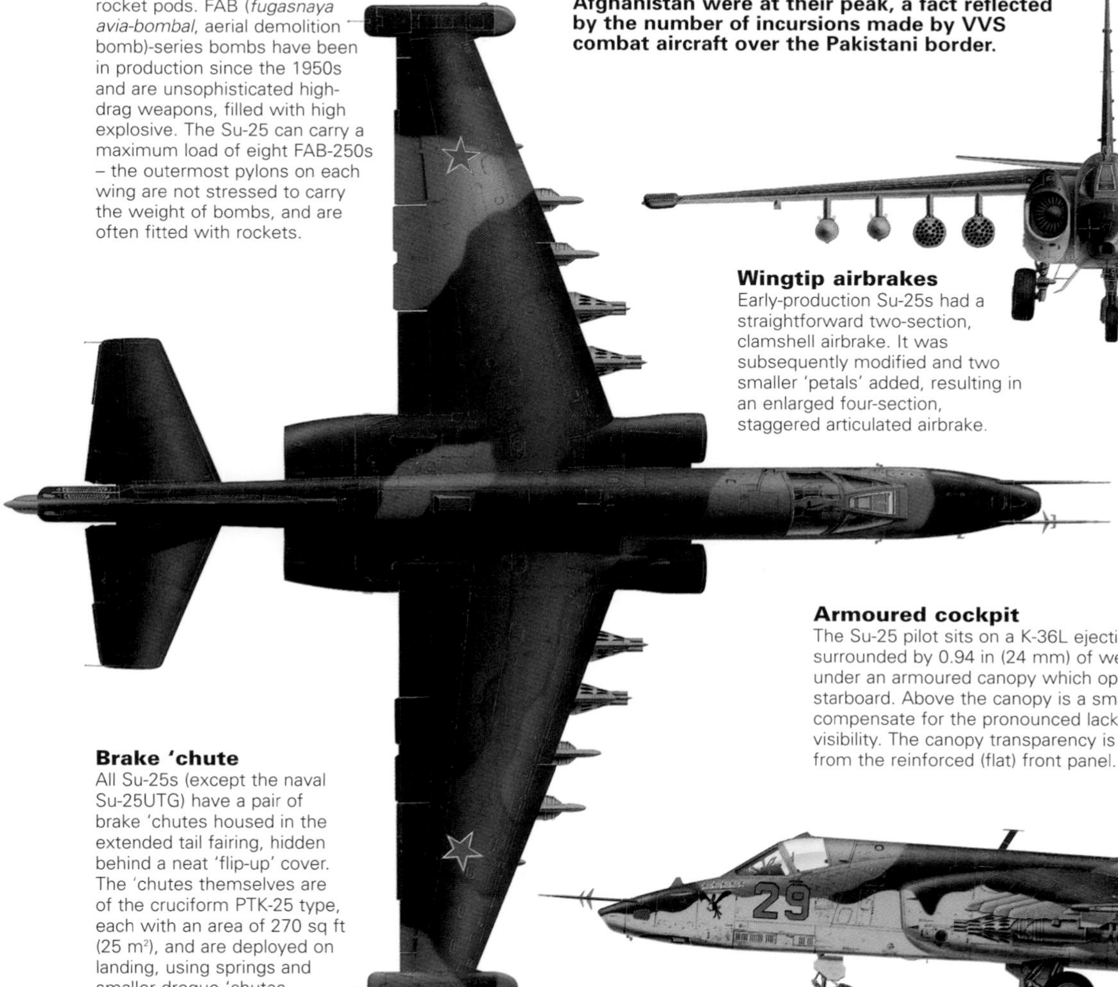

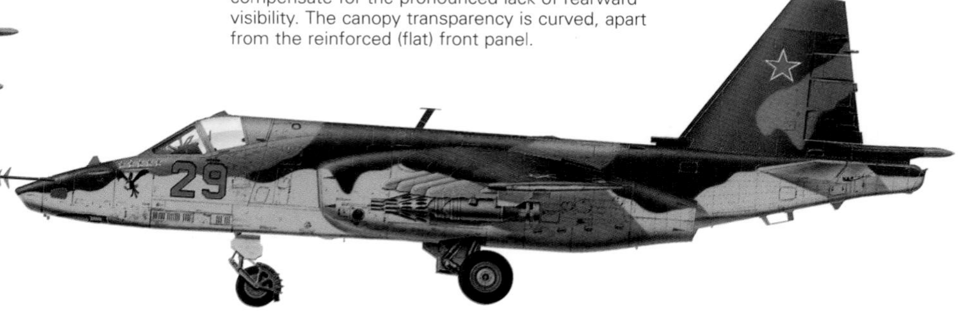

### Warload

This aircraft is seen carrying a load of four FAB-250-270 250-kg (551-lb) bombs and four UV-32M rocket pods. FAB (*fugasnaya avia-bombal*, aerial demolition bomb)-series bombs have been in production since the 1950s and are unsophisticated high-drag weapons, filled with high explosive. The Su-25 can carry a maximum load of eight FAB-250s – the outermost pylons on each wing are not stressed to carry the weight of bombs, and are often fitted with rockets.

### Grach

It was in Afghanistan that the *grach* (rook) marking, which has become synonymous with the Su-25 in Soviet (and Russian) service, first appeared. The origins of the cartoon bird are unclear, but the marking soon appeared as nose-art on virtually all the aircraft that served in Afghanistan.

### Wingtip airbrakes

Early-production Su-25s had a straightforward two-section, clamshell airbrake. It was subsequently modified and two smaller 'petals' added, resulting in an enlarged four-section, staggered articulated airbrake.

### Undercarriage

The nose gear of the Su-25 is offset to port, and fitted with a mudguard to reduce the risk of debris ingestion to the engines. The main undercarriage uses levered suspension legs, an oleo-pneumatic shock absorber and low-pressure tyres to enhance rough-field performance.

### Armoured cockpit

The Su-25 pilot sits on a K-36L ejection seat, surrounded by 0.94 in (24 mm) of welded titanium, under an armoured canopy which opens to starboard. Above the canopy is a small mirror to compensate for the pronounced lack of rearward visibility. The canopy transparency is curved, apart from the reinforced (flat) front panel.

### Brake 'chute

All Su-25s (except the naval Su-25UTG) have a pair of brake 'chutes housed in the extended tail fairing, hidden behind a neat 'flip-up' cover. The 'chutes themselves are of the cruciform PTK-25 type, each with an area of 270 sq ft (25 $m^2$), and are deployed on landing, using springs and smaller drogue 'chutes.

***Ungainly and angular, the Su-25 became a familiar and much-feared sight over Afghanistan. This aircraft carries a pair of drop tanks and four of the formidable S-24 unguided rockets.***

# Operational history

**Likened to the famous Il-2 'Shturmovik' of World War II due to its rugged strength and ground-attack ability, the Su-25 has proven to be a highly capable warplane, acquitting itself well in theatres ranging from Afghanistan to Angola.**

In December 1979 the Soviet army entered Afghanistan to suppress the expansion of Muslim fundamentalism and send warning signals to Iran and Pakistan. This was a first-class opportunity to test the new types of weapons then entering service with the Russian forces. In early March 1980 the decision was taken to carry out some of the T-8 (later re-designated the Su-25) developmental tests in conditions that were as similar as possible to those found on the battlefield. The T-8-1D and T-8-3 developmental examples of the 'Frogfoot' as well as the Yak-38 'Forger' VTOL attack aircraft were tested during this operation under the codename 'Romb-1' (rhombus). The 'Romb' group was not intended to participate in combat missions, but to carry out state acceptance tests. Pilots were warned however that, if necessary, the division commanding officer could demand their support.

The operational base of the group was in Shindand in western Afghanistan. The aircraft were deployed on 16 April 1980 and stayed for 50 days exactly, until 5 June. The sorties were flown to an Afghan tank exercise ground about 5 miles (9 km) from Shindand, where weapons delivery techniques were practised and refined. With the second week of testing, the aircraft were called upon by the army to destroy targets which were particularly difficult to attack, for instance bunkers in ravine slopes. No opposition from the ground was encountered during the operation but, with the expansion of the war, flight-testing had to be finished quickly in order to form an operational Su-25 combat unit.

## Fighting 'Frogfoot'

The first front-line unit to be equipped with the Su-25 was the 200th Independent Attack Air Flight, formed on 4 February 1981 at Sital-chai airfield in Azerbaijan. In April 1981 the flight obtained the first 12 production Su-25s from the Tbilisi factory. In the evening of 18 June, they left their home airfield for the flight to Shindand in Afghanistan. Several days later, the aircraft were conducting combat missions against mujaheddin guerrillas.

Soon the flight grew into a regiment, the 60th Independent Attack Air Regiment. From then on, for some years, one of the three flights of the regiment rotated to Afghanistan, the other two remaining based at Sital-chai.

During the early stages of the air war over Afghanistan there was little AAA from the mujaheddin guerrillas. The breakthrough for the rebels came in 1984 when, via the CIA, hand-held SAM sets such as Strela and Redeye were acquired. During the first month of their use, six 'Frogfoots' were lost. The Su-25s were equipped with flare/chaff dispensers but the pilots, caught in the heat of combat, often failed to deploy them. Sukhoi designers analysed several solutions and selected an automatic launching device that released flares whenever the armament release switch on the control column was pressed.

This solution was sufficient until 1986 when the mujaheddin took delivery of General Dynamics FIM-82A Stinger SAMs. Four Su-25s were destroyed in three days, with two pilots lost. The Stingers tended to detonate close to the engine exhaust nozzles, piercing the rear fuel tanks and causing fires to break out which could burn through control cables, or inflict damage on the farmost engine. To prevent both engines from being damaged by a single hit and also to prevent damage spreading from one to the other, a 0.2-in (5-mm) thick armour plate was inserted between the two engines. Measuring about 5

***Designed to absorb small arms and cannon fire, and even SAM hits, the Soviet Su-25s acquired an enviable reputation for survivability. In Afghanistan, the Su-25 enjoyed a lower loss rate than any other Soviet fast-jet type in-theatre.***

**Above: To counter the threat of the mujaheddin's SAMs, especially the FIM-82A Stinger, the flare capacity of the Su-25 was increased from 128 to 256 by the addition of four dispensers to the top of the engine nacelles.**

**Left: The Su-25 can carry a vast array of stores on 10 underwing hardpoints. The most common load over Afghanistan was two or four S-24 240-mm rockets on the outer pylons, with small bombs inboard.**

ft (1.5 m) long, the plate acted as a giant shield and fire-wall. A new inert gas fire-extinguisher was installed, which could be activated by the pilot. These modifications proved a great success, dramatically reducing the Su-25's loss rate. Although many were hit, not one Su-25 equipped with the inter-engine armour was lost to a Stinger. One example was damaged by two Sidewinders fired by a Pakistani F-16, but was still able to limp back to base.

## Combat losses

Twenty-three Su-25s were lost in action in Afghanistan, these aircraft representing about 10 per cent of Soviet fixed-wing losses during the war. Altogether, the 'Frogfoot' made 60,000 operational sorties. The cockpit armour of the Su-25 proved particularly successful and no Su-25 pilot was killed by projectiles or shrapnel. Several Su-25 pilots were awarded the Soviet Union's highest honour, being decorated as Heroes of the Soviet Union. Afghanistan was not the only war from which the designers of the Su-25 could draw lessons based on real combat experience. Azeri forces used Su-25s in their war against Armenia during 1992. And, from late 1992, the Georgians used Su-25s against Abkhazian units fighting for independence, who themselves were supported by Russian forces whose equipment included the Su-25.

One of the earliest incidents of this brief but bloody conflict (which lasted until the end of 1993) was an engagement on 27 October 1992 involving two Georgian Su-25s, and two Russian Su-25s which were escorting Mi-8s delivering humanitarian relief. None of the aircraft was shot down. Six Georgian Su-25s were lost later in the war, together with a Russian Su-25, the pilot of which successfully ejected, only to be decapitated by his captors. Following the secession of Abkhazia, the last Georgian Su-25 was shot down on 5 November, while conducting operations against rebel Zviadist forces who supported former President Zviad Gamsakhurdia.

## Gulf war and beyond

Delivered from 1988-89, Angola's single unit of 14 'Frogfoots' has seen extensive combat against UNITA rebels. The aircraft have been crippled by shortages of fuel and spares, and it is not known how many remain in service today.

Iraq received 30-45 Su-25s from 1986 to 1987. The aircraft played only a minor role in the long war with Iran, delivering 'dumb' bombs and chemical weapons. At the start of Operation Desert Storm, the aircraft were immediately dispersed, many being hidden under camouflage in the open.

Two Su-25s were credited to Lt Robert W. 'Gigs' Hehemann, an F-15C pilot of the USAF's 36th TFW. He shot them down on 6 February 1991 as they attempted to flee to safety in Iran to join six others already there. More examples were almost certainly destroyed in their shelters. The Su-25 'Frogfoot' has established itself as a highly-capable attack platform with an impressive combat record. Sukhoi has, accordingly, continued to develop ever more sophisticated 'Frogfoot' variants, which have yet to see combat.

**Above: Many of Iraq's Su-25s were lost during Desert Storm. At least two were claimed as air-to-air 'kills' while many others, such as this example, were lost on the ground.**

**Left: In all, 14 (including two two-seater) Su-25s were delivered to Angola during 1988-89. The aircraft have seen active combat operations against UNITA rebels.**

# Sukhoi Su-27 'Flanker'

Above: The Su-27M (Su-35) was developed as an advanced multi-role derivative of the Su-27. It has entered every recent international fighter competition without success.

## Introduction

**Sukhoi's Su-27 'Flanker' represents the jewel in the crown of the Russian aerospace industry. The basic variant is without peer as a long-range interceptor, while advanced derivatives look set to dominate Russian military aviation into the 21st century.**

Massive, and with sufficient internal fuel capacity to enjoy an unmatched radius of action, the Su-27 'Flanker' was originally designed to meet the challenging requirements of the Soviet air defence air arm, the IA-PVO. In addition to long range, the Su-27 also has an effective multi-spectral suite of sensors, with radar, infrared, and laser rangefinding. In certain circumstances, the Su-27 can actually detect, locate and identify its targets without using radar, and thus without betraying its presence to enemy radar warning receivers. The Su-27 enjoys great 'combat persistence' with up to 12 hardpoints for a range of sophisticated air-to-air missiles, including up to eight beyond-visual-range R-27 missiles. But the 'Flanker' is much more than just a long-range bomber destroyer.

Air show audiences have watched transfixed as Su-27s have performed manoeuvres which no Western front-line jet can duplicate, demonstrating predictable and safe handling characteristics in the extreme corners of the envelope. This gives the Su-27 pilot unparalleled agility in a low-speed fight, and allows him to 'point' the nose far away from the direction of flight to aim his weapons in an off-axis 'snapshot'.

Like any fighter, the Su-27 has its weaknesses. Its radar is powerful, but onboard computer processing capacity is inadequate, and the system cannot always

The basic Su-27 design has spawned major advanced derivatives, the most fundamentally changed of which is the Su-27IB (OKB Su-34) long-range strike aircraft. This marries the Su-27's fuselage with a new forward section featuring side-by-side seating and a 'platypus' nose. The Su-27IB and related naval Su-32FN are being offered to supplant the heavier bombers of Long Range Aviation, albeit while serving with Frontal Aviation regiments.

***With its upgraded radar, the two-seat Su-30MK has been developed as a multi-role strike fighter. It carries an impressive array of air-to-air and air-to-surface weapons, including precision-guided missiles. The Su-30MKI has been exported to India, which may retrofit its aircraft with canard foreplanes and thrust-vectoring nozzles.***

automatically prioritise all targets. The pilot can become swamped with information, and to maintain adequate situational awareness must rely on ground control or an AWACS platform. Similarly, the cockpit is at least a generation behind contemporary Western fighter cockpits, unnecessarily increasing pilot workload. Much of the Su-27's extraordinary agility is available only at low all-up weights, and when fully laden with fuel and weapons its limitations are more restrictive. In many respects, and with the important exception of range, the smaller MiG-29 is a better all-round fighter.

***Above: In common with many of the world's air arms, the Russian air force chooses to show off its front-line equipment in the form of a dedicated aerobatic team. The 'Russian Knights' have served to demonstrate the Su-27 on a number of international tours.***

## Original design flaws

The Sukhoi Design Bureau overcame many obstacles in getting the Su-27 into service. The original T10 design was seriously flawed and had to undergo a fundamental redesign before it was suitable for operational use in even its original, rather narrow role. Since then, the Sukhoi Design Bureau (OKB) has improved and refined the aircraft to fulfil a variety of roles. The OKB has been cushioned from the worst effects of the cutbacks by its political pre-eminence. Thus, while its rivals languish in the doldrums, Sukhoi is kept relatively busy developing and marketing advanced derivatives of the original Su-27, such as the Su-27M, Su-27IB and Su-30, as well as export versions.This seems to have ensured that the re-equipment of the Russian air force would be based around variants of the Su-27. Once used primarily as an IA-PVO long-range air defence interceptor, the Su-27 and its close relatives will soon dominate Frontal Aviation and Naval Aviation as well. If the advanced production variants of the MiG-29 remain unbuilt, today's political realities will have succeeded in killing off the Su-27's lightweight competitor. The 'Flanker' will finally represent the single future fighter for the Russian air forces. This marks a final realisation of the original plan which resulted in the Su-27, which had originally called for a single tactical Prospective Frontal Fighter.

***Right: Sukhoi's political pre-eminence has secured the future of the 'Flanker'. Rivals claim (with some justification) that when a Sukhoi and a non-Sukhoi design have competed for Russian state funding, the Sukhoi aircraft has inevitably 'won', even when it has been inferior, or less suitable for the particular requirement. This is exemplified by the Su-27K (Su-33) naval variant, which won in the face of competition from the arguably more capable Mikoyan MiG-29K.***

# The first 'Flankers'

**Starting life as the problematic Sukhoi T-10, the impressive Su-27 'Flanker' underwent a lengthy and difficult development period.**

**Wings**
The T-10-1 had provision for four underwing hardpoints, and four small fences are visible on the upper surface of the wing. The wingtip of this T-10 does not have provision for missile carriage.

## T-10-1

**This is the first prototype Sukhoi T-10, as it appeared late in the development phase of the type. It displays a number of differences from the production Su-27 'Flanker'.**

**Cockpit canopy**
The need to give the pilot a good all-round view was in vogue in the mid-1970s when the type was designed. Production 'Flankers' had a cockpit canopy that was both re-shaped and strengthened.

**Radar-less nose**
The T-10s were completed long before the intended radar was ready and thus had ballast-filled metal nose-cones to maintain the aircraft's centre of gravity.

**Powerplant**
This aircraft was powered by a pair of Lyul'ka AL-21F-3 turbojets which also powered the MiG-23 and Su-24. They provided 17,200 lb st (76.5 kN) at full military power, and 24,800 lb st (110.5kN) in full afterburner.

When the Sukhoi Su-27 was conceived, few would have dared to predict the scale of its eventual success. In fact, its early history was so disastrous that cancellation of the entire project seemed a real possibility on several occasions. The Su-27 was conceived during 1969, after the Sukhoi OKB won a design contract to design a long-range interceptor to replace the Tu-128 'Fiddler', Su-15 'Flagon' and Yak-28P 'Firebar' in IA-PVO service. From an early stage, it was decided that the new Sukhoi aircraft would have a limited frontal aviation role as a long-range escort fighter for strike aircraft like the Su-24 'Fencer' and as a complement to Mikoyan's MiG-29.

### Demanding role

The growing importance of low-level penetration tactics dictated that the new fighter should be capable of look-down/shootdown intercepts. Moreover, the increasing use of stand-off weapons such as cruise missiles made it necessary to intercept targets at very long range (preferably before their weapons could be launched), and to be capable of intercepting low-flying missiles. As if these requirements were not difficult enough, Sukhoi was instructed that the new fighter should be capable of destroying 'enemy fighter aircraft which protect the target zone', which was taken as a directive that the new fighter should be able to outperform the new American F-15 in air-to-air combat.

### First flight

The first prototype, given the bureau designation T-10-1, made its maiden flight on 20 May 1977 at Zhukhovsky. The aircraft was powered by AL-21F-3 engines, as used by the Su-17, with the afterburner nozzles completely enclosed within the rear fuselage, like those of the Su-24 'Fencer'. Spotted at Zhukhovsky (then erroneously referred to by Western intelligence agencies as Ramenskoye) by a US satellite, the aircraft was allocated the provisional reporting name of 'RAM-J'. A handful of these images was eventually seen by the press, but the quality of the released images was so poor that little could be inferred about the new fighter. In 1985, this prototype aircraft provided the Western aviation press with its first useful glimpse of the Su-27, when stills from a TV documentary about the Sukhoi OKB were released, and the machine can now be seen in the air force's museum at Monino, near Moscow.

### Configuration

The aircraft was of typical late 1960s/early 1970s configuration, with twin vertical tailfins, widely-spaced underslung engines, and a blended wing/forebody, with some features reminiscent of some aspects of the rival US F-15 and F-14. Since Western analysts at that time believed that Soviet engineers were both backward and incapable of any original thought, this led inevitably to accusations that Sukhoi had copied one or other of the US aircraft. The wing was very clean, with a drooping leading edge but no leading-edge slats and no anti-flutter weights, and with conventional outboard ailerons and inboard flaps. The root was swept at about 80°, and the main part of the leading edge at 44° out to the gracefully curving tip. Four small fences were added on the inboard panels, perhaps before the first flight. The twin fins were uncanted and were mounted on top of the engine nacelles, just outboard of the centreline. Box section beams on the sides of the nacelles carried the slab tailerons. The main undercarriage units were mounted in the wingroots, retracting forward and swivelling through 90° to lie horizontally in the wing. Large forward undercarriage doors, hinged on their leading edges, acted as airbrakes. The tall nose gear was located well forward, below the windscreen, retracting aft.

The design team, drawing on extensive work carried out by the Central Aerodynamics Institute, TsAGI, chose to use what the Russians call an 'integrated airframe' in which forebody and wing are blended together to form, in effect, a single, unified lifting body. This blending (also used on the American F-16) gives a smaller wetted area (and thus lower drag) and greater internal volume for fuel and avionics. The configuration allowed a smooth change in cross-sectional area, even at the canopy and air intakes, significantly reducing wave drag. The Su-27's very high internal fuel

*This frame from a film shown on Soviet TV was the West's first look at the Su-27. Showing the T-10-1 landing and taking off, the film revealed the aircraft's obvious similarity to the (then) current generation of American fighters.*

*This T-10 displays the wing shape to good advantage. The wing was changed on the production aircraft to use the anti-flutter weights as wingtip missile racks, while the prototypes made use of primitive leading edge spikes.*

capacity is partly a result of this, but mainly as a result of the fighter's sheer size.

The first and second prototypes were built by the OKB itself, in its Moscow 'workshop', albeit using wings and tails from the Komsomolsk-na-Amur production plant. The second prototype reportedly incorporated some improvements, including a flattened leading edge with moveable slats, canted tailfins and, according to some sources, was the first T-10 with the full standard fly-by-wire control system (originally developed for the T-4/Su-100). It also had an extra 2,204 lb (1000 kg) of internal fuel over the first aircraft's 19,841-lb (9000-kg) capacity. The T-10-2 was lost after a control system malfunction led to severe resonance, Yevgeny Soloviev being killed when he ejected outside seat parameters.

The next two prototypes, T-10-3 and T-10-4, were also built by the Bureau, but these were powered by the definitive production standard AL-31F (albeit with underslung accessories and gearboxes). T-10-3 made its maiden flight on 23 August 1979, and was followed by T-10-4 on 31 October. Five further prototypes were built by the production plant at Komsomolsk (T-10-5, T-10-6, T-10-9, T-10-10 and T-10-11), but these were powered by the AL-21F.

## Design shortfalls

While accidents were rocking the programme, information about the new US F-15 began to flood in, and it became clear that the T-10, which was failing to meet its own performance requirements, would be no match for the American fighter. The problems were being caused by higher-than-expected drag figures, a performance shortfall from the engines, excessive specific fuel consumption figures and the excess weight of the newly-developed avionics systems which, since they were mainly fitted in the nose, also tended to increase the longitudinal stability of the aircraft. The aircraft also suffered from flutter problems, and these necessitated the provision of anti-flutter weights on the leading edges of the tailfins, tailplanes and wings, and the removal of one pair of overwing fences. It was clear that, to meet its original requirement, the new fighter would need to undergo a major redesign, and Sukhoi received permission to undertake this on condition that output of the Su-25 attack aircraft would not be affected.

## Second attempt

Accordingly, the next two prototypes under construction at the OKB's Moscow facility, T-10-7 and T-10-8, were completed to a wholly new standard, which was claimed by the OKB to be an 'entirely new aircraft' retaining only the 'T-10 designation, ejection seat and mainwheels'. The redesign was personally supervised by Mikhail Simonov, who reportedly came up with the new designation T-10S (T-10 Simonov) for the revised design. The two prototypes thus became T-10S-1 and T-10S-2. Even after work had begun on the two redesigned aircraft, Komsomolsk continued working on T-10 prototypes to the original configuration, for use as equipment and avionics testbeds. Some sources suggest that some 20 original-configuration T-10s were produced, but little evidence can be found to support this contention, and it seems that only nine flew.

## New wing

The new aircraft was not an entirely 'clean sheet of paper' design, but it did represent a very major redesign. The key to the redesign was an entirely new wing. The LERXes were improved to give more lift (thereby helping to destabilise the heavier, equipment-packed nose) and the wing lost its curved tips, replacing these with massive flutter weights which doubled as wingtip missile launch rails. The ailerons (which had suffered from reversal problems because of the flexibility of the wing) and the original flaps were deleted and replaced by inboard flaperons. Less obviously, but no less importantly, the fuselage was extensively redesigned. Changes to the nose and forward fuselage were the most obvious, with a more capacious radome and reduced forward fuselage cross-section, but with increased cross-sectional area and less height immediately aft of the cabin. A GSh-30-1 cannon was fitted in the starboard wing-root, the same weapon as is used by the rival MiG-29.

The fins were increased in size and were moved outboard on to the booms which supported the tailplanes. The combined airbrake/main gear doors had caused severe tailplane flutter and were thus replaced by a spine-mounted airbrake. The undercarriage itself was refined, with canted-forward main oleos and a completely repositioned forward-retracting nose gear, located much further aft to improve the ground turning circle and to reduce the risk of debris entering the intakes. Development of the T-10S was expedited by the continued use of the surviving original T-10s as engine, armament, instrumentation and equipment testbeds, and for pilot training.

The original T-10s had a short, broad, flat beaver tail between their engine nozzles, capped by a dielectric fairing. On the T-10S, this was replaced by a much longer cylindrical tail boom which reduced drag and served as a location for the aircraft's twin braking parachutes and chaff/flare launchers. The T-10S-1 made its maiden flight in the hands of Vladimir Ilyushin (shortly before his retirement) on 20 April 1981. This was, at last, an aircraft of which Sukhoi could be proud and which fulfilled some of the enormous potential of the original design.

*The first T-10 survives today as an exhibit in the famous collection located at Monino. The addition of tailfin and taileron leading edge anti-flutter weights is visible.*

# Su-27 'Flanker'
## Record-breaking development

*Above: Many of the records set by the P-42 still stand, and the aircraft today languishes in open storage on one of Zhukhovskii's crowded ramps. There have been suggestions that the aircraft may one day form the centrepiece of an OKB museum.*

*Left: The first T-10 was fitted with distinctive leading-edge anti-flutter weights on the wings and fins. The engine nozzles were entirely contained within the rear fuselage.*

**After a difficult birth, the 'Flanker' had the potential to become one of Russia's most capable fighters. As a prelude to its entry into front-line service, Sukhoi set out to establish a number of records with a stripped-down example.**

The first T-10S looked very much like the production Su-27 that we know today, although it still had uncropped vertical fins with horizontal tops, and lacked the second canopy frame, level with the back of the ejection seat. Extensive trials with a number of aircraft eventually resulted in the adoption of small vertical fins mounted below the booms which carried the tailplanes and vertical fins, these improving both directional stability and spin characteristics. The early 'flat-topped' tailfins were used by a significant number of early production Su-27s, perhaps sufficient to equip one complete regiment.

Early 'Flankers' had an extraordinarily high attrition rate, one being lost in a fatal accident which claimed the life of Sukhoi test pilot Alexander Komarov. Another was written off after losing virtually an entire wing, although the pilot Nikolai Sadovnikov actually managed to land the aircraft. Both accidents were caused by an uncommanded pitch-up which ripped off the newly installed leading-edge flaps, causing tailfin damage and loss of the outboard wing panels. One solution was to reduce the area of the leading-edge flaps, while another was to reduce their extension angle. Other problems were less easy to solve.

It is known that the Su-27 suffered problems with its avionics, although details remain unclear. It is widely believed that at one time about 50 aircraft (often quoted as 'hundreds') were in open storage at Komsomolsk awaiting serviceable radars so that they could be delivered. These problems delayed service deliveries (for trials and evaluation) until 1986, although the first production Su-27 had been rolled out in November 1982.

### Beating the US

One of the T-10S prototypes was destined to play a further part in the Su-27 story, providing shocking confirmation that, in the field of performance at least, comfortable assumptions of Western superiority would need to be reconsidered. Under the designation P-42, the aircraft was prepared for a series of world record attempts, challenging the records set by the specially stripped F-15 Streak Eagle. The P-42 was stripped of all radar, armament and operational equipment and lightened for its record attempts, under the direction of Rollan G. Martirosov. In the interests of saving weight, the leading-edge flaps were disabled and locked shut, and their actuators were removed, while the tail sting, wingtips and fin-caps were also removed. The rear fuselage was left with a spade-like straight trailing edge, inset from the engine nozzles. The normal radome was replaced by a lightweight aluminium fairing, and the aircraft was stripped of paint, and highly polished. Ventral fins were not fitted. In the documentation given to the FAI, the engines of the P-42 were described as being TR-32U afterburning turbofans, rated at 29,955 lb st (133.25 kN) with afterburning. The Su-27's standard brakes could not hold the P-42 at anything approaching full power and, instead, the aircraft was anchored to a heavy AFV by twin cables and an electric lock. The standard brakes may even have been removed to save weight.

Among the 27 world records (for time-to-climb and level

*The T-10-1 was flown with dummy R-60 (AA-8 'Aphid') missiles underwing, and with dummy R-27 (AA-10 'Alamo') missiles between the engine nacelles. The value of the main gear doors as airbrakes is also clear.*

***The first prototype Su-27UB was broadly equivalent to early production series single-seaters. It made its maiden flight on 7 March 1985, but remained unknown in the West until shortly before the 1989 Paris Air Salon, when the first photographs were released.***

speed) set by the P-42 between 1986 and 1988 were five absolute time-to-height records previously held by America's F-15. On 27 October 1986 Victor Pugachev reached 9,625 ft (3000 m) in 25.373 seconds, and attained 19,250 ft (6000 m) in 37.050 seconds on 15 November. A succession of record-breaking flights followed, culminating in a staggering 49,210-ft (15000-m) climb in 70.33 seconds, almost seven seconds faster than the F-15 Streak Eagle. The P-42 remains in open storage at the OKB's facility at the LII's Zhukhovskii airfield, where it could be returned to flight status if another record attempt becomes necessary – however unlikely that may be.

## Production powerplant

Production Su-27s and later T-10 aircraft were powered by the production-standard Lyul'ka (MMZ/Saturn) AL-31F, which necessitated a redesigned intake to cope with the greater flow of air, although the differences are not visibly apparent. T-10S-1 also introduced the meshed intake foreign object damage (FOD) protection screens which pop up from the intake floor on start-up and retract after take-off. It may also have introduced the louvered auxiliary intakes below the inlet ducts which provide air during high-Alpha flight. FOD screens were primarily designed to minimise the chance of foreign object ingestion when taking off from or landing at rough, semi-prepared strips – a routine procedure for Soviet combat squadrons.

The AL-31F has proved to be a major success story, being as reliable, robust and maintainable as it is powerful. It has a remarkable time between overhauls (TBO), by Soviet standards, of 1,000 hours and a life of 3,000 hours, although every 100 hours the engine is subjected to checks by monitoring equipment. The only serious problem that remained with the aircraft was its excessive fuel consumption.

Many test aircraft were known by a T-10 series numerical designator, but it is unknown whether this reflected their sequential position in the overall tally of T-10s produced, or whether the sequence was restarted with the first T-10S. For example, it is unclear whether the aircraft designated T-10-17 was the 17th Su-27 completed, or whether it was the 17th T-10S. This practice carried through until the T-10-25, which was utilised as a naval trials development aircraft. Other early 'Flankers', such as the T-10-20R, were intended for further record attempts.

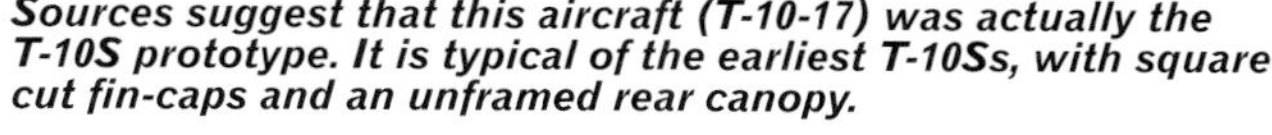

***Sources suggest that this aircraft (T-10-17) was actually the T-10S prototype. It is typical of the earliest T-10Ss, with square-cut fin-caps and an unframed rear canopy.***

## Two-seat trainer

As small numbers of Su-27s began entering service, operating from bases in the Kola Peninsula, the need for a two-seat continuation trainer soon became apparent. In fact, Sukhoi had intended to develop a two-seater early in the 'Flanker' programme, but delays encountered in the development of the single-seater had resulted in the temporary halt of a trainer variant. After all the difficulties of the single-seater, Sukhoi decided that the two-seat trainer variant would differ from it as little as possible, and would retain the overall dimensions of its predecessor, with the second pilot seated in tandem in a highly-stepped cockpit. The two-seat trainer version of the Su-27 is fully combat-capable and, unlike Mikoyan's MiG-29UB, is able to retain the standard radar.

Designated Su-27UB (T-10U), the prototype first flew in the hands of Nikolai Sadovnikov in 1985. Although built to broadly the same standard as early single-seaters, production two-seaters lacked cropped fin-caps and the distinctive chaff/flare dispenser box fairings flanking the tail sting. The primary role of the Su-27UB has always been to provide conversion and continuation training (including training in instrument flying), along with carrying out a number of civil aeromedical test programmes.

Further development of the tandem-seat Su-27UB airframe has resulted in the Su-27PU, an interceptor capable of operating autonomously for up to 10 hours on combat-air-patrol (CAP) duties. Other variants include the Su-27P, which is equipped with an enormous internal fuel tank, and the stripped Su-27PU which currently serves with the 'Test Pilots' school. The Su-30M has a limited ground attack capability, and there is also the highly capable Su-30MK strike variant.

Sukhoi continues to develop its 'Flanker' family despite Russia's current economic crisis. Upgraded early models remain in service, alongside later variants, and remain potent adversaries.

***This aircraft (possibly T-10-10) was probably the first Su-27 to incorporate all of the features associated with early production 'Flankers'. A complete load of 'Apex' and 'Alamo' missiles is carried.***

# Su-27 'Flanker-B'

*The impressive Sukhoi Su-27 'Flanker-B' displayed to the public at air shows is a far cry from the original Sukhoi T10 'Flanker-A'. This 'Flanker-B' displays to advantage the revised wing shape, reprofiled rear fuselage with ventral fins, new radome shape, repositioned nosegear and single dorsal airbrake.*

**The Su-27 'Flanker' represents one of the jewels in the crown of the Russian aerospace industry. Available for export on the world market, the capable and agile 'Flanker-B' emerged after a major re-design of the less than successful prototype T10 'Flanker-A'.**

After the dramatic failure of the original T10 'Flanker-A' to live up to expectations, two partially complete airframes were finished to a revised design, under the new designation T10S ('S' for 'series').

## Major changes

The wings had a reduced leading-edge sweep, lost their fences, had increased area (667 sq ft/62 m$^2$ from 639 sq ft/59 m$^2$) and were given square-cut tips mounting missile launch rails, the latter also acting as anti-flutter weights. The trailing-edge flaps and separate outboard ailerons were replaced by single-section flaperons extending out from the root to about 60 per cent span.

The tailfins were increased in size and moved outboard to slender booms beside the engine nacelles and were returned to the vertical, unlike those of most of the T10s. Ventral strakes were fitted below the same tailbooms to enhance directional stability and increase spin resistance.

The tailplanes were also increased in size (span, chord and area) and gained distinctive cropped tips. The flat, shallow, spade-like beaver tail between the engine nozzles was replaced by a lengthened cylindrical tail sting, tipped by a conical fairing, which reduced drag, provided a housing for enlarged twin braking parachutes and provided space for chaff/flare dispensers. The fuselage cross-sections were reduced and the wing fillets were of reduced radius.

The nose was lengthened and refined in shape, with a more bulbous radome and with considerably more droop, while the nosewheel was moved aft. The oleos of the main undercarriage units were altered to slope forward, allowing them to retract better into the wing/fuselage centre-section. The undercarriage doors were also redesigned, with a large dorsal airbrake replacing the forward doors, which had functioned as speed brakes. Even the cockpit canopy was redesigned, being given a longer, flatter, more streamlined profile. The definitive AL-31F engines (with top-mounted accessories gearboxes) were housed in redesigned nacelles. Gridded intake screens were added in the main intakes, to reduce the danger of FOD ingestion during take-off and landing. The aircraft initially lacked the extended tail-cone of the production Su-27.

## Development flights

The first T10S (the former T10-7) made its maiden flight on 20 April 1981, with Vladimir Ilyushin at the controls, but was lost on 3 September 1981, due to fuel system problems, Ilyushin ejecting safely.

The second T10S was lost on 23 December 1981 due to uncommanded pitch-ups after the separation of the new automatic flaps (later re-designed), killing pilot Alexander Komarov.

These accidents aside, the Su-27 had clearly been transformed, and its pilots raved about its handling and performance characteristics. A decision to produce the type was taken in 1982, and the first production aircraft was rolled out in November of that year.

## Development problems

Despite the re-design, the Su-27's problems were far from over. Production-standard radar deliveries were slow, and the aircraft also suffered from fuel system and engine problems. Stability problems necessitated severe flight restrictions until the flight control system could be corrected. Apart from a handful of aircraft used for ongoing development work, most were rolled off the line straight into storage outside the factory. Production was actually halted during mid-1986, while Su-27s flying at Zhukhovskii and Akhtubinsk were used to solve the various problems.

*Four Su-27 'Flanker-Bs' formate on a Beriev A-50 'Mainstay' AEW&C aircraft in a pose symbolic of the air defence role. In reality, the A-50 is more used to controlling MiG-31 'Foxhound' interceptors than 'Flankers'.*

# Su-27 'Flanker-B'

**This Sukhoi Su-27 'Flanker-B' is unusual in that it displays a large shark design along the port engine bay, which may have been applied for the aircraft's participation in the massive 1995 VE-Day flypast over Moscow. It was operated by the 760th ISIAP of the Air Forces Training Centre based at Lipetsk, which was primarily tasked with the training of weapons instructors and the development of tactics.**

**Colour scheme**
The majority of Russian air force (VVS) Sukhoi Su-27s wear the two-tone blue air superiority scheme as displayed on this aircraft. Many different shades of blue have been noted over the years.

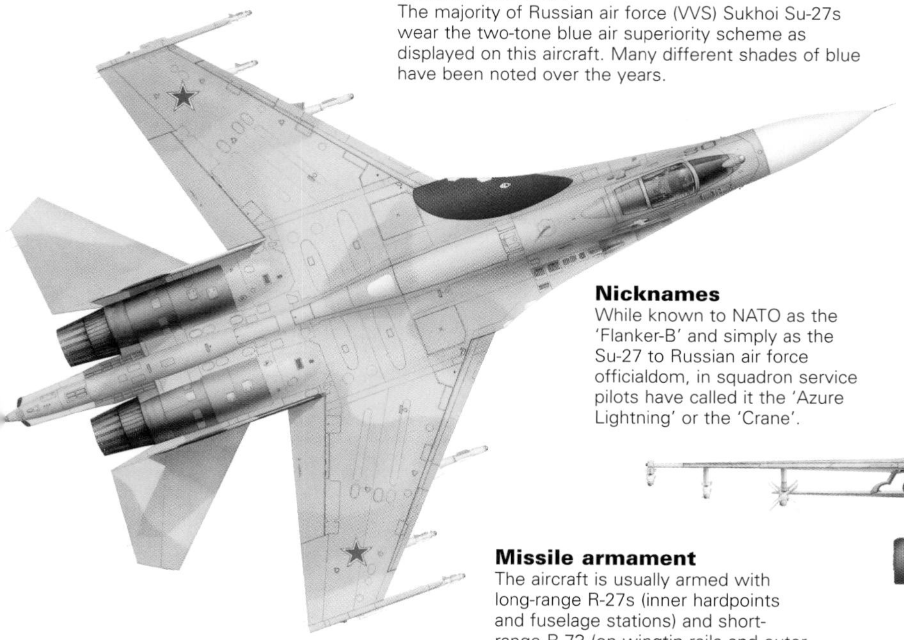

**Fin profile**
Pre-series 'Flanker-Bs' sported a square-cut, flat top to the fins, with a large anti-flutter mass protruding forward. Early production series 'Flanker-Bs' retained the anti-flutter mass, but displayed 'pointed' fins. This aircraft is a late-series 'Flanker-B', which had 'pointed' fins with no anti-flutter masses.

**Nicknames**
While known to NATO as the 'Flanker-B' and simply as the Su-27 to Russian air force officialdom, in squadron service pilots have called it the 'Azure Lightning' or the 'Crane'.

**Missile armament**
The aircraft is usually armed with long-range R-27s (inner hardpoints and fuselage stations) and short-range R-73 (on wingtip rails and outer wing hardpoints) air-to-air missiles.

**Weapons stations**
Most 'Flanker-Bs' are fitted with three hardpoints under each wing, one under each engine nacelle and two in tandem on the centreline. Some have provision for an extra hardpoint under each wing.

**Radar and radome**
This 'Flanker-B' is equipped with the NIIP N-001 radar (NATO designation 'Slot Back 2'). Early aircraft had a green painted radome and dielectric panels – on later-series aircraft these features are white. The radar is backed up by an OEPS-27 electro-optical complex IRST (infra-red search and track), located in front of the cockpit.

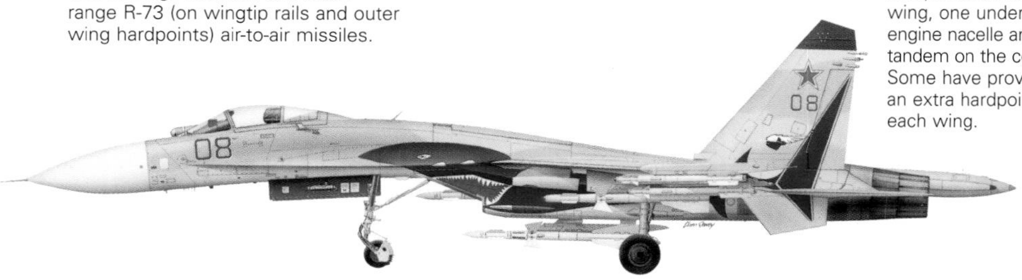

Fortunately, the T10S flight test programme did at least progress smoothly in one area – that of engine development – with many of the AL-31F's teething problems having already been solved.

## 'Flanker-B'

The earliest T10Ss differed in small details from the definitive production Su-27. The early aircraft had slightly different fin-caps, without the top of the trailing edge being cropped. The early pre-series aircraft were also fitted with long nose probes. Western intelligence agencies allocated the aircraft the reporting name 'Flanker-B' to differentiate the new configuration from the original T10.

## Early-series 'Flanker-Bs'

Small numbers of Su-27s began entering service in late 1986, flying from bases in the Kola Peninsula, probably with an evaluation/development unit. They had distinctive anti-flutter weights on the leading edges of the tailfins, which have been removed in recent years.

## Later-series 'Flanker-Bs'

The first major improvement to the Su-27 came with the addition of box-like fairings to each side of the cylindrical tail sting. They accommodated 28 upward-firing triple-shot APP-50 (L-029) chaff/flare dispensers, housing 84 chaff/flare cartridges, on the upper surface. A total of 32 dispensers (96 cartridges) augmented the four set into the top of the tail sting. The fairings extended back as far as the hinged brake chute compartment cover and were each tipped by a dielectric antenna fairing.

Dark-green nose radomes were replaced by white radomes on the production line, and later aircraft had all dielectric panels and fairings in white. The radome was actually also increased in diameter and length.

In the very latest production series, maximum take-off weight was increased by 10,360 lb (4700 kg) to 72,750 lb (33000 kg). Some late-production 'Flankers' have an extra pair of underwing pylons, bringing the total to 12.

Apart from the increased number of chaff/flare dispensers and new rear-hemisphere RHAWS antennas, the late-series Su-27 is believed to have the same avionics and equipment fit as its predecessor.

## Export 'Flanker-Bs'

Under the designation Sukhoi Su-27SK (Series Kommercial), the 'Flanker-B' has been exported to China, Ethiopia, Vietnam and, reportedly, to Syria. It seems likely that the aircraft has a slightly different version of the radar (probably lacking current Russian IFF) and reduced anti-ECM capability. The type also lacks the full-standard Russian air force EW capabilities.

***The 'Flanker-B' is the Russian air force's (VVS) most capable long-range fighter. The Sukhoi OKB also built into the design the ability to deliver air-to-ground munitions, although this capability has not been pursued widely by the VVS.***

***This aircraft displays the wingtip- mounted Sorbtsiya ECM pods that can replace the missile launch rails on late-production series 'Flanker-Bs'. It is adorned with the 'Lipetsk Aces' colour scheme featuring the Russian national colours.***

# Su-27UB 'Flanker-C'

*An Su-27UB leads in three of the* **Russian Knights** *during the team's first overseas visit to RAF Scampton, home of the* **Red Arrows**. *The two-seat example takes an active part in the team's displays and is also used for refresher training and publicity flights.*

**Designed shortly after its single seat-relative, the Su-27UB is a fully combat-capable trainer, in service with most 'Flanker' operators. More recently, export and naval variants have also been produced.**

Plans for a two-seat conversion and continuation trainer version of the Su-27 were drawn up at an early stage of the programme, but were put on hold while problems with the single-seater were addressed. It is understood that a two-seat basic T10 was due to be the next aircraft to be produced in the OKB experimental workshops when the original T10 design was abandoned.

When the single-seat fighter had to be redesigned, it was decided that every effort should be put into getting the operational aircraft right, and work on the Su-27UB went ahead only very slowly. After all of the difficulties and problems with the single-seater, it was decided that the two-seat trainer version would differ from it as little as possible, and would retain the same overall dimensions and centre of gravity, as far as was possible. Sukhoi's own figures would suggest that the provision of the second cockpit has been achieved with minimal reduction in internal fuel capacity. Aerodynamic, structural, equipment and systems changes were also kept to an absolute minimum. Wind-tunnel testing confirmed that the Su-27UB had the same characteristics as the single-seat fighter, and this was later to be confirmed in flight-testing.

The two-seat trainer version of the Su-27 is thus fully combat-capable, unlike the two-seat MiG-29UB. The aircraft retains its 'Slot Back' radar and differs from the single-seater only in having a second cockpit behind the first. The cockpits are highly stepped, and are covered by a single upward-hinging canopy, which probably produces slightly more drag than the cockpit canopy of the single-seater. The backseater benefits by enjoying the best view forward over the nose of all Russian tandem-seat trainer versions of front-line fighters. The increased keel area forward, produced by the new cockpit canopy, is compensated for by a slight increase in tailfin area. This was achieved by adding a full-chord section below the rudder, retaining the same planform from the bottom of the rudder up to the fintip. The Su-27UB is also slightly heavier than the single-seater (2,470 lb/1120 kg heavier empty, 2,515 lb/1140 kg heavier at normal take-off weight, and with a 4,749-lb/2150-kg increase in MTOW). This resulted in the least possible impact on performance, with a 44-mph (70-km/h) reduction in low-level speed, a 96-mph (155-km/h) reduction at altitude, a 100-ft (30-m) increase in landing distance and a 328-ft (100-m) increase in take-off run. Fuel load is slightly reduced, with a marginal impact on range and endurance figures, but this is not operationally significant. Some sources suggest that fuel load was actually increased, by refining the shape of the spine, but this seems unlikely.

The dorsal airbrake has been lengthened by one fuselage frame, changing its shape and area. It is believed that its maximum extension angle is rather smaller than that of the single-seater's airbrake.

The first Su-27UB prototype flew on 7 March 1985, piloted by Nikolai Sadovnikov. The Su-27UB prototype and the first few production two-seaters were built to broadly the same standard as early series production single-seaters, but without production-style cropped fin-caps and without the distinctive chaff/flare dispenser box fairings flanking the

*With the first pictures only emerging in 1989, the Su-27UB made its public debut at the Paris Air Salon at Le Bourget later that year, less than one year after the MiG-29's ground-breaking appearance at Farnborough. Two aircraft attended the show, though it was the single-seater that carried out the most dazzling displays, notably the Pugachev Cobra manoeuvre.*

***Above:** The means by which the first Su-27KUB was produced, namely fitting a newly-built forward fuselage to an existing Su-27K pre-production airframe, are readily apparent in this view of the aircraft taxiing at Zhukhovskii. Naval 'Flankers' have twin-wheel nose gear and a beefed-up main undercarriage.*

***Below:** The Ukraine's inherited 'Flanker' fleet included as many as 10 trainer examples and these serve alongside their single-seat cousins with the 62nd BAP and 831st IAP at Myrhorod.*

tail sting. The most familiar photos of the aircraft show it with cropped fin-caps and white dielectric panels, but these features were added after the first flight, together with the code 01. Most production two-seaters, however, have been delivered in the later configuration, with the increased number of chaff/flare dispensers. Maximum take-off weight was increased by 6,724 lb (3050 kg) to 73,854 lb (33500 kg) in the last production series. Production of the Su-27UB has been undertaken by the Joint Stock Company Irkutsk Aircraft Manufacturing Association since 1986, and it is not known how many Su-27UBs were produced in Moscow and at Komsomolsk before 1986. The first picture of the Su-27UB was not published until early 1989, shortly before the variant made its debut at the 1989 Paris Air Salon at Le Bourget.

The primary role of the Su-27UB has always been one of providing conversion and continuation training (including training in instrument flying, for which a track-mounted blind-flying curtain is provided).

*Russian 'Flanker' regiments typically have three or four two-seaters on charge. The rear cockpit (according to Sukhoi) gives a better view than that of an F-15B/D Eagle and, unusually for Russian two-seaters, contains no periscope for the instructor.*

Su-27UBs have also been used for a number of other roles, offering a unique high-Alpha, high-*g*, long-range and very high-speed capability in a multi-seat aircraft. One of the best-known test Su-27UBs is used for aeromedical experiments and for the training of aviation medicine specialists at Lipetsk, alongside Su-27s used by the Russian aviation medicine establishment. Other Su-27UBs have been used as chase aircraft and for test-pilot training. Outside Russia, most nations that operated the 'Flanker' as part of the Soviet Union, such as Ukraine and Belarus, continue to operate small numbers of the trainers left after the Russian withdrawal.

## Foreign trainers

The Su-27UBK designation is applied to two-seat Su-27UBs built for export customers. The aircraft is broadly equivalent to a Russian late-production Su-27UB, with extended chaff/flare dispenser fairings on each side of the tail sting. The Su-27UBK is a very rare beast, since only two (one of them coded '04') were delivered with China's first batch of 'Flankers' and, as far as is known, the Vietnamese order did not include any two-seaters. Subsequent Chinese batches may include further pairs of Su-27UBKs, but the total number of aircraft involved will doubtless be small.

## Two-seat naval 'Flanker'

The most recent addition to the two-seat family is the navalised Su-27KUB. Previously, Su-33 pilots had trained on the Su-25UTG, but this was found to be inadequate. As a result, the Su-27KUB was designed; looking like a cross between the Su-33 and the Su-34, the new aircraft has side-by-side seating and a full combat suite retaining the 12 hardpoints of its single-seat cousins. As with many Russian projects, financial constraints will determine whether or not this much-desired aircraft will fully enter Naval Aviation service.

## Su-27LL-PS

Although the advantages of thrust-vectoring engine nozzles (especially in improving take-off and landing characteristics) were made clear by the F-15 S/MTD, Sukhoi was slow to begin productive work on vectoring nozzles for the Su-27M. A single Su-27UB was modified to take a two-dimensional (pitch: up/down) nozzle, although early reports suggested that this would be used for trials in support of the Gulfstream/Sukhoi SSBJ (Supersonic Business Jet), and particularly for noise footprint measurements. It is now thought that this explanation was largely disinformation, and that the testbed was actually used for trials in support of the Su-27M project. The Su-27UB testbed, reportedly designated as the T10U-16, or as the Su-27LL-PS, was fitted with a lengthened fairing aft of the port engine. This incorporated an articulated end-piece which allowed different flat-shaped nozzle positions to be simulated, although it is unclear whether it could be actuated in flight, at least initially. The aircraft (based at Zhukhovskii with the LII Gromov Flight Research Centre fleet) began trials in 1989 (a year after the S/MTD, although the US aircraft had two, fully-vectoring nozzles which were so advanced that they were almost good enough to be adopted there and then by a production aircraft). Oleg Tsoi vectored the engine in flight for the first time on 31 March 1989, after the first flight with the new engine nozzle on 21 March. The Su-27LL-PS soon confirmed the advantages of thrust-vectoring previously demonstrated by the US aircraft. Steps were made to incorporate more advanced nozzles in the Su-27M, while the OKB also hoped that funding would be made available for similar nozzles to be fitted to the Su-27K. The thrust-vectoring Su-27 flew much later than has previously been supposed. Sukhoi's chief designer, Mikhail Simonov, had claimed a first flight in 1988, and some Western authors had assumed the participation of a vectoring aircraft in the ski-jump trials at Saki in the mid-1980s after they were shown a cleverly edited film at the 1991 Paris Air Salon. Research data gathered from the Su-27LL-PS project prompted development of the super-manoeuvrable Su-37 and the Su-30MKK.

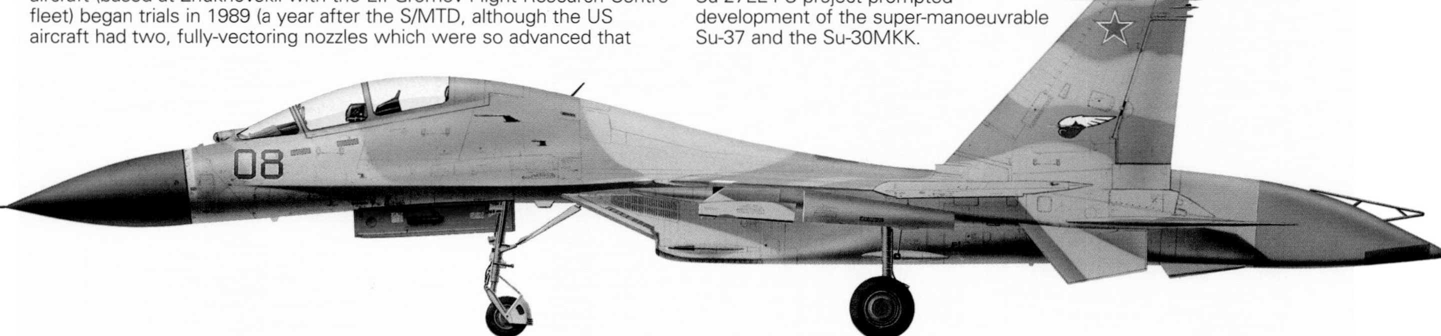

# Su-27K Briefing

*Service introduction of the Su-27K made it eligible for a separate NATO reporting name. The aircraft is understood to be known by the ASCC reporting name 'Flanker-D'. The reporting name is unlikely to be used, however, since the aircraft's correct designation (and the OKB's Su-33 designation) are widely known and used.*

**The ability of the Russian navy to project air power has been given a massive boost with the deployment of its sole carrier, the *Admiral Kuznetsov*, and its air wing of potent Su-27K interceptors.**

Development of a navalised, shipborne version of the Su-27 was launched in the early-1980s at the same time as the Soviet carrier programme. The aircraft was seen as a single-role fleet air defence aircraft, which would form one element in a mixed air wing alongside a new AWACS platform and the MiG-29K multi-role strike fighter. As such, the Su-27K was developed from the basic air force Su-27, and not from the enhanced multi-role Su-27M then also under development.

Several Su-27s tested different aspects of the intended Su-27K production configuration, including canards for approach handling tests and an arrester hook. Three T10s (-3, -24 and -25) and an early Su-27UB were used for the crucial early take-off trials from a dummy carrier deck. The first 'deck' take-off was made from the dummy deck at Saki on 28 August 1982, by Nikolai Sadovnikov flying the T10-3. The dummy deck was subsequently rebuilt to incorporate a ski-ramp identical to that fitted to the first Soviet carrier, *Tbilisi*, which was intended to reduce the take-off run.

The three T10s were followed by a batch of T10K (Su-27K) prototypes, each of which differed slightly from the others. The first Su-27K prototype (T10K-1, coded '37') followed the T10-24 and made its maiden flight on 17 August 1987. Between five and eight subsequent prototypes were built to a standard which approximated more closely to the intended production configuration. All featured twin nosewheels, wing and tailplane folding, and double-slotted trailing-edge flaps.

The Su-27K prototypes were also all fitted with abbreviated tail stings and square-section arrester hooks; none had brake chutes.

*The Su-27K pilots of the Severomorsk wing have the distinction of being at the cutting edge of naval aviation. All helmets have the fittings for helmet-mounted sights, allowing high off-boresight engagements with the Vympel R-73 missile. The average age of the aircrew here shows that the navy required very experienced pilots to form its first naval 'Flanker' wing.*

Later prototypes also had an extra pair of inboard underwing weapons pylons, raising the total number to 12, including the wingtip stations.

## Carrier trials

Carrier landing trials began on 1 November 1989, when Victor Pugachev landed the second Su-27K aboard the carrier *Tbilisi*, becoming the first Russian pilot to land a conventional aircraft aboard the carrier. The second prototype (T10-39) was the first full-standard Su-27K, fitted with all 'naval' features. Takhtar Aubakirov (in the MiG-29K) made the first ski-jump take-off from the *Tbilisi* and was followed by Pugachev in the Su-27K.

Russian naval pilots began carrier operations on 26 September 1991. Service trials were highly successful and led to State Acceptance Trials, which were successfully passed in 1994.

Had the Soviet Union's ambitious plan to build four aircraft-carriers reached fruition, perhaps as many as 72 production Su-27Ks would have been required simply for their air wings. However, the end of the Cold War led to a massive down-scaling of the USSR's carrier programme. With the *Admiral Kuznetsov* (formerly *Tbilisi*, and before that *Brezhnev*) the only carrier left for service with the Russian navy, both the AEW aircraft and MiG-29K programmes were abandoned.

If only one fixed-wing type was to be procured for the new carrier, logic would have dictated that it should be the multi-role MiG-29K. However, the political influence of Sukhoi's chief designer, Mikhail Simonov, was such that the Sukhoi aircraft was selected for production and service, and the Russian navy was forced to accept the aircraft's (and thus the carrier's) more limited role.

The Su-27K does enjoy some significant advantages over the MiG-29K, primarily exceptional range performance. Before entering service, the production Su-27K was redesignated Su-33 by the OKB, but the aircraft remains a navalised version of the basic IA-PVO interceptor, with

*An Su-27K runs up to full power on the* **Admiral Kuznetsov**. *Early in the Russian carrier programme, it was decided that time constraints precluded the development of a steam catapult, and that they would be fitted with ski ramps instead. The Su-27K therefore makes unassisted take-offs, using a combination of restrainers and take-off ramps.*

the same basic 'Slot Back' radar and with only a very limited ground-attack capability. It is uncertain whether the AV-MF uses the Su-33 designation.

### First operational cruise

The *Kuznetsov*'s first truly operational deployment took place in early 1996, when it spent two months in the Mediterranean. The ship's complement included the Su-27K-equipped 1st Squadron of the Severomorsk Regiment. Although a production batch of 18 Su-27Ks has reportedly been built, the *Kuznetsov*'s complement included the last Su-27K prototype in addition to at least 10 production Su-27Ks.

Despite the apparent abandonment of the MiG-29K, sources suggest that production of this aircraft is still under consideration. If it does enter service, the Russian navy will have obtained its originally favoured aircraft mix, and the carrier will be a more versatile weapon.

A more advanced carrierborne Su-27 (reportedly to have been designated Su-27KM, or T10KM) based on the Su-27M has been proposed, but has not materialised in the light of the massive drawdown in Russia's armed forces following the end of the Cold War. However, it remains possible that the existing Su-27Ks could be usefully upgraded to improve their capabilities. Incorporating the modifications of the Su-27SM mid-life upgrade would add a Zhuk radar and would give compatibility with the R-77 (RVV-AE 'AMRAAMski') missile and a wide range of advanced air-to-surface precision-guided weapons, and uprated AL-31FM or AL-35 turbofan engines.

It can be seen that a relatively high level of air-to-ground capability could be incorporated into existing Su-27Ks by retrofit, perhaps as part of a mid-life upgrade, making these aircraft significantly more useful and reducing the attractiveness of a MiG-29K purchase.

### Su-27K armament options

Service Su-27Ks have been seen carrying the usual IA-PVO load-out of R-27 (AA-10 'Alamo') and R-73 (AA-11 'Archer') AAMs, although the extra pair of underwing hardpoints actually allows the carriage of two additional R-27s, bringing the beyond-visual-range (BVR) armament to eight missiles. The R-27 is available in a number of versions, and those carried by the Su-27K include the R-27EM which has improved capability against sea-skimming targets, even cruise missiles flying only 10 ft (3 m) above the water. The aircraft will be among the first to receive the R-27AE which will introduce active radar terminal homing.

Service Su-27Ks have also been seen carrying an unusual centreline pod, provisionally identified as a reconnaissance pod, or an equipment pod associated with some kind of carrier landing system. Alternative stores may include a centreline fuel tank, or a UPAZ buddy inflight-refuelling store. A range of unguided bombs and rockets (podded and large-calibre single rounds) and the Kh-31 (AS-17 'Krypton') ASM can be carried underwing. None of these alternative stores has been photographed under production Su-27Ks, which seem to fulfil a pure fleet air defence role. One weapon frequently ascribed to the Su-27K is the gigantic Kh-41, an air-launched version of the 3M80 'Moskit' anti-ship missile, sometimes known under the codename ASM-MSS.

## Su-27K (Su-33)

**'Red 64' is assigned to the 1st Squadron of the Severomorsk Regiment, AV-MF, and was one of those aircraft deployed aboard the *Admiral Kuznetsov* during its first operational cruise in 1996.**

**Unit markings**
The unit badge of the 1st Squadron, Severomorsk Regiment is worn on the fins and consists of a diving sea eagle. Some aircraft also carry the post-Soviet St Andrew's flag insignia of the Russian navy.

**Flight control system**
Despite the presence of canard foreplanes, the Su-27K retains the analog fly-by-wire flight control system of the baseline Su-27, and does not have the Su-27M's digital unit.

**Radar limitations**
The Su-27K's 'Slot Back' radar has plenty of power and range, but has inadequate processing power for autonomous operations, with poor mass raid discrimination, threat prioritisation and multi-target tracking. This makes the aircraft dependent on GCI or AWACS control. Fortunately, the pilot's situational awareness is increased by the use of datalinking, and by using suitable tactics.

**Shortened tail sting**
The Su-27K's tail fairing was shortened to prevent it from striking the deck during a high-Alpha touchdown, which in turn forced the designers to reduce the number of chaff/flare dispensers and relocate them further forward.

**Wing modifications**
The Su-27K features new double-slotted flaps which span almost the entire length of the trailing edge. The inboard flap sections operate symmetrically as flaps, while the outboard sections operate differentially as drooping ailerons at low speeds.

**Analog cockpit**
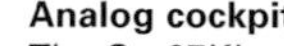
The Su-27K's cockpit is very similar to that of the baseline Su-27, with a handful of new controls for actuating the tailhook and wing folding. Conversion to the carrierborne variant is thus extremely straightforward, and there is no dedicated two-seat version.

# Su-30 family

*While not attaining any domestic sales, the Su-30 family of aircraft – including the K, MK, MKI (first prototype illustrated) and MKK – looks set to achieve considerable export success. India and China, Russia's two biggest export customers, are both investing in variants.*

**Born out of the unsuccessful long-range Su-27PU, the Su-30, in both single- and two-seat forms, has become the dominant 'Flanker' on the export market and also looks set to influence future Su-27 design.**

In the 1980s, the PVO expressed a desire to have a dedicated combat version of the Su-27UB that would be used as a long-range interceptor as well as a command post to vector single-seat 'Flankers'. The need for such an aircraft arose from the geographical nature of the then Soviet Union, which was vast and barren, with little in the way of airfield networks. It was also envisaged that the long-range 'Flankers' could provide cover for the Soviet navy, the result being the Su-27PU. However, this aircraft was ultimately not adopted by the PVO so Sukhoi redesignated it as the Su-30, which would be able to carry basic air-to-ground weapons. It was soon realised that the basic Su-30 would not be capable or versatile enough and so the multi-role, long-range fighter/fighter-bomber Su-30M was built. Export aircraft would thus go under the designation Su-30MK.

With its modernised radar, the Su-30 enjoyed a degree of latent ground attack capability and the type was initially offered as a replacement for the MiG-25BM in the SEAD (Wild Weasel) role. A TV display was added, bringing compatibility with the KAB-500KR guided bomb, and with Kh-29T missiles, together with provision for the ARK-9 datalink pod on the rear centreline pylon. This latter pod allowed the aircraft to carry the Kh-59M (AS-18 'Kazoo') TV-guided missile. The laser-guided Kh-29L (AS-14 'Kedge') used the laser channel of the upgraded OLS-27 for target designation.

As well as the normal range of air-to-air weapons associated with the basic Su-27, the Su-30MK can also carry up to eight RVV-AEs, with two on the centreline, two under the nacelles, and two under each wing. In the ground attack role, weapons options are much the same as for the Su-34, although sometimes fewer examples of each weapon type are carried by the Su-30. The Su-30MK, for instance, carries only two Kh-59M 'Kingbolts' or four Kh-25Ms (on twin carriers on the central underwing pylons). Four rocket pods can be carried on the same twin carriers. The two variants each carry six Kh-29T ASMs or KAB-500 laser-guided bombs.

One weapon offered only with the Su-30MK is the SPPU gun pod, two of which can be carried on the central underwing hardpoints, facing forward or aft.

The Su-30M made its maiden flight on 14 April 1992 in the hands of G. Bulanov and V. Maximenov and was 'Blue 56', which was demonstrated at Dubai in 1993, albeit with very little fanfare. This aircraft was fitted with an inflight-refuelling probe and offset IRST, and was displayed carrying a range of weaponry.

'Blue 321' was painted in camouflage and laden with air-to-ground weapons for static displays at a variety of international air shows and exhibitions. The multi-role Su-30M was offered to the Russian air forces as a low-cost alternative to the Su-27IB to replace the Su-24, but was never seriously considered. The aircraft was then described as having a coherent pulse-Doppler radar, a helmet-mounted target designator and the ability to carry up to six PGMs. After the 1993 Dubai air show, Mikhail Simonov claimed that the two-seat Su-30M had not been procured, but that the

***Derived from the T10PU-6, the second Su-30MKI first flew on 23 April 1998. When it finally enters service, India's MKI will be the dominant aircraft in that region, with only the MKKs of China, a nation with some enmity towards the Indians, posing a threat.***

***When Sukhoi first began to hawk the Su-30 around the export market, the aircraft it used were '321' (pictured right), which was little more than a repainted Su-27UB, and '603' (seen left), which could be argued to be the first true Su-30MK due to the fact that it was configured specifically as a demonstrator for potential overseas customers.***

**Left: The rear cockpit of the Su-30M is similar to that of the Su-27UB. It retains full dual controls and appears to have a combined HUD repeater, radar and TV display.**

**The advanced export single-seat Su-30KI wore this unusual black and two-tone grey 'splatter' camouflage for its displays at MAKS'99 and LIMA'99 in Malaysia. These colours were those of Indonesia, which ordered the aircraft, but failed to pay for them.**

Su-27IB would be bought in small numbers to act as pathfinders for a single-seat version of the Su-30M.

## Export aircraft

The Su-30MK designation is reserved for export versions of the Su-30M. The Su-30M prototypes and demonstrators effectively became demonstrators and prototypes for the Su-30MK when the chance of a Russian air forces order finally vanished.

The familiar Su-27UB demonstrator seen at numerous Western air shows was repainted in camouflage (and recoded '321') to serve as an Su-30MK demonstrator. Although it has frequently been laden with the type of sophisticated air-to-ground weaponry which one might expect to see on an Su-30MK, the aircraft's transformation was literally only skin deep. The aircraft has no inflight-refuelling probe, and remains to all intents and purposes a standard Su-27UB. At the 1993 Paris Air Salon, Sukhoi nevertheless maintained that the aircraft was the 'prototype Su-30MK', but was careful not to allow access to the rear cockpit, which might have given the game away.

## Su-30MKI

In late 1996 it was announced that India had signed a $1.5 billion contract for the supply of 40 Su-30MK fighter-bombers. The same contract was part of a $3.5 billion arms deal which also covered India's MiG-21 upgrade, weapons and a licence-production agreement for an eventual total of 100 Su-30 aircraft. India's Su-30s are designated Su-30MKI and differ from the standard MK by means of improved agility achieved through the addition of canards and thrust-vectoring AL-37FU engines. One other feature was that several of the systems, such as the HUD and satellite navigation system, would be built by Sextant Avionique of France, although the all-important fire control system is Russian-built.

The first MKI flew on 1 July 1997 and was equipped with AL-31FP thrust vectoring nozzles, giving it superb manoeuvrability. A second prototype flew in the following year. However, India had already received eight Su-30Ks ('commercial' version of the Su-30), though without canards and thrust vectoring, as a stop-gap measure. Later, 10 canard- equipped Su-30MKs were added. Currently, there are 18 Su-30Ks, serving with No. 24 'Hunting Hawks' Squadron at Pune. However, the 'Flankers' in service have been beset with problems and have attracted criticism from India's government auditor. India is set to receive six fully-equipped Su-30MKIs as well as 26 additional partially upgraded Su-30MKs which will be later modified, alongside the Su-30Ks, to Su-30MKI standard, although it looks unlikely that this will happen by the scheduled date.

## Paris 1999 disaster

In an effort to market the Su-30MKI, Sukhoi displayed the aircraft first at Bangalore at the AeroIndia '98 show and then at Le Bourget, near Paris, in June 1999. The Sukhoi aircraft was expected to be the star of this show, with an extravagant display being planned, but on 12 June, on a flight before the show officially started, the aircraft crashed. However, some gain was made out of the calamity, with the K-36DM ejection seats receiving praise as the crew escaped unscathed despite ejecting at less than 328 ft (100 m). The second MKI made a more successful display at the Moscow MAKS'99 air show later that year.

## Su-30KI and Su-30MKK

Early in the Su-27's career, Sukhoi marketed export examples of the 'Flanker-B' as the Su-27SK. During the mid-1990s, it was decided to upgrade this aircraft and the result was the Su-30KI single-seat tactical fighter. The aircraft is fitted with a retractable refuelling probe and a satellite navigation system. Furthermore, the Su-30KI's weapons suite has been enhanced through the introduction of RVV-AE medium-range AAMs and a range of air-to-ground weaponry. It is envisaged that further steps will be taken on the Su-30KI programme, leading to increasingly advanced systems, finances and orders permitting. The Su-30KI has been displayed at several air shows but has yet to secure any orders.

The Su-30MKK is a multi-role twin-seat fighter, also derived from the Su-27SK. Equipped to perform a range of air superiority and strike missions, the aircraft is fitted with 12 hardpoints carrying a total of 17,636 lb (8000 kg) of various stores with which the Su-30MKK can take off, along with a full load of fuel, a capability not possessed by other 'Flankers'. The first MKK flew on 19 May 1999 and, following the completion of tests, the first export orders were placed by China, which has agreed on 88 aircraft, with the first deliveries early in 2001.

**Also appearing at MAKS'99 was the Su-30 ('302'), which on one day was liberally armed with dumb bombs, while on another, flew with R-73s, R-77s and Kh-31s, thus reflecting the aircraft's true multi-role capability. Unpainted, the Su-30 flew alongside the Test Pilots Su-27PDs.**

*Wearing show number 343, Su-32FN '44' takes-off at the 1997 Paris Air Show. The naval strike variant of the Su-27IB, the Su-32FN is described by Sukhoi as a shore-based, long-range all-weather attack aircraft.*

# Su-27IB, Su-32FN and Su-34

## Briefing

**The side-by-side seating Su-27 variants are radical developments of the original 'Flanker' interceptor, and their evolution has been shrouded in confusion and not a little mystery. What is clear is that they promise a deadly combination of long-range 'reach' and powerful attack 'punch'.**

Although Sukhoi's Su-27 has always had a secondary ground-attack capability, Sukhoi chose to develop a dedicated two-seat attack version of the 'Flanker'. This radically-rebuilt aircraft was dubbed the Su-27IB (*Istrebitel Bombardirovschik*/fighter-bomber) and had the Bureau designation T10V-1.

The prototype, which first flew on 13 April 1990, was converted from an Su-27UB trainer, with a new side-by-side armoured cockpit section (including the nose gear) grafted onto the existing fuselage. The Su-27IB has a distinctive long, flattened nose, which led to the nickname 'platypus'. The aircraft is also fitted with small canards on the long chines running back to the leading edge of the wing.

Western perception of the Su-27IB was muddied when TASS released a photograph of the prototype ('Blue 42') apparently landing on the carrier *Tiblisi*. It was announced that this aircraft was the 'Su-27KU', a carrier training version – though it had no arrestor hook! The reasons behind this 'disinformation' are still unclear. Photographs of the Su-27IB, this time carrying a heavy warload, were released after the aircraft was presented to Russian and CIS air force commanders during the Minsk-Maschulische 'display' in 1992. Later that year the same aircraft flew in public, at the Moscow air show.

### Production variants

The designation Su-34 was applied, by Sukhoi, to the production version of the Su-27IB, for the Russian air force. The first pre-production Su-34 ('Blue 43') was rolled out from Sukhoi's Novossibirsk plant in 1993, making its maiden flight on 18 December.

The full-standard Su-34 (Bureau designation T10V-2), is fitted with 12 hardpoints and can carry up to 17,640 lb (8000 kg) of weapons. It is cleared to carry virtually the full range of Russian air-to-surface ordnance. This could include a total of 34 100-kg (220-lb) AB-100 bombs under various pylons, or a triple cluster of 250-kg (550-lb) AB-250s under each hardpoint for a total of 22 bombs, or 12 500-kg (1,100-lb) AB-500 bombs. Alternatively, the Su-34 can carry up to seven KMGU cluster bomb dispensers, a variety of unguided or laser-guided rockets, or a number of precision-guided missiles, such as the KAB-500 or the KAB-1500.

The cockpit of the aircraft uses a mix of conventional instruments and multi-function CRT displays (in the central console, shared by the two crew). Only the pilot has a HUD. Both crew are seated on K-36DM ejection seats. The large forward cabin gives the pilots room in which to move around on long-duration missions. There is also a small food heater and even a chemical toilet.

*This photograph of the Su-27IB prototype, labelled as the 'Su-27KU', caused great confusion for many years, with even Sukhoi denying that the Su-27IB designation existed.*

*The Su-34 and Su-32FN all have a large tail 'sting' which may be capable of housing a targetting and guidance radar for a rear-firing defensive missile system.*

### Long-range strike

Although the Su-34 might be considered to be a replacement for the air force's Su-24s in the tactical strike role, it may also replace Tupolev's Tu-16 and Tu-22M in some roles, such as that of a long-range stand-off missile carrier. The Su-34 has already been proposed as a potential launch platform for the Novator ASM-MS Alfa long-

***This is the first pre-production Su-34 (Sukhoi Bureau designation T10V-2) which is the Russian air force version of the Su-27IB. The air force itself still appears to use the Su-27IB designation.***

range hypersonic cruise missile. The Alfa is primarily an anti-shipping weapon and it seems that Sukhoi is now directing its efforts towards earning a maritime strike role for the Su-34.

### Maritime role

When Sukhoi first presented the Su-34 ('45', the T10V-5 which had first flown on 28 December 1994) at the 1995 Paris Air Show, it did so using the surprise designation Su-32FN. The aircraft was described as an all-weather, 24-hour maritime strike aircraft, equipped with the Sea Snake sea-search and attack radar. An (unlikely) anti-submarine capability was even attributed to the aircraft, when Sukhoi stated that it could carry up to 72 sonobuoys and be fitted with a MAD system in the tail 'sting'. The Su-32FN is certainly capable of carrying all existing Russian anti-ship/air-to-surface missiles. The Su-32FN returned to Paris in 1997 when another aircraft ('44') took part in the flying display for the first time. It is unclear how many Su-27IB/Su-34/Su-32FN aircraft have been built to date, but it is probably less than six.

Sukhoi is understood to have a preliminary purchase agreement for 12 Su-34s with the Russian air force and has also received enquiries from a number of overseas nations. The Su-27IB/ Su-34 was earmarked to replace all of Russia's tactical strike aircraft by 2004, but only eight aircraft were available at the end of 2003. Indeed, Sukhoi will be lucky if it receives even small future orders from the Russian air force (Su-27IB/ Su-34) and navy (Su-32FN).

## Sukhoi Su-27IB

**The Su-27IB (known to the Bureau as the T10V-1) was unveiled in the early 1990s under the guise of a side-by-side two-seat trainer, for carrier operations. It was given the spurious designation 'Su-27KU'. Sukhoi repeatedly denied the Su-27IB designation, as that pointed to the aircraft's true combat role, and made strenuous efforts to conceal all documentation that referred to the 'Su-27IB'. For example, at the 1992 Minsk-Maschulische, a display board describing the aircraft as the Su-27IB was covered before photographers could reach it. Today, Sukhoi is now more open about the aircraft's role and has attempted to split the Su-27IB into dedicated land attack (Su-34) and maritime attack (Su-32FN) variants. The aircraft seen here, 'Blue 42', was the Su-27IB prototype which first flew on 13 April 1990 – the first of a new breed of larger attack 'Flankers'.**

**Canard foreplanes**
Canards were first flown on the T10-24 (Su-27K) during May 1985 and were later included on several 'Flanker' variants, including the Su-27IB. These foreplanes increase take-off performance by generating extra lift forward of the centre of gravity, but are also used as control surfaces in their own right.

**Armament**
This aircraft is seen carrying IR-guided R-73 (AA-11 'Archer') air-to-air missiles (AAMs) outboard and longer-range radar-guided R-77 (AA-12 'Adder') AAMs inboard. Underwing it carries a Kh-29L/AS-14 'Kedge' (port) or Kh-29T (starboard) with two KAB series LGBs inboard and two Kh-31 (AS-14 'Krypton') air-to-surface missiles (ASMs) under each intake.

**Nose shape**
The Su-27IB has an entirely new nose section grafted on at the wing leading edge. The cockpit is provided with side-by-side seats and has been moved forward to give a better view over the broad, flat nose, to which the aircraft owes its 'platypus' nickname. Chines flow back to join the leading edge root extensions on each side. When a radar is fitted (to production-standard aircraft), it is probably only carried in the very forward portion of the nose.

**Tailfins**
The Su-27IB has the same increased height tailfins as those of the Su-27UB but, surprisingly, lacks ventral fins, despite its massive forward 'keel' area.

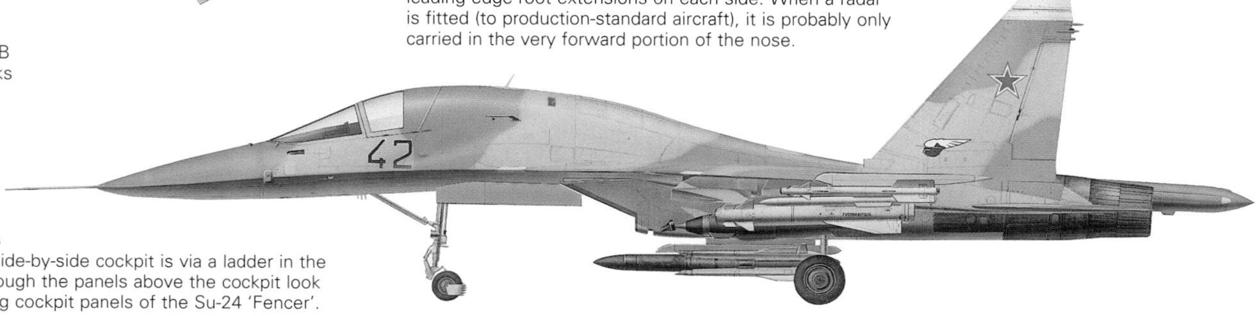

**Cockpit access**
Access to the new side-by-side cockpit is via a ladder in the nosewheel bay, although the panels above the cockpit look similar to the opening cockpit panels of the Su-24 'Fencer'.

# Su-27M (Su-35 and Su-37) variants

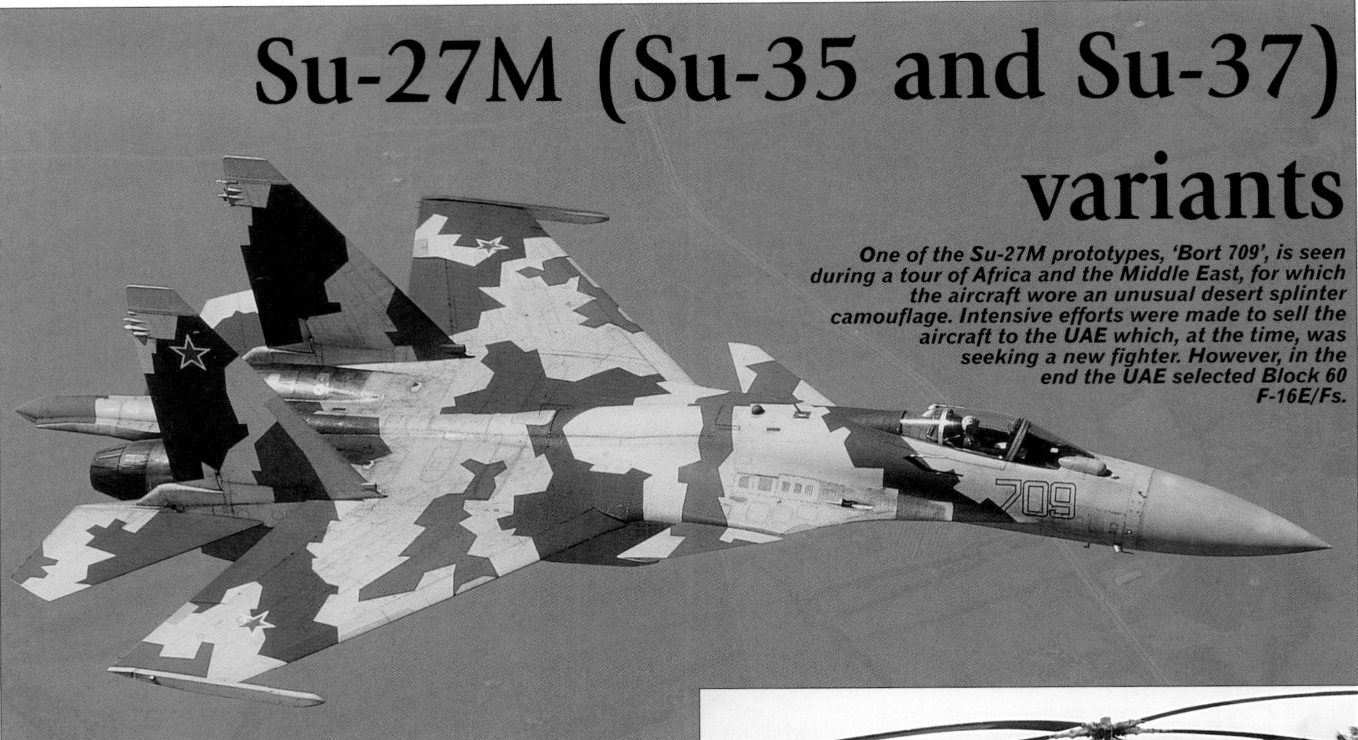


*One of the Su-27M prototypes, 'Bort 709', is seen during a tour of Africa and the Middle East, for which the aircraft wore an unusual desert splinter camouflage. Intensive efforts were made to sell the aircraft to the UAE which, at the time, was seeking a new fighter. However, in the end the UAE selected Block 60 F-16E/Fs.*

**Sukhoi has taken its basic Su-27 variant, already viewed as one of the most capable all-weather air-superiority fighters of the day, and produced a succession of ever more potent models. Although no firm sales have been achieved, the West has been reminded that, despite its current economic crisis, Russia can still produce fighters equal to the latest Western designs.**

*One of the prototype Su-27Ms is now part of the large collection of Russian aircraft on display at the Monino air museum on the outskirts of Moscow. Its camouflage has been faded and bleached by summer sun and winter snow.*

Sukhoi OKB ensured continuing financial support for its advanced Su-27 derivative, initially designated Su-27M, by the simple expedient of re-designating it as Su-35. The project to develop an advanced version of the Su-27 was launched during the early 1980s, before the initial variant had entered service, with the primary aim of producing an aircraft with better dogfighting characteristics. A proof-of-concept aircraft with moving canard foreplanes, the T-10-24, initially flew during 1982, and was the first of a confusing array of converted production aircraft used as flying testbeds, and newly-built Su-27M 'prototypes'.

The Su-27M is equipped with a completely new flight control system, with four longitudinal and three transverse channels. The channel for the canard foreplane also functions as a redundant channel. To compensate for the canards, the tailfin area has also been increased on some Su-27M prototypes, and the new, square-topped tailfin will be incorporated into production Su-35s. In addition to aerodynamic and control system improvements, Sukhoi has been working on vectoring engine nozzles and on various avionics upgrades that have been incorporated into both production Su-35 and its later derivative, the Su-37.

The Su-27M was originally planned to incorporate the NIIP N011 multimode low-altitude terrain-following/avoidance radar, with a search range of up to 54 nm (62 miles; 100 km) against an advancing target, and 30 nm (34 miles; 55 km) against a retreating target. The radar is reported to have the ability to track 15 targets and and engage four to six simultaneously. A Phazotron Zhuk-27 and Zhuk-Ph phased-array radar is currently under development as an alternative to the N011 or to be retrofitted to production Su-35s. Such a radar would have the ability to track 24 air targets, and enable the aircraft to ripple-fire six to eight of its AAMs.

As well as constituting a highly capable air-to-air threat, Sukhoi has been keen to point out the Su-35's ability to carry a wide range of air-to-surface weapons and to operate as a multi-role strike fighter.

## Heavyweight fighter

Primary air-to-surface weapons compatible with the Su-35 are known to include the passive radar-homing Kh-31P (AS-17 'Krypton'), the similarly-guided ASM-M, the TV-guided Kh-29T (AS-14 'Kedge'), and the KAB-500T TV-guided bomb. The Su-35 can carry up to six of any of these weapons, below the nacelles and under the inboard and centre underwing pylons. Alternatively, up to four GBU-1500T TV-guided bombs or similarly-guided AGM-TVS missiles (known to be the Kh-59M or AS-18 'Kazoo') can be carried underwing.

In addition to its wide range of offensive armament, the Su-35 has a comprehensive defensive/offensive EW suite. The ECM system is designed to give individual or mutual (formation) protection against a wide range of threats, many of which have been pre-programmed (512 sample threats are carried on board) including the ground-based Hawk, Patriot, Roland, Crotale and Gepard, and air threats/targets which include the F-14, F-15, F-16,

*'Bort 710' was the penultimate Su-27M prototype, the last aircraft being converted to serve as the Su-37 testbed. Mounted beneath the wingtip are R-73 (AA-11 'Archer') short-range AAMs.*

B-1B and B-52. The passive RHAWS gives 360° coverage horizontally, and 30° above and below the aircraft's flight path.

The advanced 'Flanker' was formally redesignated Su-35 by the Sukhoi OKB during 1993, but the Soviet air force confusingly continues to designate the aircraft as the Su-27M. The first two prototypes were built in the bureau's own Moscow workshops and were followed by a batch of between five and nine aircraft built at Komsomolsk. The first prototype made its maiden flight on 28 June 1988, more than two years before the basic Su-27 'Flanker-B' was in large-scale squadron service.

Like most advanced 'Flanker' variants, the Su-35 is equipped with an IFR probe below the port side of the cockpit. Its installation necessitated the relocation of the electro-optical sensor ball from the centreline to the starboard side of the windscreen, which is one of the distinguishing features of the Su-35 model. The second Su-35 prototype, 'Bort 707', was fitted with a modern glass cockpit. Subsequent Su-35s were built on production tooling at the Komsomolsk na Amur plant, and differed from earlier models in their modified tailfins and revised and strengthened nose undercarriage.

## Future uncertain

These final modifications brought an end to the prototype batch of Su-27Ms. By 1993 flight-testing had been completed, although there was still no agreement on which radar was to be fitted to production aircraft. This has led to the Su-35 programme becoming extremely late, mainly through lack of funds and competition from Mikoyan's resurrected and cheaper MiG-29SMT. Despite the enormous capabilities offered by the Su-27M, the fighter's future remains in doubt. The Russian air force has expressed interest in the rival MiG-29SMT, which is not only as capable, but offers far greater commonality with existing MiG-29s. Sukhoi has nevertheless vowed to continue development of the 'Su-35', hoping for an order from a foreign state. It would be viewed as a sad irony if one of the ultimate 'Flanker' variants were to lose its position to advanced MiG-29 variants.

### Russia's TV star

The latest Su-27 variant, the Su-37 (pictured below), is a derivative of the Su-27M, equipped with thrust-vectoring (TV) engine nozzles. The prototype was actually the last Su-27M prototype (which had previously flown with 'standard' powerplants installed). Photographs of the new variant were first made public in 1995, and showed the aircraft resprayed in a disruptive sand-brown splinter camouflage in an effort to attract potential Middle East customers. The aircraft also displayed the new AL-37FUs (pictured right). The AL-37FU (FU standing for *Forsazh Upravleniye*, or afterburner-controlled) is not just an AL-31 with vectoring nozzles; it also has an entirely new fan and forward section. There are claims that the AL-37FU powerplant is fully interchangeable with the baseline AL-31, meaning that any standard Su-27 could be retrofitted with the new engine, although it is uncertain how well the thrust vectoring could be incorporated into the old-style flight control system software. Should this prove successful, two-seat Su-30MKs for India are scheduled to be the first early-generation Su-27s to be fitted with the new engine. Currently being developed for the Su-37 by Saturn/Lyulka are three-dimensional AL-37 PP engines which have reached an advanced stage of development. If these are incorporated into later aircraft, 'off-axis' manoeuvring would be increased considerably.

The cockpit of the Su-37 incorporates numerous modifications compared with that of front-line 'Flankers', the most significant of which is the sidestick controller in place of the usual centre stick. Other changes are the installation of three CRT display screens on each side of the main panel, and a quadruplex digital flight control system. Mounted in the nose is a large radome housing the Phazotron N011 Zhuk 27 multimode low-altitude terrain-following/terrain-avoidance radar.

The aircraft first flew with its new engine nozzles on 2 April 1996 although these were initially locked in position. The aircraft completed 50 flights before its appearance at the 1996 Farnborough SBAC air show (pictured left). These flights were mainly in the hands of Yevgeni Frolov and Igor Votintsev, both highly-experienced Sukhoi test pilots. Despite the impressive capabilities of this new 'Flanker', the Su-37 has yet to enter front-line service with any nation.

# Transall C.160

Above: The first prototype Transall C.160 (D-9507) is seen here in a 1963 Nord publicity photograph in formation with one of the company's N.262s. D-9507 underwent flight tests at the Centre d'Essais en Vol based at Istres in southern France.

Left: The C.160's relatively high-aspect ratio wing was chosen to fulfil the demands of relatively short-field performance with good cruise speed and fuel economy.

## Franco-German tactical airlifter

**The result of the first large-scale collaboration between aircraft companies from two nations, the C.160 has proved to be a reliable, effective transport aircraft in over 30 years of service.**

International aircraft programmes are commonplace today, so it is easy to forget that they were a rarity in the history of aviation until comparatively recently. Even the specifications issued on behalf of NATO began by fostering winner-takes-all competitions, instead of mutual collaboration. Within the transatlantic alliance, pairs of countries also began looking at joint programmes during the 1960s, and though France and the UK were sufficiently experienced to initiate advanced projects (such as the SEPECAT Jaguar and Aérospatiale/BAC Concorde), the position was different with West Germany.

Still building up experience and confidence after a 10-year hiatus following World War II, the German aviation industry was not yet ready for designing a complex combat aircraft. It was, however, building the Nord Noratlas transport under licence, and a joint-venture successor to that aircraft, involving the French originator, appeared a viable proposition. Bilateral talks held in January 1959 were encouraging, so France and West Germany agreed to form a Transporter Allianz (transport alliance), abbreviated to Transall.

Three firms and three assembly centres were responsible for the first-generation aircraft: Nord (later part of Aérospatiale) at Melun Villaroche; Hamburger Flugzeugbau (later part of MBB) at Finkenwerder; and Weser Flugzeugbau (later part of VFW-Fokker) at Lemwerder. No fabrication was duplicated, so that Nord built the centre and outer wing sections, engine nacelles and landing-gear control units; Weser contributed fuselage centre-sections, landing-gear panniers and doors; and Hamburger built the front and rear fuselage, fin and loading ramp. For a designation, the partners chose C.160 to reflect the widely-recognised 'C' (cargo) prefix and the aircraft's wing area in square metres. The latter number also turned out to be the quantity funded by the two partners: West Germany had a need for 110 and France 50 (excluding prototypes).

Built in France, the first C.160 made its maiden flight from Melun on 25 February 1963, to be followed by two more prototypes, two static test airframes and six pre-production C.160As, shared between the three assembly centres. Unlike the situation in most other international programmes, the firms involved did not build aircraft exclusively for their home air force, with the result that the Armée de l'Air and Luftwaffe operate C.160s from Aérospatiale, MBB and VFW. Almost the sole differences between the individual models are the national insignia and distinguishing designations – C.160D for West Germany (Deutschland) and C.160F for France.

### Turboprop power

Viewed from without, the C.160 is unquestionably a tactical transport of modern design. In common with most of its contemporaries, the design began with the premise that turboprop power is the most efficient over short and medium ranges. Propellers require ground clearance, and freight-loaders like a fuselage to be as close to the ground as possible.

Thus, the wing is mounted in the shoulder position as a compromise. To avoid the cumbersome stowage of stalky,

***Left:* This 'lizard'-type camouflage replaced the initial grey and green scheme applied to the Luftwaffe's C.160Ds. A total of four squadrons (staffeln) assigned to three wings (Lufttransportgeschwader) currently operate the type.**

***Below:* A C.160D of LTG 61, Luftwaffe, demonstrates a drop out of both deployment doors at the rear of the cabin. A load of 88 paratroopers can in theory be carried, but 60-75 is a more common load.**

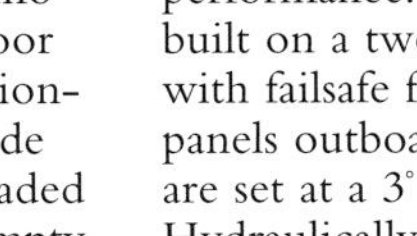

multi-wheeled landing-gear units in the engine nacelles, the mainwheel bogies are transferred to panniers at each side of the fuselage, in which partial movement through the retraction cycle allows the aircraft to 'kneel' for the easier loading of bulky cargo. The complex, twin-boom tail structure having fallen out of fashion since the days of the Noratlas, the C.160 mounts a conventional tail unit above hold level, so that a rear ramp is available for straight-in loading and unloading.

In round figures, the Franco-German specification called for an aircraft grossing 110,231 lb (50000 kg) and capable of hauling 17,637 lb (8000 kg) over 746 miles (1200 km) out of a semi-prepared airstrip. To simplify maintenance requirements the C.160's designers opted for two powerful turboprops instead of four of medium output, and therefore chose the Rolls-Royce Tyne 20 Mk 22. Conveniently, this 6,100-shp (4549-kW) powerplant was being built under licence in slightly different form by Hispano-Suiza in France for the Breguet Atlantic, assisted by MAN in Germany and Belgium's FN-Herstal. Ratier-FIGEAC produced the four-bladed, fully-feathering and reversible-pitch propellers under Hawker Siddeley licence.

Its manufacturer might be loath to admit it, but the C.160 does include one concession to 19th century technology: the internal dimensions of the cargo hold conform to the international loading gauge for railway freight. Clearly a highly practical consideration, this convention results in the hold having a useful width of 10 ft 4 in (3.15 m) and a height of 9 ft 9⅓ in (2.98 m); length is 56 ft 5½ in (17.21 m), giving a floor area of 583.9 sq ft (54.25 m²) and a usable volume of 4,944 cu ft (140 m³). Lashing points are arranged on a 20-in (50.8-cm) grid with individual strengths of 11,023 lb (5000 kg) or 26,455 lb (12000 kg).

## Cabin capacity

The C.160's rear door is split athwartships, the forward portion lowering hydraulically to truck-bed height and the aft component raising to the fuselage roof to give loading clearance. There is a paratroop door on each side of the fuselage, immediately to the rear of the landing gear panniers, while first-generation C.160s also have a freight door on the forward, port side. For para-dropping, the maximum individual load is 17,637 lb (8000 kg), although vehicles such as light tanks and earth-movers of up to double that weight can be accommodated on the reinforced floor when transported conventionally. Other loads can include three jeeps (with partly-loaded trailers plus crews), two empty three-tonne trucks, or one empty five-tonne truck.

Up to 93 passengers can be carried on canvas seats, these taking three people 90 minutes to install. The passenger total decreases to between 61 and 88 in the case of fully-equipped paratroops, who require more space for their equipment and room to exit freely. A full stick of paratroops can be dropped within 30 seconds. In the casevac role, 62 stretchers and four attendants is the maximum load.

Aerodynamically and constructionally, the C.160 is a cantilever monoplane, with the comparatively high aspect ratio of 10:1 for economic cruise performance. The wings are built on a two-spar structure, with failsafe features, and the panels outboard of the engines are set at a 3° 26' dihedral. Hydraulically-operated double-slotted flaps occupy the inboard two-thirds of the trailing edge, with ailerons at the extremities. The outboard panels also house air brakes and spoilers, both of which are powered by a duplicated hydraulic system.

One of the lesser-known aspects of the wing design is the fact that provision was made for the rapid attachment of an auxiliary jet engine, such as the Rolls-Royce RB162-86 of 5,250-lb (23.6-kN) thrust, under each outer section. Such fitments have never been adopted in service, even on the nine C.160s bought by South Africa – the sole direct military export customer.

Of conventional design, the fuselage is an all-metal semi-monocoque structure, basically circular, but with a flattened bottom. Two tandem pairs of wheels are stowed in each fuselage pannier, complemented by steerable twin nosewheels. Low-pressure tyres permit operations from semi-prepared airstrips, although German C.160s have also flown exercises from stretches of the autobahn.

An internal winch assists in the loading of heavy cargoes and, for crew and passenger comfort during medium-altitude cruise flight, the cockpit and hold can be pressurised. The complete aircraft structure is stressed to withstand high gust and manoeuvre loads of up to 3*g* at low level as well as the static loads incurred when landing on semi-prepared airstrips.

### Civilian service

At the 1965 Paris Salon, Nord displayed a model of a proposed 130-150 seat passenger version. By late 1967, the design had been refined and was to be powered by two Pratt & Whitney JT3D jet engines. Both propeller- and jet-powered versions never entered production, although some examples have found their way into civilian use. In 1973 four C.160Fs were modified for nocturnal mail operations by Air France under the designation C.160P. Three C.160Ps and three C.160NGs were also operated by Pelita Air of Indonesia (left), transporting cargo between the nation's many islands.

# Nouvelle Génération

**The Transall remains the workhorse of the Armée de l'Air's Comandement de la Force Aérienne de Projection (CFAP) transport fleet. The basic transport was delivered in two variants, the basic C.160F and the improved C.160NG.**

*A C-160NG demonstrates its low altitude delivery capability. Partly as a result of conducting relief operations in war zones, the C.160NG has been equipped with new self-protection equipment, including Type 507 chaff/flare dispensers attached to the fuselage and a Thomson-CSF Sherloc RWR and Elta missile approach warning system.*

Production of the first generation Transall originally ended in 1972, after the delivery of three prototypes, six pre-production aircraft, and 169 production aircraft.

Some 110 C.160Ds were delivered to the German Luftwaffe (20 of which subsequently went to Turkey), nine C.160Zs went to South Africa and 50 C.160Fs were delivered to the Armée de l'Air. The small size of the French order was always surprising, since it was barely sufficient to support a single Escadre de Transport, especially once some aircraft started to be diverted to the Night Postal Service, where they wore French civil registrations.

In fact, the first generation Transall now equips only two of ET 61's three squadrons, ET 1/61 'Touraine' and ET 3/61 'Poitou' based at Orléans-Bricy, with ET 2/61 'Franche-Comté' having re-equipped with the Lockheed Martin C-130H/H-30 Hercules.

*Of a total 23 C.160NG aircraft delivered with fixed refuelling probes, 10 are provided with a fuel dispensing capability via a hose-drum unit (HDU) within the port undercarriage pannier.*

It thus came as no surprise when it was decided to reopen the French (former Nord) production line at Bourges, using German-built parts. This would eventually provide a further 23 transport aircraft, allowing the Armée de l'Air to equip four full squadrons, with six more aircraft being delivered in more specialised configurations, and with six further aircraft being delivered to Indonesia (for use by Pelita Air Services).

Aérospatiale had hoped to receive orders for a minimum of 40 civil Transalls, including three for the Night Postal service, though in the event, the Indonesian aircraft would be the only additional orders.

The new Armée de l'Air transports were designated as C.160NGs (Nouvelle Génération) and differed from the C.160F in having additional fuel capacity (with an extra centre-section fuel tank) and improved avionics. The new C.160NGs also feature an inflight-refuelling capability with a fixed probe mounted above the cockpit.

*Home-based at BA 105 Evreux-Fauville, 64e Escadre de Transport was originally responsible for the Armée de l'Air's entire fleet of new-build C.160NGs, with operations shared between two squadrons: ET 1/64 'Béarn' and ET 2/64 'Anjou'.*

*Despite the fleet-wide Rénové upgrade programme, the Armée de l'Air's C.160 Transall fleet is now fast approaching the end of its useful life, and operations in Bosnia, Kosovo, Africa and Timor has led to a more intensive utilisation than initially forecast.*

Ten of the 23 transport aircraft were completed in tanker/transport configuration, with a hose-drum unit in the rear of the port undercarriage sponson. Five more aircraft have provision for this equipment to be rapidly fitted, to allow them to be re-roled as tankers if required. The Transall C.160NGs were delivered to ET 2/64 'Anjou' and then ET 1/64 'Béarn' squadrons at Evreux-Fauville.

In addition to the two main Transall wings (ET 61 with the early aircraft and ET 64 with the NGs) the type also serves with GAM (Groupe Aérien Mixte) 56 'Vaucluse' (a single aircraft used in the Special Forces support role) and detached with ETOM (Escadron de Transport d'Outre Mer) 50 'Réunion' at Saint Denis, Réunion; ETOM 55 'Ouessant' at Dakar-Ouakam, Senegal; ETOM 58 'Antilles' at Fort-deFrance-Lamentin in the French Antilles, and with ETOM 88 'Larzac' in Djibouti.

## Sigint platform

Two of the initial 25 aircraft ordered by the Armée de l'Air were built as C.160G Gabriel Sigint aircraft, with an extensive suite of Elint and Comint equipment and with a correspondingly impressive array of prominent receiver antennas on the fuselage and wings. These were delivered to EE 54 'Dunkerque' at Metz-Frascaty in 1988. The Gabriel aircraft have found plenty of 'trade' during the post-Cold War period, and have been used in Desert Storm, and during subsequent operations over the Balkans and in the Middle East.

## Communications post

Four more C-160NGs were added to the Armée de l'Air order in 1982, these being delivered to EE 59 'Bigorre' at Evreux-Fauville as C.160H ASTARTE radio relay aircraft in 1988. The ASTARTE aircraft form a vital part of the RAMSES communications network, providing unjammable very low frequency relay to allow communication with French nuclear submarines while submerged. Hardened against the effect of electro-magnetic pulse, the ASTARTE aircraft have distinctive conical guides projecting from the tailcone and rear ramp for the aircraft's trailing antennae. They are understood to incorporate the same inflight refuelling tanker gear as some of the transport aircraft. However, the aircraft's role disappeared when French SSBNs were withdrawn from the deterrent role, and the unit had been due to disband or change role in late 2002.

Production of the second-generation Transall ended again in 1985. Since then the Armée de l'Air Transalls have undergone a number of modernisation and upgrade programmes. Between 1994 and 1999, all 65 or 66 surviving transport aircraft received an upgraded cockpit with a new head-up display and a new EFIS 854 TF Electronic Flight Instrumentation System, together with a flight management system with two Gemini 10 computers and a new radio management system, under the so-called Rénové programme. The aircraft also gained a new navigation suite, with an inertial reference unit (IRU), an attitude and heading reference unit (AHRU) and a global positioning system (GPS). After upgrade the aircraft were re-designated as C.160Rs, though the former C.160NGs continued to be distinguished by their inflight refuelling probes.

The Gabriel and ASTARTE aircraft had already received these modifications, and therefore were not part of the Rénové programme.

## Further upgrade

Some 22 Transalls (in two batches of 11, and presumably mainly consisting of the surviving C.160NGs, perhaps plus the two Gabriel aircraft) are being further upgraded with a new self defence suite, including a Sherloc Radar Warning Receiver, a missile approach warning system and new chaff/flare dispensers.

In the long term, the C.160 will be replaced by the new Airbus Military A400M, once known as the European Future Large Aircraft (FLA). In the interim, however, attrition losses and withdrawals of older aircraft have resulted in some shortfall in tactical airlift capacity, and this has been made good by the introduction of the CASA CN.235M-200, which are jokingly known as 'Transallitos' in Armée de l'Air service. In the short term, the surviving Transalls reportedly require a life extension and/or fatigue rectification programme if they are to achieve their programmed out of service date.

*Originally intended to enable transport between France and North Africa, the Transall family boasts a significant rough-field capability, as evidenced by this **C.160NG** take-off from a dirt strip. Typical payloads for the **C.160NG** include up to 68 fully-equipped paratroops.*

# Tupolev Tu-160 'Blackjack'

## Soviet super bomber

**As part of the Soviet Union's nuclear triad, the Tu-160 'Blackjack' offered an intercontinental bombing ability together with stealthy design and fiercesome firepower. However, following the demise of the Soviet Union, the Tu-160 has, like so many other ventures, proven too costly and difficult to maintain, and only a small number remain in service.**

*Above: The purpose of the long, straight fairings on the sides of the rear fuselage is unknown. They may house a digital databus, which would require a long, unbroken area, and are similar to fairings seen on various 'Bear' sub-types.*

*Top: Conceived as a counterpart to the B-1, to which it is externally similar, there are some notable differences in that the Tu-160 has 79 per cent more engine power and, although appreciably larger, has a smaller radar cross-section.*

The Tu-160 'Blackjack' is the largest-ever Soviet bomber, dwarfing the similar-looking American B-1B, and is the heaviest combat aircraft ever built. The Soviet bomber was heavily influenced by the original Rockwell B-1A, which first flew on 23 December 1974, but which was cancelled by President Carter in 1977. Originally designated Product 70, the Tu-160 made its maiden flight on 19 December 1981 at Zhukhovskii, in the hands of Boris Veremei. Spotted by a prowling US spy satellite three weeks before this, on 25 November 1981, the new aircraft received the reporting name 'Ram-P' before being re-designated 'Blackjack'. Parked between a pair of Tu-144 'Chargers', the aircraft revealed many features in common with the American B-1, although comparison with the Tu-144 showed the Soviet aircraft to be very much bigger.

When the B-1A project was reborn as the cheaper, less complex B-1B, all thoughts of high-level penetration had been abandoned, and the less sophisticated aircraft was expected to use low-level flight (where it was limited to subsonic speeds) and a reduced radar cross-section to penetrate enemy defences. Back in the USSR, there was no such cost-cutting exercise, and the Tu-160 remained committed to both low-level penetration (at transonic speeds), and high-level penetration at speeds of about Mach 1.9.

The variable-geometry wings, with their full-span leading-edge slats and trailing-edge double-slotted flaps, confer a useful combination of benign low-speed handling and high supersonic speed. Wing sweep is manually selected, with three settings: 20° for take-off and landing, 35° for cruise, and 65° for high speed flight. The trailing edge of the inboard section of the flaps (immobilised when the wings are swept back) has no fuselage slot to retract into when the wing is swept. Instead, therefore, it folds upwards to be aligned with the aircraft centreline, thereby acting as a fence. Some aircraft have a 'double-jointed' folding section which can fold up to be a fence at either 35° or 65°.

The Tu-160 has a crew of four, sitting in side-by-side pairs on Zvezda K-36D ejection seats. The crew enter the cockpit via a ladder in the rear part of the nose gear bay. The pilot and co-pilot are provided with fighter-type control columns, and although the aircraft has a fly-by-wire control system, all cockpit displays are conventional analogue instruments, with no MFDs, CRTs or HUD. In front of the cockpit is the long, pointed radome for the terrain-following and attack radar, with a fairing below it for the forward-looking TV camera used for visual weapon aiming. Intercontinental range is assured by the provision of a fully-retractable inflight-refuelling probe.

### Missile payload

The Tu-160's offensive warload is carried in two tandem weapons bays in the belly. These are each normally equipped with a rotary carousel which can carry either six RK-55 (AS-15 'Kent') cruise missiles or 12 Kh-15S AS-16 'Kickback' 'SRAMskis'. The RK-55 has a range in excess of 1,864 miles (3000 km) and a 200-kT nuclear warhead.

The development programme of the Tu-160 was extremely protracted, and at least one prototype is believed to have been lost. Series production was at Kazan and continued until January 1992. Even after the aircraft entered service, problems continued to severely restrict

*Ukraine's 'Blackjacks' were variously scrapped under the terms of the START 1 treaty, or passed to Russia . Even though they were repainted following the break-up of the Soviet Union, they were rarely flown.*

***Like the B-1B or Su-24, the Tu-160 uses a variable-geometry wing to reconcile the conflicting demands of supersonic flight and low-speed handling. Wing sweep is conducted manually with settings of 20° for take-off and landing, 35° for cruising flight and 65° for a high-speed supersonic dash.***

operations. A shortage of basic flying equipment was a major irritation to aircrew, while a lack of ear defenders and anti-vibration boots for groundcrew resulted in deafness in some men. Problems with the aircraft's ejection seats led to a situation in which they could not be adjusted to suit individual crew members, and reliability of the aircraft, its engines and systems bordered on the unacceptable. Operations were supported by teams from the Kazan factory and the Tupolev OKB, who continued to deliver aircraft before a common standard and configuration were agreed upon. Thus, wingspans, equipment fit, and intake configuration differ from aircraft to aircraft. As a result of these problems and Tupolev's lack of money, along with a declaration by President Yeltsin over the building of further strategic bombers, no more Tu-160s will be built.

## 'Blackjack' today

Nineteen completed Tu-160s were delivered to the two squadrons of the 184th Heavy Bomber Regiment (GvTBAP) at Priluki in the Ukraine from May 1987. These were left at the base under Ukrainian command after the disintegration of the USSR. A deal for the purchase of these aircraft by Russia fell through in 1997, though the Ukrainians did allow American intelligence officials to spend some time examining one of the bombers for an undisclosed price – the Americans were not allowed to remove any parts of the aircraft, however. This deal particularly upset the Russians who deeply resent the friendliness of the West with former Soviet Republics such as the Ukraine, especially those who operate similar front-line equipment. Soon, under the provision of the Strategic Arms Reduction Treaty (START) 1 treaty, the aircraft were scrapped, with the wings and tail being cut from the fuselage and the latter cut into three sections. The engines and avionics may be retained for commercial use, however.

Russia currently operates about 15 Tu-160s, around six of which are supposedly operational, though it is likely that only two are mission-capable. Russia will rely upon modified Tu-22M3s until the emergence of new bombers such as the proposed Tu-60S. At one point, plans existed to use a modified Tu-160 (Tu-160SK) as a carrier for the Burlak space vehicle, in the same way that the American Pegasus is to be launched by an L-1011 TriStar and later it seemed that a US company might operate three 'Blackjacks' as atmospheric launch platforms, but this deal fell through.

## Tu-160 'Blackjack-A'

**Wearing a white scheme, presumably as protection against nuclear flash (like Britain's V-bomber force of the 1960s), this Tu-160 was part of the 184th Heavy Bomber Regiment, based at Priluki in the Ukraine.**

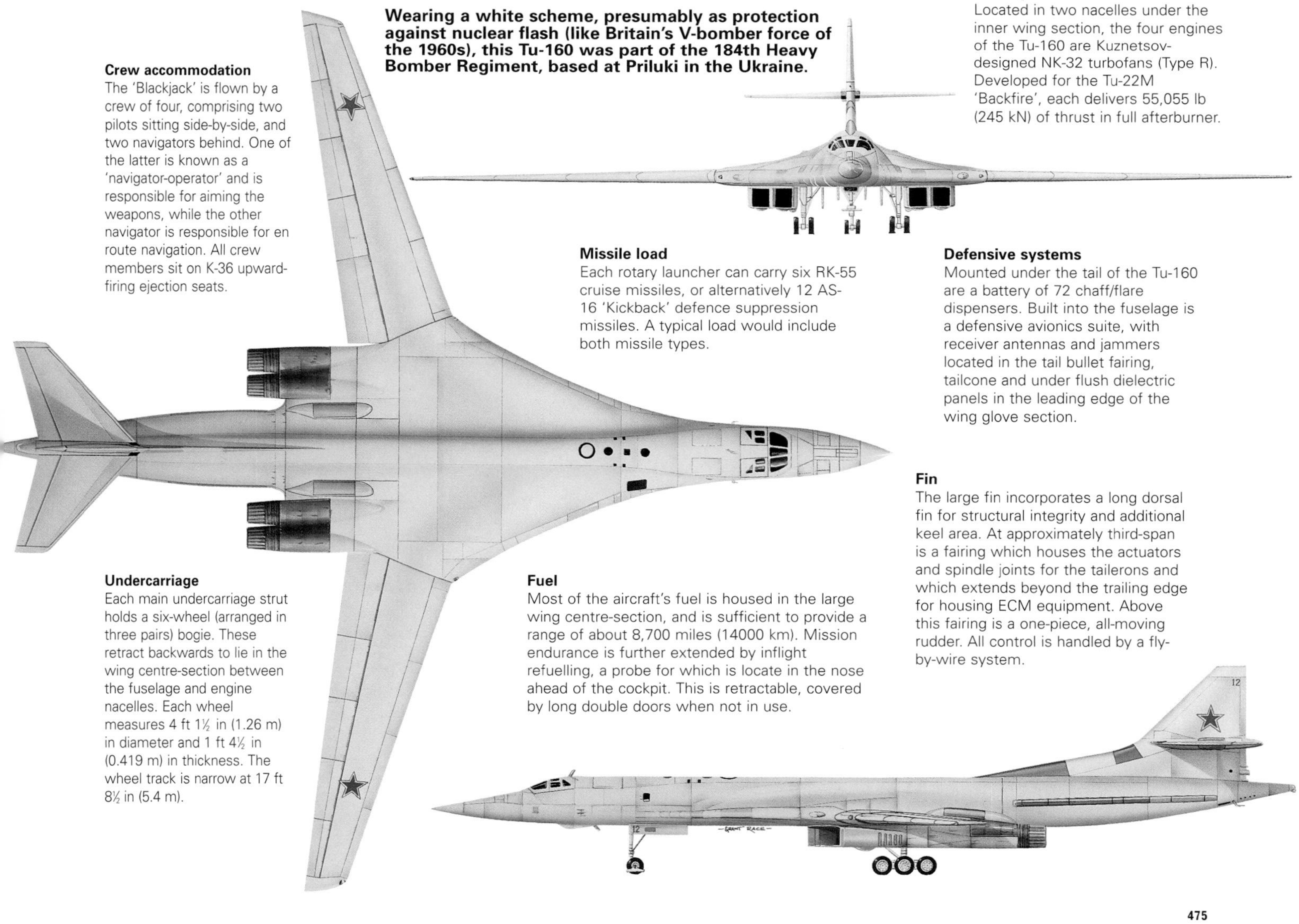

**Crew accommodation**
The 'Blackjack' is flown by a crew of four, comprising two pilots sitting side-by-side, and two navigators behind. One of the latter is known as a 'navigator-operator' and is responsible for aiming the weapons, while the other navigator is responsible for en route navigation. All crew members sit on K-36 upward-firing ejection seats.

**Powerplant**
Located in two nacelles under the inner wing section, the four engines of the Tu-160 are Kuznetsov-designed NK-32 turbofans (Type R). Developed for the Tu-22M 'Backfire', each delivers 55,055 lb (245 kN) of thrust in full afterburner.

**Missile load**
Each rotary launcher can carry six RK-55 cruise missiles, or alternatively 12 AS-16 'Kickback' defence suppression missiles. A typical load would include both missile types.

**Defensive systems**
Mounted under the tail of the Tu-160 are a battery of 72 chaff/flare dispensers. Built into the fuselage is a defensive avionics suite, with receiver antennas and jammers located in the tail bullet fairing, tailcone and under flush dielectric panels in the leading edge of the wing glove section.

**Fin**
The large fin incorporates a long dorsal fin for structural integrity and additional keel area. At approximately third-span is a fairing which houses the actuators and spindle joints for the tailerons and which extends beyond the trailing edge for housing ECM equipment. Above this fairing is a one-piece, all-moving rudder. All control is handled by a fly-by-wire system.

**Undercarriage**
Each main undercarriage strut holds a six-wheel (arranged in three pairs) bogie. These retract backwards to lie in the wing centre-section between the fuselage and engine nacelles. Each wheel measures 4 ft 1½ in (1.26 m) in diameter and 1 ft 4½ in (0.419 m) in thickness. The wheel track is narrow at 17 ft 8½ in (5.4 m).

**Fuel**
Most of the aircraft's fuel is housed in the large wing centre-section, and is sufficient to provide a range of about 8,700 miles (14000 km). Mission endurance is further extended by inflight refuelling, a probe for which is locate in the nose ahead of the cockpit. This is retractable, covered by long double doors when not in use.

# Tupolev Tu-22/22M Introduction

**Developed as supersonic successors to the first generation of Soviet nuclear bombers, the Tu-22 and Tu-22M have adopted an important maritime role in addition to strikes against strategic land targets. The exact nature of their role remained a constant source of debate in the West until the end of the Cold War.**

*Large supersonic, sub-strategic bombers are largely a relic of the past in Western air arms, yet the Tu-22M3 remains in widespread Russian and Ukrainian service and in early 2004, India was again looking into acquiring four of the type.*

*The Tu-22M3 'Backfire-C', of which 268 were built, was the second and final major production version. It entered service in 1983.*

Tupolev's mighty Tu-22 'Blinder' and Tu-22M 'Backfire' represented a class of medium bomber that had largely disappeared in the USAF by the 1960s. Although they were designed for strategic nuclear missions they were not intended for intercontinental strikes. Instead, they were produced for two distinctly different missions: continental strikes against strategic land targets in Europe and Asia, and strikes against US Navy carrier battle groups. However, the true nature of the role of the 'Backfire' became a source of fierce debate in the West, and the type became perhaps the best-known icon of the late Cold War era.

Tupolev's work on what became the Tu-22 (known to the design bureau as Samolet 105A) began in the early 1950s and gathered pace in 1954 when the subsonic Tu-16 'Badger' entered service. The new bomber was intended as a supersonic replacement for the 'Badger', but in the event the older aircraft proved far more successful in service. In June 1958, when Samolet 105A finally took to the air for the first time, speed was still seen as the best defence for a bomber. The Tu-22's high-altitude supersonic dash speed made it a considerable worry to NATO planners.

The aircraft entered service in 1961 in its Tu-22B variant, designed to drop free-fall bombs. In addition to large nuclear weapons, the aircraft could also carry conventional weapons, including the enormous FAB 9000 weapon of 9000 kg (19,840 lb). Problems abounded with the new type, and the Tu-22B was not a success. The Tu-22R introduced an important reconnaissance role for the type, especially in the maritime environment. Subsequent development included several electronic variants.

## Missile carrier

At the turn of the 1960s, the surface-to-air missile replaced the manned interceptor as the biggest threat to the strategic bomber. One way to defeat SAMs was to employ stand-off weapons which could be launched from outside the missile's deadly envelope. Accordingly, the 'Blinder' was redesigned as the Tu-22K to carry a single Kh-22 (AS-4 'Kitchen') missile, which could have either a conventional or a nuclear warhead. Development was protracted, and it was not until 1967 that the Tu-22K/Kh-22 combination achieved full operational status.

Missile-carrying 'Blinders', supported by reconnaissance and EW variants, were largely aimed at US Navy carrier battle groups, although a list of strategic land targets was also drawn up. In the mid-1970s the advent of the F-14 Tomcat and its ultra-long-range Phoenix missiles severely undermined the ability of the Tu-22 to perform its maritime mission. By that time, the follow-on Tu-22M was entering service.

A handful of 'Blinders' continues to serve today, although the vast majority have been withdrawn. The Tu-22 was exported to Libya and Iraq, and saw considerable action employed to drop conventional free-fall bombs. Libyan 'Blinders' were used to attack Tanzanian targets in 1979 in support of Uganda, and the following year undertook the first of several raids in Chad and Sudan. Iraqi Tu-22s staged many raids during the long Iran-Iraq conflict, while Soviet 'Blinders' were used sporadically during the Soviet occupation in Afghanistan.

## 'Backfire'

In the 1980s, no aircraft was more argued about than the Tupolev Tu-22M 'Backfire', and it became a key factor in the SALT 2 arms limitation talks. Its genesis dated to 1959, when serious discussions were held about providing a successor to the Tu-22. It evolved from a political minefield as a relatively low-risk fallback option to the Mach 3-capable Sukhoi T-4 bomber, which in the event only reached prototype status.

*In order to train prospective Tu-22M crews, Tupolev produced the purpose-built Tu-134UBL. This version of the well-known airliner has ROZ-1 attack radar housed in the extended nose.*

***Above: The wedge-shaped intakes easily distinguish the Tu-22M3 'Backfire-C' from previous models. They allowed the aircraft's dash speed to be raised above Mach 2.***

***Left: Despite being difficult to fly, and extremely unpopular, the Tu-22 enjoyed a lengthy career, notably in the reconnaissance and EW roles.***

Although it was essentially a completely different aircraft, the 'Backfire' used the Tu-22M (M=modified) designation to ease its political progress through the Soviet system. It was called Samolet 145, or Project YuM by the design bureau.

Drawing on data from TsAGI (Central Aero- and Hydrodynamic Institute), Tupolev designed the aircraft with variable-geometry wings, permitting a considerable increase in fuel load. Unlike the revolutionary Sukhoi T-4, the Tu-22M was based on a development of the Tu-22's weapon system, and retained the Kh-22 missile as its prime armament. Most missions would employ just one missile carried in a recessed centreline bay, although wing pylons could mount a further two missiles on short-range missions. Conventional free-fall bombing capability was retained.

After a small run of Tu-22M0 and Tu-22M1 aircraft, the main production version – the Tu-22M2 'Backfire-B' – was introduced. Its range performance sparked immediate controversy as American agencies simply could not believe that it was an intermediate-range aircraft. The USAF and Defense Intelligence Agency calculated a combat radius of around 3,500 miles (5630 km), which put the aircraft firmly into the 'strategic' camp, while the CIA was quoting a 2,100-mile (3380-km) radius. This confusion was exploited considerably by the Soviets, who steadfastly refused to reveal any data about the aircraft. Eventually, the Soviets agreed to remove refuelling probes from the aircraft.

When range data finally became available, the lower estimates of the CIA were shown to be nearer the mark. Indeed, the Tu-22M was intended for exactly the same European/Asian land targets and US Navy carrier targets as its predecessor, the Tu-22 'Blinder'.

## 'Backfire' development

Tu-22M2s entered service in 1976 and immediately proved to be far better than the 'Blinders'. Continued development produced the Tu-22M3, which had a reprofiled nose and wedge-shaped intakes, among other improvements, which raised dash speed to Mach 2.05 and improved range by around one-third. New weapons were also introduced, including the Kh-22MA low-altitude version of the standard Tu-22/22M missile and Kh-15 (AS-16 'Kickback') high-speed missile, available either as the Kh-15P with nuclear warhead or Kh-15A with high-explosive.

'Backfires' saw brief action during the fighting in Afghanistan, and were used in 1995 over Chechnya. Ironically, the Chechen rebel leader, Dzhokar Dudayev, was a former Tu-22M3 pilot.

Tupolev's Tu-22 'Backfire' is still Russia's premier bomber, with around 200 believed to be in service with both air force and navy regiments. Ukraine also operates numbers of Tu-22M2s and Tu-22M3s. Despite the adoption of the satellite as the prime tool of maritime surveillance, small numbers of 'Backfires' are configured for the oceanic reconnaissance mission.

***With the break-up of the Soviet Union, Tupolev was permitted to undertake a limited sales campaign for the 'Backfire', based on the Tu-22M3. Iran and China have been linked to the type, but only India seems close to a purchase.***

# Tu-22: 'Blinder' variants

**Of the handful of supersonic medium bombers produced during the Cold War, Tupolev's Tu-22 'Blinder' was manufactured in larger numbers than any other. Although it was an extremely unpopular aircraft with its crews and accidents were common, a surprising number of variants was produced.**

*Above: Tu-22RD 'Blinder-C' '36' is a reconnaissance aircraft ('R') fitted with a flight refuelling probe ('D'). This aircraft still has its rearward-firing gun barbette, later replaced by ECM systems.*

*Right: The absence of a second pilot's seat in the Tu-22 bomber made a trainer version essential. The raised second cockpit is visible on this Tu-22U 'Blinder-D'.*

The need for a supersonic bomber that could out-run the new generation of supersonic interceptors then being developed resulted in the Tupolev design bureau putting forward its Samolet 105 design, built as the Tu-22 'Blinder'.

The configuration of the aircraft was unusual compared to contemporary bombers, particularly in terms of the location of its engines. They were mounted above the fuselage at the base of the tail, improving the air flow into the engines and minimising engine damage due to debris ingestion on take-off. Little thought had been given to the consequences for engine maintenance once in service, and this would later become a nagging problem with the design. The engine configuration had design drawbacks as well, requiring reinforcement of the tail structure, as well as an extension of the nose to give the aircraft a suitable centre of gravity. Nevertheless, the aerodynamics of the design were deemed sufficiently good to warrant these penalties. The basic configuration of the aircraft was optimised for subsonic cruise speeds, with supersonic dash capability up to Mach 1.5 when penetrating enemy air defences.

The type first flew on 21 June 1958 from Zhukhovskii. Many types of engine were considered for the aircraft, including Kuznetsov NK-6s and the VD-7M, which was chosen to power the second prototype, the Samolet 105A. Production aircraft had VD-7Ms and, later, RD-7Ms. Wind tunnel tests had started to reveal the nature of the 'area-rule' for supersonic flight and this was incorporated into the 105A. A thinner wingroot on this aircraft also led to the adoption of separate nacelles for the undercarriage.

## Conventional bomber

The Tu-22 was originally designed to be a free-fall bomber, but the increase in the sophistication of surface-to-air missiles and the threat of interceptor aircraft led bomber designers in the 1960s to look at ways of producing a stand-off capability. Thus, only 15 Tu-22B 'Blinder-Bs' were built as such and were used mainly for training within the Soviet services. The only export customers, Iraq and Libya, did receive Tu-22B aircraft, but they were late-build Tu-22R aircraft modified to the free-fall bomber standard.

## Reconnaissance aircraft

The second version produced, the Tu-22R 'Blinder-C', was equipped with wet film camera equipment in the nose and weapons bay. The aircraft was oriented towards traditional military reconnaissance, especially naval, but did retain a bombing capability. A total of 127 Tu-22Rs was built, making it the most common 'Blinder' model manufactured. Aircraft fitted with inflight refuelling receiver equipment were re-designated as Tu-22RDs. Adding improved ELINT reconnaissance gear to the aircraft produced the Tu-22RK, or Tu-22RKD if equipped with a refuelling probe. Another upgrade of the reconnaissance equipment on the Tu-22RD in the early 1980s produced the Tu-22RDM.

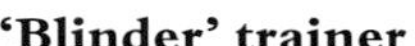

## 'Blinder' trainer

The 'Blinder' was a difficult aircraft to fly, being very different from the subsonic 'Badger' from which most crews were converting. A dedicated trainer version was required because the aircraft only had a single cockpit. To overcome this problem, the Tu-22U ('Blinder-D') was produced, with a second raised cockpit above the first. The prototype was completed in 1960 and a total of 46 of the aircraft was produced.

## Missile carriers

The political climate in Moscow in the early 1960s had moved opinion away from

***The electronic warfare version of the 'Blinder' was the Tu-22P 'Blinder-E'. This aircraft, a Tu-22PD, is one of 55 'Blinders' of which the Ukrainian air force took control in 1993/94.***

***Left:* The 'Blinder's' high landing and take-off speeds resulted in many accidents. Downward-firing ejection seats gave the crews little chance to escape in such an emergency.**

***Below:* The 'Blinder' was powered by two RD-7M engines, mounted either side of the tail. This position caused maintenance headaches for the groundcrew, with the engines perched 20 ft (6 m) above the ground.**

bombers to missile systems. In order for the Tu-22 to survive, the aircraft needed to have the ability to carry stand-off attack missiles. The type was re-designed to carry the Kh-22 cruise missile, the development of which was as long and protracted as that of the aircraft. Taking to the air for the first time in early 1961, a total of just 76 Tu-22K missile carriers (also given the ASCC codename 'Blinder-B') was built at state aviation plant No. 22 in Kazan. These included the improved Tu-22KD with upgraded engines. Although intended to replace the Tu-16 in both air force and navy service, insufficient numbers were built to replace the air force 'Badgers'. Only a handful of Tu-22K missile carriers were delivered to the Soviet navy for trials. Tu-22Ks built to use an anti-radar version of the Kh-22 missile were designated Tu-22KPs, distinguished by having a 'pitchfork' aerial on the right side of the nose. Anti-radar missile carriers with a refuelling probe were called Tu-22KPDs.

## Electronic warriors

An electronic warfare version, the Tu-22P 'Blinder-E', was built in the early 1960s. It also was used in the electronic jamming role. A total of 47 Tu-22P-1s and Tu-22P-2s was built, the two versions varying in the precise configuration of their electronics package. As was the case with the other Tu-22 variants, the aircraft were upgraded with the RD-7M-2 engines and refuelling probe from 1965, and redesignated the Tu-22PD. Eventually, the electronic warfare package was improved, leading to the Tu-22P-4, Tu-22P-6 and Tu-22P-7 variants. The Tu-22PD was usually issued on the basis of one squadron per regiment of Tu-22K missile carriers, to provide EW support.

Several Tu-22s have been modified serving as test beds for new systems, as Tu-22LLs. At least one may still be in service at Zhukhovskii.

## Unpopular 'Shilo'

Although an aesthetically pleasing design, the Tu-22 was widely dreaded by the Long-Range Aviation crews, who nicknamed it the 'Shilo' (awl – a pointed tool for piercing wood or leather). It was pronounced 'unflyable' by some bomber pilots. The situation was at its worst in the 1960s, due to uncorrected technical problems, and led to a number of instances of the crews refusing to fly the aircraft. This was exacerbated when the Tu-22K missile carrier was pushed into service prematurely, with a resultant high accident rate. Inherent design flaws in the aircraft, which made it both difficult to operate and to fly, led to a continual string of upgrade and modification programmes intended to fix the lingering problems. The use of downward-firing K-22 ejection seats made ejection during take-offs and landings impossible.

# TU-22P 'BLINDER-E'

**The TU-22P was the final production version of the 'Blinder' and was intended to serve chiefly alongside the Tu-22K as an escort jammer. One squadron of 'Blinder-Es' was generally allocated to each Tu-22K regiment. The Tu-22P played a small but important role during the final years of its front-line career in the Soviet Union, when it escorted Tu-22M2 'Backfires' on bombing missions over Afghanistan.**

### Design and performance goals

The Tu-22's 'waisted' fuselage came as a result of the drag-reducing 'area rule' considerations imposed on its design. A supersonic dash capability (Mach 1.5) was essential for the Tu-22B bomber's original intended Hi-Lo-Hi attack profile. The ability to launch missiles at supersonic speed later became an important consideration for the Tu-22K.

### Handling qualities

The Tu-22 did not have a reputation as a pilot's aircraft and could be very difficult and dangerous to fly. The aircraft could not be allowed to slow down to less than 180 mph (290 km/h) on approach, as this risked an uncontrollable pitch-up and stall.

### Refuelling the Tu-22

Aerial refuelling was one of the most difficult operations for an inexperienced crew. The Tu-22 flight controls were not delicate, and many inexperienced pilots found themselves closing in on the refuelling drogue much too quickly and being forced to abandon the link-up, with a fast descent to the right. Some pilots needed almost 45 minutes to secure a link-up.

# 'Backfire' variants

## Tu-22M0 and Tu-22M1 'Backfire-A'

Promoted by Tupolev as an upgrade of the Tu-22 'Blinder', the Samolet (Aircraft) 145 (later Tu-22M) was an entirely new aircraft. The first prototype, Tu-22M0, was delivered to the Flight Test Institute (LII) at Zhukhovskii in the summer of 1969, just two years after the project had been given the go-ahead by Brezhnev and the Council of Ministers, it being favoured over Sukhoi's delta-winged T-4. The Tu-22M0 completed its first test flight on 30 August 1969, and a pre-production run of 10 aircraft was planned. Nine pre-series Tu-22M0s were built at Kazan in 1969-71. However, the Tu-144-derived Kuznetsov NK-144-22 engines were inefficient, limiting the Tu-22M0's range to 2,573 miles (4140 km), well below expectations. The final Tu-22M0 introduced several production features, including the rear defensive gun position in place of the aircraft's previous large ECM fairing (à la Tu-22KD). The distinctive wing-mounted undercarriage fairings of the Tu-22M0 were abandoned on later aircraft. A single Tu-22M0 (below and bottom) is preserved at Monino, east of Moscow, and has carried the serials 'Blue 33' and 'Red 33'. The Tu-22M1 first series production aircraft (centre, note fintop fairing) incorporated new Kuznetsov NK-22 engines, offering 10 per cent more thrust.

Following the completion of Tu-22 production, Tu-22M1 manufacture was scheduled to begin at State Aviation Plant No. 22 at Kazan in 1971. The Tu-22M1 introduced revised wingroot landing gear, and increased wingspan, although problems persisted. Only nine Tu-22M1s were built from 1971-72, and operational trials were conducted by the 185th Guards Heavy Bomber Aviation Regiment/13th Guards Heavy Bomber Aviation Division, Poltava, Ukraine, under the command of P. S. Denikin, later head of the Russian air force. Other airframes were perhaps used in trials carried out by naval regiments, but the problematic Tu-22M1 never reached quantity production.

## Tu-22M2 'Backfire-B'

Known to its crews as 'Dvoika' (Deuce), the Tu-22M2 'Backfire-B' (above and below) was the definitive production variant of the Tu-22M series. Production lasted from 1972 to 1983, and a total of 211 airframes was completed. Initially fitted with a refuelling probe on the nose, this was later deleted under SALT (Strategic Arms Limitation Treaty), removing the aircraft's intercontinental range. Other recognisable Tu-22M2 features include the conventional splitter-plate intakes and twin tail guns. Typical offensive load for the Tu-22M2 comprised a single centreline Kh-22 ASM; alternatively, free-fall bombs could be carried on multiple-ejector racks (inset). In addition to service with the Long-Range Aviation branch of the air force, the Tu-22M2 was delivered to the Northern and Black Sea Fleets of Naval Aviation, replacing the Tu-16K. Training (supported by the Tu-134UBL crew trainer) was carried out at the 43rd Flight Personnel Combat Training and Conversion Centre at Ryazan.

### Tu-22M3 'Backfire-C'

Introducing new NK-25 engines, an improved and strengthened wing and revised forward-raked air intakes, the Tu-22M3 (below and below right) succeeded the Tu-22M2 on the Kazan production line, and was accepted for service in 1983. Optimised for low-level operations, with support from A-50 AWACS platforms and escort interceptors, the first aircraft were deployed to the 185th Guards Heavy Bomber Aviation Regiment, and 268 Tu-22M3s were built before production was halted in 1993. The Kh-22 remained a principal weapon; however, the Tu-22M3 introduced a new weapon to the 'Backfire' inventory, with up to six Raduga Kh-15A, or Kh-15P nuclear-armed (NATO AS-16 'Kickback') ASMs carried on an internal rotary launcher. The Tu-22M3 also carries a new Ural ECM system. In the late 1980s, work on the Tu-22MP (a Tu-22M3 variant) began, but this dedicated EW-escort jammer, a replacement for the Tu-16P, had not yet entered service by the time 'Backfire' production came to an end. A further Tu-22M3 sub-variant is the Tu-22M3(R) quick-reaction strategic reconnaissance aircraft, the first being accepted for navy use following conversion in 1984. Twelve more Tu-22M3(R)s were later accepted for service, and their equipment includes a large bomb-bay sensor package, and possibly SLAR and Miass ELINT systems. The Tu-22M2 had made the combat debut of the 'Backfire' as a conventional bomber over Afghanistan, and the Tu-22M3 took over these duties in January 1988, with the 402nd Heavy Bomber Regiment being deployed to Mary-2 airbase in Turkestan. Sixteen Tu-22M3s were operational in anti-mujaheddin manoeuvres, dropping bombs of up to FAB-3000 (3000-kg/6,614-lb) size. The final Afghan missions were completed in early 1989, but Russian Tu-22M3s saw further action in the Chechen conflict in 1995, principally involved in attacks near Grozny. Although developed primarily as a low-level attack aircraft for Long-Range Aviation, the Tu-22M3 is best known as a medium-range maritime strike platform through its exploits with the Soviet, and now Russian, naval fleets. The only other operator of the 'Backfire-C' is Ukraine (below left), with aircraft in service with two units (184 and 185 TBAP).

# Tu-22M3 'Backfire-C'

**Prior to the dissolution of the Soviet AV-MF (Aviatsiya Voyenno-Morskoyo Flota), the Tu-22M3 was operated by subordinated regiments (MRAPs) of missile-carrying bombers (also including Tu-16Ks and Tu-22M2s) within naval aviation divisions (MRADs). Today, the Tu-22M3 fleet is divided between two divisions of two regiments each, comprising the Russian navy's Northern Fleet (regiments at Lakhta and Olenya) and Pacific Fleet (two regiments at Alekseyevka), as well as a small number with the Naval High Command, based at the Ostrov Naval Aviation training base.**

**Carrier group strike**
Attacks against NATO carrier battle groups were the most high-profile missions likely to be encountered by Soviet AV-MF 'Backfire' crews. AV-MF 'Backfire' tactics ensured that at least seven aircraft from each strike package would have a chance of scoring a direct hit on the targeted aircraft-carrier. For greater efficiency, the Tu-22M3 can work in concert with Tu-95RT 'Bear-D' ELINT/over-the-horizon (OTH) target designator aircraft.

**Crew training**
AV-MF Tu-22M crews are trained in the Tu-134UBL, seating 12 trainees and carrying Tu-22M instrument panels. The older Tu-134Sh-1 is a dedicated navigator trainer with 13 trainee stations and practice bomb MERs. The single Tu-134UBK was developed exclusively for AV-MF Tu-22M crews, and carries PNA radar, a bombsight and a Kh-22 acquisition round.

**Bomb bay**
Within the Tu-22M3's internal weapons bay, the MKU-6-1 rotary launcher can carry six Kh-15 (RKV-500B/NATO AS-16 'Kickback') tactical cruise missiles. A further four weapons can be carried externally on the outer wing stations. The conventional Kh-15A carries an active radar seeker; the Kh-15P has a passive anti-radar seeker.

**Kh-22 attack profile**
Following a Mach 2.5 steep terminal phase dive, a single example of the Kh-22 'Kitchen' anti-shipping weapon can tear a 215-sq ft (20-m²) hole in the side of a ship, before burning its way 39 ft (12 m) into the vessel, ensuring the destruction of the internal bulkheads. The standard Kh-22 carries a 2,205-lb (1000-kg) high-explosive warhead (Kh-22P/N variants carry a 3.5-kT nuclear warhead) and possesses a range of 340 miles (550 km) when launched at high altitude.

***The Raduga Kh-22 (NATO AS-4 'Kitchen') ASM is the primary anti-shipping weapon of the Tu-22M3 – up to three examples can be carried.***

**Tail armament**
Tu-22M3 defensive armament is provided by a single twin-barrelled GSh-23 cannon in the tail barbette. Ammunition supply is 1,200 rounds of PIKS infra-red decoy and PRLS chaff ammunition. The gun is aimed using the PRS-4 'Krypton' radar or supplementary TP-1 TV sight.

# Tu-95/Tu-142 'Bear'

## Introduction

**As the result of one of the most outstanding aircraft designs ever, Tupolev's 'Bear' became synonymous with the threat posed to the West by Soviet military power.**

At the height of the Cold War 'Bears' could be found in places half a world away from the nearest Soviet airbase thanks to their prodigious range. The type proved to have great and varied capabilities, performing all with great efficiency, and the 'Bear' is still an important part of Russia's front-line forces. Its crews love it, and sometimes the same aircraft has previously been flown by the pilot's father. No other aircraft so fully exploits the potential of the turboprop, to the extent that jet speed is combined with the economy of slow-turning propellers. And, along with the C-130 Hercules, no other military aircraft in history has achieved a production in excess of 35 years.

### Boeing B-29 roots

Moreover, the Tupolev Tu-95 'Bear' (as it is called by ASCC/ NATO) has its roots in Seattle before World War II. There, Boeing designers planned the Model 345, which flew in 1942 as the B-29. In 1944 three B-29s made forced landings in Siberia, and the design was pirated by the Soviets.

The result was the Tu-4, almost identical to the B-29 except for its fuel tanks, engines and armament. This was enlarged and further developed into the Tu-80, which was further enlarged into the Tu-85. But by the time the first Tu-85 was flying, in January 1950, it was clear that turboprops could enable engine power to be doubled, trebled or even quadrupled. An engine of such power was already well ahead in development, so the Tu-85 was cancelled. The large and growing OKB (Experimental Construction Bureau) of A. N. Tupolev was given the task of designing a bomber to use this new awesomely powerful gas-turbine engine.

*Perhaps the most photographed 'Bear' was the Tu-95RTs 'Bear-D'. These reconnaissance machines were typically spotted shadowing Western naval fleets or probing NATO's borders.*

The NK-12 turboprop that subsequently emerged was powerful enough to propel the bomber at jet speeds, requiring Tupolev to build an airframe with swept wings and tail surfaces. These features, combined with the 'Bear's' massive contra-rotating propellers would later cause much consternation among western observers.

The fuselage of the new bomber was simply that of the Tu-85, but with a slight stretch. The tail was, of course, new, but was very similar to that designed a few weeks earlier for the Type 88 (later Tu-16 'Badger'), while the wing also owed much to this design. Another completely new feature was the landing gear. The whole aircraft had to stand much higher off the ground than either the Tu-85 or Tu-88, so the twin-wheel nose gear had to be exceedingly tall. The main gears not only had to be high but also matched to a weight 75 per cent greater than that of the Tu-85, so the answer chosen was a four-wheel bogie. As in the Tu-88 this was hydraulically retracted backwards into large streamlined boxes projecting far behind and below the wing, faired at the front into the inner engine nacelles.

### New answers

Tupolev had previously relied almost totally upon B-29-type systems, but the Tu-88 and the new bomber, the Type 95,

*Armed in its Tu-95MS-16 form with up to 16 RKV-15B (AS-15 'Kent') nuclear-armed cruise-missiles , the 'Bear-H' offered perhaps the greatest and potentially most devastating threat to the West.*

***In 2004 Russian forces retained the 'Bear' in service for three main missions. The Tu-95MS-6 'Bear-H' continued to handled the nuclear-strike role, while the Tu-142M 'Bear-F' flew ASW/MR missions and a handful of Tu-142MR 'Bear-Js', as shown, handled communications with Russian submarines.***

began to meet more severe demands and perforce had to introduce new answers. Because of the higher speeds, higher altitudes and greatly increased structural loads the skin gauges had to be increased, cabin pressure raised and the flight control system modified.

## Strategic bomber

The Type 95 was designed purely as a long-range strategic bomber, competing against the four-jet Myasishchyev M-4 in answer to a Stalin directive of late 1949 that Soviet design teams should produce turbine-engined intercontinental bombers. Initially the M-4 was the preferred choice of Soviet Long-Range Aviation, but flight testing showed that it could not meet the specified radius of action and it was never a major combat weapon. In contrast, while nobody was very surprised that the Tupolev aircraft could meet the range requirement, its speed and altitude capability proved better than expected. All-round performance was far higher than that of any previous propeller aircraft in history, and it still is today, 45 years later.

The original bomber's fuselage retained most features of the Tu-85, thus its cross-section was identical to that of the B-29, and the crew of 10 was similarly accommodated in three pressurised compartments, an isolated one in the extreme tail and large compartments, ahead of and behind the wing, linked by a tunnel crawlway. Armament comprised five powered turrets, two dorsal, two ventral and one in the tail, each with twin NR23 cannon. As in the B-29, the strong bulkhead joining the strongest of the four spars in the left and right inboard wings inevitably divided the bomb bay into two compartments front and rear, of equal size. Each could accommodate a single thermonuclear bomb or a wide range of conventional bombs.

## 1955 first flight

The prototype Tu-95 flew in early 1955. Seven aircraft took part in the July 1955 Aviation Day display at Tushino, shocking Western observers. Little did they know that this new and unusual bomber could boast world-beating performance and would be a continuous threat to the US and its NATO allies for almost four decades. Even fewer could have predicted that this threat would take so many forms, and that it would even terrorise the West's submarines on a global scale.

***Right: Only one nation received export 'Bears', the Indian Navy initially taking five downgraded Tu-142ML 'Bear-Fs'. Around eight such machines were available for ASW/MR work in early 2004.***

***Below: Western citizens became familiar with images of 'Bears' and Western interceptors. Here a pair of USAF F-4Es from Keflavik, guided by an E-3A AWACS, formates on a Tu-95RT on 28 September 1980.***

# 'Recce' and 'comms'

*As familiar as Pooh? The 'Bear' variant most likely to be encountered by NATO was the Tu-95RTs 'Bear-D', a type commonly engaged on shadowing missions against Western naval forces.*

**As a reconnaissance and communications relay aircraft the 'Bear' once again found tasks at which it excelled. In the 21st century all of the recce 'Bears' have gone, but the comms 'Bear-J' serves on.**

First identified in August 1967, the Tu-95RTs 'Bear-D' was the first model of the basic Tu-95 to have no provision for bombs or missiles. Some 53 'Bear-Ds' were built, 52 of them as new-build airframes, for Soviet naval aviation. The type was designed primarily to provide vital targeting information for submarines launching anti-ship missiles, but an important adjunct to this was the provision of reconnaissance. For this latter role the Tu-95RTs was equipped with sensors for the provision of electronic, radar and photographic recce.

## Missile guidance

Typical AShMs cannot be left with a large CEP (circular error probability), as could the huge AS-3 'Kangaroo'. Not only must they have precision guidance but the guidance must take into account the varied movements of the target. Even if the missile has a terminal homing capability, it must still receive continuous guidance throughout its flight until near enough to the target for its own homing guidance to be activated and locked-on to the correct target. Over the open ocean radar ranges are considerable, but the guidance problem is still severe. It is especially difficult for launch platforms on the Earth's surface such as warships, whose radar horizon, even with high antennas, may be 80 miles (129 km) or less. 'Bear-D' was developed to operate in collaboration with surface ships and, primarily, submarines armed with P-6 AShMs. The 'Bear' provided target information to the submarine, whose computer then selected the most valuable target before the commander gave the order to fire. The missile was then guided by a controller on the submarine, using a radar scope, until it was close enough to the target for its active terminal guidance system to take effect. Using this method, the Mach-1.3 P-6 could be launched at its maximum range of 186 miles (300 km).

*Fuel-efficient turboprop engines, capacious fuel tanks and the ability to inflight-refuel gave 'Bear-D' a phenomenal reach on its long-range reconnaissance missions.*

'Bear-D' was able to communicate its radar data reliably and in real time with Soviet submarines via a data link. The aircraft relied on two primary detection sensors, both of them radars with horizontally scanning antennas. The smaller unit under the nose was known to NATO as 'Short Horn' and used to transmit data gathered by the larger 'Big Bulge' radar beneath the centre fuselage. 'Short Horn' was also used for navigation.

'Bear-D' retained the Elint blisters and camera ports on both sides of the rear fuselage, as first seen on the upgraded 'Bear-C' bomber, together with most of the added antennas. An extra item was a streamlined blister under the fuselage about 8 ft (2.44 m) behind the 'Big Bulge' radar. Another, more prominent, new feature was a large streamlined fairing on the tip of each tailplane. These contained antennas for the Alfa system that was connected with the aircraft's targeting/recce role. In April 1970 aircraft of this type took off

*Some observers suggested that the Tu-142MR's under-fuselage fairing might be a buddy refuelling pod. The aircraft is often seen in close company with 'Bear-Fs' and was thought to have a comms-support role.*

***Intercepts of prowling 'Bear-Ds' were commonplace. In this instance a VF-41 F-4J Phantom II flying over the Atlantic from USS Franklin D. Roosevelt has made contact. These encounters were generally good natured, although rumours persist of 'Bears' scoring at least two manoeuvre kills over RAF Lightnings.***

from a base in the Kola peninsula, carried out exercises in collaboration with Soviet naval forces in the Iceland-Faroes gap and then continued south to land in Cuba. This surprised NATO forces and marked the beginning of a new era in which Tu-95 and Tu-142 aircraft routinely operated from bases far from the Soviet Union: San Antonio de los Banos (Cuba), Conakry (Guinea), Belas (Angola), Okba ben Nafi and other bases in Libya, two bases in Ethiopia, two in Mozambique and Cam Ranh Bay in Vietnam. The bases in Cuba, Angola and Vietnam subsequently supported 'Bear-D' (and other) aircraft on permanent detachments for many years.

## Tu-95MR 'Bear-E'

First identified in about 1968, having become operational in late 1963/early 1964, this aircraft is a 'Bear-A' bomber rebuilt for long-range reconnaissance with the Soviet air force. The main change was that the bomb bay of 'Bear-A' was gutted and re-equipped with three pairs of large optical cameras plus a seventh camera at the rear on the right. These were mounted in a giant detachable pallet whose underside stood proud of the fuselage profile. The pallet also held the environmental control systems associated with the reconnaissance package and may have been able to accommodate an IRLS (infra-red linescan) and possibly a SLAR (sideways-looking airborne radar). The type's radar system was fully integrated with its cameras, this set up proving very reliable in use.

'Bear-E' retained the bomber's navigator station in the glazed nose. Above this was added evidence of the Tu-95MR's other key system – an inflight-refuelling probe. Just four Tu-95MRs were built, the last of them being devoid of inflight-refuelling equipment, while the other three employed their probes to good effect. Indeed, during testing of the inflight-refuelling installation, three hook-ups with M-4-4 tankers were made. One of these was at night, the 'Bear' taking 100,000-lb (45372 kg) of fuel. 'Bear-E' also featured a pair of lateral Elint blisters on the sides of the rear fuselage. Various other extra avionics antennas were also added, including a small blister radome under the forward fuselage (in line with the inner propellers). All of the 'Bear-E's retained the defensive armament of six 23-mm cannon. After around two decades of front-line service the Tu-95MRs were converted as Tu-95U trainers, in which guise they served into the early 1990s.

## Tu-142MR 'Bear-J'

The last production Tu-142 variant, codenamed 'Bear-J' by NATO, was based on the Tu-142MK 'Bear-F Mod 3' airframe. In early 2004 a number of Tu-142MRs remained in service with Russian naval aviation, tasked with duties similar to those performed by the USA's E-6A Mercury TACAMO, i.e. long-range communications duties, and using VLF radios to communicate with missile carrying submarines. 'Bear-J' may also be used to relay commands to other naval units, surface or submarine.

The Tu-142MR appears to have larger ADF sense aerials on its spine, with a large blister fairing on the top of the fuselage between the wingroots. This may house satellite communications gear. 'Bear-J' also has a distinctive communications antenna 'spike' projecting forwards from its fin cap.

A large pod projecting down from the forward weapons bay contains the winch for the VLF trailing wire antenna that is reeled out to allow long-range communications with submarines.

***Right: Taken from a US Navy interceptor, this close-up of a 'Bear-D' rear fuselage reveals just how many antennas and sensors littered the skin of the machine. The large blisters house ECM equipment. Note also the ventral gun turret.***

***Below: 'Bear-D' served on at least into the early 1990s. By this time, the type's intensive operations were beginning to take a toll however, and crashes were not uncommon.***

**In its bomber and missile-carrying forms, the 'Bear' terrorised the West for more than three decades. Tu-95MS-6 remains a key front-line warplane in 2001.**

# Bombers and missile carriers

*'Bear-H' is a formidable warplane, which remains effective in the early years of the 21st century. Originally intended to augment the Tu-160 fleet, the Tu-95MS is Russia's primary strike platform.*

As the original 'Bear' variant, the Tu-95 'Bear-A' proved disappointing in testing and was built to the extent of just two examples. One of these aircraft was therefore rebuilt as the improved Tu-95M with greater power and higher weights. This new standard was still slightly lacking, but was put into production as a free-fall nuclear bomber, entering service around 1958. Subsequent variants included the Tu-95A 'Bear-A' nuclear-weapons transport and the Tu-95MA bomber, while the last of the 'Bear-As' eventually saw out their days as Tu-95U 'Bear-A' trainers.

## The missile age

From 1960 onwards, the strategic importance of free-fall bombing diminished as missiles became available as nuclear deterrents. Accordingly, in 1955 two 'Bear-As' were modified to serve as prototypes for the Tu-95K 'Bear-B'. The new aircraft was designed to carry and launch the huge Mikoyan-Gurevich Kh-20 (AS-3 'Kangaroo') missile.

Production Tu-95Ks entered service from 1960, some 47 aircraft being built. 'Bear-B' differed from the original bomber in several obvious respects. Instead of a glazed nose it had a huge missile-guidance radar, called 'Crown Drum' by NATO, which filled the entire nose. The Kh-20 was carried recessed under the fuselage, with its nose inlet faired over by a curved windshield, which would be discarded on launch of the missile. Most 'Bear-Bs' retained the original defensive armament of three 0.91-in (23-mm) turrets.

Some 28 Tu-95Ks were later fitted with a nose inflight-refuelling probe as Tu-95KD 'Bear-Bs'. These aircraft were joined by 23 production KDs and in the late 1960s the survivors of all these Tu-95KD and Tu-95K airframes were upgraded to Tu-95KM 'Bear-C' and Tu-95K-20 'Bear-C' standard, respectively. 'Bear-C' featured a thoroughly upgraded nav/attack system and compatibility with the modernised Kh-20M missile. In addition, a number of KMs were fitted with underwing sampling pods for the collection of samples over above-ground nuclear-test sites, primarily in China. By the early 1970s however, it was clear that improving Western defences had made the 'Bear-C'/Kh-20M combination obsolete and action was taken to combine the 'Bear' airframe with the new Kh-22 (AS-4 'Kitchen') missile.

*Above: The giant Kh-20 missile was carried semi-recessed in the 'Bear's' former bomb bay. Kh-20 weighed 19,731 lb (8950 kg), had a yield of 800 kT, and a CEP of around 1 mile (1.60 km).*

## 'Bear-G' takes shape

A scheme to modify the 'Bear' design for the carriage of up to three 'Kitchens' was first mooted in 1963. It was not until 1973 that such a scheme became a necessity however, delays preventing the first Tu-95KM conversion to Tu-95K-22 'Bear-G' standard from making its first flight until 30 October 1975. Missile firings were first accomplished in 1981, but the modified Tu-95KMs and new-build Tu-95K-22s did not become operational until 1987. As such, their time in service was relatively short, the type fading from the front line in the late 1990s.

The modification to 'Bear-G' standard involved the addition of a new, larger radar unit in the nose; the addition of an ECM thimble radome below the refuelling probe; deletion of the tail turret in favour of a new tail-cone containing ECM equipment and numerous other changes. Later in their lives, some K-22s were fitted with underwing sampling pods similar to those of 'Bear-C'. The Tu-95K-22 perhaps represented the ultimate expression of the original Tu-95 bomber, the next attack variants being developed from the even more capable Tu-142 airframe.

## Tu-95MS 'Bear-H'

Having developed the superlative Tu-142MK for the ASW role, Tupolev began working on a cruise missile-carrying variant of the aircraft in the 1970s. The machine was intended to take on a role similar to that of the B-52, with several missiles being carried on rotary launchers. Designed for the Kh-55 (AS-15 'Kent') missile, 12 of which were to be carried on two launchers, the Tu-142MS proved capable of carrying six missiles due to centre of gravity concerns. It was decided that the production of the Tu-142MS would be built alongside the Tu-142MK and would be

*Right: Tu-95K was the original missile-carrying 'Bear'. This machine was of the early production standard without the inflight-refuelling probe that was later added.*

***With the Tu-95KD came an inflight-refuelling probe. This compensated for the loss of range caused by the weight and drag penalty of the Kh-20 missile and its associated systems. In fact, the Tu-95K had a range some 2,608 miles (4200 km) less than that of the Tu-95A.***

designated Tu-95MS. In the meantime however, an experimental Tu-95M-55 was built as a test platform aimed at proving the various systems of the new missile-carrier. This made its first flight on 31 July 1978 and had accomplished a huge amount of useful test flying before crashing fatally on 28 January 1982.

The new 'Bear H' was based on the airframe of the Tu-142M, but with a shorter fuselage ahead of the wing. It features a redesigned cockpit section and a new nose profile which accommodates a totally new radar, along with other missile-guidance and navigation-related equipment. The compact nature of this new installation, combined with centre-of-gravity considerations, resulted in the shorter forward fuselage. A prototype for the new series was produced by modifying a production Tu-142MK and this completed its first flight in September 1979. Other features of the aircraft to become clear at this stage were its revised powerplant of four more-powerful NK-12MP engines and seven-person crew.

The Tu-95MS 'Bear-H' went into production during 1983 and it soon became clear to NATO observers that, like 'Bear-F Mod 4', 'Bear-H' had a long cable conduit running externally along the left side of its fuselage, one end disappearing into the nose radome and the other into the rear pressure cabin. The fuselage had a small ram air inlet on each side, but no large Elint blisters nor camera ports as had been seen on previous 'Bears'. In fact, apart from the aft ADF sense strake, almost the only excrescence was a small flat-topped dome above the forward fuselage. At the rear, the tail had the extended-chord rudder common to all Tu-142M variants. As there were no remotely controlled turrets, the lateral sighting blisters were no longer needed, but the tail gunner and turret were retained. The turret was of a totally new origin, never seen previously. The central power-aimed section had an increased arc of fire and carried a pair of GSh-23L guns. In fact, this turret was identical to that employed by the Tu-22M2.

'Bear-H' nominally became operational in 1982, before series production was properly underway. The type was built in two basic variants, the Tu-95MS-6 'Bear-H' armed with up to six RKV-500A (Kh-55/AS-15 'Kent') cruise missiles on a rotary launcher in the bomb bay, and the Tu-95MS-16 with the rotary launcher of the MS-6 and the capacity to carry up to 12 additional weapons underwing. This gave the MS-16 a truly awesome weapon load of up to 18 'Kents', although a load of 16 was probably more normal. Later, in accordance with the SALT-2/START armament-limitation treaties, the MS-16s were reduced to MS-6 standard and in 2004 this type continued to form the backbone of the Russian bomber force.

## Experimental bombers

Two experimental bomber 'Bears' are worthy of note. In 1993 a Tu-95MS was converted as the Tu-95MA for a new missile programme, but nothing more was heard of this after flight testing.

A previous experimental model, the Tu-95V was flown in the late 1950s. This aircraft was designed to carry a thermonuclear weapon of terrifying size. The 80,000-lb (36298-kg) weapon required the 'Bear-A's' bomb bay to be enlarged and reinforced. In the event, political considerations delayed the detonation of such a weapon until 1961. On 30 October that year, the Tu-95V dropped a single thermonuclear weapon weighing 40,000 lb (18149 kg) over Novaya Zemlya.

The resulting explosion had a yield of between 75 and 120 megatons, the bomb sending a clear signal to the West that the Soviets had a thermo-nuclear capability. The Tu-95V disappeared into obscurity before re-emerging as a transport for the Tu-144 'Charger' programme and served into the 1980s as a trainer.

***Right: To a degree the Tu-95MS has a role similar to that of America's B-52. It is a long-range load carrier that ought not to be able to survive in a modern combat environment, but remains viable thanks to its ability to launch long-range stand-off missiles.***

***Below: Such has been the longevity of the Tu-95 that several generations of Western interceptors have shadowed it. This Tu-95MA 'Bear-A' has a US Navy Crusader for company.***

*The Tu-142MK ('Bear-F Mod. 3') introduced new generation ASW equipment, including RGB-55A sonobouys, and entered service in 1980. The type can be identified by its MAD boom at the top of the vertical fin (unlike the Tu-142), but lacks the thimble radome of the definitive Tu-142MZ.*

# Maritime 'Bears'

**The final Tu-142 ASW aircraft left the Taganrog facility in 1994, bringing to a close 'Bear' production. However, the type continues to fulfil an important naval role within India and Russia.**

Development of a Tu-95 variant optimised for anti-submarine warfare (ASW) duties was officially initiated in 1963. Based upon the airframe of the Tu-95RTs, the Tu-142 would introduce a search and track system and an ASW weapon system. The new aircraft would carry a sophisticated and accurate navigation system that was also part of the weapons system targeting hardware. Tupolev's earlier attempts at an ASW platform based on the 'Bear' (the Tu-95PLO proposed in the early 1960s) had been rendered abortive by the lack of such a powerful sensor system.

A further role for the Tu-142 would be that of electronic reconnaissance, utilising Kvadrat-2 and Kub-3 EW systems. In accordance with Soviet military doctrine, the Tu-142 was required to be capable of operations from unprepared airstrips: as a result the aircraft incorporated a new undercarriage with six wheels on each main unit, accommodated in increased size nacelles.

Further refinements included an increased area wing housing new rigid metal fuel tanks, and a defensive electronic countermeasures suite. From the second prototype onwards, the cabin was lengthened by 3.42 ft (1.50 m), providing space for new systems.

*Left: Escorted by a pair of Su-33s, this Tu-142MZ ('Bear-F Mod. 4) represents the ultimate expression of the ASW Tu-142. The type introduced a more powerful NK-12MP turboprop, replacing the original NK-12MV.*

## RTs commonality

The prototype Tu-142 first flew on 18 July 1968. Compared to the Tu-95RTs, with which it retained much commonality, the Tu-142 had ventral and dorsal cannon turrets removed, and the large dielectric radome for the Upseh system replaced by a smaller fairing for the infra-red system. A new antenna system positioned in fairings on the horizontal stabiliser tips replaced the Arfa system carried by the Tu-95RTs 'Bear-D'.

## Service entry

During May 1970 the first production Tu-142s were delivered for operational test and evaluation by Soviet navy ASW units, during which they were tasked with tracking the movement of nuclear submarines.

After the successful completion of trials and the completion of testing of the Berkut-95 search radar, the Tu-142 was declared operational in December 1972. Attaining initial operational capability was hampered by slow deliveries, the 12 aircraft received (of 36 ordered) by the AV-MF in 1972 were fitted with the original 12-wheel main undercarriage units, as carried by the first prototype. In service, the Tu-142's rough field capability was found to be of limited utility. Furthermore, the aircraft's performance was hampered by its weight, and these two factors were consequently dealt with by the introduction of a modification plan.

The modified Tu-142 introduced a crew rest area for long duration flights, and the main landing gear units were replaced by lighter examples, resulting in an 8,000 lb (3,630 kg) weight reduction and improved flight characteristics. This modified aircraft received no new designation (only 18 Tu-142s were built before production switched to

*The late production Tu-142 ('Bear-F Mod. 1') was a reduced weight version, with the larger main landing gear units replaced with strengthened four-wheel units, similar to those of the standard Tu-95.*

***A Tu-142 'Bear-F Mod. 1' banks to reveal its ventral side-looking radar unit optimised for maritime surveillance and weapons bay doors (aft). Three different types of explosive sound sources (ESS) are used in conjunction with sonobouys.***

the Tu-142M) but received the reporting name 'Bear-F Mod. 1'. In 1972 the Kuibyshev facility produced its last aircraft, and this became the standard configuration for production aircraft, which were now to be delivered as the Tu-142M ('Bear-F Mod. 2') from the Taganrog plant. The Tu-142M was equipped with the extended cockpit and new undercarriage, but other equipment remained unchanged compared to earlier aircraft. As a result of their similarity with the final Tu-142s delivered from Kuibyshev, the Taganrog-built aircraft were known by the AV-MF as Tu-142s, despite their Tu-142M factory designation.

## New submarine threats

Development of more 'stealthy' submarines, together with operational experience, indicated that conventional acoustic-band sonobouys with trigger devices were becoming less effective against their intended targets. Instead, sonobouys with explosive sound sources (ESS) would have to be used for detecting more modern submarines. The Tu-142MK ('Bear-F Mod. 3') combined improved sonobouy equipment with a Korshun target acquisition system. The first example successfully completed its first flight on 4 November 1975, and subsequently began equipment trials in April 1978. The new Korshun radar, avionics suite and ASW equipment proved problematic, and it seemed likely that it could become obsolete even before it entered service.

As a result, in July 1979, a year before the Korshun-equipped Tu-142M entered service it was declared that the aircraft needed substantial upgrading. However, production of the Tu-142M (Tu-142MK) began during 1978, superseding that of the baseline Tu-142M, with the AV-MF electing to use its own designation system to identify the new aircraft. Aircraft equipped with the new ASW system became known as Tu-142Ms, whilst older aircraft retained the Tu-142 designation.

***Right: Indian Naval Aviation received eight Tu-142MKEs (export Tu-142MK 'Bear-F Mod. 3s' with slightly less sophisticated equipment) in the 1980s. The aircraft fly with INAS 312, based at Arrakonam.***

## Improved capability

The first three Korshun-equipped Tu-142MKs entered service in November 1980, introducing a magnetic anomaly detector (MAD), a new navigation system to provide automatic flight control inputs, and an improved ECM capability.

The Tu-142 continued to be updated and improved throughout the course of its long production run. The ultimate ASW 'Bear' variant proved to the Tu-142MZ 'Bear-F Mod. 4' with a more sophisticated ASW system than its predecessors, further improved ECM and new engines and APU.

Further upgrade programmes aimed to improve the Tu-142's likelihood of success against modern 'quiet' nuclear-powered submarines. The ultimate 'Bear' ASW suite was advanced Korshun-KN-N-STS of the Tu-142MZ, combining the Korshun with the Nashatyr-Nefrit (ammonia/jade) ASW complex, including the Zarechye sonar (hence Tu-142MZ).

In addition to production RGB-1A and RGB-2 sonobouys associated with the Berkut STS, the Tu-142MZ can carry RGB-16 and RGB-26 sonobouys in conjunction with its new ASW systems. The additional equipment effectively doubled the aircraft's efficiency, reducing sonobouy expenditure by 1.5 times. Submarines could now be detected while travelling at depths of 2,624 ft (800 m) in rough seas.

After state acceptance trials beginning in 1987, during which it conducted trials with the latest nuclear-powered submarines then operated by the Soviet Northern and Pacific Fleets with excellent results, the Tu-142MZ, the last 'Bear', was declared fully operational with the AV-MF in 1993.

***Left: A Tu-142M taxies out at Kipelovo, the centre of Russian naval 'Bear' operations. The airbase is home to around 40 remaining ASW-tasked Tu-142M and Tu-142MZs, as well as Tu-142MR 'Bear-Js'.***

***Below: The Tu-142M 'Bear-F Mod. 2' is equipped with the extended cockpit and twin-axle main undercarriage gear found on all but the first aircraft. The new designation served to identify airframes built at the Taganrog facility (from 1972) rather than at Kuibyshev.***

# Vought A-7 Corsair II

*With a long and proud history, A-7 Corsair IIs were involved in every major American action from Vietnam to Desert Storm. The pinpoint accuracy of this much-loved aircraft mean that it is sorely missed.*

## Introduction

**The A-7 Corsair II flew its last combat mission in Operation Desert Storm, after which it was put out to pasture to make space for a new generation of hi-tech warplanes. Having acquired a superb reputation in a number of conflicts, it is, today, missed by many.**

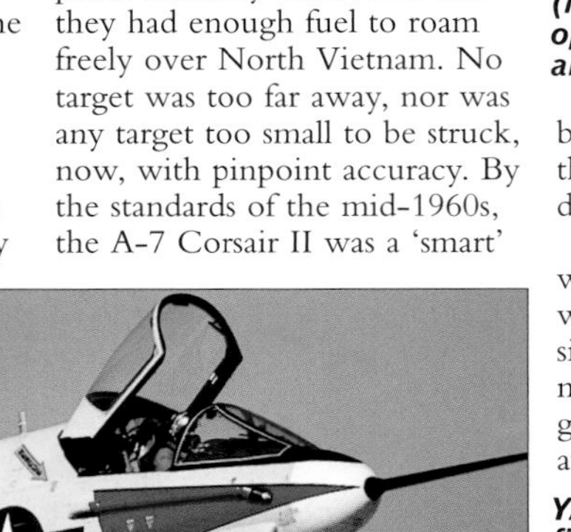

*Greece operates four units of A-7s, including the E and TA-7H variants. The principal duty of the Greek and Portuguese (latterly the other European operator of the aircraft) A-7s is anti-shipping.*

The little, snub-nosed A-7 no longer flies in American colours. But for 30 years the distinctive A-7 fought in every conflict that came its way, and established a dominant position as a superb one-place, subsonic attack aircraft.

Pilots called it the SLUF (Short Little Ugly F★★★★★) and loved it with a passion. Ground combat commanders liked the A-7 because it offered a new standard of accuracy when it unleashed bombs on a target, the bombs often being aimed at enemy troops a short distance from 'friendlies'.

The Corsair II's economical turbofan engine also gave it the 'legs' to rove in enemy territory and strike at will. When the A-7 replaced the tiny A-4 Skyhawk in the Gulf of Tonkin in 1967, pilots suddenly discovered that they had enough fuel to roam freely over North Vietnam. No target was too far away, nor was any target too small to be struck, now, with pinpoint accuracy. By the standards of the mid-1960s, the A-7 Corsair II was a 'smart' bomb-carrying warplane before the world's air forces began developing 'smart bombs.'

The A-7 was a straightforward, shoulder-wing aircraft with swept flight surfaces, provision for in-flight refuelling and narrow-track tricycle landing gear. Despite its somewhat awkward appearance, it was a

*YA-7A, BuNo. 152580, was the first prototype and was rolled out of the LTV hangars at NAS Dallas on 13 August 1965. Its first flight was on 27 September of the same year. It was named Corsair II in honour of the Chance Vought F4U Corsair of World War II.*

***Right:* Developed for combat-crew training, the A-7K was a two-seater based on the A-7D. The aircraft, 31 of which were built, only equipped ANG units and this example (the prototype A-7K, 73-1008) was part of the 152nd Tactical Fighter Training Squadron, Arizona ANG.**

***Below:* Sidewinders and bombs arm this A-7E as it heads across the Arabian peninsula on the way to attack Iraqi targets. Only two US Navy light attack units, based on the USS Kennedy, used A-7s in the 1991 Gulf War.**

very conventional design except for its continuous-solution NWDS (navigation and weapon delivery system) which was the most advanced such system of its era.

The pilot sat very far forward, at the very tip of the nose, well ahead of the nose wheel. He – or she, since the A-7 was the first combat aircraft to be flown by female aviators, first inducted into the US Navy in 1974 – could not even see the swept wings from the cockpit. Visibility was good, and the SLUF was easy to handle when taxiing on the ground and when flying in the 'pattern' around an airfield or aircraft-carrier.

## Corsair heritage

It would have been a brilliant design, except that the A-7 Corsair II lacked sufficient power to go along with a fine airframe, weapons-hauling capability, accuracy and range. Even later versions of the SLUF with improved engines never provided enough thrust to give the pilot a comfortable margin of flexibility.

The A-7 Corsair II came from a Dallas, Texas, company that had built US Navy warplanes for decades, having been founded by Chance Milton Vought who died in 1930. It was in 1964 that the US Navy chose Vought to build a new attack aircraft based upon its much-admired F-8 Crusader supersonic fighter. Created on the drawing board by the same design team that had fashioned the Crusader, the new aircraft bore a strong family resemblance but lacked the grace and beauty of its predecessor. One critic scoffed that the Corsair II showed only an incomplete resemblance to the Crusader because, "Somebody must have stepped on the blueprints."

The first pre-production Corsair II completed its maiden flight on 27 September 1965, almost exactly a decade after that of its Crusader forebear. By then, the US was deeply committed to a build-up in Vietnam. Early A-7s were in the combat zone within two years of that first flight.

The navigation and weapons delivery system of the A-7 is primitive by today's standards but in 1967 was the most advanced in the world. Pilots were delighted that they could actually 'pickle' a bomb on a specific building, or on the centre of a bridge, even if the target was in a congested area. The development of laser-guided and other precision weapons was occurring at the same time that the A-7 was appearing on carrier decks, and over time the Corsair II gained the ability to carry 'smart' bombs.

On a typical mission, a Corsair II carried 1,000 rounds of ammunition for its internal General Electric M61A1 cannon and up to 15,000 lb (6804 kg) of bombs or missiles on six wing and two fuselage pylons. The A-7 had a maximum speed in clean conditions of 661 mph (1065 km/h) and a radius of action of 550 miles (885 km) when carrying eight 500-lb (227-kg) bombs. It weighed 42,000 lb (19051 kg) when fully loaded for take-off.

Although Vought had not previously had the US Air Force as a customer, the USAF adopted the A-7 (although not the Corsair II nickname). In Vietnam, USAF SLUFs excelled in the 'Sandy' mission, escorting rescue helicopters which were picking up downed airmen in enemy terrain. The long reach of the A-7 was demonstrated when one pilot, helped by a single air refuelling, flew a nine-hour mission .

## Final flurry

The A-7 became a staple aircraft of the Air National Guard, and with Greece and Portugal. Thailand later acquired ex-US Navy aircraft. A small number of two-seat models was employed for training and electronic warfare duties.

Very late in the career of the Corsair II, just a year before Operation Desert Storm in which the US Navy flew the type in combat for the last time, Vought built and flew two prototypes of an extensively redesigned, much more advanced, version with afterburning engines and new avionics systems. Flight tests revealed great promise, but by then the digital age had arrived and newer warplanes were achieving new standards of load-carrying capability, range, and accuracy. The second-generation Corsair II never went into production.

***Above:* Engulfed in steam from a catapult track, this A-7E is prepared for launch from the USS Kennedy. The aircraft's outer stores stations are fitted with triple ejection racks carrying cluster bombs, while defensive AIM-9s are mounted on fuselage rails.**

***Right:* It was during Vietnam that the Corsair II first saw combat and it was in this conflict, due to its superb performance, that its reputation was forged.**

*Aside from successful operations with the US Navy and Air Force, the A-7 Corsair II found only three foreign operators, Greece, Portugal, and, more recently, Thailand. For a time, the Corsair II was seen as likely equipment for both Pakistan and Switzerland. The A-7G was proposed for Switzerland and the Swiss evaluated two modified USAF A-7D aircraft at Emmen in April 1972.*

# A-7s abroad

**Primarily a maritime strike and close support aircraft, the Vought A-7 Corsair II has proved its versatility in its adoption as a land-based attack platform and an air-defence asset, with front-line units currently operational in Europe and Asia.**

## Pakistan

In 1976, Pakistan was offered a total of 110 new-build A-7 Corsair IIs, in part funded by Saudi Arabia. Deliveries of the aircraft were dependent upon the abandonment of Pakistani plans to buy a French nuclear reprocessing plant, a condition that was refused by Prime Minister Bhutto. The A-7 sale was thus withdrawn by President Jimmy Carter, who also managed to prevent the sale of the reprocessing plant. Later, the Carter administration offered Pakistan 100 F-5Es, but these were in turn rejected by the new Pakistani Head of State, General Zia. Relations between the US and Pakistan worsened during the period, and culminated in Pakistan's withdrawal from SEATO and CENTO, and the burning down of the US embassy in Islamabad. During the later 1970s, without A-7s, the Pakistan air force (Pakistan Fiza'ya) was forced to revert its force of Mirage 5PAs and IIIEPs to a more ground-attack optimised role, backed up by a number of US-delivered B-57 Canberras. In 1983, Pakistan began receiving the Nanchang A-5C 'Fantan', a dedicated ground-attack aircraft of similar performance to the Corsair II.

## Thailand

The most recent Vought A-7 customer, the Royal Thai Navy Air Division (RTNAD), or Kongbin Tha Han Lur Thai, received its 14 ex-US Navy A-7E maritime strike aircraft in 1995. Additionally, a total of four ex-USN TA-7E two-seat trainers was delivered, and all are currently operated by 104 Squadron, based at Naval Air Station U-Tapao. Following evaluation of the Nanchang A-5 and upgraded A-4 Skyhawk, an $81.6 million (Bht2.04 million) contract was placed with the USN in early 1994. Following pilot and technical training at NAS Meridian, and Corsair refurbishment at the US Naval Air Depot, Jacksonville, Florida, the first Thai TA/A-7Es were delivered in July 1995, entering service with 104 Squadron at U-Tapao, at the Sattahip naval base. An ex-USAF airfield of the Vietnam War era, the airfield has the only runway in Thailand long enough (6,560-8,200 ft/2000-2500 m) to support A-7 operations. The TA/A-7E is in fact the second Vought Corsair type to be flown by the RTNAD and its predecessors, following the V-93S Corsair two-seat biplane, flown by the naval air arm in the 1930s.

## Portugal

Portugal's A-7P Corsair II fleet uniquely retained the 20-mm Colt Browning Mark 12 cannon and TF30 powerplant of the early A-7A/B models, while incorporating the electronics suite, HUD and navigation fit of the A-7D/E. The initial A-7P programme for the Força Aérea Portuguesa (FAP) included 50 TF30-P-408-powered airframes, as well as spares and support equipment. Under a $198 million 1982 contract, Vought refurbished and modernised 20 stored A-7A airframes, although deliveries of the first batch of 20 aircraft actually began in late 1981, and were completed by mid-1982. A second batch of 30 A-7Ps was delivered from October 1984. The initial location for the A-7P fleet was BA5 (Air Base 5), near Monte Real close to the Portuguese coast, with the aircraft flown by Esquadra 302 of Grupo Operacional 51, a former F-86 operator. Maintenance for the fleet is provided by the FAP overhaul facility at Alversa, outside Lisbon. Deliveries of the two-seat TA-7P variant for the FAP began in May 1985. Currently flown from BA5 at Monte Real, the current TA/A-7P fleet is separated between Esquadra 302 and Esquadra 304, and orders have been followed up with another 20 A-7As for use as spares sources. FAP Corsair IIs are tasked with tactical air support for maritime operations (TASMO), air interdiction (AI) equipped with fuselage side-mounted AIM-7P Sidewinder AAMs, and offensive/defensive air support (OAS/DAS). Precision attack capability has been enhanced by the introduction of the AGM-65A Maverick to the FAP inventory. For defensive purposes, the aircraft are fitted with AN/ALQ-101 jamming pods, as well as standard RWR and chaff/flare dispensers. Until the arrival of the air-defence optimised F-16 Fighting Falcons of Esquadra 210, FAP A-7Ps regularly deployed to the Azores (based at BA4 Lajes) in order to practice their ACM skills, and the Sidewinder-armed Corsair II fleet was supported by similarly armed T-38 Talon 'fighters', before the latter were withdrawn from service in June 1993. The FAP retired the last of its Corsair IIs on 9 July 1999 and under the Peace Atlantis II programme, it is replacing one of its Corsair II squadrons with 16 ex-AMARC F-16As, and four two-seat F-16Bs.

## Greece

Switzerland's decision not to buy the A-7 resulted in Greece becoming the first export customer for the A-7 Corsair II. The first A-7 Corsair II (159662) for the Hellenic air force (Elliniki Polimiki Aeroporia, or EMA) flew on 6 May 1975, with Vought test pilot Jim Read at the controls. Single-seat Corsair IIs destined for Greek service were designated A-7H, and deliveries followed a programme that had been instigated in 1974, and was completed with the delivery of the 60th single-seat A-7H example, arriving at Athens in 1977. Greece's first two-seat Corsair IIs (TA-7Hs) were delivered during July 1980, following their purchase with assistance from grant aid, which was initiated in 1978. Five two-seaters were originally delivered, comprising new production airframes. Greece initially operated three squadrons of A-7Hs, 354 'Perseus' Mira (squadron) of the 110th Pteriga Machis (wing) being based at Larissa in Thessalia in northeast Greece, and the 388 Mira and 340 Mira of the 115th Pteriga Machis being based at Souda Bay, near Iraklion in Crete. When first delivered, the five TA-7Hs (essentially similar to the USN's TA-7Cs) were divided among existing A-7H squadrons, with two aircraft serving with each unit. 388 Mira operated the TA/A-7H only briefly, prior to converting to the F-4 Phantom II. Today, Greece's Corsair II force is separated between four of the EPA's five fighter-bomber units (the other unit, 361 MVE flying the Cessna T-37B/C). Of the 60 single-seat A-7Hs and five two-seat TA/A-7Hs delivered from the mid-1970s until 1980, approximately 45 remain operational. Based at Souda, 340 MV 'Alepou' and 345 MV 'Lailaps' fly the remainder of the initial delivery batch. Meanwhile, at Araxos, 335 MV 'Tigreis' and 336 MV 'Olympus' fly around 70 ex-US Navy A-7Es and TA-7Cs, delivered between 1993/94 in order to replace the TF/F-104G Starfighter fleet. These surplus USN aircraft were reworked at NAS Jacksonville, prior to delivery to the EMA, and were delivered to the last two Starfighter units, which gave up their final aircraft in March 1993. The two Corsair II units based at Souda are tasked with the maritime attack role, replacing F-84Fs, with a secondary air defence role armed with AIM-9L Sidewinders. During 1990, 340 MV at Souda took part in an exchange with the Harrier GR.Mk 5s of No. 1 Squadron, based at RAF Wittering. The Souda-based TA/A-7H fleet currently shares its base with veteran T-33A trainers, ex-Luftwaffe Do 28Ds, and an AB 205A search and rescue detachment. Greece has expressed interest in upgrading and modernising its Corsair II although, following the end of the USAF-sponsored YA-7F programme, any major move to increase the effectiveness of the fleet seems unlikely.

On the export market the Lynx has proved a force to be reckoned with. The Portuguese navy maintains a force of five Super Lynx Mk 95s.

# Westland Lynx

## Multi-role helicopter

**Under the design leadership of Westland, the Lynx emerged as an effective medium-lift helicopter which, in dedicated army and navy variants, effectively fulfils the disparate anti-tank and battlefield reconnaissance roles, as well as flying anti-surface vessel and ASW missions.**

Above: In August 1978, the Lynx AH.Mk 1 became operational with the BAOR. This aircraft was photographed just after launching a TOW missile from its starboard-side launch tubes.

The Lynx is a compact helicopter design suited to ASW and other naval roles, as well as to multi-role armed and unarmed land missions. Of conventional, mainly light alloy, construction, the Lynx nevertheless introduced glass-fibre access panels, doors and fairings, and also made use of composites in the four main rotor blades. The later production Super Lynx and Battlefield Lynx introduced more advanced composite blades with swept tips developed under the British Experimental Rotor Programme (BERP), offering improved speed and reduced vibration.

The pilot and co-pilot or observer are seated side-by-side. Maximum high-density seating is provided for one pilot and 10 armed troops on lightweight bench seats. The Super Lynx has a chin-mounted Sea Spray or AlliedSignal RDR 1500 360° scan radar. For armed escort and anti-tank missions, the army version can be equipped with 20-mm cannon, rocket pods or up to eight HOT, Hellfire or TOW air-to-surface missiles. For the ASW role, armament typically includes two Sting Ray homing torpedoes, or up to four Sea Skua or two Penguin AShMs. More than 400 have been built for the UK and several export customers, and the type remains in production.

### Development

After the end of World War II, Westland decided to branch out into the new rotary-wing field. Initially building heavily-modified Sikorsky models under licence, the company began designing its own machines when it was left as the only manufacturer, following a rationalisation of the British helicopter industry in 1959/60. Westland began work on a series of proposals for future military helicopters. One of these was the W.3, to be powered by the Pratt & Whitney PT6A turboshaft engine and targeted at Naval/Air Staff Requirement 358 for a medium helicopter for the RAF and RN. Several variants, re-designated W.13, were projected before the Army's General Staff Operational Requirement 3335 was issued in October 1964. This called for a multi-role helicopter capable of carrying a crew of two and seven fully-armed troops at a speed of 170 mph (274 km/h).

A requirement issued in June 1966 added yet another twist, this time detailing a specific need

Most of the Lynx airframe is of conventional aluminium alloy, but the aircraft did introduce a number of innovations. Not least of these was its rotor system, with its main rotor hub and inboard flexible arm portions being built as a titanium monobloc forging.

***Above:** Westland built a single Lynx 3 demonstrator as a heavier and more powerfully-armed version of the aircraft. The machine featured a WG.30 tailcone, revised engines and intakes, and BERP rotor blades.*

for a helicopter capable of operating from frigates and destroyers in high-sea states.

### French involvement

France had a parallel requirement for this and other types, and the W.13, together with the SA 330 Puma and the SA 341 Gazelle, formed part of the Anglo-French agreement signed on 22 February 1967. Westland was given W.13 design leadership and proceeded with the development of a medium helicopter to fulfil Britain's requirements, as well as French demands for an armed reconnaissance and ASW helicopter.

The official go-ahead was given in July 1967 and work was stepped up. The task was made easier with the development by Rolls-Royce of the 900-shp (670-kW) RS.360 turboshaft, which had begun life at Bristol Siddeley as the BS.360. However, Rolls-Royce had difficulties in achieving the required thrust, and the first flight of the Lynx, as it was now known, was delayed by some eight months. The first of 13 prototypes finally lifted off on 21 March 1971, flown by Ron Gellatly, followed by the third on 28 September, and the fourth and second on 8 and 24 March 1972, respectively. Once the engines, named Gem from 1971, had delivered the maximum rated power, the Lynx quickly demonstrated its capabilities, setting two world records with a maximum speed of 199.92 mph (321.74 km/h).

The first British Army Lynx AH.Mk 1 became airborne on 12 April that same year, while the Royal Navy HAS.Mk 2 first flew on 25 May, but was lost in an accident on 21 November 1972. The naval version differed in having a lengthened nose to accommodate a radar scanner and a wheeled undercarriage. The second HAS.Mk 2 made the first at-sea landing on 29 June 1973. Eight more aircraft were used on the military development programme and the first production Lynx AH.Mk 1 for the AAC with Gem 2 engines, flew on 11 February 1977.

***Below:** Sud Aviation, later Aérospatiale, took responsibility for 30 per cent of Lynx development and production. The Aéronavale received a total of 40 Lynx HAS.Mk 4(FN) helicopters for use in the anti-submarine warfare role.*

### More power, more speed

Second-phase development produced the naval Super Lynx and army Battlefield Lynx, to which standards later UK Mk 8 and 9 models were built, alongside those for export customers. Both the Super Lynx and Battlefield Lynx, as well as having the BERP main rotor and reversed direction tail rotor for improved control, also have increased take-off weight, all-weather day/night capability and extended payload range.

Current versions are the Super Lynx 100, an upgraded naval Lynx powered by Gem 42-1 turboshafts, and the Super Lynx 200 with more powerful LHTEC CTS800 engines with dual-channel FADEC and some LCD flat panel displays.

With 45 new airframes on order in mid-1999, the Super Lynx production line is at its busiest for many years. In addition to seven new aircraft being built for the German navy, 13 new Super Lynxes are in production for the Korean navy, and GKN Westland is also upgrading the 17 existing German navy Sea Lynxes and eight Lynxes in service with the Danish navy to Super Lynx standard. The upgrade programmes for the latter two are the first life-extension programmes to include the supply of new airframes into which the existing engines, flying controls, hydraulic systems, avionics and electrical systems are transferred.

In parallel with work on the existing contracts, rapid progress is also being made on the first Super Lynx 300. This latest version also incorporates LHTEC CTS800 engines, but differs from the Series 200 in introducing a full night-vision goggle compatible 'glass' cockpit. The Super Lynx 300 first flew in January 1999 with Gem 42 engines and began flight tests with the CTS800 in 2001. It has been selected by South Africa to meet its shipborne helicopter requirement, and six have been supplied to Malaysia.

***Above:** Seven Sea Lynx Mk 89 helicopters were originally delivered to the Nigerian navy. These three machines, awaiting their delivery flight aboard a Heavylift Belfast, demonstrate the standard folding main rotors of the naval variants.*

***Below:** A Royal Navy Lynx HAS.Mk 3 approaches its landing spot aboard ship. The first landing of a navy Lynx at sea was accomplished in 1973 aboard the helicopter ship, RFA* Engadine. *The navy Lynx features a robust wheeled undercarriage.*

# Army variants

**The Westland Lynx has undergone various upgrades during its service with the Army Air Corps, producing a number of distinct variants. Major export orders, however, were never forthcoming.**

## WG.13 Lynx prototypes

The first Lynx prototype (below) made its maiden flight on 21 March 1971. The aircraft was one of five prototypes which were utilised for development flying. The prototypes had an early-style rotor head, cabin doors with three windows, Rolls-Royce BS.360 turboshafts and the first three aircraft had a characteristic short-nose configuration. XW835 later adopted the civil identity G-BEAD and was re-engined with a pair of Pratt & Whitney PT6B-34s.

## Lynx AH.Mk 1

The Lynx was planned as a replacement for the Sycamore and Wessex as a battlefield utility helicopter and therefore entered service as an unarmed utility helicopter, primarily intended to transport men and material, but also for casevac and command post use. The production AH.Mk 1 differed little from the later pre-production aircraft, with the most obvious change being to the main cabin doors, which replaced the original triple 'portrait-format' windows with a single large, square window. A total of 100 examples was delivered, with a further 13 subsequently added, the type entering service with the British Army of the Rhine at Detmold in August 1978. The AH.Mk 1 was used to test a variety of anti-armour weapons, including HOT and Hellfire (below). Rocket systems were also trialled, but eventually it was TOW which was adopted as the anti-armour weapon (see below left).

## Lynx AH.Mk 1 (TOW)

The spectacular performance and agility of the Lynx led some to call for its adaptation for anti-tank duties at an early stage in its career. A TOW missile installation was quickly designed for the Lynx, with clusters of four missiles on each side of the cabin, and with an M65 gyro-stabilised sight roof-mounted above the left side of the cockpit. The Lynx's origin as a utility helicopter meant that it had a spacious cabin which could be used to accommodate up to eight 'reloads' or Milan missile teams, making it a much more potent anti-tank asset than the earlier Scout. Following trials, some 60 Lynx AH.Mk 1s were retrofitted with TOW from 1981; the missile has since been upgraded to Improved TOW (ITOW) standard with an enhanced warhead.

## Lynx HC.Mk 28

The Qatar Police became the only export customer actually to receive the Army/Battlefield Lynx when it purchased three Lynx HC.Mk 28s. The aircraft were broadly similar to the AH.Mk 1, albeit with sand filters over the engine intakes. The first Mk 28 first flew in December 1977, and the trio was delivered in 1978. The aircraft were sold to BAe in 1991.

## Lynx AH.Mk 5 (Interim)

The AH.Mk 5 was planned as an interim version of the Lynx, primarily to test and evaluate features planned for the definitive second-generation Army Air Corps Lynx – the AH.Mk 7 – and was powered by the Gem 41-1 engine. In addition to the small batch of AH.Mk 5s for Army Air Corps evaluation and trials, three dedicated test/trial Mk 5s were ordered for the RAE/MoD. After trials, one of the aircraft (above) was adopted by the Empire Test Pilots School.

## Lynx AH.Mk 7

The second-generation AH.Mk 7 differs from the AH.Mk 1 in a number of ways. The larger tail rotor rotates in the opposite direction and the aircraft has provision for massive engine exhaust suppressors (not always fitted). The Gem 42 powerplant drives British Experimental Rotor Programme (BERP) rotor blades which are now standard on all AH.Mk 7s and the aircraft has a higher (10,750-lb/4876-kg) all-up weight, along with airframe strengthening and a redesigned tailcone. Improved survivability is a key part of the AH.Mk 7 and, in addition to the infra-red suppressors, an ALQ-144 IRCM jammer is fitted under the root of the tailboom and the crew are provided with armoured seats. The AH.Mk 7 can also be fitted with a door-mounted general-purpose machine-gun (GPMG), regularly used on deployment in Bosnia (below) and Northern Ireland; it is believed that a 0.5-in (12.7-mm) gun can also be fitted. Other new equipment includes a Brightstar infra-red landing light, NVG-compatible external lights and a Sky Guardian 2000 RWR. A total of 107 AH.Mk 1s was converted to AH.Mk 7 standard.

## Lynx AH.Mk 7 'Granby'

Army Air Corps Lynxes deployed during Operation Granby were fitted with new sand filters on their engine intakes, IR suppressors and Sky Guardian 200-13 RWRs. The aircraft were camouflaged in two-tone sand and stone, and received white recognition stripes: three around the boom, three beneath the fuselage and one around the nose.

## Lynx AH.Mk 7 'Chancellor'

The Lynx's roles in Northern Ireland had long included surveillance, and the type had used Heli-Tele to record demonstrations and incidents. At least one Lynx had its capability enhanced by the fitting of new 'Chancellor' equipment. This consisted of a digital video camera and FLIR and a downlink carried on a 'Chancellor' ball on an angled, articulated arm on the port side of the cabin. The aircraft also featured a fairing or strengthening strap, running along the bottom of the cabin door, and had an unusual, non-standard blade antenna below the nose and another under the tailboom.

## Lynx AH.Mk 9

When a contract was placed for a batch of new Lynxes to support the British Army's 24 Airmobile Brigade, the decision was taken that these aircraft (intended as utility transport helicopters) would utilise an extremely 'crashworthy' wheeled undercarriage, like that developed for the Lynx 3. By allowing rolling take-offs, the revised undercarriage also permits a higher all-up weight of 11,300-lb (5126 kg) and an uprated gearbox allows 1,840-shp (1373-kW) of power to be delivered from the Gem 42 engines. Like the AH.Mk 7, the Mk 9 lacks provision for TOW armament, but can carry the IR-suppressors and has an audio *g* warning system. The AAC ordered 16 new-build examples and a further eight were converted from Mk 7s. After an accident the aircraft are now fitted with cabin seats and are able to carry six fully-equipped airborne troops (with Milan), or nine soldiers in 'light order'.

## Army Lynx demonstrator, G-LYNX

The 102nd production Lynx was completed as a demonstrator for Westland. After working as an armament trials aircraft, it was converted for an attempt on the world helicopter speed record. To solve the problem of excessive main rotor flow separation, drag and torsion, the BERP project, jointly sponsored by Westland and the MoD, was initiated to develop a new blade. With its distinctive 'paddle' tip, the new blade cured the problems and, with more powerful Gem 60 engines with water-methanol injection, redirected exhaust pipes, a WG.30-style tailplane and a host of other weight/drag-saving measures, the Lynx was ready for the attempt. On the evening of 11 August 1986 the aircraft achieved a ratified figure of 249 mph (400.87 km/h) over a 15-km (9.32-mile) course, becoming the first helicopter to break the 400 km/h (248.5 mph) mark.

## Lynx T800 demonstrator

After being returned to something close to AH.Mk 1 standard, G-LYNX was later fitted with a pair of Allison-Garrett LHTEC T800 engines, each rated at 1,350 shp (1007 kW). The T800 (selected for the RAH-66 Comanche) fitted well into the Lynx airframe, with only minor changes to its nacelle contours. The aircraft was also fitted with a reduction gearbox and more efficient IR-suppressors. Re-serialled as ZB500, the aircraft demonstrated a 50 per cent improvement in hot-and-high performance and further engine integration and performance envelope work was carried out before the aircraft was placed in storage in 1992.

## Lynx 3

The Lynx 3 designation was applied to a family of second-generation 'Super Lynxes' formally announced on 21 June 1982. After France and Germany withdrew from the project to pursue their own project, which became the Tigre, Westland continued development as a private venture. Marketed as a versatile assault helicopter, the Lynx 3 was based on the AH.Mk 1 airframe, but incorporated major changes. These included a fixed wheeled undercarriage, side-facing intake filters, the rear fuselage and tail unit of the WG.30 and a stretched fuselage with a 1-ft (30-cm) fuselage plug. Other features included increased fuel capacity, heavyweight hardpoints and a thickened tailboom. The project was abandoned in 1987 due to a lack of orders.

# UK naval variants

**As a small ship's helicopter the Lynx is without peer. Thanks to its small size, manoeuvrability, harpoon recovery gear and negative-force rotor, it can operate in much higher sea states than its rivals.**

## Lynx HAS.Mk 2

The Lynx HAS.Mk 2 was the baseline Royal Navy Lynx, a dedicated ASW platform optimised for 'small ship' operation. Basically similar to the original Army AH.Mk 1, the HAS.Mk 2 had a fixed wheeled tricycle undercarriage in place of skids, and naval features including a 'deck-lock' harpoon, a two-bag flotation system and a folding tailboom. The basic Lynx's rotor system was also well-suited to small ship operation, providing quick response to control inputs and high control power, both useful for precise positioning over a rolling flight deck, and for ensuring an accurate and firm touch down. The new naval version also had hardpoints to allow the carriage of weapons, including two Mk 44 or Mk 46 torpedoes, or two Mk 11 depth charges, or up to four Sea Skua anti-ship missiles. Its bulged nose housed radar in the form of a Seaspray Mk 1, though the prime purpose of the set was to provide illumination for the semi-active radar homing Sea Skua missile, and to improve all-weather capability The naval version entered service before the AH.Mk 1. HAS.Mk 2 production for the Royal Navy totalled 60 new-build aircraft. Fifty-three HAS.Mk 2s were subsequently converted to HAS.Mk 3 standards.The Lynx HAS.Mk 2 entered service with No. 700L Squadron when it formed on September 1976. This functioned as a joint Royal Navy/Royal Netherlands Navy Intensive Flying Trials Unit, and at full strength operated six RN HAS.Mk 2s and two Dutch Lynx Mk 25s. One of the unit's aircraft deployed aboard HMS *Sirius* in 1977. The unit disbanded on 16 December 1977, and formed the nucleus of the Lynx training squadron, No. 702, which formed on 3 January 1978. No. 702 Squadron also functioned as the HQ Squadron for Lynx-equipped Ships Flights until 1 January 1981, when No. 815 Squadron took over as the HQ unit. The first operational deployment of the Lynx took place from 8 February 1978, aboard the 'Leander'-class frigate *Phoebe*. The aircraft was subsequently deployed aboard, 'Tribal'-, 'Leander'- and Type 21 frigates, Type 42 destroyers, and later aboard Type 22 and Type 23 frigates. As the maritime threat to the Royal Navy evolved and intensified, the Lynx HAS.Mk 2s were modified to fulfil new roles, including the ASV (Anti-Surface Vessel) mission, autonomous ASW, and the Electronic Counter Surveillance Measures task. Sea Skua ASMs, a towed MAD 'bird' and ESM were all retrofitted to most HAS.Mk 2s after delivery, to allow them to assume their new duties.

## Naval Lynx 3

The Naval Lynx 3 (not to be confused with the HAS.Mk 3) was developed in parallel with the Army Lynx 3. A mock-up was revealed in September 1985, with 360° radar in an undernose radome, an overnose PID, a WG.30-style tail rotor and pylon, and a lowered tailplane. The version was soon abandoned in favour of advanced derivatives of the HAS.Mk 3.

## WG.13 prototype batch

The first example of a naval Lynx was XX469 (below, foreground) which differed from earlier test aircraft by having a more bulbous nose representative of the Seaspray radar installation. The naval aircraft also had conventional tricycle undercarriage rather than the skids of the Army variants. XX469 was lost in 1972 and XX510 took over its trials duties. Testing by the MoD and Aéronavale continued until the late 1970s and the emergence of the HAS.Mk 2.

## Lynx HAS.Mk 3

The Lynx HAS.Mk 3 (above) was a modestly improved derivative of the Royal Navy HAS.Mk 2, with transmission, dynamic system and powerplant improvements. The new variant's improved performance and payload capabilities were accompanied by some new items of operational equipment, including Racal Decca MIR-2 Orange Crop ESM. The aircraft was fitted with a new four-bag flotation system, and was fitted with new towed MAD (Magnetic Anomoly Detector), ESM and the Sea Skua ASM. New-build aircraft were delivered between March 1982 and April 1985. They were augmented by the conversion of all surviving HAS.Mk 2s to 3 or 3S standards. The Lynx HAS.Mk 3 serves only with No. 702 (training) and No. 815 Squadrons, No. 829 having disbanded in March 1993. Since entering service, the HAS.Mk 3 fleet has been subject to a series of modifications, as detailed below.

**Lynx HAS.Mk 3GM (above right)**: There were three standards of 'Gulf Modification' among the 14 aircraft deployed during Operation Granby, of 18 or 19 aircraft originally 'Granby Modified' and all re-designated as HAS.Mk 3GMs. All aircraft are understood to have been fitted with MIR-2 ESM. LORAL Challenger IR jammers were fitted above the cockpit doors, but these were removed in-theatre to save weight, because the naval Lynxes were not felt to face a credible threat from shoulder-launched SAMs. Royal Navy Lynxes operating in Desert Storm scored 17 direct hits with their Sea Skua missiles and sank 12 Iraqi vessels.

**Lynx HAS.Mk 3S:** The Lynx HAS.Mk 3 was re-designated with the addition of an 'S' for 'secure' suffix after the addition of dual GEC-Marconi AD3400 UHF secure speech radios. It has been reported that the third batch of new-build HAS.Mk 3s was delivered to this standard.

**Lynx HAS.Mk 3ICE (right)**: When the Lynx replaced the Wasp in the 'small ships' ASW role, it was inevitable that it would also replace the Wasps used aboard the Antarctic survey/ice patrol ship HMS *Endurance*. The Royal Navy has thus equipped a number of Lynxes for service in the Antarctic. The most obvious modification is the application of high-visibility International Orange patches on the nose and cabin doors, though the aircraft also carry a range of specialised equipment. This includes a vertical (survey) camera pod, and a cabin-mounted periscope for sighting, while Sea Skua equipment is removed to comply with the prohibition against armed aircraft in Antarctica.

**Lynx HAS.Mk 3SICE**: When equipped with AD3400 UHF Secure Speech radios, the *Endurance* Flight Lynx HAS.Mk 3ICEs are designated as HAS.Mk 3SICEs. During a seven-month voyage by HMS *Endurance* into the heart of the Antarctic in early 1999, two Lynxes became the first helicopters to operate below 73° S, exploring the Carroll Inlet, taking aerial photographs and gathering scientific data.

**Lynx HAS.Mk 3S/GM**: When equipped with, or when given provision for the various Granby modifications, Secure Speech-capable HAS.Mk 3Ss are officially known as HAS.Mk 3S/GMs.

**Lynx HAS.Mk 3CTS**: The HAS.Mk 3CTS was never intended as a front-line variant in its own right, but only as a tool for the development and evaluation (including operational evaluation) of the CTS, which also forms the heart of the ultimate Royal Navy Lynx, the HMA.Mk 8.

## Lynx HMA.Mk 8

The latest Navy Lynx variant is the HMA.Mk 8, which represents a real modernisation of the Navy Lynx design, and which parallels the Army's AH.Mk 7 upgrade. Designated HAS.Mk 8 until late 1995, the aircraft then became the HMA.Mk 8. If the HAS.Mk 3 modernised the Navy Lynx for the needs of the 1980s, the HMA.Mk 8 transformed the type into a state-of-the-art maritime helicopter for the new millenium. The new variant introduced 920-shp (686-kW) Gem 42 Series 200 engines, and an improved rotor system with the better tail rotor of the AH.Mk 7. The aircraft gained a number of new systems which enhance its surveillance and ASV capabilities, and which give a higher degree of autonomy. The HMA.Mk 8 will introduce digital radar processing for the old 180° Seaspray, this upgrade resulting in a change of designation to HMA.Mk 8 DSP (Digital Signal Processing) or HMA.Mk 8(DP). The Royal Navy's HMA.Mk 8s are now able to use the FN Herstal 0.50-in (12.7-mm) heavy machine-gun pod (HMP), regularly used by HAS.Mk 3GMs, though it is unclear whether such a weapon has received a formal release to service. Three former HAS.Mk 3CTS aircraft were used for HAS.Mk 8 development. XZ236 was used for CTS development and integration, ZD266 served as an avionics development aircraft, and ZD267 flight-trialled the new undernose radome and nose-mounted PID. Westland received a contract for the conversion of the first seven (of a planned 44 conversions) in May 1992, and subsequently received a follow-on contract for four more, as well as a contract to bring the development aircraft ZD267 to full Mk 8 standards. The first of these was delivered in July 1994 to an OEU formed within No. 815 Squadron. All seven of the initial batch were delivered by mid-1995. The first HMA.Mk 8s went to No. 702 Squadron (the Lynx training unit) from February 1996, and the type made its first sea deployment (aboard HMS *Montrose*) in late 1995. MoD plans originally called for the conversion of all surviving Lynx HAS.Mk 3s to the new standard.

# Foreign operators

**Naval Lynx variants have sold well abroad, Westland tailoring the aircraft to the individual needs of customers, with revised engines/transmissions and operational equipment.**

## Brazil – Lynx Mk 21, Super Lynx Mk 21A

Brazil's ASW/ASV-roled Mk 21 was closely based on the baseline RN HAS.Mk 2, though they are armed with Sea Skua ASMs, Mk 9 depth charges or Mk 46 torpedoes. The first made its maiden flight on 30 September 1977; nine were built, the last flying on 14 April 1978. They were locally referred to as SAH-11s, and equipped Esquadrão de Helicopteros de Esclarecimento e Ataque 1 (HA-1) at São Pedro da Aldeia from 1978. The Lynxes are most commonly seen aboard the 'Niteroi'-class (Vosper-Thorneycroft Mk 10) frigates.

Brazil took delivery of 14 Super Lynxes, nine newly-built and five produced by the conversion of Mk 21s, in a £150 million deal signed in 1993. Broadly equivalent to the Portuguese Mk 95, the Brazilian Lynxes were equipped with the 360° SeaSpray 3000 radar and have provision for FLIR, recce pods or a 'dunking' sonar. The aircraft are powered by the 1,120-shp (836-kW) Gem 42-1, with composite main rotor blades and the reverse direction tail rotor. The first airframe for conversion made its first flight in its new configuration on 23 March 1996. The first new-build Mk 21A (N4001) made its maiden flight on 12 June 1996.

## France – Lynx Mk 2(FN), Mk 4(FN)

Based on the RN HAS.Mk 2, but with the higher (10,500 lb/4763 kg) all up weight normally associated with the Gem 4-engined Dutch Lynx Mk 27, the Aéronavale Mk 2 (pictured) also had an ASV capability from the start, the latter being added to the RN variant only by retrofit. The French OMERA-Segid ORB31W radar replaced the usual Seaspray, while armament in the ASV role comprised Aérospatiale AS 12 ASMs. Twenty-six were built; the first flying on 24 October 1979. The Aéronavale's Lynx Mk 4 was the French equivalent to the British HAS.Mk 3, though the dynamics, transmission and powerplant changes were not accompanied by any major improvement. Fourteen Mk 4s were produced. The French Lynxes have been improved and modernised in service, and now have BERP main rotor blades.

## Argentina – Lynx Mk 23

Acquired for use in the ASW role aboard Argentina's two ex-RN Type 42 destroyers (*Hercules* and *Santisima Trinidad*), Argentina's two Lynx Mk 23s first flew on 17 May and 23 June 1978, and were similar to the baseline RN HAS.Mk 2, and to the Brazilian Mk 21. Both deployed to Port Stanley in the wake of the Argentine invasion of the Falklands, but played little part in the war that followed. One (0735/ 3-H-42, above) was lost in an accident on 2 May 1982, and the other was grounded then or soon afterwards. It was sold to Denmark in November 1987 (together with the Navy's entire Lynx spares holding).

## Denmark – Lynx Mk 80, Mk 90, Super Lynx Mk 90B

Denmark acquired 10 Lynxes (eight Mk 80s and two Mk 90s) for fishery protection duties with the Sovaernets Flyvetjeneste (Naval Flying Service). Twin-engined safety and the ability to refuel in flight while hovering above a vessel (HIFR – Helicopter In Flight Refuelling) were crucial capabilities for the Danes. All of the Danish Lynxes were based on the HAS.Mk 3, with Seaspray radar. The first batch of eight of these new helicopters was newly-built as Lynx Mk 80s, the first aircraft making its maiden flight on 3 February 1980. Two more aircraft were acquired in 1987/1988 to replace two of the original aircraft (which had crashed in 1985 and 1987), these being designated as Mk 90s. In service, the surviving Danish aircraft have been upgraded and further upgrades are planned under a recently announced MLU. When modified, the aircraft will be designated Lynx Mk 90B.

## Netherlands – Lynx Mk 25, Mk 27, Mk 81, STAMOL Lynx

The first six Dutch Lynxes were broadly equivalent to the HAS.Mk 2, and were procured for use in the SAR role. They made their maiden flights between 23 August 1976 and 16 September 1977. The UH-14As were also used for training, utility transport and for support of the Royal Netherlands Marine Corps' BBE anti-terrorist unit. The Netherlands Navy's Mk.27 was based on the basic Lynx HAS.Mk 2, although it was powered by 1,120-shp (836-kW) Gem 4 Mk 1010 engines. Optimised for the ASW role, the 10 Mk 27s were intended to operate from 'Tromp'-, 'Kortenaar '-and 'Van Speijk'-class frigates. The first made its maiden flight on 6 October 1978. The new version was fitted with Alcatel (now Thomson-CSF) DUAV-4A dipping sonar, and was armed with one or two Mk 46 torpedoes. The third batch of Dutch Lynxes were HAS.Mk 3-based ASW aircraft, and were locally designated SH-14C. The first SH-14C made its first flight on 9 July 1980. The SH-14Cs initially lacked dipping sonar, but were instead fitted with a Texas Instruments AN/ASQ-81(V)2 magnetic anomaly detector. This was found to be less effective than sonar and was removed, and the SH-14Cs were relegated to training and utility duties. Under the STAMOL (SH-14D) programme 22 surviving Dutch Lynxes were upgraded to a common standard, essentially that of the dipping sonar-equipped SH-14B. Other changes included an upgraded engine, new rotor blades and advanced avionics. A new radar was also planned, but later abandoned for budgetary reasons, though a FLIR was installed.

## Malaysia – Super Lynx 300

In September 1999 Westland announced the sale of six Super Lynxes to the Royal Malaysian Navy, to replace elderly Westland Wasps. At the time no specific version or equipment fit was announced.

## Norway – Mk 86

The Norwegian air force (Luftforsvaret) ordered six Lynxes for use by the civil Kystvakt (Coast Guard) for SAR, fishery patrol and environmental control duties. The first made its first flight on 23 January 1981. Assigned to the air force's No. 337 Skvadron at Bardufoss, the aircraft operate mainly from three Coastguard 'Nordkap'-class patrol vessels in the North Atlantic (north of 65° N).

With the same Gem 4 Mk 1010 engines and increased AUW as the Dutch Mk 27, the six Norwegian Lynx Mk 86s were only semi-navalised, lacking the normal folding tailboom of the navy Lynx. They are equipped with Seaspray radar and, in addition to the usual UHF, HF and VHF/AM radios, have a police/emergency service VHF/FM radio. The TANS is connected to the Agiflite camera, which allows navigational data to be imprinted on photos of border/territorial water violations. A rescue hoist is used for SAR and for winching inspectors down to vessels being examined. It is also used to lift a fuel line to allow HIFR. The aircraft have been used intensively, and will eventually be replaced by the NH90.

## Portugal – Super Lynx Mk 95

Portugal selected the Super Lynx to meet its requirement for a shipborne ASW helicopter. Always the preferred choice of the Portuguese Navy, five Super Lynxes were ordered on 2 November 1990. Although designated as a 'Super Lynx' by Westland, and though nominally 'based on the HMA.Mk 8', the Portuguese Navy Lynx Mk 95s lacks the distinctive overnose Passive Identification Device (PID) associated with third-generation Royal Navy Lynxes, or the overnose FLIR associated with the Mk 88A. The aircraft does have a Racal RNS252 GPS-aided INS, together with a Bendix AN/AQS-18(v) 'dunking' sonar and Bendix RDR 1500 radar in an undernose radome, and was the first Super Lynx variant with these features. Five Mk 95s were produced for service on Portugal's 'Vasco da Gama'-class (MEKO 200) frigates, and are shore-based at Montijo, near Lisbon. Three of the Portuguese Super Lynxes are new-build, but the first two were produced through conversion of ex-Royal Navy HAS.Mk 3s. The first converted Mk 95 made its maiden flight on 27 March 1992. The first new-build aircraft flew for the first time on 9 July 1993.

## South Korea – Super Lynx Mk 99

South Korea ordered Super Lynxes in 1988, making it the first export customer for the type, despite their aircraft's late numerical designation. This was reportedly allocated at Korea's request, the number 9 reportedly having connotations of good fortune in Korea! Although labelled as a Super Lynx, the Korean Mk 99 lacked the later reverse direction composite tail rotor and the composite BERP main rotor blades. The aircraft did have the new undernose radome, however, housing Seaspray 3 radar. Purchased for service aboard the Korean Navy's 'Sumner'- and 'Gearing'-class destroyers, the 12 new-build Lynx Mk 99s are shore-based at Chinhae with No. 627 Squadron. As well as the 360° Seaspray Mk 3 radar, they may be armed with Mk 44 torpedoes or Sea Skua ASMs. The first Mk 99 made its maiden flight on 16 November 1989, and deliveries were made between July 1990 and May 1991. The serial No. 90-0704 was omitted for reasons of superstition, '4' being considered 'unlucky'.

## South Africa – Super Lynx 300

In August 2003, South Africa signed a contract for four helicopters to be based on the Super Lynx 300 configuration for use in the ASW and anti-surface unit roles.

## Nigeria – Lynx Mk 89

The last HAS.Mk 3-based Lynx variant was Nigeria's Mk 89, which was broadly similar to the Mk 88 used by the Kriegsmarine, albeit without the Bendix sonar, and with folding tailboom. The Nigerian Lynxes have 1,135-shp (847-kW) Gem 43-1 Mk 1020 engines with improved hot and high performance. Three aircraft were supplied for use by No. 101 Sqn, the first making its maiden flight on 29 September 1983.

## Pakistan – Lynx HAS.Mk 3 (Pakistan)

Pakistan signed an agreement for the purchase of three second-hand Royal Navy basic standard Lynx HAS.Mk 3s in June 1994, with an option to purchase three more. They were acquired for service aboard three of the six ex-Royal Navy Type 21 frigates also purchased by Pakistan. The aircraft were refurbished to 'half-life' standards prior to delivery, but have Sea Skua HIE (Helicopter Installed Equipment) removed.

## Qatar – Lynx Mk 28

The Qatar Police became the only export customer to actually receive the Army/Battlefield Lynx when it purchased three Lynx HC.Mk 28s. These were the first helicopters actually delivered under the AOI deal, and were broadly similar to the original Lynx AH.Mk 1 used by the Army Air Corps, albeit with sand filters over the engine intakes. The first Mk 28 first flew on 2 December 1977, and the trio was delivered in 1978. The Qatari Lynxes had a relatively short career however, and were sold back to BAe, and then to the UK MoD, in 1991.

## (West) Germany – Lynx Mk 88, Super Lynx Mk 88A

The German Navy's Lynx Mk 88 was based on the RN HAS.Mk 3. Like the Danish and Norwegian aircraft, the Mk 88s lacked tail rotor folding, although they were always intended to deploy aboard small ships. Optimised for ASW duties, the aircraft were fitted with Bendix AN/AQS-18(v) 'dunking' sonar. Nineteen were built for service with Marinefliegergeschwader 3 at Nordholz, in three batches of 12, two and five aircraft. The first of these made its maiden flight on 26 May 1981. The 17 survivors are being converted to Super Lynx standards as Mk 88As, which involves 're-airframing' the aircraft, together with the incorporation of various new systems.

Seven new-build Mk 88A aircraft (pictured) were also ordered in a £100 million contract signed in September 1996, the first of these flying on 1 May 1999. Mk 88A 83+21 is pictured. The Mk 88A is similar to the Brazilian Mk 21A, and includes a 360° GEC-Marconi Seaspray 3000 radar and an overnose FLIR turret containing a GEC Sensors MST FLIR, in a turret installation.

# New generation

*ZT800 was the first production Super Lynx 300, making its maiden flight on 27 January 1999. The latest Super Lynx variant, it later incorporated LHTEC CTS800 engines and a night vision goggle (NVG) compatible 'glass' cockpit.*

**The 'second phase' of Lynx development witnessed the introduction of the naval Super Lynx, which as well as securing numerous export orders, has also served as the basis for the Navy's latest Lynx Mk 8.**

It is perhaps unusual that the most fiercely fought battle for orders for shipboard helicopters is being decided by derivatives of helicopters which first entered service more than 25 years ago. Arguably the leading 'contender' is GKN Westland's Super Lynx, which combines the agility and compact dimensions of the original Lynx with new levels of performance and new avionics and systems.

The basic Super Lynx is a relatively modest improvement over the first-generation aircraft, and some have been produced by new-build production, and others by conversion of existing Lynx airframes. Specifications of the Super Lynx differ according to particular customer requirements, and some traditional major 'Super Lynx' features are missing from some examples.

The first Super Lynxes produced were 12 Mk 99s for the South Korean Navy, which retain the original main rotor of the standard Lynx, and lack the newer reverse-direction composite tail rotor. An initial batch of 12 Super Lynx Mk 99s was delivered from 1990, and was followed by a follow on batch of 13 similar Mk 99As. The aircraft are fitted with a new 360°-scan version of the original Seaspray Mk 3 360°-radar, but lack any form of overnose PID (passive identification device). A new feature of the Super Lynx Mk 99A is the introduction of an all-composite tailpane.

*The Brazilian navy's 14 Series 100 Super Lynx Mk 21As retain conventional cockpit instrumentation and carry the original Rolls-Royce Gem 42-1 turboshafts and Seaspray 360°-radar.*

## RN 'Super Lynxes'

Although they are not referred to as Super Lynxes, the Royal Navy's Lynx HMA.Mk 8 helicopters are equivalent to Super Lynx standards, with composite BERP composite main rotor blades, uprated Gem 42 Series 200 engines, full authority digital engine control (FADEC) and improved avionics, although these aircraft (mostly converted from earlier HAS.Mk 3s) retain the original forward-looking Seaspray radar, albeit in a new undernose 'chin' radome. Unusually, they also incorporate a new PID in the shape of a GEC Sea Owl FLIR, mounted atop the nose. The HMA.Mk 8's Racal RAMS 4000 central tactical system (CTS) greatly reduces crew workload by centrally processing sensor data, and presenting mission information on a multifunction CRT display.

The next Super Lynx customer was Portugal, which took delivery of the first of five Super Lynx Mk 95s in 1993. The Portugese Super Lynxes feature the lightweight, low cost Bendix RDR 1500 radar, and lack any overnose PID or FLIR, but do feature composite BERP main rotor blades, a reverse direction composite tail rotor, and

*Above: The RN's HMA.Mk 8 has its original Seaspray Mk 1 radar in a new chin radome, and a BAE Systems Sea Owl thermal imager on a gimballed mount in the former radar position.*

*Below: Portugal ordered five Mk 95 Super Lynx in 1990, with Racal RNS252 GPS-aided INS and Doppler 91 nav systems and some American equipment, including AN/AQS-18 sonar and Honeywell radar.*

***Above:* Initially ordered in 1988, South Korea's Mk 99/99A Super Lynxes can be armed with Sea Skua anti-ship missiles, and serve aboard 'Sumner'- and 'Gearing'-class destroyers.**

***Left:* Brazil ordered nine Mk 21As (plus five conversions from Mk 21s). The first upgraded example, flown on 22 December 1995, was followed by the first new-build helicopter which flew in 1996.**

advanced avionics. The aircraft also have the Bendix AN/AQS-18(V) dunking sonar and a Vesta datalink. The first two Portugese Lynx Mk 95s were produced through the conversion of refurbished and zero-lifed ex-RN Lynx HAS.Mk 2s, but the remainder were new-build aircraft.

Since 1999, new-build Lynx fuselages have been capable of absorbing a significant increase in MTOW, and this has helped encourage a number of existing Lynx customers to upgrade early Lynx versions to Super Lynx standards, using new airframes and Super Lynx systems and avionics, to which existing engines, flying controls, hydraulics, electrics and some avionics are then transferred.

The first such rebuilt Super Lynxes were five Brazilian Mk 21s (which became Mk 21As), which were delivered alongside nine new-build Mk 21As. The Brazilian Super Lynxes may have been the first with Westland's new bolted main rotor head, which raised maximum weight to 11,750 lb (5330 kg). These aircraft feature undernose Seaspray 3000 radar but lack overnose PID or FLIR, and deliveries began in 1996.

While Germany ordered seven new-build Super Lynx Mk 88As in 1996, it has also decided to upgrade surviving Mk 88s to the same standard using new-build Lynx fuselages. Modification kits are supplied to Eurocopter, which undertakes the actual conversions. The first conversion returned to Westland's Yeovil plant for flight trials, verification and customer acceptance, but the remainder will be redelivered direct from Eurocopter.

The German Super Lynxes are similar to the Brazilian aircraft, with composite BERP main rotors, the reverse direction tail rotor (which improves hover performance at high AUW), and undernose Seaspray 3000 radar. Unlike the Brazilian navy aircraft, however, the German Super Lynxes have an overnose GEC Sensors MST FLIR for passive detection and identification of targets.

### Third generation Lynx

A new Super Lynx has now emerged, powered by US-built turboshaft engines. The company's demonstrator, G-LYNX, flew as the private venture Battlefield Lynx 800 demonstrator with CTS800 engines in 1991. The aircraft was subsequently used as the de facto Super Lynx Series 200 demonstrator. The Series 200 combined standard Super Lynx avionics and cockpit with the new engines and electronic power systems, but was soon superseded by the more extensively redesigned Series 300, which flew in prototype form (initially with Gem engines) on 27 January 1999.

The Super Lynx failed to win orders in Australia and New Zealand, where the rival Super Seasprite was selected – largely for its lower price tag and better ASM-carrying capabilities – but did beat the SH-2 to win Malaysia's requirement in 1999, and has also been selected by South Africa.

South Africa will receive newly-built Super Lynx Series 300s, as has Malaysia, with six-screen glass cockpits and advanced avionics, and with the internationally-designed 1,334-shp (995-kW) LHTEC (Light Helicopter Turbine Engine company) CTS800 engines instead of the original Gem 42s. These new engines offer greater reliability and maintainability, and bring a 30 per cent increase in power.

Westland continues to aggressively market the Super Lynx, whose compact dimensions and 'over-sized' capabilities continue to make it the shipboard helicopter to beat. Lynx develop- ment also continues, and Westland has explored the possibility of producing a very high speed 'Compound' version, with a cabin-mounted wing 'off-loading' the main rotor in forward flight.

***The German navy's Mk 88A is a Series 100 machine with 360°-Seaspray 3000 radar, FLIR turret, Rockwell Collins GPS, Racal Doppler 91 and RNS252 INS. Upgrading of 17 existing Lynx Mk 88 airframes is being undertaken by Eurocopter Germany at Donauwörth.***

# INDEX